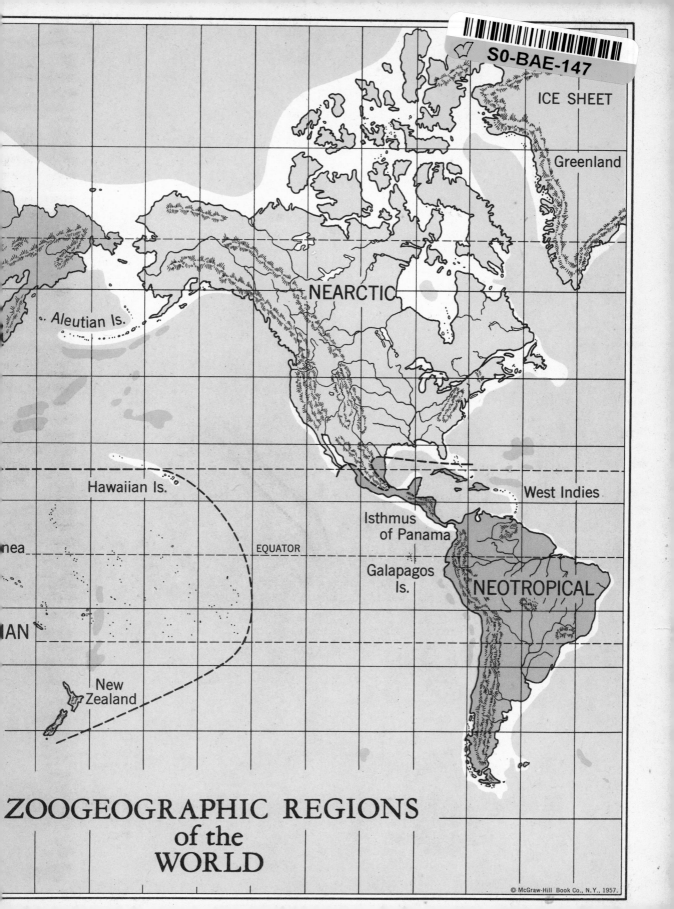

ICE SHEET

Greenland

NEARCTIC

Aleutian Is.

Hawaiian Is.

West Indies

Isthmus
of Panama

nea

EQUATOR

Galapagos
Is.

NEOTROPICAL

IAN

New
Zealand

ZOOGEOGRAPHIC REGIONS
of the
WORLD

McGRAW-HILL PUBLICATIONS IN THE ZOOLOGICAL SCIENCES

E. J. Boell, Consulting Editor

GENERAL ZOOLOGY

McGRAW-HILL PUBLICATIONS IN THE ZOOLOGICAL SCIENCES

E. J. Boell, Consulting Editor

Baitsell · HUMAN BIOLOGY
Breland · MANUAL OF COMPARATIVE ANATOMY
Chapman · ANIMAL ECOLOGY
Haupt · FUNDAMENTALS OF BIOLOGY
Hyman · THE INVERTEBRATES: PROTOZOA THROUGH CTENOPHORA (Vol. I)
      THE INVERTEBRATES: PLATYHELMINTHES AND RHYNCHOCOELA (Vol. II)
      THE INVERTEBRATES: ACANTHOCEPHALA, ASCHELMINTHES, AND ENTOPROCTA (Vol. III)
      THE INVERTEBRATES: ECHINODERMATA (Vol. IV)
Leach · FUNCTIONAL ANATOMY OF THE MAMMAL
Mayr, Linsley, and Usinger · METHODS AND PRINCIPLES OF SYSTEMATIC ZOOLOGY
Metcalf and Flint · FUNDAMENTALS OF INSECT LIFE
Mitchell · A TEXTBOOK OF GENERAL PHYSIOLOGY
Mitchell and Taylor · LABORATORY MANUAL OF GENERAL PHYSIOLOGY
Pearse · ANIMAL ECOLOGY
Quiring · FUNCTIONAL ANATOMY OF THE VERTEBRATES
Rogers · TEXTBOOK OF COMPARATIVE PHYSIOLOGY
Senning · LABORATORY STUDIES IN COMPARATIVE ANATOMY
Shull · EVOLUTION
Shull · HEREDITY
Shull, LaRue, and Ruthven · PRINCIPLES OF ANIMAL BIOLOGY
Shull, LaRue, and Ruthven · LABORATORY DIRECTIONS IN PRINCIPLES OF ANIMAL BIOLOGY
Snodgrass · PRINCIPLES OF INSECT MORPHOLOGY
Storer and Usinger · GENERAL ZOOLOGY
Storer · LABORATORY MANUAL FOR GENERAL ZOOLOGY
Storer and Usinger · ELEMENTS OF ZOOLOGY
Weichert · ANATOMY OF THE CHORDATES
Weichert · ELEMENTS OF CHORDATE ANATOMY
Weichert · REPRESENTATIVE CHORDATES
Welch · LIMNOLOGY
Wieman · AN INTRODUCTION TO VERTEBRATE EMBRYOLOGY
Wolcott · ANIMAL BIOLOGY
Wolcott and Powell · LABORATORY GUIDE IN ANIMAL BIOLOGY

There are also the related series of McGraw-Hill Publications in the Botanical Sciences, of which Edmund W. Sinnott is Consulting Editor, and in the Agricultural Sciences, of which R. A. Brink is Consulting Editor.

GENERAL ZOOLOGY

TRACY I. STORER *Professor of Zoology, Emeritus*
University of California, Davis

ROBERT L. USINGER *Professor of Entomology*
University of California, Berkeley

THIRD EDITION

McGRAW-HILL BOOK COMPANY, INC.
New York   Toronto   London   **1957**

II

PREFACE

This text provides a general introduction to zoology, primarily for students in colleges and universities. The subject matter has been carefully arranged to facilitate readings in connection with either lectures or laboratory work and for reference use. Part I deals with the general principles of animal biology. After a brief introduction and some history of zoology, the frog is discussed as a type animal to establish basic ideas of structure and function. Then follow chapters dealing with the finer structures of the body and the organization of these into special systems for carrying on essential life processes. Succeeding chapters consider the more general phases of animal existence—reproduction, heredity, distribution, and evolution.

In Part II, following an introduction to the classifying and naming of animals, each chapter describes the structure and physiology of common and representative types belonging to a major group—from the one-celled protozoans to man. The accounts of natural history and reproduction show how structure and function serve in the life histories of these and related animals. Some of the many interrelations between animals and their environments are discussed, and there is frequent mention of the importance to mankind of various animals, both useful and harmful. The broader relations of animals are dealt with further in the general chapters on distribution and evolution.

The synopses of classification are a special feature, having been extracted from authoritative original sources and organized into a uniform pattern. They are intended first to show the extent, diversity, and relationships of the animals comprising each of the larger groups, together with something of their mode of occurrence and their interrelations with other animals and with mankind. A second purpose is to facili-

tate identification of specimens down to the order and, in some cases, to the family. Common or notable representatives are mentioned by scientific and common names, using North American examples principally. Since the living animals are but the existing members of a continuous procession of animal forms that have occupied the earth down through time, the geological ranges of groups and various fossil representatives (marked †) are mentioned.

The lists of references at the ends of chapters are provided for the enquiring student or teacher who wishes further information on a subject. Certain "classical" references—by Mendel, Darwin, and others—are cited so that the reader may become acquainted with a few of the major contributions to biological thought. Because of the international scope of science, including zoology, comprehensive works in foreign languages are included. The lists have been revised throughout to include significant new books and other important recent literature.

Technical words in the text are distinguished by different type faces, as follows: anatomical and other terms, *humerus, monohybrid;* scientific names of genera or species, *Rana pipiens, Mus*; names of families and higher systematic groups, CULICIDAE, PROTOZOA, etc. Throughout the summaries of classification the pattern is: Phylum **ARTHROPODA,** Class *INSECTA*, Order **Diptera,** Family TABANIDAE.

Preparation of a third edition has afforded opportunity for both changes and additions. Many constructive criticisms from teachers, students, and other users of the earlier editions have been carefully considered, and those consistent with the general plan of the book and the space available have been included. An introductory account of the physical and chemical properties of matter has been added preceding the discussion of protoplasm. The former chapter on organs and organ systems has been expanded and divided (Chaps. 4 to 10) with addition of considerable basic material on physiological processes. The patterns of classification for coelenterates, flatworms, echinoderms, and the larger subdivisions of the arthropods have been substantially revised and minor changes made for other phyla and classes. Some significant results from the ever-expanding research in biology and zoology are incorporated; examples are biochemical-physiological processes, enzymes, gene structure and mode of action, ecological concepts, etc.

Most of the illustrations are original. Anatomical figures, wherever possible, were made from special dissections and those of bilateral animals are shown from the left side to facilitate comparisons. In series showing embryological or larval development, the individual figures are brought into comparable positions so that changes during growth or metamorphosis can be traced or compared directly with drawings of the adult animals.

The illustrations have undergone substantial revision for this edition; many have been modified, others replaced by better figures, and a considerable number of new ones added. The labeling of all figures has been changed from hand lettering to printed type. Mrs. Emily P. (Thompson) Reid continues to be our artist-collaborator. She has a sympathetic interest in the new illustrative materials, having provided many original ideas in planning drawings besides her skill in execution. For previous editions she provided most of the figures of invertebrates, some of vertebrates, and many in the general chapters. Others in the latter two groups were made by Norman C. Bilderback and W. Schwartz. Some photographs were furnished by J. R. Slevin, the National Zoological Park, the San Diego Zoological Society, and others. These, together with illustrations used through the courtesy of various publishers, are credited as to source in the legends.

Besides the many persons acknowledged as helping in the previous editions, this edition has been aided by the following: A. W. Bell (earthworm circulation and details elsewhere); J. W. Durham (classification of echinoderms); Richard M. Eakin (review of Chap. 11); Cadet Hand (classification of coelenterates); Frank A. Pitelka (aid in revision of his biome map— see back end papers); McKnight and McKnight, Bloomington, Ill. (their North American map as base for biome map); Hans Ris (photomicrographs of mitosis); Ray F. Smith (review of Chap. 13); R. A. Stirton (aid with Fig. 14–15); and Robert W. Storer (review of Chap. 34). Our colleagues in the biological sciences at Davis and Berkeley have provided assistance with many problems. Readers and users of the book, since it first appeared in 1943, have provided a continuing generous flow of suggestions and minor corrections. To all who have helped this enterprise we extend grateful appreciation.

TRACY I. STORER
ROBERT L. USINGER

CONTENTS

Part I

GENERAL ANIMAL BIOLOGY

Fig. 1-1. Some common representative animals and the environments in which they live.

1 INTRODUCTION

An enormous variety of animals now inhabits the earth, and many other kinds have lived and died out during past geological time. Animals differ from one another in size, structure, manner of life, and other features. Mankind has acquired a vast amount of detailed knowledge about animals—enough to fill a large library—but there is still much more to be learned and many questions have arisen.

What is life? What is an animal? In what ways are the various kinds of animals alike or unlike in structure, internal bodily processes, and modes of life? How do animals carry on their ordinary activities? How are the different kinds related to one another? In what ways does man resemble and differ from other living things? How is he affected by various animals, and how have his activities influenced those about him? The answers to many of these questions are provided by the *science of zoology* (Greek *zoön,* animal + *logos,* discourse) that deals with various aspects of animal life.

BIOLOGY

1-1. Science (Latin *scientia,* knowledge) is exact knowledge or tested and verified human experience. A scientist is a person who has chosen to spend his life in the advancement of knowledge. He probes into the unknown, he asks questions, and he seeks answers by carefully planned observations and experiments. He uses the scientific method, which involves absolute honesty in both thought and action and requires strict discipline in all work.

The raw materials of science are *facts,* the real state of things in contrast to beliefs, vague impressions, or superstitions. Simple facts—that fire is hot, water is wet, etc.—may be determined by direct observation, but even these gain precision by the use of scientific instruments and permit observations by one person to be compared with those of others. In many fields of science progress is dependent upon the instruments that are available, and the development of a new tool such as the electron microscope or the cyclotron opens up new subjects and methods not even suspected earlier.

The records of science are accumulated facts or *data* (sing., *datum*). Qualitative data deal with different kinds of things, and quantitative data with dimensions, weights, or other facts that can be expressed in numerical terms.

The scientific method may be illustrated by a common observation—that moths are attracted to candle flame. To the scientist this suggests a general principle or relation of cause (light) and effect (attraction). He sets up a temporary working explanation or *hypothesis*—that moths react positively to light. Then he plans experiments to test the hypothesis. Various kinds of moths are exposed to lights of different intensity and wavelength. If the experiments support the hypothesis, the scientist can formulate a

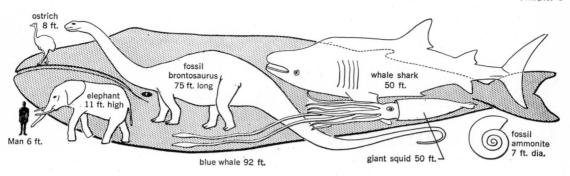

ostrich
8 ft.

elephant
11 ft. high

Man 6 ft.

fossil
brontosaurus
75 ft. long

whale shark
50 ft.

fossil
ammonite
7 ft. dia.

blue whale 92 ft.

giant squid 50 ft.

Fig. 1-2. The largest animals as compared with man. About 1/200 natural size. (*Adapted from C. R. Knight.*)

more definite **theory** to explain the observed facts. In this case the theory might state that certain kinds of moths are attracted to light in the blue portion of the spectrum but are repelled by longer wavelengths that appear to us as yellow or red. Such a theory then becomes the basis for extensive trials over a period of years. As a result of such scientific study and deduction, electrical manufacturers have produced yellow lights that are considered to be "insectproof," not attractive to insects. Moths destructive to agricultural crops can be sampled and even lured to their death by "light traps." Finally, through repeated proof as to cause and effect, a theory may be restated as a general **principle** or **law**—but even this is never beyond criticism. New facts may be discovered that require the principle to be restated or discarded. Thus the scientific method accepts no knowledge as completely fixed or infallible but constantly seeks added evidence to test and to formulate basic principles of nature.

1-2. Specialized fields of science. The average person has more or less **common knowledge** about animals. A child learns that dogs bark and are covered with hair, that birds fly and are covered with feathers, and many similar facts. Much detailed information of this sort is known to primitive peoples who live in the wild and to farmers whose livelihood depends on an understanding of nature. Other people may develop a special interest in **natural history** and

study such matters as the habits of birds or other conspicuous animals. The science of zoology includes these kinds of information together with all other knowledge about animals, both popular and technical. With **botany,** the science of plants, it forms **biology** (Gr. *bios,* life), the science of living things. Biology in turn is one of the natural sciences that have to do with the phenomena of nature. Some other natural sciences are geology—earth structure; mineralogy—substances in the earth's crust; physiography—surface features of the earth; and meteorology—weather and climate. The natural sciences may be contrasted with the **physical sciences**—physics dealing with the properties of matter and chemistry with its constitution.

In ancient times one man such as Aristotle (Greek, 384–322 B.C.) might master the entire field of science, and only a century ago Louis Agassiz (1807–1873) and some others knew and could teach all the natural sciences. With the subsequent great increase in knowledge this is no longer possible and scientific fields have of necessity been divided and redivided. A scientist now must specialize in one field or related parts of a few. Although unfortunate in some respects, specialization has made for much more rapid advance in both science and industry. A scientist has, therefore, the problem of working in a particular branch of knowledge yet endeavoring to develop a broad vision of the world about him.

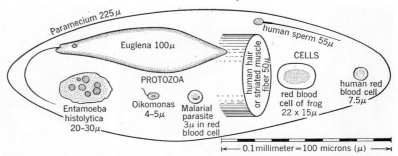

Fig. 1-3. Some of the smallest animals and some animal cells, all included within the outline of a *Paramecium*. Magnified about 450 times.

Scientific publications are the means of communication between scientists throughout the world. They have grown progressively until about a half million separate articles now are published each year. Any one scientist finds difficulty in keeping abreast of current publications and to do so must rely in part on special abstracting journals, reviews, and digests.

Some principal subdivisions of zoology and the chapters where they are discussed are:

ANATOMY (Gr. *ana*, up + *temno*, cut), structure as revealed by dissection.

MORPHOLOGY (Gr. *morphe*, form), structure as a whole. (Chaps. 2, 4–10, 16–36)

HISTOLOGY (Gr. *histos*, tissue), microstructure of tissues. (Chap. 3)

CYTOLOGY (Gr. *kytos*, hollow), structures and functions within cells. (Chap. 3)

PHYSIOLOGY (Gr. *physis*, nature), living processes or functions within animals. (Chaps. 2–10, 16–36)

NUTRITION (L. *nutrio*, feed), use and conversion of food substances. (Chap. 5)

EMBRYOLOGY (Gr. *en*, in + *bryo*, swell), growth and development of the new individual within the egg. (Chap. 11)

GENETICS (Gr. *genesis*, origin), heredity and variation. (Chaps. 12, 14)

PATHOLOGY (Gr. *pathos*, suffering), nature, symptoms, and cause of disease.

PARASITOLOGY (Gr. *para*, beside + *sitos*, food), study of animals that live and subsist on or in other animals. (Chaps. 13, 16–27)

NATURAL HISTORY, life and behavior of animals in their natural surroundings. (Chaps. 2, 13, 16–36)

ECOLOGY (Gr. *oikos*, house), relations of animals to their environments. (Chaps. 2, 13, 16–36)

ZOOGEOGRAPHY (Gr. *zoön*, animal + geography), distribution of animals in space. (Chap. 13)

PALEONTOLOGY (Gr. *palaois*, ancient + *ont*, being), fossil animals and their distribution in time. (Chaps. 13, 14, 16–36)

EVOLUTION (L. *e*, out + *volvo*, roll), origin and differentiation of animal life. (Chap. 14)

TAXONOMY (Gr. *taxis*, arrangement + *nomos*, law), classification of animals and principles thereof. (Chaps. 15, 16–36)

PSYCHOLOGY (Gr. *psyche*, mind), the animal mind.
SOCIOLOGY (L. *socius*, companion), societies of animals and of man. (Chaps. 13, 26, 36)

Zoology is also divided for the study of particular animal groups that are of special interest or importance into such fields as:

PROTOZOOLOGY, study of the one-celled animals, or PROTOZOA. (Chap. 16)

ENTOMOLOGY, study of insects; further subdivided into insect taxonomy, economic entomology, etc. (Chap. 26)

ORNITHOLOGY, study of birds. (Chap. 34)

MAMMALOGY, study of mammals. (Chap. 35)

1-3. Living vs. nonliving matter. Most living things or organisms can be distinguished readily from nonliving materials by a few simple criteria: form and size, chemical composition, organization, and others discussed below. The dormant seeds of plants and the eggs of most animals appear inert, but when placed under proper conditions each will reveal its living nature.

Some nonliving things show one or more attributes of the living. A crystal of an inorganic chemical like table salt has such definite organization that it can be identified by its physical features; it can grow by additions on the exterior. The flame of a candle has distinctive form, size, and color; in the presence of oxygen the wax is burned to yield carbon dioxide and heat, somewhat like the "burning" of food within an animal's body. The crystal and flame, however, lack other basic attributes of living matter such as irritability and reproduction. Perhaps on the border between living and nonliving matter are the viruses (par. 14-2); they can reproduce, but some also can be crystallized (Fig. 1-4).

 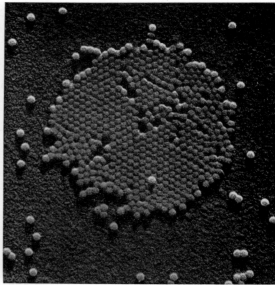

Fig. 1-4. Nonliving vs. living things. *Left.* Crystals of quartz (long, white) and of iron pyrites. About natural size. *Right.* Crystallized form of the poliomyelitis virus that lives and multiplies in cells of animals, including man. ×110,000. (*Electron microscope photo from W. M. Stanley.*)

The main differences between living and non-living things are:

FORM AND SIZE. Each kind of living organism usually has a definite form and characteristic size (Figs. 1-2, 1-3), within certain limits; most of them are also arranged as definite individuals. A whale, a flea, or any common plant is recognized by such features. Nonliving materials vary widely in such respects, as from a sand grain to a mountain or a drop of water to an ocean.

CHEMICAL COMPOSITION. Living organisms are composed chiefly of carbon, hydrogen, oxygen, and nitrogen in various but definite proportions, together with small amounts of other chemical elements. These materials are organized into complex organic molecules, often of great molecular weight, and collectively form the living substance or protoplasm (Chap. 3). The same and other chemical elements occur as compounds in nonliving minerals, but the molecular weights are small (below 2,000).

ORGANIZATION. The parts of each living organism are composed of complex microscopic cells, and these are assembled into interrelated systems for performing the life processes. The living plant or animal rearranges and recombines the chemical elements for its needs. Rocks and minerals cannot recombine materials like a living system; any of their structural features such as crystal pattern depend on the chemicals present and mode of formation.

METABOLISM. Various vital processes, collectively known as **metabolism**, are constantly taking place within living organisms—intake and use of food, respiration, secretion, and others. Nonliving things have no metabolic changes.

IRRITABILITY. The living organism and its parts react to changes in the environment. These act as stimuli that produce responses by the organism. Stimuli may be external, such as heat, light, moisture, pressure, or contact, or else internal. The degree of response is often disproportionate to that of the stimulus, and the organism is often not permanently altered by the stimulus. When inanimate materials react, there is a definite quantitative relation between the intensity of the environmental change and the reaction produced, as in the expansion of a metal by heat.

Fig. 1-5. Plants vs. animals. *Left.* Venus' fly-trap, a plant that closes its leaf blades to catch insects for food. *Center.* Euglena, a one-celled organism "claimed" by both botanists and zoologists (par. 16-10). *Right.* Colonial hydroid, a marine animal of plant-like form (par. 18-13).

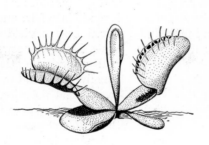

REPRODUCTION. Each kind of living organism has the ability to duplicate itself in kind—pine seeds produce pine trees and not oaks, and chicken eggs yield little chicks and not ducklings or puppies. Organisms reproduce by using materials within their bodies (Chap. 11). Nonliving things cannot reproduce.

GROWTH AND LIFE CYCLE. Living organisms grow by development of new parts between or within older ones and may replace parts during life. Each individual has a definite life cycle—birth, growth, maturity, life span, and death. If nonliving things increase, they do so by external addition, as with crystals, and there is no orderly cycle of change.

1-4. Animals vs. plants. Children learn to distinguish between ordinary animals and plants, but some living organisms are not easy to place. In general, animals can move about or move parts of the body, but so can a few plants such as the Venus' fly-trap that closes its leafy "jaws" to catch insects. Many animals become fixed early in life: sponges, sea anemones, oysters, barnacles, etc. Others are both fixed and of plant-like form, such as hydroids and bryozoans (Fig. 1-5). A few lower organisms seem truly intermediate between the ANIMAL KINGDOM and PLANT KINGDOM: the one-celled microscopic *Euglena* moves and takes food like an animal but contains chlorophyll like a plant, hence is claimed by both zoologists and botanists.

The principal differences between animals and plants are:

FORM AND STRUCTURE. In animals the body form is rather constant, the organs are mostly internal, the constituent cells are within delicate membranes, and the tissues are bathed in a solution containing sodium chloride (NaCl). Growth is usually differential, producing changes in proportions of body parts with age. The plant body is often variable, organs are added externally, the cells are usually within thick rigid walls of cellulose, and sodium chloride is toxic to most plants. Growth is usually terminal, at the ends of organs, and often continues throughout life.

METABOLISM. Animals require complex organic materials as food, obtained only by eating plants or other animals. Food is broken down (digested) and rearranged chemically within the body. Oxygen (O_2) is needed for respiration. The end products of metabolism are chiefly carbon dioxide (CO_2), water (H_2O), and urea, $(NH_2)_2CO$. Most plants utilize carbon dioxide from the air together with water and inorganic chemicals obtained in solution from the soil. By photosynthesis—the action of sunlight on the green pigment, chlorophyll—these simple materials are formed into various organic compounds, and oxygen is released as a by-product (Fig. 13-1).

IRRITABILITY. Most animals have a nervous system and can respond quickly to stimuli. Plants have no such system, and their responses are slower.

1-5. Animal life of the world. About one million kinds or species of living animals are known, and new sorts are constantly being discovered. Some are enormously abundant, others are present in moderate numbers, and still others are rare. For convenience in study and to indicate relationships between the different kinds, the Animal Kingdom is divided into various groups, large and small (Chap. 15).

Every kind of animal has its own special requirements for life, determined by its structure and its needs as to food, shelter, and reproduction. Different parts of the earth's surface are covered variously with salt or fresh waters or with soil or rocks of many types. Tropical regions receive more heat from the sun than those near the poles, and the amount of moisture in the atmosphere or precipitated as rain or snow varies from place to place. Therefore the physical environment on different parts of the earth is diverse. This influences the kinds of plants that grow on various portions of the land, and the plant cover in turn influences the types of animals that can live in any one place. In consequence, the numbers and kinds vary widely on different parts of the earth (Chap. 13).

No animal species lives entirely to itself. Each is influenced in various ways by both the physical environment and the other plants and animals that make up its biological environment. Most animals are affected by enemies, diseases, and competitors. The total of all these interactions comprises the "web of life" or the "balance of nature," a dynamic complex of forces, physical and biological, that affects every living organism, including man.

1-6. Relations of animals to man. Primitive races "live off the land" by gathering wild seeds and fruits and capturing various kinds of animals to provide food (Chap. 36). The larger human populations in civilized countries cannot subsist on wild supplies but must produce their own food: cultivated grains (wheat, corn, rice) and domesticated animals (cattle, sheep, swine, and poultry). Both primitive and civilized peoples levy on animals in fresh and salt waters—fishes, oysters, crabs, and others—for a further supply of animal protein; but the resources of the sea are not inexhaustible and the aquatic harvest has declined where overexploited.

Man is dependent upon animals in many ways other than for food. The wool of sheep and the pelts of various fur-bearing mammals provide clothing, bird feathers are used in pillows and quilts, hides supply leather and glue, hair is made into felt, and the glands and other internal organs yield many medicinal preparations. Honey, beeswax, tortoise shell, and natural sponges are other useful animal products. The livestock and meat-packing industries, the commercial fisheries, the fur trade, and beekeeping provide profitable employment for thousands of persons.

Among the harmful animals the larger predatory mammals are no longer dangerous to man in civilized countries, but they kill domestic livestock and useful wild animals. The insects and rodents that feed upon crop plants, grasses, herbs, or trees take a toll that amounts to millions of dollars annually and necessitates large expenditures for control. Other insects and the "house" rats and mice damage and destroy stored foods and property. Some insects, spiders, scorpions, and snakes are dangerously poisonous. The many kinds of parasites—protozoans, worms, insects, and ticks—bring illness and death to man, his domestic livestock, and useful wild species. Disease organisms carried by animals have exercised a dominant role in the history of mankind down through the ages; examples are the protozoan parasite of malaria and the virus of yellow fever, both carried by mosquitoes, the bacteria of plague transmitted by fleas, and the typhus spread by lice and fleas.

HISTORY OF ZOOLOGY

1-7. Early zoology. Prehistoric man had a practical interest in animals that provided food, clothing, and other essentials and in the wild beasts that menaced him. Later, animals came to have a part in his religion, medicine, and art. The Cro-Magnon peoples made paintings of animals and some animal statues (Fig. 1-6) in the caves of southwestern Europe. Much later the ancient civilizations about the eastern Mediterranean produced pottery, sculpture, and tapestries that show notable skill in portraying animals. The languages of all primitive races include many terms pertaining to animals; and as these differ from tribe to tribe, they indicate

Fig. 1-6. Animal drawings by prehistoric men in caves of western France and northern Spain—horse, woolly mammoth, ibex, bison, bog elk, rhinoceros, cow and bull; part of a ceiling fresco of bison. Some originals were in color. (*After copies by Breuil, far reduced.*)

that knowledge of animals is as old as the languages themselves.

One of the first known civilizations was that of Babylon, where clay models were made of organs in the human body and the heart was thought to be the center of intelligence. The Egyptians had some knowledge of animals, and before 1500 B.C. they used the parts and excretions of animals for medical treatments. The domestication of animals by early civilizations (Chap. 36) yielded practical information on breeding, growth, and nutrition.

The early eastern Greeks, however, made the first real contributions to biology, and they were the first to speculate on the origin of the universe and of the earth and its animal inhabitants. Anaximander (611–547 B.C.) believed that living things arose from a primordial mud, with a sequence from lower life up to man who had arisen from a fish form. Xenophanes (sixth century B.C.) recognized fossils as animal remains and inferred that the presence of marine forms up on mountains indicated the latter had once been beneath the sea. Empedocles (fifth century B.C.) is said to have rid a town of malaria by draining the nearby swamps. The oldest zoological document is a Greek medical work of

the fifth century B.C., with a simple classification of edible animals, chiefly fishes. Best known of early Greek physicians was Hippocrates (?460–370 B.C.); his writings show a high level of scientific thought and a "modern" approach to medicine. Students of today subscribe to the oath of Hippocrates when admitted to the practice of medicine.

Aristotle (384–322 B.C.) was the first zoologist of record and one of the greatest. He studied under Plato, taught Alexander the Great, lectured to pupils at the Lyceum in Athens, and wrote extensively on philosophy, politics, and other topics besides zoology. His *Historia animalium* of nine "books" (about 500 pages in a modern printed translation) includes a miscellany on the structure and habits of animals native to Greece, Macedonia, and Asia Minor. The parts based on personal observations (and dissections?) are accurate, but some from other sources are erroneous. He showed how animals could be grouped according to structure, habitat, and habits, but offered no system of classification (Chap. 15). Parts of other manuscripts by Aristotle, *On the Parts of Animals* and *On the Reproduction of Animals*, also survive. He followed the development of the chick embryo,

centaur   mantichora   merman

unicorn   dragon   chimaera

Fig. 1-7. Mythical animals. Creatures of the imagination figured in early books and on sculptures, mosaics, vases, and tapestries. A unicorn supports the arms of England, and St. George's dragon is stamped on British coins. (*After Ashton, Curious creatures in zoology, Cassell & Co., Ltd., London.*)

knew that drone bees develop by parthenogenesis, and that the young of some sharks develop within the mother. Aristotle insisted on the importance of observation, recognized the regularity and law inherent in biological phenomena, and used the inductive method of forming conclusions from observed facts. The human body served him as a reference in comparative discussions. He conceived an evolutionary development from lower to higher forms, which he ascribed to a supreme "guiding intelligence."

The Romans were mostly practical administrators and soldiers and made few contributions to zoology. Pliny the Elder (A.D. 23–79) compiled an encyclopedic *Natural History* of 37 books, covering all natural phenomena and their applications, wild and domestic animals, animal husbandry, medicine, and other topics. Although there was little new material and much of fancy and fable among the 20,000 items culled mainly from other writings or tales, the work served for over 1,500 years as a major source of natural-history information. A few other Roman writers on biology were Lucretius (96–55 B.C.), M. T. Varro (116–27? B.C.), Virgil (70–19 B.C.), and Celsus (A.D. 30?).

Galen (A.D. 130–200?), a Greek physician who later lived in Rome, was the last great biologist of antiquity. He was influential in developing a coherent system of physiology. Since dissection of human bodies was rarely possible, he used other animals, especially the Barbary ape. He described various internal organs and the blood vessels, showing that the arteries and left side of the heart contained blood and not air as believed by earlier writers; he also inferred that arteries and veins must be connected. He gave good accounts of the brain and nerves, and by experiment differentiated sensory and motor nerves. Food, he assumed, was "transformed" in the stomach, passed to the liver, and there converted into blood. Galen localized various qualities of the soul in different body parts and believed that all organs had been created in the most perfect form; hence, his long and detailed writings were acceptable in the ages of Christianity that followed. For a thousand years they were considered infallible and served as almost the only text on medical anatomy in western Europe.

A downward trend in scientific inquiry began before Greek civilization ended; it continued throughout the years of the Roman Empire and the centuries when Europe was overrun by barbarians. After Galen a thousand years elapsed with no biologist who made critical observations. The church held the people to narrow and dogmatic beliefs and discouraged original inquiry. Older writings were copied repeatedly with commentaries (and errors), but no copyist himself ever looked at the animals to verify that which he copied. Pliny, Galen, and Aristotle were the chief sources of biological information. Aristotle's writings were acceptable to the church because he believed that the earth was the center of the universe and that a supreme intelligence directed all natural phenomena.

Meanwhile, in the Near East, men continued to read the old Greek writings. They did some original work in mathematics, astronomy, and chemistry, but little in biology. Later, the biology of the Greeks was translated into Arabic and spread with Mohammedism, even to Spain. In Europe, universities were founded in the eleventh to thirteenth centuries, under control of the church, and the Arabic copies of Greek authors were then translated into Latin.

The revival of learning, or Renaissance, was a slow process. Two friars at the University of Paris were important in this change: Roger Bacon (English, 1214?–1294) had an especial interest in optics and in the philosophy of learning and of science; Albertus Magnus (Bavarian, 1200–1280) wrote a treatise *On Animals* that was a commentary on Aristotle but with some original observations. An interest in travel for commerce and discovery brought to Europe some knowledge of animals in distant lands. Important among early travelers were Marco Polo (1254–1323), Vasco da Gama (1469?–1524), Columbus (1446?–1506), and Magellan (1480?–1521). Practical anatomy, with dissection, began with Mondino (1270?–1326) at Bologna, Italy. Rediscovery of Greek and Roman statuary brought a revived interest in accurate portrayal of the human body and of animals and plants by the Italian Renaissance painters. Among the latter was Leonardo da Vinci (Italian, 1452–1519), an engineer and inventor, a famous painter, an anatomist of the human and animal bodies, and a physiologist. He pioneered in many fields, but his findings remained in notes and drawings that were not published until many years later.

1-8. Manuscripts and printing. All early human records were manuscripts (L. *manus*, hand + *scribo*, write) on clay tablets and later on sheets of papyrus or parchment. The Greek library of the second century B.C. at Alexandria had over 700,000 scrolls, or "books," and both the Romans and Arabs later had similar but smaller libraries. Ancient documents survived by being copied repeatedly, but many were lost. The oldest copies of Aristotle and Pliny date from about the ninth century A.D. Upon the invention of printing (about A.D. 1450) copies of the older works were multiplied in number and made available to many more persons. Printing was thus an important aid in the revival of learning.

1-9. Natural history. General works on animals after the Renaissance were patterned on Aristotle but gradually included increasing amounts of original observation. A few notable early authors and their works were Konrad Gesner (Swiss, 1516–1565), *Historia animalium* (1551 and later), of five volumes and over 3,500 pages, the first illustrated work on zoology, with many good figures; Guillaume Rondelet (French, 1507–1566), *De piscibus marinis* (1554), including all sorts of marine animals from the Mediterranean and the first figure of a dissected invertebrate; Pierre Belon (French, 1517–1564), *Histoire naturelle des étranges poissons marins* (1551), dealing with sea anemones to whales and figuring the attachment of the embryo whale to the mother—one of the earliest zoological books printed in a language other than Latin.

From the sixteenth century to the present day there has been an unending series of natural-history works dealing variously with one species or a larger group, with certain or all animals of a region (faunal works), or with the entire animal kingdom. A famous comprehensive treatise was the *Histoire naturelle* of Georges, Comte de Buffon (French, 1707–1788), director of the Jardin des Plantes in Paris. The *Histoire* covered animals, plants, and minerals in 44 volumes (1749–1804) and was completed by assistants after the author died. It was often reprinted and was translated into English and German.

1-10. Human anatomy and physiology. Andreas Vesalius (Belgian, 1514–1564), who studied at

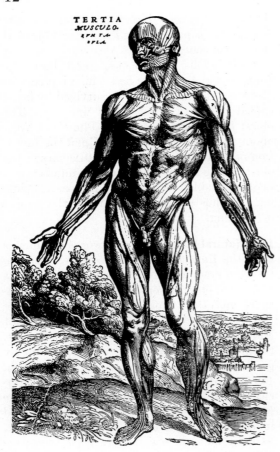

Fig. 1-8. First accurate portrayal of the human body. Much reduced from plate in *De fabrica corporis humani*, Vesalius, 1543.

Paris and at Padua in Italy and later taught anatomy, was a powerful factor in the return to original observation. Finding that Galen's writings were incomplete and erroneous, he made original dissections and published a large text *On the Structure of the Human Body* (1543). This book is notable for careful figures of the skeleton and muscles (Fig. 1-8).

William Harvey (English, 1578–1657) introduced the experimental method and quantitative deductions into physiology. He had been a student at Padua in Italy, where scientific study was on a high level. Harvey's researches, after returning to England, dealt with the circulation of the blood. His book *De motu cordis* (1628) described the way in which the blood

fills and then empties from the auricles and then the ventricles by the muscular contractions of these chambers (direct observations on lower animals); how blood spurts from a cut artery in keeping with the contractions of the heart; and how, when a vein is clamped, it empties on the side toward the heart but becomes engorged behind the clamp (experiment). Finally (by quantitative calculations), he showed that so much blood is pumped through the heart in an hour or day that it must be recirculated constantly. It could not, as earlier believed, all be generated in the liver from food as "natural spirits" for a single passage in the blood vessels. In *De generatione animalium* (1651) he described the embryology of the chick and of lower forms and inferred that mammals are produced from eggs.

1-11. The microscope (Fig. 1-9). Prior to invention of the microscope (Gr. *mikros*, small + *skopos*, watcher), animals invisible to the unaided eye and the finer structures in larger animals were unknown. Hand lenses for magnification (and reading spectacles) were known in the thirteenth century or earlier. The first compound microscope with two separated lenses is ascribed to J. and Z. Janssen, spectaclemakers of Middleburg, the Netherlands, in 1590–1591, but Galileo is considered the effective inventor. The best modern compound microscopes now magnify about 2,000 times and resolve objects about 1.0 micron (μ) apart. The ultraviolet microscope (1903) magnifies up to 10,000 times and will resolve to about 0.1 μ. Since 1934 the electron microscope with magnifications to 30,000 times or more has been used with extremely thin preparations of many biological materials to learn the finer architecture of cell parts. The phase microscope, a recent development, differentiates many details of structure in living cells.

1-12. Early microscopists. Robert Hooke (English, 1635–1703) was the first to report the presence of cells in plant tissue; his *Micrographia* (1665), with 83 plates of figures, described many minute objects. The real founder of microanatomy for both plants and animals was Marcello

Fig. 1-9. Development of the microscope. (*a*). One of Leeuwenhoek's "microscopes," about 1673, a simple magnifier used in sunlight. (*b*). Robert Hooke's microscope, 1665, with lamp and condenser to concentrate light on the object. (*c*). Modern compound microscope.

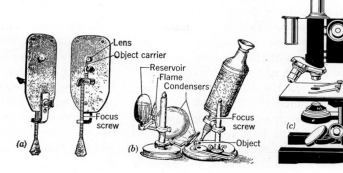

Labels on figure: Lens, Object carrier, Reservoir, Flame, Condensers, Focus screw, Focus screw, Object, (a), (b), (c)

Malpighi (Italian, 1628–1694), who investigated tissues and organs, fresh, cooked, or injected. He described the finer anatomy of the lungs, liver, and spleen and saw capillaries joining arteries and veins. He also wrote a detailed account of the anatomy of the silkworm (1669), including the structure and respiratory function of the spiracles and tracheae. Another work described the development of the chick (1672). Antony van Leeuwenhoek (Dutch, 1632–1723) was a self-taught individual who ground his own lenses and made simple microscopes, some with magnifications up to 270 times. His discoveries included blood corpuscles, spermatozoa, striated muscles, protozoans, and rotifers and were reported in a long series of letters to the Royal Society of London. The student of elementary zoology retraces in some degree the work of these early microscopists and the host of others that have followed down to the present day.

1-13. Classification and nomenclature. For centuries, naturalists either listed their animals in no particular order or followed the system extracted from Aristotle. Plant classification began in the sixteenth century and was advanced by John Ray (English, 1627–1705). He was the first to narrow the concept of a species to organisms of like kind derived from similar parents, to recognize variation in species, and to establish larger groups based upon anatomical features. Besides a three-volume work on plants (1686–1704), he published small books on quadrupeds and serpents (1693) and on insects (1705).

The earliest great taxonomist was Carolus Linnaeus (Swedish, 1707–1778). The growing knowledge of plants and animals in the eighteenth century was leading to confusion; descriptions were wordy, and species were designated by names that varied with locality and country. Linnaeus established a universal system of classification and nomenclature with concise descriptions. Beginning in 1735 he published a *Systema naturae* that passed through 12 editions, the last in 1768. It was a methodical catalogue of plants, animals, and minerals, arranged in larger and subsidiary groups. He gradually evolved a binomial nomenclature by which each kind of organism is designated by a genus and a species name (par. 15-9). This was first employed consistently for animals in his tenth edition (1758), which is the starting point for the binomial nomenclature used today. Linnaeus stimulated great interest in collecting and classifying. He believed in special creation and the fixity of species, later noting some variations.

1-14. Embryology. Aristotle knew about the development of certain animals, but details of chick embryology were first published by Fabricius (1621), Harvey (1651), and Malpighi (1672). Karl Ernst von Baer (German, 1792–1876), the "father of modern embryology," established the germ-layer theory and introduced the comparative viewpoint in his *Development of Animals* (1828; 1837). Francis Balfour (English, 1851–1882) summarized the knowledge up to his day in a masterly *Comparative Embryology* (1880–1881).

1-15. Comparative anatomy. Practically all early anatomical studies were treatises on separate animals. Then Baron Georges Cuvier (French, 1769–1832) established comparative anatomy as a new branch of biology. He made independent studies at the seashore, and from 1797 on did research at the Jardin des Plantes in Paris. His *Leçons sur l'anatomie comparée* (1801–1805) gathered the fruits of his earlier studies, and his work on the animal kingdom (*Règne animal*, 1816) included his theory of types. H. Milne-Edwards (French, 1800–1885) introduced the idea of division of physiological labor and wrote a treatise on comparative physiology and anatomy (1857–1881). Richard Owen (English, 1804–1892) developed the concepts of analogy and homology; his three-volume *Comparative Anatomy and Physiology of Vertebrates* (1866–1868) is still useful.

1-16. Paleontology. The nature of fossils as relics of animals that had lived in former times was noted by Xenophanes, by Leonardo da Vinci, and by Steno (1638–1686), but it was Cuvier who founded the science of paleontology. His *Ossemens fossiles* (1812–1813) was based on specimens from rocks near Paris. He believed in the fixity of species and that there had been a succession of catastrophes through time, each of which had killed off all life, after which new life had been created. The theory that fossils were remains of animals that had perished in the Biblical deluge was current before and after Cuvier's time, but final recognition of their true nature was established by the work of Charles Lyell (Scottish, 1797–1875) and his successors. Jean Baptiste Lamarck (French, 1744–1829) did for invertebrate paleontology what Cuvier had accomplished for vertebrates.

1-17. Histology and the cell theory. In 1665 Hooke had figured the dead cells in cork, and van Leeuwenhoek later depicted the nuclei in blood corpuscles, but no early microscopist had any hint of cellular structure as a general phenomenon. François Bichat (French, 1771–1802) issued a treatise on membranes, or "tissue." In 1823 Hunter figured blood cells with a "nucleus," and in 1824 René Dutrochet (French,

1776–1847) announced that plants and animals were composed of cells. In 1833 Robert Brown (English, 1773–1858) described nuclei in plant cells. In 1838 M. J. Schleiden (German, 1804–1881) put forth the thesis that cells were the units of structure in plants, and next year his coworker Theodor Schwann (German, 1810–1882) applied the thesis to animals. This generalization, the cell theory, has been one of the most fruitful of all biological concepts and is the basis of all understanding of the structure and functions within living organisms (Chap. 3).

1-18. Evolution. Up to the end of the eighteenth century belief in special creation was general and there were only vague speculations on the origin of organisms and their differentiation. Lamarck was the first to propose a general theory of evolution based upon influences of the environment, the effects of use and disuse of organs, and the inheritance of acquired characters. This was set forth in his *Philosophie zoologique* (1809). Cuvier strongly opposed Lamarck's theory in debates before the French Academy of Sciences in 1830 with Geoffroy Saint-Hilaire (French, 1772–1844). The convincing arguments of Charles Robert Darwin (English, 1809–1882) finally established the theory of evolution based on natural selection (1859) as a guiding principle for all subsequent biological work (Chap. 14).

1-19. Heredity and genetics. The Greeks knew that some characteristics were transmitted from generation to generation' in man, but little attention was given to heredity for many centuries. Darwin learned some facts from practical breeders, but did not know the mechanics of inheritance. The pioneer definitive work on this subject was done by Gregor Johann Mendel (Austrian, 1822–1884) and published in 1866 (Chap. 12) but lay unnoticed until a revival of interest in the subject in 1900. Since then the new science of genetics has made enormous strides, both practical and theoretical.

1-20. Biological education. Until less than a century ago there was only meager training in science, including biology, and that was mainly

Fig. 1-10. Some leaders in the development of zoology and related sciences.

by lectures. Louis Agassiz (1807–1873), a Swiss zoologist and student of Cuvier, later professor at Harvard University, initiated the present practice of firsthand study and dissection of specimens by students. He also carried popular instruction to laymen by public lectures on zoology in many American cities. His dictum "Study nature not books" today is applied at all levels, from nature study in the lower schools to the wide offerings of college and university instruction in the biological sciences.

MODERN BIOLOGY

Today zoology is an ever-widening field of study in which rapid strides are being made by many investigators. Older subjects, such as comparative anatomy, classification, and embryology, are pursued from increasingly enlightened viewpoints. Experimental zoology, genetics, and the physiology of tissues and cells are explored by refined methods and instruments. New fields have opened and expanded in the study of hormones, vitamins, enzymes, mineral metabolism, and physicochemical processes. "Tagged" chemical elements made radioactive by one or another means are fed or injected and traced in animal bodies to determine the manner of storage, utilization, and disposal of components in food and body metabolism. The older descriptive natural history of wild animals is being supplanted by quantitative measurements and by the study of individuals and populations, which yields a clearer understanding of events and processes in nature.

1-21. The study of zoology. Many students have some general knowledge about certain kinds of animals, gained from everyday experiences in country or city, or from museums and zoological gardens. To expand this knowledge, the beginning course in zoology provides a general account of the animal kingdom, the kinds and numbers of animals, the structure of representatives of different groups, the bodily (physiological) processes, and the ways that animals live. To this is added an understanding of how animals grow and reproduce, the principles of inheritance (heredity), the distribution of animal life over the earth today and in past geological time, and finally how the existing kinds of animals came into being—the theory of organic evolution. Further work in zoology is designed to expand the student's knowledge beyond the limits of an introductory course and to deal with other aspects of the subject.

The requirements for successful study of zoology are simple: (1) ability to observe carefully and to report accurately that which is seen; (2) absolute honesty in all work—a prime requirement in all branches of science; (3) clear thinking to arrive at dependable deductions or inferences from observations; and (4) a judicial attitude to appraise the relative values of conflicting evidence and to arrive at appropriate conclusions—but with a willingness to abandon or alter such conclusions in the presence of evidence pointing in another direction. Skill in attaining all these requirements may be gained even in an elementary course.

Some kinds of zoological study can be made of living animals in their natural environments; others are possible when the animals are held captive or reared in the laboratory; and still other types of study require that the animals be preserved as specimens. For the last they are preserved in alcohol or formaldehyde (most invertebrates, fishes, etc.), or dried (shells of mollusks, pinned insects, stuffed birds and mammals, etc.), or mounted on microscope slides (minute animals). Collections of specimens, labeled with place, date of collection, name of collector, and other data are maintained for study in public and private museums or in university laboratories and by many individuals. The specimens serve for identification, classification, anatomical studies, and other purposes, including teaching. Many "amateur naturalists" (persons who make their living in other kinds of work) contribute to the advance of zoology by collecting, preserving, and studying specimens and publishing the results of their studies.

The purposes in studying zoology are several. Some knowledge of animals and of the basic principles of biology is part of a well-rounded education. Many persons find pleasure in learning about animals, and some develop a special interest in particular groups—birds, insects, fishes, or others—which they follow as a side line of interest beyond the duties of their daily lives. And a knowledge of those animals of practical importance to mankind is essential in our advancing civilization.

REFERENCES

The vast literature of zoology includes thousands of separate books and many periodicals, both technical and popular. The items listed here and in other chapters are a few selected works in which the student will find elementary and advanced materials dealing with various aspects of zoology. There are many elementary textbooks of zoology and animal biology that deal with parts or all of the animal kingdom and with various general biological phenomena and principles.

The following works include systematic accounts of the animal kingdom:

HARMER, S. F., and A. E. SHIPLEY (editors). 1895–1909. The Cambridge natural history. London, Macmillan & Co., Ltd. 10 vols. PROTOZOA to MAMMALIA.

LANKESTER, E. R. (editor). 1900–1909. A treatise on zoology. London, A. & C. Black, Ltd. 8 vols. Incomplete; omits annelids, insects, land vertebrates, etc.

PARKER, T. J., and W. A. HASWELL. 1897. A text-book of zoology. London, Macmillan & Co., Ltd. 1940–1941. 6th ed. Rev. by Otto Lowenstein and C. Forster-Cooper. 2 vols., lv + 1,528 pp., 1,173 figs. PROTOZOA to MAMMALIA.

SEDGWICK, A. 1898–1900. A student's text-book of zoology. London, Swan Sonnenschein & Co. 3 vols., 2,565 pp., illus. PROTOZOA to MAMMALIA.

The principal comprehensive works in foreign languages are:

BRONN, H. G., and OTHERS. 1859– . Klassen und Ordnungen der Tier-reichs. Leipzig. "6 vols." (actually about 50, still incomplete).

CLAUS, C., KARL GROBBEN, und ALFRED KUHN. 1932. Lehrbuch der Zoologie. 10th ed. Berlin, Springer Verlag, OHG. xi + 1,123 pp., 1,164 figs.

DELAGE, M. Y., et E. HÉROUARD. 1896–1902. Traité de zoologie concrète. Paris. 5 vols. Incomplete; chiefly lower invertebrates.

GRASSÉ, PIERRE-P. (editor). 1948– . Traité de zoologie, anatomie, systématique, biologie. Paris, Masson et Cie. 17 vols. planned, 10 issued to date.

KÜKENTHAL, W., und T. KRUMBACH (editors). 1925– . Handbuch der Zoologie eine Naturgeschichte der Stämme des Tierreichs. Berlin, Walter De Gruyter & Co. "7 vols." (actually 14 or more, still incomplete).

PERRIER, J. O. E., et R. PERRIER. 1893–1928. Traité de zoologie. Paris, Masson et Cie. 10 vols., 3,610 pp., 2,352 figs.

The following deal with invertebrates:

BORRADAILE, L. A., and F. A. Potts. 1935. The Invertebrata. 2d ed. New York, The Macmillan Co. xv + 725 pp., 483 figs. Modern, technical. PROTOZOA to TUNICATA.

BROWN, F A., JR. 1950. Selected invertebrate types. New York, John Wiley & Sons, Inc. xx + 597 pp., 235 figs. PROTOZOA to TUNICATA.

BULLOUGH, W. S. 1950. Practical invertebrate anatomy. London, Macmillan & Co., Ltd. xi + 463 pp., 168 figs. PROTOZOA to CEPHALOCHORDATA.

CARTER, G. S. 1952. A general zoology of the invertebrates. 3d ed. New York, The Macmillan Co. xxviii + 421 pp., 172 figs. General problems, physiology, ecology.

GALTSOFF, P. S., F. E. LUTZ, P. S. WELCH, J. G. NEEDHAM, and OTHERS. 1937. Culture methods for invertebrate animals. Ithaca, N.Y., Comstock Publishing Associates, Inc. xxxii + 590 pp., 82 figs.

HYMAN, L. H. 1940. The invertebrates: Protozoa through Ctenophora. Vol. 1, xii + 726 pp., 221 figs. 1951. Platyhelminthes and Rhynchocoela. Vol. 2, vii + 550 pp., 208 figs. Acanthocephala, Aschelminthes, and Entoprocta. Vol. 3, vii + 572 pp., 223 figs. 1955. Echinodermata. Vol. 4, vii + 763 pp., 280 figs. 1955. New York, McGraw-Hill Book Co., Inc. Modern, general; other volumes planned.

LIGHT, S. F. 1954. Intertidal invertebrates of the central California coast. Rev. by R. I. Smith and others. Berkeley, University of California Press. xiv + 446 pp., 138 figs.

MacGINITIE, G. E., and NETTIE MacGINITIE. 1949. Natural history of marine animals. New York, McGraw-Hill Book Co., Inc. xii + 473 pp., 282 figs.

MINER, R. W. 1950. Field book of seashore life. New York, G. P. Putnam's Sons. xv + 888 pp., 251 pls. Atlantic coast invertebrates.

PENNAK, R. W. 1953. Fresh-water invertebrates of the United States. New York, The Ronald Press Co. ix + 769 pp., 470 figs.

PRATT, H. S., and OTHERS. 1935. Manual of the common invertebrate animals exclusive of insects. 2d ed. New York, The Blakiston Division, McGraw-Hill Book Co., Inc. xviii + 854 pp., 974 figs. Chiefly for North America; keys for identification.

RICKETTS, E. F., and JACK CALVIN. 1952. Between Pacific tides. 3d ed. Rev. by Joel W. Hedgpeth. Stanford University, Calif., Stanford University Press. xiii + 502 pp., 46 pls., 134 figs. Marine invertebrates, arranged by habitats.

WARD, H. B., G. C. WHIPPLE, and OTHERS. 1918. Fresh-water biology. New York, John Wiley & Sons, Inc. ix + 1,111 pp., 1,547 figs. Chiefly invertebrates; keys for identification.

YONGE, C. M. 1949. The sea shore. London, William Collins Sons & Co., Ltd. xvi + 311 pp., 40 col. pls., 88 figs. Ecology of British marine invertebrates (and fishes).

Comprehensive books on animal physiology include:

PROSSER, C. L. (editor). 1950. Comparative animal physiology. Philadelphia, W. B. Saunders Co. ix +

888 pp., 312 figs. Deals with PROTOZOA to MAM-
MALIA, but subject matter arranged by physio-
logical processes.
SCHEER, B. T. 1948. Comparative physiology. New
York, John Wiley & Sons, Inc. x + 563 pp., 72
figs. By groups, from PROTOZOA to VERTEBRATES.

A few books on the history of zoology are:

GABRIEL, M. L., and SEYMOUR FOGEL. 1955. Great ex-
periments in biology. Englewood Cliffs, N.J.,
Prentice-Hall, Inc., xiii + 317 pp. Excerpts from
notable original works by Hooke, Pasteur, Mendel,
and others.
GARRISON, F. H. 1929. An introduction to the history
of medicine. 4th ed. Philadelphia, W. B. Saunders
Co. 996 pp., illus.
LOCY, W. A. 1925. The growth of biology. New York,
Henry Holt & Co., Inc. xiv + 481 pp., 140 figs.
NORDENSKIÖLD, E. 1924. The history of biology. New
York, Alfred A. Knopf, Inc. x + 629 + xv pp., illus.

PEATTIE, D. C. 1936. Green laurels: the lives and
achievements of the great naturalists. New York,
Simon & Schuster, Inc., xxiii + 368 pp., illus.
SINGER, CHARLES. 1953. A history of biology: a general
introduction to the story of living things. Rev. ed.
New York, Abelard-Schuman, Inc., Publishers.
xxxv + 603 pp., 194 figs.

Two index periodicals for finding original articles
are:

Biological Abstracts. 1926–   . Baltimore, Union of
American Biological Societies. Comprehensive listing of new scientific literature in biology with abstract of each article; indexed by author and subject.
Zoological Record. 1864–   . London, Zoological Society of London. Annual volumes listing new books
and papers in zoology; indexed by author, subject
matter, and systematic position of the animals
discussed.

2 THE FROG AS A REPRESENTATIVE ANIMAL

The body of any animal has a definite form (morphology) and is composed of various structural parts, both gross and microscopic. These enable it to carry on the activities necessary for life, the *physiological processes* within its body and the *external relations* with its environment. The frog is convenient for an introductory study because of its size and availability and because it shows many resemblances in form [1] and function to the higher vertebrates and man (Chaps. 4–10, 33–36). The details of its structure can be determined easily by dissection, its physiology is well known and readily demonstrated, and its life habits, or *natural history,* are simple and easily observed. The following account will apply to any common species (Fig. 2-1; Chap. 32).

2-1. Habits and external relations. Frogs live in water and in moist places on land, thus are amphibious (Gr. *amphi,* both + *bios,* life). Each kind lives in a particular sort of surroundings, or *habitat,* such as marshes, pools, or streams. On land a frog rests with its short angular forelegs upright and the long hind legs folded beside the body. When disturbed it jumps by suddenly extending the hind legs and

---

[1] As compared with other lower vertebrates the frog is not entirely "typical." Its specializations include a flat skull with few bones, only four front toes, few vertebrae, and no exoskeleton of scales.

feet. In the water it swims by alternately flexing and extending the hind legs, the broad webs between the toes pushing against the water and carrying the animal forward. It may float with all legs extended and only the eyes and nostrils above water; from this position it can turn and dive to the bottom by swimming.

The frog does those things which enable it to survive as an individual and to continue as a species. It must find live *food* of proper kind and amount, chiefly insects and worms, which are caught by a quick flip of the sticky mucus-coated tongue and swallowed entire. Motionless animals or objects are ignored, and undesirable food is rejected. The frog seeks *shelter* in the water to escape enemies, to avoid unfavorable weather, to moisten its skin, and to absorb water. In winter, for protection from freezing, it burrows into the mud of a pond for a "winter sleep," or hibernation. Frogs seek shallow quiet water as a *breeding place* where their jelly-coated eggs are laid and fertilized. The eggs develop into embryos that hatch out as tadpoles or larvae. These feed and grow in the water and later transform into young frogs (Fig. 2-20). Various *enemies* eat frogs, thus reducing their numbers; snakes, turtles, herons, raccoons, and man are the chief enemies. From them frogs try to escape by leaping away, diving into water, and hiding in the bottom debris.

Fig. 2-1. The leopard or grass frog (*Rana pipiens*) and the bullfrog (*Rana catesbeiana*).

Certain internal parasites and some *diseases* tend also to reduce the frog population. The *competitors* of frogs include other animals living in the same habitat that seek insects and similar food.

2-2. Organ systems and physiological processes. The body (like that of most animals) consists of several *organ systems,* each specialized by structure and function to carry on some essential physiological process such as digestion, circulation, etc. These systems are integrated to work harmoniously with each other. Each system is composed of several *organs,* which individually perform some part of the general function; in the digestive system, the mouth is for food taking, the stomach for storage and digestion, and so on. An organ, in turn, is formed of several layers or parts known as *tissues;* and each tissue is composed of many microscopic

cells, usually of like kind. The wall of the stomach contains four principal tissue layers, including digestive and gland cells, muscle cells, connective tissues, and others. The many substances comprising the cells are known collectively as *protoplasm* (Chap. 3). The frog's body includes the following organ systems (Fig. 2-3):

1. Body covering (skin).
2. Skeletal system.
3. Muscular system.
4. Digestive system.
5. Circulatory system.
6. Respiratory system.
7. Excretory system.
8. Endocrine system.
9. Nervous system and sense organs.
10. Reproductive system.

2-3. External features. The *head* and *trunk* are broadly joined, and there are two pairs of *legs,* or *limbs;* there is no neck region or tail. The entire animal is covered by soft smooth moist *skin.* The head (Fig. 2-2) bears a wide *mouth* for taking food, two small *nostrils* (external nares) near the tip of the snout that serve in respiration, two large spherical *eyes* (organs of sight), and behind each eye a flat *eardrum* or *tympanic membrane* that receives sound waves. Each eye has a fleshy opaque upper *eyelid* and a lesser lower lid. Beneath these is a transparent third eyelid (nictitating membrane) that can move upward over the eyeball to keep it moist in the air and as a protection when under water. At the hind end of the body is the *vent,* or *anus,* a small opening through which are discharged undigested food wastes, the liquid excretory waste (urine) from the kidneys, and the

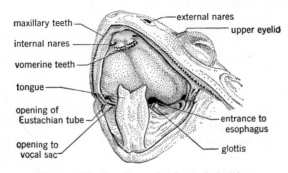

maxillary teeth
internal nares
vomerine teeth
tongue
opening of Eustachian tube
opening to vocal sac
external nares
upper eyelid
entrance to esophagus
glottis

Fig. 2-2. Head and mouth of a male bullfrog.

sex cells (eggs or sperm) from the reproductive organs.

The short *front leg* (arm) comprises an upper arm, forearm, wrist, and hand; the latter has a small palm with tubercles beneath, four fingers (digits), and a vestigial "thumb." The inner digit is thickened on males, especially in the breeding season. Each *hind leg* includes a thigh, shank or lower leg, ankle (tarsal region), and the long foot with a narrow sole (metatarsus) and five slender toes connected by broad thin webs

A frog is *bilaterally symmetrical,* with equivalent right and left sides. Structures on or toward the central longitudinal axis are termed *medial,* and those toward the sides are said to be *lateral.* The regions of the body are the *anterior end,* which moves forward; the opposite or *posterior end;* the back or *dorsal surface,* which is habitually uppermost; and the lower or *ventral surface* (Fig. 15-3). The latter comprises the broad *throat* beneath the head; the chest, thorax, or *pectoral region* adjacent to the forelegs; the belly, or *abdomen,* behind; and the *pelvic region* between the hind legs.

2-4. Mouth cavity. Within the *upper* and *lower jaws* is the broad *mouth cavity.* This narrows behind as the *pharynx,* which connects to the gullet, or esophagus. The flat *tongue* is attached anteriorly to the mouth floor but notched and free behind and has *taste buds* in small papillae on its upper surface. The mucus-coated posterior end can flip forward through the open mouth to capture food. Swallowing is accomplished by raising the mouth floor, in which a flat *hyoid cartilage* is embedded, and is aided by depressing the eyeballs. The upper jaw is margined by fine conical *maxillary teeth,* and the roof of the mouth has two patches of *vomerine teeth.* These all attach to the bone surfaces and are replaced if lost. They serve only to hold food. Near the vomerine teeth are two openings. the *internal nares,* connecting with the nostrils, through which air passes to and from the mouth cavity in respiration. The *glottis* is a median ventral slit in the pharynx, behind the tongue, that guards the entrance to the

lungs. It is opened for breathing but closes while food is being swallowed. Behind each eyeball and near the corner of the mouth there opens a small *Eustachian tube;* this connects to the middle ear chamber beneath the eardrum and allows the air pressure to be equalized on the two surfaces of the eardrum. Male frogs of many species have openings into two *vocal sacs* in the throat; these can be inflated to amplify the croaking notes.

2-5. Internal structure. If the ventral skin and muscular body wall are cut away, the *internal organs* or *viscera* will be found inside the large *body cavity* or *coelom.* A smooth transparent membrane, the *peritoneum,* lines the cavity (parietal peritoneum) and covers the organs (visceral peritoneum). Most of the organs are suspended from the middorsal region by double layers of peritoneum known as *mesenteries* through which blood vessels and nerves connect to the organs (Figs. 2-4, 2-5).

Far anterior in the coelom is (1) the reddish pear-shaped *heart* within a tissue sac (pericardium) filled with watery lymph. Beside the heart are (2) the two thin-walled elastic *lungs,* and behind these is (3) the firm brown *liver* of three rounded lobes with (4) the sac-like greenish *gall bladder* between the middle and right lobes. Parts of the digestive tract include (5) the short *esophagus* above the liver, (6) the long whitish *stomach* along the left side, (7) the slender and coiled *small intestine,* and (8) the bigger and dark *large intestine* or *rectum* that passes posteriorly. Along the fore part of the small intestine is (9) a slender irregular and whitish *pancreas.* Behind the stomach lies (10) a rounded reddish *spleen.* At either side of the middorsal line, above the peritoneum, are (11) two long dark *kidneys.* The *bladder* (12) is a thin-walled sac midventrally at the posterior end of the coelom. Between the intestines and kidneys are (13) the *gonads* or *sex organs.* A female has two large *ovaries,* containing many small dark spherical eggs, and two convoluted whitish *oviducts* extending along the dorsal wall of the coelom. In a male there are two small dark bean-shaped *testes.* To each sex organ is

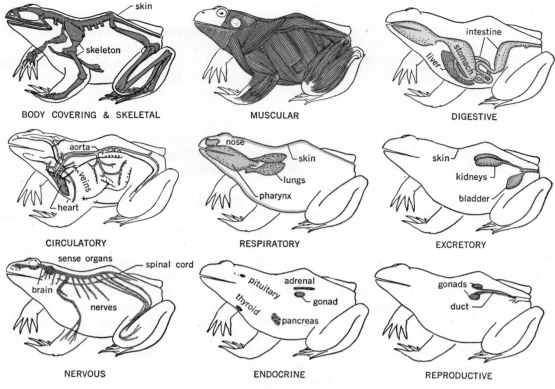

BODY COVERING & SKELETAL

MUSCULAR

DIGESTIVE

CIRCULATORY

RESPIRATORY

EXCRETORY

NERVOUS

ENDOCRINE

REPRODUCTIVE

Fig. 2-3. The separate organ systems of a frog.

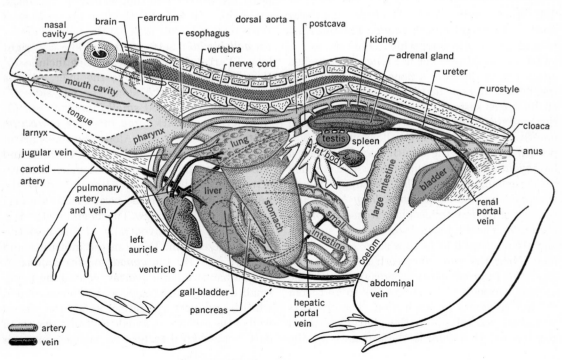

Fig. 2-4. The frog. Internal structure.

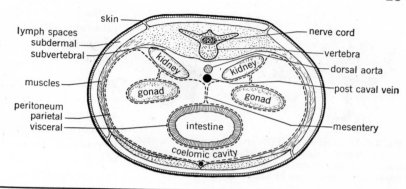

Fig. 2-5. The frog. Diagrammatic cross section of the body to show relations of the peritoneum (broken lines) to internal organs. The skin is multilayered (compare Fig. 2-6).

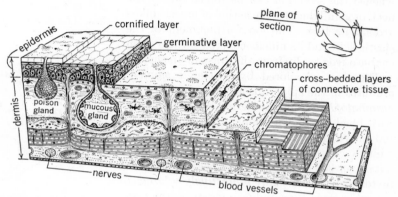

Fig. 2-6. The frog's skin. Enlarged stereogram showing the component cell layers, fibers, glands, and other details (compare Fig. 4-1, human skin). The section is cut at 45 degrees to the main body axis as indicated in the small outline figure.

connected (14) a branched **fat body.** The rectum and the ducts from the kidneys and sex organs all enter (15) the **cloaca,** which opens at the anus.

2-6. Body covering. The thin flexible **skin** over the entire animal provides physical protection, excludes disease organisms, serves in respiration, and is the means of water absorption, as a frog does not drink. As in all land vertebrates, it comprises an outer stratified **epidermis** and a **dermis** beneath, both of several cell layers (Fig. 2-6). In the epidermis, the basal cells (germinative layer) produce successive layers of cells that move outward and flatten, the outermost becoming a thin cornified covering. Every month or so during the summer, a new layer forms beneath and the old covering is molted, or sloughed off; it splits down the back, is worked off in one piece by the "hands," and usually is swallowed. The dermis is mainly of connective tissue. Its outer spongy portion con-

tains glands and pigment cells over a dark-staining layer of granules or fibers. The deeper part is a compact bed of crossed connective tissue fibers, each layer at about 45 degrees with the body axis, making the skin flexible either along or across the body. In and beneath the dermis are nerves and blood vessels, the latter of importance in cutaneous (skin) respiration. The skin of frogs and toads, unlike that of other vertebrates, is attached to the body only along certain lines (Fig. 2-5).

The glands produce useful fluids, or **secretions,** that pass out on the epidermis through fine ducts. The many small **mucous glands** secrete a colorless watery fluid that keeps the skin moist, glistening, and sticky. If a frog is roughly handled or chloroformed, the scarcer but larger **poison glands** pour out a thick whitish granular alkaloidal secretion with a burning taste that protects the animal in some degree from enemies. Each gland has a spherical base of secreting cells discharging into a central cavity,

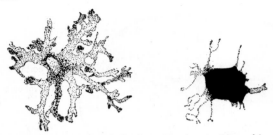

Fig. 2-7. One pigment cell (chromatophore) of frog skin. *Left.* Pigment dispersed throughout cell. *Right.* "Contracted," pigment concentrated into center of cell; extended processes of cell invisible. (*After Hewer.*)

whence the secretion can be forced out of the neck or gland duct by the action of muscle fibers around its base. The loose attachment of the elastic skin and its mucus-covered surface often enable a frog to slip from the grasp of an enemy.

The skin is colored by scattered **pigment granules** in the epidermis and pigment cells, or **chromatophores,** in the dermis—melanophores with black or brown pigment, lipophores with red or yellow, and guanophores that contain whitish crystals. The skin of a tadpole may have over 300 chromatophores per square millimeter. Frogs are usually **protectively colored** to resemble their surroundings, green on the dorsal and lateral surfaces and pale to whitish beneath. There is no green pigment; the prevailing color results jointly from the pigments that absorb some light rays and reflect others (chemical color) and the microscopic structure in outer layers of the skin that reflects some colors and changes others (physical color due to interference phenomena). Dark spots are due to groupings of melanophores and golden flecks to yellow lipophores. On most amphibians the patterns are stable, but the colors of some undergo marked changes. Darkening results when the pigment granules in the chromatophores are spread out and cover other elements in the skin, and paling occurs when they are concentrated (Fig. 2-7). Changes in color result from both external conditions and internal states; low temperature produces darkening, whereas under higher temperatures, drying, or increased light, the color pales. Some of these changes are induced through the eyes, as experimentally blinded frogs do not change. Pigment control

is due in part to a hormone (intermedin) of the pituitary gland, in part to a hormone of the adrenal glands, and in part to the nervous system.

2-7. Skeletal system. The body framework is a jointed internal skeleton that supports the soft parts, protects vital organs, and affords attachments for muscles used in movement and locomotion. In an early frog larva it is entirely of soft gristle or **cartilage,** but many parts later become hard **bone** (Chap. 3). Cartilage persists on the ends of limb bones to form smooth joint surfaces and in parts of the skull and limb girdles. The skull, vertebral column, and sternum

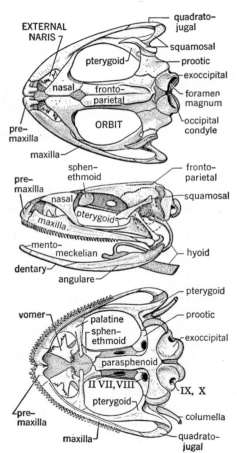

Fig. 2-8. Skull of bullfrog in dorsal, lateral, and ventral views. Lower jaw and hyoid cartilage shown only in lateral view; cartilage stippled. II, X, etc., exits for cranial nerves.

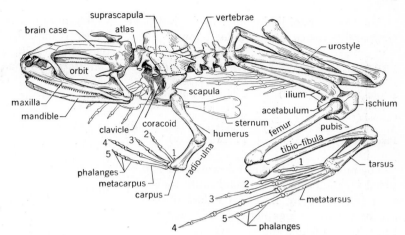

Fig. 2-9. Skeleton of the bullfrog.

comprise the *axial skeleton,* and the limbs and girdles form the *appendicular skeleton* (Figs. 2-8, 2-9; Table 4-1).

The broad flat skull comprises (1) a narrow brain case, or *cranium;* (2) the paired *sense capsules* of the nose and ear and large *orbits* for the eyes; and (3) the *jaws, hyoid,* and cartilages of the *larynx* (visceral skeleton). The cranium is roofed mainly by the frontoparietals, the nasals cover the nasal capsules, the prootics house the inner ears, and posteriorly each exoccipital bone bears a rounded *occipital condyle.* The two condyles fit depressions in the first vertebra and permit slight movement of the head on the spinal column. Between the condyles is the large opening, or *foramen magnum,* through which the brain and nerve cord connect. Each half of the upper jaw (maxillary arch) includes a premaxilla and maxilla with teeth and a quadratojugal, all fused to the cranium. The lower jaw (mandibular arch) on each side is a rod-like (Meckel's) cartilage, encased by the dentary and angulosplenial bones; the latter bone articulates to the quadrate cartilage on the cranium.

The spinal or *vertebral column* supports the body, connects to the head and limbs, and protects the nerve cord. It consists of nine *vertebrae* and a slender *urostyle.* It is short, of few segments, and scarcely flexible, unlike the column in most vertebrates. Each vertebra is made up of a spool-like *centrum* surmounted by a *neural arch* to house the nerve cord. Above the arch is a low *neural spine,* at either side is a broad *transverse process,* and at either end is a pair of *articular processes* that fit to similar processes on adjacent vertebrae. There are no ribs.

The anterior or *pectoral girdle* is a ∪-shaped framework around the thorax that shelters organs within and supports the fore limbs; it is attached to the vertebrae by muscles. Each half includes a broad cartilaginous *suprascapula* dorsally, a narrower *scapula* laterally, and the slender *clavicle* and wider *coracoid* ventrally. The latter join to the midventral breastbone, or *sternum,* which is largely cartilaginous and of several parts (epi-, omo-, meso-, and xiphisternum from before backward). Where the scapula and coracoid meet there is a shallow depression (glenoid fossa) in which the head of the humerus articulates.

The posterior or *pelvic girdle* is a stout rigid V-shaped frame that connects the hind limbs to the vertebral column and transmits the power in locomotion from the hind limbs to the body. It consists of three bones on each side, the long *ilium* anteriorly, the *ischium* posteriorly, and *pubis* ventrally. Where these join, there is a cup-like socket, the *acetabulum,* in which the head of the femur of the hind limb articulates. Each ilium has a long process, parallel to the urostyle, that attaches to a stout transverse process on the ninth (sacral) vertebra.

The two pairs of limbs differ in size but have comparable bones and parts as follows:

FORE LIMB (*arm*)
Humerus (*upper arm*)
Radius and ulna (fused)
  (*forearm*)
Carpals (*wrist*)
Metacarpals (*palm of hand*)
Phalanges (*fingers*)

HIND LIMB (*leg*)
Femur (*thigh*)
Tibia and fibula (fused)
  (*shank or lower leg*)
Tarsals (*ankle*)
Metatarsals (*sole of foot*)
Phalanges (*toes*)

The most complete skeletal protection is provided for the brain by the solid skull; the nerve cord is in a bony flexible conduit of neural arches with openings between adjacent vertebrae through which spinal nerves pass; the vertebrae, pectoral girdle, and sternum encircle the thorax; the pelvic girdle shields the abdomen dorsally; and the limb skeletons afford only support.

The form of each bone is related to the function it serves. **Fixed** bones of the brain case and pelvic girdle are immovably joined to each other, but most of the bones are **movable** with smooth **articular surfaces** at the joints where one bone moves on another. At the shoulder and hip there are **ball-and-socket joints** that permit rotation of the movable member (humerus, femur); **hinge joints** that allow movement in one plane occur at the elbow, knee, and elsewhere (Fig. 4-4). Movable bones are attached to one another by **ligaments** formed of dense connective tissue and also by the muscles and tendons that operate them. The centrum of each vertebra and each long bone in a limb or foot comprises a larger central **diaphysis** and a smaller **epiphysis** at either end. The fixed bones are joined to each other, and each epiphysis to its diaphysis by irregular and interlocking **sutures.** The latter remain cartilaginous throughout life in a frog; hence, its bones may continue to grow. In birds and most mammals, however, each suture becomes bony at a certain age, after which increase in size is impossible (par. 4-5).

2-8. Muscular system. The body of a frog or any other vertebrate contains three kinds of muscle fibers—smooth, cardiac, and striated—

which differ in microscopic structure and physiology (Chap. 3). The external muscular system (Figs. 2-10, 2-11) consists of **skeletal** or **voluntary muscles** that are attached to the bones; under willful control they produce movement and locomotion. Each is made of many parallel striated fibers, bound together by connective tissue. The opposite ends are fastened to separate bones or other parts by extensions of the connective tissue. The more central or less movable end is called the **origin,** and that on the more distal or movable part is the **insertion.** Many muscles have the connective tissue extended as a slender **tendon** that inserts at some distance from the muscle itself. On the lower limb segments, feet, and toes, some tendons pass under transverse (annular) ligaments that serve as pulleys. The **action** of a muscle is to contract, or shorten in length, so that the two structures to which it is attached are brought closer together. Muscles are commonly arranged in opposed groups. The following are the general types, as to mode of action, with an example of each:

FLEXOR, bends one part on another; *biceps,* flexes forearm toward upper arm.
EXTENSOR, straightens or extends a part; *triceps,* extends forearm on upper arm.
ABDUCTOR, draws a part away from axis of body (or of a limb); *deltoid,* draws arm forward.
ADDUCTOR, draws a part toward axis of body (or of a limb); *latissimus dorsi,* draws arm up and back.
DEPRESSOR, lowers a part; *depressor mandibulae,* moves lower jaw down to open mouth.
LEVATOR, elevates or raises a part; *masseter,* raises lower jaw to close mouth.
ROTATOR, rotates a part; *pyriformis,* raises and rotates femur.

Voluntary muscles are of three general structural forms: (1) broad thin sheet muscles, such as the external oblique and transversus that form a flexible wall for the abdomen; (2) slender ribbon-like muscles, usually with restricted origin and insertion, such as the biceps or deltoid; and (3) sphincters with the fibers in circular arrangement, as in the sphincter ani that constricts to close the anus.

In many movements of body parts, several muscles act together, some contracting more than others; such coordination is directed by

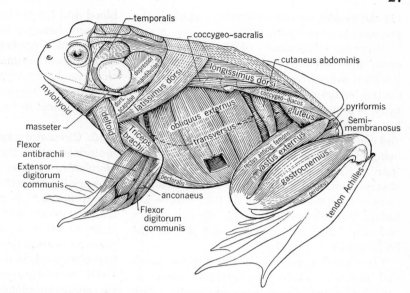

Fig. 2-10. Muscles of the bull-frog.

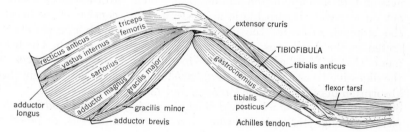

Fig. 2-11. Muscles of the bull-frog on ventral surface of left hind leg.

the nervous system. Each fiber or group of fibers has end plates of motor nerves that convey the impulses to stimulate contraction (Fig. 10-9*D*).

2-9. Digestive system. An animal needs food to supply materials for growth and maintenance, for replacement or repair of parts, for energy to move, and for producing sex cells. Plants synthesize the materials they need for life and growth from simple chemical substances in the soil and air. Animals by contrast require complex organic substances as food and obtain these by eating plants or other animals. Their food must be subjected to the physical and chemical changes of *digestion,* before it can be *absorbed* and used in the body. The system serving this function consists of the *digestive tract* and the *digestive glands.* The tract is es-

sentially a tube that extends from the mouth to the anus, being of differing diameter and structure in its several parts.

The small animals taken as food into the mouth are lubricated by the mucus secreted there (a frog lacks salivary glands) and pass through the *pharynx* to enter the *esophagus.* This is lined by glands that secrete an alkaline digestive fluid and has muscular walls that move the food along. Food passes at once to the *stomach,* which is an organ for storage and digestion, larger at the anterior or cardiac end and tapering to the posterior or pyloric end. The thick stomach wall is of four layers: (1) the *mucosa,* or inner lining, with many glands; (2) the *submucosa,* a network of connective tissue containing blood and lymph vessels and nerves; (3) the *muscularis* with both circular and longitudinal bundles of smooth muscle fibers; and

(4) the **serosa,** or outer covering, which is the peritoneum (Figs. 3-14, 5-5).

Muscular contractions of the stomach wall crush the food into smaller particles and mix it with the digestive secretions. These secretions contain **enzymes** or digestive ferments. An enzyme is a chemical substance, an organic catalyst, that speeds up certain chemical reactions and converts large amounts of material without being changed or used up itself in the process (par. 3-15). Each kind of digestive enzyme changes certain classes of food substances into simpler compounds (Chap. 5) that can be absorbed through the wall of the digestive tract and enter the blood. Food is not part of the body until it is absorbed.

The digestive enzymes in the frog's stomach and intestine include pepsin, trypsin, and erepsin, all of which act on proteins; lipase, which acts on fats; and amylopsin and maltase, which act on starches. Hydrochloric acid secreted in the stomach activates the digestive fluid secreted in the esophagus. The muscular movements that mix and gradually move food along the digestive tract are termed **peristalsis.** Some absorption may occur in the stomach, but most of the mixed and finely divided contents is passed through the **pyloric valve** (a sphincter muscle) at the posterior end and enters the **small intestine.** The intestinal wall is comprised of four tissue layers as is the stomach.

Two large **digestive glands,** the liver and pancreas, supply secretions to the small intestine besides those from glands in the intestinal wall. The **liver** is a large multilobed gland that secretes **bile.** This passes through bile capillaries and is stored in the **gall bladder,** then moves through the **bile duct** to the small intestine when food enters the latter. The bile serves to emulsify fats. The **pancreas** is a multicellular gland producing several digestive enzymes that pass into the **pancreatic duct,** which joins the common bile duct. Most digestion and absorption take place in the small intestine. Undigested residues are slowly moved by peristalsis into the **large intestine,** are formed into feces, and finally passed out through the **cloaca** and **anus.** Absorbed materials travel by way of the blood and lymph to various parts of the body for immediate use in growth or activities or for storage. Much reserve food is stored in the liver as glycogen (animal starch), a carbohydrate that can be converted into glucose for use in the body as needed. Fats may be stored at various places in the body.

2-10. Circulatory system. The transporting of materials within the body is performed by the **circulatory system.** Its principal functions are to carry (1) oxygen and carbon dioxide between the respiratory organs and body tissues; (2) digested foods and water from the digestive tract to other organs; (3) stored foods from place to place as needed; (4) organic wastes and excess minerals in solution, together with water, to the excretory organs; and (5) hormones from the endocrine glands where they are produced to the places where they are used. The system consists of the heart, arteries, capillaries, veins, and lymph vessels, together with the fluid blood and lymph. The heart is a chambered muscular pump that forces the fluids to circulate constantly through the closed system of tubular elastic vessels.

The **blood** is a clear fluid **plasma** containing free cells, or **blood corpuscles** (Fig. 2-12). The plasma comprises water, distinctive blood proteins, and mineral salts, including about 0.65 per cent of sodium chloride; it is the medium that carries soluble materials. The **red blood cells** or **erythrocytes** are elliptical, flattened, and nucleated. They contain a yellow to red respiratory pigment, **hemoglobin,** that serves to carry oxygen to the tissues. Each cell measures about 0.014 by 0.023 mm. (14 by 23 μ), and they number 400,000 or more per cubic millimeter of blood. The **white blood cells,** or **leucocytes,** are colorless and nucleated; they number about 7,000 per cubic millimeter and are of several kinds (Chap. 6). Most of them can move independently by amoeboid movement. Certain kinds (phagocytes) police the body against invading bacteria or other foreign organisms and remove dead or old tissue cells. When a blood vessel is injured, the blood **coagulates,** or forms a clot, to stop up the

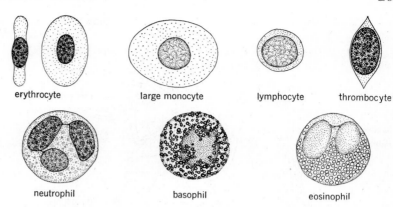

erythrocyte   large monocyte   lymphocyte   thrombocyte

Fig. 2-12. Blood cells of the frog. Nuclei dark, and granules shown as small circles.

neutrophil   basophil   eosinophil

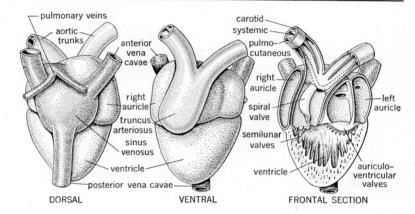

Fig. 2-13. Heart of bullfrog, enlarged.

DORSAL   VENTRAL   FRONTAL SECTION

wound and prevent loss of blood. Certain small spindle cells, or *thrombocytes,* floating in the plasma provide the substance thrombin that acts upon the fibrinogen in the plasma to bring about clotting. Blood cells are formed chiefly in the *marrow* contained in cavities within the bones. Some are formed in the *spleen,* which also disposes of old cells.

The *heart* is a connected series of chambers enclosed by muscular walls (Fig. 2-13). It consists of (1) a conical thick-walled *ventricle* posteriorly; (2) the left and right *auricles* anteriorly, with thin muscular walls; (3) a thin triangular *sinus venosus* dorsally; and (4) a stout tubular *truncus arteriosus* that leads forward from the anterior base of the ventricle. *Valves* between the chambers prevent backward flow of blood. The auricles are separated by an interauricular septum. In the truncus is a thin, flat, and twisted spiral valve. The heart is covered

by a thin membrane, the *pericardium,* and is enclosed in a sac of the same material.

The *arteries* are blood vessels (Fig. 6-4) that carry blood away from the heart. They are lined by a glassy-smooth endothelium and have stout walls containing smooth muscle cells and connective tissue fibers to maintain the *blood pressure* produced by contractions of the heart. The arteries branch again and again into successively smaller vessels, with thinner walls, that extend to all parts of the body. The finest arteries (arterioles) connect to the microscopic *capillaries,* which have walls only of endothelium and are scattered densely among tissue cells of the body. Here food and oxygen are distributed through the capillary walls, some plasma and lymph cells escape, and both carbon dioxide and other wastes are taken into the blood. The capillaries join to form small *veins,* and these in turn combine into larger veins that carry

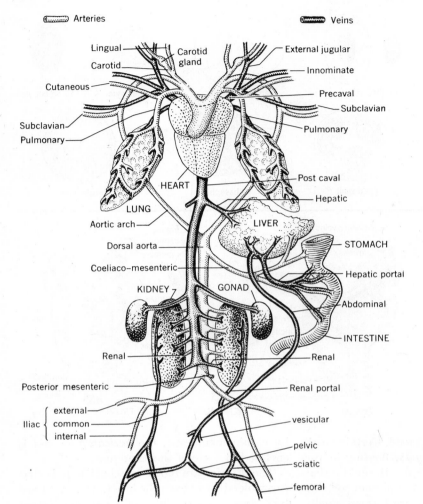

Arteries

Veins

Lingual
Carotid
Carotid gland
External jugular
Innominate
Cutaneous
Precaval
Subclavian
Subclavian
Pulmonary
Pulmonary

HEART
Post caval
Hepatic

LUNG
Aortic arch
LIVER
Dorsal aorta
STOMACH
Coeliaco–mesenteric
Hepatic portal
KIDNEY
GONAD
Abdominal
Renal
INTESTINE
Renal
Posterior mesenteric
Renal portal
Iliac { external
common
internal
vesicular
pelvic
sciatic
femoral

Fig. 2-14. Circulatory system of the bullfrog in ventral view showing principal arteries and veins in relation to the internal organs.

blood toward or to the heart. Their structure is essentially like that of the arteries, but the walls are thinner, with less muscle and connective tissue, since the blood pressure in veins is lower than in arteries.

The course of circulation (Figs. 2-15, 6-6) is thus: Blood accumulates in the sinus venosus, which contracts to force it into the right auricle. Blood from the lungs accumulates in the left auricle. The two auricles then contract and force their contents into the ventricle. Earlier it was thought that when the ventricle contracted the spiral valve deflected unoxygenated blood from the right side into the pulmocutaneous arch and oxygenated blood from the left

side into the carotid and systemic arches. By injecting opaque but inert materials into the blood stream and quickly making X-ray photographs (Foxen and Wells), it was found that the two streams mix. Cutaneous respiration, both in water and on land, is thought to compensate for failure of all unoxygenated blood to be pumped to the lungs.

The left and right branches of the truncus subdivide into three major vessels or "arches," the common *carotid* to the head, the *systemic* to the body and viscera, and the *pulmocutaneous* to the lungs and skin. Where the carotid divides, there is a spongy carotid gland to equalize blood pressure in the vessels beyond.

Fig. 2-15. Plan of the circulation (flow chart) in a frog or other land vertebrate, with both blood vessels (solid lines) and lymph vessels (broken lines); arrows indicate the direction of flow.

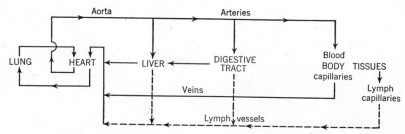

The two systemic arches curve around the esophagus to join as a median *dorsal aorta* extending posteriorly below the vertebrae. Each pulmocutaneous artery divides into a *pulmonary artery* to capillaries in the lungs and a *cutaneous* artery branching on the inner surface of the skin. The arterial system has the pattern of a tree, with repeated branchings (Fig. 2-14).

The venous system is somewhat more complex. Two *precaval veins* return blood to the sinus venosus from veins in the head, fore limbs, and skin. A median *postcaval vein* collects from the kidneys, gonads, and dorsal musculature. There are also three special venous paths. (1) Two *pulmonary veins* return blood that has been oxygenated in the lungs to the left auricle; all other veins deliver eventually to the sinus venosus and right auricle. (2) The *hepatic portal system* gathers blood from the digestive tract (stomach and intestines) and carries it to the liver. There the veins break up into capillaries, and then the blood is assembled in hepatic veins that enter the postcava. The hepatic portal circulation allows some materials in blood from the digestive tract to be either stored or filtered out during passage through the liver. In the frog the hepatic portal also receives an abdominal vein that collects from the hind limbs (femoral veins), bladder, and ventral body wall. (3) The *renal portal system* gathers blood from the hind limbs (sciatic and femoral veins) and posterior body wall and divides into capillaries within the kidneys. This blood is collected by the renal veins and returns to the heart in the postcaval vein.

The *lymphatic system* includes many delicate *lymph vessels* of varied diameter and shape that penetrate the organs and tissues but are difficult to see. Frogs and toads, unlike other vertebrates, have also several large *lymph sacs* or spaces between the skin and body (Fig. 2-5). Behind the shoulder girdle and beside the anus are two pairs of *lymph hearts* that pulsate frequently in a living frog. Dorsal to the coelom and peritoneum there is a large *subvertebral lymph sac* about the kidneys. The watery *lymph* in these structures contains leucocytes but lacks red cells and some proteins of blood plasma. It filters out from blood capillaries into the tissues, enters the lymph vessels, and later returns to the veins. Some small openings (stomata) in the peritoneum communicate with lymph vessels.

2-11. Respiratory system. The energy for life and growth is derived by the oxidation, or "physiological burning," of absorbed food. This is analogous to the burning of coal in the presence of oxygen to yield heat and carbon dioxide ($C + O_2 \rightarrow CO_2 + $ heat). *Respiration* is the process of supplying oxygen to the body; the removal of carbon dioxide that results from metabolism is really a matter of excretion but is commonly discussed as part of respiration. The oxygen–carbon dioxide exchange between the air or water and the blood is termed *external respiration,* and that between the blood and body cells is *internal respiration.*

The *respiratory organs* of a frog are the *lungs, skin,* and *lining of the mouth cavity.* They all have moist surfaces (epithelium) close over blood vessels. Oxygen from the air dissolves in the surface moisture and diffuses inward to the blood, whereas carbon dioxide passes in the opposite direction. The *hemoglobin* in red blood cells combines with oxygen where plentiful and releases it as the blood passes through body tissues where oxygen is scarcer and needed. The

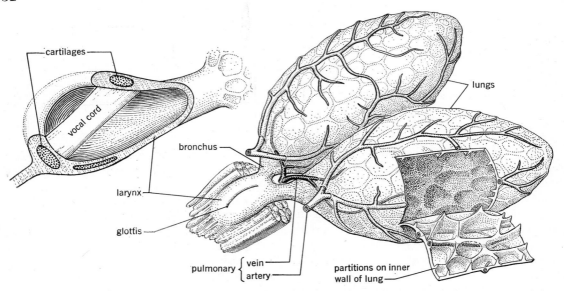

Fig. 2-16. Respiratory organs of the bullfrog in laterodorsal view with left lung cut open to show partitions on inner surface. Enlarged sketch at upper left shows larynx opened along mid-line with right vocal cord in place.

hemoglobin enables the blood to transport much more oxygen than if the latter were dissolved in the plasma. Carbon dioxide, however, is carried mainly by the plasma. The laws of simple diffusion of gases probably account for the exchanges in respiration, as the concentration of oxygen in the air (about 20 per cent) is far greater than in blood, and that in the blood is greater than in tissues; the reverse is true for carbon dioxide.

The frog's *lungs* (Fig. 2-16) are two thin elastic sacs with shallow internal folds that increase the inner surface to form many small chambers, or alveoli. These are lined with capillaries of the pulmonary circulation. Each lung connects by a short *bronchus* to the voice box or *larynx* behind the glottis. The mechanics of breathing involve *inspiration,* or drawing in air, and *expiration,* or forcing it out, both performed with the mouth closed. At inspiration (1) the glottis closes, the mouth floor is depressed, and air is drawn through the nostrils into the mouth cavity and pharynx; (2) the nostrils close (by valves), and the mouth cavity is compressed to force the air through the opened glottis into the lungs. At expiration the muscles of the body

wall contract to force air from the lungs out the mouth cavity and nostrils. Much of the frog's respiration, however, is performed by merely pumping air in and out of the mouth cavity, where the gaseous exchange occurs through the mucous membranes of its lining. The frog's skin contains large blood vessels that serve in respiration either in air or water and especially during hibernation. Oxygen dissolved in the water then passes through the moist skin to the blood, and carbon dioxide moves in the reverse direction. The frog tadpole respires by *gills* (Fig. 32-4) which are slender extensions of the epithelium of the pharynx containing many blood capillaries; their function is comparable with that of the skin or lung of a frog (Fig. 7-2).

The *larynx* is reinforced by cartilages and contains two elastic bands, the *vocal cords.* When air is forced vigorously from the lungs, the cords vibrate and produce croaking notes, the pitch of the sound being regulated by muscular tension on the cords.

2-12. Excretory system. The animal body is a delicately balanced system from which excess materials and the wastes, or end products, of

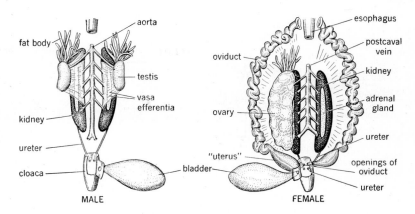

Fig. 2-17. Excretory and reproductive organs (urogenital system) in ventral view. Cloaca opened ventrally to show entrance of ducts (enlarged), and bladder turned aside. Aorta and arteries shown in male, postcaval vein in female (compare Fig. 2-14); left ovary omitted.

metabolism must be removed. The process of removal is termed *excretion*. Some wastes are disposed of by the skin and lungs, others are discharged from the liver in the bile, and some are excreted from the intestine with the feces. The principal *excretory organs* of the frog are the two long brown *kidneys* (Fig. 2-17), dorsal to the coelom and peritoneum. The kidneys are selective filters that remove soluble organic wastes (especially urea), excess mineral salts, and water gathered from the body cells and fluids by the blood (Chap. 8).

Each kidney is a compact mass of about 2,000 *renal corpuscles* bound together by connective tissue. A renal corpuscle comprises (1) a coiled knot, or *glomerulus,* of small arteries within (2) a double-walled cup, or *Bowman capsule,* that is connected to (3) a *uriniferous tubule* surrounded by capillaries (Fig. 8-5). The latter joins through collecting tubules to the *ureter* (Wolffian duct), a fine white tube that extends along the outer margin of the kidney to the dorsal wall of the cloaca. Blood with both oxygen and wastes is brought to the kidneys in the renal arteries, which divide into arterioles in the glomeruli and continue as capillaries about the tubules; the renal portal veins also join to these capillaries. Blood reduced in wastes leaves the kidneys by the renal veins. On the ventral surface of each kidney are many ciliated funnels (nephrostomes) that may drain wastes from the coelom. They connect to uriniferous tubules in frog larvae and later to the renal veins.

The liquid waste collected in the kidneys is the *urine.* It passes down the ureters to the cloaca and may be voided at once through the anus or may be stored temporarily in the thin-walled *bladder* connected to the ventral side of the cloaca. The daily output of urine in summer amounts to about one-third of the frog's weight.

2-13. Endocrine glands. Like other vertebrates, the frog has several endocrine or ductless glands that produce substances known as *hormones.* The latter are also called *internal secretions* because they are carried by the blood instead of being passed out through ducts. The hormones regulate various physiological processes (see general discussion in Chap. 9).

At the base of the brain is a minute *pituitary gland,* of three lobes. The *anterior lobe,* in larvae and young, secretes a *growth-stimulating hormone* that controls growth, especially of long bones, and also affects the thyroid. Removal of the gland in larvae delays their growth, and they do not change into frogs; replanting the gland restores these functions. Feeding or injecting an extract of the gland produces larvae of greater than normal size. In adult frogs the anterior lobe secretes a *gonad-stimulating hormone* responsible for release of ova or sperm from the reproductive organs. If two or more fresh anterior lobes are implanted on successive days in an adult but nonbreeding female, her eggs will soon mature and be laid. Similar implants into a male will

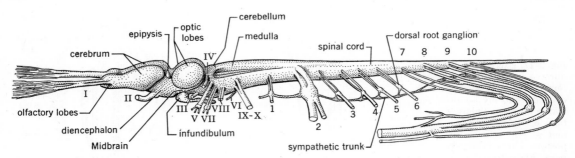

Fig. 2-18. Nervous system of the bullfrog in laterodorsal view, with the nerves and sympathetic trunk of the left side. I–X, cranial nerves; 1–10, spinal nerves (Table 10-1).

hasten sexual maturity, the clasping reflex, and the discharge of spermatozoa. The *intermediate lobe* produces *intermedin,* which regulates the behavior of chromatophores in the skin. Its removal is followed by a marked bleaching due to concentration of the pigment (Fig. 2-7); if then implanted, the pigment spreads and normal coloration results. The *posterior lobe* evidently regulates water intake by the skin; its removal seems to inhibit molt of the cornified epidermis and to cause deposition of pigment there.

The small *thyroid gland* behind the hyoid cartilage produces *thyroxin,* which regulates general metabolism. The gland enlarges and its secretion increases in larvae before they metamorphose into frogs. If removed, the larvae do not transform. If the gland or its extract is injected into young bullfrog larvae, which normally have a two-year larval life, their metamorphosis is hastened.

The *pancreas* secretes, besides digestive enzymes, the hormone known as *insulin,* which regulates sugar metabolism. This is produced by special cell groups, the *islets of Langerhans.* Its action is less conspicuous in the cold-blooded frog than in birds and mammals.

Along the ventral surface of each kidney is a slender *adrenal gland* that produces *epinephrin* (adrenalin). This hormone causes increased blood pressure and also contracts dark pigment in the skin.

2-14. Nervous system. The complex physiological processes of the many organs within the body and the frog's relations with its external environment are controlled and coordinated by the *nervous system* (Fig. 2-18). This is an intricate structure composed of nerve cells, or *neurons* (Chap. 3). The *central nervous system* comprises the brain and spinal cord, and the *peripheral nervous system* includes the paired cranial and spinal nerves together with the sympathetic nervous system.

The *brain* is housed in the "brain box," or cranium. In dorsal view it shows (1) two *olfactory lobes* with nerves to the nasal chambers; (2) two *cerebral hemispheres* closely joined to the preceding and also attached to (3) the median *diencephalon,* or 'tween-brain. Behind this are two rounded *optic lobes,* supported on (4) the *midbrain* below, and followed by (5) a small transverse *cerebellum;* this is over (6) the open-topped *medulla oblongata,* which tapers to join the spinal cord. The diencephalon has a dorsal *pineal body* or *epiphysis.* Below the diencephalon is the *optic chiasma* (crossing of the optic nerves) followed by the *infundibulum* as a bluntly triangular outgrowth, with the *hypophysis,* or *pituitary gland,* at its posterior end.

The *cavities* within the brain are the first and second *ventricles* in the cerebral hemispheres; these connect to a third ventricle in the diencephalon. From the latter a small aqueduct of Sylvius leads to the fourth ventricle located in the medulla. The fourth ventricle is continuous with a minute central canal through the spinal cord. Cerebrospinal fluid fills the ventricles and other cavities and surrounds the brain. Metabolic exchanges for the brain are performed by arteries and veins over its surface and by two dense networks of blood vessels, the **anterior choroid plexus** over a dorsal opening in the diencephalon and the **posterior choroid plexus** above the medulla. The brain and spinal cord are surrounded by two membranes, a thicker **dura mater** adhering to the enclosing bones and a delicate **pia mater** close over the nervous tissue itself. Ten pairs of **cranial nerves** extend from various parts of the brain to sense organs, muscles, and other structures (Table 10-1).

The functions of the brain have been determined by studying the behavior of frogs after experimentally injuring or removing parts and by stimulation with electric currents. The olfactory lobes serve the sense of smell. The cerebral hemispheres are areas of memory, intelligence, and voluntary control in higher animals, but in the frog their function is less clear. Removal impairs memory, the frog is lethargic, and its movements are more machine-like. The diencephalon is related to vision and balance. The optic lobes inhibit reflexes in the spinal cord, each controlling the opposite side of the body. In higher vertebrates the cerebellum is a center of coordination; in the frog it controls equilibrium in part. The medulla directs most bodily activities. If all the brain but the medulla is removed, the frog can leap, swim, capture and swallow food, recover normal position if inverted, and breathe normally. Death soon follows removal of the medulla.

The **spinal cord** extends backward from the medulla and within the neural arches of the vertebrae, to end as a slender filament in the urostyle. It has lengthwise dorsal and ventral **fissures** and contains a **central canal** already noted. The outer **white matter** is chiefly of nerve fibers, and the inner **gray matter** consists largely of nerve cells. Ten pairs of **spinal nerves** emerge from the cord, between the vertebrae, as shiny white strands on the dorsal wall of the abdomen above the peritoneum. Each nerve has two roots. The **sensory** or **dorsal root** carries nerve impulses from parts of the body *into* the spinal cord, and on this root is an enlargement, or **ganglion,** containing nerve cells. The **motor** or **ventral root** comprises fibers that transmit directive impulses *outward* from the cord to the tissues. The two roots of each join outside the cord as a nerve that extends to a definite part of the body or limbs. On either side, the large second or **brachial nerve** joins in a network, or **brachial plexus,** from which nerves run to the fore limb and shoulder region. The seventh to ninth form a **sciatic plexus** that distributes to the hind limb.

The **sympathetic nervous system** shows as two thread-like nerve strands above the dorsal wall of the coelom. Each has 10 ganglia and many fibers connecting to the brain, spinal cord, and viscera. The system directs many internal (vegetative) functions that are not under conscious or voluntary regulation such as the rate of heartbeat, secretion of digestive juices, muscular movements in the stomach and intestine, and the muscular "tone" of blood vessels (compare Fig. 10-5).

2-15. Sense organs. Changes in either the external or internal environment of an animal act as stimuli that affect **sensory structures,** or **receptors,** in its body. The receptors are connected to sensory nerves and give rise to nerve impulses, which are transmitted to the central nervous system. Each kind of stimulus affects a particular kind of receptor. We know accurately only the sensations of man; from these we interpret the sensory reactions of lower animals. In the frog, microscopic receptors for **touch** (tactile stimuli) are present under the epidermis. Others probably respond to irritating substances such as strong chemicals and possibly to heat. The tongue bears small papillae containing **taste buds.** The sense of **smell** is ascribed to endings of the olfactory nerves in the nasal cavities.

The vertebrate **ear** serves two functions: **hearing** and adjusting the **equilibrium** of the body. The latter sense resides in the semicircular canals and ampullae of the inner ear (Chap. 10). The frog has an **eardrum** (tympanic membrane) exposed on either side of the head to receive sound waves from air or water. Vibrations induced in an eardrum are transmitted across the space beneath (middle ear) by a rod (columella) connecting the eardrum and inner ear. The latter lies within the prootic bone and contains a lymph-filled compartment with sensory endings of the auditory nerve (eighth cranial) where sound impressions are registered. Frogs are insensitive to most sounds but react to the croaking notes of males during the breeding season.

The *eye* is the most complex of vertebrate sense organs and responds to *light* or electromagnetic radiation of certain frequencies. The frog's eyes are much like those of man (Fig. 10-15). The *eyeball* lies in the orbit, beneath the eyelids; it is moved by six muscles attached to its outer surface. Its structure is analogous to that of a camera, having a transparent biconvex lens that forms an image on the sensitive interior. The outer *sclerotic coat,* of connective tissue, forms a supporting case, with the *cornea* as a transparent front. The next or *choroid coat* contains blood vessels and much black pigment to exclude all light save that entering the front. The innermost layer or *retina* contains the *rods* and *cones,* receptors for vision, that connect to the *optic nerve* (second cranial). Inside the cornea, part of the choroid coat is specialized as the *iris,* a pigmented disc with a central opening, or *pupil,* through which light enters the spherical *lens* just behind. The pupil contracts or dilates to regulate the amount of light entering the eye. The frog's lens does not change in either shape or position, and its eye is like a "box camera" for forming images of objects beyond a certain minimum distance. The space before the lens contains a watery *aqueous humor,* and that behind, a jelly-like *vitreous humor,* both serving to maintain the form of the eyeball.

2-16. Reproductive system. The organ systems discussed previously are all concerned with the life of the individual animal, whereas the *reproductive system* serves to maintain the frog as a species. It consists of the reproductive organs or *gonads,* which produce sex cells, and the *reproductive ducts* through which these cells leave the body (Fig. 2-17). Frogs are of two *sexes,* the *females* which lay eggs or *ova* (sing. *ovum*),

and the *males* which produce sperm or *spermatozoa* to fertilize the eggs and cause them to develop into new individuals. Each individual frog is either female or male, the sexes being separate.

The female's two gonads, or *ovaries,* are attached dorsally in the coelom, near the kidneys, each supported by a mesentery (mesovarium). In early spring the ovaries of an adult contain several thousand small black eggs that swell out the abdomen, but a summer specimen has only a small mass of grayish ovarian substance. Each ovary is a hollow sac of four to seven lobes with thin double walls, and every egg is enclosed in a delicate follicle formed of cells between the two layers. The ovary is supplied with arteries that bring materials for growth of the ova. Along either side of the middorsal line of the coelom is a whitish convoluted *oviduct;* its anterior end is an open ciliated funnel (ostium) and its posterior end joins dorsally to the cloaca.

When the eggs become mature, in the breeding season, each follicle ruptures (because of a pituitary hormone) and the eggs escape into the coelom. There they are moved anteriorly by the action of cilia covering the peritoneum and enter the oviduct funnels. They are moved down the ducts by cilia on lengthwise ridges lining the interior. Between these ridges are gland cells; these secrete albuminous material to form the jelly coatings that swell out around the eggs after laying (Fig. 2-20). At 22 to 25°C. the eggs pass through the oviduct in about 4 hours, and they may be accumulated in the enlarged posterior portion (uterus) before being laid by passing out the cloaca.

The male has two small bean-shaped *testes* attached near the kidneys by mesenteries (mesorchia). Each testis is a mass of coiled *seminiferous tubules* where spermatozoa are produced. The minute sperm, when mature, enter several fine ducts, or *vasa efferentia,* that connect to uriniferous tubules in the anterior part of the kidney. The sperm then pass down the tubules and ureter (which are joint urinogenital canals) and may be stored in the dilated posterior end, or *seminal vesicle,* of the ureter. At mating, the sperm are discharged through the cloaca to fertilize the eggs. Mature and functional sperm are present from August to May in the leopard frog, *Rana pipiens*.

Anterior to the gonads in both sexes are paired finger-like growths, the *fat bodies*. These provide reserve nutriment, possibly helping in the formation of the sex cells, and serve for subsistence during hibernation. They are largest just prior to hibernation and far reduced after breeding. They are of special importance during the breeding season for the males, which then take little or no food. The fat bodies are used up in frogs kept for some time at laboratory temperatures, and females then may also draw on their yolk-laden eggs for sustenance.

Mature females and males differ in most species of frogs and toads in features called *secondary sexual characteristics.* Males have heavier arm muscles, shorter but stouter inner fingers, and roughened "nuptial pads" on the fingers. Male toads and tree toads have a median resonating pouch on the chin, and there are paired pouches in some frogs. The eardrum is larger in the male bullfrog and green frog, and the two sexes of some toads differ in coloration. In birds and mammals such differences are due to endocrines (Fig. 9-6), but this is not clearly so in all amphibians. Implants of testes into female toads produce thick nuptial pads such as occur in males.

2-17. Natural history and life cycle.
Frogs require a damp environment so that the soft glandular skin will be kept moist, and most species live in or near ponds or streams (Fig. 2-19). They are "cold-blooded" or variable-temperatured (poikilothermous); the body temperature is dependent upon that of the environment. A few live in cold regions, in high mountains or even within the Arctic Circle, but frogs are most abundant as to species and individuals in the moist regions of temperate or tropical lands. They reproduce, feed, and grow during warm weather and hibernate where the winter is cold. In this inactive state, all metabolism in the body drops to a low level and the heartbeat is very slow.

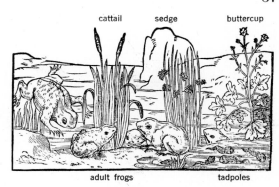

cattail   sedge   buttercup

adult frogs   tadpoles

Fig. 2-19. The earliest illustration of frogs and tadpoles in their natural habitats. (*From Rondelet, De piscibus marinis*, 1551 A.D.)

Each species of frog has a definite time of spring emergence, based upon temperature, and most species proceed at once to reproductive activities (Fig. 2-20). The males gather in appropriate waters and begin croaking to attract the females. The latter, when their eggs are "ripe," enter the water where each is clasped by a male. He mounts her back and grips his forelegs around her thorax, with the roughened nuptial pads on his inner fingers pressed tightly against her breast. As the female extrudes her eggs, the male discharges milt, or seminal fluid containing spermatozoa, to fertilize them. The jelly coats about the eggs swell and adhere to plant stems or other objects, the eggs from each female forming a large tapioca-like mass. Development starts at once, and each egg becomes an embryo, which after some days emerges from the jelly as a small "polliwog," tadpole, or larva. It has an ovoid head-and-body, a slender compressed tail, and horny jaws used to scrape green algae from objects in the water for food. The intestine is then long and spirally coiled in the abdomen. The larva has three pairs of external gills on the pharynx and later these are replaced by three pairs of internal gills within the gill slits (Fig. 32-2). Later the hind legs appear, but the forelegs are hidden under a membrane (operculum) over the ventral surface of the body. Finally, after some weeks or months, depending upon the species of frog and the prevailing temperature, the larva undergoes a metamorphosis. Its lungs

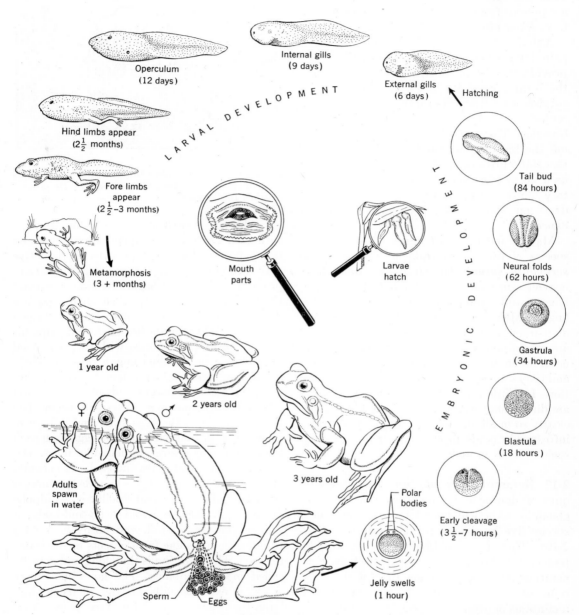

Operculum
(12 days)

Internal gills
(9 days)

External gills
(6 days)

Hatching

L A R V A L   D E V E L O P M E N T

Hind limbs appear
(2½ months)

Fore limbs
appear
(2½–3 months)

Metamorphosis
(3 + months)

Mouth
parts

Larvae
hatch

1 year old

2 years old

3 years old

Adults
spawn
in water

Sperm

Eggs

Jelly swells
(1 hour)

Polar
bodies

Early cleavage
(3½–7 hours)

Blastula
(18 hours)

Gastrula
(34 hours)

Neural folds
(62 hours)

Tail bud
(84 hours)

E M B R Y O N I C   D E V E L O P M E N T

Fig. 2-20. Life cycle of the frog. (*Partly after Rosel,* 1758.) Magnified figures show newly hatched tadpoles clinging to vegetation by their adhesive "discs," and the face of an older larva with its dark horny jaws and minute "teeth." (Compare Fig. 32-2.)

have developed, and it seeks shallow water to gulp down air. The forelegs burst out, and the part larva–part frog lives at the water's edge as its mouth widens, its gills and tail are reabsorbed, and its intestine shortens. The tadpole becomes a frog, and after one or more years becomes sexually mature and reproduces.

Each female lays many hundred eggs. Some eggs fail to develop, and some are eaten by enemies. Many larvae are eaten by fishes, snakes, turtles, or water insects, some larvae die because the water dries up before they transform, and young frogs are victims of many enemies. Of the great numbers of eggs laid each season, only a few become adult frogs; but under usual conditions these are enough to maintain the frog as a species.

REFERENCES

(See also Chap. 32)

GAUPP, E. 1896–1904. A. Ecker und R. Wiedersheim's Anatomie des Frosches. 2d ed. Brunswick, Germany, Friedrich Vieweg & Sohn. 3 vols., 1,774 pp., 500 figs. A classic, with great detail.

HOLMES, S. J. 1928. The biology of the frog. 4th ed. New York, The Macmillan Co. ix + 396 pp., 112 figs. Simple account of structure, physiology, and behavior.

MARSHALL, A. M. 1928. The frog: an introduction to anatomy, histology and embryology. 12th ed. London, Macmillan & Co., Ltd. xi + 182 pp., 40 figs.

3 MATERIALS OF THE ANIMAL BODY

Every animal is an integrated combination of structural parts and systems that perform the various physiological processes essential for life. The larger features of structure and function in the frog are described in Chap. 2. The organ systems are dealt with in greater detail in Chaps. 4 to 10. The materials and finer components of the animal body are discussed in the present chapter.

A. PHYSICAL AND CHEMICAL BACKGROUND

3-1. Matter, weight, and gravity. The substance of the universe, the earth, and living organisms is termed *matter.* Under different environmental conditions of temperature and pressure, any particular kind of matter may be in one of three physical states—solid, liquid, or gas. Water, a common type of matter, may be variously solid ice, fluid water, or water vapor. Animal shells and skeletons are mostly of solids, the blood plasma and much of the content of body cells is fluid, and gases are present in lungs or dissolved in body fluids. Almost any animal comprises matter in three states.

The *mass* or quantity of matter in any object or body is one of its basic attributes. Certain forces attract any two bodies of matter, the degree of attraction being dependent upon their masses and distance apart. The attraction between the earth and that of any animal or other object on or near its surface is termed *gravity,* and the value of this force is its *weight.*

The force of gravity keeps animals against the surface of the earth or any solid object on which they may be. It acts more rapidly in air than in a heavier medium such as water where resistance to movement is greater. The weight of any given animal would be less on the moon (small mass) but much greater on Jupiter (larger mass). The volume relation of weight of any object in reference to some standard (such as water) is termed its *specific gravity.* That of a gas is low, whereas that of metals such as iron or gold is high. Among animals specific gravity, and particularly the weight–surface area relationships, determine their habits and influence the types of environments in which they can live. Bats, birds, and insects are able to fly because of their extensive wing surfaces, and some aquatic invertebrates swim and float readily because they have much surface in relation to weight. The effective specific gravity of any aquatic animal is less than that of a comparable land dweller because the former is buoyed up by the weight of water it displaces.

Because of another property or force, *inertia,* a body at rest tends to remain so and one in motion tends to continue in motion. Inertia is directly related to mass. A child's wagon requires less force to start into motion (overcoming inertia) than an automobile, but the wagon meets more surface resistance to motion and tends to stop sooner than the heavier vehicle. The same is true of animals. An insect has less inertia than a bear, hence it can start and stop more quickly. In the absence of gravity and friction with the air, water, or ground, a body once set in motion would continue on indefinitely; but on the earth resistance of the surroundings eventually overcomes the inertia of movement. Any animal, large or small, must exert propulsive power to remain in motion.

3-2. Cohesion and adhesion. For particles of matter of submicroscopic size (molecules; see par. 3-4) other forces operate: that of **cohesion** tends to keep particles of the same kind together and that of **adhesion** those of different kinds. Cohesion of molecules at the surface of a body of water (or other fluid) produces an elastic skin-like effect termed **surface tension** that tends to make the surface minimum in extent. This tension has an appreciable elastic strength; it will support a clean needle laid on the surface. Water striders and other insects can "walk" on the surface film because their feet are covered by a nonwettable wax that does not break the cohesive force. Surface tension rounds up rain water as drops, and microscopic amounts of oil within animal cells are formed into spherical droplets by this force. Adhesion and surface tension are responsible for the rise of fluid in a fine capillary tube. An insect that falls with its wings on the surface film of a pool may be unable to rise again because of adhesion between its wings and the water. All the phenomena named—gravity, inertia, cohesion, surface tension, and adhesion—are involved in the structural make-up and bodily processes of animals at both gross and microscopic levels.

3-3. Energy. Another important basic component of our universe is **energy,** "the capacity to do work." All activities of living organisms are expressions of energy; examples are the movements of animals, the digestion and use of food,

and the transmission of nerve impulses. Energy may be manifested in several ways: *motion,* such as the flight of an insect; *heat,* an increase in temperature (due to random movements of particles within matter); *chemical change* or reaction as in the digestion of food; *electric current,* flow of impulses along the course of a nerve; and *light,* transmission of units called photons. All these forms, which are more or less interconvertible, are termed **kinetic energy,** the energy of motion (Gr. *kinein,* to move). A second kind is **potential energy,** literally the energy of position. An upraised hand or foot has potential energy, but as it swings to throw or kick a ball this is converted to the kinetic energy of motion. According to the Einstein equation $(e = MC^2)$ matter and energy are interconvertible, but this is a phenomenon of nuclear fission (atomic bombs) and such **atomic energy,** a third type, is rare in living organisms.

Two basic laws govern all energy conversion. The law of **conservation of energy** states that in any system the total quantity of energy remains unchanged. In an animal the total received in food is expended in movements, digestion, and other bodily processes, or lost as heat radiated into the environment. None has actually been "lost" to the system of which the animal is a part. The law of **degradation of energy** holds that heat is the end form of all energy transformations and that all forms of energy may be entirely transformed into heat, but that heat may never be transformed completely into the other forms. The energy received by an animal is variously converted in the internal economy of its body, but all that is involved in motion, friction, chemical conversions, or even nerve impulses, finally becomes heat that is transferred to its environment.

The energy in the world, in last analysis, all derives from the sun. Solar radiation is responsible for the development and growth of plants upon which in turn practically all animals depend (Chap. 13).

3-4. Structure of matter. In everyday experience we learn to recognize some of the thou-

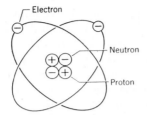

Chapter 3

Fig. 3-1. Model of presumed structure of a helium atom.

sands of kinds of matter or substances to which names are given—water, iron, sugar, etc. Mere inspection, however, may not show whether any particular substance is pure—of one kind— or a mixture of two or more. Ordinary water, for example, usually contains both oxygen (a gas) and salts (solids), in solution. To learn the actual properties of water alone it must be rid of other substances. The science of chemistry is devoted to learning the precise nature of different substances in pure form and mixtures and their reactions with one another.

Chemical research has shown that each kind of pure substance consists of ultramicroscopic units called **molecules.** In turn each molecule is made up of one or more **chemical elements.** The particles of an element are termed **atoms.** A molecule of water consists of two atoms of hydrogen and one of oxygen. For convenience in stating chemical facts and describing chemical reactions the names of elements are represented by symbols: H for hydrogen, O for oxygen, C for carbon, and so on. The formula for the water molecule is therefore H_2O, that of the gas oxygen is O_2, and that of common table sugar is $C_{12}H_{22}O_{11}$. In all, 92 naturally occurring chemical elements have been identified, named, and studied.

By indirect methods we have learned that atoms, in turn, are composed of even smaller particles. No one has been able to see the ultra-minute molecules, atoms, or smallest components; but many careful physical experiments and calculations have made it possible to count and determine their weight, learn their electrical charges, and compute their speed of travel. From these and other data the structural make-up of molecules and atoms has been visualized and models of many have been made.

3-5. Atomic structure. The atom is considered as having a spherical outline with a central **nucleus** around which are one or more ultimate particles called **electrons,** each revolving in an orbit (Fig. 3-1). The make-up of an atom thus roughly resembles our solar system with its central sun (nucleus) and revolving planets (electrons). In both there is a vast amount of space between the components. If an atom were enlarged to a sphere 100 feet in diameter, the nucleus would be perhaps a half inch through. Around the nucleus electrons would be whirring so fast as to be a faint blur.

The nucleus is composed of **protons,** each of which bears a single positive charge, and also **neutrons** that are uncharged. For every positively charged proton in the nucleus there is an electron, negatively charged, in one of the orbits. The entire atom, therefore, is neutral, as the positive and negative charges are equal.

The atoms of the various chemical elements differ from one another in the number of neutrons, protons, and electrons each contains (Fig. 3-2). The combining of chemical elements (ions) to form compounds (molecules) rests on transfer of electrons from one kind of atom to another (Fig. 3-3).

Different kinds of atoms contain one to seven concentric orbits, each with one or more electrons. The elements can be arranged in a **periodic table** according to the number of electrons (or protons) each contains. Hydrogen has 1 electron (and 1 proton), whereby its atomic number is one; helium has 2; sodium has 11; and so on. The atomic weight is an arbitrary number assigned to each kind of atom with reference to oxygen (16) as a standard; sample atomic weights are hydrogen 1, sodium 23, uranium 235.

By means of atomic fission isotopes can be made of most elements (some also occur in nature). An isotope has essentially the same chemical properties as the original element but differs in atomic weight; some kinds spontaneously release electrons from the nucleus, hence are radioactive. Carbon 14 (atomic weight) so produced is essentially like its "parent," carbon 12, but is radioactive; it can be

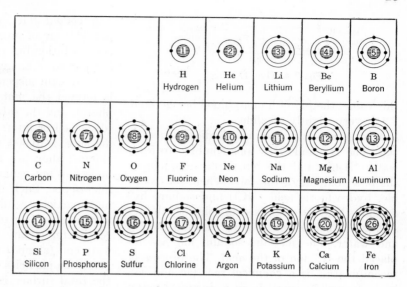

Fig. 3-2. First part of the Periodic Table diagraming the structure of atoms. The central number represents the nucleus and its net positive charge—the atomic number. Small black dots represent planetary electrons, negatively charged, in their respective orbits. The atoms shown include those of elements common (C, H, O, N) or essential (Na, P, etc.) in living matter; still others are present in minute amounts as trace elements (Fe, Si, etc.). Five kinds of atoms are omitted between calcium and iron.

incorporated into a carbon-containing substance that is fed to or injected into an animal, and the course of that type of atom can be traced in its passage in various parts of the body by means of a device to record radioactivity called the Geiger counter. Research with isotopes in plants and animals is serving to reveal some of the most intimate and fundamental details of their chemical processes.

3-6. Ions, electrolytes, and compounds. When the outer orbit contains fewer than half the total number of electrons that it can hold it may lose one or more; if more than half it may gain electrons. A change in number of electrons

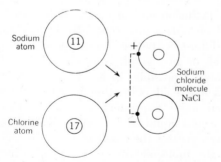

Fig. 3-3. Chemical union of sodium and chlorine to form sodium chloride (table salt). Transfer of one electron leaves the sodium atom in the compound with one positive charge (11 in nucleus, 10 electrons), and the chlorine becomes negatively charged (17 in nucleus, 18 electrons).

changes the electrical nature of the atom—gaining electrons it becomes negative, but losing any it becomes positive. An atom thus changed is termed an *ion;* with an excess of electrons it becomes an *anion* (having a negative charge; in an electric field it moves toward the anode or positive pole); with a deficit it becomes a *cation* (going to the cathode or negative pole). A solution containing ions will conduct an electric current, hence is termed an *electrolyte.*

A substance formed by the joining of two or more different kinds of atoms is a *compound.* Any compound that releases H^+ atoms (ions) when dissolved in water is called an *acid.* Common examples are hydrochloric acid, acetic acid (in vinegar), and lactic acid (in sour milk). A *base* or *alkali* is a compound that in solution releases OH^- ions. Caustic soda ($NaOH$) and ammonia water (NH_4OH) are household examples. Both acids and alkalies, in strong concentration, are severe irritants and will "burn" the skin and the delicate coverings of the eyes and mouth.

The strength of an acid or alkali is indicated by the relative number of hydrogen (H^+) or hydroxyl (OH^-) ions present in a given solution. This is represented by an exponential value termed the *pH*, where a value of 7 is neutral (Fig. 3-4). Most body fluids are close to

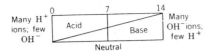

Fig. **3-4.** The pH range.

this value, the pH of human blood being about 7.3 or very slightly alkaline.

Mixing an acid and an alkali produces a *salt.* The H^+ and OH^- ions combine to form water (H_2O), and the remaining ions join as the new compound, the salt. When, for example, hydrochloric acid (HCl) and sodium hydroxide (NaOH) are mixed in solution, the result is the compound sodium chloride (NaCl) and water. The metallic sodium ion has replaced the H^+ ion of the acid. The process of recombination is a *chemical reaction* and can be expressed in symbols as a *chemical equation,* thus:

$$HCl + NaOH \rightarrow NaCl + H_2O$$

The arrow indicates the course of the reaction. If the reaction is reversible, as is true of many biological reactions in living organisms, a dual symbol $\rightleftharpoons$ is used.

3-7. Mixtures. When a substance is mixed with any fluid the result is variously a solution, suspension, or colloid. In a *solution* the molecules or ions of dissolved substance (the solute) soon become evenly distributed throughout those of the liquid (the solvent). Many acids, bases, salts, and other compounds (e.g., sugars) form true solutions in which the solute soon disappears from view and the solvent becomes clear. One liquid may be dissolved in another, such as alcohol in water, and a gas may be dissolved in a fluid as oxygen does in water. If, however, the dispersed particles are of larger size (groups of molecules) a *suspension* results; mixing clay or flour in water yields a cloudy product; if allowed to stand undisturbed it will slowly clear as the particles settle to the bottom. An *emulsion* is a mixture of a fluid and fine particles or droplets of another liquid; milk containing droplets of cream (butterfat) and mayonnaise (oil, vinegar, raw egg) are examples.

A *colloid* (Gr. *kolla,* glue) results when the particles are of intermediate size—too large to enter solution but too small to settle out. Glue is a colloid of animal gelatin in water; the particles remain suspended indefinitely. The water is termed the *matrix* (continuous or external phase), and the other material is the *inclusion* (dispersed or internal phase). Colloid particles measure 1/10,000 to 1/1,000,000 mm. in diameter; they are larger than most chemical molecules but cannot be seen with an ordinary microscope. Such division of matter into minute particles results in an enormous increase in ratio of surface to volume. Thus a solid cubic centimeter of any substance has a surface of 6 sq. cm. (about 1 square inch), but when dispersed as particles 1/100,000 mm. in diameter the total surface is about 6,000 sq. meters or 1⅜ acres! The large surfaces provided by colloid dispersion in living matter are important for the chemical changes constantly in progress there. Colloids do not diffuse through membranes (par. 3-8) and when dried usually are masses of indefinite form; by contrast, crystalloids (e.g., salt, sugar) diffuse readily and when dried produce crystals of regular and characteristic structure. A colloid system may be either a semirigid *gel* or a more fluid *sol* (like gelatin in water when cold, then warmed). In living matter which is largely colloidal these states may interchange during metabolic processes.

3-8. Diffusion and osmosis. Molecules in any kind of matter are constantly in motion, and the differences between states of matter—solid, liquid, or gas—result from the relative degree of motion possible. In a solid such as iron or brick the field of motion is extremely small. When more movement is possible the substance is a liquid, and when the limit of motion is even greater the result is a gas. In a fluid or gas the molecules move out in all directions until they are evenly distributed throughout the available space. Under a high-power microscope a suspension of minute particles shows a dancing "Brownian movement" of the particles resulting from the repulsion between mole-

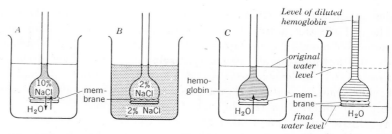

Fig. 3-5. Simple diffusion and osmosis. *Left. A.* End of thistle tube containing 10 per cent salt solution is covered by a permeable membrane and inverted in a beaker of pure water. *B.* Salt diffuses out through the membrane, and water diffuses in until solution is of same strength on both sides (equilibrium). *Right. C.* Hemoglobin solution in tube, pure water in beaker. *D.* Molecules of hemoglobin are too large to pass pores in *semi*permeable membrane, but water diffuses inward, diluting hemoglobin solution; level of fluid becomes higher in tube but lower in beaker.

cules. Movement of molecules from places of higher to lower concentration is termed **diffusion.** If an odoriferous gas (e.g., hydrogen sulfide) is released in one corner of a room, it quickly diffuses and can be smelled in any part of the air. When a solid such as sugar or salt is immersed in water, it quickly **dissolves** and shortly molecules of the compound are uniformly spread throughout the water, as one can confirm by withdrawing a drop in a pipette from any portion.

The forces that repel one molecule from another result in a **diffusion pressure** proportional to the number of molecules present per unit volume of space. If two gases are enclosed in a container, each becomes diffused equally, and the total pressure is the sum of the two partial pressures. In like manner there is diffusion pressure in a solution when a quantity of any substance is dissolved in a fluid.

If a vessel containing water is divided in two by a metal partition, then sugar may be dissolved in one compartment and salt in the other, but the two will not mix. If, however, the partition is of collodion, cellophane, or parchment, sugar will diffuse through from the first compartment to the second, and salt in the opposite direction. The thin sheet acts as a **permeable membrane** having submicroscopic pores that permit the molecules of sugar and of salt to pass. Many of the finer structures in animal bodies are surrounded by **semiperme-**

able membranes that are selective in their action. Such membranes regulate the movement of food substances, respiratory gases, other essential materials, and of wastes between body parts. Some membranes permit passage of larger molecules than others, and the rate of passage varies with the kind of membrane and the kinds and amounts of material on the two sides.

When unequal concentrations of dissolved substances occur on the opposite sides of a semipermeable membrane, the resulting differences in diffusion pressure force exchange of water and of the dissolved substances through the membrane until there is equilibrium (equal diffusion pressure) on the two sides. The diffusion of water through a semipermeable membrane is termed **osmosis** (some authors use this term also for diffusion of dissolved substances). When two fluids contain equal concentrations of dissolved substances they are said to be **isotonic.** Solutions used to immerse living cells or tissues for study are made isotonic with the natural fluids that surrounded them in the body, as to the kinds and amounts of the principal salts (0.9 per cent NaCl for mammalian blood or tissues, etc.). A *hypo*-tonic solution has a lower osmotic (diffusion) pressure than that in the material with which it is being compared, and a *hyper*-tonic one has more.

Two experiments with artificial semipermeable membranes (collodion or cellophane) will demonstrate (Fig. 3-5) diffusion and osmosis. The end of a thistle tube is covered by a semipermeable membrane and inverted in a beaker; the thistle tube contains 10 per cent salt solution (NaCl; molecular weight, 58), and the beaker contains only pure water (*A*). Some salt will diffuse through the membrane from the thistle tube to the beaker and some water from the beaker to the thistle tube until an equilibrium occurs with equal parts of salt and water in each (*B*). When a solution of hemoglobin is placed in the thistle tube (*C*), however, water will move from the beaker to the thistle tube by osmosis, whereby the level of fluid rises in the tube and lowers in the beaker (*D*). This results because hemoglobin molecules are too large (molecular weight, 63,000 to 68,000) to pass through pores in the membrane. These experiments show processes involved in transfer of materials across membranes of living cells in animal bodies.

3-9. Animal form and function. The basic properties of matter are of great importance in the structure and physiology of animals. An animal has mass that is acted upon by the force of gravity to keep it on the earth or any object upon which it rests. Because of inertia it remains in one position unless it expends force (power of muscles) to move. When in motion friction with the air, water, or soil tends to reduce its movements and continued expenditure of energy (muscle action) is needed to keep it traveling. Cohesion and adhesion keep the various microscopic parts of the body attached to each other, and surface tension affects the form of liquids within the body and its cells.

The animal requires energy to make bodily movements and for the essential processes of its internal organs. The energy is derived from food which is variously transformed by digestion and metabolism (Chap. 5). The end product of energy transformations of all kinds, from a nerve impulse to violent use of muscles, is heat which is eventually transferred to the animal's environment.

Chemical processes in the body result from interactions of the ions, atoms, and molecules that form the substance of the animal. As detailed in later chapters, there are nervous and chemical controls operating constantly in the functions of the body to maintain a relatively steady internal environment. When the normal pattern becomes deranged, illness or death ensue. "Life" may be regarded as an enormously complex system of interacting physical and chemical processes that are intricately and delicately balanced.

B. PROTOPLASM

The living substance in the cells of all plants and animals is called *protoplasm.* It is a complex mixture of various materials, including water, mineral salts, and many organic compounds. The latter are known in nature only as components or products of living organisms. In different species and in the parts and organs of any one animal the protoplasm differs in its chemical, physical, and biological properties. It has, however, certain common characteristics which are discussed below.

3-10. Chemical composition. Protoplasm contains about 20 of the 92 natural chemical elements. The proportions of these and the specific compounds into which they are organized differ in various animals and in the different cells and tissues of any one animal. These elements are among the most common in the rocks, soils, and waters of the earth; they are present in foods taken by animals, in their useful products or secretions, and in the wastes of animal metabolism. An average percentage chemical composition of animal protoplasm (by weight and apart from intercellular substance) is as follows:

Oxygen (O)	76.0	Potassium (K)	0.3
Carbon (C)	10.5	Iron (Fe)	0.01
Hydrogen (H)	10.0	Magnesium (Mg)	0.02
Nitrogen (N)	2.5	Calcium (Ca)	0.02
Sulfur (S)	0.2	Sodium (Na)	0.05
Phosphorus (P)	0.3	Chlorine (Cl)	0.10

Traces of silicon (Si), copper (Cu), aluminum (Al), manganese (Mn), boron (B), cobalt (Co), iodine (I), fluorine (Fl), and bromine (Br) are also present in many animals. No single element is peculiar to living things, but carbon and nitrogen are more abundant in protoplasm than among inanimate materials.

3-11. Water, salts, and gases. Protoplasm contains much water (H_2O), various salts (NaCl, $CaCO_3$, etc.), and some gases, especially oxygen (O_2) and carbon dioxide (CO_2). *Water* makes up from 80 to 95 per cent of the weight, being more abundant in young cells or animals than in older ones and in the lower aquatic animals than in the higher terrestrial types. Water (1) is the best solvent for inorganic substances and for many organic compounds; (2) favors the dissociation of electrolytes dissolved in it; (3) has high surface tension; (4) has great fluidity; and (5) has a large capacity to absorb heat. All the necessary processes of protoplasm are dependent upon these characteristics of water, and the life of organisms on this earth would be impossible without it. Watery body fluids (lymph and blood plasma), with both inorganic and organic content, surround cells in the animal body and transport materials within it. Terrestrial animals usually have a suitable body covering and other means to restrict undue loss of water.

The *inorganic salts* are chiefly those found in sea water, notably sodium chloride (NaCl), and are present in small concentrations; the ions of these are important in the composition of protoplasm, its chemical activities and electrical properties, and for growth, maintenance of health, and reproduction. The skeletons or shells of many animals are composed of inorganic salts—especially calcium carbonate, $CaCO_3$, and calcium phosphate, $Ca_3(PO_4)_2$—secreted by specific cells or tissues.

3-12. Organic compounds. These are the compounds of carbon with hydrogen, oxygen, often nitrogen, and sometimes other elements. Carbon, with four bonds, becomes grouped in "chains" and rings, thus:

Its free bonds become joined by hydrogen, oxygen, nitrogen, hydroxyl (OH) and other radicals, and certain other elements. Collectively the "organic" compounds include all those present in the protoplasm of plants and animals together with many new kinds synthesized by chemists. Protoplasm consists mainly of three types: carbohydrates, lipids, and proteins.

1. CARBOHYDRATES are compounds of carbon, hydrogen, and oxygen, generally with the latter two in a 2 to 1 ratio, as in water. Starches with the formula $(C_6H_{10}O_5)_x$—where x may be 200 to 300—are common as stored food substances in plants. The cellulose forming the walls of plant cells has the same empirical formula as starch, but x is much larger, and the molecule is of different structure; cellulose is relatively insoluble and can be digested by only a few animals. Starches eaten by animals are broken down (hydrolyzed) into simple sugars by certain digestive enzymes before being absorbed. Glycogen $(C_6H_{10}O_5)_x$—where x is small—is stored in animal tissues and used for energy. For transport in the blood, glycogen is

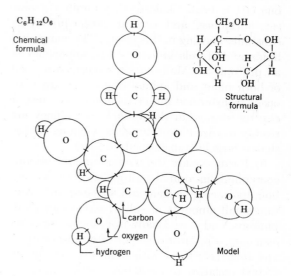

Fig. 3-6. Three ways of picturing the glucose molecule. *Chemical formula,* a shorthand description. *Structural formula,* relative positions of the atoms and the bonds between them. *Model,* "architecture," showing spatial relations.

transformed into glucose (Figs. 3-6, 5-7; par. 5-11). Lactose, or milk sugar ($C_{12}H_{22}O_{11}$), is a carbohydrate present in the milk secreted by all mammals to nourish their young.

2. LIPIDS are fatty and related substances that contain carbon and hydrogen, with less oxygen than in carbohydrates. They are all "greasy" and are soluble in organic liquids such as ether, chloroform, or benzene, but rarely in water. Some are fluid at ordinary temperatures, such as cod-liver oil and whale oil; others are solid fats, such as butter, lard, and tallow; and a few are waxes, like that in the human ear or that produced by bees. The true fats, both liquid and solid, are combinations of glycerol (glycerin) and fatty acids, of which oleic acid ($C_{18}H_{34}O_2$) in olive oil is an example. Fats may be decomposed (saponified) by alkalies such as sodium or potassium hydroxide, yielding glycerol and soaps, which are soluble in water. The compound lipids may contain nitrogen, with or without phosphorus, in addition to carbon, hydrogen, and oxygen; lecithin, abundant in egg yolk, is an example. The sterols are complex wax-like lipids, with many carbon and hydrogen atoms and at least one OH radical. Cholesterol, vitamin D, some sex hormones, and certain cancer-producing substances belong in this group. The compound lipids and sterols are essential components of all protoplasm. Many fats are received in food of both plant and animal origin and are variously transformed either for immediate use or else for storage in the animal body. They are readily oxidized in protoplasm, yielding energy that is largely transformed into heat.

3. PROTEINS are the most abundant organic compounds in animal protoplasm. Besides carbon, hydrogen, oxygen, and **nitrogen,** they contain small amounts of sulfur, sometimes phosphorous, and occasionally iron, iodine, or other elements. Protein molecules often are complex and relatively huge with molecular weights of 35,000 (gelatin) to 5,000,000 (hemocyanin) or more. Thus, lactoglobulin in milk has a molecular weight of about 42,000 and an approximate formula of $C_{1864}H_{3012}O_{576}N_{468}S_{21}$. Proteins are infinite in variety, those in each type of tissue in each kind of organism being more or less different from all others. Protein molecules are being built up and broken down constantly in animal cells, but biochemists have yet to create such molecules in the laboratory.

The basic structural units or "building blocks" in proteins are called amino acids, characterized by nitrogen in an amino radical (NH_2); 23 kinds are known. All have the following basic formula ("BF"), but the R component is different in each kind:

The simplest, glycine, is "BF" + H with one hydrogen atom in the R position; three other amino acids and their major functions are as follows:

CYSTINE
hair growth, etc.

THYROXIN
bodily metabolism

TYROSINE
pigment formation

Animals make 15 amino acids but derive the other 8 from plants. Amino acids evidently are joined in various ways by the action of enzymes (par. 3-15) to form peptides. "Simple" proteins consist entirely of amino acids; examples are the soluble proteins in blood serum, milk albumen, and egg white and the very insoluble ones known as keratins that form cuticle, hair, and nails. "Conjugated" proteins are those containing other radicals or organic compounds besides amino acids; the hemoglobins in red blood cells and nucleoproteins of cell nuclei are examples.

A nucleoprotein is composed of a protein with nucleic acid (containing phosphorus). The chromatin of cell nuclei (par. 3-17) is rich in this acid, which makes possible staining the chromatin with basic dyes. Nucleic acid is also a basic component of viruses. In animals a succession of digestive enzymes serves to reduce nucleic acid and its derivatives for absorption or elimination.

Protoplasm contains additional organic substances, some of unknown composition, that either direct the activities of individual cells or tissues or else control and coordinate the activities of the entire animal. These regulatory substances include enzymes (par. 3-15), vitamins (par. 5-14), respiratory pigments (par. 7-9), and hormones (Chap. 9).

3-13. Physical characteristics. Typically protoplasm is a translucent, often grayish, slimy substance, somewhat viscous, but capable of flowing. Its structure has been variously considered to be (1) granular; (2) foam-like or alveolar; (3) an emulsion; or (4) fibrillar or reticular, of small fibers or threads. Actual differences in kind, difficulties in observing the fine details, and changes incidental to removing protoplasm from living organisms or the fixing of tissues for study are responsible for some differences in the interpretation of its structure.

3-14. Biological activities. Living organisms and the protoplasm of which they are composed are characterized by activity and change. A human being develops as an embryo, is born, grows, lives actively, and dies. Within its protoplasm, as in all animals, many processes are going on constantly. In contrast to nonliving materials, protoplasm is characterized by (1) *metabolism,* the physical and chemical changes by which materials are transformed and used for growth, maintenance, and repair and to yield energy; (2) *irritability,* the response to stimuli from changes in its environment; and (3) *reproduction,* the ability of an organism or its parts to produce new individuals of its own kind. Constructive metabolism (anabolism) includes the synthesis of the products of digestion into compounds, often more complex, which are incorporated into the protoplasm, stored for later use, or formed into essential products such as secretions. By destructive metabolism (catabolism, dissimilation), various components are broken down (oxidized, etc.) to simpler compounds, providing energy for work or heat, with consequent yield of waste products. Both types are occurring simultaneously in living protoplasm, but anabolic processes, leading to growth, predominate during embryonic development and early life.

3-15. Enzymes. Many reactions between chemical substances in the living body proceed with extreme rapidity; yet the same substances, when removed from the body, react slowly if at all. The difference is due to the presence in animal cells and tissues of organic catalysts, known as *enzymes,* each responsible for a specific type of reaction. A catalyst is a compound that speeds up a chemical reaction without affecting the end point or being combined in the end products. A minute amount of enzyme will transform large amounts of a substance; the enzyme pepsin, in pure form, will digest 50,000 times its weight of boiled egg white in 2 hours. Most enzymes are named for the reactions they promote; the enzyme lact*ase* splits lactose (milk sugar) into 2 simpler sugars, and sucr*ase* divides sucrose (table sugar) into glucose and fructose.

Digestion, respiration, secretion, excretion, and other vital processes depend upon enzymes. Some biologists believe there may be a thousand kinds in one animal cell. Each enzyme acts on one class or kind of chemical substance (carbohydrate, fat, protein) and in a particular constructive or destructive type of reaction (Chap. 5). Many enzymes bring about hydrolysis: by action of the enzyme a molecule of water is added to the molecule acted upon and the combination then separates into two molecules. Other enzymes may carry the breakdown still farther. During digestion, for example, carbohydrates are ultimately reduced to simple sugars, fats to fatty acids and glycerol, and proteins to amino acids. Many enzyme reactions are reversible—under one set of conditions a substance is split into two products, but under other circumstances the two will be synthesized into the original material.

Enzymes are protein in nature. Many lose their catalytic power when heated to 40 or 50°C., and this may be one reason many animals die at such temperatures. Each kind does best at some particular temperature and at a certain pH, for example, pepsin at pH 1.5 (HCl, in the stomach), but trypsin at 7 to 8.6 (mildly alkaline, in the intestine). Some 20 to 30 enzymes have been crystallized, but none synthesized. Many enzymes are formed as inactive **zymogens** in the cells where they are produced but require the presence of another substance, an **activator,** to become functional. Thus the inactive trypsinogen, secreted in the pancreas, becomes the active protein-splitting enzyme, trypsin, only after it has passed through the pancreatic duct into the small intestine and been activated there by enterokinase secreted by cells in the intestinal wall. With some enzymes a second substance, or **coenzyme,** is necessary for their functioning. Several vitamins (B_1, B_2, B_6; Table 5-1) are involved in certain enzyme systems.

3-16. Buffers. Protoplasm can "live" only within rather close physical and chemical limits, including (1) temperatures between about 0°C. (32°F.) to 40 or 45°C. (104 or 113°F.); (2) presence of oxygen gas within certain pressures; (3) definite and limited concentrations of salts; and (4) a delicate balance between H^+ and OH^- ions—the **acid-base equilibrium** (regulation of pH). This equilibrium is maintained by **buffers** which are salts of weak acids that can furnish base (usually Na or K) to form salts of strong acids and release weaker acid. Blood, for example, contains dissociated carbonates of sodium and potassium—salts of carbonic acid. Should a stronger acid (hydrochloric, lactic) appear as a result of metabolism, the protective buffer action replaces it by weaker acid; a sample reaction is:

$$NaHCO_3 + HCl \rightarrow NaCl + H_2CO_3$$

| sodium bicarbonate | hydrochloric acid | sodium chloride | carbonic acid |

Sea water is buffered by bicarbonate to a pH of about 8.1, one of its favorable features as an environment for animals. Isotonic salt solutions (Ringer's and Locke's) used for studies of animal tissues are buffered with bicarbonate.

C. CELLS

3-17. History. The finer structures of living organisms were unknown until after invention of the compound microscope (about 1591). In 1665 Robert Hooke reported that cork and other plant materials contained many small partitions separating cavities that he named **cells.** In 1824 René Dutrochet stated that ". . . plants are composed entirely of cells, and of organs that are obviously derived from cells . . .", and that the same applied to animals. In 1833 Robert Brown described the nucleus as a central feature in plant cells. In 1838 M. J. Schleiden put forth the thesis that cells were the unit of structure in plants; and in 1839 his coworker Theodor Schwann applied the thesis to animals. This generalization is known as the **cell theory.** Greater emphasis was given at first to the cell wall and less to the contents. In 1840 Purkinje named the cell contents protoplasm. Research during the past century has extended the theory and shown that the cell contents are far more important than the wall and that intercellular material is produced by certain cells. According to the cell theory *all animals and plants are composed of cells and cell products.* The cell is the fundamental unit, both structural and physiological, in all organisms, and there is a constant exchange of matter and energy within cells in the process of living. In multicellular animals the cells are integrated for proper functioning, whereas in unicellular animals the cell and organism are one. A multicellular animal generally starts life as a single cell that divides repeatedly to form its body.

Most animal cells are minute (Fig. 3-7). The unit of measure used is 0.001 millimeter (mm.), a **micron** (plural, *micra;* symbol, μ). The best light microscope resolves structures measuring about 0.2 μ. Still finer details of cells are revealed by the ultra and electron microscopes (and X-ray diffraction); for these, dimensions are stated in terms of the **angstrom unit, A** (1,000 A = 0.1 μ). Cells vary somewhat in size, but each kind in a particular species of animal is fairly uniform. The smallest cells known are those of bacteria at the limits of visibility of the microscope. Human blood cells average 7.5 μ in diameter, and many other cells are from 10 to 50 μ in size; some nerve cells in large animals are several feet in length. The largest cells are the yolks of bird and shark eggs; that of the chicken is about 30 mm. in diameter (Fig. 11-8) and of the ostrich about 80 mm.

The typical animal cell (Fig. 3-8) is bounded by a **cell** or **plasma membrane** (only a few molecules thick) surrounding the **cytoplasm** that

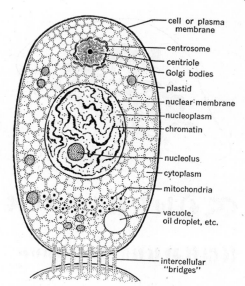

Fig. 3-8. Diagram of an animal cell. Not all parts shown will be present or seen in any one cell, either living or fixed and stained.

fills the interior of the cell. In the cytoplasm there is a smaller distinct structure, the **nucleus.** The cytoplasm is translucent and viscous and contains submicroscopic fibrils. Near the nucleus there is a globular **centrosome** (cell center) containing one or two dot-like **centrioles.** The cytoplasm contains other inclusions such as (1) **mitochondria** (chondriosomes), formed as fibrils or globules 0.5 to over 1 μ in size that have a part in oxidative processes; (2) **Golgi bodies** (lipochondria), thought to serve in producing secretions; (3) **microsomes,** 0.06 to 0.25 μ in size, related to cell metabolism; (4) **fat,** as droplets or as yolk in egg cells; (5) **vacuoles,** filled with either granular or fluid material; and (6) **secretion granules,** especially in gland cells, that are transformed to pass out as secretions. These and other inclusions serve various purposes in cell physiology, not all understood; some require special techniques to be seen.

The nucleus is commonly oval or spherical but in some kinds of cells is long or lobed; it may be centered in the cytoplasm or at one side or end. It is surrounded by a distinct **nuclear membrane** enclosing the nuclear sap (karyolymph). Most important within the nucleus

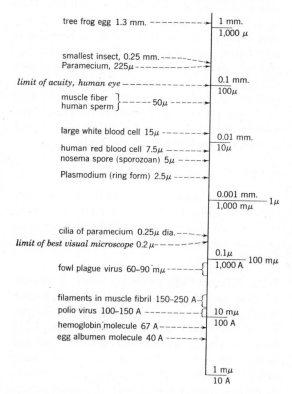

Fig. 3-7. Relative sizes of animal cells and some parts of cells. Each major scale division is 1/10 of that above. 1 millimeter (mm.) = 1,000 micra; 1 micron (μ) = 1,000 millimicrons; 1 millimicron (mμ) = 1,000 angstrom units (A). Visual microscope magnifies about 10 to 2,000 $\times$; electron microscope about 5,000 to 100,000 $\times$ or more.

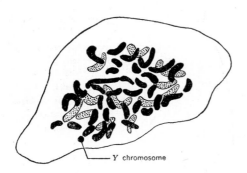

— Y chromosome

Fig. 3-9. The 48 human chromosomes. *Above.* During mitosis in an embryonic mesenchyme cell; deeper-lying chromosomes are stippled; the Y chromosome of the male is marked. × 1500. *Below.* Arranged in homologous pairs to show differences in size and shape. (*After Evans and Swezy*, 1931.)

is the *chromatin,* seemingly of isolated granules but actually parts of continuously spiraled filaments, the *chromonemata.* Chromatin is so named because it stains intensely with basic dyes such as hematoxylin; chemically it is mainly of nucleoprotein. Each nucleus usually contains a spherical *nucleolus* (one or more). The nucleus controls much of cell metabolism; if removed the cell cannot perform anabolic activities and lives only a short time. An isolated nucleus cannot form cytoplasm.

The study of cell structure and activity is known as *cytology.* For most cytological study, cells or pieces of tissue are fixed (killed) in chemical reagents or by freezing, cut in thin sections (10 μ or less), mounted on microscope slides, and stained to differentiate the internal details. Care is necessary that these procedures do not alter the original structures in the cells. Living cells may be treated with "vital dyes" that stain and render parts more visible without injury. Apparatus for microdissection permits removal of cell parts or injection of reagents for special studies. Isolated cells and

tissues may be kept alive to grow for days (or years) in nutrient solutions. The phase microscope and the electron microscope are new research tools permitting study of the finer details of cell structure.

Studies of cells formerly dealt mainly with their physical features as seen in thin stained sections. In recent years new methods of study and new tools of research are being devised by biochemists to learn the exceedingly complex reactions constantly in progress in every living cell. Although of microscopic size, the cell is an amazing unit where many chemical substances undergo a wide variety of interaction and change—synthesis of new materials, use of food and energy to provide for movement, secretion, or other activities, and rendering of waste products into forms not harmful. Any cell is at least as intricate as an entire petroleum refinery that receives the mixture of hydrocarbons in petroleum, refines and modifies some for fuel and lubricants, and synthesizes many new and different organic compounds to serve various purposes in our modern everyday life. All that was said previously about protoplasm (par. 3-10 to 16) actually applies to the cells which are the metabolic units of the body.

D. CELL DIVISION

Growth in organisms is chiefly by multiplication of cells. In the unicellular Protozoa, the animals themselves are multiplied; in other animals the number of cells in the individual is increased.

3-18. Mitosis. Cells multiply chiefly by *mitosis,* a rather complex process that involves, importantly, an equal division of the nuclear chromatin in kind and amount (Figs. 3-10, 3-11). Cell division by mitosis is common to all animals from amoeba to man and in all plants except bacteria and blue-green algae. Mitosis is active during embryonic development, in growth, in repair of injury, and in replacement of body covering at molting. It is also the process involved in malignant growths (tumors, cancer). As seen in living cells it is a continuous dynamic process, but for convenience in

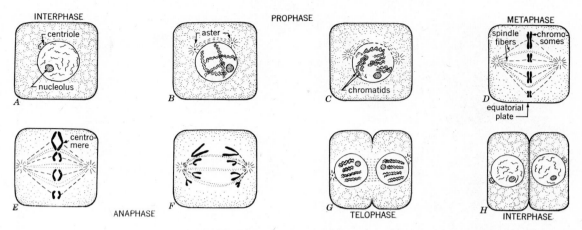

Fig. 3-10. Mitosis: Division of nuclear materials and cytoplasm of one cell into two; diagrammatic.

study is divided into several stages, as follows: (1) prophase, (2) metaphase, (3) anaphase, and (4) telophase. Cells not undergoing mitosis are said to be in the interphase, or are called metabolic cells, because metabolic processes are going on constantly within them.

PROPHASE. The centrosome usually contains two centrioles (if but one, this divides); the two move to opposite sides of the nucleus. Around each centriole fine short radiating fibers appear in the cytoplasm to form an *aster;* and other longer *spindle fibers* extend between the separating centrioles.

Meanwhile the chromatin within the nucleus becomes evident as distinct chromosomes that shorten, thicken, and stain deeply. Each chromosome is actually composed of two wavy parallel filaments, the *chromatids* (daughter chromosomes). In the cells of any one species the several chromosomes are of characteristic size and shape—long or short, thick or thin, and shaped like a rod, **J,** or **V** (Fig. 3-10). Careful microscopic preparations show a constriction or dot (centromere) where the two arms of a chromosome join; this is the point of attachment by spindle fibers. Toward the end of the prophase the nuclear membrane and nucleolus disappear, the chromosomes become associated with the spindle fibers and move toward the equatorial plane of the cell.

The total number of chromosomes present at the end of the prophase is the *diploid number.* This is constant and characteristic in any species of animal for all its cells except mature germ cells. The chromosome number ranges from 2 to about 250 but usually is less than 50 in different kinds of animals.

METAPHASE. The chromosomes lie radially in an equatorial plate across the cell, midway between the two asters, each chromosome being connected to the spindle fibers. Other fibers extend continuously between the poles. The two halves of each chromosome become more evident.

ANAPHASE. The halved chromosomes move apart, those of each group toward its respective pole (centriole). In living cells there is an active pulling back and forth of the opposing sets as they separate. Each daughter chromosome consists of an equivalent half of the material formerly in one chromosome.

TELOPHASE. As the groups of daughter chromosomes end their polar movement they become less conspicuous, a nuclear membrane forms about each group, a nucleolus is produced in each, each centriole divides into two, and the spindle disappears. Finally a cell membrane appears across the former plane of the equatorial plate. When this has ended, mitosis is complete. The chromosomes in each daughter

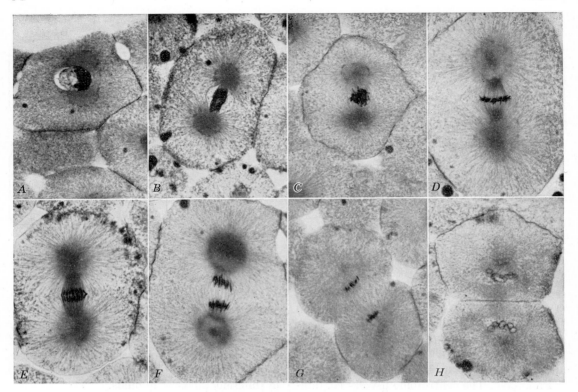

Fig. 3-11. Mitosis in egg (blastula) of whitefish. PROPHASE. *A.* Centrosome divides. *B, C.* Centrosomes at opposite poles, chromosomes becoming evident, nuclear membrane disappears. METAPHASE. *D, E.* Chromosomes centered on equator of spindle, and (*E*) each divides into two. ANAPHASE. *F, G.* Chromosomes move toward poles, spindle lengthens, centrosomes less evident. TELOPHASE. *H.* Nuclear membrane forming around chromosomes, cytoplasm of the two cells separated by membrane between. (*Photomicrographs by Dr. Hans Ris.*) Compare Fig. 3-10.

cell revert to the pattern of the interphase or metabolic cell.

The duration of a complete mitotic cycle depends on the species of animal, the age of the individual, the particular tissue involved, the temperature, etc. The total time of a mitosis has been determined as 9 minutes for *Drosophila* cleavage and 67 to 205 minutes for chick mesenchyme cells. In both cases the longest stage was the prophase.

3-19. Significance of mitosis. The equal division of chromatin whereby each daughter cell receives half of that in each parent chromosome is of great significance from the standpoint of heredity (Chap. 12), since the genes or determiners of hereditary characters are believed to be carried by the chromosomes and to split with the latter. Such partitioning distributes identical lots of genes to all cells in the body.

3-20. Amitosis. Direct nuclear division, or *amitosis,* has been reported in several types of cells and tissues; the nucleus simply constricts and separates into two portions without formation of spindles or chromosomes. This may occur without division of the cytoplasm, resulting in a syncytium, or multinucleate cell. Many cases of cells undergoing amitotic division are considered to have been abnormal or pathological.

E. TISSUES

The parts of any multicellular animal consist of different kinds of cells. Those of similar structure and function are arranged in groups or layers known as *tissues,* hence multicellular animals (METAZOA) are "tissue animals." In each tissue the cells are essentially alike, being of characteristic size, form, and arrangement, and they are specialized or differentiated, both structurally and physiologically, to perform some particular function such as protection, digestion, or contraction, whence there is a division of labor between different tissues. *Histology,* or microscopic anatomy, is the study of the structure and arrangement of tissues in organs, in contrast to gross anatomy which deals with organs and organ systems by dissection (Fig. 3-12).

The cells in a multicellular animal may be divided into (1) *somatic cells* or *body cells* (and their products), constituting the individual animal throughout its life, and (2) *germ cells* having to do only with reproduction and continuance of the species (Chap. 11). There are four major groups of somatic tissues: (1) epithelial or covering; (2) connective or supporting, including vascular or circulatory; (3) muscular or contractile; and (4) nervous.

3-21. Epithelial tissues. These cover the body, outside and inside, as in the skin and the lining of the digestive tract (Fig. 3-12). The cells are compactly placed, bonded together by intercellular cement for strength, and often supported below on a basement membrane. Struc-

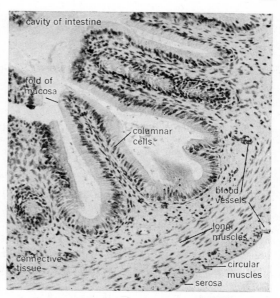

Fig. 3-12. Section of frog intestine (duodenum). Photomicrograph shows how several kinds of cells and tissues combine to form an organ.

turally the cells may be (1) squamous, or flat; (2) cuboidal; (3) columnar; (4) ciliated; or (5) flagellated (see Fig. 3-13). The tissue may be either (6) simple, with the cells in one layer; or (7) stratified, with multiple layers. Functionally an epithelial tissue may be protective, glandular (secretory), or sensory.

Simple squamous epithelium is of thin flat cells, like tiles in a floor; such cells form the peritoneum that lines the body cavity and the endothelium of the inner surface of blood vessels in vertebrates. Stratified squamous epithelium forms the outer layers of the human skin

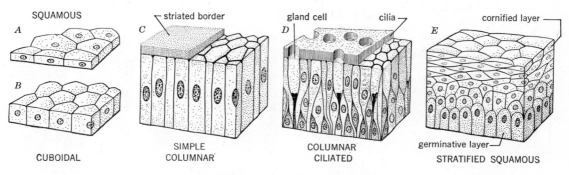

Fig. 3-13. Types of epithelial tissues.

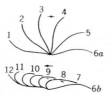

Fig. 3-14. Action of an individual cilium. 1–6*a*, forward stroke, in direction of arrow, cilium rigid; 6*b*–12, recovery stroke, cilium bends from base to tip. (*After Gray, 1928.*)

(Fig. 4-1) and lines the mouth and nasal cavities. Cuboidal epithelium, with cube-like cells, is present in salivary glands, kidney tubules, and the thyroid gland. Columnar epithelium consists of cells taller than wide, with their long sides adjacent; this type lines the stomach and intestine of vertebrates.

A *ciliated cell* bears on its exposed surface numerous short hair-like protoplasmic processes known as *cilia* (Fig. 3-14). These beat in one direction, the adjacent cilia acting in unison, so that small particles or materials on the surface are moved along. Cuboidal ciliated epithelium lines the sperm ducts of earthworms and other animals, and columnar ciliated epithelium lines the earthworm's intestine and the air passages (trachea, etc.) of land vertebrates. The embryos and young larvae of many aquatic animals are covered with ciliated cells by which they are able to swim about. A *flagellated cell* has one or more slender whip-like cytoplasmic processes or *flagella* on the exposed surface; such cells line the digestive cavities of hydra and sponges.

Protective epithelium guards animals from external injury and from infection. It is one-layered on many invertebrates but stratified on land vertebrates. In the latter case, the basal columnar cells (stratum germinativum) produce successive layers of cells by mitosis; these pass outward, flatten, and lose their soft protoplasmic texture, to become cornified or "horny," as they reach the surface (Fig. 3-13*E*). The epithelium on the earthworm secretes a thin homogeneous *cuticle* over its entire exterior surface, and the body covering on arthropods is similarly produced. Nails, claws, hairs, and feathers are produced by special groups of epithelial cells.

Glandular epithelium (Fig. 3-15) is specialized for secreting products necessary for use by an animal. Individual gland cells of columnar type (goblet cells) that secrete mucus occur on the exterior of the earthworm and in the intestinal epithelium of vertebrates. The multicellular salivary and sebaceous glands of man and various mammals are lined with cuboidal cells. The secretions may be either sticky (mucous) or watery (serous).

Epithelial cells specialized to receive certain kinds of external stimuli are called *sensory cells.* Examples are those in the epidermis of the earthworm (Fig. 24-2) and on the tongue and nasal passages of man (Figs. 10-10, 10-11).

3-22. Connective and supportive tissues. These serve to bind the other tissues and organs together and to support the body. They derive from embryonic mesenchyme cells with fine protoplasmic processes. Tissues of this group

Fig. 3-15. Types of glandular tissues.

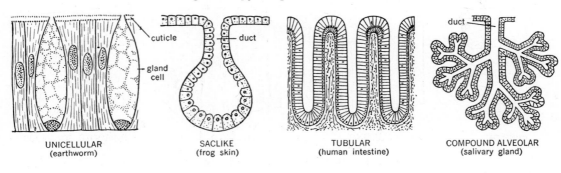

UNICELLULAR (earthworm)   SACLIKE (frog skin)   TUBULAR (human intestine)   COMPOUND ALVEOLAR (salivary gland)

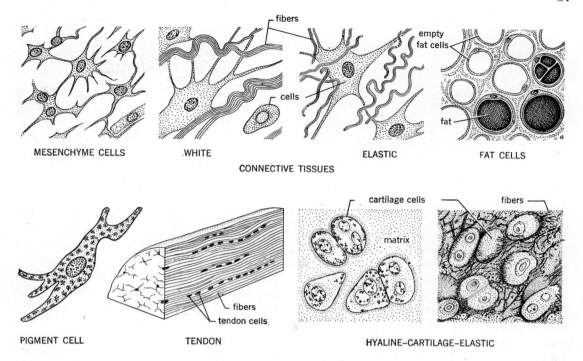

MESENCHYME CELLS   WHITE   ELASTIC   FAT CELLS

CONNECTIVE TISSUES

PIGMENT CELL   TENDON   HYALINE–CARTILAGE–ELASTIC

Fig. 3-16. Types of supportive tissues.

later become diverse in form; some produce fibers and other intercellular substance, the cells becoming less conspicuous. The supportive tissues include reticular, fibrous, and adipose types together with cartilage, bone, and pigment (Fig. 3-16).

Reticular tissue is a network of cells with stiff interconnected protoplasmic fibrils, the spaces between being filled with other types of cells; it makes the framework of lymph glands, red bone marrow, the spleen, and other organs. *Fibrous connective tissue* consists of scattered cells, rounded or branched in form, with the intercellular spaces occupied by delicate fibers. The *white* (collagenous) *fibers* are made of many fine parallel fibrils, pale in color and often wavy in outline, forming bundles that are crossed or interlaced, but not branched; they occur commonly in tendons and around muscles and nerves. *Elastic fibers* are sharply defined and straight, bent, or branched; they bind the skin to the underlying muscles, attach many other tissues and organs to one

another, and are present in walls of the larger blood vessels and elsewhere. Both kinds of fibers occur in the wall of the intestine and in the deeper part (dermis) of vertebrate skin. In *adipose* or *fat tissue* the cells are rounded or polygonal, with thin walls and the nucleus at one side; they contain droplets of fat, which may form larger globules. Fat is usually dissolved out in prepared microscopic sections, leaving only a framework of cell outlines.

A *tendon* is a bundle of parallel white fibers surrounded by a sheath of the same material, with inward projections of the sheath that form septa, or partitions. *Cartilage* (gristle) is a firm yet elastic matrix (chondrin) secreted by small groups of rounded cartilage cells embedded within it and covered by a thin fibrous perichondrium. *Hyaline cartilage* is bluish white, translucent, and homogeneous; it covers joint surfaces and rib ends and is present in the nose and in the tracheal rings. It is the skeletal cartilage in the embryos of all vertebrates and in the adults of sharks and rays. It

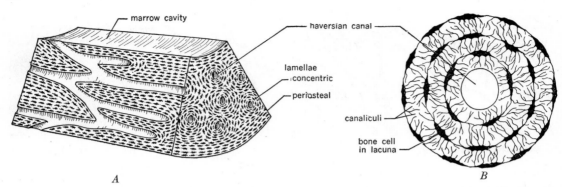

Fig. 3-17. Structure of bone (enlarged and diagrammatic). *A.* Portion of a long bone in longitudinal and cross section. *B.* Three concentric lamellae around a Haversian canal, as seen in a thinly ground cross section.

may become impregnated with calcareous salts but as such does not become bone. *Elastic cartilage* containing some yellow fibers is present in the external ears of mammals and in the Eustachian tubes. *Fibrocartilage,* the most resistant type, is largely of fibers, with fewer cells and less matrix. It occurs in the pads between the vertebrae of mammals, in the pubic symphysis, and about joints subject to severe strains.

True *bone* or *osseous tissue* occurs only in the skeletons of bony fishes and land vertebrates (Fig. 3-17); it is unlike the limy skeletons of invertebrates. Bone is a dense organic matrix (chiefly collagen) with mineral deposits, largely tricalcium phosphate, $Ca_3(PO_4)_2$, and calcium carbonate, $CaCO_3$; the mineral part averages about 65 per cent of the total weight. Bone develops either as replacement for previously existing cartilage (cartilage bone) or follows embryonic mesenchymal cells (membrane bone). Both types are produced by *bone cells* (osteoblasts). The cells become separate but retain many minute protoplasmic connections with one another and with blood vessels. Bone is, therefore, a living tissue that may be reabsorbed in part or changed in composition. During the life of an individual the proportion of mineral gradually increases and the organic material decreases, so that bones are resilient in early youth and brittle in old age.

A bone (Fig. 4-4) is covered by thin fibrous *periosteum,* to which muscles and tendons attach. Within the periosteum are bone cells that function in growth and repair. The mineral substance is deposited in thin layers, or *lamellae.* Those beneath the periosteum are parallel to the surface. Inside, especially in long bones, are many small tubular *concentric lamellae,* forming cylindrical *Haversian systems,* the wall of each being of several such lamellae with a central *Haversian canal.* The systems are mainly longitudinal, but cross-connect, providing channels for blood vessels and nerves to pass from the periosteum to the interior marrow cavity of a bone. Individual bone cells occupy small spaces, or *lacunae,* between the lamellae; these connect to one another by many fine radiating canals (canaliculi) occupied by the protoplasmic processes. In flat bones such as those of the skull and in the ends of long bones, the interior lacks regular systems and is more spongy. Cross sections made by sawing such bones show the bone fibers are arranged like beams in arches and trusses to resist compression from the exterior. A slice of bone ground microscopically thin will show the lacunae and canaliculi, which then become filled with air and appear black by refraction. The central cavity in a long bone is filled with soft, spongy *yellow marrow* (containing much fat); the ends and spaces in other bones contain *red marrow,* where blood cells are produced.

Pigment cells or *chromatophores* provide the color of many animals (Fig. 2-7).

3-23. Vascular or circulatory tissues. The blood and lymph that serve to transport and dis-

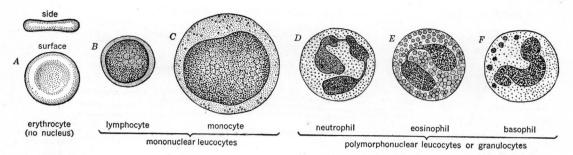

side

surface

A

B

C

D

E

F

erythrocyte
(no nucleus)

lymphocyte   monocyte

mononuclear leucocytes

neutrophil   eosinophil   basophil

polymorphonuclear leucocytes or granulocytes

Fig. 3-18. Human blood cells. Erythrocyte about 7.5 μ in diameter. Nuclei of leucocytes are dark (Table 6-1).

tribute materials in the body consist of a fluid *plasma* containing free cells, or *corpuscles* (Fig. 3-18; Table 6-1). Colorless **white blood cells,** or **leucocytes,** are present in all animals with body fluids; some have the function of "policing" the body by engulfing bacteria and other foreign materials, when they are known as **phagocytes.** Certain white blood cells can move and change shape, hence are called **amoebocytes** (amoeba-like). The leucocytes of vertebrates can pass through the walls of blood vessels and invade other tissues of the body. Vertebrate blood also contains **red blood cells,** or **erythrocytes,** colored red by a pigment, **hemoglobin,** that serves for transport of oxygen. Those in mammals are nonnucleated, biconcave, and usually round, but in other vertebrates they are nucleated, biconvex, and oval. The fluid plasma transports most materials carried in the blood stream; it is colorless in vertebrates, but that of some invertebrates is colored either blue or red by dissolved respiratory pigment (hemocyanin, hemoglobin, etc.).

3-24. Muscular or contractile tissues. Movements in most animals are produced by long, slender **muscle cells** (Fig. 3-19) that contain minute fibers or myofibrils. When stimulated, they shorten in length or contract, thus drawing together the parts to which the muscles are attached.

In **striated muscle** the fibrils have alternate dark and light crossbands of different structure or density, producing a distinctly cross-banded or striated appearance; the dark bands shorten and broaden upon contraction. The cells are cylindrical, scarcely 50 μ in diameter; but some

measure an inch or more in length. Each cell is surrounded by a delicate membrane (sarcolemma) and contains several to many long nuclei. The vertebrates have groups of striated muscle cells surrounded by connective tissue sheaths to form **muscles** of various shapes. These sheaths either attach to the periosteum on bones or gather to form tendons by which the muscles are attached to the skeleton (Fig. 4-4). The simultaneous contraction of many fibers causes a muscle to shorten and bulge, as easily seen in the biceps of the upper arm. Striated muscle in vertebrates is attached to the skeleton, hence is called **skeletal muscle;** being under conscious control, it is also termed **voluntary muscle.**

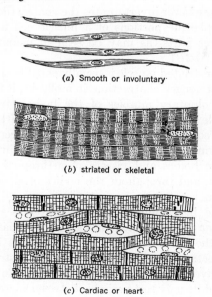

(*a*) Smooth or involuntary

(*b*) striated or skeletal

(*c*) Cardiac or heart

Fig. 3-19. Types of muscular cells and tissues.

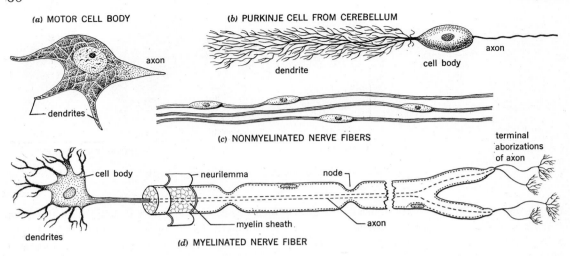

Fig. 3-20. Types of nerve cells.

Nonstriated or *smooth muscle* consists of delicate spindle-shaped cells, each with one central oval nucleus and homogeneous fibrils; the cells are arranged in layers, or sheets, held by fibrous connective tissue. Such muscle is found in the internal organs or viscera of the vertebrate body, as in the walls of the digestive tract, blood vessels, respiratory passages, and urinary and genital organs; hence it is also called *visceral muscle;* not being under control of the will, it is also termed *involuntary muscle.* In some lower invertebrates the contractile and protoplasmic portions of a muscle cell are of distinct parts, as may be seen in nematodes (Fig. 20-2*B*).

Nonstriated muscle is usually capable of slow but prolonged contraction; in mollusks, it forms the voluntary muscles of the body. Striated muscle can contract rapidly but intermittently and requires frequent rest periods; it occurs in the wing muscles of the swiftest flying insects, in the bodies and viscera of arthropods generally, and throughout the bodies of all vertebrates.

The heart muscle of vertebrates is called *cardiac muscle;* it has delicate cross striations, and the fibers are branched to form an interconnecting network. Cardiac muscle is striated yet involuntary; throughout the life of an individual its only rest period is between successive contractions of the heart.

3-25. Nervous tissues. Nervous systems are composed of nerve cells, or **neurons.** The neurons are of varied form (Fig. 3-20) in the systems of different animals and in the several parts of any one system. The individual neuron usually has a large cell body, a conspicuous nucleus, and two or more protoplasmic processes. The process that transmits stimuli to the cell body is the *dendrite,* and that carrying impulses away from it is the *axon.* In a large animal an individual neuron may be several feet long. Bipolar cells have one dendrite and one axon; multipolar cells have a multiple dendrite and single axon. The dendrite is often short and commonly much branched (like a tree) near the cell body, whereas the axon may be short or long and is unbranched save for an occasional collateral fiber. A group of nerve-cell bodies, with their conspicuous nuclei, when outside the central nervous system, is termed a *ganglion* (pl. ganglia).

A group of fibers or processes, bound together by connective tissue, is a *nerve.* The central nervous system of animals consists of an aggregation of nerve cells and fibers. Among these is the *neuroglia* (or glia), of several cell types, that seems to serve as delicate packing to hold neurons apart. Nerve fibers without any surrounding sheath are termed *nonmyelinated* (nonmedullated) and are gray in appearance. A *myelinated* fiber has the axon surrounded by

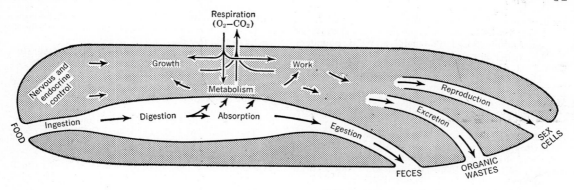

Fig. 3-21. Diagram of the essential functions in an animal.

a sheath of myelin containing fatty material and appears white. A delicate membrane, or **neurilemma** (Schwann sheath), surrounds both types of fibers. The neurilemma sheath seems to play an important role in the regeneration of damaged nerve fibers. The myelin substance is constricted at intervals, forming the **nodes of Ranvier.** Nonmyelinated fibers are common among invertebrates; and among vertebrates they are found in the sympathetic system and in certain fiber tracts of the spinal cord (internally) and brain (externally). In nerves and on the outside of the spinal cord the myelinated fibers give those parts a whitish appearance.

F. ORGAN SYSTEMS

Every animal, small or large, must carry on a variety of essential functions (Fig. 3-21). Basically these may be reduced to growth, maintenance, and reproduction; all other functions serve these major needs. Actually the bodily operations are complex. In the various groups of the Animal Kingdom, from lowest to highest, there is progressive increase in bodily complexity to carry on these functions. A series of *organ systems* has evolved to serve the various needs. The systems and their principal functions are as follows:

1. Body covering or integument—protection from the environment
2. Skeletal system—support (and protection) of the body
3. Muscular system—movement and locomotion

4. Digestive system—reception and preparation of food
5. Circulatory system—transport of materials
6. Respiratory system—exchange of oxygen and carbon dioxide
7. Excretory system—disposal of organic wastes and excess fluid
8. Endocrine glands or system—regulation of internal processes and adjustments to exterior environment
9. Nervous system (and sense organs)—regulation of internal processes and adjustments to exterior environment
10. Reproductive system—production of new individuals

Most of the invertebrates and all the vertebrates have the systems just mentioned. In some cases functions are performed without special structural parts being present. Coelenterates, for example, lack respiratory and excretory organs, and the flatworms and roundworms have no circulatory or respiratory organs. An organ that continues in use maintains its efficiency, but if unused it tends to degenerate. In sedentary animals and many parasites various organs have disappeared. Thus, the tapeworm, which absorbs nutriment directly from its host, has no digestive tract; and insects such as fleas, lice, and others of burrowing or parasitic habits have no wings.

REFERENCES

Some books dealing with protoplasm, cells, and tissues are:

Dahlgren, Ulric, and W. A. Kepner. 1908. A textbook of the principles of histology. New York, The Macmillan Co. xiii + 515 pp., 470 figs.

DE ROBERTIS, E. P. D., W. W. NOWINSKI, and F. A. SAEZ. 1954. General cytology. Translated by Warren Andrew. 2d ed. Philadelphia, W. B. Saunders Co. xi + 456 pp., 162 figs.

GREEP, R. O. (editor). 1954. Histology. New York, The Blakiston Division, McGraw-Hill Book Co., Inc. xi + 953 pp., 648 figs.

MAXIMOW, A. A., and W. BLOOM. 1952. A textbook of histology. 6th ed. Philadelphia, W. B. Saunders Co. x + 616 pp., 580 figs.

NONIDEZ, J. F., and W. F. WINDLE. 1953. Textbook of histology. 2d ed. New York, McGraw-Hill Book Co., Inc. xv + 528 pp., 326 figs.

SEIFRIZ, WILLIAM. 1936. Protoplasm. New York, McGraw-Hill Book Co., Inc. x + 584 pp., 179 figs.

WILLIER, B. H., P. A. WEISS, and VIKTOR HAMBURGER (editors). 1955. Analysis of development. Philadelphia, W. B. Saunders Co. xiii + 735 pp., 248 figs. Discusses structure and function of cells.

WILSON, E. B. 1928. The cell in development and heredity. 3d ed. New York, The Macmillan Co. xxxvi + 1,232 pp., 529 figs.

The following works variously discuss the animal (or human) body and the organ systems and their physiology. They will serve as general references for Chaps. 4 to 10 that follow.

AMBERSON, W. R., and D. C. SMITH. 1948. Outline of physiology. 2d ed. New York, Appleton-Century-Crofts, Inc. xi + 502 pp., 193 figs. Emphasizes historical development of physiology.

BALDWIN, ERNEST. 1949. An introduction to comparative biochemistry. 3d ed. Cambridge, England, University Press. xvi + 164 pp., 12 figs. Biochemical processes and adaptations in both aquatic and terrestrial animals.

CARLSON, A. J., and VICTOR JOHNSON. 1953. The machinery of the [human] body. 4th ed. Chicago, University of Chicago Press. xxi + 663 pp., 223 figs.

FULTON, J. F. (editor). 1955. A textbook of physiology. 17th ed. Philadelphia, W. B. Saunders Co. xliii + 1,275 pp., 600 figs.

HANSTRÖM, BERTIL. 1939. Hormones in invertebrates. Oxford, Clarendon Press. xi + 198 pp., 13 pls., 21 figs.

HEILBRUNN, L. V. 1952. General physiology. 3d ed. Philadelphia, W. B. Saunders Co. xiii + 818 pp., 123 figs.

HOUSSAY, B. A., and OTHERS. 1955. Human physiology. Translated by J. T. Lewis and O. T. Lewis. New York, McGraw-Hill Book Co., Inc. xvi + 1,177 pp., 504 figs.

MARSLAND, DOUGLAS. 1951. Principles of modern biology. New York, Henry Holt & Co., Inc. xv + 757 pp., illus.

PACE, D. M., and B. W. McCASHLAND. 1955. College physiology. New York, Thomas Y. Crowell Co. xxi + 615 pp., 315 figs. Man and various lower animals.

PINCUS, GREGORY, and K. V. THIMANN (editors). 1948–55. The hormones: physiology, chemistry and applications. 3 vols. New York, Academic Press, Inc.

PROSSER, C. L. 1950. Comparative animal physiology. Philadelphia, W. B. Saunders Co. ix + 888 pp., 312 figs.

ROMER, A. S. 1955. The vertebrate body. 2d ed. Philadelphia, W. B. Saunders Co. viii + 644 pp., 390 figs.

SCHEER, T. B. 1948. Comparative physiology. New York, John Wiley & Sons, Inc. x + 563 pp., 73 figs. PROTOZOA to VERTEBRATES.

TURNER, C. D. 1955. General endocrinology. Philadelphia, W. B. Saunders Co. xi + 553 pp., 171 figs.

WEISZ, P. B. 1954. Biology. New York, McGraw-Hill Book Co., Inc. xviii + 679 pp., illus.

WILLIAMS, R. H. (editor). Textbook of endocrinology. 2d ed. Philadelphia, W. B. Saunders Co. xii + 776 pp., 173 figs.

4 BODY COVERING, SKELETON, AND BODY MUSCLES

In all but the lowest animals the external body covering, the supporting framework or skeleton, and the muscles that serve for movements and locomotion are variously interrelated. The kind of covering, the type of skeleton, and the arrangement of muscles in each group depend on its ancestry, the sort of environment it inhabits, and its mode of life. Among invertebrates the functions of protection and support are often combined in a firm external skeleton with the muscles inside. The most efficient designs are among the insects and other arthropods which have jointed body segments and appendages with many individual muscles attached to inward projections of the covering skeleton. By contrast, the vertebrates, almost from their beginning, have had a separate body covering or integument and an internal jointed framework or skeleton with muscles on the outer surfaces; both hinge and ball-and-socket joints are present. The muscles of vertebrates, by their size and arrangement, are largely responsible for bodily shape.

A. BODY COVERING

4-1. Invertebrates. The body in all animals has some covering to conserve the protoplasm within, to give physical protection, and to exclude disease organisms. Many protozoans (e.g., *Amoeba*) are covered only by the delicate cell membrane, whereas others (*Paramecium*) also have a firm elastic pellicle. All multicellular animals are covered by a tissue, the **epidermis.** On many soft-bodied invertebrates of the water or moist environments on land, such as coelenterates, flatworms, and slugs, this is a single layer of cells. The epidermis on many worms secretes an external, noncellular **cuticle** as additional covering; this is delicate on earthworms but resistant on flukes, tapeworms, and roundworms. On insects, snails, and some other animals the epidermis secretes a protective external skeleton or shell (Fig. 4-2).

The coverings of terrestrial arthropods include a cuticle and usually a thin layer of wax as well; therefore they resist the loss of body fluids. This arrangement, with other adaptations to life in air, enables the insects, spiders, and relatives to inhabit dry environments.

4-2. Vertebrates. The body covering is a **skin,** or **integument,** consisting of an outer **epidermis** over an underlying **dermis** that contains blood vessels, nerves, and pigment. On fishes the thin epidermis contains many glands that provide mucus to lubricate the exterior of the body. Sharks and rays have enamel-covered exposed scales, and most bony fishes are protected by dermal scales that sheathe the body. The land vertebrates (amphibians to mammals) have a **stratified epidermis** of several cell layers (Figs.

63

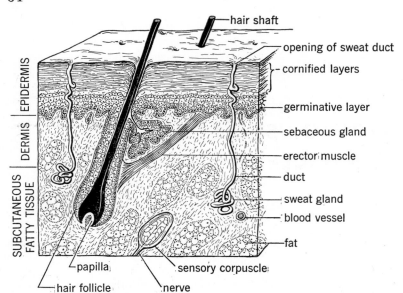

hair shaft

opening of sweat duct

cornified layers

germinative layer

sebaceous gland

erector muscle

duct

sweat gland

blood vessel

fat

EPIDERMIS

DERMIS

SUBCUTANEOUS FATTY TISSUE

papilla

hair follicle

sensory corpuscle

nerve

Fig. 4-1. Section of human skin, enlarged and diagrammatic.

2-6, 4-1). The outermost layer becomes hardened, or *cornified,* as a more resistant covering and is continually renewed by growth of new layers from the base of the epidermis. Amphibian skin is glandular and moist, as in the frog. On reptiles, birds, and mammals the cornified part is dry and tougher, the better to resist wear in dry environments. It also limits the loss of moisture by evaporation and thus conserves body fluids. The skin of reptiles usually contains dermal *scales* that afford added physical protection, and on lizards and snakes the cornified exterior is molted at intervals. Birds are covered by *feathers;* these are dry, nonliving, cornified products of the epidermis that insulate the body, provide streamlined exterior contours of bodily form, and make the broad surfaces of the wings and tail used for flight. The skin of most mammals is covered by *hairs,* another type of cornified epidermal product, also serving for insulation. Both feathers and hair are replaced periodically by molt of the old, and growth of new coverings. (Skins of some mammals and reptiles can be tanned—rendered insoluble—to serve as leather.)

Only the birds and mammals with their heat-conserving body coverings are "warm-blooded" (homoiothermous), with regulated body temperatures. All other animals are "cold-blooded" (poikilothermous) like the frog, their body temperatures following closely those of the environments in which they live. Seals, whales, and other aquatic mammals have deep layers of fat (blubber) under the skin that insulate their bodies from heat loss in the water.

The human skin (Fig. 4-1) resembles that of other mammals but is scantily haired on most parts and is thin (epidermis, 0.07 mm.; dermis, 2.5 to 5 mm.). Evaporation of the watery perspiration secreted by the *sweat glands* helps to cool and regulate the body temperature in hot environments.

Besides the skin, other cornified epidermal products include the horns of cattle and sheep (but not the calcareous antlers of deer), the claws, nails, hoofs, and horny pads on the feet of various land vertebrates, the beak and shank coverings on birds, and the outer scutes on turtle shells. Cornified materials are all highly insoluble proteins (keratins) that are quite resistant to wear and to chemical disintegration. Some other keratins are the horny coverings on fish eggs and the horny skeletons of bath sponges and sea fans (coelenterates).

4-3. Pigment and coloration. An important protective device in the body covering of many animals is the *coloring matter* or *pigment.* Protection is gained by the pattern of pigment (camouflage, see Chaps. 2, 14) or by the density and extent of pigment (for protection from rays of the sun).

B. SKELETAL SYSTEMS

All animals in some phyla and some in most of the others have a firm framework or *skeleton* that gives physical support and protection for the body and often provides surfaces for the attachment of muscles. A skeleton is not absolutely necessary, however, since many aquatic invertebrates and a few land animals have none. Parts of the skeleton in arthropods and vertebrates form jointed appendages that serve as levers for locomotion. In such cases there is a close mutual relation of structure and function between the skeletal parts and muscles, whereby their interaction is more efficient.

The skeleton may be a shell or other *external* covering (exoskeleton), as on corals, mollusks, and arthropods, or *internal* (endoskeleton), as with vertebrates. It is *rigid* on corals, many mollusks, and others, but variously *jointed* and movable in echinoderms, arthropods, and vertebrates. Exoskeletons serving as defensive armor were present on fossil animals such as the trilobites, primitive fish-like ostracoderms, early amphibians (labyrinthodonts), and some ancient reptiles (dinosaurs); they occur also on living brachiopods, most mollusks, barnacles, some fishes, the turtles and tortoises, and the armadillo (Fig. 4-2).

An exoskeleton limits the ultimate size of an animal and may become so heavy that the organism must remain fixed. This is because the internal muscles cannot be large and powerful enough to move the heavy framework. The internal skeleton of a vertebrate involves far less limitation, and some vertebrates have attained to huge size; these include the brontosaurs and other fossil reptiles and the living elephants and rhinoceroses. Certain sharks and whales, whose weight is partly supported by the water, are even larger (Fig. 1-2).

Fig. 4-2. Skeletons in animals; diagrammatic. *A, B.* Protozoans. *A.* Radiolarian, framework of silica. *B.* Foraminiferan, limy shell. *C.* Sponge, many minute limy spicules. *D.* Coral, solid calcareous (limy) cup with partitions. *E.* Rotifer, firm "glassy" cuticle. *F.* Brachiopod, two limy shells. *G.* Echinoderm, internal jointed skeleton of limy plates. *H.* Mollusk, limy shell. *I.* Crustacean, complete exoskeleton with chitin. *J.* Vertebrate, skull, vertebrae, limb girdles, and limb skeleton of bone.

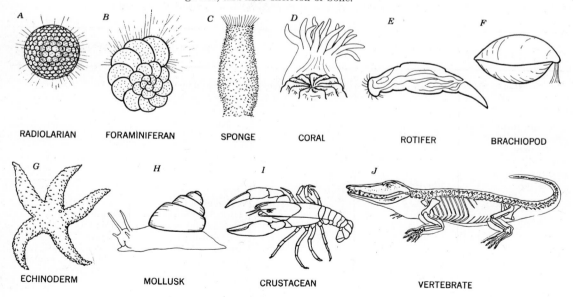

RADIOLARIAN   FORAMINIFERAN   SPONGE   CORAL   ROTIFER   BRACHIOPOD

ECHINODERM   MOLLUSK   CRUSTACEAN   VERTEBRATE

4-4. Invertebrate skeletons. Some protozoans (Sarcodina, Mastigophora) secrete or otherwise form skeletons of calcareous, siliceous, or organic substances, often of intricate pattern. Sponges secrete microscopic internal rods (spicules) or fibers of the same classes of materials. The skeletons of corals, brachiopods, echinoderms, and mollusks are mainly of lime ($CaCO_3$) and are retained throughout the life of the individual, growing at the margins and becoming thicker with age. All arthropods—crustaceans, insects, and others—are covered completely by jointed exoskeletons of organic materials containing chitin (par. 25-2). These are flexible at the joints between segments of the body and appendages but more rigid elsewhere. On crabs and related crustaceans the external covering is reinforced by internal deposits of limy salts that produce a hard "crust." The appendages number one pair per body segment (somite) or fewer and are variously developed as sensory antennae, jaws or other mouth parts, and legs for walking or swimming. Since the skeletons of arthropods when once hardened cannot expand, these animals undergo complete molt of the old covering at intervals to permit of growth; the body parts enlarge immediately after a molt, before the new covering has hardened. The se-

creted tubes in which some aquatic worms live, the cases built of bottom debris by some protozoans and certain insect larvae, and the empty snail shells used by hermit crabs all serve as protective exoskeletons.

4-5. Vertebrate skeletons. The internal skeleton has a common basic pattern with the fundamental features seen in a frog (par. 2-7). From the cyclostomes to the mammals a progressive sequence may be traced, although there are many differences in the size and form of component parts and in the presence or absence of certain elements. The essential features in a land vertebrate are given in Table 4-1. The skeleton supports the body, provides for attachment of muscles, and houses the brain and nerve cord. In all but the cyclostomes it includes framework for the jaws and the paired fins or limbs. The skeleton is of hyaline *cartilage* in adult cyclostomes and sharks and in the embryos of all higher vertebrates, but in the adults of bony fishes to mammals it is largely of *bone* with cartilage over joint surfaces and in a few other places.

Each bone in the body is built on good "engineering" principles in both gross and microscopic structure. Those subject to heavy

TABLE 4-1. General Divisions of the Skeleton in a Land Vertebrate

Axial skeleton (median)			Appendicular skeleton (lateral, paired)	
Skull	Vertebral column	Thoracic basket	Pectoral (anterior)	Pelvic (posterior)
Cranium (brain box) Sense capsules (nose, eye, ear) Visceral arches (jaws, hyoid, larynx)	Vertebrae Cervical (*neck*) Thoracic (*chest*) Lumbar (*lower back*) Sacral (*hip*) Caudal (*tail*)	Ribs (*paired; bony or cartilaginous*) Sternum (*breastbone*)	Shoulder girdle Scapula (*dorsal*) Clavicle (*anterior*) Coracoid (*posterior*)	Hip girdle Ilium Pubis Ischium
			Fore limb Humerus (*upper arm*) Radius and ulna (*forearm*) Carpals (*wrist*) Metacarpals (*palm*) Phalanges (*fingers*)	Hind limb Femur (*thigh*) Tibia and fibula (*shank*) Tarsals (*ankle*) Metatarsals (*sole*) Phalanges (*toes*)

Fig. 4-3. Vertebrae. *A.* Tail region of bony fish; both neural and hemal arches. *B.* Trunk region of bony fish. *C.* Human lumbar vertebra. *D.* Part of vertebral column (lumbar region in man) showing how the vertebrae articulate with one another, the pads between the centra, and the openings (foramina) for spinal nerves connecting to nerve cord.

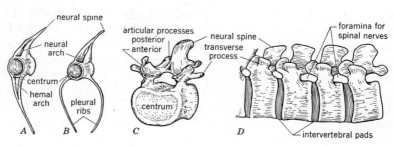

stresses are reinforced within, and where stout muscles or tendons attach, the exterior is roughened. Long bones are tubes—a given amount of material is more rigid when formed as a tube than a solid rod. Also thin layers give greater strength than a solid mass, as in plywood, hence the lamellae of bone (par. 3-22) afford further stiffness.

Flat bones, such as those in the skull, grow so long as the junctions between any two are cartilaginous but cease growing when bony sutures develop between them. A "long" bone—limbs, fingers, centra of vertebrae—is composed of a central *diaphysis* with a cap or *epiphysis* at each end; these start as three centers of ossification in the embryo. A layer of cartilage connects each epiphysis to the central portion. Growth in length (Fig. 4-4) is by extension of the cartilage, then that in contact with the bone is converted to bony tissue. Increase in length is possible so long as the junction remains cartilaginous. A long bone increases in diameter by deposit of bony tissue on the exterior; at the same time some bony substance is removed from the interior cavity. Repair of fractures in any bone is by much the same process.

Calcium salts for bone, derived from food, are carried in small amount by the blood (10 mg. per 100 ml. of blood). Regulation of calcium metabolism is directed by the parathyroid glands (par. 9-5). When the blood calcium declines, bones are "robbed" of calcium, as may occur during pregnancy.

4-6. Vertebral column. In all chordates the first skeletal element to appear in the embryo is a slender unsegmented and gelatinous rod, the *notochord,* that extends along the body axis between the digestive tract and the nerve cord. It persists thus throughout life in amphioxus and cyclostomes, but in fishes and higher types is later surrounded and supplanted by the backbone, or *spinal column,* of separate vertebrae (Fig. 4-3). The spool-like *centrum* of each vertebra has a dorsal *neural arch* to enclose the nerve cord. In the tails of fishes each vertebra has also a ventral *hemal arch* around the main artery and vein; this arch is spread open in the body or trunk region and forms rib-like structures shielding the internal organs. In land vertebrates the centrum bears a pair of *transverse processes* as points of attachment for the true ribs of these animals (except frogs). At either end of the centrum are two *articular processes* by which one vertebra may turn slightly on those directly before and behind. The vertebral column of fishes comprises only *trunk* and *tail* regions, but in salamanders, reptiles, and mammals there are five regions: neck, or *cervical;* chest, or *thoracic,* with ribs; lower back, or *lumbar;* pelvic, or *sacral,* joining the hind-limb girdle; and tail, or *caudal.* The caudal vertebrae are few in man and birds. Long-bodied swimming vertebrates have the vertebrae numerous and much alike, as seen in eels and similar fishes, in some salamanders (*Siren*), in some fossil reptiles, and in whales. The living snakes that literally swim on land have many vertebrae (Fig. 33-7). The ribs of land vertebrates usually join ventrally to a breastbone, or *sternum,* but this is lacking in snakes. The sternum of birds has a large median keel for attachment of the stout flight muscles (Fig. 34-5).

4-7. Skull. This structure, which frames the vertebrate head, begins in the embryo as cartilage and consists of (1) the *cranium,* or brain box, which houses the brain; (2) three pairs of *sense capsules* for the organs of smell, sight, and hearing; and (3) the *visceral skeleton,* which is a series of paired arches providing the jaws, the support for the tongue (hyoid apparatus), and the supports for the gill region. It continues in this state in adults of sharks and rays, but in bony fishes and higher forms the cartilaginous cranium is replaced by numerous bones; also the capsules and upper jaw become more completely joined to the cranium. In land vertebrates parts of the visceral arches are put to other uses (Fig. 14-7). Both the general form and detailed structure of the skull in adults of various vertebrates are diverse, and a comparative study from fishes to mammals shows many differences, including reduction in the number of bones; yet there is an underlying continuity in pattern throughout the entire series.

4-8. Limbs. Cyclostomes have no lateral appendages, but the sharks and bony fishes have two pairs, the *pectoral* and *pelvic fins,* with skeletal elements consisting of *fin rays.* Each pair is supported on a framework, or girdle (Chaps. 30, 31). Land vertebrates have two pairs of *limbs* in place of the fins, and these are supported by the *pectoral* and *pelvic girdles,* respectively, as in the frog. Each limb characteristically ends in five *toes,* or *digits.* The component bones of the girdles and limbs are homologous from amphibians to mammals, although variously modified in adaptation to special modes of life (Fig. 14-2). Loss of digits, fusion of other bones, and reduction or complete loss of fins, limbs, and girdles have occurred in various vertebrates. Some salamanders have only four or three toes on each foot, and no living bird has more than three "fingers" or four toes. Reduction in number of toes occurs in many mammals, the horse being an extreme case, with only one functional toe on each foot (Fig. 14-13). The radius and ulna and the tibia and fibula are fused in many species that have slight rotational movement of the limbs. The limbs and digits are far reduced in some salamanders and lizards and are absent in a few lizards and all snakes. Whales and sirenians have no hind limbs, and among fishes the eels lack pelvic fins. Vestiges of the limbs or girdles in whales, boas, and other limbless vertebrates indicate that these animals have descended from ancestors with limbs.

C. MUSCULAR SYSTEMS

The ability to contract is a fundamental property of protoplasm, but in most animals the contractions that bring about changes in shape or form and locomotion are produced by special fibrils or muscular tissues (par. 3-24). Most multicellular animals that are capable of locomotion have opposed sets of muscles to perform these movements.

4-9. Invertebrates. Simple protozoans such as *Amoeba* can contract or extend the one-celled body in any direction (par. 16-4). Others of

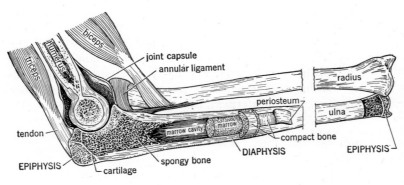

Fig. 4-4. Structure of a long bone and a joint; human elbow region in lengthwise section. The rounded end (trochlea) of the humerus fits the (semilunar) notch in the olecranon (base of ulna) to make a hinge joint, enclosed in the articular capsule. The ulna, a typical long bone, has a central tubular shaft (diaphysis) with a cap (epiphysis) at each end. Growth in length occurs in cartilage areas between shaft and ends. The ends are covered with smooth articular cartilage.

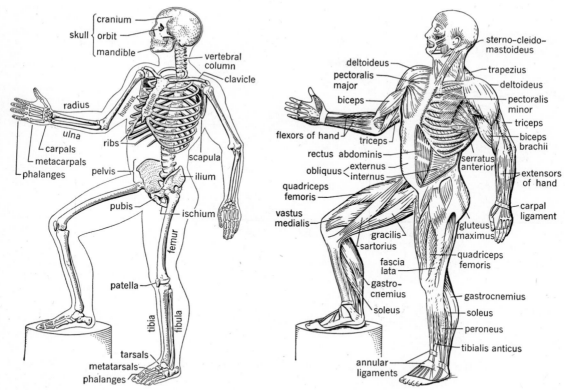

Fig. 4-5. The human skeleton. (Typically of the "vertebrate" pattern; compare Figs. 2-9, 35-2.)

Fig. 4-6. Superficial muscles of the human body (pectoralis major and external oblique removed on left side).

more specialized structure such as the stalked *Vorticella* have special contractile fibrils (myonemes). The body wall of coelenterates contains ⊥-shaped epitheliomuscular cells with contractile fibers in the basal part; these cells lie in opposed sets in the body wall (Fig. 18-2), whereby the body can be reduced in either length or diameter. Flatworms usually have muscle fibers in three directions—longitudinal, transverse, and dorsoventral (Fig. 19-4B); contraction of those in any one plane will force the soft but fluid-filled body to extend in the other planes, much as the human tongue can be moved. In roundworms the muscle cells somewhat resemble those of coelenterates, but all are aligned against the body wall and parallel to the main body axis (Fig. 20-2). The alternate contraction of fibers along opposite sides of the body enables the worm to bend and straighten, but it can neither twist freely nor extend the

body in length. In an earthworm the body wall includes two layers of muscles, an outer circular and an inner longitudinal layer (Fig. 24-4). Contraction of the outer layer causes the fluid-filled body to lengthen, and action of the longitudinal muscles shortens it. The crustaceans, insects, and other arthropods are the only invertebrates that depart from the "layer" arrangement of muscles; they have many separate muscles, varied in size, arrangement, and attachments, that move the body segments and the parts of the jointed legs and other appendages. These muscles are fastened to the internal surfaces of the exoskeleton and act over hinge joints between adjacent parts. A caterpillar may have 2,000 separate muscles.

4-10. Vertebrates. The muscles of vertebrates attach to parts of the skeleton. In the fish-like forms—cyclostomes to permanently gilled am-

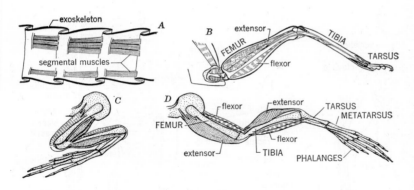

Fig. 4-7. *A*. Internal segmental muscles of an arthropod, connected to hardened, jointed, telescoping parts of exoskeleton. *B*. Internal muscles in leg of an insect. *C, D*. Hind leg of frog showing two pairs of opposed muscles: extensor vs. flexor. In *C* the leg is folded or *flexed* by contraction (thickening) whereby the origin and insertion of each muscle are brought closer together. In *D* the leg is *extended* by contraction of the opposed muscles. (*Adapted partly from Guyer, Animal biology, Harper & Brothers.*)

Fig. 4-8. Locomotion in the toad, a four-footed animal. Beginning at the upper left, the 15 figures show the normal pattern of limb movement; 1 to 4 sequence in flexing the limbs. (*After J. Gray*, 1939.)

phibians—and the limbless reptiles, the muscles are predominantly segmental (Fig. 33-3). They alternate with the vertebrae and provide the undulating movements by which the animals travel. In land vertebrates, from frogs to mammals, the nonsegmental muscles that move the limbs and head are larger and more important (Figs. 2-10, 4-6). In the higher forms some segmental muscles persist, however, between the vertebrae and the ribs and in the rectus abdominus muscles of the ventral body wall. The contraction of muscles is controlled by end plates of motor nerve fibers that attach to the muscle fibers (Fig. 10-9*E*).

4-11. Muscle and nerve. In a living animal the contraction (shortening) of a muscle results from impulses passing from the central nervous system along a nerve. Luigi Galvani (Italian, 1737–1798) was first to show that an electric impulse would cause muscular contraction. When a frog leg was suspended on a copper hook and touched to an iron plate, a spasmodic contraction occurred. He thought this resulted from "animal electricity," but Alle-

sandro Volta (Italian, 1745–1827) showed it was due to the electrical charge between two dissimilar metals. Such contraction may be demonstrated with a nerve-muscle preparation of the sciatic nerve and gastrocnemius muscle dissected out together from a frog (Fig. 4-9*A*). One end of the muscle is attached immovably, and the opposite end is tied to a lever that will magnify or record any change in length of the muscle. Brief electric shocks are applied to the nerve. Beginning with one too weak to produce any result and gradually increasing the intensity, a threshold of stimulation is reached at which slight contraction results. Further increase will produce a greater contraction, but soon a point is reached when still stronger impulses have no further effect. If all fibers but one in the nerve are cut and the remaining one is stimulated at increasing intensities, nothing happens until the **threshold** is reached, when the response is at once a maximum. This is the **all-or-none effect.** The graded increase in action of an entire nerve-muscle preparation results from different fibers having slightly unlike thresholds.

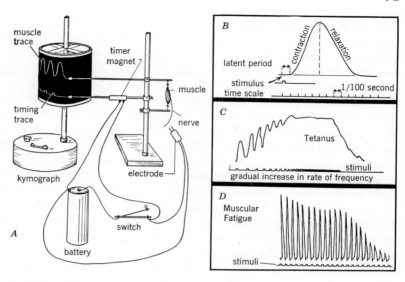

Fig. 4-9. Contraction of voluntary muscle. *A*. Nerve-muscle preparation attached to kymograph for recording contraction when nerve is stimulated by electrical impulse from battery. *B*. Diagram of normal contraction and relaxation after a single stimulus. *C*. Tetanus (maintained contraction) with increasing rate of stimuli. *D*. Fatigue resulting from repeated stimuli over a long period. (*B–D from kymograph records.*)

An individual muscle contraction follows a characteristic pattern (Fig. 4-9*B*) lasting about 0.1 second. The interval between the initial stimulus and shortening, about 0.01 second, is known as the **latent period.** Although no mechanical change occurs during this phase, reactions are taking place within the muscle which liberate the energy required for contraction. The second phase, the **period of contraction,** lasts about 0.04 second. Finally, in the **period of relaxation,** about 0.05 second, the muscle returns to its original length and physiological state. When individual shocks are well spaced in time, the muscle relaxes completely to its original length between them. But if repeated at close intervals, it does not; this state is called **clonus.** With still higher frequency of stimulus there is no relaxation but a smoothly maintained contraction, termed **tetanus.** Normal movements in the entire animal result from tetanic contractions. In man, at least when awake, some fibers in every muscle are in tetanus, and the muscles feel firm. This maintained tension or **tonus,** resistance to stretching, keeps the body in normal condition—while seated, standing, or at work. Tonus continues without fatigue because while some fibers are contracted others are relaxed and resting and there is a rotation in this role. The tone of muscles is one indication of health; in some paralyses, such as that of poliomyelitis, the muscles become flabby (atonic), whereas in other conditions they are tightly contracted (hypertonic).

The fibers in a skeletal muscle are in groups called **motor units,** each group controlled by one motor neuron. Eye muscles of man have 2 to 6 fibers per unit, those in a cat's leg up to 165. Different leg muscles of a cat include from 200 to over 600 such units. Each unit evidently follows the **all-or-none law:** its fibers either contract fully or not at all. No muscle is ever completely at rest; some units (5 per cent or so) are always contracted, even during the "complete relaxation" when a person is resting or while asleep; thereby some heat is generated. If motor stimuli to nerve end plates are experimentally blocked (by the drug curare), all muscles become relaxed, the body is limp, and it assumes the temperature of the environment, since no heat then is produced internally by muscular contraction.

4-12. Muscular contraction. Many striated muscles can contract with extreme speed (as in an insect wing) and do so repeatedly for a time. In a 100-yard dash the runner's leg muscles may contract 30 times within 10 seconds; at the end he has an "oxygen debt" that is repaid by quick heavy breathing for several minutes. In rapidly contracting muscle oxygen is used, carbon dioxide is given off, the glycogen content is reduced, lactic acid accumulates, and much heat is evolved.

From special means of study (X-ray diffraction, electron microscope) it is thought that the finest myofibrils in muscle consist of long W-shaped protein chains that fold together in contraction. The gross effects of this are seen when one flexes the upper arm—the biceps shortens and thickens. Three proteins are identified in muscular tissue: myogen (readily soluble), myosin (less so), and actin (least soluble). Solutions of myosin and actin combine as actomyosin, and this compound when concentrated experimentally becomes a gel; if formed into a thin thread and treated with a water extract of muscle (myogen), it shortens. This is presumed to be a model of contraction by the very proteins of living muscle.

The energy for muscle contraction and other biological processes is supplied ultimately by glucose ($C_6H_{12}O_6$) derived from digestion of food and carried in the blood stream. When stored (in liver, muscle, etc.) it is converted into glycogen ($C_6H_{12}O_6$)$_x$. Then, in essence, glycogen is oxidized to carbon dioxide and water:

$$C_6H_{12}O_6 + 6O_2 \xrightarrow[\text{enzymes}]{}$$

$$6CO_2 + 6H_2O + \text{energy}$$

Formerly it was thought that glycogen served rather directly for the release of energy because some of it disappears from muscle with repeated strong contractions. Actually, its conversion involves a series of intermediate reactions (not detailed here).

In addition, other substances in muscle are involved in the energy-contraction cycle, including recovery. A resting muscle contains (1) adenosine triphosphate, ATP; (2) phospho-creatine, PC; and (3) glycogen. With contraction each undergoes chemical change and *each reaction releases much energy.* Chemical analyses show that:

1. ATP is reduced to andenosine diphosphate (ADP), and this in turn to adenosine monophosphate (AMP).

2. Phosphocreatine (PC) is reduced to creatine and phosphate.

3. Glycogen is converted into lactic acid.

The energy of the three reactions above is utilized as follows:

1. Breakdown of ATP provides the actual energy for muscular contraction; the other reactions are all involved in recovery.

2. Division of PC supplies the energy to resynthesize ATP.

3. The several reactions converting glycogen to lactic acid afford energy for reforming PC from P and C.

4. Oxygen reacts with about one-fifth of the lactic acid to provide energy for reconverting the remaining four-fifths to glycogen.

Reduction of both ATP and PC are by hydrolysis (addition of water) and involve no oxidation; hence they can proceed under anerobic conditions (absence of oxygen). In contrast, the reconversion of lactic acid to glycogen is aerobic, involving use of some of the oxygen always present in muscle. The "oxygen debt" is built up by the breakdown reactions of ATP and PC, then is repaid by the lactic acid–glycogen reaction.

When a muscle becomes fatigued—incapable of further contraction—there is no ATP, little glycogen, and much lactic acid. Both PC and ATP are present and active in most or all living cells. If ATP is extracted and applied to a muscle, the latter contracts. Some investigators believe actomyosin may be the enzyme for ATP reduction. All the reactions—breakdown or synthesis—in muscles are by enzymes specific for each reaction.

Muscles contract to perform work; about 30 per cent of the energy used serves this purpose; the balance produces heat. About four-fifths of all bodily heat derives from this source. Mankind's mechanical engines convert only 12 to 25 per cent of the energy supplied into useful work; the animal body is therefore a more efficient "machine."

Fatigue—the inability to continue contraction—results from accumulation of lactic acid and depletion of glycogen and ATP. Evidently the motor end plates on muscles are rendered inactive by the lactic acid. (If formation of lactic acid is prevented by use of a poison, iodoacetic acid, muscles continue to contract.)

4-13. Muscles and bodily movements. In locomotion each pair of opposed muscles shows a rhythm of alternate activity. If more than one such pair is involved, their action shows a regular sequence. The primitive pattern, as in an eel, snake, or other slender animal, is a series of waves of contraction passing alternately along either side of the body. The movement of limbs in land forms is also alternate, in both vertebrates (Fig. 4-8) and insects. In lower vertebrates the stimulus for movement comes mainly from the environment and is controlled by nerve centers in the medulla oblongata but is modified by sensory stimuli from the eyes, nose, or other special receptors. Among invertebrates such as earthworms, crustaceans, and insects, destruction of the "brain" does not seriously disturb the normal pattern of locomotion, which depends upon stimuli from contact with the ground or other surfaces.

4-14. Cilia and flagella. Certain movable processes on cells (Chap. 3) serve in locomotion and for many vital processes in the bodies of animals. A *flagellum* is a beating whip-like process arising from a granule (blepharoplast) within a cell. Flagella occur on some protozoans, on the collar cells of sponges, and on internal cells of hydra (Chaps. 16, 17, 18). When many short processes are present, they are termed *cilia*. Cilia are moved by a fibrillar or neuromotor system (par. 16-19). External cilia provide for the locomotion of ciliate protozoans, ctenophores, rotifers, some flatworms, and aquatic larvae of many invertebrates. Cilia occur on the tentacles of bryozoans, some marine worms, and certain coelenterates, on the exterior of starfishes, and on the gills of bivalve mollusks. They line parts of the respiratory and genital tracts of vertebrates, the intestines of mollusks and earthworms, the feeding groove (endostyle) of lower chordates, and the excretory organs of many invertebrates. Some rates of beat, per second, for cilia are *Vorticella*, 6 to 8; *Stentor*, up to 42; gills of a mussel, 10; flagella in a sponge, 20.

In multicellular animals *mucus* is often secreted by gland cells adjacent to those bearing cilia, and materials trapped in the mucus are carried in one direction by the continual beating of many cilia. Cilia and mucus carry food to the mouth on anemones, bivalves, and bryozoans, and foreign particles trapped by mucus in the respiratory passages of land vertebrates are carried outward by ciliary action. The cilia in egg and sperm ducts aid in carrying sex cells to the exterior.

5 DIGESTIVE SYSTEMS AND METABOLISM

Green plants build their tissues from inorganic materials by the photosynthetic process, using energy from the sun (Chaps. 1, 13). The food of animals is obtained by eating plants or other animals. It serves two purposes, as a fuel to supply bodily energy and as a source of materials for growth and repair. After being obtained (feeding), it is broken down into simpler chemical substances (digestion) and then is taken into the cells and tissues of the body (absorption) where it is utilized (metabolism).

5-1. Feeding. Animals differ widely in their food habits. Some insects feed on the tissues or juices of a single species of plant or the blood of one kind of animal, but most animals take several or many kinds of food. Cattle, deer, rodents, and insects that eat leaves and stems of plants are said to be *herbivorous;* cats, sharks, flesh flies, and many marine animals whose food is entirely or largely of other animals are termed *carnivorous;* and man, bears, rats, and others that eat various plant and animal materials are called general feeders, or *omnivorous.*

Paramecium, some sea anemones, and certain fishes that feed on small particles, living or dead, such as plankton, are termed microphagous feeders. In contrast, most higher animals, including man, that use larger materials are macrophagous feeders. Still other animals are fluid feeders, like the mosquitoes that suck blood and the aphids that pump in plant juices.

The digestive mechanism or system in various animals (Fig. 5-1) differs in general form, structural details, and physiological processes according to the nature of the food, manner of life, and other factors. All means for taking and using food are essentially alike in that materials from the external environment are brought into intimate contact with internal membranous surfaces where digestion and absorption can take place.

5-2. Invertebrates. Many protozoans have no permanent structures for taking or digesting food. An amoeba pushes out lobes of protoplasm (pseudopodia) at any part of its one-celled body to surround an item of food; the latter is taken into a fluid-filled *food vacuole* within the cytoplasm for digestion (Fig. 16-4). In paramecium and other ciliate protozoans a permanent external *oral groove* lined by beating cilia carries food particles to a definite "cell mouth" where they pass into food vacuoles and are digested (Fig. 16-22). Drawing food to the mouth in a current of water by use of cilia is done by many animals from protozoans to lower chordates. The microscopic food of sponges is captured by and digested in flagellated *collar cells* that line certain interior canals of the animal; digestion is thus intracellular, as in protozoans. Coelenterates have a definite *mouth* connected to a sac-like *digestive cavity* (enteron) within the body that is

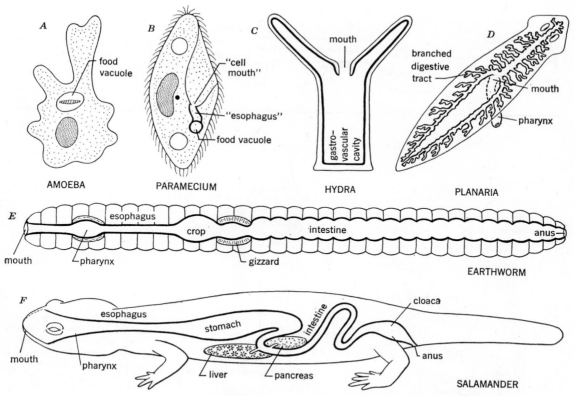

Fig. 5-1. Types of digestive systems in animals; diagrammatic. *A.* Amoeba, food enters at any place on cell surface. *B.* Paramecium, with definite cell mouth. *C.* Hydra, mouth and sac-like digestive cavity. *D.* Planaria, mouth and branched digestive tract, but no anus. *E.* Earthworm, tubular digestive tract having specialized sections, complete with terminal mouth and anus. *F.* Vertebrate, complete and partly coiled tract with specialized parts and digestive glands, anus at base of tail.

lined by a tissue layer of special digestive cells (Fig. 18-2). The flatworms (except tapeworms) have a mouth and a branched *digestive tract* extending to all parts of the body (Fig. 19-2). In both the latter groups the tract is *incomplete* in that foods enter and undigested residues pass out the same opening, the mouth. In the coelenterates and flatworms, food that has entered the digestive tract is acted upon by enzymes secreted from gland cells in the interior lining. This is intercellular digestion, in a digestive cavity, such as occurs in all higher animals; some partly digested food, however, is taken into cells lining the cavity for intracellular digestion.

In most other invertebrates the digestive tract is essentially a tube within the body. It is external in the sense of being open to the outside (mouth, anus) and separated from the interior body spaces by semipermeable membranes. It is termed *complete* because food enters the mouth and passes through various organs for storage, digestion, or absorption and any residues pass out the anus at the opposite end of the system. The parts differ in structure in animals belonging to various groups (Chaps. 20 to 27), but the names applied to them give some indication of the function of each part. An earthworm, for example, has a *mouth* with fleshy lips to grasp food, a muscular *pharynx* that sucks in the food and lubricates it by mucous secretions, a slender *esophagus* to carry

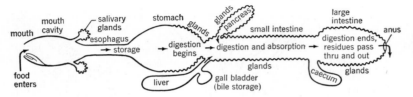

Fig. 5-2. Diagram of structure and activities in the digestive tract of a vertebrate.

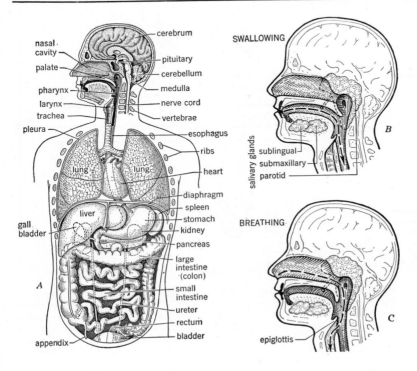

Fig. 5-3. *A.* The digestive system and other internal organs of the human body. Greater omentum supporting organs at front of abdomen removed; reproductive organs omitted. *B.* Route of food when swallowed —larynx raised against epiglottis, closing trachea. *C.* The respiratory path, trachea open.

food on to the dilated *crop* for storage, a muscular-walled *gizzard* where food is ground against particles of sand, and a long *intestine* with pouch-like lateral extensions providing a large surface for absorption of digested portions (Fig. 24-3). Undigested residues pass out the anus at the posterior end of the body. Jaws with teeth occur in the mouths of some other annelid worms, in squids and octopuses, in sea urchins, and in many arthropods. The mouth in all mollusks except the bivalves has a radula (Fig. 23-4) bearing many fine horny teeth that serve to rasp off particles of food. The mouth parts of arthropods are modified appendages; those of insects are adapted for either chewing or sucking (Chap. 26; Table 26-2).

5-3. Vertebrates.[1] The digestive system of almost every vertebrate has the following essential parts (Figs. 5-2, 5-3): (1) The *mouth* and *mouth cavity* commonly have *teeth* to grasp, tear, or chew food and a *tongue* that may help in capturing or manipulating it; in most land vertebrates the cavity contains *salivary glands* to lubricate the food and start digestion. (2) The *pharynx* contains gill slits in fishes and aquatic amphibians but has no direct digestive function. (3) The *esophagus* (gullet) is an elastic tube carrying food past the region of the

[1] For a comparison of the digestive and other **organ** systems in the various classes of vertebrates see the figures on "general structure" in Chaps. 2, 29 to 31, **33** to 35.

heart and lungs. (4) The **stomach** is a large pouch where food is stored and some digestion occurs. (5) The **small intestine,** a long slender tube, folded or coiled, is the principal region for digestion and absorption. (6) The **large intestine** (colon) is the portion where absorption is completed and undigested residues are formed into masses (feces) for expulsion through (7) the **cloaca,** which ends with (8) the **anus.** The cloaca is also an exit for excretory wastes and sex cells in sharks, amphibians, reptiles, and birds, but these pass out separate openings in most mammals. All vertebrates have two large digestive glands, the **liver** and **pancreas,** connected by ducts to the small intestine; cyclostomes have no pancreas. Typically all vertebrates have teeth except the living birds, although a few in other classes are toothless. Teeth in some fishes and reptiles and in most mammals are differentiated for piercing, shearing, crushing, or grinding, according to food habits (Chap. 36).

5-4. Food and digestion. The plant and animal foods taken by animals consist of protoplasm (Chap. 3) which is made up of proteins, carbohydrates, and fats, together with vitamins, minerals, and water. The water and inorganic salts can be absorbed from the digestive tract without change, but the protoplasmic materials must be altered before they can be utilized. The digestive system is a "laboratory" where these changes occur.

The processes of digestion, absorption, and utilization of food may, by analogy, be likened to a miscellany of large and small buildings (food), which are taken apart, the wooden portions into boards, the plumbing into pipes and fittings, and so on (digestion). Each must be of such size as to pass through a series of holes in a great wall (absorption). On the other side the various parts may be stored or recombined into new structures of different kinds from the original ones, and some are burned to supply energy (utilization).

Some foods are subjected only to chemical alteration, as with the microscopic organisms taken as food by protozoans and other small animals, the fluids of plants sucked up by bees and aphids, the blood pumped in by parasitic worms, leeches, or insects, and the larger prey taken by coelenterates and starfishes. Many other animals use food that must be reduced physically before chemical digestion can proceed effectively. This is accomplished by teeth in the mouth or elsewhere (pharynx of some fishes, stomach of crayfishes) and by grinding in the gizzard of earthworms and birds. Flesh eaters such as the sharks, large fishes, snakes, hawks, owls, cats, and others bolt down their food entire or in large pieces, and its physical reduction is accomplished by muscular action in the stomach. Other fishes and the herbivorous mammals that subsist upon plant materials chew their food thoroughly before it can be digested. Insects and many land vertebrates have salivary glands that provide secretions to moisten the food while it is being chewed and swallowed.

5-5. Digestive enzymes. The chemical aspects of digestion involve the reduction of complex organic substances in the food into simpler molecules that can be passed through cells of the digestive epithelium to enter the fluids and cells of the body. Proteins are reduced to amino acids, fats to fatty acids and glycerol, and carbohydrates to simple sugars (monosaccharides) such as glucose. These changes are performed by the digestive ferments, or enzymes (Chap. 3).

In general, these enzymes can act only upon dead protoplasm and are unable to penetrate living cells. They are produced by all animals from protozoans to mammals, but the same number or kinds of enzymes are not present in all animals. The food in a vacuole within a protozoan can be seen to change gradually in form and size as it is acted upon by enzymes. The reaction of the vacuole changes from acid to alkaline during the process, as can be shown by indicator dyes. The cytoplasm therefore has the ability to secrete enzymes and also substances to change the reaction (pH) of fluid in the vacuole. Among lower invertebrates, enzymes are secreted by cells in some or all parts of the digestive tract, but in higher animals only by glands or cells in certain portions of it. In the vertebrates, some are produced in the salivary glands or the esophagus, and others regularly in the stomach, small intestine, and pancreas.

5-6. The digestive process in man (Fig. 5-7).

The taking of food into the mouth cavity is a joint action of the lips, tongue, and teeth. The flexible lips are delicately sensitive to the physical character and temperature of the food, but not to taste. The tongue, having muscles in three planes, has great ability in movement and change of shape to handle the food; on its surface the taste buds (Fig. 10-10) are concentrated. The teeth are specialized to cut and grind the food. (In many lower vertebrates the teeth, in the absence of flexible lips, serve merely to grasp food; see Chaps. 2, 30 to 33.) Structurally, a tooth has a hard outside enamel, a filling of softer dentine, and a central living pulp supplied with nerves; the root is set in a socket of the jaw (Figs. 5-4, 35-13).

In the mouth cavity the food is lubricated by *saliva* secreted by three pairs of *salivary glands,* the submaxillary, sublingual, and parotid (Fig. 5-3*B*). About 1,000 cc. of saliva is produced per day, mostly at mealtimes. Secretion is a reflex act (par. 10-8) stimulated by savory tastes in the food or even by the sight or smell of food that literally "makes your mouth water." The intensity of the stimulus seemingly is related to the water content of the food—dry

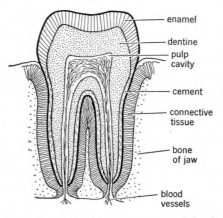

Fig. 5-4. Enlarged section of human tooth in the jaw. Compare Fig. 36-13.

bread in the mouth stimulates a copious flow, wet bread much less, and water none at all.

Saliva contains a protein, mucin, serving as a lubricant, and an enzyme, *ptyalin* (salivary amylase); the latter, in the normal alkaline medium of the mouth, reduces starches first to dextrins and then to the double sugar, maltose (malt sugar). The action is more rapid on cooked starch but, at best, is slight because food is in the mouth only a short time. Chewing aids starch digestion by breaking up the food, mixing in the enzyme, and lengthening the time of exposure to ptyalin. Starch requires about an hour for digestion. The action of ptyalin continues within the food mass in the stomach until penetrated by the acid gastric juice.

After a mouthful of food has been ground by the teeth and mixed with saliva, the tongue, by voluntary action, moves it backward into the pharynx and there presses it into a compact bolus. The remainder of the process of swallowing is involuntary, guided by a sequence of reflex movements. The soft palate rises to close the nasal cavity, then the larynx (Adam's apple) is lifted to press against the epiglottis, closing the entrance to the trachea and enlarging the opening of the esophagus (Fig. 5-3*B*, *C*). Failure in any of these reflexes results in "swallowing the wrong way"—the bolus of food enters the glottis, and choking is followed by a convulsive cough to remove the obstacle. The normal passage of a bolus through the esophagus results from a slow wave of muscular contraction down the walls of the gullet until the food passes the cardiac valve and enters the stomach.

All the movements and kneading of food in the digestive tract below the pharynx are by slow rhythmic contraction and relaxation of involuntary muscles, longitudinal and circular, in the wall of the tract. This process is known as *peristalsis.* By alternate action of the muscles, the diameter of the tract at any one place is first enlarged, then reduced. A wave of contraction moving down the esophagus carries a food bolus from esophagus to stomach. In the latter organ the alternate action kneads and mixes the food with secretions. In the intestine this movement, long continued, serves to divide and redivide the contents, to mix it thoroughly, to bring new portions against the inner wall, and to move the contents slowly along.

5-7. The stomach. This structure is a storage chamber that receives the food of a meal. Here the contents are given both physical and chemical treatment, then are passed, a little at a time, to the small intestine. Storage is mainly in the upper part (fundus) of the stomach, and muscular action chiefly in the middle (cardia) portion. The lower part (pyloric) ends with the pyloric valve, a circular muscle at the junction with the intestine. The stomach is important because its secretion has an antiseptic effect on bacteria in the food and because there is partial digestion of proteins by the gastric juice. Yet surgical removal of the stomach is not necessarily fatal in man, because food can be completely digested in the intestine.

The stomach wall contains gastric glands (an estimated 35,000,000) that secrete the gastric juice. This results from reflexes initiated by the taste or smell of food plus action of a hormone (gastrin). Pioneer studies on gastric juice were made by William Beaumont (American, 1785–1853) on a man—Alexis St. Martin—whose stomach had been partly shot away in 1822. The wound healed so that a permanent fistula (external opening) remained. Over several years Beaumont took and analyzed samples of gastric juice and tested its action on various foods; this provided the first understanding of the digestive process.

The gastric secretions include *mucin,* which further lubricates the food mass, *hydrochloric acid* (about 0.2 per cent), and enzymes. The acid reaction of gastric juice (pH, about 1.0) is well known from the unpleasant experience of vomiting. Of the gastric enzymes, *pepsin* splits proteins partly (to polypeptides such as proteoses and peptones), and *rennin* causes the casein in milk to coagulate. (Rennin extracted from stomachs of calves is used to form the "curd" in cheese making.) There is possibly a third enzyme, *gastric lipase,* having slight action on emulsified fats. An average person secretes an estimated 2,000 to 3,000 cc. of gastric juice daily.

5-8. The intestines. The small intestine is a slender tube about 25 feet long. The first 10 inches or so are the duodenum, the long central part is the jejunum, and the remaining 4 or 5 feet the ileum. When food in semifluid state (chyme) has passed through the pyloric valve into the duodenum, it stimulates secretion of the "intestinal juice" from tubular glands in the much-folded wall (Fig. 5-5). This alkaline fluid contains several enzymes. *Erepsin* continues the gastric digestion of proteins, splitting the proteoses and peptones into amino acids. The three carbohydrate-splitting enzymes are *maltase,* which converts maltose into glucose; *sucrase,* which changes sucrose (cane sugar) to glucose and fructose; and *lactase,* which divides lactose (milk sugar) into glucose and galactose.

The acid (HCl) in the chyme, upon entering the intestine, stimulates cells in the wall to release secretin from prosecretin (Fig. 5-6). This is a hormone (Chap. 9) carried in the blood stream through the heart and to the pancreas. There, independent of the nervous system, it initiates discharge into the intestine of the clear yellowish *pancreatic juice;* the daily secretion is 500 to 1,000 cc. Carbonates in this fluid neutralize the hydrochloric acid in the chyme, making the intestinal contents mildly alkaline in reaction. Enzymes in the pancreatic juice are *trypsin* (activated from trypsinogen by enterokinase from the intestinal wall) which splits intact or partly divided proteins into amino acids; *lipase,* which converts fats to fatty acids and glycerol; and *amylopsin,* which reduces entire or partly digested starches to sugars.

A third fluid, *bile* (not an enzyme), is added from the liver through the bile duct. This greenish-yellow liquid contains bile salts that facilitate digestion by physically reducing fats to small droplets (emulsification). Bile is stored in the gall bladder whence 500 to 1,000 cc. per day flows to the intestine. If the flow of bile is interrupted mechanically, as by gallstones or

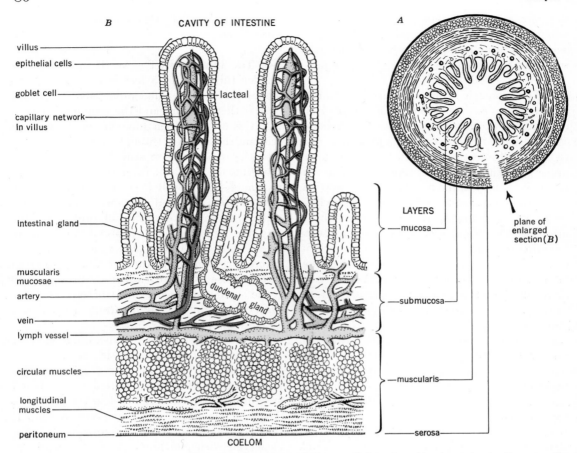

B   CAVITY OF INTESTINE   *A*

villus

epithelial cells

goblet cell

capillary network
In villus

lacteal

Intestinal gland

muscularis
mucosae

artery

vein

lymph vessel

circular muscles

longitudinal
muscles

peritoneum

duodenal
gland

COELOM

LAYERS

mucosa

submucosa

muscularis

serosa

plane of
enlarged
section(*B*)

Fig. 5-5. Structure of the small intestine (duodenum). *A.* Cross section
B. Diagrammatic cross section, enlarged.

infection of the bile duct, certain bile pigments are diverted into the blood stream and produce jaundice, with yellowing of the skin.

The *liver,* the largest "gland" in the body, besides the secretion of bile, performs several other functions related to the digestive tract and other parts of the body (Fig. 5-7). Briefly it (1) stores glucose (as glycogen) and provides a regulated supply to the body as needed; (2) serves in protein synthesis and also in the breakdown and disposal of waste nitrogenous products; (3) helps dispose of poisons; and (4) forms a substance (antianemia factor) aiding in red blood cell production—but also breaks down old red cells.

The *large intestine,* or *colon,* serves principally to dispose of undigested and indigestible residues by way of the rectum and anus and to conserve water by absorption from the mass. The food residues, together with bacteria, mucus, and dead cells from the intestinal wall, make up the feces that are expelled at intervals. The feces are characteristically colored by pigments from the bile (bilirubin and biliverdin) that are breakdown products of hemoglobin. Food usually passes from the mouth to the end of the small intestine in about 4½ hours; but residues may continue for a longer time, even beyond 24 hours, in the colon. During this time there is much bacterial action. Bacteria that survive the stomach acidity multiply rapidly, and some bring about more or less putrefaction, especially in the colon, where various toxic products and foul-smelling gases result.

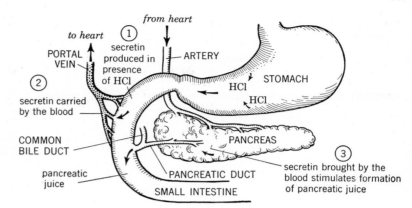

Fig. 5-6. The path and action of secretin in stimulating production of pancreatic juice.

Bacteria comprise up to 50 per cent of the dry weight of the feces.

5-9. Control of secretory activities. All digestive processes are integrated by the nervous system and hormones. Food entering the mouth stimulates salivary secretion by activating taste-bud cells from which impulses pass along sensory nerves to a "salivary center" in the medulla. From there motor fibers in the autonomic nervous system carry impulses to the salivary glands (Fig. 10-5). Simultaneously gastric juice is secreted in the stomach, as was shown by Ivan Pavlov (Russian, 1849–1936). The esophagus in a dog was severed, and the two cut ends brought out to open on the skin of the neck region. When food was placed in the animal's mouth, its stomach secreted gastric juice although no food reached the stomach. In a normal animal, when food enters the stomach, it stimulates the release of gastrin (a hormone), and this brings about the secretion of more gastric juice.

As food containing the acid gastric juice enters the intestine, the acid stimulates release of secretin, and hence of pancreatic juice (Fig. 5-6); the acid also promotes release of cholecystokinin from the intestinal wall which causes the gall bladder to discharge bile. Pancreatic juice, being alkaline, neutralizes the acid gastric juice, thereby removing the stimulus to its own secretion. Thus each stage in the digestive process influences others and results in a coordinated procedure.

5-10. Absorption. The small intestine is the principal area for absorption, the process that fulfills the purpose of digestion. Through the intestinal wall the chemical substances derived from food enter the body proper to be built into living tissues or used for energy. The wall acts as a semipermeable membrane. Its absorbing surface is increased about tenfold (to about 5 square meters) by upward of 4,000,000 minute projections, or *villi,* each containing blood capillaries and a central *lacteal vessel* (Fig. 5-5). The end products of protein and carbohydrate digestion (amino acids, simple sugars) pass through cells of the intestinal mucosa and mostly into blood capillaries connecting to the hepatic portal vein, whence they are carried to the liver. End products of fat digestion enter the lacteals which connect to the lymphatic system. Lymph vessels from the intestine join those from elsewhere in the body to form a large trunk, the thoracic duct, that in turn enters the venous system close to the heart (Chap. 6; Fig. 6-5).

5-11. Metabolism. When the products of digestion reach their ultimate destinations by way of the blood they are variously (1) broken down chemically to supply energy (catabolism); (2) stored as glycogen—animal starch—or as depot fat; or (3) built into new protoplasm (anabolism). Synthesis and breakdown are going on simultaneously in every living cell. The two processes are in dynamic equilibrium, with one or the other dominating at various times or

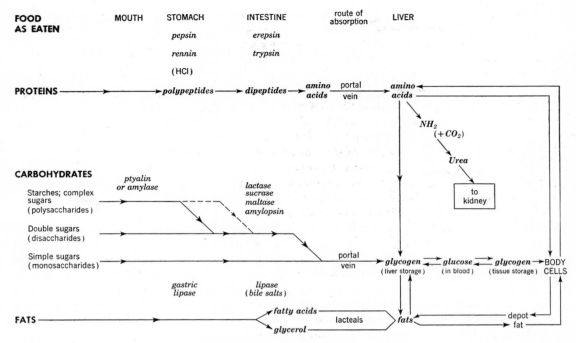

Fig. 5-7. History of food in the body—from the mouth through the processes of digestion and distribution, including some functions of the liver. Enzymes named in italics. (*Adapted from Weisz, 1954.*)

places (Figs. 5-7, 5-8). As mentioned previously (par. 4-12) catabolic processes may be represented by the oversimplified formula:

$$C_6H_{12}O_6 + 6O_2 \rightarrow 6H_2O + 6CO_2 + energy$$
(glucose)   (enzyme
                    action)

In the muscles the actual reactions are complex, but ultimately they depend upon a constant supply of glucose and oxygen.

The liver plays a central role in this process, receiving glucose in blood from the intestine and converting it into glycogen. The latter is (1) stored in the liver for use between meals when it is reconverted into glucose; (2) released into the blood stream gradually so as to maintain a rather constant glucose (blood sugar) level of about 0.1 per cent; and (3) carried to all parts of the body. The blood sugar level is largely controlled by the hormone insulin, formed by the islets of Langerhans in the pancreas (Chap. 9). Some of the lactic acid produced in the muscles is also carried by the blood to the liver where it is converted to liver glycogen. Thus there is a constant circulation of carbohydrate within the body in the following pattern:

digested
carbohydrate
↓
Liver glycogen ⇌ blood sugar (glucose) → muscle glycogen
↓   ↓
body cells   intermediate steps
↓
lactic acid
↓
$CO_2 + H_2O$ + energy

INPUT   **OUTPUT**

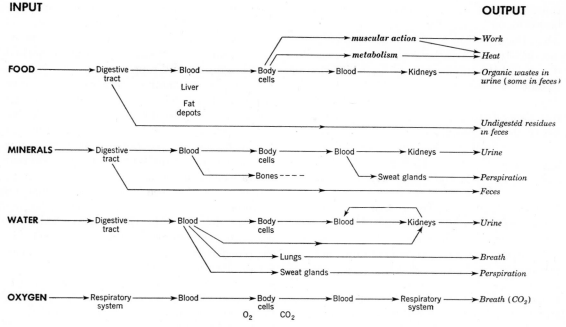

Fig. 5-8. Flow chart of input and output of the body.

When carbohydrates are taken in excess, they can be converted into fats by a method of synthesis little understood. Fats are stored in fat cells among the muscles, beneath the skin, and elsewhere in the body. Fats are also formed from fatty acids and glycerol absorbed by the lacteals and transported by way of the lymphatic system.

5-12. Utilization. The percentage of food actually absorbed of the total amount ingested is an indication of the degree or efficiency of utilization. This varies widely depending on the composition of the foodstuff and on the specific needs of each kind of animal. Meat and other materials of animal origin are almost completely utilized, 95 per cent or more being absorbed, whereas foods from plant sources are less efficient, depending on their character and the extent to which each is digested. Seeds yield higher percentages of usable food than leaf or stem materials.

A daily account of the intake and output for each group of substances shows that the animal body is in a state of balance or fluctuates around an equilibrium. Demands are greater in growing individuals or in those at hard manual labor as compared with adults in sedentary activities. The equilibrium is maintained by the selective utilization of various substances in the diet. It is upset if any essential and irreplaceable element is lacking, and also if the total of foodstuffs is not sufficient for the minimum requirements of the organism. A diet, therefore, should be both qualitatively and quantitatively adequate.

The metabolic decomposition of food in the body to yield energy is an oxidative process, corresponding to the combustion of a fuel. The heat of combustion for organic compounds is recorded in calories. (One calorie is the heat needed to raise 1 gram of water 1°C.; in metabolism the large or kilogram-Calorie is the basis: 1 Calorie = 1,000 calories.) Laboratory experiments show the fuel value for the three main classes of foodstuffs in Calories, to be as follows: carbohydrate, 4.1; protein, 5.5; fat, 9.3. Fat thus has high "fuel value" in the animal body. The amount of energy needed to maintain the vital functions of an animal is essen-

84

tially constant and is termed the standard or basal metabolism. This is the metabolic rate when the organism is at rest and no food is being digested or absorbed. For the average human adult it is about 1 calorie per kilogram of weight per hour at 37°C., or 1,700 calories per day (155 pounds or 70 kg. × 24 = 1,680). The rate depends to a large extent on the functioning of the thyroid gland (Chap. 9) and can be altered by feeding thyroid extract or by removing part of the gland. It is also influenced by age, sex, activity, and external temperature.

5-13. Kinds of food. The preceding discussion shows that the amount of food is not the only criterion for an adequate diet. A "balanced diet" is a mixture of foods containing all the substances essential for the development, growth, and maintenance of the individual. Foremost of these are the carbohydrates, fats, and proteins. Furthermore, the proteins must include most or all of the amino acids to provide the body with the building materials to synthesize its own proteins.

Certain additional substances, the *inorganic elements* (minerals) and the *vitamins,* are essential in a balanced diet. Most diets contain adequate amounts of these substances, so their need was not suspected until recent years.

Fig. 5-9. Vitamin B₁ deficiency—polyneuritis. *A.* Pigeon fed 12 to 24 days on polished rice lacking vitamin B₁. *B.* Same bird, completely normal, a few hours after receiving B₁ concentrate or food high in B₁ content. (*After Harris, Vitamins, J. & A. Churchill, Ltd.*)

Experiments have shown that minute amounts of iron, copper, zinc, manganese, cobalt, and iodine are essential micronutrients for animals; and a number of vitamins are vital for normal health, growth, and reproduction.

Iodine is an example of an essential "trace element." For several hundred years it has been known that iodine deficiency produces a disease called goiter, with a tumor-like bulge in the neck region. We now know that goiter results from the malfunction of the thyroid gland which, in the absence of iodine, cannot produce the essential metabolism-regulating hormone, thyroxin. Iodine comprises 65 per cent by weight of the thyroxin molecule, but not more than one part per million is needed in the blood stream because the thyroid gland can accumulate and store iodine until the necessary level is reached. The required minute amounts of iodine are now generally provided, in areas where it does not occur naturally, in food or water, by use of "iodized salt."

Another deficiency disease is anemia, caused by insufficient iron. Most (66 per cent) of this element in the body is contained in the hemoglobin of the blood; additional iron occurs in the liver, spleen, and bone marrow where red blood cells are formed.

Addition of minute amounts of certain antibiotics to the feed of poultry and domestic mammals has been found to increase markedly the rate of growth, evidently by reducing pathogenic organisms in the digestive tract.

5-14. Vitamins (Table 5-1). These are organic substances, mostly of plant origin, required for normal growth in animals. Their existence was suspected late in the nineteenth century when it was found that a diet of pure carbohydrates, fats, and proteins would not support life. Eijkman (Dutch, 1858–1930) was the first to produce a disease of dietary origin, polyneuritis, in fowls (Fig. 5-9) by feeding them exclusively on polished rice. The resemblance between this condition and a human illness, beriberi, led him to cure many cases in Java with an extract of rice bran. This and other nutritional factors later were named vitamins; the polyneuritis

TABLE 5-1. The Vitamins and Their Characteristics

Name, formula, and principal effect	Important sources	Physiological functions	Result of deficiency or absence (in man, except as noted)
A($C_{20}H_{30}O$) antixerophthalmic (fat soluble)	*Plant form* (carotene, $C_{40}H_{56}$) in green leaves, carrots, etc.; is changed in liver to *animal form* ($C_{20}H_{30}O$), present in fish-liver oil (shark); both forms in egg yolk and milk	Maintains integrity of epithelial tissues, especially mucous membranes Needed to regenerate visual purple in retina of eye	Xerophthalmia (dry cornea, no tear secretion), phrynoderma (toad skin) Night blindness "Nutritional roup" in birds
B *"complex"* (water soluble) Thiamine (B_1) ($C_{12}H_{17}ON_4S$) antineuritic	Yeast, germ of cereals especially wheat, peanuts, other leguminous seeds, egg yolk, liver, and lean pork	Needed for carbohydrate metabolism. Thiamine pyrophosphate is "cocarboxylase" which catalyzes metabolism of pyruvic acid to acetaldehyde and CO_2 (Stimulates root growth in plants)	Beriberi (on diet high in polished rice) Loss of appetite, with loss of "tone" and reduced motility in digestive tract Cessation of growth Polyneuritis in birds
Riboflavin ($C_{17}H_{20}O_6N_4$)	Green leaves, milk, eggs, liver, yeast	Essential for growth; forms active group of several enzymes concerned with intermediate metabolism of food	Cheilosis (inflammation and cracking at corners of mouth) "Yellow liver" of dogs "Curled-toe" paralysis of chicks
Nicotinic acid or niacin ($C_6H_5NO_2$) antipellagric	Green leaves, wheat germ, egg yolk, meat, liver, yeast	Forms active group of di- and tri-phosphopyridine nucleotides essential to cellular function	Pellagra in man and monkeys Swine pellagra in pigs Blacktongue in dogs Perosis in birds
Folic acid ($C_{19}H_{19}O_6N_7$)	Green leaves, liver, soybeans, yeast, egg yolk	Essential for growth and formation of blood cells; involved in transfer of "single-carbon" units in metabolism	Anemia (hyperchromicmacrocytic) and sprue in man Nutritional cytopenia in monkeys Slow growth and anemia in chicks and rats
Pyridoxine (B_6) ($C_8H_{12}O_3N$)	Yeast, cereal grains, milk, liver	Present in tissues as pyridoxal phosphate which serves in transamination and decarboxylation of amino acids	Anemia in dogs and pigs Dermatitis in rats Paralysis (and death) in pigs, rats, and chicks
Pantothenic acid ($C_9H_{17}O_5N$)	Yeast, cane molasses, peanuts, egg yolks, milk, liver	Forms "coenzyme A" which catalyzes addition of acetyl group to choline and other substances	Dermatitis in chicks and rats Graying of fur in black rats "Goose stepping" and nerve degeneration in pigs
Biotin ($C_{10}H_{16}O_3N_2S$)	Yeast, cereal grains, cane molasses, egg yolk, vegetables, fresh fruits	Essential for growth Functions in CO_2 fixation and oleic acid synthesis in bacteria	Dermatitis with thickening of skin in rats and chicks Perosis in birds

TABLE 5-1. The Vitamins and Their Characteristics (*Continued*)

Name, formula, and principal effect	Important sources	Physiological functions	Result of deficiency or absence (in man, except as noted)
B *"complex"* B$_{12}$ ($C_{63}H_{90}N_{14}O_{14}PCo$)	Liver, fish, meat, milk, egg yolk, oysters, bacteria and fermentations of *Streptomyces*	Formation of blood cells, growth	Pernicious anemia Slow growth in young animals Wasting disease in ruminants
C or ascorbic acid ($C_6H_8O_6$)	Citrus fruits, tomatoes; animals (except primates and guinea pigs) produce vitamin C	Maintains integrity of capillary walls; involved in formation of "intercellular cement"	Scurvy (bleeding in mucous membranes, under skin, and into joints) in man and guinea pig
D ($C_{28}H_{44}O$) antirachitic (fat soluble)	Fish-liver oils, especially tuna, less in cod; also from exposure of skin to ultra-violet radiation	Regulates metabolism of calcium and phosphorus; needed for normal growth and mineralization of bones	Rickets in young (bones soft, yielding, often deformed) Osteomalacia (soft bones), especially in women of Orient
E or Tocopherol ($C_{29}H_{50}O_2$) antisterility (fat soluble)	Green leaves; wheat-germ oil and other vegetable fats	Essential to rapid cell proliferation and differentiation in vertebrates	Sterility in male fowls and rats; degeneration of testis with failure of spermatogenesis Death of embryos "Suckling paralysis" and muscular dystrophy in young animals
K ($C_{31}H_{46}O_2$) antihemorrhagic (fat soluble)	Green leaves, also in certain bacteria as those of "intestinal flora"	Essential to production of prothrombin in liver, necessary for blood clotting	Blood fails to clot

factor was called vitamin B$_1$. In the last 30 years most of the vitamins have been isolated, crystallized, characterized chemically, and synthesized. Vitamins are effective in minute amounts. Of vitamin B$_1$ the average human being needs only 1 to 2 mg. daily, usually supplied by whole-grain bread or cereal. Well-balanced diets usually provide enough of all vitamins for normal health. Some modern advertising is at fault in claiming that people on a normal well-balanced diet need to take vitamin concentrates regularly. In some illnesses, however, large doses of certain vitamins may be prescribed to hasten recovery.

Eating habits and methods of preparing food often result in some vitamin deficiencies. White bread and canned foods are commonly deficient; the heat of cooking destroys some vitamins, and others are lost when the water is drained off after cooking. Raw fruits and vegetables are helpful in the diet because they retain their vitamins.

The restricted diets of some races of people lead to deficiency diseases (Figs. 5-10 to 5-12). Scurvy (vitamin C deficiency) was common on long sea voyages in past centuries; the British sea captains who later learned to carry limes as a food accessory to prevent scurvy were known as "lime-juicers." Beriberi is prevalent among Oriental peoples who live largely on polished rice, and pellagra among persons on diets largely of corn that is deficient in niacin.

The vitamins are unrelated chemically, but each evidently regulates one or more bodily processes. Some act as parts of enzymes, or as coenzymes, or influence enzyme systems within cells. Thiamine (B$_1$), for example, may unite with phosphoric acid to form a pyrophosphate

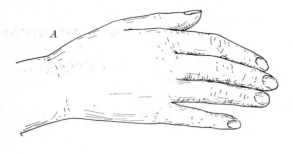

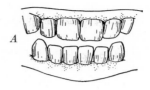

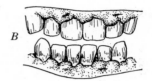

Fig. 5-11. Scurvy, from vitamin C deficiency. *A.* Normal gums of person receiving adequate supply of vitamin C in citrus, tomato juice, etc. *B.* Gums of severe scurvy, swollen and bleeding.

Fig. 5-10. Pellagra. *A.* Normal hand. *B.* Hand of person on diet lacking niacin of vitamin B complex: skin thickened, sloughing, cracking, and with extra pigment. (*After Harris, Vitamins, J. & A. Churchill, Ltd.*)

during the process of muscular contraction (par. 4-12). Thiamine pyrophosphate then acts as a coenzyme in a chemical reaction involving the breakdown of pyruvic acid with removal of CO_2. Thiamine deficiency results in an accumulation of pyruvic acid in the tissues with consequent nerve and muscle pain (beriberi).

5-15. Other digestive processes. The digestive mechanisms and processes among animals vary in many details. In some birds and insects the lower end of the esophagus is dilated into a crop for temporary storage of food. Most birds also have a stomach of two parts, a slender soft glandular proventriculus and a larger thick-walled muscular gizzard, lined by hardened secretion, where food is ground up by grit swallowed for the purpose. The cattle, deer, and other cud-chewing mammals (ruminants) have a stomach of four compartments; the first three are specializations of the esophagus and have rough cornified linings where food is abraded and also worked on by bacteria. Rodents,

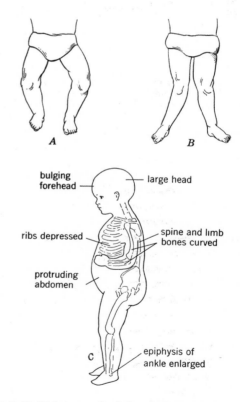

Fig. 5-12. Rickets, result of vitamin D deficiency in diet. *A, B.* Leg deformities. *C.* Other deformities, not all to be seen in any one individual. (*After Harris, Vitamins, J. & A. Churchill, Ltd.*)

horses, and some other herbivores have a large thin-walled caecum at the junction of the small and large intestines; there is some bacterial digestion of cellulose in this chamber. Man has a short caecum (Fig. 5-3), to which the vermiform appendix attaches (the latter has no known useful function and may become infected, requiring surgical removal).

Microorganisms are essential for the digestion of cellulose by certain termites and a few other wood-eating invertebrates. If the bacteria and protozoans normally in the digestive system of a termite are eliminated (by high temperature), the insect starves because it cannot produce enzymes to digest the cellulose in its diet of wood. Blood-sucking animals commonly have a special anticoagulant in the saliva that keeps the blood in a fluid state during ingestion. In scale insects and their relatives, which suck plant fluids, the terminal part of the intestine is bent back into a loop fitting into a dilated pouch of the esophagus; this "filter chamber" eliminates excess water from the highly diluted foodstuffs.

A few animals partly digest their food outside the body. The protozoan *Vampyrella* secretes an enzyme, cellulase, to dissolve the cell walls of an alga, *Spirogyra*, on which it feeds. A starfish extrudes its stomach to envelop and digest large prey. Larvae of some beetles (*Dytiscus, Lampyris,* etc.) inject a protease into their prey—tadpoles, slugs, and snails—that predigests parts of these animals, the softened food then being ingested.

6 CIRCULATORY SYSTEMS

The life processes of an animal require that food and oxygen be available continually for metabolism in all parts of its body and that wastes be removed promptly. In protozoans these interchanges are aided by streaming movements of the cytoplasm within the one-celled body; and in the simple multicellular types, the exchanges occur by diffusion between the epidermal cells and adjacent body parts. More complex animals, with organs and tissues well removed from the exterior or gut, have a *circulatory system* for internal transport (Fig. 6-1). Its essential parts are (1) the *blood,* consisting of fluid plasma and free cells or blood corpuscles; (2) the *heart* (or an equivalent structure) with muscular walls that contract periodically to pump the blood through the body; and (3) a system of tubular *blood vessels* through which the fluid is moved. The system is *closed* in vertebrates and annelids, where the vessels convey blood from the heart in various circuits among the tissues and back to the heart. Mollusks and arthropods have an *open* (lacunar) system, blood being pumped from the heart through blood vessels to various organs but returning partly or entirely through body spaces—the *hemocoel*—to the heart.

6-1. Invertebrates. Sponges, coelenterates, flatworms, and roundworms have no circulatory system. Simple diffusion serves to carry digested food, respiratory gases, and wastes between various parts of their bodies. In brachiopods, echinoderms, and some others the system is obscure. Fluid in the body spaces (coelom, pseudocoel) serves in some as a medium for circulation. Nemerteans have one dorsal and two lateral blood vessels with many cross connections. Pulsations in the walls of these serve to circulate the blood, which, surprisingly, contains red blood cells resembling those of vertebrates.

The blood of most invertebrates has relatively few free cells in the plasma as compared with vertebrates. Usually there are amoeboid corpuscles resembling white blood cells, some phagocytic (par. 6-4) and some aiding in transport of food or other substances. In insects many of the cells cling to organs and become common in the plasma only after bodily injury or during molt (then up to 30,000 or 70,000 per cu. mm. in some species). If a respiratory pigment (par. 7-9) is present to carry oxygen, it usually is dissolved in the plasma because the molecules are relatively huge (molecular weight about 2,000,000), too large to diffuse through cell membranes.

The heart of invertebrates is always dorsal to the digestive tract (Fig. 6-2). In mollusks it is short, lies within a thin pericardial sac, an consists of one or two thin-walled *auricles* that receive blood from the body and deliver it to a single muscular-walled *ventricle.* The latter contracts to force the blood through the ves-

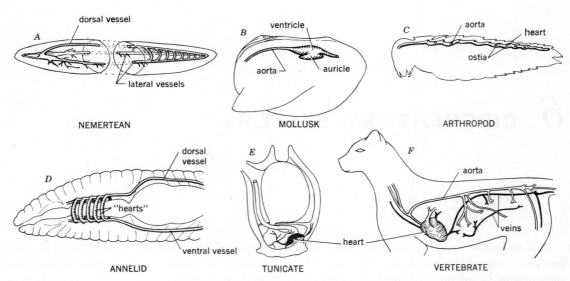

Fig. 6-1. Types of circulatory systems in animals. *A.* Nemertean (ribbon worm), simple lengthwise dorsal and lateral vessels with cross connectives. *B.* Mollusk (bivalve), dorsal heart with auricle (1 or 2) and ventricle, anterior, and posterior aortas, blood returns through body spaces (hemocoel)—open system. *C.* Arthropod (insect), dorsal tubular heart and aorta, blood returns through body spaces (hemocoel)—open system. *D.* Annelid (earthworm), dorsal and ventral vessels (and others) with cross connectives—closed system. *E.* Tunicate (sea squirt), a heart and aortas, vessels obscure; blood flow reverses. *F.* Vertebrate (mammal), chambered heart, definite aorta, arteries, and veins, with connections to respiratory organs—closed system.

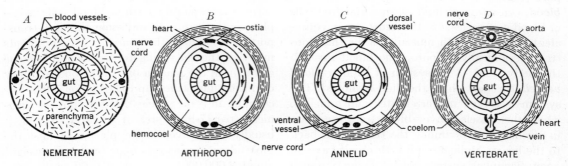

Fig. 6-2. Diagrammatic cross sections to show relations of circulatory system to body spaces and organs. *A.* Nemertean. Mere system of vessels, no heart, body filled with packing tissue (parenchyma). *B.* Mollusk-arthropod. An open system. Dorsal heart (and aortas) from which blood escapes into body spaces —the hemocoel—and returns to the heart (some mollusks collect blood from the hemocoel in veins). Coelom reduced to small cavities (in pericardial sac, gonads, etc.). *C.* Annelid. Closed system of vessels containing the blood; body spaces (between gut and body wall) a true coelom. *D.* Vertebrate. Closed system; heart ventral; a true coelom.

sels, or arteries, that distribute to various organs (Fig. 23-10). Insects and many other arthropods have the heart as a slender dorsal tube with segmentally placed lateral openings (ostia) that receive blood from the body spaces (hemocoel), and pump it through a median aorta to organs and tissues (Figs. 25-4, 26-5).

The earthworm has a closed system with several lengthwise vessels through the body and paired transverse connecting vessels in most body segments. The circulation is produced by contractions of the middorsal vessel and by five pairs of lateral hearts in anterior body segments (Fig. 24-3; Table 24-1).

6-2. Vertebrate blood.[1] In all vertebrates the blood comprises (1) a nearly colorless plasma; (2) white blood cells or leucocytes, of several kinds; (3) red cells or erythrocytes colored by the contained hemoglobin which serves to transport oxygen; and (4) smaller cells, the platelets or thrombocytes. The *plasma* carries dissolved foods, wastes, internal secretions, and some gases. Human blood plasma consists of about 92 per cent water plus proteins and other organic compounds and about 0.9 per cent of inorganic salts, chiefly sodium chloride; in health, these vary but slightly in amount. Physiological salt solution containing the same kinds and amounts of these salts can be used to dilute blood without injuring the corpuscles. An average person contains 5 to 6 quarts of blood; about 60 per cent is plasma.

6-3. Erythrocytes. The *red cells* are nucleated and oval in all vertebrates but mammals, where they are nonnucleated, biconcave, and circular

---

[1] The various functions of the circulatory system and the general structure of the blood, heart, and vessels of vertebrates are much as described for the frog (Chap. 2; Figs. 2-12 to 2-15). Human blood cells are shown in Fig. 3-18, and their characteristics are given in Table 6-1; the structure and action of the human heart are illustrated in Fig. 6-3, and the principal vessels of the human circulatory system in Fig. 6-5; the microanatomy of arteries, capillaries, and veins is indicated in Fig. 6-4; progressive differences in the heart and aortic arches of vertebrates are illustrated in Fig. 14-4; the general plan of vertebrate circulation is diagrammed in Fig. 2-15, and differences among fishes, amphibians, and birds and mammals are shown in Fig. 6-6.

(oval in camels). Mammalian red cells are nucleated, however, during their development. The red cells total about 30 trillion (3×10^{12}) in a human being; each may live to 120 days and may make 50,000 circuits in the blood stream. Red cells are more numerous in infants and in persons living at high altitudes; their numbers are altered in some diseases, being reduced in anemia. Red cells are produced chiefly in red bone marrow, and an excess supply is often stored in the spleen. Old cells are destroyed chiefly in the spleen, whence much of the hemoglobin passes to the liver; its pigment is excreted in the bile and its iron content is largely returned to the marrow.

6-4. Leucocytes. The several kinds of *white cells* have their principal activities in the tissues, and those seen in the blood stream are but a part of the "passing parade" on their way from their origins in the marrow, spleen, or lymphoid structures to the tissues or to their death. The lymphocytes, with a single rounded nucleus, are commonest in lymph vessels and in the lymph nodes along those vessels; the granulocytes, with lobed nuclei, are in the blood stream and also around tissues. The estimated life of a white cell is 12 to 13 days. Most white cells of both types can perform amoeboid movements and can crawl out between the endothelial cells lining capillaries into spaces between tissue cells. There many of them can act as *phagocytes* (Gr. *phagos*, eat) to protect the body by consuming bacteria that invade wounds. In an acute infection, such as appendicitis or pneumonia, the neutrophils and small lymphocytes increase markedly; the total leucocyte count will rise from a normal of about 8,000 or 10,000 to 20,000 or 30,000 per cubic millimeter, to battle the infection. The whitish pus of an infected area consists of dead leucocytes, tissue cells, and blood serum.

The *blood platelets* or *thrombocytes* are an obscure but essential element of the blood. They are more or less disc-shaped, much smaller than red cells, and without nuclei. When injured, they disintegrate, releasing thromboplastin, which initiates the clotting process.

6-5. Functions of the blood. The blood performs a variety of duties for the many parts of the body. Some were listed previously, but all may be mentioned here to show the importance of this fluid circulating medium. It serves to carry:

1. Oxygen and carbon dioxide between respiratory organs and tissues (pars. 7-9, 7-10).
2. Water and digested foods from the digestive tract to other organs (par. 5-10).
3. Stored foods from one organ or tissue to another as needed (par. 5-11).
4. Organic wastes, excess minerals in solution, and water to the excretory organs (par. 8-3).
5. Hormones from the glands where produced to the places of use (Chap. 9).

Besides these miscellaneous transport functions the blood acts to regulate the pH of tissues within narrow limits by means of buffers such as phosphates and carbonates; the blood is slightly alkaline with a pH relatively constant at 7.4. Its role in water balance between the tissues and excretory structures is all-important, and it does this at such a rate that the water content of the blood does not vary appreciably in a normal individual. In the "warmblooded" birds and mammals the blood, by differential distribution between the internal organs and the body surface, serves to maintain the temperature of the entire body within close

TABLE 6-1. Average Characteristics of Human Blood Cells

Kinds of cells and average number per cubic millimeter of blood	Structure; color with Wright's blood stain;[1] diameter (μ = 0.001 mm.)	Source	Function
Erythrocytes (red blood cells): 5,000,000 (in males) 4,500,000 (in females)	Nonnucleated, circular, biconcave; orange-buff; 7.5 to 7.7 μ (8.6 μ in fresh blood)	Endothelium of capillaries in bone marrow	Transport oxygen; remain in blood vessels
Leucocytes (white blood cells): 8,000 to 10,000 1. GRANULOCYTES *a. Neutrophils,* 65 to 75% *b. Eosinophils,* 2 to 5% *c. Basophils,* 0.5%	Colorless in life Nucleus of lobes joined by thread, stains dark lilac; cytoplasm granular, pale blue; 10 to 12 μ Granules stain weakly Granules few, eosin (red) Granules deep blue	Reticuloendothelial cells outside capillaries of bone marrow	Amoeboid; can leave blood vessels and enter tissues; defend against infection
2. LYMPHOCYTES, 20 to 25%	Nucleus single, large, round, deep blue; scant cytoplasm, clear blue; 6 to 10 μ	Lymphoid tissue, spleen, and lymph glands	Nonmotile; related to immunity
3. MONOCYTES, 2 to 6%	Nucleus single, large, round, deep blue; much cytoplasm, muddy blue; 12 to 15 μ	Spleen and bone marrow	Very motile; phagocytic
Platelets: 200,000 to 400,000	Small, refractile, no nucleus; dark blue to lilac; 2 to 4 μ	Cytoplasmic fragments of megakaryocytes in bone marrow	Provide substance needed in clotting

[1] A stain containing two special kinds of dyes, methylene blue and eosin, together with sodium bicarbonate and methyl alcohol.

limits. And the blood finally is the defense mechanism against foreign organisms, having therefore a major role in maintaining normal health and opposing the effects of disease.

6-6. Clotting. When a blood vessel is cut, the issuing blood is soon stopped by a protective *clot.* The injured tissues and disintegrating *blood platelets* release *thromboplastin* (thrombokinase) which, in combination with *calcium ions* always present in the plasma, acts upon *prothrombin,* also in the blood, to produce *thrombin.* (Prothrombin is produced in the liver when vitamin K is present.) Thrombin converts a soluble blood protein, *fibrinogen,* into *fibrin,* which becomes a mass of fine fibers entangling corpuscles to form the clot. Diagrammatically the process is as follows:

$$\text{thromboplastin}$$
$$\downarrow$$
$$\text{prothrombin} + \text{calcium} \rightarrow \text{thrombin}$$
$$\text{thrombin} + \text{fibrinogen} \rightarrow \text{fibrin}$$
$$\text{fibrin} + \text{blood cells} \rightarrow \text{blood clot}$$

The fluid residue from a clot is the blood serum. A further substance, heparin, prevents the formation of thrombin in blood flowing normally within blood vessels. Decrease in the number of platelets lengthens the clotting time. Blood withdrawn for transfusion or for laboratory use is kept from clotting by addition of sodium citrate. In certain male persons known as "bleeders" clotting is long delayed or fails; a slight cut or tooth extraction may result in death by loss of blood (hemorrhage). This condition is caused by a sex-linked hereditary disease (hemophilia) transmitted by females but manifested chiefly in males; among females only those rare individuals homozygous for the defect experience the disease.

6-7. Antibodies. When a "foreign protein" (i.e., not naturally in the body) is injected into the blood of an animal, a specific protective substance, or *antibody,* usually is formed. Thus, if a small (sublethal) dose of rattlesnake venom is injected into a pigeon, the bird's plasma, after several days, will contain antibodies ca-

pable of neutralizing a much larger dose of venom. The venom has served as an *antigen* stimulating some tissues to produce an antibody which is carried mainly in the blood plasma. Bacteria and other organisms may serve as antigens. Recovery from any germ-caused disease results from the production of antibodies, which often confer a degree of *immunity,* transient or permanent, to further attack by the organism in question. Human beings and domestic animals are now rendered immune to certain diseases by injecting the dead or attenuated organisms (vaccine) of a particular disease or the immune serum (antitoxin) from a horse or other animal that has previously been immunized. Examples are vaccines for smallpox and typhoid fever, and antitoxins for diphtheria, tetanus, and snake bite. Antibodies occur in the globulin fraction of blood plasma. The injecting of gamma globulin, obtained from whole blood of donors, may increase the immunity of the recipient to various diseases including measles and poliomyelitis.

6-8. Human blood groups. If red blood cells from one person are mixed with blood plasma of another individual, the cells remain separate in some cases but become clumped, or agglutinated, in others. This is a matter of great practical importance when blood from a healthy donor is sought for transfusion into the veins of a sick or wounded person; should clumping occur, the patient may die instead of being helped. The blood of donor and patient must be "compatible." Extensive tests show that two types of *antigens* (agglutinogens) called *A* and *B* occur in the red cells of different persons, and the plasma contains two kinds of *antibodies* (agglutinins) known as *a* (*anti-A*) and *b* (*anti-B*). There are four *blood groups* among human beings: group O, having antibodies *a* and *b* but no antigens; group A, antibody *b* and antigen *A*; group B, antibody *a* and antigen *B*; and group AB, antigens *A* and *B* but no antibodies. The results of mixing cells of any one group with plasma of another are summarized in Table 6-2. Blood-group characteristics are inherited and remain constant throughout life. Blood of any anthropoid ape is like one or another human group; monkeys and lower mammals also have blood groups but not identical with those of man. Other antigens (*M, N*) are present in human red cells, but their significance is not clear.

Sterile dried plasma, without corpuscles, now serves extensively for blood transfusion. It keeps indefinitely under varied climatic conditions, needs only to be mixed with sterile water before injection, and involves no problem of agglutination.

TABLE 6-2. Results of Mixing Cells and Serum of Human Blood Groups

−, *compatible; no agglutination*
+, *not compatible; agglutinates*

			Blood group			
			O	A	B	AB
			Antigen in red cells			
			None	*A*	*B*	*AB*
Blood group	O	Antibodies in serum	*a, b*	−	+	+	+
	A		*b*	−	−	+	+
	B		*a*	−	+	−	+
	AB		None	−	−	−	−

6-9. The Rh factor. About 85 per cent of white persons have another antigen in their red blood cells, and their blood is known as Rh+ (Rh positive); those lacking this substance are termed Rh− (Rh negative), the difference being due to heredity. If Rh+ blood is repeatedly transfused into an Rh− individual, the antigen stimulates production of anti-Rh agglutinin. This is called iso-immunization, since both the antigen (Rh) and antibody (anti-Rh) are in the same species.

An Rh− individual receiving blood from Rh+ donors shows no reaction at first, but later becomes iso-immunized; if then transfused

with Rh+ blood there is a severe reaction, usually fatal. The anti-Rh agglutinins cause hemolysis of the Rh+ transfused blood.

An Rh− mother bearing an Rh+ fetus (that received the Rh+ factor from the father) may become immunized by Rh+ fetal erythrocytes entering the maternal circulation. Then in second or later pregnancies the maternal anti-Rh agglutinins cross the placenta, enter the fetal circulation, and hemolyze the fetal red cells, commonly with fatal results. This disease (erythroblastosis) in the fetus or newborn results in loss of about 1 pregnancy in 50 among the white women of the United States. Once so immunized, such a mother, with a homozygous father (Chap. 12), is unlikely to bear a living child.

6-10. The lymphatic system. Within the tissues of the body there is a fluid in contact with individual cells and with the blood capillaries, known as the *tissue fluid* or *lymph*. Essentially it is a plasma filtrate, a fluid which originates from seepage or percolation of water plus solutes through capillary walls. The lymph plays a vital role in transport between cells, as also in diffusion and in immunity. It is primarily extracellular but may return to the blood through the lymphatic system. Between the cells in all tissues there are minute channels where fluid collects. These channels converge to form fine, thin-walled *lymph vessels* with valves. Most lymph vessels are so delicate as not to be seen in anatomical preparations. They become larger in the thorax and there unite to form the *thoracic duct* which empties into the venous system near the heart (Fig. 6-5). The lymphatic system carries fluid in only one direction, from the tissues to the blood and heart (Fig. 2-15). Scattered along the system are many *lymph nodes*. Besides producing lymphocytes, the nodes defend the body from infection by intercepting disease organisms. Throat infections, for example, may be accompanied by swelling of lymph nodes in the neck.

The *spleen* is a part of the lymphatic and circulatory systems capable of acting as a res-

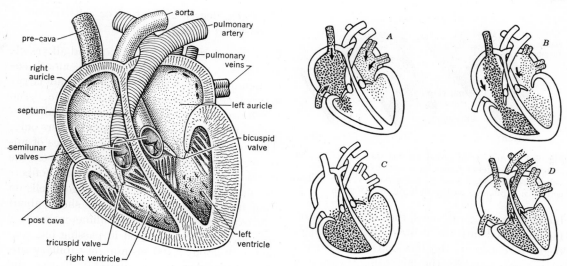

Fig. 6-3. The mammalian (human) heart (frontal section, ventral view) and (A–D) its mode of action. Arrows indicate paths of blood flow. Heavy stipple, unoxygenated blood; light stipple, oxygenated blood. A. Auricles filling from veins. B. Blood entering relaxed ventricles. C. Auricles contracting, ventricles filling. D. Ventricles contracting, blood forced into aorta and pulmonary arteries. The aorta and pulmonary artery actually emerge from the dorsal side (rear) but are shown here to aid in tracing the flow of blood. (*Modified from Best and Taylor, The human body and its functions, Henry Holt and Co., Inc.*)

ervoir to hold a fifth to a third of all blood; it serves to regulate the volume of blood elsewhere in circulation. In addition it produces white cells (lymphocytes) and destroys old red cells.

6-11. The heart. The entire circulatory system in any vertebrate is composed of the heart, the blood vessels (arteries, arterioles, capillaries, and veins), and the lymphatic channels and nodes. The heart comprises a series of chambers with slight or heavy muscular walls that receive blood from the veins and pump it through the arteries. In the two-chambered heart of fishes (1 auricle, 1 ventricle) all blood passing through the heart is unoxygenated; amphibians and most reptiles have two auricles that receive blood from the body and lungs, respectively, and a single ventricle; in birds and mammals the four-chambered heart (2 auricles, 2 ventricles) is really a dual structure, the right side pumping only from the body to the lungs, and the left side from the lungs to the body (Figs. 6-3 and 14-4).

Heart (cardiac) muscle has an innate power of rhythmic contraction from the time it is first formed in the embryo. This remarkable independence can be seen readily in the frog. A heart, removed from the body, will contract for some minutes; and if immersed in physiological saline solution that supplies essential elements and nutrients (NaCl, KCl, CaCl$_2$, etc., and glucose), beating may continue for several days. The primary regulation of heartbeat rests with groups of specialized cardiac muscle cells. The *"pace-maker"* (sino-auricular node, high in wall of right auricle) initiates contraction of the auricles. After a brief delay it stimulates a second center (auriculo-ventricular node, in septum between auricles), which, in turn, affects a band of fibers (bundle of His) on the walls of the ventricles to start ventricular contraction. The heartbeat also is under nervous control (vagus nerve, sympathetic system) and is further influenced by some hormones and certain drugs.

The sequence of heart action is as follows (Fig. 6-3): The thin-walled auricles fill with

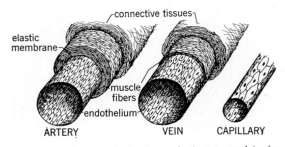

Fig. 6-4. Structure of blood vessels (not to scale). An artery has a thicker muscular layer than a vein, and a vein is usually larger than its corresponding artery. The wall of a capillary consists only of endothelium.

blood from the great veins, then contract, moving the blood into the ventricles. As the latter begin to contract, the bicuspid and tricuspid valves are closed by the increasing pressure of the blood. The semilunar valves are still closed, so the blood is blocked in all directions and its pressure rises. When pressure in the ventricles exceeds that in the arteries, the semilunar valves open and blood spurts into the arterial system. Then the cycle is repeated. The only rest for heart muscle throughout life is in the short intervals while the chambers are filling.

The heart in a quiet normal person contracts about 72 times per minute and pumps about 60 cc. of blood per "beat." The total volume of blood is about 6,000 cc., and all of it could pass through the heart in 100 beats. During a life of 70 years the heart may contract three billion times and move nearly two hundred million liters of blood. In some small birds and mammals the heart beats 200 to 400 times per minute.

Blood moves from the heart in a series of spurts, which in an exposed artery as on the wrist or temple may be felt as the "pulse," greatest as the heart is contracted (systole) and least when filling (diastole). The pressure declines at progressive distances from the heart because of frictional losses, especially in the arterioles; and the returning flow in the veins is practically smooth. Typical pressures for man, in millimeters of mercury, are arteries, 120/80 (systolic/diastolic); capillaries, 30/10; veins, 10/0. Pressure is influenced by rate of heartbeat, degree of dilation or constriction of vessels, and other factors.

6-12. Blood vessels. The heart and all vessels are lined throughout with a glassy-smooth endothelium. The walls of the aorta and larger arteries contain heavy layers of elastic tissue and muscle fibers (Fig. 6-4), but the small arterioles are covered by smooth muscle fibers only. The capillary walls, where all exchanges of nutrients, gases, and wastes occur between the blood stream and tissues, have no muscle fibers but possess many contractile (Rouget) cells on their outer surfaces. Frog muscle shows about 400 capillaries per square millimeter in cross section, and 1 cc. of blood in passing has contact with about 2,700 sq. mm. of capillary surface. In a dog the comparable figures (by Krogh) are 2,600 capillaries and 5,600 sq. mm. Capillaries in the skeletal muscles of a man may have a total length of 60,000 miles and a surface area of about $1\frac{1}{2}$ acres.

Veins are thin-walled, with connective tissue fibers but few muscles; unlike the arteries, they collapse when empty. The walls of all blood vessels are elastic, and vasomotor nerve fibers control the muscle fibers, causing arterioles to dilate or contract so as to alter the amount of blood passing to any region. The veins are provided with a series of valves that aid in maintaining the flow of blood back to the heart. The blood in man helps to control the body temperature by regulating the loss of heat. Excess heat acts through a nerve center in the medulla to permit dilation of superficial blood vessels in the skin where heat may be lost; chilling results in contraction of such vessels. In a resting dog the rate of blood flow per second is 300 to 500 mm. in large arteries and 0.5 mm. in capillaries.

6-13. Blood circulation in vertebrates. The paths of blood circulation are similar in principle in all vertebrates but differ in details depending on the complexity of the heart (1 or 2 auricles and ventricles) and on the type of respiration (gills or lungs) (Fig. 6-6). The circulation of the blood in man was first demonstrated by William Harvey (1578–1657), an English physi-

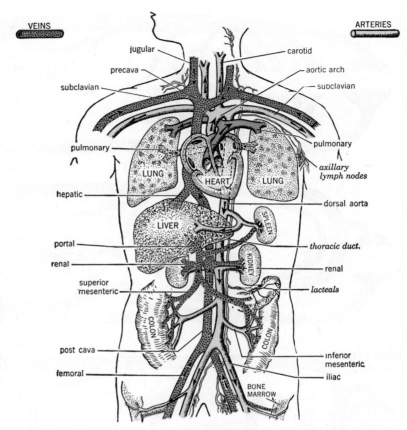

VEINS

ARTERIES

jugular

carotid

precava

aortic arch

subclavian

subclavian

pulmonary

pulmonary

axillary lymph nodes

LUNG

HEART

LUNG

hepatic

dorsal aorta

SPLEEN

LIVER

thoracic duct.

portal

KIDNEY

renal

renal

lacteals

superior mesenteric

COLON

COLON

inferior mesenteric

post cava

iliac

femoral

BONE MARROW

Fig. 6-5. Principal blood vessels of the human circulatory system in relation to internal organs; stomach, small intestine, bladder, and sex organs omitted. The thoracic duct of the lymphatic system and a few lymph nodes are shown in yellow and labeled in italics.

cian, early in the seventeenth century. Harvey tied a ligature above the elbow and saw enlargements at the location of valves in the veins of the forearm. When he held his finger on a vein and pressed the blood out above that point, he noticed that the vein remained empty. (Anyone can repeat this experiment on his own arm.) By this and other experiments he deduced that blood flows along the veins toward the heart. Harvey reasoned that the blood must enter the extremities through the arteries and pass somehow to the veins, but it remained for the Italian anatomist, Marcello Malpighi, to discover the capillaries 33 years later.

In man, the *path of circulation* is essentially as follows: The blood arriving from various parts of the body passes into the precaval and postcaval veins to enter the right auricle; it is poor in oxygen, dark red in color (*blue*, Fig. 6-5), and carries carbon dioxide. From the right

auricle it flows through the tricuspid valve (Fig. 6-3) to the right ventricle, and thence, as the result of a strong contraction of the heart muscle (systole), through the semilunar valve and along the pulmonary artery to the lungs.

In the lungs the blood courses through many small capillaries in membranes covering the alveoli (Fig. 7-3*C*), where it becomes reoxygenated (*red*, Fig. 6-5) and gives up its carbon dioxide (par. 7-10). Thence it flows into larger vessels and to the pulmonary veins entering the left auricle. Through the bicuspid valve it reaches the left ventricle, where, by powerful muscular contraction (systole), it is forced into the aorta, the largest and most stout-walled vessel in the body. The aorta divides first into several large arteries that in turn branch and subdivide to supply all parts of the body. The blood travels along the arteries to microscopic arterioles, and thence to the nonmuscular cap-

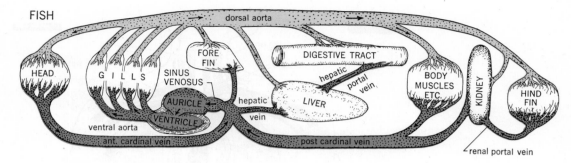

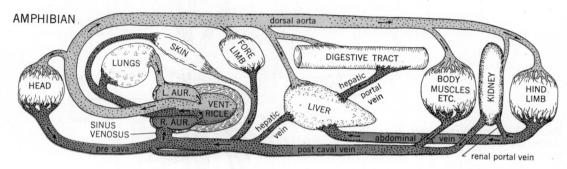

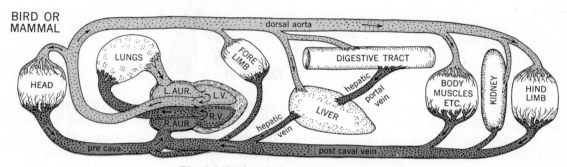

Fig. 6-6. Paths of blood circulation in vertebrates. Fish, one auricle and one ventricle (Figs. 30-4, 31-3). Amphibian, two auricles and one ventricle (Fig. 2-13). Bird or mammal, two auricles and two separate ventricles (Figs. 34-7, 35-4). Arrows indicate paths of blood flow. Blue, unoxygenated blood; red, oxygenated blood. (Compare Fig. 14-4.)

illaries in the tissues. Diffusion through the capillary walls is the means for interchange of water, gases, salts, and soluble organic materials between the blood and the cells composing the body.

The most direct route for return of blood to the heart is through the systemic part of the venous system. Capillaries join to form venules, and these merge to form veins, finally collecting in the two great veins, precaval and postcaval.

In addition to the complete cycle outlined there are several vital side paths. Arterial blood in the abdomen enters a system of capillaries lining the walls of the stomach and intestines where digested food is absorbed; then the blood passes into the portal vein to the liver. There it spreads through another system of capillaries, where food substances may be stored in liver cells and other essential processes take place as described in par. 5-11. To complete this important side route, blood from the liver gathers in the hepatic vein and flows to the postcaval vein.

An equally essential path takes arterial blood through a double system of capillaries in the kidneys (par. 8-2; Fig. 8-5), whence it returns to the heart. The blood is the chief regulatory mechanism of the body; during its passage through the kidneys, excess water and wastes are removed to maintain a relatively uniform condition (steady state) in the body as a whole.

In the heart of a human fetus the partition between the two auricles is incomplete, and also there is a connection (ductus arteriosus) between the pulmonary artery and aorta. These both serve to shunt blood around the developing but nonfunctional lungs. (Oxygen then is obtained through the placenta.) At birth, when air breathing begins, a flap closes the wall between the auricles, and the ductus arteriosus is constricted. If the ductus remains open, blood bypasses the lungs, resulting in a "blue baby," deficient in oxygenation of the blood, a condition which can be corrected by surgery.

The heart and circulatory system are so important in many bodily activities that any disturbance in their own functions is serious. High blood pressure (hypertension) puts added strain on both the heart and vessels, and may end in rupture of an artery, extensive hemorrhage, and death. "Hardening of the arteries" (arteriosclerosis) is another circulatory ailment, particularly in older persons. A common and serious disease is coronary thrombosis—closure or stoppage by a spasm or clot of some of the coronary vessels supplying blood to the heart muscle itself. The injury is not repaired, and a local deficiency in circulation results. The remaining coronary vessels have an added load, and the heart becomes less efficient. If the victim is otherwise healthy, he may survive with a program of lessened general activity; but if the heart is already weakened, the result is usually fatal.

Other activities in the circulatory system include formation of red cells in the bone marrow, the service of the spleen in storing blood, and that of the spleen and liver in destroying old red cells.

6-14. Integration of the circulatory system. The heart and blood vessels are controlled by the nervous system and also by certain substances in the blood. The circulatory system is sensitive to slight changes in the body, and its performance is complex because so many organs and functions are involved. The simple act of walking, for example, brings adjustments in heartbeat, blood pressure, and distribution of blood. The muscular activity requires oxygen and produces carbon dioxide. By chemical and nervous stimulation, the oxygen demand increases arterial pressure and dilates the capillaries, making for a greater flow of blood. The rate of heartbeat quickens from a reflex stimulated by increased pressure in the right auricle. Other reflexes stimulate constrictor and dilator centers in the medulla (Chap. 10), decreasing blood flow to inactive areas and hastening it where needed. Meanwhile the hypothalamus is activated and epinephrin (adrenalin) is secreted, resulting in constriction of blood vessels in the skin and viscera and dilation of those in the muscles. All these changes tend in one direction and, unless checked, would lead to excessive heartbeat and a blood pressure so high it would endanger fine blood vessels of the brain. But sensory elements in the aortic arch and carotid sinuses, acting through the medulla, cause a relaxation of arterial muscles and decrease in heart rate. The various parts of the circulatory system thus are integrated and operate with sensitive checks and balances.

6-15. Aortic arches (Fig. 14-4). Six pairs of aortic arches appear in the embryos of all vertebrates, proceeding from a ventral aorta at the anterior end of the heart and passing between the gill slits that develop in the sides of the pharynx. The first and second pairs soon disappear. In adult fishes, arches 3 to 6 lead to the gills where respiratory exchanges occur and then all join above to form the dorsal aorta; similarly, arches 4 to 6 supply the gills in permanently gilled salamanders. Among land vertebrates, arch 3 forms the common carotid artery on each side, arch 5 disappears, and arch 6 becomes the pulmonary artery.

7 RESPIRATORY SYSTEMS

All animals need oxygen for the metabolism in their cells and must dispose of the resulting carbon dioxide. The exchange of these gases is termed *respiration.* Some animals can exist for months on fats or other foods stored in their bodies, many can live a shorter time without water, but few survive long without oxygen, since none is stored in the body. Most animals obtain the oxygen from their environments. The air contains 21 per cent of oxygen (210 cc. per liter), but water holds only 0.7 per cent or less (7 cc. per liter); the oxygen in the water molecule (H_2O) is not available for respiration.

Animal life undoubtedly originated in the sea where a host of animal types still live, deriving their oxygen from that dissolved in the water. In the course of geological time various animals have become terrestrial, and therefore air-breathing. This change required major adaptive modifications including new methods of respiration.

7-1. Oxygen and carbon dioxide. Ordinary respiration in different animals is performed by various *respiratory organs* or *systems,* such as the body covering, gills, lungs, or tracheae. These structures are unlike in appearance but fundamentally the same in function (Figs. 7-1, 7-2); each comprises a moist permeable membrane through which molecules of oxygen and carbon dioxide diffuse readily. In accordance with the laws of gases each gas acts independently of others. When a difference in diffusion pressure (par. 3-8) exists on the two sides of a membrane, more molecules pass toward the region of lesser pressure than in the opposite direction. The partial pressure of oxygen in the air or water is greater than within an animal body, where it is constantly being used up, so that oxygen tends to enter any suitable membrane surface. The partial pressure of carbon dioxide is greater within the animal, so that it tends to pass outward. These exchanges occur simultaneously. In many small animals the exchange of gases is direct, from air or water through membranes to tissue cells; but it is more complex in larger species and those with dry or nonpermeable exteriors. In the latter, respiration consists of two stages: *external respiration,* the exchange between environment and the respiratory organs; and *internal respiration,* the exchange between the body fluids and the tissue cells. A third stage, the utilization of oxygen in the cells, is a part of metabolism (par. 5-11).

The term "respiration" is normally associated with free oxygen. But some intestinal parasites and muck-inhabiting invertebrates live where there is little or no oxygen in their environment. These anaerobic animals may obtain energy in the absence of free oxygen by the metabolism of foods (glycogen; fats?) in their bodies.

Fig. 7-1. Types of respiratory mechanisms in animals. IN WATER (below). *A.* Protozoan, diffusion through cell wall. *B.* Mayfly nymph (insect), tracheal gills. *C.* Salamander, blood gills. *D.* Mosquito larva, aquatic with tube for breathing free air. IN AIR (above). *E.* Earthworm, diffusion through moist body wall to blood vessels. *F.* Land snail, moist lung inside body. *G.* Land vertebrate, pair of moist lungs inside body. *H.* Insect, system of air ducts (tracheae) throughout body.

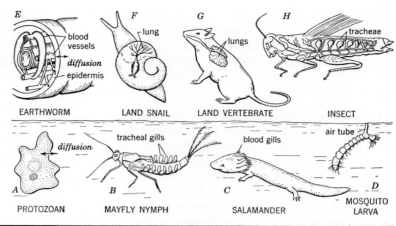

Fig. 7-2. Equivalent nature of various respiratory mechanisms in different animals living in water or air; diagrammatic.

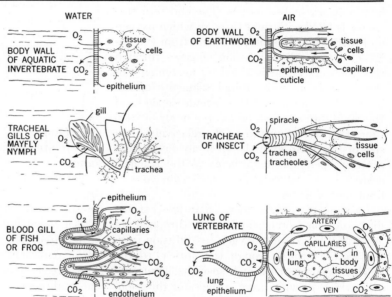

7-2. Respiratory mechanisms. Animals obtain oxygen by one or another of five principal methods: (1) simple diffusion from water or air through a moist surface into the body (amoeba, flatworm); (2) diffusion from air or water through thin body tissues to blood vessels (earthworms, etc.); (3) from air (through spiracles) or from water (through tracheal gills) to a system of air ducts (tracheae) to the tissues (insects); (4) from water through gill surfaces to blood vessels (fishes, amphibians); (5) from air through moist lung surfaces to blood vessels (land snails, land vertebrates).

7-3. Simple diffusion. Many aquatic animals obtain air directly from their environments. In a protozoan, gaseous exchange takes place through the cell membrane to and from the surrounding water. In sponges, coelenterates, and other lower soft-bodied invertebrates, the gases diffuse through epithelial cells and thence to those deeper in the body. Some endoparasites are bathed in the body fluids of their hosts from which they absorb oxygen and to which they give up carbon dioxide. Terrestrial flatworms can live in damp places where respiratory diffusion is possible through the moist epidermis. Direct diffusion would be inadequate for large animals because their internal organs are distant from the outer surface. Terrestrial species must conserve bodily water and cannot afford a large moist exterior for respiration by diffusion.

7-4. Tracheae. Insects, isopods, some arachnids, and *Peripatus* have fine tubes leading in from the body surface that branch to all interior organs and tissues. These are called *tracheae.* They develop as ingrowths of the body wall and are lined with chitin. Each ends in microscopic tracheal cells that extend as intracellular *tracheoles,* sometimes forming a capillary network in the tissues. The end of a tracheole is filled with fluid through which oxygen and carbon dioxide diffuse to and from the adjacent tissue cells. Diffusion of gases through the tracheal system is aided by movements of the thoracic and abdominal segments of the body. The efficiency of this scheme depends on the rapid diffusion rate of oxygen in air (45,000 times that in water) and on the relatively small size of tracheate animals. In many insects the exterior openings or *spiracles* of the tracheal system have valves (lids) which can close to limit loss of water.

Larvae of dragon-flies, may-flies, stone-flies, and some other tracheate arthropods are aquatic. They obtain oxygen by diffusion from the water, either through the cuticle to the tracheal system or through specialized *tracheal gills* which provide more surface for diffusion. Adult water beetles and bugs swim to the surface and take down a silvery bubble of air under the wings from which oxygen diffuses into the tracheal system.

7-5. Blood gills. In most higher animals respiration is aided by a blood transport system. Its simplest form is seen in the earthworm where oxygen diffuses through the body wall into superficial blood vessels and then passes to the tissue cells. In the frog the moist skin and the lining of the mouth cavity serve similarly. Many aquatic animals, however, have a more efficient mechanism—*blood gills*—of many slender filaments covered by delicate epidermis and containing capillary networks. The O_2—CO_2 exchange occurs between the surrounding water and the blood within. Free, dissolved oxygen diffuses inward from the water. Cold water holds more oxygen than warm water, and the "white water" of fast-flowing streams has more than the still water of ponds or stagnant swamps. The small amount of oxygen dissolved in water limits the density of animal populations, but aquatic plants partly offset this by releasing oxygen during photosynthesis.

The gill filaments of salamander larvae (Fig. 32-2) and those of some marine worms are merely exposed to the water, but tube-dwelling annelids, aquatic crustaceans such as the crayfish (Fig. 25-5), and many aquatic mollusks have special means to force water over the gills. The gills of lower vertebrates are in chambers at the sides of the pharynx, and water taken into the mouth (nostrils in amphibians) is forced out over the filaments (Fig. 31-6).

7-6. Lungs. All "land vertebrates," including the aquatic reptiles, birds, and mammals, have *lungs* essentially like those of a frog. A lung is a chamber lined by moist epithelium underlaid by a network of blood capillaries, where atmospheric air can be used. Basically, a lung is like a blood gill but invaginated rather than evaginated. The reptile lung contains many interior partitions, and those of birds and mammals are elaborately subdivided, affording large internal respiratory surfaces. The finer lung branches or *bronchioles* end in microscopic compartments, the *alveoli,* surrounded by many blood capillaries (Fig. 7-3C), where respiratory exchanges occur. Bird lungs are dense, and air is forced through the bronchioles to and from a series of thin-walled *air sacs* (Fig. 34-9); these occupy spaces between internal organs and around or in some bones. The air sacs serve mainly to dissipate excess body heat and are not entirely essential for respiration. Some mollusks and arachnids have lungs similar in principle to the vertebrate type (Figs. 23-4, 27-3).

7-7. The human respiratory system. The mouth and nose communicate with the lungs

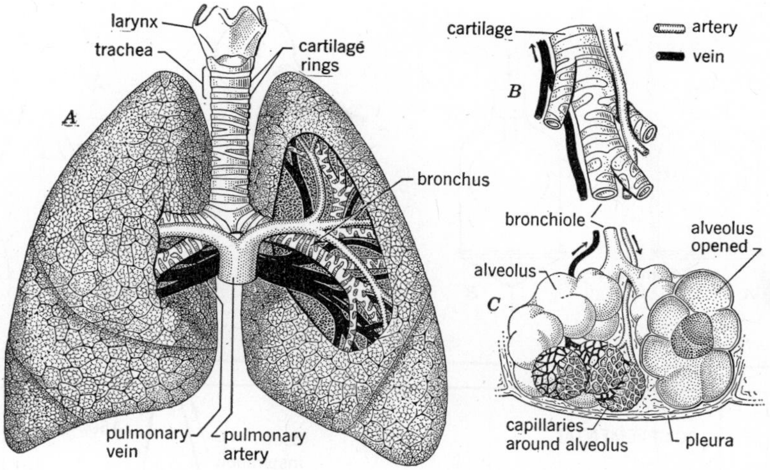

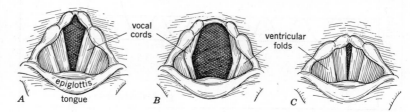

Fig. 7-3. Human respiratory system. *A.* Larynx, trachea, and lungs in ventral view; left lung opened. *B.* Part of a bronchiole, with cartilages; small blood vessels adjacent. *C.* Alveoli and capillaries; diagrammatic.

Fig. 7-4. Human larynx and vocal cords and their action. *A.* Larynx viewed from base of tongue—vocal cords as in normal breathing. *B.* In deep inhalation. *C.* When singing a high note. (*Kimber et al., Textbook of anatomy and physiology, The Macmillan Co.*)

through a series of special structures. The **glottis** is an opening in the floor of the pharynx, protected above by a lid or epiglottis, and supported by a cartilaginous framework, the **larynx.** The latter connects to a flexible tube, the **trachea,** or windpipe, that extends into the thorax and forks into two **bronchi,** one to each **lung** (Fig. 7-3).

In the nose the entering air is filtered, warmed, and moistened. This is accomplished by a thick layer of mucous membrane lining the nasal cavities. The mouth serves as an alternate route for air, and the pharynx is a passage for air from either the nose or mouth to the larynx (Fig. 5-3B).

The larynx, or voice organ (Fig. 7-4), is in the front part of the neck. It is broad above, triangular in shape, and consists of nine cartilages moved by muscles; it contains two folds of mucous membrane with embedded fibrous, elastic ligaments, the **vocal cords.**

The voice is produced by air forced from the lungs to vibrate the vocal cords, and the positioning of the cords is changed to produce vari-

ous kinds of sounds. The sound waves so created pass through the pharynx, mouth, and nasal cavities, which act as resonating chambers; these parts, together with the tongue and lips, are important in speech. The size of the larynx varies in different individuals; at the time of puberty it grows more rapidly in males than in females, resulting in change to a deeper and lower voice.

The trachea and bronchi are reinforced against collapse by rings of cartilage. In the lungs the bronchi branch into many bronchial tubes and **bronchioles** (Fig. 7-3C), with successively thinner walls. Each bronchiole ends in a sac-like atrium, having on its surface many small irregular chambers, the **alveoli** or air sacs. The latter are surrounded by blood capillaries where the respiratory exchanges occur. The human lungs have 700,000,000 or more alveoli; the entire inner surface is estimated as about 90 square meters, more than one hundred times the area of the skin.

The substance of the lungs is porous and spongy. The right lung is larger, broader, and

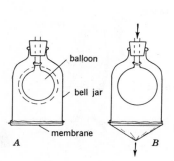
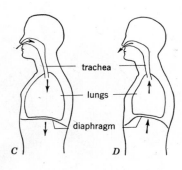

Fig. 7-5. Mechanism of breathing. *Left. A.* Semifirm rubber balloon in bell jar covered at bottom with flexible membrane. *B.* When membrane is pulled down, space inside is increased and pressure of air through tube causes balloon to expand. *Right. C.* When chest box is expanded and diaphragm drawn down, air enters through nose and trachea, expanding lungs to fill chest cavity. *D.* When ribs and diaphragm relax, air is forced out.

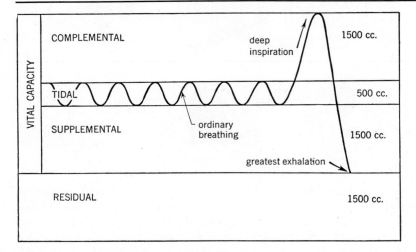

Fig. 7-6. Lung capacity and breathing in man. Ordinary respiration exchanges only the tidal air (10 per cent); deep breathing flushes most of the lung (3,500 cc., or 70 per cent); the residual air changes only by diffusion. (*Winton and Bayliss, Human physiology, J. & A. Churchill, Ltd., The Blakiston Co.*)

1 inch shorter than the left, owing to the asymmetrical positions of heart and liver. The **diaphragm** is a dome-shaped muscular partition that separates the thorax, containing the heart and lungs, from the abdominal cavity. Under normal conditions the lungs occupy fully the airtight thoracic cavity because the atmospheric pressure of air in the alveoli keeps them expanded against the inner surface of that cavity. If air enters the thoracic cavity, by accident or in the treatment of pulmonary disease, the lung collapses.

7-8. Breathing. This essential process consists of movements, partly voluntary, that alter the size of the thoracic cavity and therefore the lung capacity. At inspiration the ribs are raised and muscles in the diaphragm contract to flatten the latter; the thoracic space is thus enlarged and pressure about the lung is lessened, whereupon air passes down the trachea and into the lungs. Expiration results from lessening the volume of the thorax by relaxing the muscles controlling the ribs and diaphragm (Fig. 7-5).

Only about one-sixth of the total amount of air flows in and out of the lungs with each quiet respiratory movement (Fig. 7-6). The average composition is, of course, different for atmospheric air (20.96 per cent oxygen) and expired air (16.02 per cent oxygen). There is a net loss of 4.94 per cent oxygen and a gain of 4.34 per cent carbon dioxide. The nitrogen in air (79 per cent) is inert and has no part in respiration. In the lungs there is a gradient, owing to diffusion through the residual air, so that the alveolar air contains only 14 per cent oxygen. The rate of breathing is controlled mainly by a respiratory center in the medulla of the brain, and this in turn is stimulated by an excess of carbon dioxide in the blood. The respiratory rate increases during vigorous exercise because of the greater production of carbon dioxide in muscular metabolism. A person may "hold his breath" for a limited time, but as the carbon dioxide increases in the blood, the stimulus becomes too strong to be resisted. The respiratory rate is also subject to nervous control of other sorts, as seen in emotional states of anger or excitement. If breathing stops due to suffocation, death soon follows unless respiratory movements are restored artificially by alternately applying and releasing pressure on the ribs to simulate breathing and bring about gaseous exchange. The lungs of a newborn baby are inflated with the first breath after interruption of the placental circulation.

The air at high altitudes is rarefied (lesser barometric pressure), and a given volume contains less oxygen than at sea level. This affects normal respiratory needs of men and animals. A mountain climber or a person in an airplane must use a tank of oxygen and face mask to obtain adequate oxygen. Planes operating above 10,000 feet usually have the air pressure inside raised (pressurized) to provide ease for passengers in breathing.

A person who enters the water without an artificial supply of air can hold his breath and remain submerged about 2 minutes, then must come up to breathe and repay the oxygen debt incurred. For continued submergence commercial divers wear a metal helmet connected to a hose supplying air under pressure, and "skin divers" use a tank of compressed air (aqualung) and face mask for the same purpose. In both cases the air provides oxygen and also serves to keep the lungs inflated. The maximum safe limit for experienced divers is toward 200 feet; beyond that depth the water pressure is too great for the thorax to perform normal respiratory movements. Deep submergence and the consequent heavy pressure force some nitrogen into solution in the blood plasma; a diver must rise slowly, stopping at intervals, else the bubbling release of nitrogen causes painful decompression sickness, or "the bends."

7-9. Respiratory function of the blood. After oxygen has crossed the alveolar membrane, it must be delivered to the tissue cells where needed. In man and most higher animals this transport is accomplished by the blood. The process is complicated because mere diffusion is not adequate to meet the needs of large active animals. Human blood plasma carries in solution only 2 or 3 per cent of the total oxygen. The remainder is transported by the red pigment, *hemoglobin,* with which it enters into combination in the erythrocytes or red corpuscles. The process is as follows: After diffusion into the alveolar capillaries, the oxygen unites with the hemoglobin because the tension of the gas is lower in the blood than in the alveoli. The combined oxyhemoglobin then travels in the circulation to the tissues where oxygen tension is lower than in the arterial blood. There oxygen is freed to diffuse to the cells, and the deoxygenated hemoglobin returns to the lungs in the venous blood. The total oxygen capacity of the human blood averages about 1,200 cc., and 100 to 350 cc. of oxygen passes into the tissues at each circuit. In an hour the body at rest uses about 15 liters (4 gallons) of oxygen, and in strenuous exercise up to 280 liters (75 gallons).

Hemoglobin itself is a so-called "respiratory pigment," formed by the union of red *hematin,* which contains iron, with a colorless protein, *globin.* The unique feature of hemoglobin is that a given amount may combine with different amounts of oxygen, depending on the tension of the gas in contact with the system. Thus the reaction is reversible and may be represented by the generalized equation $Hb_4 + 4O_2 \rightleftharpoons 4HbO_2$, where Hb stands for a molecule of hemoglobin. HbO_2 is oxyhemoglobin, of bright-red color, in contrast to the duller hemoglobin. The respiratory pigment in most mollusks and arthropods is *hemocyanin* (with copper instead of iron). When oxygenated, hemocyanin is blue rather than red.

7-10. Carbon dioxide. Respiration involves the exchange of two gases, and it might be inferred that disposal of carbon dioxide is a reversal of the inward flow of oxygen. Actually the mechanism of carbon dioxide transport is somewhat different. Some carbon dioxide is necessary to maintain the buffer system of the blood and tissues. About one-third of the excess carbon dioxide unites directly with the hemoglobin in red blood cells, and the remainder is transported in the plasma as bicarbonate while en route to the lungs. The exact mechanism is complex, involving the so-called "chloride shift" by which chloride ions pass into the red cells and bicarbonate ions pass out to maintain the necessary acid-base equilibrium of the blood at a pH of about 7.4. The process is facilitated by an enzyme, carbonic anhydrase, in the red blood corpuscles.

7-11. Ventilation. It has long been assumed that "fresh" air must be provided for human respiration. This appears logical at first thought, but experiments seem to prove that air in a poorly ventilated room does not differ appreciably in oxygen and carbon dioxide content from air in a well-ventilated room. The injurious effects of poor ventilation actually are due to interference with the heat-regulating mechanism of the body. The combination of accumulated body odors plus an increase in temperature and moisture leads to a feeling of inertia or fatigue. For greatest comfort the air in a room should be moderately cool, should contain some moisture, and should be undergoing slight movement.

8 EXCRETORY SYSTEMS AND REGULATION

A. EXCRETION

Excretion is the process of ridding the body of wastes resulting from metabolism. The protoplasm and fluids of an animal, be it protozoan or human, comprise a delicately balanced physicochemical system, and it is the function of the excretory system (Fig. 8-1) to maintain this constant internal environment. Excess water, gases, salts, and organic materials, including metabolic wastes, are excreted, whereas substances essential for normal functions are conserved.

Excretion deals mainly with disposal of nitrogenous materials. During digestion the nitrogen-bearing proteins are reduced to amino acids and absorbed; some then go to body cells for building new proteins. In the vertebrates other amino acids pass to the liver (Fig. 5-7) and are reduced for elimination through the kidneys. Among mammals and amphibians the end product is mostly urea, formed by action of the liver enzyme arginase; in birds and land reptiles (also some snails and many insects) the nitrogenous waste is mainly insoluble uric acid. Marine teleost fishes excrete up to a third of the nitrogen as trimethylamine oxide. Many aquatic invertebrates eliminate the nitrogen as ammonia; this compound is highly toxic but readily disposed of because an excess of water is present. A few animals excrete amino acids directly.

8-1. Excretion in invertebrates. The simplest appearing method of excretion is to pass wastes through the cell membrane into the surrounding water, as occurs in many protozoans. *Amoeba, Paramecium,* and various other fresh-water protozoans have one or more **contractile vacuoles** that accumulate excess water from within the cytoplasm and periodically discharge to the exterior so as to maintain the normal fluid balance within the cell body. Ammonia is the chief excretory product. The means of disposal of excretions by protozoans is obscure. Excretions of sponges and coelenterates diffuse from body cells into the epidermis and thence into the water.

Among insects and a few other arthropods the principal excretory organs are slender **Malpighian tubules** (Fig. 8-2A, B), attached to the anterior end of the hind-gut and closed at their inner ends; these tubules collect wastes from the body fluids and discharge them into the hind-gut. Both urates and carbon dioxide are received in solution from the blood; water and other materials are reabsorbed in the lower parts of the tubules. The final excretions, including uric acid crystals, carbonates, oxalates, and sometimes urea or ammonia, pass out with the feces. The fat body of insects is also a depository for organic wastes and is the chief excretory mechanism in springtails (COLLEMBOLA), which lack Malpighian tubules. The exoskeleton renders excretory service in some invertebrates, including insects, since nitrogenous materials deposited in it are eliminated when the animal molts. The white pigment in wings of cabbage butterflies, formed from uric acid, is clearly an excretory product.

The commonest excretory organs in many animals are tubular structures, the **nephridia** and **coelomoducts.** Primitively these were arranged one pair to a body somite, but they have become variously modified in the course of evolution (Figs. 8-3, 8-4). Flatworms and ribbon worms have many *flame cells* (protone-

phridia, inner ends closed; Fig. 8-2C) scattered among the body cells from which wastes are drawn to pass out in a branched system of ducts (Fig. 19-3). In the earthworm, each somite contains a pair of **nephridia** (metanephridia, inner ends open; Fig. 8-2D). The inner end of each has a ciliated funnel, or **nephrostome,** draining from the coelom, and around the long tubule are blood vessels whence wastes are also drawn; the tubule ends externally as a small ventral **nephridiopore** (Fig. 24-6). Mollusks and some other invertebrates have one or two pairs of nephridia-like organs that drain from the body or blood (Fig. 23-9); nephridia also occur in the chordate amphioxus (Fig. 28-12).

In some annelids, mollusks, arthropods, and in the chordates the principal excretory organs

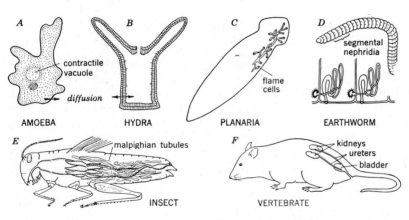

Fig. 8-1. Types of excretory mechanisms in animals. *A.* Amoeba, contractile vacuole and diffusion from cell surface. *B.* Hydra, diffusion from cells. *C.* Planaria, many flame cells connecting to ducts ending in a common excretory pore(s). *D.* Earthworm, two nephridia in each body somite emptying separately through body wall. *E.* Grasshopper, series of fine Malpighian tubules connected to end of midgut. *F.* Vertebrate, two kidneys with ducts to a single bladder discharging to exterior. .

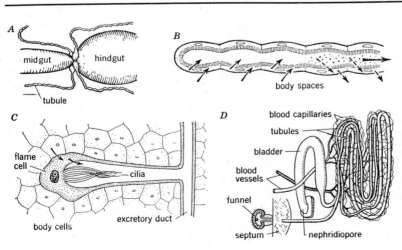

Fig. 8-2. *A.* Malpighian tubules of insect attached to gut. *B.* Section of one tubule showing entry of excretions from body spaces (→), reabsorption routes for water and some other materials (--→), and exit route of wastes (→). *C.* Planarian flame cell draws fluid wastes from surrounding body cells; bundle of cilia drives fluid into excretory duct. *D.* Earthworm nephridium receives fluid wastes from coelom through funnel and also by diffusion from surrounding blood vessels.

Fig. 8-3. Basic patterns of vertebrate excretory systems in relation to circulatory system and coelom; diagrammatic (Table 8-1). *Pronephros.* Segmental. Ciliated ducts gather fluid waste from coelom; a knot (glomus) of blood capillaries adjacent. *Mesonephros.* Segmental. Some with open ciliated ducts, others without; branch from duct around knot of blood capillaries forming a glomerulus. *Metanephros.* Nonsegmental. Concentrated groups of glomeruli draining to one large duct; no opening to coelom (compare Fig. 8-5).

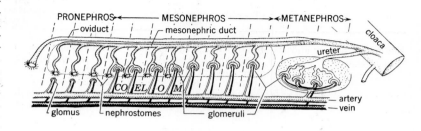

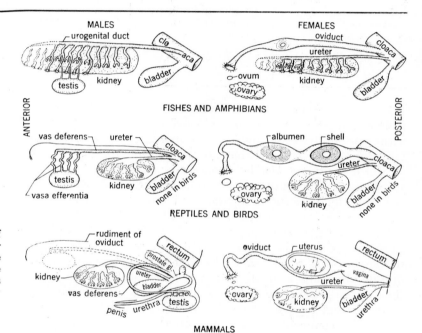

Fig. 8-4. Urogenital systems of vertebrates; only one side or half of each is shown. For the male mammal the primitive (embryonic) positions of testis and vas deferens are shown by broken lines.

are coelomoducts, probably derived from genital ducts, but now variously modified to remove wastes from the body cavity. Crustaceans have two pairs, the "antennal" (green) and "maxillary" glands; each has an end sac with a duct opening at the base of an appendage. Only rarely are both developed in the same stage of a single species.

8-2. The vertebrate kidney. The principal excretory organs in a vertebrate are two *kidneys.* They are short and posterior in all but the fishes and salamanders, where they extend along most of the body cavity. The kidneys of lower vertebrates—cyclostomes to amphibians—and the embryonic kidneys of the higher groups develop segmentally, a pair per body somite (pronephros, mesonephros); some tubules have nephrostomes opening to the coelom, thus somewhat resembling the nephridia of earthworms (Figs. 8-3, 8-4; Table 8-1). The adult kidneys of reptiles, birds, and mammals (metanephros) are nonsegmental and drain wastes only from the blood.

TABLE 8-1. Types of Kidneys in the Vertebrates

	Pronephros or head kidney	Mesonephros or mid-kidney	Metanephros or hind kidney
Embryonic history and adult structure	First to appear in embryo; develops segmentally, far forward in body cavity; each unit with a nephrostome opening from the coelom; no glomeruli	Develops segmentally in middle part of body cavity; some nephrostomes open to coelom, but excretion chiefly by glomeruli	Last to develop; not segmental; posterior in body cavity; no nephrostomes; many glomeruli; all excretion from blood stream
FISHES AND AMPHIBIANS	*Functions in larva*; disappears in adult	*Becomes functional kidney of adult*	(Not developed)
REPTILES, BIRDS, AND MAMMALS	Appears transiently in embryo and soon disappears	Appears after pronephros; *functions during embryonic life*, disappearing before hatching or birth; duct persists as vas deferens in male	Last to appear; *becomes functional kidney throughout life*

From each kidney, of whatever type, a common collecting duct, the **ureter,** carries the waste posteriorly. In amphibians, reptiles, and birds the two ureters discharge into the **cloaca,** to which a **urinary bladder** connects in amphibians and some reptiles. The waste, or **urine,** is always fluid except in reptiles and birds, where the semisolid excretions (uric acid) are voided as a white paste (guano) with the feces. In most mammals the ureters connect directly to the bladder, whence a median duct, the **urethra,** discharges to the exterior, passing through the penis in the male. The interrelated excretory and reproductive systems of vertebrates are commonly termed the **urogenital system.**

Each human kidney (Fig. 8-5) consists of an inner **medulla** and an outer **cortex,** the latter containing about a million excretory units, or **nephrons.** A nephron is made up of (1) a **Malpighian** or **renal corpuscle** composed of a globular double-walled **Bowman capsule** around a clump of arterioles, or **glomerulus;** and (2) a **tubule,** both convoluted and straight, surrounded by blood capillaries. The corpuscle is about 0.2 mm. in diameter, and the tubule is 0.015 to 0.025 mm. in diameter by 50 to 60 mm. long. The 2 million nephrons of a man,

end to end, would extend for nearly 50 miles. All the tubules discharge into a central cavity (pelvis) of the kidney that connects to the ureter.

8-3. Kidney function. The first step in urine formation is filtration. Wastes and other materials are brought in the blood stream by the renal arteries to the arterioles. According to the generally accepted theory of kidney function (by Cushny), protein-free fluid passes from the arterioles in the glomerulus through the Bowman capsule. This process takes place because of the pressure of the blood; the fluid in the capsule has the same percentage composition as blood plasma minus the colloids to which the membranes are impermeable. The second step is differential reabsorption by cells of the tubules—mostly in the ascending limb of the loop of Henle and the distal convoluted tubule. Reabsorption involves work with the use of oxygen and the expenditure of energy. This is illustrated by materials such as glucose that are present in the blood and in the glomerular filtrate but not in normal urine. Such substances are reabsorbed completely and in a direction opposite from that expected by simple diffusion.

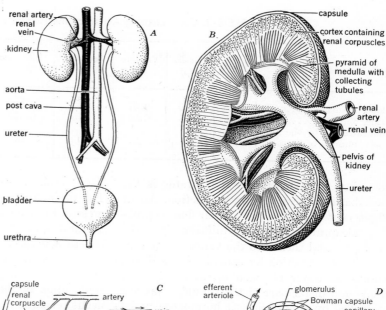

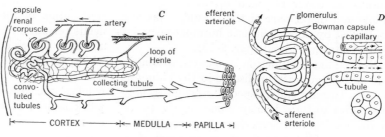

Fig. 8-5. The human excretory system. *A.* Entire system, ventral view. *B.* One kidney in median section. *C.* Relations of renal corpuscles, tubules, and blood vessels. *D.* One renal corpuscle and adjacent tubule (shown also in cross section)—solid arrows show flow of blood, broken arrows the excretory path. *C* and *D* diagrammatic and much enlarged.

The most remarkable feature of reabsorption by the tubules is its selectivity. For example, about 1,140 grams (2½ pounds) of salt (NaCl) passes from the glomeruli into the tubules each day—but normally only 4 to 8 grams (0.14 to 0.28 ounce) of this leaves the body in the urine. The rest is reabsorbed into the blood stream. Urea, on the other hand, is constantly being removed; it is about half (30 grams daily) of all solids in the urine, where it is in much higher concentration than in the blood plasma (Table 8-2). Materials like glucose, sodium, and calcium are called "high-threshold substances" because they are reabsorbed in considerable quantities, little or none being left to pass out in normal urine; those reabsorbed in small quantities (urea, uric acid, etc.) are termed "low-threshold substances." In addition to glomerular filtration and reabsorption, there is some direct tubular excretion of waste products difficult to metabolize in the body.

The capacity of the human kidneys is truly remarkable. They comprise scarcely ½₀₀ (0.5 per cent) of the total body weight, yet receive 20 per cent of the blood volume pumped by the heart. About 1,700 quarts of blood flows through the kidneys each day, but only about 180 quarts is filtered, and of this fluid 178 quarts is reabsorbed; thus only 1 or 2 quarts passes off as urine. In other words, an amount equal to the entire volume of blood is filtered by the tubules about 30 to 36 times per day.

Urinary output is controlled in several ways. Filtration, or diffusion of fluids from blood plasma through the glomerular membranes to the capsular space, is directly influenced by blood pressure. This, in turn, is affected by epinephrin from the adrenal medulla which constricts the blood vessels of the glomeruli. Another hormone, cortin, from the adrenal cortex, affects reabsorption of sodium and chloride in the kidney tubules and the elimination of

TABLE 8-2. Concentrating Action of the Human Kidney

	Water	Sodium (Na)	Chloride (Cl)	Potassium (K)	Phosphate (PO$_4$)	Sulfate (SO$_4$)	Uric acid	Urea
Blood plasma, %	92	0.30	0.37	0.02	0.009	0.002	0.004	0.03
Urine, %	95	0.35	0.60	0.15	0.150	0.180	0.050	2.00
Concentration by the kidney, number of times....	..	1	2	7	16	90	12	60

potassium. The reabsorption of water is the most basic process of kidney function. About 80 per cent of that in the tubular fluid is probably recaptured by direct diffusion into the capillaries and thence to the venous system as a result of attraction by colloids in the blood. Additional water is taken up in the loop of Henle and distal part of the tubule, a process controlled by an antidiuretic hormone secreted by the pituitary gland (par. 9-10).

Normal kidney function is essential to health, and any irregularity or disease in the kidney is serious. Certain salts, especially oxalates, may crystallize to form kidney stones in the pelvis of the kidney and sometimes require removal by surgery. The content of the urine may be altered by other abnormal conditions. Urinalysis, therefore, may give useful clues to the general state of bodily function, healthy or otherwise. Abnormal constituents of the urine may be albumin, excess glucose, acetone bodies, cell casts, pus, blood, or bile pigments. It is a remarkable fact that removal of one kidney, and even part of the second kidney, does not entirely hinder the total excretory process in man.

8-4. The bladder and urination. The urine forms at a fairly constant rate, about 1 cc. per minute. It passes down the ureters to accumulate in the urinary bladder, whence it is expelled at intervals through the urethra. The bladder is a hollow, pear-shaped organ low in the front of the abdominal cavity. It, like the stomach, can adapt to change in volume without altering the internal pressure. The smooth muscle of the bladder wall accommodates to increase in volume until about 300 cc. of urine has accumu-

lated; then a sensation of fullness develops. The desire to urinate may, however, be suppressed by voluntary control of the external urethral sphincter until the total content is 700 to 800 cc. Urination, or emptying of the bladder, is controlled by several reflex mechanisms which involve stretching followed by contraction of the bladder wall with simultaneous relaxation of the sphincters. Even small amounts of urine can be passed by straining, which increases the pressure in the abdomen and compresses the bladder. When the urine reaches the urethra, urination continues by reflex action, even though pressure is discontinued.

8-5. Other means of excretion. In higher animals, including man, some wastes are eliminated other than by the principal excretory organs. Metabolic CO_2 is disposed of by routes described in Chap. 7. Water is eliminated through the lungs, up to 240 cc. (8 ounces) per day in man. Some other excretory products are voided with the feces, including wastes of heavy metals (iron and calcium), bile pigments excreted by the liver during the breakdown of hemoglobin, and more or less water.

The skin of man, by its sweat glands (Fig. 4-1), also serves for the elimination of water, together with salts, traces of CO_2, and some nitrogenous waste. The loss through perspiration is usually small, but during active sweating as much as 3 gallons of water may be lost in a day. Under such circumstances salt (NaCl) needed in the body's economy must be replaced by eating salty foods or salt tablets; also the supply of vitamin C must be adequate. Perspiration is only incidentally excretory, its primary function being temperature regulation. It is also influenced by fright and emergency situations in which a "cold sweat" occurs.

B. REGULATION IN THE BODY

8-6. Homeostasis. The famous French physiologist Claude Bernard said, "All the vital mechanisms, varied as they are, have only one object, that of preserving constant the conditions of life in the internal environment." All living organisms maintain a more or less **steady internal state,** known as homeostasis, regardless of extremes in their external environment. In general the degree to which a particular group has achieved independence of its environment is a measure of its evolutionary progress; some generalized protozoans are affected by nearly every factor in the medium surrounding them, whereas man is variously independent, by one means or another.

Reflex activity of the nervous system and hormones of the endocrine system are the bases of all steady-state control. Every part of the animal body during all stages of growth and reproduction is under their influence. The situation of even the simplest animal is so intricate and little understood that regulatory processes generally are considered piecemeal, in terms of a few readily measurable criteria, rather than as an integrated whole. Osmotic pressure, hydrogen ion concentration, and temperature are three of these criteria, and each is intimately connected with water.

8-7. Osmoregulation. Water is taken in with food and also to some extent by absorption in aquatic forms. It is the universal solvent and carrier in protoplasm, and no organism can be independent of this essential fluid. Because of its property of diffusing across membranes, water is the vehicle for maintenance of the steady state.

The body fluids of all animals are remarkably similar in salt content and resemble that of sea water, suggesting that life originated in the sea at some remote time. Regulation of osmotic pressure (par. 3-8) is simple for most soft-bodied marine invertebrates because their body fluids are in equilibrium (isotonic) with the surrounding water; pressures are the same inside and outside. Fresh water contains only about $\frac{1}{100}$ the salt concentration of sea water. Body fluids of fresh-water animals have a higher salt content than the surrounding medium, and water tends to diffuse inward; the excess is disposed of in various ways. Protozoans do so by means of the contractile vacuole, which usually is absent in marine forms. Other fresh-water animals have nephridia, Malpighian tubules, or kidneys to excrete the surplus. This work of excretion requires energy, as evidenced by the higher respiratory rate of fresh-water animals as compared with closely related marine species.

Aquatic vertebrates maintain osmotic balance in different ways, depending on their evolutionary history. Among bony fishes fresh-water forms have blood with higher salt content than the surrounding medium, but the reverse is true in marine forms. Water enters fresh-water fishes through semipermeable membranes of the gills and mouth, whereas it tends to leave the body of marine forms. In fresh-water forms the excess water is excreted by the kidneys; salts are maintained at proper concentration in the blood by absorption through special cells in the gills. Among marine species water deficiency is avoided by swallowing sea water and absorbing it, salts and all, from the gut. The resulting excess salts are removed by secretory cells in the gills. The kidneys of fresh-water fishes have well-developed glomeruli to filter out large amounts of water, but in marine forms the glomeruli are reduced and little water is discharged as urine. The eel, salmon, and some other migratory fishes live alternately in both fresh and salt waters; presumably their glomeruli are nonfunctional while in the sea. The blood of elasmobranch fishes has about the same salt content as in bony fishes but also contains up to 2 per cent of urea. The latter increases the osmotic pressure in marine elasmobranchs slightly above that in the surrounding medium; water tends, therefore, to enter rather than pass out as in marine bony fishes. Urea is retained in elasmobranchs by a special absorbing segment of the kidney tubule, and the gills are impermeable to urea.

8-8. Water regulation of land animals. Terrestrial animals experience the hazard of desiccation, and many of them have an impermeable cuticle to resist loss of water from the body surface. Also, means have developed whereby precious water is reabsorbed by the kidneys (occasionally by cells in the rectum).

In man the excretion or retention of water depends on the state of hydration of the body as a whole. Excessive sweating decreases the volume of fluid that passes out in the urine, whereas drinking quantities of fluid increases the urinary output. Water balance is controlled to a certain extent by thirst, which varies remarkably with the state of hydration, and by kidney action, which is influenced by the antidiuretic hormone secreted by the posterior lobe of the pituitary. In the absence of this hormone, reabsorption by the kidney tubules decreases. The control mechanism is automatic, because an increase of osmotic pressure in the blood causes increased secretion of the hormone. This, in turn, stimulates reabsorption and thus conserves water. Alcohol inhibits secretion of the antidiuretic hormone and thus has a dehydrating effect. Caffeine acts as a diuretic by increasing the glomerular filtration rate and by reducing reabsorption of water by the tubule cells.

8-9. Regulation of pH. The hydrogen ion concentration of most body fluids varies, but it is usually between pH 7 and 8. The regulatory mechanism by the blood, in this case, is the buffering action of such inorganic ions as phosphates and carbonates. Ion pairs, like $^=HPO_4$ and $^-H_2PO_4$, and $^=CO_3$ and $^-HCO_3$, act as buffers by combining with excess H^+. For example, the $^=CO_3$ forms $^-HCO_3$, resulting in a decrease of carbonate, an increase in bicarbonate, and the elimination of free H^+ ions. When the blood becomes too alkaline, this reaction is reversed. A considerable amount of acid or base thus may be absorbed without altering the pH of body fluids.

8-10. Heat regulation. The metabolism in an animal produces heat (which can be measured and stated in calories; see Chap. 5). The body temperature at any given time, however, is a function of the heat produced, conserved, and lost. In most animals metabolism is low and the body temperature does not differ much from that of the environment. Such animals are called cold-blooded, though actually their body fluids may be comparatively warm or cold, following the fluctuations in outside temperature. Birds and mammals are warm-blooded, or even-temperatured (homoiothermous); to maintain this condition their energy production goes up as the outside temperature goes down, and thus the body temperature remains nearly constant. The normal temperature by mouth in man is about 37°C. (98.6°F.). This varies within a few degrees for various reasons, of which the most important is infection. Regulation is effected by the nervous system, which acts literally as a thermostat.

In cold weather metabolism is increased through muscular activity, including the involuntary act of shivering, and some of this energy is in the form of heat. During warm weather, excess heat is lost in two ways. Blood vessels in the skin are dilated so that heat is taken to the surface more rapidly, and the activity of the sweat glands is increased. The actual loss of heat is largely through radiation from the body surface and utilization of heat in the process of evaporating water. Excessive humidity hinders evaporation and is the cause of discomfort on hot, moist days. Clothing produces no heat but holds a layer of warm moist air between it and the skin and thus reduces the loss of heat by evaporation and radiation. Evaporation through increased respiration is an important means of regulating temperature in animals such as dogs that do not perspire.

8-11. Hibernation. Many cold-blooded animals hide away in sheltered places during the low temperatures of winter to avoid death by heat loss or freezing. Their temperature becomes practically that of the surroundings, and metabolism drops to a very low level when they are thus in "winter sleep," or hibernation. Some warm-blooded animals such as ground squirrels, chipmunks, and certain bats also hibernate during the colder parts of the year, when their food is scarce. The body temperature then follows that of the surroundings. During this period normal heat regulation is interrupted and the whole physiology of the animal becomes modified—rate of heartbeat, oxygen consumption, and metabolism all are far reduced.

8-12. Hormonal control. Ultimately it appears that the various parts of the pituitary gland (Chap. 9) are primarily responsible for control of specific hormones which, in turn, maintain particular equilibria in the body's steady state. Thus thyroxin, secreted by the thyroid, regulates general metabolism, the parathyroid glands control calcium metabolism, and insulin, secreted by the islets of Langerhans in the pancreas, maintains the blood glucose level. Absence of insulin causes the well-known disease diabetes.

8-13. The blood in regulation. In higher animals the circulating blood is the vehicle for maintenance of the steady state. Besides carrying the raw materials and waste products of metabolism, it transports water, hormones, and enzymes, and it also serves as a defense mechanism against the invasion of harmful organisms. Blood cells have a direct phagocytic action, but the blood also plays a vital role in the immunity of the body against infection. When a foreign protein (bacterial or toxin) is introduced into the blood and threatens to upset the "steady state," antibodies usually are formed. These are very specific and confer immunity for periods of from a few months or several years to the total length of life of the individual (par. 6-7). The body fluids of every animal are in a more or less steady state of equilibrium with all of the materials and infectious agents in its environment. This intricate system breaks down occasionally with serious and even fatal results. Some individuals become hypersensitive to particular proteins, such as certain kinds of pollens that cause hay fever or asthma.

8-14. Organizational levels. The so-called "steady state" is not a single, static condition but a dynamic equilibrium of many systems which change in successive stages of development. Furthermore, it exists at various levels. There is the cellular steady state by which individual cells are maintained in equilibrium with their environment, there is regulation at the tissue level, at the organ level, and finally at the level of the whole organism. Regulation and the steady state are at the basis of life.

9 THE ENDOCRINE GLANDS

Glands are cells or groups of cells specialized in structure and function to produce substances needed in bodily processes; these are synthesized from ingredients obtained in the blood or lymph. Most glands discharge their products through ducts and are called glands of external secretion (exocrine). The salivary glands and liver, for example, have ducts carrying secretions to parts of the digestive tract, whereas the mammary and sweat glands discharge through openings on the body surface. In addition there are other glands, without ducts, whose secretions are carried by the blood stream to various parts of the body. These are the *glands of internal secretion, ductless glands,* or *endocrine glands,* and their products are called *internal secretions, hormones,* or *endocrines.* Minute amounts of these endocrine substances exercise profound regulatory control over many bodily functions, stimulating or inhibiting the development, growth, and activities of various tissues and influencing the behavior of the individual.

9-1. Control by endocrines. Most or all endocrine activities are interrelated and work together so that we may speak of an endocrine system. It acts in conjunction with the nervous system to regulate bodily functions. This situation is like that in a factory where rapid decisions are made on the spot by workers and foremen (analogous to nerve impulses in the body), whereas long-term adjustments and general policies are laid down by top management (endo-

crines in cooperation with parts of the nervous system).

The exact mechanism by which endocrines influence physiological processes is unknown. They may act as catalysts or participate directly in chemical reactions. Most of them are of low molecular weight and diffuse freely to bring about prompt responses. Also they are oxidized or destroyed readily so that their effects are not permanent unless a continuing supply is available. Knowledge of hormone chemistry has advanced by synthesis of two hormones, thyroxin and epinephrin (adrenalin); the molecules are rather simple. Experiments show that hormones are not specific for the animals in which they are produced but will influence bodily processes in many others. Adrenalin, for example, has an effect in protozoans and various crustaceans besides man and other vertebrates. Cross effects even have been found between plants and animals. Auxin, the growth hormone of plants, will stimulate the protozoan *Euglena viridis;* and some animal hormones stimulate growth in root tips of plants which by decapitation have been deprived of a supply of their own growth hormone. Hormones seemingly are fundamental substances that probably appeared early in biochemical evolution. The full extent of their occurrence in organisms is unknown.

9-2. Invertebrate hormones. There is evidence of hormones in nematodes, annelids, some other

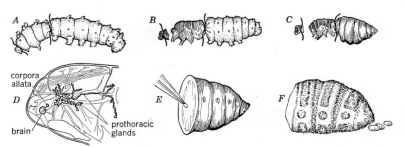

Fig. 9-1. Endocrine control of metamorphosis in larvae of the Cecropia moth. *A.* Ligatures tied behind head and thorax before NSH is secreted; no metamorphosis. *B.* Ligatures tied after NSH reached thorax; GDH activated, head and thorax transform. *C.* Ligatures applied still later; GDH throughout body, metamorphosis complete. *D.* Position of corpora allata and prothoracic glands in head of larva. *E.* Brain and prothoracic glands from chilled larva implanted in isolated abdomen of pupa. *F.* Hormones produce metamorphosis to adult form, and eggs laid! Stipple, larva; lines, pupa; hairy, adult. (*After C. M. Williams, Biological Bull.,* 1952, 1948.)

worms, mollusks, and arthropods. In crustaceans a substance produced in the **sinus gland** on the eyestalk influences the chromatophores. The pigments—white, red, and yellow (also black, brown, and blue)—are variously spread or condensed so that the body color comes to resemble the environment of the individual.

Molting and metamorphosis in insects are controlled by internal secretions. In bugs (*Rhodnius*) a hormone from the **corpus allatum** behind the brain inhibits metamorphosis (par. 26-31), whereas another from neurosecretory cells in the **pars intercerebralis** of the brain induces molting and differentiation. Metamorphosis of the overwintering pupa into an adult in the silkworm moth (*Platysamia cecropia*) results from interaction of two hormones (Fig. 9-1). In nature, the cold of winter is necessary to end the rest period (diapause) that precedes metamorphosis. After chilling, a growth and differentiation hormone (GDH) is secreted by prothoracic glands anterior in the thorax, its production being triggered by another hormone (NSH) from the neurosecretory cells. Experiments demonstrating these endocrine activities are as follows: (1) A normal pupa does not transform if kept over winter at room temperature but does so after being stored at 5°C. (2) If a chilled and an unchilled larva are joined surgically (parabiosis) so their blood streams mingle, both will transform; hormone from the one circulates in the other. (3) If a chilled pupa is dissected into two parts, head-thorax and abdomen, the first transforms into normal foreparts of an adult, but the second does not. If, however, brain and prothoracic glands are then implanted in the second, it becomes a normal abdomen, which may lay eggs! (4) If the brain is removed from eight chilled larvae, the larvae then grafted to one another in a chain, and a brain transplanted into the first, the whole series will transform in sequence.

In early larval life the corpora allata secrete an inhibitory or status quo hormone (SQH). Removal of corpora allata in a young larva is followed by premature pupation, metamorphosis, and emergence of a miniature adult. Evidently SQH suppresses action of GDH in early larval life; prior to pupation, however, secretion of SQH lessens, whereupon GDH can act.

9-3. Hormones of vertebrates.[1] In the higher vertebrates and man (Fig. 9-2) the endocrine glands include the pituitary, thyroid, parathyroids, islets of Langerhans, adrenals, gonads, parts of the gastric and intestinal mucosa, and, in some mammals, the placenta. The pineal and thymus were earlier thought to produce inter-

[1] See also endocrines of the frog (par. 2-13), control of secretory activities in digestion (par. 5-9), iodine and the thyroid (par. 5-13), regulation of excretion (pars. 8-3, 8-8, 8-12), endocrines and reproduction (par. 11-24), and endocrine effects in birds (pars. 34-13, 34-20).

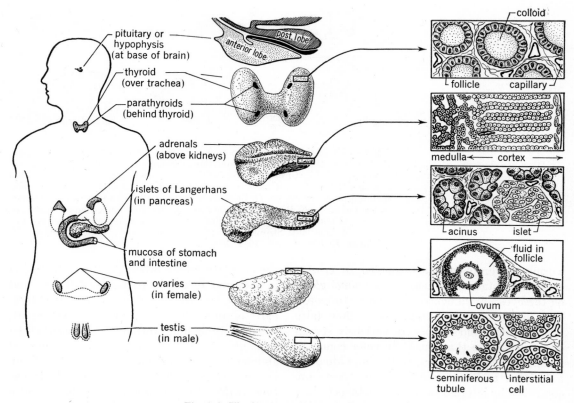

Fig. 9-2. The human endocrine glands. *Left.* Position in body. *Center.* Form of each (not to same scale). *Right.* Enlarged details of cellular structure.

nal secretions, but there is no clear-cut evidence to support this view. The location, structure, and functions of the endocrine glands are enough alike throughout the vertebrates to suggest a homologous series, differing as to details.

Knowledge of vertebrate endocrines has advanced enormously through experimental research since about 1920. Endocrine functions are studied by (1) removing the glands from either young or adult animals; (2) implanting them into subjects of various ages; (3) feeding the gland substance or an extract of it; (4) injecting the extract into the body; and (5) observing individuals with diseased glands. Deficiency of a particular secretion is termed *hypo-*, and an excess, *hyper-*. With the thyroid, for example, a scant supply is referred to as hypothyroidism, and an excess results in hyperthyroidism. The science of endocrinology has im-

portant applications in human medicine and some bearing on the production of domesticated animals. The structure and function of the endocrines are described here with particular reference to man.

9-4. Thyroid. This gland, of two lobes joined by an isthmus, lies on either side of the trachea below the larynx. It consists of many spherical closed sacs or follicles of microscopic size that are lined with cuboidal cells and surrounded by blood vessels and nerves. The follicles are filled with a colloid containing the active principle, *thyroxin* ($C_{15}H_{11}O_4NI_4$; about 65 per cent of iodine by weight), which regulates the general metabolism of the body as well as its growth and sexual development. Normal function produces a varying amount of thyroxin depending on age, sex, and other factors. With decreased

Fig. 9-3. Disorders of the thyroid. HYPERTHYROIDISM. *A.* Exophthalmia, protrusion of the eyeballs. *C.* Goiter, overgrowth of the thyroid gland. HYPOTHYROIDISM. *B.* Cretin child, result of deficient thyroid secretion. (*B, after Hoskins, The tides of life, W. W. Norton & Co., Inc.; C, after Robinson, Our mysterious life glands, Eugenics Publishing Co.*)

A   *B*   *C*

production the person is less active, listless, and feels "cold," because of lowered general metabolism. This condition may be overcome by a daily dose of a few milligrams of thyroid extract (prepared from beef thyroid). Overgrowth or overfunction in man speeds up bodily activities (basal metabolism), increasing both heat production and heartbeat. This condition is usually relieved by removing part of the gland surgically to reduce the amount of thyroxin in the body. Extreme cases of hyperthyroidism often exhibit nervous excitability and exophthalmic goiter or protrusion of the eyeballs (Fig. 9-3*A*). If the thyroid is removed in a young animal, skeletal growth is arrested and sexual maturity fails; if removed from tadpoles, they do not transform into frogs. Normal development is restored, however, if thyroid is implanted or fed or an extract of it is injected.

A deficiency of iodine in the soil and water occurs in glaciated areas and in other places far from the sea, such as the Great Lakes region, the Alps, and the Himalayas. Chronic enlargement of the thyroid, known as *goiter,* often occurs to compensate for the deficiency (Fig. 9-3*C*). If the deficiency is severe, *cretinism* results among children. Cretins (Fig. 9-3*B*) are dwarfed in size, with thick puffy skin and coarse facial features, the basal metabolism is decreased, and the sexual organs do not develop; mental growth is seriously retarded, many are imbeciles or idiots, and deaf-mutes are common. Comparable deficiency in adults causes *myxedema,* characterized by thick, puffy skin, scant dry hair, lowered metabolism, disturbance of sexual function, and mental lethargy. Treatment with thyroid extract, if commenced early, stimulates

young cretins to normal development and commonly restores myxedematous adults. In regions of deficiency the addition of iodine to the diet, as iodized salt, prevents the occurrence of such defects.

9-5. Parathyroids. Behind or partly embedded in the thyroid are two pairs of small oval *parathyroids.* Their secretion regulates the concentration of calcium in the blood plasma and affects the calcium metabolism in the body. Removal of the glands is followed by muscular twitchings and spasmodic contractions of increasing violence, leading to severe convulsions (parathyroid tetany) and death. Injection of parathyroid extract stops these effects. Overproduction of parathyroid secretion raises the level of calcium in the blood, and calcium may be withdrawn from the bones.

9-6. Gastric and intestinal mucosa. There is evidence of several hormones produced in cells lining the stomach and small intestine that control secretion of digestive enzymes. Secretin (Fig. 5-6) from the intestinal wall stimulates secretion of the pancreatic juice, and gastrin from the mucosa of the stomach serves similarly for gastric juice (par. 5-9).

9-7. Islets of Langerhans. Within the substance of the pancreas, in addition to the glandular tissue providing digestive enzymes that pass through the pancreatic duct to the intestine, there are many small groups of cells, of different form and staining reaction, not connected to the duct. These *islets of Langerhans* produce the endocrine *insulin,* which regulates the metabolism of carbohydrates, including sugars, and of fats. Disease in the islets or removal of the pancreas is followed by an increase of sugar in the blood and urine, a condition known as *diabetes.* Formerly this was fatal in children and young adults and a considerable cause of death in older people, but its effects can now largely be prevented by daily injection of insulin.

In some diseases an excess of insulin is produced, resulting in a drastic reduction in the level of blood sugar. This is comparable to the condition caused by injecting an overdose of insulin into a diabetic. The resulting insulin shock is not unlike some forms of drunkenness and can be overcome by eating sugar and thus raising the level of sugar in the blood. For medical purposes insulin is extracted from the pancreas of cattle and sheep obtained in slaughterhouses.

9-8. Adrenals (suprarenals). These two glands lie adjacent to the anterior or upper end of the kidneys and have an unusually rich blood supply. Each consists of an outer *cortex* and inner *medulla,* of different microscopic structure. In frogs the adrenal lies along the ventral surface of the kidney, and in sharks the cortex and medulla are separate structures.

The medulla produces *epinephrin* (adrenalin), which, injected into an animal, causes contraction of smooth muscle fibers in some arterioles, chiefly in the abdomen and skin, with consequent rise in blood pressure, while arterioles in skeletal muscle are relaxed and the heart is stimulated. Epinephrin relaxes smooth muscle on the bronchioles of the lung (hence relieves attacks of asthma) and retards muscular movements in the intestine; it also hastens the transformation of glycogen into glucose. One or two parts per billion of epinephrin are normal in the blood stream of man; but under emotional stress, such as fear or anger, additional amounts are suddenly secreted, and blood is shifted from the viscera to the muscles and the brain, so that the individual is ready for "fight or flight." This hormone is also produced in many invertebrates and has been synthesized in the laboratory.

Unlike other endocrine glands, removal of the adrenal medulla by surgery, which stops the secretion of epinephrin, results in no significant disturbance. Possibly the autonomic nervous system can take over in the absence of adrenalin so that this hormone may have a strictly emergency function. Adrenalin is unique in another respect in that its secretion is under nervous control.

The cortex or outer part of the adrenal produces several endocrine substances. Chemically these are steroids, some of the more important being desoxycorticosterone, corticosterone, and cortisone. The last named is beneficial in treating some types of arthritis.

Complete removal of both adrenals is followed by death in 10 to 15 days. Earlier symptoms are loss of appetite, vomiting, weakness and prostration, reduction in bodily temperature and metabolism, and loss of water and sodium chloride from the blood. Destruction of the adrenal cortex (Addison's disease) in man results in bronzing of the skin, gradual decline, and finally death.

9-9. Gonads, or sex glands. The testes of the male and ovaries of the female are the *gonads,* or *primary sex organs.* The sperm ducts, associated glands, and penis of the male and the oviducts, uterus, and vagina in the female are the *accessory sex organs;* these are related in various ways to reproduction (Chap. 11). External differences between the sexes, or *secondary sexual characteristics,* appear in many animals upon attaining sexual maturity. The gonads, besides producing eggs and sperm, respectively, secrete hormones that affect the accessory organs and sexual characteristics. Other endocrine glands, especially the pituitary and thyroid, also influence the sexual structures and functions.

The thick neck, deeper voice, and belligerent manner of bulls, the antlers of male deer, and the larger comb, wattles, and spurs and crowing habits of roosters are some familiar secondary sexual characteristics. Castration, or removal of the gonads, before sexual maturity, produces striking changes in the form and temperament

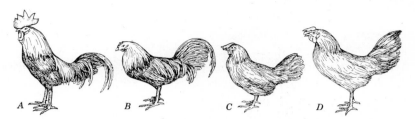

Fig. 9-4. Effect of sex hormone in fowls. *A.* Normal male, long comb and wattles, slender body. *B.* Castrated male (capon), scant comb and wattles, heavier body, resembles female. *C.* Normal female. *D.* Castrated male later receiving engrafted ovary—bigger size, larger comb and wattles, longer feathers on neck. (*After Finlay,* 1925.)

of these animals. The steer (castrated bull) has a smaller neck and more cow-like voice and is docile; the castrated deer grows no antlers; and the capon (castrated rooster) has smaller comb and spurs and does not crow (Fig. 9-4). In all such castrates the secondary characters are lacking, the accessory sex organs are reduced, sexual behavior is slight or absent, and the individuals tend to accumulate fat.

The endocrine of the testis responsible for these changes is ***testosterone*** ($C_{19}H_{30}O_2$), evidently produced by the *Leydig* or *interstitial cells* between the seminiferous tubules. If this hormone is injected into a castrated individual, the accessory sex organs enlarge, the secondary sexual characters develop, and the behavior becomes that of a normal (uncastrated) animal.

Follicles of the ovary produce a female sex hormone, ***estradiol*** (and related estrogenic hormones), responsible for the phenomenon of estrus, or "heat," in female mammals. Removing the ovaries from an immature female prevents her from becoming sexually mature, the accessory sex organs remain infantile, and the sex instincts are not shown. Injecting estradiol into a castrated female corrects these effects. If injected into a normal (uncastrated) but immature female, sexual maturity is quickly brought about, the accessory organs develop, but the ovaries remain infantile.

The accessory reproductive organs of females, especially after estrus, are controlled by another ovarian hormone, ***progesterone*** (progestin); this is produced by the corpus luteum that forms in a Graafian follicle of the ovary after discharge of the ovum. Progesterone, together with estradiol, prepares the uterus for receiving a fertilized ovum. Both hormones, directly or indirectly, induce enlargement of the mammary glands for their subsequent function; later the lactogenic hormone of the pituitary stimulates milk secretion. A third ovarian hormone, ***relaxin,*** facilitates birth by relaxing ligaments of the pelvic girdle.

9-10. Pituitary. At the base of the brain is the ***pituitary gland,*** or ***hypophysis,*** formed during embryonic development of (1) an anterior lobe from a pouch (Rathke's pocket) on the roof of the mouth, and (2) a posterior lobe from the infundibulum of the brain. In an adult human being it consists of four parts: anterior, intermedia, posterior (nervosa), and tuberalis. The entire gland weighs only about half a gram, but it has an enormous influence on the growth and functioning of the entire body. The secretions are of two types as to mode of action. Some (e.g., thyrotropic hormone) influence the activity of particular "target" organs, mostly other endocrine glands; others (growth-stimulating hormone) control metabolic activities of the tissues generally.

An extract of the posterior lobe affects smooth muscle, causing a rise in arterial blood pressure by contraction of all blood vessels (thus being unlike epinephrin); it also contracts smooth muscle in the intestine, gall bladder, ureters, urinary bladder, and uterus. These effects may be due to either one or two hormones. A commercial extract, ***pituitrin,*** produces all these ef-

A   B

C

D

Fig. 9-5. Disturbances due to unbalance in growth hormone of anterior pituitary gland. *A.* Normal woman, age 25 years. *B.* Same individual, age 42, advanced acromegaly—heavy brow ridges, nose, and lips, and lengthening of jaw. (*After Robinson, Our mysterious life glands, Eugenics Publishing Co.*) *C.* Normal dachshund. *D.* Littermate that received hypophysis implants for 35 weeks. (*After Evans et al., 1933.*)

fects. In cold-blooded vertebrates *intermedin* from the intermediate lobe causes extension of the melanophores, or pigment cells.

The anterior lobe of the pituitary produces several distinct hormones that affect other endocrine glands and also various parts of the body. Thus, the rate of production of thyroid hormone depends on the supply of thyrotropic hormone from the anterior pituitary. The principal anterior pituitary hormones and their effects are as follows (see also par. 11-24):

1. GROWTH-STIMULATING. Excessive secretion of this hormone or overgrowth of the gland causes *gigantism.* If this occurs during early youth, it results in lengthening of the long bones; human giants 8 to 9 feet tall are produced by extreme overfunction. An excess later in life causes *acromegaly,* in which the forehead, nose, and lower jaw become massive and the facial skin is thick and coarse (Fig. 9-5). Deficiency of this hormone results in *dwarfing,* the individual retaining the proportions of a child.

2. GONADOTROPIC. In female mammals this hormone (1 or more) causes normal growth of the Graafian follicle in the ovary. When injected into immature females it causes precocious sexual maturity within a few days; overdoses in rats cause a doubling or trebling of the number of eggs (up to 33) released from the ovaries at one time. In male mammals it stimulates growth of both the seminiferous tubules and interstitial tissue. Im-

plantation of pituitary gland into amphibians results in rapid maturing and laying of eggs within a few days. Removal of the pituitary is followed by atrophy of the gonads and the accessory sex organs.

3. LACTOGENIC. This hormone stimulates milk secretion in the mammary glands of mammals and secretion of "crop milk" in pigeons; it is present in birds when they are "broody."

4. ADRENOCORTICOTROPIC. Growth and secretory activity of the adrenal glands are stimulated. One of these products is the adrenocorticotropic hormone, ACTH, which in turn stimulates the secretion of other hormones, including cortisone.

5. THYROTROPIC. The growth and secretory activity of the thyroid gland are regulated by this hormone of the anterior pituitary.

6. DIABETOGENIC. This substance increases the sugar content of the blood (thus being antagonistic to insulin).

9-11. The endocrine glands as a system. The several glands of internal secretion, located at separate places in the body, are of unlike origin and structure, and their secretions differ chemically (proteins, steroids, polypeptides, and others). The pituitary is a center that integrates this rather loose "system." Its secretions travel in the blood to influence all the other endocrine glands (and in addition various other organs and tissues). All the endocrine glands have nerve fibers to and from the nervous system.

10 NERVOUS SYSTEMS AND SENSE ORGANS

A. NERVOUS SYSTEMS

All living protoplasm is excitable or irritable. Because of this, every organism is sensitive to changes or stimuli from both its external and its internal environments; to these it responds or reacts in various ways. Every type of organic response, from the simplest action of an amoeba to the most complex bodily function or mental process in man, results from this fundamental characteristic of excitability. To perceive stimuli, to transmit these to various body parts, and to effect responses, most animals have a *nervous system* (Fig. 10-1). This system (together with endocrine glands in some) serves also to coordinate and integrate the functions of cells, tissues, and organ systems so that they act harmoniously as a unit.

10-1. Stimulus and response. Any physical or chemical change capable of exciting an organism or its parts is a *stimulus.* Common external stimuli derive from temperature, moisture, light, gravity, contact, pressure, oxygen supply, salt concentrations, and odors (chemical emanations). Internal stimuli result from the quantity of food, water, oxygen, or wastes in the body and from fatigue, pain, disease, or other conditions. Some stimuli act directly upon cells or tissues and elicit a direct response (*e.g.*, sunburn), but most animals have various kinds of specialized receptors (sense organs) to receive stimuli.

A *receptor* is a cell or organ having an especial sensitivity (lowered threshold) to some particular kind or kinds of stimulus, as the eye to light and the ear to sound. *Exteroceptors* receive stimuli from the external environment, and *interoceptors* from within the body, as with hunger or thirst. (See also proprioceptors, par. 10-15.) Receptors induce the transmission of nerve impulses through the nervous system; the impulses, in turn, excite terminal structures, or *effectors,* to bring about responses.

Some stimuli are gradual and response is slow, as in the chilling that precedes a sneeze; others are abrupt and produce a quick response, like the jab of a pin. Beyond a certain minimum there may be no quantitative relation between the intensity of a stimulus and the kind or magnitude of the responses that it produces (the all-or-none effect); this depends upon the kinds of cells or organs excited and their physiological condition. Several weak stimuli in rapid succession may bring a response although each individually is too slight to do so; this is called the summation effect. Upon being excited, muscles contract to produce movements and gland cells pour forth the secretions previously synthesized within them.

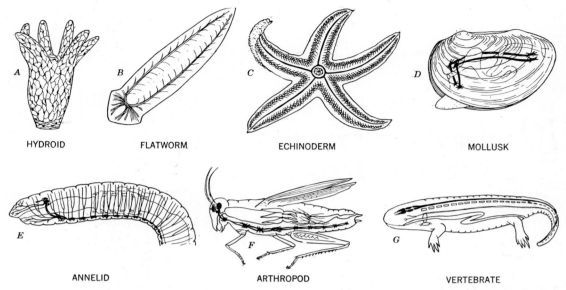

A HYDROID   *B* FLATWORM   *C* ECHINODERM   *D* MOLLUSK

E ANNELID   *F* ARTHROPOD   *G* VERTEBRATE

Fig. 10-1. Nervous systems in animals (heavy black). *A*. Hydroid, nerve net throughout body. *B*. Flatworm, ganglia in "head" region, two nerve cords. *C*. Echinoderm, nerve ring around mouth, median nerve in each arm. *D*. Bivalve mollusk, three pairs of ganglia and connectives. *E*. Annelid, a "brain" of ganglia in anterior end, double solid ventral nerve cord, segmental ganglia and nerves. *F*. Arthropod, similar to earthworm. *G*. Vertebrate, brain in head, single hollow dorsal nerve cord with paired segmental nerves.

10-2. Neurons and nerves. Nervous systems are composed of nerve cells, or *neurons,* with cell processes known as *dendrites* and *axons.* The neurons are of varied form (Fig. 3-20) in the systems of different animals and in the several parts of any one nervous system. According to the "neuron theory" each neuron is a distinct anatomical unit, having no protoplasmic continuity with other neurons, and also is physiologically distinct. Injury to the nucleus or cell body destroys a neuron but does not always affect adjacent neurons. The neuron is the functional unit of the nervous system, which consists solely of neurons in orderly arrangement, they alone performing the nervous functions. Between any two neurons related in function there is a delicate contact, or *synapse;* this is a "physiological valve" that passes nerve impulses in only one direction, from the axon of one neuron to the dendrite of the other. A *nerve* consists of one to many *nerve fibers* (axons or dendrites) bound together by connective tissue and including blood vessels to supply nutrients

and oxygen. A large nerve contains many fibers —like the wires in an electric cable.

The *nerve impulse* that passes along a nerve fiber involves both chemical and electrical change. It requires the presence of oxygen and produces a minute but measurable amount of carbon dioxide, also a rise in temperature. The impulse moves like the burning of a trail of gunpowder; once ignited (stimulated) it travels at a uniform speed with the same intensity throughout. A wave of electrical change accompanies the impulse. In the resting nerve fiber the exterior has a positive charge and the interior a negative one—hence the fiber is "polarized." As the impulse passes, the two charges neutralize one another. Then there is a refractory period (0.001 to 0.005 second) during which the depolarized fiber cannot carry another stimulus. Chemical change during this time reestablishes polarization, and the fiber again can conduct. The myelin sheath around a fiber possibly insulates the fiber so its impulse does not spread to adjacent fibers.

A nerve impulse travels 6 to 12 meters per second in a lobster, 28 to 30 meters per second in a frog, and up to 120 meters per second in some mammalian fibers. Transmission is slower in nonmyelinated fibers than in those with a myelin sheath. There is a short delay in passage at each synapse. An impulse, upon reaching the finely branched ends of an axon, causes the latter to produce a chemical *neurohumor* which sets up an impulse in the next neuron. Acetylcholine is produced in most synapses including those at effectors on skeletal muscle. In at least some sympathetic synapses the neurohumor is sympathin, a substance like adrenalin. The presence of acetylcholine would continue to stimulate the next neuron but for the fact that an enzyme, cholinesterase, quickly inactivates it.

Sensory or *afferent neurons* are those which conduct impulses from receptors to or toward the central nervous system; and *motor* or *efferent neurons* conduct from the central nervous system to various effectors. Still other *adjustor neurons* (internuncial or associative) in the brain and nerve cord join variously between sensory and motor neurons. Some nerves contain only sensory fibers, others only motor fibers, and many are mixed nerves including both types. A *ganglion* is a unit containing the cell bodies of few or many neurons, and certain ganglia in the brain are known as *centers*. In all but the lowest animals the nervous system may be termed a receptor-adjustor-effector system or a sensory-neuromuscular mechanism.

10-3. Invertebrate nervous systems (Fig. 10-1). Most protozoans show no structures for coordination, but many ciliates such as *Paramecium* have a definite system of fibrils or a *neuromotor apparatus* (Figs. 16-23, 16-30); this evidently receives stimuli, conducts impulses, and coordinates movements of the cell body. In sponges the cells about the openings (oscula) in the body wall contract slowly if touched, and these reactions may be communicated to nearby cells, but there are no definite nerve cells or structures. Hydra and other coelenterates have a diffuse *nerve net* around the body in or under the epi-

thelium, but no central ganglion. The net is composed of nerve cells (protoneurons) that are unlike typical neurons in being joined to one another by protoplasmic processes. They connect both to receptors (modified epithelial cells) in the epidermis and to the bases of epitheliomuscular cells that contract slowly to alter the body shape. Nerve nets occur in some other animals and even on the blood vessels of vertebrates.

In bilaterally symmetrical animals the nervous system is linear, usually comprising one or more pairs of *ganglia* or a *brain* in the anterior end joined to one or more *nerve cords* that extend posteriorly through the body. The nerve cords of invertebrates are all ventral and solid, and nerves pass from the ganglia and cords to various organs. Flatworms have two anterior ganglia, with nerves to the head region, and two separated nerve cords which are joined by cross connectives. In mollusks, annelids, and arthropods the paired anterior ganglia (supraesophageal, subesophageal) lie above and below the esophagus and are joined by connectives. The more specialized mollusks lack ventral nerve cords but have large ganglia joined by connectives in the head, foot, and viscera. In annelid worms and the more primitive arthropods, also some insects and their larvae, the two ventral nerve cords have a pair of ganglia and a pair or more of nerves in each body segment. In the higher crustaceans, insects, and arachnoids the ventral ganglia are concentrated anteriorly. Starfishes and other echinoderms have a radially arranged nervous system in keeping with their symmetry.

10-4. Vertebrate nervous systems. In all vertebrates the nervous system has a comparable embryonic origin (par. 11-19) and is always single, hollow, and dorsal to the digestive tract. In basic pattern it is like that of the frog (Fig. 2-18) and consists of (1) the *central nervous system* with large anterior *brain* (Figs. 10-2, 10-3) connected to a spinal or *nerve cord,* and (2) the *peripheral nervous system* of 10 or 12 pairs of *cranial nerves* from the brain, a pair of *spinal nerves* from the cord for each primi-

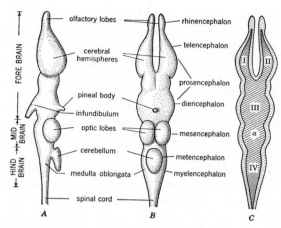

Fig. 10-2. Pattern of the vertebrate brain. *A*. Left side. *B*. Dorsal surface. *C*. Frontal section with the ventricles (I–IV) numbered; *a*, aqueduct.

tive body segment, and the **autonomic** (or sympathetic) **nervous system** (Fig. 10-5). The description of the frog's nervous system will suffice for almost any vertebrate save for proportional differences in the brain, the length of the spinal cord, and the number of cranial and spinal nerves.

10-5. Brain. Parts of the brain are in linear arrangement in the adult shark (Fig. 30-6) and frog. In higher vertebrates this primitive **brain stem** becomes folded or flexed, and the **cerebrum** and the **cerebellum** become progressively enlarged (Fig. 10-3) until in mammals and especially in man (Fig. 10-7) the cerebrum overlies all other parts. Furthermore, the outermost gray matter, or **cortex,** of the cerebrum is both thickened and increased in area, so that it becomes folded or convoluted. In man it contains several billion neurons and their synapses, comprising about three-fourths the weight of the entire nervous system. The cortex is the seat of all conscious sensations and actions, memory, the will, and intelligence; its increase in bulk among the higher vertebrates is in keeping with their greater mental abilities. There is, however, no exact correlation between brain size and intelligence (par. 36-8). The cerebellum is concerned with muscular coordinations and shows especial development in fishes and birds

whose movements are quick and well balanced. The connections and functions of the cranial nerves are given in Table 10-1.

10-6. Spinal cord and nerves (Fig. 10-4). The outer **white matter** of the spinal cord is of bundles of myelinated fibers connecting between various parts of the brain and the nuclei of spinal nerves and adjustor neurons. The inner **gray matter** contains adjustor neurons and the nuclei of motor neurons; nuclei of sensory neurons are in the **dorsal root ganglia** of spinal nerves. If the dorsal root of a spinal nerve is cut, any sensory impulses from the entering fibers fail to reach the cord and brain. Destruction of the ventral root blocks all motor control by fibers in that nerve. The ventral roots are

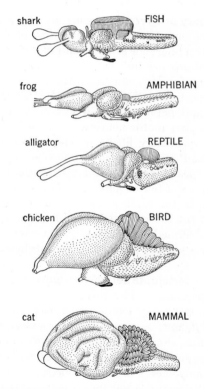

Fig. 10-3. The brains of representative vertebrates showing progressive increase, especially in the cerebral hemispheres and cerebellum. *Olfactory lobes,* clear; *cerebrum,* lightly stippled; *optic tracts and lobes,* coarsely stippled; *base of midbrain,* wavy lines; *cerebellum,* vertical lines; *medulla oblongata,* horizontal dashes; *pituitary body,* black. Stubs of cranial nerves are outlined.

TABLE 10-1. The Paired Cranial Nerves of Vertebrates

Number and name of nerve	Origin (in brain)	Distribution (external connections)	Function (chiefly as in man)
I Olfactory	Olfactory lobe (or bulb)	Olfactory epithelium in nasal cavity	*Sensory:* smell
II Optic	Optic lobe on midbrain	Retina of eye	*Sensory:* sight
III Oculomotor	Floor of midbrain	Eye: 4 muscles of eyeball; iris, lens, upper lid	*Motor:* movements of eyeball, iris, lens, and eyelid
IV Trochlear	Floor of midbrain (emerges dorsally)	Eye: superior oblique muscle of eyeball	*Motor:* rotation of eyeball
V Trigeminal	Side of medulla	Top and sides of head, face, jaws, and teeth	*Sensory:* forehead, scalp, upper eyelid, side of nose, teeth. *Motor:* movement of tongue and of muscles used in chewing
VI Abducens	Side of medulla	Eye: external rectus muscle of eyeball	*Motor:* rotation of eyeball
VII Facial	Side and floor of medulla	Tongue (anterior $\frac{2}{3}$), muscles of face, of mastication, and of neck	*Sensory:* taste. *Motor:* facial expression, chewing, movement of neck
VIII Auditory (acoustic)	Side of medulla	Inner ear: (1) organ of Corti in cochlea (2) semicircular canals	*Sensory:* (1) hearing (2) equilibrium
IX Glossopharyngeal	Side of medulla	Tongue (posterior $\frac{1}{3}$); mucous membrane and muscles of pharynx	*Sensory:* taste and touch. *Motor:* movements in pharynx
X Vagus (pneumogastric)	Side and floor of medulla	Pharynx, vocal cords, lungs, heart, esophagus, stomach, and intestine	*Sensory:* vocal cords, lungs. *Motor:* pharynx, vocal cords, lungs, esophagus, stomach, heart; inhibits heartbeat
XI * Spinal accessory	Floor of medulla	Muscles of palate, larynx, vocal cords, and neck	*Motor:* muscles of pharynx, larynx, and neck
XII * Hypoglossal	Floor of medulla	Muscles of tongue (and neck)	*Motor:* movements of tongue

* Nos. XI, XII are lacking in amphibians, fishes, and cyclostomes.

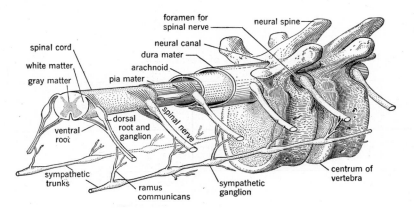

Fig. 10-4. The human spinal cord, spinal nerves, and sympathetic nervous system in relation to the vertebrae and the membranes (meninges) about the cord.

Labels in figure: foramen for spinal nerve, neural spine, spinal cord, neural canal, white matter, dura mater, gray matter, arachnoid, pia mater, ventral root, dorsal root and ganglion, spinal nerve, sympathetic trunks, ramus communicans, sympathetic ganglion, centrum of vertebra

variously injured or destroyed in poliomyelitis, leading to impairment of muscular function.

10-7. Autonomic nervous system (Fig. 10-5). The somatic nerves (cranial, spinal) connect mainly to skeletal muscles and direct the adjustment of an animal to its surroundings. By contrast, the *autonomic nervous system,* of ganglia and fibers connecting to all smooth muscles, glands, and the viscera, deals with the internal environment of the body. It controls routine (vegetative) functions such as the rate of metabolism, the action and tone of internal muscles, and maintaining the constancy (homeostasis) of components in the blood, lymph, and tissue fluids. In birds and mammals, it closely regulates the body temperature by increasing metabolism and fluffing out the feathers or fur in cold weather or by promoting loss of heat in a warm environment.

The thoracolumbar portion, or *sympathetic system,* includes two lengthwise chains of connected ganglia along the trunk vertebrae and aorta. Efferent fibers from the spinal cord pass in spinal nerves to enter the sympathetic ganglia as preganglionic fibers. Upon leaving, as postganglionic fibers, those of each group unite as a *plexus,* then distribute to various organs, as with the nerves from the coeliac plexus to the stomach, liver, etc. Afferent sympathetic fibers pass directly from organs to the dorsal roots of spinal nerves and into the spinal cord. Still other fibers connect to the erector muscles of the hairs and to sweat glands and small blood vessels.

The craniosacral portion, or *parasympathetic system,* includes fibers in certain cranial nerves, to the iris of the eye (III), the glands and mucous membranes of the mouth (V, VII), and the heart, lungs, stomach, and upper small intestine (X or vagus); and other fibers from sacral nerves connect to organs in the lower abdomen.

Most visceral organs and some others are innervated by both systems, and the two have more or less opposite effects. The parasympathetic promotes secretion of saliva and digestive juices, increases muscular activity of the intestine, constricts bronchioles in the lungs, slows the heartbeat, and constricts the pupil and adjusts the eye for near vision. In contrast, the sympathetic increases heartbeat, slows gastrointestinal action, dilates the bronchioles, etc. By increasing secretion of epinephrin from the adrenal glands (par. 9-8) it also mobilizes bodily resources for emergencies—fright, flight or fight, and injury. The epinephrin constricts blood vessels of the skin and viscera, dilates those of the heart and skeletal muscle, releases glucose from the liver for muscle metabolism, and accelerates the clotting time of the blood.

10-8. Types of response. Certain responses in animals can be classified readily, but others cannot because they differ from one another in degree and not in kind. Among lower animals many are invariable, whereas in higher forms the variable responses predominate. The amoeba exhibits many fixed responses, yet it can learn in a simple way. Man's behavior is highly variable, but he has many constant and involuntary responses.

The essentially unvarying type of response by which an animal orients itself toward or away from a given stimulus is termed a *taxis*. (The term tropism now is reserved for the turning movements of plants.) A fish that heads into a current so that the two sides of its body are stimulated equally by flowing water exhibits positive *rheotaxis* (Gr. *rheos*, current), and an insect that climbs directly upward in opposition to gravity is said to show *negative geotaxis* (Gr. *geos*, earth). The moth that flies directly to a light is *photo-positive* or shows positive phototaxis (Gr. *photos*, light), whereas a cockroach that scuttles for cover when spotted by a light at night is *photo-negative* (negative phototaxis). These several types of response are considered to depend upon reflexes.

The simplest invariable coordinated response involving a nervous system is a *reflex act* and occurs in animals with nerve cords and nerves, such as annelid worms, arthropods, and vertebrates. When the human leg is bent and suspended freely and the knee tendon is tapped, the leg jerks forward. This knee-jerk reflex is an automatic, unlearned, and involuntary response to the stimulus. The *reflex arc* (Fig. 10-6A) (1) involves a receptor excited by the stimulus and (2) induces a nerve impulse in the dendrite of a sensory neuron, which passes through the nerve-cell body (in the dorsal root ganglion) and along the sensory axon into the gray matter of the spinal cord. There the impulse (3) crosses a synapse, or center of correlation, to (4) a second conductor, the motor (efferent) neuron, and continues out its axon in the ventral root to (5) the end organ in contact with an effector; if the latter is a muscle, it is excited to contract. Other simple reflexes are winking of the eyelids when an object is thrust before the eyes and sudden secretion of tears by the tear glands when a bit of dust lodges on the cornea. A reflex may or may not evoke a conscious sensation.

Few if any reflexes in vertebrates are really simple. The majority are *compound reflexes*

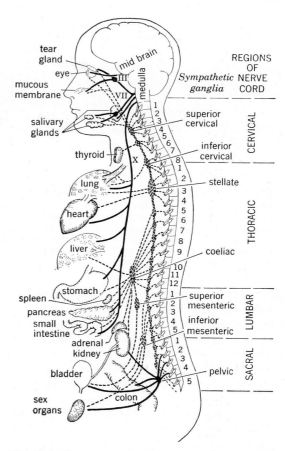

Fig. 10-5. The autonomic nervous system of man and its connections with the central nervous system and the internal organs; diagrammatic and simplified. *Sympathetic trunk and main ganglia* (coeliac, etc.), heavy stipple; *sympathetic nerves*, broken lines; *parasympathetic nerves*, heavy solid lines; *cranial nerves*, III, VII, (IX), X; *spinal nerves* numbered for each region of spinal cord.

wherein an impulse entering on one sensory neuron influences several motor neurons through intermediate or *adjustor neurons* (Fig. 10-6B, C); or impulses from several sensory neurons are compounded to act on one motor neuron. *Allied reflexes* are combined to produce a harmonious effect, such as the muscular movements in a person when walking or in an earthworm or caterpillar when crawling. These actions may be modified or inhibited through *association neurons* extending to other portions of the nerve cord and to the brain (Fig. 10-6D). *Chain re-*

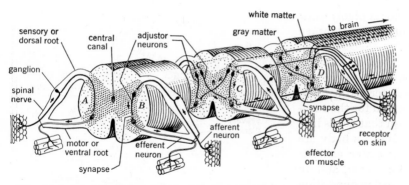

Fig. 10-6. Simplified stereogram of the vertebrate spinal cord and nerves to show relations of neurons involved in reflex arcs. *Afferent neurons*, solid; *efferent neurons*, outlined; *association neurons*, broken lines; *receptors*, as in skin; *effectors*, as on muscles. Arrows show paths of nerve impulses. Each nerve contains many fibers. *A*. Simple reflex arc. *B*. Reflex arc with one adjustor neuron. *C*. Reflex arc with cross connections. *D*. Reflex arc with cross connections and also others to and from the brain.

flexes act in sequence, the response of one becoming the stimulus for the next. A frog reacts to a nearby moving insect by opening its mouth and flipping its tongue forward and back; the captured prey in the mouth stimulates receptors there to bring about closing of the mouth and to start swallowing reflexes in the pharynx and esophagus.

By training, a reflex may be conditioned to follow upon some environmental stimulus other than the original one that evoked it. In a dog the sight of food induces reflexly a flow of saliva, whereas the ringing of a bell does not. The Russian physiologist Pavlov rang a bell whenever food was offered to a dog. After some repetitions the mere sound of the bell, without food, induced salivary secretion in the animal. This Pavlov termed a ***conditioned reflex.*** Many human acts become conditioned reflexes, often of complex character. Repeated performance of a particular act or procedure becomes a ***habit*** by some more or less enduring change in the mode of response to a stimulus. Many of the routine activities of human beings are thus reduced to habits so that they are induced by particular stimuli without the intervention of conscious control. Dressing oneself, for example, is first learned as a conscious procedure but grows to be a habit. In time it becomes a series of chain and conditioned reflexes, mostly automatic—

but not invariable; one may "absent-mindedly" pick up or put on the wrong garment or shoe.

An ***instinct*** is a complex pattern of behavior that is derived by heredity, hence unlearned. Compared with a reflex it is more elaborate but more adaptable. Most instincts serve to maintain the individual or the species. In many kinds of animals the choice and means of using food are instinctive acts throughout life, whereas instincts pertaining to reproduction are manifested only when the individuals become sexually mature. Among animals that live more than one year the reproductive instincts are active only during the breeding season. The migrations of birds and fishes and the manner of making nests and caring for young among insects and vertebrates are governed entirely or largely by instinct. The mud dauber wasp exemplifies a complex cycle of instincts. Each female makes a tube of mud; then just before it is sealed, she captures spiders and paralyzes them with her sting, lays an egg on each, and seals them in the tube. The wasp larvae hatch and feed on the living prey, and when mature the young wasps cut their way out. The parent female never sees her offspring, but her instinctive behavior, and later that of the young, serves to maintain the species. In social insects such as the honeybee (par. 26-14) each caste has

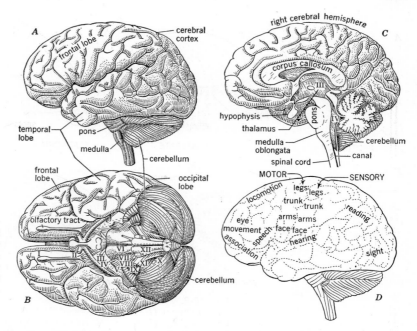

Fig. 10-7. The human brain. *A.* Left side. *B.* Ventral surface; I–XII, cranial nerves. *C.* Median section; III, IV, ventricles. *D.* Left side, showing localization of certain functions on the surface of the cerebral cortex.

separate instincts that function together for the well-being of the colony.

Beyond hereditary taxes, reflexes, and instincts are the higher aspects of nervous function by which these innate *patterns of behavior* become modified in adaptation to special needs. These grade upward to the display of *intelligence* among the higher vertebrates and man, in which the brain contains a greater number and more intricate arrangement of conduction paths and larger numbers of association neurons in the cerebral cortex. All the neurons ever to be present develop early in the life of an individual, but new associations and pathways are established throughout life according to the kinds and intensity of stimuli received and the patterns of behavior developed. There is a functional localization for certain sensory and motor phenomena in the cortex; these have been ascertained (Fig. 10-7*D*) partly by experiment and partly by study of the effects of brain injuries. A discussion of the nature of consciousness, memory, and the will is beyond the scope of this text.

10-9. Sensory pathways. After an impulse reaches the spinal cord it follows specific sensory pathways to higher centers. These differ for various types of stimuli. Injury to the spinal cord results in loss of sensitivity on the afflicted side in the case of touch and pressure, but on the opposite side with pain and temperature. In the first, the afferent neurons from sense organs for touch and pressure enter the spinal cord and immediately turn upward on the same side to the medulla oblongata. There the impulse is transmitted across a synapse and activates a secondary neuron, axons of which cross the medulla and turn up to end in the *thalamus.* This structure, in the brain stem, acts as the sensory relay station; from there the impulse is transmitted to the cerebral cortex for conscious appreciation and integration.

Stimuli for pain and temperature enter the spinal cord through the dorsal roots, and into afferent neurons ending in the dorsal horn of the gray matter. Passing a synapse, an impulse enters a secondary neuron that crosses the spinal cord at the same level and then turns upward on the side opposite the original sensory receptor to ascend past the medulla directly to the thalamus. Thence the impulse goes to the cerebral cortex. In both cases there is a crossing over between sensory receptor and cerebral cor-

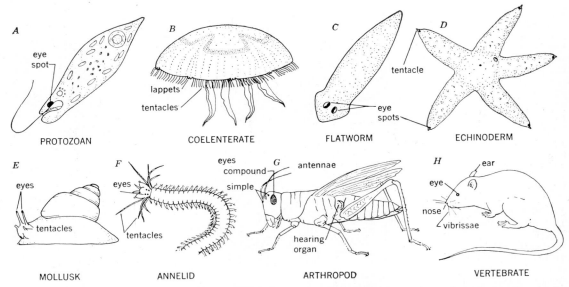

Fig. 10-8. Sensory devices and sense organs in various types of animals. *A.* Protozoan (*Euglena*), "eyespot." *B.* Coelenterate (jellyfish), lappets and tentacles. *C.* Flatworm (*Euplanaria*), eyespots. *D.* Echinoderm (starfish), tentacle and eyespot on end of each arm. *E.* Mollusk (land snail), eyes and tentacles on head. *F.* Annelid worm (sandworm), eyes and tentacles on head. *G.* Arthropod (grasshopper), both compound and simple eyes and antennae on head; hearing organ on thorax. *H.* Vertebrate (mammal), eyes, ears, and nose, also sensory hairs on tip of head.

tex, but at different levels. Thus injury to one side of the cerebral cortex, as in cerebral hemorrhage, results in loss of sensation on the opposite side of the body.

B. SENSE ORGANS

Receptors that yield conscious sensations are called **sense organs** (Fig. 10-8). The functions of these are well known only in man; we cannot always determine their functions clearly in animals. The human "special senses" are **touch,** including contact, pressure, heat, and cold; **taste,** for certain substances in solution; **smell,** for volatile chemicals and gases in the air; **hearing,** for vibrations in air, water, or solids; and **sight,** for light waves. Compared with man, the dog has a more delicate sense of smell, the cat hears sounds of higher pitch, the eagle has keener sight, and the honeybee responds to light farther into the violet but less of the red. Sensory structures are located so as to meet the

environment, being around the body in sessile animals and more numerous anteriorly in bilaterally symmetrical species.

10-10. Touch. Tactile receptors are common on the tentacles of coelenterates and annelid worms and the antennae of arthropods; the latter commonly have tactile hairs on the body (Fig. 26-4D). On vertebrates, tactile receptors occur over most of the exterior surface. Some are **free nerve endings,** and others are special **corpuscles** that contain the sensory nerve terminations (Fig. 10-9). In man these are most sensitive and closely spaced on the face and palmar surfaces of the fingers. At the finger tip a pressure of only 3 grams per square millimeter is detected and two points 2.3 mm. apart will receive separate sensations, whereas on the back of the body the minima are 48 grams and 67 mm.

10-11. Taste and smell. A common **chemical sense** to irritating chemicals is present in the human mouth and nasal cavities and over all the

Fig. 10-9. Receptors and effectors, the end organs related to sensory and motor nerves. *A.* Free sensory nerve endings in cornea of eye. *B.* Meissner corpuscle (sensory) under human epidermis. *C.* Nerve endings on gland cell in pancreas. *D.* Motor fibers on muscles in frog. *E.* Motor end plates on muscle fibers in rabbit. (*Adapted from Cajal, Histology, The Williams & Wilkins Co.*)

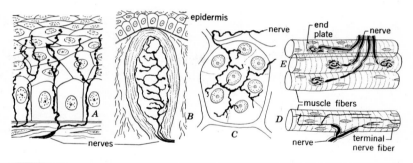

Fig. 10-10. The mechanism of taste in man. *A.* Dorsal surface of tongue. *B.* Two types of taste papillae in section and enlarged. *C.* Relative sensitivity on the tongue for the four tastes. *D.* Section of a taste bud; enlarged and diagrammatic. (*Partly after Parker, Smell, taste and allied senses in the vertebrates, J. B. Lippincott Co.*)

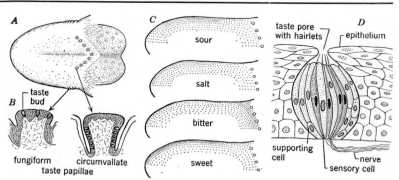

body in amphibians, fishes, and other aquatic animals. ***Taste,*** or gustation, is the perception of dissolved materials by ***taste buds.*** These are groups of narrow receptors with fine tips in a small external pore (Fig. 10-10). They are usually in or about the mouth but occur over the body in catfishes and carp and on tarsi of butterflies. Human taste buds distinguish sweets, salts, acids, and bitter (alkaloidal) substances, and differ in sensitivity as to the concentrations of various materials that can be detected: cane sugar, 1 part in 200; table salt, 1 in 400; hydrochloric acid, 1 in 15,000; and strychnine, 1 in 2,500,000. The olfactory organs of fishes and other aquatic animals respond like taste buds to substances dissolved in the water.

Besides their ordinary service, the taste buds may help in maintaining the constancy of the body's internal environment. Rats suffering from experimental dietary or endocrine deficiencies, when offered a choice of foods or solutions, chose those containing the needed substances.

Smell, or olfaction—"taste at a distance"—depends in man on slender neurons with directly exposed tips that lie in mucous membranes high in the nasal cavity (Fig. 10-11). Eddy currents of air carry volatile substances directly to these cell endings, which have much greater sensitivity than taste buds. Man can detect oil of peppermint at 0.024 mg. per liter of air and artificial musk at 0.0004 mg. per liter. Much of our "taste" for food depends upon smell, as shown by the fact that when a cold congests the nasal membranes all food tastes much alike. The sense of smell is vastly more delicate among wild mammals and insects and serves them variously in finding food and mates and sometimes in avoiding enemies. In some moths the odor of a female may attract a male for a mile or more.

10-12. Equilibration. A *statocyst* (Fig. 10-12) is a small organ of equilibration in which a particle rests among hair-like projections on sensory cells. A change in position of the animal brings the particle, or ***statolith,*** against one or another of the receptors, which transmits an impulse indicating the body position in respect to gravity. In mollusks the statolith is a small

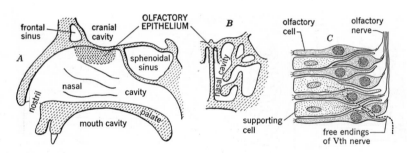

frontal sinus   cranial cavity   OLFACTORY EPITHELIUM   B   olfactory cell   olfactory nerve   C

Fig. 10-11. The mechanism of smell (olfaction) in man; diagrammatic. A. Section of the head showing olfactory epithelium on lateral wall of right nasal cavity. B. Transverse section of nasal cavity. C. Enlarged microscopic section of the olfactory epithelium. (*Adapted from Parker, Smell, taste and allied senses in the vertebrates, J. B. Lippincott Co.*)

limy concretion, whereas in the crayfish (par. 25-14) a particle of sand serves this purpose. The inner ear of most vertebrates has three fluid-filled semicircular canals (Fig. 10-13*A*) in separate planes. On each canal is a swelling or **ampulla,** a statocyst-like organ of equilibrium, that contains one to many limy particles (otoliths) over sensory "hair cells." Tilting the head or moving the body shifts the otoliths or causes movement of fluid in one or more canals. In turn, these stimulate the hair cells that connect to nerves and bring about reflex muscular movements whereby the body is righted. If a cat is inverted and dropped, the mechanism of equilibration acts to rotate the body so that the animal lands on its feet.

10-13. Hearing. The organ of hearing in mammals (Fig. 10-13) has an external sound-collecting appendage, or **pinna,** around a tubular **external auditory canal.** At the end of the canal, sound waves act to set the eardrum, or **tympanic membrane,** into vibration. These movements pass through three **auditory ossicles** (malleus, incus, stapes) and produce vibrations in the fluid filling the spiral **cochlea** of the inner ear. In the latter are many **hair cells,** each evidently the receptor for a particular frequency, that induce stimuli in the auditory nerve. Lower land vertebrates have no pinna, the cochlea is represented by a small outgrowth (lagena), and one bone (columella) replaces the three ossicles. The human ear responds to sound frequencies of about 30 to 10,000, or higher, per second. Sound receptors among invertebrates occur mainly in certain insects (Fig. 26-15).

10-14. Light and sight. Photoreceptors sensitive to light are present in earthworms (Fig.

24-2), and there are "eyespots" on various coelenterates and mollusks. From such simple structures various types of eyes have been developed (Fig. 10-14). Among arthropods there are both simple and compound eyes (Fig. 25-8; pars. 25-14, 26-10). The cephalopod mollusks have eyes much like those of vertebrates, but they are derived differently.

The **eye** in all vertebrates (Fig. 10-15) is much as described for the frog. It is of the "camera" type with a lens which focuses images of external objects on the receptors in the **retina,** as on a photographic film. The receptors consist of **rods** (about 115 million in a human eye), which form colorless sensations in dim light, and the **cones** (6.5 million), which are active in strong light and are sensitive to both white and colors.

After exposure to bright light, some time is needed for dark adaptation (vision in very dim light). The rods contain a protein pigment, visual purple or rhodopsin, that is bleached by light and must be present for vision in the dark. Rhodopsin is related to carotene compounds, and vitamin A is considered a stage in its regeneration; severe vitamin A deficiency inter-

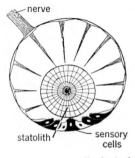

Fig. 10-12. Statocyst of a mollusk (enlarged section).

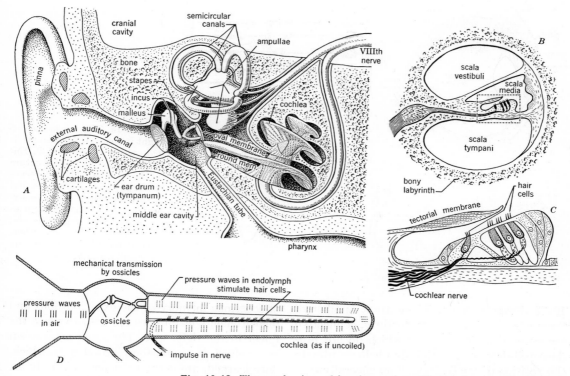

Fig. 10-13. The mechanism of hearing and equilibrium in man. *A.* General structure of the ear. *B.* Cross section of one part of cochlea (area of Fig. *C* in dotted lines). *C.* Enlarged section through spiral organ of Corti with sensory hair cells. *D.* Diagram of sound transmission from the air to an impulse in the auditory nerve.

feres with dark adaptation, producing "night blindness."

The human eye is sensitive to a visible spectrum from violet to red (397 to 723 mμ, and most acute at 510 mμ = yellow); it cannot perceive vibrations of other wavelengths. Focusing in mammals is accomplished by change in curvature of the lens through action of the ciliary muscle, whereas in birds the lens moves to and fro as in a camera. The size of the opening or pupil in the iris diaphragm, which admits light to the interior, is changed reflexly according to the intensity of the light. Many mammals, some birds, and a few other vertebrates have *binocular vision* in that both eyes can focus on an object in part of the visual field. Such vision facilitates detecting movement in the line of sight toward or away from the viewer and enables man and some animals to judge distances accurately.

Fig. 10-14. Eyes of some invertebrates, seen in median section. *A.* Medusa (coelenterate). *B.* Beetle larva (insect). *C.* Snail (mollusk). *D.* Cuttlefish (mollusk). (*Altered from Claus, Grobben, and Kuhn.*)

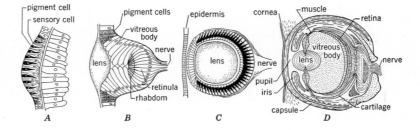

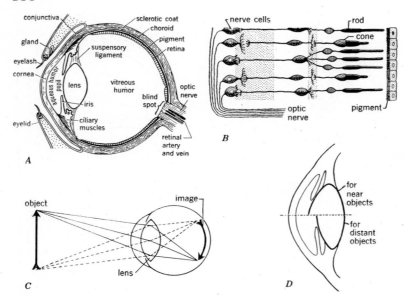

Fig. 10-15. The mechanism of sight in man. *A*. Median vertical section of the eye. *B*. Enlarged diagram of the structure of the retina. *C*. The lens serves to form an image (reduced and inverted) on the retina in the way a camera lens produces an image on the photographic film. *D*. Changes in shape of the lens (accommodation) to focus on near and distant objects.

10-15. Proprioceptors. There are a number of "sense organs" in muscles, tendons, connective tissues, and skeletal tissues which do not produce well-defined sensations but help coordinate the position of the limbs and are generally concerned with the so-called "kinesthetic sense." These are the *proprioceptors.* The simple act of touching a particular part of the body when the eyes are shut is learned by practice and involves unconscious memory of the exact tensions and displacements of muscles required to place the finger in the right spot. The same mechanism is involved in more complicated acts which, once learned, are carried out unconsciously as, for example, piano playing, skating, riding a bicycle, or typewriting. To a certain extent the proprioceptors are responsible for maintenance of posture.

11 REPRODUCTION AND DEVELOPMENT

The ability to produce new living individuals is a basic characteristic of all plants and animals. Early biologists understood correctly how the higher animals reproduce, but for centuries it was believed that many forms of life arose from nonliving materials by *spontaneous generation*—worms and tadpoles from mud and flies from the carcasses of dead animals. These erroneous ideas were gradually abandoned after Francesco Redi (Italian, 1626?–1697) showed in 1668 that maggots and flies are produced from meat only if living flies have laid eggs on such material. Yet only a century ago it was thought that bacteria and other microorganisms could develop spontaneously. In 1861, Louis Pasteur (French, 1822–1895) proved that when bacterial cultures were heated to kill the organisms and properly stoppered to prevent reinvasion by germs or their spores from the air, they would remain without life. The principle of *sterilization* that he demonstrated is the basis for destroying microorganisms by heat or chemicals. It is used in present-day surgery and medicine, in preserving food by canning, in the keeping of *pasteur*-ized milk, in safeguarding public water supplies, and in other aspects of modern life.

All reliable evidence indicates that new life comes only from preexisting life (*omne vivum ex vivo*); this is the process of *biogenesis,* or *reproduction.*

A. REPRODUCTION

11-1. Asexual reproduction. This occurs (Fig. 11-1) when new individuals derive from one "parent," and no special reproductive structures are involved. It occurs in many plants and lower animals. Protozoans such as *Paramecium* multiply by *binary fission,* in which an individual divides into two halves, usually equal, after which each grows to the original form. The nucleus divides, and then the cytoplasm. Multiple fission, or *sporulation,* occurs in the sporozoans (*Plasmodium*, etc.), where the nucleus divides repeatedly and then the cytoplasm fragments, so that a part of it surrounds each of the many daughter nuclei (Chap. 16). *Budding* is a type of reproduction in which a new individual arises as an outgrowth, or *bud,* on an older animal, that grows to the form and size of the latter. Budding of sponges, coelenterates, bryozoans, and tunicates results in colonies of many individuals. Fresh-water sponges also produce internal buds, or *gemmules* (Chap. 17), each of several cells, within a common dense covering. These escape, and later each gemmule produces a new individual. Bryozoans have internal buds known as *statoblasts* which develop into new individuals.

In some flatworms (Turbellaria) and ribbon worms (Nemertinea) an individual may *fragment* itself into two or more parts, each

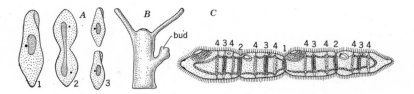

Fig. 11-1. Types of asexual reproduction. *A.* Binary fission in *Paramecium. B.* Budding in *Hydra. C.* Fragmentation in a flatworm, *Microstomum;* numbers indicate the sequence of fission planes that will divide the animal into 16 parts. (*After von Graf.*)

capable of growing to be a complete animal. Some sea anemones reproduce from fragments at the base of the stalk.

11-2. Regeneration. The capacity to replace or *regenerate* parts lost by injury or otherwise is allied to growth after fragmentation. Young animals and species low in the evolutionary scale usually have greater regenerative powers than older or higher animals. A cutting of willow or geranium in moist soil will grow into a complete plant, and pieces of some hydroid coelenterates if put in sand under sea water will form complete animals. When a flatworm (*Euplanaria*) is cut into pieces, each will usually regenerate to form a complete but smaller individual (Fig. 11-2). Starfishes and other echinoderms regenerate lost arms or other parts. Appendages of crabs and other crustaceans and the tails of some salamanders and lizards may be cast off under stress, a process termed *autotomy* (Gr. *auto*, self + *toma*, to cut). Then the animal regenerates the lost part. Regeneration may involve either a local part or a complete reorganization of tissues to produce organs and other structures anew.

Regeneration (and embryonic differentiation) have been explained by the axial-gradient theory of Boveri, Child, and others. This involves different rates of metabolic activity in the parts of an animal, highest commonly at the anterior end and lowest posteriorly. A short anterior fragment of a planarian would have a high metabolic rate and may produce a second head, whereas a short piece removed toward the posterior end leaves the main axial gradient undisturbed and a tail end will regenerate. Complete reversal of polarity may occur if a fragment of the hydroid *Tubularia* is "planted" upside down, when the former basal end will produce a mouth and tentacles.

11-3. Sexual reproduction. Most animals and plants increase by a process in which new individuals develop from sex cells produced by the parents. This is *sexual reproduction.* Typically two cells of different kind (male and female) join to create a new individual. Even protozoans have some reproductive processes resembling the sexual phenomena of higher animals (par. 16-24). In the *conjugation* of ciliates (*Paramecium*, etc.) two individuals of apparently like kind fuse together, exchange micronuclear materials, and then separate to continue binary fission. Among sporozoans (*Plasmodium*, etc.) two kinds of individuals (macrogametes and microgametes) are formed at certain stages; these fuse permanently in pairs to continue the life cycle. In the colonial flagellate, *Volvox*, the same or different colonies yield two kinds of free individuals that combine in pairs, one of each, and give rise to new colonies.

In multicellular animals, *sex* is the total of all structural and functional characteristics that distinguish *male* ($\male$) and *female* ($\female$). Both produce free *sex cells,* or *germ cells.* Those of males are minute and known as sperm, or *spermatozoa* (Gr. *sperma*, seed + *zoon*, animal); the female releases somewhat larger *eggs,* or *ova*

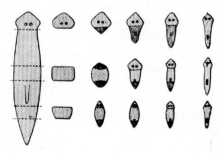

Fig. 11-2. Regeneration in a flatworm, *Euplanaria.* Portions cut from an entire worm (indicated by broken lines) gradually regenerated (dark stipple) to form entire small worms. (*After Stempell.*)

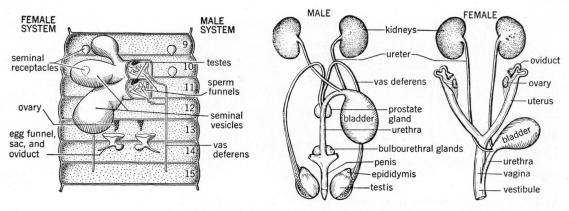

Fig. 11-3. Reproductive systems. *Left.* Earthworm (monoecious), both systems in one individual. *Right.* Cat (dioecious), male and female systems in separate individuals.

(sing. *ovum*). Besides the necessary differences in reproductive organs, individuals of the two sexes may differ in external or internal form, in physiology, in behavior, and, among higher animals, even in psychological characteristics.

The germ cells are produced in organs known as *gonads,* the sperm in *testes* (sing. *testis*), or spermaries, and the ova in *ovaries.* These are the *primary sex organs,* and the only sex structures present in coelenterates. Most animals have ducts lined with glands and other parts associated with the gonads to form a *reproductive system* that aids in the reproductive process (Fig. 11-3). Any or all of these parts are single, paired, or multiple in different animals (Chaps. 18 to 36).

If both male and female systems are in one individual, as in flatworms and earthworms, the animal is termed *monoecious* (Gr. *monos*, one + *oecium,* house). In nematodes, arthropods, various other invertebrates, and practically all vertebrates each individual is either male or female; the sexes are *separate,* and such animals are *dioecious* (Gr. *di*, two + *oecium*). The term *hermaphrodite* is applied to monoecious species and also to occasional abnormal individuals of dioecious species that contain both male and female systems. A condition known as *protandry* occurs in some oysters and the hag fishes (cyclostomes) where the same gonad produces sperm and eggs alternately.

11-4. Reproductive systems. There is variety in the structural details of the reproductive systems of different animals, but all have a basic similarity in pattern, even between the two sexes (Table 11-1). In the *male* reproductive system the spermatozoa are produced in a series of compartments, or tubules, of the *testis* (Fig. 11-4). Thence they travel through small

TABLE 11-1. The Essential Features of Reproductive Systems

Sex	Gonads (produce sex cells)	Sex ducts	Accessory glands	Storage (of sperm)	Terminal organs (extrusion or transfer)
Male ($\male$)	Testis (*spermatozoa*)	Vasa efferentia, vas deferens	Sperm activating	Seminal vesicle	Penis
Female ($\female$)	Ovary (*ova*)	Oviduct (+ uterus)	Albumen, yolk, shell	Seminal receptacle	Vagina (+ ovipositor)

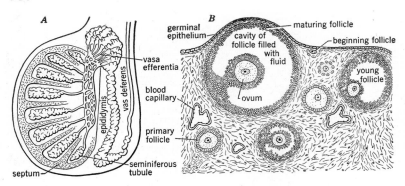

Fig. 11-4. The gonads of mammals. *Left.* Section of a testis. *Right.* Small section of an ovary, much enlarged, with several Graafian follicles.

ducts, or **vasa efferentia,** to a larger duct, or **vas deferens.** The lower end of the latter often is enlarged as a **seminal vesicle.** The vas deferens either leads directly to the exterior or through a copulatory organ, or **penis,** in species which mate for transfer of sperm directly from male to female. **Accessory glands** providing secretions to activate the sperm or for other purposes are sometimes present along the sperm duct. In mammals these are the prostate and bulbo-urethral glands.

The **female** reproductive system produces the ova as individual cells in the **ovary.** In some animals each ovum during its growth is surrounded by follicle cells, as in the frog. The mammalian egg grows in a special **Graafian follicle** that enlarges as the egg matures and finally ruptures to release it (Fig. 11-4*B*). Fluid in the follicle contains hormones important in reproduction (par. 11-24). Ovaries of mammals and some other animals are solid, those in a frog are sac-like, and those of insects comprise several tubular ovarioles. The ovum usually acquires its yolk while still in the ovary. Mature eggs are released from the ovary and moved down the conducting tube, or **oviduct,** by the action of muscles in its walls or by cilia lining its interior. **Glands** in the wall of the oviduct may surround the egg with various materials such as the albumen (egg white) and shell in reptiles, birds, and some other animals. The lower part of the duct is enlarged as a temporary storage reservoir for eggs in some species. This part is expanded as the **uterus** in mammals and other animals that retain the eggs for development inside the body. In species

that copulate, the terminal part of the female tract is specialized as the **vagina** to receive the male's penis; some have also a **seminal receptacle** for storage of the sperm received.

11-5. Origin of sex cells. There is much interest in the ultimate origin of the sex cells because they give rise to new individuals and serve to transmit hereditary characteristics between successive generations. The doctrine of germinal continuity by August Weismann (German, 1834–1914) held that the sex cells, or **germ plasm,** comprised a substance apart from external influences and from the body, or **somatoplasm.** For each new generation the parent germ plasm produces both the body (soma) and the germ plasm of new individuals. The continuity of germ plasm is clear in some invertebrates (*Ascaris, Sagitta, Miastor*) where one cell in the early cleavage of the egg can be traced as the ultimate origin of the future sex cells. In birds, mammals, and others, however, no such early recognition of future germinal material is possible. Indeed, all the early ova in young mammals degenerate, and others form later from germinal epithelium (modified peritoneum) over the ovaries. We now recognize a direct continuity in the chromosomes whereby each cell of the new animal contains the hereditary mechanism established in the egg (zygote) as it starts to develop.

The gonads appear during embryonic development in some animals but do not enlarge until the individuals approach sexual maturity; in others they form at the latter stage. Early germ cells in the gonads multiply by mitosis

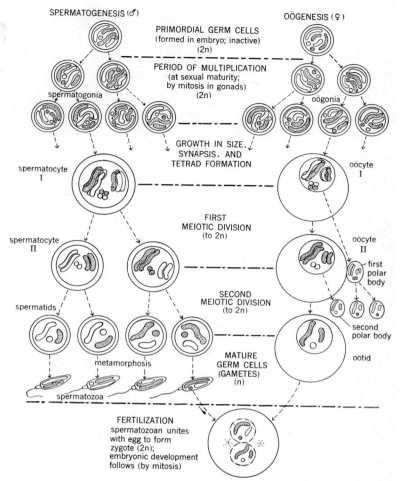

Fig. 11-5. Maturation of germ cells and fertilization; diagrammatic. The maturation process is similar in the two sexes as to nuclear divisions and chromosomes, but differs as to the cytoplasm. The species is assumed to have 6 chromosomes (diploid number); chromosomes derived from the previous generation are shown as white (maternal) and stippled (paternal), respectively.

like somatic cells (epithelium, muscle, etc.); every chromosome divides longitudinally into strictly equivalent halves so that each daughter cell receives an identical set of chromosomes. The nucleus in each contains a dual set of chromosomes, the *diploid number,* $2n$ (except in some "haploid" bees, etc.). In every pair, one chromosome was derived from the male parent and the other from the female parent of the individual in question. The two members of each pair are termed *homologous chromosomes.* At the approach of sexual maturity the

germ cells multiply rapidly; they are then known as *spermatogonia* in the male and as *oögonia* in the female. Before being able to participate in reproduction, however, their physical and physiological characteristics must change.

11-6. Maturation and meiosis. The process by which spermatogonia become spermatozoa and oögonia become ova is known as *gametogenesis* or *maturation,* and the resulting matured cells are called *gametes* (Figs. 11-5 to 11-8). The

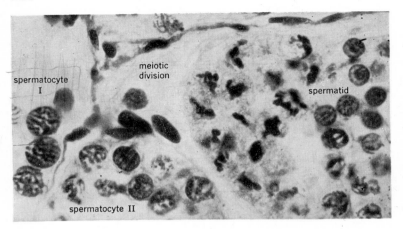

spermatocyte
I

meiotic
division

spermatid

spermatocyte II

Fig. 11-6. Spermatogenesis in testis of a salamander (*Aneides lugubris*). Stages are recognizable by the 4:2:1 ratio of volume in spermatocyte I, spermatocyte II, and spermatid.

accompanying nuclear changes are termed *meiosis.* The gametes of the male and female differ in form, size, and physiology, but the meiotic changes in their nuclei are comparable.

Meiosis consists of two nuclear divisions that follow one another without an interval, known as the *first and second meiotic* (maturation) *divisions.* These differ from mitosis in two important features: (1) The final number of chromosomes in a gamete is only half (or the haploid number, n) of that present in a spermatogonium or oögonium (or somatic cell), and the set of chromosomes in a matured gamete includes but one member from each homologous pair that was present in the unmatured cells. (2) There is a random assortment in this reduction so that each gamete receives either *one or the other* member of each pair. Hence, when two gametes of opposite sex later join in fertilization, the chromosome number in the new individual will be that of the species ($2n$). The manner of division and segregation of the chromosomes during maturation, together with the random meeting of eggs and sperm in fertilization, afford a logical basis for many of the observed phenomena of inheritance on the premise that the chromosomes are the bearers of the determiners, or genes, for hereditary characters. The random sorting provides for variation in the characters that will appear in different individuals of the new generation (Chap. 12).

11-7. Spermatogenesis. As a male matures sexually, the spermatogonia in the testis multi-

ply by mitosis until many are present; then maturation begins. Each spermatogonium increases in size and is termed a *primary spermatocyte.* During the prophase of the *first meiotic division,* the diploid number of chromosomes ($2n$) appears in the nucleus, each chromosome being a single strand of particles (chromomeres). The 2 chromosomes of each homologous pair come to lie more or less parallel to one another, a phenomenon called *synapsis* (conjugation). Soon each chromosome divides longitudinally (or the one produces a second) to yield 2 chromatids, but the latter do not immediately separate. Every bundle then includes 4 components (chromatids) and is termed collectively a *tetrad.* There is no further splitting of chromosomes during maturation.

In each primary spermatocyte the chromosomes shorten and thicken; a spindle forms with the tetrads arranged at random on the equatorial plate. At the metaphase the paternal and maternal pairs of chromatids separate slightly; at the anaphase one pair goes to one pole of the spindle and the other pair to the opposite. From different tetrads the manner of segregation is by chance—free assortment. Some maternal and some paternal pairs of chromosomes go to one pole, and those of opposite origin to the other pole. Each of the resulting 2 cells (with n chromosomes or $2n$ chromatids) is called a *secondary spermatocyte.*[1]

[1] Further details are as follows. At the beginning of meiosis the chromosomes first appear as long filaments with the chromomeres spaced out on the chromonemata,

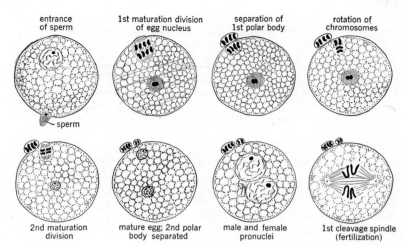

Fig. 11-7. Maturation of the ovum, sperm entrance, and fertilization in the roundworm, *Ascaris megalocephala.*

Shortly a spindle forms in each secondary spermatocyte, and the chromosomes take an equatorial position, when the *second meiotic division* occurs. The two chromatids of each pair separate as distinct chromosomes and go to opposite poles of the cell; the resulting 2 cells are called *spermatids.* A primary spermatocyte thus yields 4 spermatids, each containing n chromosomes, the haploid number. From each pair of homologous chromosomes in a primary spermatocyte, any one spermatid contains one representative, either paternal or maternal.

Following the second division, each spermatid undergoes a *metamorphosis.* Much of the cytoplasm is cast out, and the nucleus compacts to a small (densely staining) head. Behind this

is a mid-piece containing one or two centrioles, and the posterior end of the cell becomes a slender cytoplasmic tail. This is the mature male gamete, or *spermatozoan.* Both maturation and metamorphosis are usually completed before the sperm escapes from the testis.

11-8. Oögenesis. The gonads of females produce fewer sex cells than those of males. The egg acquires most of its physical features before maturation. In the ovary the oögonia become *primary oöcytes,* often enlarging with the addition of yolk. Synapsis, tetrad formation, and chromosome reduction occur as in the male; the division spindle forms near the cell margin. At the first meiotic division practically all the cytoplasm remains with one nucleus to form the *secondary oöcyte;* the other nucleus passes out on the surface of the cell as a microscopic *first polar body.* Likewise, in the second meiotic division, the cytoplasm with one nucleus forms the *oötid,* and the other nucleus is passed out as the *second polar body.* The chromosome content of an oötid results from chance assortment as with a spermatid. With slight change in nuclear position the oötid becomes a female gamete, or *ovum.* Thus each oögonium yields but one ovum; yet the nuclear divisions that produce the ovum and polar bodies are equivalent to those by which four spermatozoa are derived. In different species, meiosis either occurs in the ovary, or after the egg is set free, or requires

---

like beads on a rosary (leptotene stage). The homologous chromosomes then pair, side by side, eventually joining along their entire length (zygotene-synapsis). The pairs then shorten and thicken (pachytene), and during this stage each individual chromosome splits longitudinally (or reproduces) to yield 2 daughter chromatids (the tetrad, latterly called bivalent). At this time transverse breaks may occur whereby parts of the pair of daughter chromatids of one chromosome may be exchanged for equivalent parts of the 2 chromatids of the other homologous chromosome (this is crossing over; Fig. 12-8; par. 12-16; the points of crossing over are termed chiasmata). Then the homologous chromosomes (each of 2 chromatids) begin to separate (diplotene stage) and there is further contraction in length (diakinesis). Finally they become arranged in an equatorial plate, the two members of each homologous pair having their centromeres toward opposite poles of the cell.

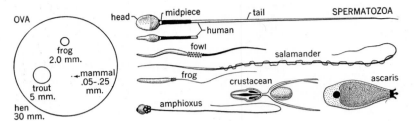

Fig. 11-8. The gametes of several animals. Ova, natural size, diameters in millimeters. Spermatozoa, greatly enlarged, but not to same scale. (*Mostly after Retzius.*)

that a sperm must penetrate the egg cytoplasm before it will be completed.

11-9. Gametes. The gametes of various animals differ in form and size, and those of the two sexes in any one species are quite unlike (Fig. 11-8). The ovum (any covering or shell being disregarded) is spherical or oval and nonmotile and may contain yolk to nourish the newly developing individual. The largest ova are those of some sharks (180 by 140 mm.), the human ovum is only about 0.15 mm. in diameter, and some invertebrate eggs are even smaller. Spermatozoa are motile and able to swim in fluid. While usually thread-like, some are amoeboid and others of peculiar shapes. Their size is usually microscopic; those of man are 52 to 62 μ long, but sperm of a toad (*Discoglossus*) measure 2,000 μ (2 mm.). The sperm cell is a minute fraction of the egg in volume; with human gametes the ratio is about 1 to 195,000. Enough human ova to provide the present world population of two billion people could be put in a top hat and the sperm to fertilize them in a thimble!

11-10. Fertilization. The union of a mature spermatozoan and an ovum is known as *fertilization,* and the resulting cell is a *zygote.* The joining of two haploid (n) nuclei yields a zygote with the diploid number ($2n$) of the species. Fertilization involves the physical entry of the sperm and also physiological processes in both egg and sperm. A sperm cannot effect the fertilization of an unmatured egg. Fertilization is irreversible and usually species-specific; only in exceptional cases will "foreign" sperm fertilize an egg. Fertilization stimulates the egg to active cleavage and development; also it provides for combining hereditary characteristics from both

parents. In different species, sperm penetrate the egg at various stages during maturation, but fusion of the egg and sperm nuclei occurs only after maturation in the egg is completed. Experimental evidence suggests that the outer (cortical) portion of the egg secretes a substance, *fertilizin,* to which the sperms react in effecting fertilization. On some eggs a *fertilization membrane* forms after entrance of one sperm; the egg cytoplasm then separates slightly from its cell membrane. Additional sperms may enter (polyspermy) eggs with much yolk, but only one fuses with the egg nucleus.

A few monoecious or hermaphroditic animals may be self-fertilizing; but *cross-fertilization,* the combining of gametes from two different individuals, is the general rule. A monoecious animal commonly produces its eggs and sperm at different times; if formed simultaneously they are usually self-sterile.

In *external fertilization* (1) the eggs and sperm are shed freely into open water (many invertebrates, some marine fishes); (2) the male and female are close together, as over a nest, when eggs and sperm are extruded (lampreys, trout); or (3) there is simultaneous extrusion of eggs and sperm by clasped pairs (frogs and toads). In *internal fertilization* (4) the male places sperm packets or spermatophores on the bottom of a pond or stream and one or more is taken into the seminal receptacle of the female (aquatic salamanders); or (5) by definite copulation sperm are transferred by the male into the female's vagina, later to fertilize eggs in her reproductive tract (nematodes, some mollusks, earthworms, arthropods, some fishes, all reptiles, birds, and mammals). Many water dwellers practice internal fertilization, and it is necessary for all terrestrial species, because sperm can travel only in a fluid medium. In vertebrates having internal fertilization, the sperm are moved up the oviduct where the eggs are usually fertilized.

11-11. Artificial insemination. In some mammals normal copulation may be replaced by artificial insemination; seminal fluid (semen) is removed from a male and placed in the vagina of a female to initiate pregnancy. This is a common practice for some domestic animals; the desirable characteristics of a high-quality stallion or bull may be transmitted to hundreds of offspring rather than to relatively few as by ordinary mating. Semen may be shipped long distances for such use. About 5,000,000 dairy cows are now so inseminated annually in the United States. Under medical supervision, artificial insemination is used among human beings in special cases, when a husband is sterile or when some physiological abnormality in husband or wife prevents normal conception.

11-12. Cryptorchidism. In males of most terrestrial mammals, upon reaching sexual maturity, the testes descend from the abdominal cavity into the scrotum, either permanently or during the mating season. Failure to descend, a condition termed cryptorchidism, renders a testis sterile. If both testes remain abdominal, no viable sperm are produced because of the higher temperature within the abdomen as compared with the scrotum. Descent is considered to be conditioned by a pituitary hormone.

11-13. Special types of sexual reproduction. Development of an egg without the entrance of a sperm is known as *parthenogenesis* (Gr. *parthenos*, virgin + *genesis*, origin). It occurs in rotifers (Fig. 21-7), plant lice and thrips, many ants, bees, and wasps, and some crustaceans; males are unknown in some species of thrips and rotifers. Aphids have successive generations of parthenogenetic females during the spring and summer; then both sexes are produced by parthenogenesis. These mate in ordinary sexual reproduction, and the females lay fertilized eggs from which females hatch the next spring to continue parthenogenesis (Fig. 26-32). The

queen honeybee produces fertilized eggs (with sperm from her seminal receptacle) that develop into females, either workers or queens; but she also lays unfertilized eggs that yield haploid (n) males or drones (par. 26-17). Spermatogenesis in the latter is of a peculiar type, omitting a reduction division.

Larvae of the gall fly (*Miastor*) produce eggs that develop parthenogenetically to yield other larvae. In the liver flukes (TREMATODA) one larval stage, the sporocyst, produces unfertilized eggs that give rise to another known as the redia (par. 19-9). Such parthenogenesis among larvae is termed *paedogenesis.* The larvae of some salamanders (AMBYSTOMIDAE) may become sexually mature, mate, and produce fertile eggs, a phenomenon called *neoteny.*

Mature eggs of some sea urchins, frogs, and other animals that normally are fertilized may be induced to develop by *artificial parthenogenesis,* as demonstrated by Jacques Loeb in 1900. The stimuli employed included shaking, heat, dilute organic acids, and hypertonic solutions (water with greater than normal concentrations of salts). By pricking thousands of frog eggs with needles, Loeb induced development in many eggs, obtained over 200 tadpoles, and reared nearly 100 individuals (both sexes) through or beyond metamorphosis. The frogs were diploid as to chromosome number. One "fatherless" rabbit has resulted from artificial stimulation of an egg later implanted in the uterus of a female. Means for inducing artificial parthenogenesis are diverse, but all successful methods achieve the same result—activation of the egg.

Polyembryony is the production of two or more individuals from one egg by separation of the cells in early stages of cleavage. This occurs in cases of identical twins in man, also in some armadillos (4 young per egg), in bryozoans, and in some parasitic HYMENOPTERA. In the last-named group some eggs produce single embryos and others yield from 8 to about 1,000.

11-14. Reproduction in general. Most species have definite *reproductive seasons.* In temperate and cold regions these are usually in spring

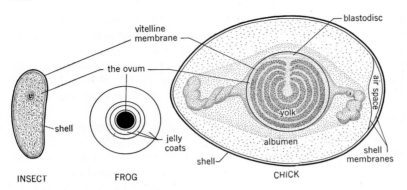

Fig. 11-9. Protective coverings of some animal eggs.

or summer when food is abundant and other conditions for survival of the offspring are favorable. Many invertebrates do not reproduce until the environmental temperature reaches a certain minimum. Other species are influenced by the kind of food available. With some birds and mammals the increasing length of daylight acts on the gonads through the pituitary gland to induce breeding.

Most animals are *oviparous;* the females release or lay eggs (Fig. 11-9) from which the young later hatch out. Many aquatic invertebrates, most insects, and all birds are of this sort. Other animals give birth to living young. Some of them are *ovoviviparous,* producing eggs with much yolk that develop within the oviducts ("uterus") of the female. Certain insects, sharks and lizards, and the garter snakes and rattlesnakes are examples. The mammals and occasional other animals (*Peripatus, Salpa*) are *viviparous,* producing small eggs that are retained and nourished in the female's uterus.

The *number of eggs* produced by each female is inversely proportional to the average chance for survival of any one offspring to complete maturity. If the hazards are great, the number is large. Some parasites produce millions of eggs, the codfish up to 6,000,000 a year, a brook trout up to 5,600, a quail averages 14, a robin 3 to 5, a deer or sheep 2 or 1, and the horse only 1. Some species produce several batches of eggs or broods of young. The *rate of development* until hatching is rather constant in birds and mammals, but with other animals it varies according to environmental temperature or other factors. The approximate time required is characteristic for each species, ranging from a few hours or days for some invertebrates to months for large mammals—9 months in mankind and 20 months in the elephant.

Many animals have special *breeding habits* that make for greater success in reproduction. These include courting performances that bring the sexes together for mating, nests to provide protection for eggs, and parental care of eggs and young. Eggs are carried on the body or in brood pouches by females of some crustaceans, insects, and spiders and by one or the other sex in certain fishes and amphibians. Birds sit on and incubate their eggs, and heat from the parent's body causes the eggs to develop at a uniform rate. In mammals, development of the young within the mother's uterus achieves a similar result. Young of some ants, bees, and wasps are provided with food in the nest, the termites and social bees feed and tend the young in their colonial nests, the nestlings of birds are fed with food gathered by the parents, and young mammals are nourished by milk secreted from the mammary glands of their mothers.

11-15. Sex ratio. The numerical relation between the sexes in a species is the sex ratio. Theoretically there should be equal numbers of male- and female-producing gametes. Actually there is either a differential in their production or in mortality among embryos or later stages. In mankind the primary ratio is high, but males experience greater mortality both prenatal and postnatal. The ratio is important in livestock production, and there would be decided prac-

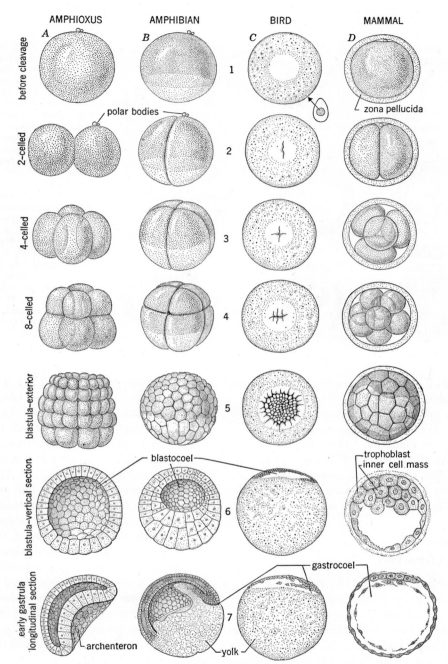

AMPHIOXUS   AMPHIBIAN   BIRD   MAMMAL

before cleavage

polar bodies

zona pellucida

2-celled

4-celled

8-celled

blastula–exterior

blastula–vertical section

blastocoel

trophoblast
inner cell mass

early gastrula
longitudinal section

gastrocoel

archenteron

yolk

Fig. 11-10. Sample stages of cleavage and gastrulation in eggs of chordates. *A.* AMPHI-
OXUS, cleavage holoblastic, little yolk; egg diameter 0.1 mm. (*After Hatschek.*) *B.* FROG,
modified holoblastic cleavage, much yolk; diameter 2 mm. (*Various sources.*) *C.* BIRD,
meroblastic discoidal cleavage in small blastodisc on large yolk mass; diameter 30 mm.
(*After Blount; and Patten, Early embryology of the chick, The Blakiston Co.*) *D.* MAM-
MAL, cleavage holoblastic, practically no yolk; an outer trophoblast and an inner cell
mass formed in blastula (6); gastrula formed by migration of endoderm cells from
inner cell mass (7); egg surrounded during early cleavage by zona pellucida (from
Graafian follicle of ovary) which later disappears. (*After Gregory; and Patten, Embryology of the pig, The Blakiston Co.*)

147

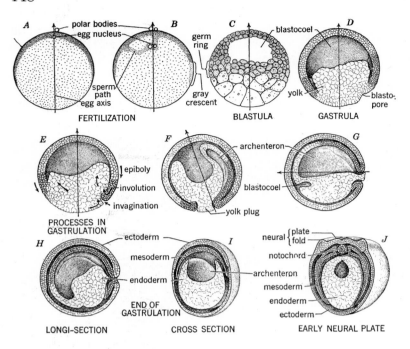

Fig. 11-11. Early embryology of the frog. Long arrow indicates egg axis. *A.* Sperm at surface of egg. *B.* Entrance path of sperm (in plane of paper) bisects gray crescent and determines plane of first cleavage. *C.* Late blastula. *D.* Blastopore formed, gastrulation begins. *E.* Processes in gastrulation. *F, G.* Gastrulation continues, rotation of egg on axis, anteroposterior and dorsoventral relations established. *H, I.* Gastrula completed. *J.* Beginning of organ systems. *D–H.* Longisections. *I, J.* Cross sections. (Compare Figs. 11-8, 11-10, 2-16.) (*A–C, E–G redrawn by permission from W. C. Curtis and M. C. Guthrie, Textbook of general zoology, John Wiley & Sons, Inc.; D, H–J, redrawn from H. Spemann, Embryonic development and induction, Yale University Press.*)

tical benefit if sex could be controlled to produce more females.

The sex ratio is usually stated as numbers of males per 100 females. Some well-known ratios after birth are mankind, 103 to 107:100; horse, 98.3; cattle, 107.3; sheep, 97.7; pig, 111.8; dog, 118.5; rabbit, 104.6; house mouse, 100 to 118; chicken, 93.4 to 94.7; pigeon, 115. The ratio varies with race or breed, season, and other factors.

B. DEVELOPMENT

The starting point for the production of a new individual by sexual reproduction is the activated egg, or *zygote.* Repeated mitotic divisions result in many cells that differentiate to form the tissues and organs of the developing individual, or *embryo.* This is the process of embryogeny (Gr. *embryo + genesis,* generation), and the science that deals with the subject is *embryology.* The following account outlines the early development of the frog (Figs. 2-20, 11-11) and mentions some features of development in salamanders, birds, and mammals.

11-16. Blastula. Soon after an egg is fertilized, the single-celled zygote becomes two cells, the two divide into four, and so on. This process of *cleavage* partitions the egg substance into an increasing number of smaller cells, or *blastomeres,* each with an equal number of chromosomes. As cleavage continues, the cells become arranged in the form of a hollow ball, or *blastula,* within which a *blastocoel* (segmentation cavity) appears. Two major regions are evident, an upper *animal hemisphere* or pole of small dark cells with little yolk and an opposite *vegetal hemisphere* below of larger pale-colored cells rich in yolk granules. Between them is a *germ ring* or *marginal zone* of medium-sized cells.

Cleavage is termed holoblastic when an entire egg cell divides, as in the frog; it is meroblastic when only part of the protoplasm divides, as in the chick (Fig. 11-10).

11-17. Gastrula. Cleavage is followed by the complex process of *gastrulation.* Cells of the vegetal and marginal regions gradually move inward and are overgrown by those of the animal hemisphere. A double-walled cup results, as might be produced by pushing in one side of a hollow rubber ball. This is termed a *gastrula.* The blastocoel is gradually obliterated, and the cavity resulting from gastrulation is the primitive gut, or *gastrocoel* (archenteron). The external opening of the archenteron is called the *blastopore.*

When complete, the gastrula consists of (1) an outer layer of *ectoderm,* from cells of the animal hemisphere; (2) an inner layer, of *endoderm* (entoderm), from cells of the vegetal hemisphere; and between these, (3) a third layer, of *mesoderm,* derived from the marginal zone. These are the *germ layers* from which various tissues and organs will form. The ectoderm will produce the external covering of the body, the nervous system, and the sense organs; the endoderm provides the lining of the digestive tract, its glands, and associated structures; and the mesoderm gives rise to the supportive tissues, muscles, lining of the body cavity, and other parts (Table 11-2).

Gastrulation involves three related activities (Fig. 11-11*E*): (1) the yolk-laden endoderm cells of the vegetal hemisphere push or cup inward (invagination); (2) the germ ring, and especially the dorsal lip of the blastopore, is

TABLE 11-2. General Outline of Embryonic Differentiation in a Vertebrate

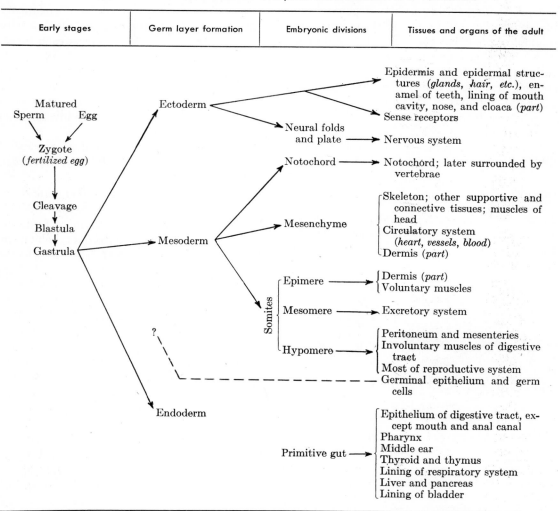

inturned (involution); and (3) the ectoderm grows downward eventually to cover the cells of the vegetal hemisphere (epiboly, or overgrowth).

11-18. Body symmetry and axes.[1] An *egg axis* may be visualized through the animal and vegetal poles. A *gray crescent* forms usually on a meridian 180 degrees from the point of sperm entrance and is bisected by the first cleavage plane. The latter then proves to be the future median plane of the embryo; hence the path of sperm entrance establishes bilateral symmetry. The dorsal lip of the blastopore, where endoderm and marginal zone meet, grows over the cells of the vegetal hemisphere as gastrulation proceeds; when all the endoderm is inside, the original egg axis has rotated about 90 degrees. The former lower end of the axis is then at the completed blastopore, marking the posterior end of the future animal, so that the longitudinal body axis is indicated. The plate of mesoderm cells inturned at the upper lip of the blastopore indicates the dorsal region; and shortly after gastrulation the paired neural folds on the surface, forward from the blastopore, provide an external indication of the dorsal surface.

11-19. The embryo. After gastrulation the *differentiation* of the embryo begins. From the three germ layers there are outpocketings, inpocketings, thickenings, divisions, and other

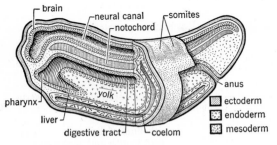

Fig. 11-12. Stereogram of early frog embryo cut away to show beginnings of organ systems.

---

[1] The movement and fate of local portions of the egg may be determined by spotting the surface with vital dyes that stain but do not injure the protoplasm and then tracing the subsequent location of these color spots.

changes that lead to establishment of the organs and organ systems (Fig. 11-12).

The nervous system starts dorsally as a pair of *neural folds.* The ectoderm between these sinks down, and the folds come together to form a *neural tube* (canal), enlarged at the anterior end to become the *brain.* On either side, between the neural tube and ectoderm, a line of cells forms the *neural crests* that will produce the dorsal or sensory roots of spinal nerves to grow into the cord. Motor roots later push out ventrally from the cord. The early brain is of three primary vesicles, *fore-, mid-,* and *hind brain.* The forebrain produces the cerebral hemispheres and diencephalon, and from the hind brain the cerebellum and medulla oblongata are derived. A rounded *optic vesicle* grows laterally on either side of the forebrain; as each meets the ectoderm on the side of the head region, the latter is stimulated to form a thickened *lens vesicle* that subsequently produces the lens of the eye. Meanwhile, the outer surface of each optic vesicle becomes concave by invagination and forms the *retina.*

The endoderm of the primitive gastrocoel becomes the inner lining of the *digestive tract.* Anteriorly, at the future pharynx, three outpocketings of the tract on either side meet three corresponding inpocketings from the side of the neck; these break through to form the *gill slits.* A single ventral outpocket, behind the pharynx, forms the *liver bud,* later to yield the liver and bile duct. An inpocketing of ectoderm (stomodeum) forms ventrally on the head region, and a similar one (proctodeum) at the posterior end. In later embryonic life these break through to join the endoderm of the digestive tract, the stomodeum becoming the *mouth cavity* and the proctodeum becoming the anal canal, both lined by ectoderm. During larval life a ventral outpocket of the pharynx grows posteriorly, with two lobes, and gives rise to the *larynx, trachea,* and *lungs.*

During gastrulation mesoderm forms between the ectoderm and endoderm. Cells in its mid-dorsal part become arranged as a solid rod, the *notochord,* between the nerve tube and primitive gut, to serve as a supporting body axis

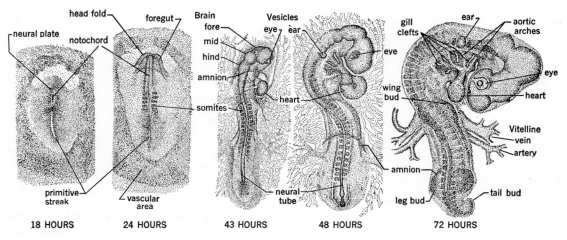

18 HOURS   24 HOURS   43 HOURS   48 HOURS   72 HOURS

Fig. 11-13. The chick embryo during the first 72 hours of development ($\times$ 8⅓). Gastrulation (Fig. 11-10*C*) probably occurs before the egg is laid. At 21 hours of incubation the first somite appears; after 26 hours the heart begins beating and food material is brought by vitelline veins from the yolk surface (not shown). During the second day the anterior end turns so that the left side of the embryo lies toward the yolk; this turning is completed on the fourth day. At 48 hours the amnion covers the anterior two-thirds of the embryo. (*After Patten, Early embryology of the chick, The Blakiston Co.*)

Mesoderm at either side of the notochord grows down as a curved plate between the ectoderm and endoderm, and the two meet ventrally under the yolk mass. The thin lower part (hypomere) of each plate splits into two layers. The outer is applied to the ectoderm and becomes the *parietal peritoneum,* the inner surrounds the gut (and other organs later) to make the *visceral peritoneum* (and smooth muscle of the gut), and the space between the layers is the body cavity or *coelom.* The uppermost mesoderm (epimere) at either side of the nerve tube and notochord forms a lengthwise series of segmental blocks or *somites.* Each somite differentiates into three parts: a thin outer part (dermatome) becomes the *dermis* of the skin, a thick inner part (myotome) later gives rise to the *voluntary muscles,* and nearest the notochord a scattering of cells (sclerotome) grow about the nerve tube and notochord to form the *vertebrae* (axial skeleton), first of cartilage but later replaced by bone. Between the ventral plates and the somites a third portion (mesomere) is the forerunner of the *excretory system* and parts of the reproductive system.

Further details of embryonic development are too many to follow here. After some days (depending on the species of frog and the water temperature) the embryo escapes from its gelatinous covering to hatch as a tadpole, or *larva.* Shortly it begins to feed and grow. Development continues for some months, and then a *metamorphosis* occurs by which the larva transforms into a frog (Fig. 2-20).

11-20. Development of the chick (Figs. 11-10*C*, 11-13). Eggs of birds, reptiles, and many fishes contain so much yolk that cleavage of the entire mass is impossible. The process begins in a small area of protoplasm, or *blastodisc,* at the animal pole. By superficial (meroblastic) cleavage a plate of cells is formed that corresponds to the spherical blastula of a frog. This splits to form two layers of cells, ectoderm and endoderm. A median *primitive streak* then develops forward from the posterior end of the ectoderm, and from its anterior portion parallel edges turn up to form *neural folds.* The *notochord* appears between the neural tube and endoderm, as in the frog. The endoderm spreads in a flat sheet

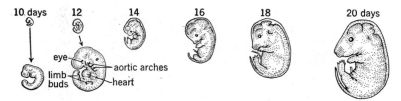

Fig. 11-14. The rat embryo from the tenth to twentieth day of gestation, nearly natural size; 10- and 12-day stages also enlarged about three times. Early development is slow; third day: 8-cell stage, in oviduct; fourth to seventh days: blastula, in uterus; eighth day: primitive streak; tenth day: somites 1 to 6 (comparable with 25-hour chick). After the embryonic membranes and placenta are formed growth is rapid and birth occurs 21½ to 22 days after fertilization.

over the surface of the yolk mass. Mesoderm forms between the ectoderm and endoderm at either side of the notochord, then splits into two sheets with the future coelomic cavity between; somites develop in the mesoderm at either side of the notochord. Meanwhile, a **head fold** appears at the anterior end of the primitive streak; this contains the first evidence of the future brain and fore-gut. The subsequent development of the chick embryo has much in common with that of the frog, as to the way in which organs become established. Gill pouches and **gill slits** appear in the first few days but soon close. The endoderm and mesoderm on all sides spread around the yolk to form a **yolk sac** (Fig. 11-15) that is enclosed by the ventral body wall just before hatching. A calcareous **egg tooth** forms on the tip of the beak, by which the embryonic bird cracks the shell and hatches out as a chick.

11-21. Development of the mammal (Figs. 11-10D, 11-14). The eggs of the lowest living mammals (MONOTREMATA) resemble those of birds in being of some size, with much yolk,

and are laid externally. Eggs of all the higher or placental mammals are minute, practically yolkless, and retained within the female's body for development. The entire egg divides, and a yolk sac is formed. This has been taken to mean that the mammals are derived from a stock (the reptiles) with large-yolked eggs, but in acquiring other means for developing and nourishing the embryo they have not lost all features of their former mode of development. After the gastrula stage, the development of a mammalian embryo resembles the early embryogeny of the bird; gill pouches and slits appear but soon close.

11-22. Embryonic membranes (Fig. 11-15). The embryos of reptiles, birds, and mammals have a series of **embryonic membranes** that protect against desiccation and shock and serve in respiration, excretion, and other necessary functions during embryonic life. These are the **amnion, chorion, yolk sac,** and **allantois;** each is composed of two layers of embryonic tissue. The amnion forms a closed sac about the embryo and is filled with a watery **amniotic fluid**

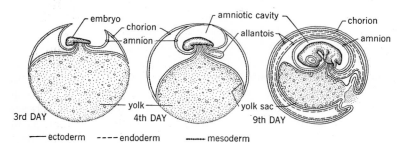

Fig. 11-15. Three stages in development of the embryonic membranes of the chick; diagrammatic longitudinal sections; shell, shell membranes, and albumen omitted; compare Figs. 11-4, 11-12B.

Fig. 11-16. *A.* Entire reproductive tract of female cat, with uterus cut open to show the position of one embryo of the six present. *B.* One embryo removed from uterus with the zonary placenta cut open, and part of embryonic membranes removed to show relations of umbilical cord, blood vessels, and membranes.

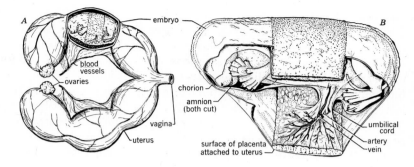

to keep the embryo moist and protect it against shock or adhesions. The chorion surrounds the amnion. The yolk sac in reptiles and birds gradually incorporates the yolk into the digestive tract for nourishing the embryo. The allantois pushes out from the hind-gut to lie against the chorion and shell membranes. Blood vessels then grow out on its surface to serve as an embryonic respiratory and excretory organ. All these membranes are ruptured and discarded when the young hatch.

11-23. Placenta and umbilical cord. The minute mammalian egg passes down the oviduct to lie on the inner surface of the maternal uterus. An amnion soon forms and fills with fluid. The chorion and allantois grow out and make contact with the uterus, whereby embryonic blood vessels on the allantois are brought close to maternal blood vessels in the uterine wall. Processes, or *villi,* of the chorion become embedded in depressions of the uterine surface, and the resulting joint embryonic-maternal structure is called the *placenta* (Fig. 11-16). Nutrients and oxygen then pass from maternal blood vessels through several intervening cell layers to the blood of the embryo, and carbon dioxide and excretory wastes move in the opposite direction; but there is no direct connection between maternal and embryonic circulations. The degree of intimacy between maternal and embryonic structures and the form of placenta vary in different mammals. The placenta may be *diffuse,* with scattered villi (pig and cow); *discoidal,* or disc-like (bats, rodents, and mankind); or *zonary,* a cylindrical band (cats and other carnivores). The human placenta is com-

plex; some lining tissues of the uterus disappear, and embryonic blood vessels on the chorionic villi are bathed in maternal blood (Fig. 36-5). Any developing embryo that has acquired characteristic mammalian form is called a *fetus.* From the ventral surface of its abdomen a soft flexible *umbilical cord* extends, conveying two arteries and a vein that connect to embryonic capillaries in the placenta. When the fetus has completed its growth, *birth* (parturition) occurs. The maternal vagina dilates, and slow rhythmic contractions of the uterus gradually force the fetus to the exterior. The amnion is either ruptured in this process or is quickly torn by the mother, so that the newborn young may breathe air; soon the umbilical cord is severed. The embryonic part of the placenta either passes out with the fetus or descends later, as the "afterbirth," and is usually eaten by the parent.

11-24. Role of hormones in reproduction. Hormones (Chap. 9) regulate the sequence and timing of events in reproduction. This is best understood in vertebrates, especially mammals, where several hormones of the anterior pituitary are highly important, together with others originating in the reproductive organs. First, a *growth-stimulating hormone* (GSH) causes a young individual to become sexually mature. (If the pituitary is experimentally removed, the reproductive organs remain infantile, the individual is sterile, and no sexual cycle occurs.) In a normal mature female the *follicle-stimulating hormone* (FSH) promotes growth of the ovum and Graafian follicle (Fig. 11-4); then the follicle itself releases a hormone, *estradiol* (an estrogen), that brings on sexual behavior (estrus) for mating. After the ovum is discharged from its follicle, the *luteinizing hormone* (LH) from the pituitary stimulates cell growth whereby the ruptured follicle becomes a *corpus luteum.* This structure in turn (influenced by lactogenic hormone, or prolactin, LTH, also from the pituitary) secretes a hormone, *progesterone,* that affects cells lining the uterus, preparing them for the implantation of a fertilized egg. If pregnancy results the corpus luteum persists, increasing in size, and its secretion (LH) prevents growth or maturing of other ovarian follicles (thus being antagonistic to FSH). Upon birth of the young, the *lactogenic hormone* (LTH) stimulates milk production in the mammary gland. After birth the corpus luteum and its secretion decline, permitting FSH to promote ovulation once more. In the event that implantation fails or pregnancy is interrupted, the corpus luteum and supply of LH are reduced, whereupon FSH again can act.

The placenta, besides serving for exchange of food, respiratory gases, and wastes between parent and embryo, also produces hormones—estradiol and progesterone—until near the end of pregnancy. A third hormone, *gonadotropin,* also is formed, and some of it is excreted in the urine. The modern human "pregnancy test" depends upon demonstrating the presence of this last hormone in a sample of urine. *Relaxin,* another placental hormone, relaxes pelvic ligaments in anticipation of birth.

Besides hormones of the anterior pituitary and reproductive tract, those from other endocrine glands (thyroid, parathyroid, etc.) have a part in processes related to reproduction. The human menstrual cycle (par. 36-12) is regulated by FSH and LH as described above. In male animals reproductive activities also are under hormonal control (par. 9-9).

11-25. Processes in development. Aristotle and the Romans recognized that mating of a male and female was necessary for the production of offspring in mankind, the domestic animals, and some animals in nature, but the causal relation of copulation to birth of young is still unknown

to some primitive peoples. Spermatozoa were discovered by Hamm and van Leeuwenhoek in 1677 and soon were thought to have a bearing on development. In 1824 Prevost and Dumas showed that if seminal fluid of frogs was filtered to remove the sperm before being poured over unfertilized eggs, the latter failed to develop. Penetration of the egg by sperm, and union of the sperm and egg nuclei in fertilization were first observed in sea urchin eggs by Oskar Hertwig and Fol, independently, in 1875. Meanwhile, embryologists had two contrasted theories to explain development. The *preformation theory,* supported by Harvey and Malpighi, was well established by 1720 and was later elaborated by Bonnet (1720–1793), Von Haller (1708–1777), and others. It assumed that either the egg or the sperm contained a "germ" completely preformed but minute and invisible, which expanded or enlarged to visible size and form during development. Some artists even figured the "homunculus" (little man) presumed to occur in the head of a human sperm. Bonnet's theory of "encasement" assumed that, if the "germ" contained a complete individual, then each germ in turn must contain those for succeeding generations in smaller scale, like a series of boxes one within another; all germs were assumed to have been created in the beginning. On this fantastic premise someone calculated that Eve, the mythical mother of the human race, must have contained over 200 million homunculi! The opposing *theory of epigenesis* by Wolff (1759) and others assumed that the egg lacked internal organization and some outside force (vis essentialis) was responsible for its development. Modern descriptive and experimental embryology has shown that the cytoplasm of eggs has some preformed elements and that both external and internal factors operate in development.

11-26. Organization. The eggs of various species differ in degree of organization before and after fertilization. In those of some jellyfishes and echinoderms the individual blastomeres may be separated, up to the 16-celled stage, and each will produce a complete but proportionately smaller embryo; eggs of amphioxus will do likewise in the 2-celled stage; and if the blastomeres at the 2-celled stage of a salamander are carefully separated, two complete embryos may result if cleavage is bilateral. In these cases of "indeterminate cleavage" each blastomere, if parted, can produce a separate and complete individual. By contrast, the separation of blastomeres or cell groups during cleavage in eggs of ctenophores, some mollusks (*Dentalium*), annelids, and tunicates (*Styela*) will result in each producing only that part of the embryo which it would form in an undisturbed egg. Such "determinate cleavage" indicates organization of material in the egg prior to cleavage. One part may influence another, as is shown in eggs of amphioxus or of amphibians that are only partly separated in the 2-celled stage, and yield ➤-shaped embryos with two anterior ends. If dorsoventral separation is attempted in the early gastrula of a salamander, the upper part may produce a well-formed embryo and the lower only a mass of cells.

Evidence of subsequent organization in the egg and of the time or stage in which it occurs has been derived for amphibians by vital staining and by transplanting small areas of the embryo. By many studies of this type an elaborate "presumptive organization" has been demonstrated in the late blastula and early gastrula, and the existence of the several processes earlier described (par. 11-17) has been confirmed. Between the 2-celled stage (when each blastomere may produce a separate embryo) and the end of gastrulation, materials for each major region of the early embryo have become differentiated (Fig. 11-17).

The dorsal lip of the blastopore proves to be a region of strong influence in determining subsequent embryonic growth. If at the beginning of gastrulation a piece of presumptive epidermis is planted in the dorsal lip, it will be carried in and contribute to the production of muscle segments, gut wall, or other organs, depending upon where it arrives; in any case, it contributes to either mesoderm or endoderm derivatives and not to ectoderm. Pieces of presumptive mesoderm transplanted into the ectoderm of a

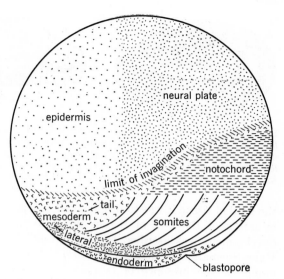

Fig. 11-17. Localization of formative areas on the egg of a salamander (*Taricha* or *Triturus*) at the start of gastrulation. Epidermis and neural plate will derive from ectoderm, lateral plate, somites, and notochord from mesoderm. (*Modified from Vogt.*)

gastrula will become epidermis (ectoderm). Later, however, if part of the dorsal lip is transplanted to the ectoderm, it will induce the formation there of a secondary embryo on the host embryo. The notochord and other dorsal-lip derivatives come from the transplant, but the nervous tissue arises from the local host ectoderm that otherwise would have become epidermis (Fig. 11-18).

Further evidence of time sequence in organization has been obtained by exchanging transplants of presumptive epidermis and neural plate (both ectodermal) between embryos of two salamanders that have eggs of different color. Dark presumptive epidermis from *Taricha taeniata* transplanted to the neural-plate region of the light-colored *T. cristata* became neural plate if moved during the early gastrula stage but continued as dark epidermis, even in the brain, if transplanted in the late gastrula. The reverse transplant produced opposite results. In the early transplant the region determined the nature of the subsequent differentiation, whereas in the later one the material that was transplanted was already "determined" as to

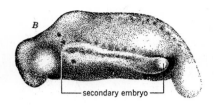

secondary embryo

Fig. 11-18. Effect of an organizer. *A.* Neural fold stage of a newt (*Taricha taeniata*); visible part in white is secondary neural plate induced by implanted organizer from another species (*T. cristata*). *B.* Side of an early embryo (*T. taeniata*) with secondary embryo showing ear vesicles, nerve tube, 2 rows of somites, and tail bud. (*After Spemann and Mangold, 1924.*)

the kind of tissue it was to produce. Such determination of the fate of tissues in embryonic development was ascribed to "organizers" by Hans Spemann (German, 1869–1941). An example of the presence of organizers in later stages is to be seen in the development of the lens for an eye only in the presence of an optic vesicle. If the vesicle is removed, no lens develops; and if the vesicle is transplanted from the head to elsewhere in the body, a lens may develop wherever an optic vesicle touches ectoderm.

REFERENCES

BARTH, L. G. 1949. Embryology. New York, The Dryden Press, Inc. xii + 330 pp., 194 figs. Emphasis on processes and controlling factors, many diagrams.

BRACHET, JEAN. 1950. Chemical embryology. New York, Interscience Publishers, Inc. xiii + 533 pp., 123 figs.

DAWYDOFF, C. 1928. Traité d'embryologie comparée des invertébrés. Paris, Masson et Cie. xiv + 930 pp., 509 figs.

FLEXNER, L. B. 1955. Gestation. New York, Josiah Macy, Jr., Foundation. 238 pp., 97 figs. Structure and function of mammalian placenta.

HAMILTON, W. J., J. D. BOYD, and H. W. MOSSMAN. 1952. Human embryology. 2d ed. Baltimore, The Williams & Wilkins Co. viii + 432 pp., 433 figs. Includes excellent chapter on comparative vertebrate development.

HUETTNER, A. F. 1949. Comparative embryology of the vertebrates. Rev. ed. New York, The Macmillan Co. xviii + 309 pp., 197 figs.

HUXLEY, J. S., and G. R. DE BEER. 1934. The elements of experimental embryology. London, Cambridge University Press. xiii + 514 pp., 212 figs.

KORSCHELDT, E., and K. HEIDER. 1936. Vergleichende Entwicklungsgeschichte der Tiere. New ed. 2 vols. Jena, Germany, Gustav Fischer Verlagsbuchhandlung. xx + 1,314 pp., 1,312 figs. General embryology.

LILLIE, F. R. 1952. The development of the chick. 3d ed. Rev. by H. L. Hamilton. New York, Henry Holt & Co., Inc. xi + 624 pp., illus. The American classic.

MACBRIDE, E. W. 1914. Text-book of embryology. Vol. I. Invertebrata. London, Macmillan & Co., Ltd. xxxii + 692 pp., 468 figs. Sponges to tunicates.

NEEDHAM, JOSEPH. 1934. A history of embryology. London, Cambridge University Press. xviii + 274 pp., illus. Scholarly review of ideas regarding development up to 1814.

NELSEN, O. E. 1953. Comparative embryology of the vertebrates. Philadelphia, The Blakiston Co. xxiii + 982 pp., 380 figs.

PARKES, A. S. (editor). 1952. Marshall's Physiology of reproduction. 3d ed. 2 vols. London, Longmans, Green & Co., Ltd.

PATTEN, B. M. 1931. The embryology of the pig. 2d ed. Philadelphia, The Blakiston Co. ix + 327 pp., frontispiece, 168 figs. Only complete account of a mammal other than man.

———. 1951. The early embryology of the chick. 4th ed. Philadelphia, The Blakiston Co. xiii + 244 pp., 102 figs., some colored.

RUGH, ROBERTS. 1951. The frog: its reproduction and development. Philadelphia, The Blakiston Co. x + 336 pp., illus.

SPEMANN, HANS. 1938. Embryonic development and induction. New Haven, Conn., Yale University Press. xii + 401 pp., 192 figs. Experiments on amphibian embryos.

WILLIER, B. H., P. A. WEISS, and VIKTOR HAMBURGER (editors). 1955. Analysis of development. Philadelphia, W. B. Saunders Co. xii + 735 pp., 248 figs. Factors and processes affecting embryonic growth and differentiation.

12 HEREDITY AND GENETICS

"Like tends to beget like," in animals and plants—the young of dogs are always puppies and those of cats always kittens, never puppies. Yet offspring usually differ among themselves and from their parents in varying degree. Two purebred collies will produce pups that grow to resemble their parents closely, whereas the chance mating of two mongrel dogs often yields a litter of varied types. The ancient Greeks knew that blue-eyed parents have blue-eyed children, that baldness and squint eyes follow in successive generations, and that certain eye defects run in particular families. This passage of characters from one generation to another is called *inheritance* or *heredity.*

Heredity is resemblance based upon descent, the occurrence in living organisms of qualities, either expressed or hidden, that are derived from their ancestors. It involves physical and physiological characteristics, instincts, and even psychological features in higher animals and man. Differences among individuals of a species are called *variations.* These are of two types: *somatic* or *environmental variations* due to food, temperature, or other external factors; and *hereditary* or *germinal variations* that appear in certain offspring without reference to the environment. The science of *genetics* seeks to account for the resemblances and differences due to heredity, their source, and their development.

Genetics aids agriculture by improving the form, yield, resistance to disease, and other features of domesticated animals and cultivated plants. Some knowledge of human heredity has been obtained, parts of which have practical application. Genetics has helped the study of evolution, of embryology, and of other sciences. It has a cultural value in dispelling many faulty beliefs regarding inheritance.

Little of value was learned about heredity until the eighteenth century, when knowledge developed about sexuality in plants and plant hybridization. Kölreuter (German, 1733–1806) and others produced various fertile hybrids by artificial pollination and described the characters of both parent and hybrid plants. But they had no clear understanding of the hereditary process.

12-1. Mendel. The person who first made decisive experiments in heredity and who formulated the basic laws of genetics was Gregor Johann Mendel (1822–1884), a monk in the Augustinian monastery at Brünn, Austria (Fig. 1-10). He recognized heredity as of major importance for understanding organic evolution. He saw clearly that all earlier hybridizers had failed to discover any general laws of inheritance because they had neither traced individual characters through successive generations nor kept complete numerical records of their results. Mendel therefore planned careful experiments to overcome these difficulties. He chose the

157

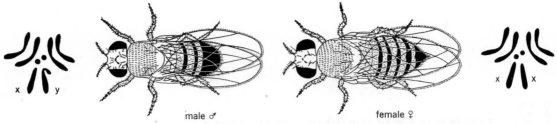

Fig. 12-1. The fruit fly, *Drosophila melanogaster*, used for studies in genetics. Much enlarged. Diploid sets of chromosomes shown, with sex chromosomes marked (XY, XX). Male fly smaller with abdomen marked by three black bands, the last extending beneath the rounded posterior end. Female larger, abdomen swollen but pointed, with five black bands not joined ventrally.

garden pea (*Pisum*) for study and spent two years in selecting races with distinctive and contrasted characters and in making certain that each original stock was pure. During the next six years he made many crosses, by artificial pollination, and carried each through three or more generations. Mendel kept count of all plants and seeds of each kind produced, analyzed the results, and from them deduced the two most important fundamental laws of heredity. His report (44 pages) of 1866 in an obscure periodical was brought to world-wide attention only in 1900 by three other investigators who independently had then reached similar conclusions.

Discovery of Mendel's findings gave great impetus to the study of heredity, and an enormous amount of careful work has since been done by many geneticists working with various plants and animals. Of especial value has been use of the fruit fly, or pomace fly, *Drosophila melanogaster*, by W. E. Castle, T. H. Morgan, and others. This small insect (Fig. 12-1) is reared easily in bottles provided with food, or "culture medium," for the larvae; a pair will produce 200 or more offspring, with successive generations every 10 to 14 days. Such abundant material made it possible to investigate problems requiring many individuals and generations and to apply mathematical analysis to the results.

12-2. Monohybrid cross. This is a cross in which the parents differ in one pair of alternative characters. When a true-breeding black guinea pig and a white individual are mated (Fig. 12-2), all the (hybrid) individuals of the next (F_1)[1] generation are black, no matter which parent is black and which is white. These black hybrids, when crossed among themselves, yield in the following (F_2) generation a population of which, *on the average*, three-fourths are black, like the black grandparent, and one-fourth are white, like the white grandparent. The character of white coat disappears in the F_1 and reappears unchanged in the F_2. If the F_2 white animals are then crossed among themselves, only white individuals result (F_3), whereas among the black F_2 animals some ($\frac{1}{3}$) produce only blacks and the others ($\frac{2}{3}$) produce both blacks and whites, as in the F_2 generation. Thus, as Mendel said, when two contrasting characters are brought together in a cross, one is **dominant** (expressed or evident) in the next (F_1) generation, and the other is **recessive** (latent, or recedes from view). In the following (F_2) generation these two characters are **segregated,** in an average 3 to 1 ratio. We may, therefore, state in modern terms **Mendel's first law:** *The factors for a pair of characters are segregated.* The factors responsible for a pair of alternative or contrasted characters, such as Mendel studied, are now termed **alleles** (allelomorphs).

Some examples of simple (monohybrid) characteristics in domestic animals are as follows (recessives in parentheses):

CATS: tabby (black or blue); short hair (long hair or Angora).

CATTLE: black or Angus (red); polled or hornless (horned); white face (colored face).

DOGS: gray (black); stumpy tail (normal tail).

HORSES: black (chestnut); trotting (pacing).

[1] The parental generation is designated as P, the first generation of offspring as the F_1 (first filial), the second as the F_2, and so on.

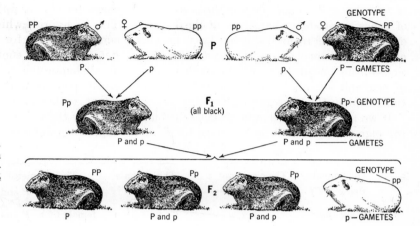

Fig. 12-2. Monohybrid cross. Inheritance of coat color in guinea pigs when pure-breeding black and white parents are mated.

SHEEP: white fleece (black fleece).
SWINE: black (red); belted (solid color); uncleft hoof (normal hoof).

12-3. Mechanism of heredity. Mendel was the first to differentiate between the actual visible character and that "something" which caused its production. Obviously the character cannot be present in the germ cells that join in fertilization to produce a new individual, but something representing it and responsible for its production is there. This is now called the *gene* or *factor* for the character. A gene is the unit of inheritance that is transmitted in a gamete and controls the development of a character, by interaction with the other genes, the cytoplasm, and the environment.

Since the gametes are the only materials that pass onward from parents to form new individuals of the next generation, the mechanism of heredity must be sought in them. It will be recalled (Chap. 11) that (1) in meiosis each cell destined to become a gamete receives, by random sorting, either one or the other member of each pair of homologous chromosomes; (2) at fertilization there is a random meeting of an egg and a sperm; (3) the chromosomes of the egg nucleus and sperm nucleus join as a zygote; and (4) during embryonic growth and later, each cell in the new individual receives by mitosis an equal and like number of chromosomes

derived from the zygote. As inheritance in sexual reproduction involves the transmission of characteristics from both parents, the chromosomes are considered to be the means by which this occurs. Certain experiments have shown that (1) an egg deprived of its nucleus and then "fertilized" by a sperm produces an individual with only paternal characteristics; (2) mature eggs caused to develop by artificial parthenogenesis result in animals with only maternal characteristics; and (3) some cytoplasm may be removed from certain eggs, and yet if the egg nucleus is fertilized by a sperm the resulting individual contains characteristics of both parents. Thus hereditary transmission of characteristics is dependent upon the nucleus rather than the cytoplasm.

The modern *chromosome theory of heredity* assumes that genes are ultramicroscopic units contained in the chromosomes. Their physical and chemical nature is largely unknown. In the giant salivary gland chromosomes of *Drosophila* (Fig. 12-10), many crossbands can be seen, which possibly are the location (loci) of the genes. Some indirect evidence on the presence and arrangement of genes in chromosomes is discussed later (par. 12-16).

12-4. Explanation of the Mendelian ratio. Hybrid individuals result from combining two gametes of different heredity, and a process of segregation must take place in the germ cells of such hybrids to account for the sorting out of genes to produce characters in the F_2 generation. Mendel realized this but knew nothing of the actual mechanism. The reduction divisions during maturation, and the random union of egg and sperm, both discovered since his time, explain this segregation.

If we represent the dominant gene for black (or pigmented) coat in guinea pigs by P and

Individual animals such as the parents that are "pure," containing like genes for any one character (PP or pp), are termed **homozygous.** The F_1 hybrid, which appears black and yet contains a gene for white (Pp), is said to be **heterozygous;** it contains two kinds of genes of an allelomorphic pair. The entire genetic constitution of an individual, both expressed and latent, makes up its **genotype;** and its appearance, or the assemblage of characters that are expressed or evident, constitutes its **phenotype.**

Parents		F_1		F_2
The animals	Their gametes	The animals	Their gametes	The animals
Black (PP)	P		male ($\male$) P and p	1 Black (PP)
		Black Pp		2 Black (Pp)
white (pp)	p		female ($\female$) P and p	1 white (pp)

the recessive gene for white by p, then the genetic formulas for the parents (which contain the diploid number of chromosomes) are PP and pp and for their respective (haploid) gametes are P and p. When the gametes of the parents join in fertilization, all the resulting offspring of the F_1 generation will be Pp and black. When the F_1 forms gametes, each sex will produce both P and p gametes. The possible combinations for the F_2 will be PP (black), Pp and pP (black), and pp (white), giving an average ratio of 3 blacks to 1 white individual.[1] The events in this cross may be outlined as shown above.

Both the parents and two of the F_2 (PP and pp) are homozygous, but the F_1 hybrid and two of the F_2 (Pp) are heterozygous; the F_1 hybrid is a black phenotype, and its genotype is Pp. In the F_2, the whites are homozygous recessives; of the blacks, $\frac{1}{3}$ are homozygous dominants yielding only blacks, and $\frac{2}{3}$ are heterozygous. The analysis may be restated as shown below with phenotypes, genotypes, and gametes bracketed for the parental, first filial, and second filial generations respectively.

Many other characters have been found to follow Mendel's first law.

P			F_1			F_2	
phenotypes	genotypes	gametes	phenotype	genotype	gametes	phenotypes	genotypes
Black	PP	P			$\male$ P and p	3 Black	1 PP
			Black	Pp			2 Pp
white	pp	p			$\female$ P and p	1 white	1 pp

---

[1] Random sorting of chromosomes and meeting of eggs and sperm are matters of chance (par. 12-3), and the numbers of individuals with contrasting characteristics actually obtained in any cross rarely correspond exactly to the theoretical ratio expected. Thus, in one monohybrid mating Mendel obtained 7,324 pea seeds— 5,474 round (dominant) and 1,850 wrinkled (recessive), a ratio of 2.96 to 1 rather than the expected 3 to 1. In another experiment (8,023 seeds) the ratio was 3.01 to 1. The differences between actual results and theoretical ratio in any given case are explainable by a **law of probability** which deals with the chance that any one

event will happen rather than its alternative. This may be illustrated by tossing a coin. In any single toss the chances are even (50:50) that either heads or tails will come up. Sometimes heads will come 2, 3, or more times in sequence, but the chances of this decrease with each successive toss. Eventually, with many trials, tails will appear as frequently as heads, realizing the expected ratio. Inheritance of sex in man (par. 12-13) follows a 50:50 ratio in the main, like the coin, yet occasional large families have all sons or all daughters! According to the laws of probability such cases may be expected but are rare.

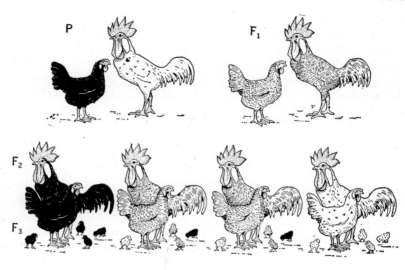

Fig. 12-3. Incomplete dominance of a Mendelian character in the Andalusian fowl. The "blue" fowls are lightly stippled. (*Modified from Hesse-Doflein.*)

	P			F₁			F₂	
phenotypes	genotypes	gametes	phenotype	genotype	gametes		phenotypes	genotypes
Black	*BB*	*B*			♂ *B* and *b*		1 Black	*BB*
			Blue	*Bb*	↓⤬↓		2 Blue	*Bb*
splashed					♀ *B* and *b*		1 splashed	
white	*bb*	*b*					white	*bb*

12-5. Incomplete dominance.

With some characters the F₁ hybrid is intermediate between the parents. Such incomplete dominance occurs in the Andalusian fowl, where the mating of a black and a splashed-white produces "blue" offspring in the F₁, and the F₂ results are in the ratio: 1 black, 2 blue, 1 splashed white (Fig. 12-3). The homozygous dominant is black, the heterozygous individuals are blue, and the homozygous recessive is splashed white, as outlined beneath Fig. 12-3. Mendel's first law obviously applies here as well as in cases of complete dominance, but the heterozygous individuals, being blue, are easily recognized.

12-6. Backcross.

Offspring that show the dominant character in a cross are alike phenotypically but may be either heterozygous or homozygous for that character. To determine their genotype the *test cross* or *backcross* is used, mating the dominant hybrid with a pure recessive individual. If, with guinea pigs, the black individual under test is homozygous (*PP*), all the offspring from a backcross with the recessive (*pp*) will be black (*Pp*); if, however, it is heterozygous (*Pp*), the offspring will be about equally black (*Pp*) and white (*pp*). Thus:

Backcross		
phenotypes	genotypes	gametes
Black	·*Pp*	*P* and *p*
		↓⤬↓
white	*pp*	*p* and *p*

Offspring	
phenotypes	genotypes
2 Black	*Pp*
2 white	*pp*

In practical genetics the backcross is used as a rapid means for "purifying" (rendering homozygous) desirable stocks.

12-7. Dihybrid cross.

When parents differ in two pairs of characters, the F₁ offspring are termed *dihybrids;* in such crosses Mendel found that each pair of characters is inherited independently of the other. This may be illustrated

(Fig. 12-4) in the case of the guinea pig where black or pigmented coat (P) is dominant to white (p) and rough or rosetted coat (R) is dominant to smooth (r). The mating of a black rough animal to a smooth white one may thus be outlined:

P

phenotypes	genotypes	gametes
Black, Rough	$PPRR$	PR
white, smooth	$pprr$	pr

F$_1$

phenotype	genotype	gametes
		PR Pr
Black, Rough	$PpRr$	
		pR pr

Four kinds of gametes are formed by each sex, and the Punnett checkerboard will show the 16 matings possible to produce the F$_2$ generation.

dihybrid cross. There are $9 + 3 = 12$ black to $3 + 1 = 4$ white offspring, and $9 + 3 = 12$ rough to $3 + 1 = 4$ smooth individuals. The ratio of 3 dominant to 1 recessive in each case follows Mendel's first law, as in a monohybrid cross. This shows the independence of each pair of characters, which is **Mendel's second law:** *When races differ from each other in two (or more) pairs of factors, the inheritance of one pair of factors is independent of that of the other(s).*

The four phenotypes involve nine different genotypes as shown in the analysis of the F$_2$ population; $PPRR$, $PPrr$, $ppRR$, and $pprr$ are homozygous, and the other five are heterozygous. The appearance of new phenotypes and genotypes in dihybrid (and multihybrid) crosses is a practical means to obtain strains of animals or plants with combinations of characters different from those of the parents. In this cross, there are two new types of homozygous indi-

Possible matings for the F$_2$ generation					Analysis of the F$_2$ generation			
	Male gametes				Phenotypes			
	PR	Pr	pR	pr	9 Black Rough	3 Black smooth	3 white Rough	1 white smooth
PR	$PPRR$ Black Rough	$PPRr$ Black Rough	$PpRR$ Black Rough	$PpRr$ Black Rough	Genotypes			
Pr	$PPRr$ Black Rough	$PPrr$ Black smooth	$PpRr$ Black Rough	$Pprr$ Black smooth	1-$PPRR$ 2-$PPRr$ 2-$PpRR$ 4-$PpRr$	1-$PPrr$ 2-$Pprr$	1-$ppRR$ 2-$ppRr$	1-$pprr$
pR	$PpRR$ Black Rough	$PpRr$ Black Rough	$ppRR$ white Rough	$ppRr$ white Rough				
pr	$PpRr$ Black Rough	$Pprr$ Black smooth	$ppRr$ white Rough	$pprr$ white smooth				

(Leftmost label, vertical: Female gametes)

The F$_2$ phenotypes include 9 black rough (any with PR genes) like the dominant parent and 1 white smooth (pr) like the recessive parent. Two new combinations have appeared, of which there are 3 black smooth (Pr) and 3 white rough (pR). The 9:3:3:1 ratio is characteristic of a

viduals—black smooth $(PPrr)$ and pure white rough $(ppRR)$.

12-8. Multihybrids. In a *trihybrid cross* each gamete carries 3 genes; 8 kinds of F$_1$ gametes are possible in each sex, giving 64 combinations

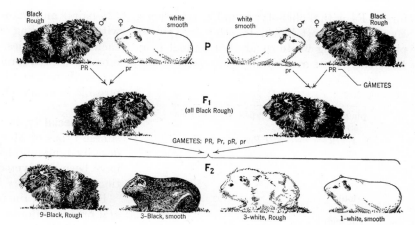

Fig. 12-4. Dihybrid cross, with guinea pigs differing in two independent pairs of Mendelian characters of the hair—color and arrangement.

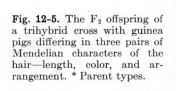

9–Black, Rough 3–Black, smooth 3–white, Rough 1–white, smooth

Fig. 12-5. The F₂ offspring of a trihybrid cross with guinea pigs differing in three pairs of Mendelian characters of the hair—length, color, and arrangement. * Parent types.

27–Short, Black, Rough 9–Short, white, Rough 9–Short, Black, smooth 3–Short, white, smooth

9–long, Black, Rough. 3–long, white, Rough 3–long, Black, smooth 1–long, white, smooth

Analysis of the F₂ Generation of a Trihybrid Cross

Phenotypes							
27 Short Black Rough	9 Short Black smooth	9 Short white Rough	9 long Black Rough	3 Short white smooth	3 long Black smooth	3 long white Rough	1 long white smooth
Genotypes							
1-SSPPRR 2-SSPPRr 2-SSPpRR 2-SsPPRR 4-SSPpRr 4-SsPPRr 4-SsPpRR 8-SsPpRr	1-SSPPrr 2-SSPprr 2-SsPPrr 4-SsPprr	1-SSppRR 2-SSppRr 2-SsppRR 4-SsppRr	1-ssPPRR 2-ssPPRr 2-ssPpRR 4-ssPpRr	1-SSpprr 2-Sspprr	1-ssPPrr 2-ssPprr	1-ssppRR 2-ssppRr	1-sspprr

for the F_2, with 8 phenotypes and 27 genotypes. By crossing a short, black, smooth-haired guinea pig with a long white rough-coat animal (Fig. 12-5) the results are as follows:

P		
phenotypes	genotypes	gametes
Short Black smooth	*SSPPrr*	*SPr*
long white Rough	*sspPRR*	*spR*

F_1		
phenotype	genotype	gametes
		SPR *SPr*
		SpR *Spr*
Short Black Rough	*SsPpRr*	
		sPR *sPr*
		spR *spr*

Increasing the numbers of independent factor pairs greatly enlarges the chance for new combinations, thus:

Pairs of factors, n; kinds of F_1 gametes by each sex, 2^n; possible combinations for F_2 zygotes, 4^n; kinds of phenotypes in F_2, 2^n; different genotypes in F_2, 3^n.

The great variability seen in human beings may be due to the large number of chromosomes (24 pairs) and many genes involved, together with intermingling of races through time. Since each gamete carries structurally different chromosomes, each probably with one to many genes, there are millions of F_2 combinations possible in mankind.

12-9. Special types of inheritance. Besides the simple types of Mendelian inheritance already described, many others of more complex nature have been discovered that involve the interaction of two or more factors.

For example, the form of comb differs in several breeds of domestic fowls, but each remains true within its breed (Fig. 12-6). The Wyandotte has a low regular **rose** comb with papillae, the Brahma a narrow, higher three-ridged **pea** comb, and the Leghorn and others an upright blade, or **single** comb. When fowls with rose (or pea) and single comb are crossed, the former is dominant, and the F_2 averages 3 rose (or pea) to 1 single. If rose is crossed with pea, however, the F_1 hybrid bears a walnut comb (resembling half a walnut meat) and the F_2 gives 9 walnut, 3 rose, 3 pea, and 1 single. The results differ from ordinary dihybrids because the F_1 resembles neither parent, and two other types appear in the F_2. This is a case of **interaction of supplementary factors** in a cross involving two pairs of factors that affect one structure, the comb. If the dominant gene for rose is represented by R and its allele by r and those for pea by P and p, respectively, the results may be explained thus:

P		F_1		F_2			
genotypes and phenotypes	gametes	genotype and phenotype	gametes → ↓	*RP*	*Rp*	*rP*	*rp*
			RP	*RRPP* walnut	*RRPp* walnut	*RrPP* walnut	*RrPp* walnut
RRpp rose	*Rp*		*Rp*	*RRPp* walnut	*RRpp* rose	*RrPp* walnut	*Rrpp* rose
		RrPp Walnut	*rP*	*RrPP* walnut	*RrPp* walnut	*rrPP* pea	*rrPp* pea
rrPP pea	*rP*		*rp*	*RrPp* walnut	*Rrpp* rose	*rrPp* pea	*rrpp* single

Fig. 12-6. Comb characters of male fowls. (*Adapted from Punnett, Mendelism, The Macmillan Co.*)

pea   rose   walnut   single

Single comb is thus a double recessive (*rrpp*), rose comb contains either one or two *R* genes but only recessive *p* genes, pea comb has either one or two *P* genes but only recessive *r* genes, and walnut appears whenever at least one each of *R* and *P* are present.

Another modified two-factor ratio occurs in the color of Duroc-Jersey swine, where both factors are necessary for full color (red), either one alone yields partial color (sandy), and the absence of both yields colorless (white) animals.

12-10. Cumulative factors. In some cases either of two independent genes may alone produce a character but, when acting together, cause it to be accentuated; such *cumulative genes* are quantitative in expression. The pigmentation of Negro skin is an example, according to Davenport. A pure-blooded Negro has two pairs of genes for black (melanin) pigmentation, *BB* and *B'B'*, whereas a pure-blooded white carries the paired *bb* and *b'b'* for nonblack. Mating of such individuals results in mulatto offspring (F₁) with skin of intermediate color; two of the latter in turn will have children of different skin colors. Thus:

one full-colored Negro (4 *B* or *B'* genes), four dark mulattoes (3), six half-color mulattoes (2), four pale mulattoes (1), and one white-skinned (no dominant genes). The last might have other Negro characteristics, however, since racial features assort independently. Marriages between pure-blooded whites and mulattoes yield white and mulatto offspring in various proportions, depending on the genotype of the mulatto parent.

12-11. Lethal factors. Various species of plants and animals carry *lethal factors* which, when homozygous, stop development at some stage, and the individual dies. Their presence is usually detected by an abnormal ratio in the offspring. A conspicuous case is that of the yellow race of the house mouse, *Mus musculus*, which never breeds true. If a yellow mouse is mated to some nonyellow, half the young are yellow and half are nonyellow, a ratio to be expected from mating a heterozygous animal (yellow) with a homozygous recessive (any nonyellow such as agouti). If two yellows are mated together, the young average 2 yellow to 1 nonyellow, whereas the expected ratio among the

P		F₁		F₂			
genotypes and phenotypes	gametes	genotype and phenotype	gametes →	*BB'*	*Bb'*	*bB'*	*bb'*
			↓ *BB'*	4	3	3	2
bbb'b' white	*bb'*		*Bb'*	3	2	2	1
		BbB'b' Mulatto	*bB'*	3	2	2	1
BBB'B' Negro	*BB'*		*bb'*	2	1	1	0

The figures in the checkerboard indicate the number of genes for black color in each individual; the offspring average, as to skin color,

young would be 1 pure yellow to 2 heterozygous yellow to 1 nonyellow, but the "homozygous yellow" dies as an embryo. The "creeper fowl" with short, crooked legs behaves genetically like the yellow mouse. Other lethals are known in *Drosophila*, cattle, sheep, hogs, and horses; and some human defects are thought to be due to such factors.

12-12. Multiple alleles. All the examples discussed previously involve pairs of alternative factors. In many other cases more than two alternative factors affect the same character; these are called *multiple alleles.* Thus, in the domestic rabbit, among various color forms, there are the normal "wild" type, the complete albino with solidly white coat and pink eyes, and the "Himalayan" albino with pink eyes and a white coat except for black or dark brown on the ears, nose, and feet. The albino is a simple recessive to the wild type, and the Himalayan albino is likewise recessive to the wild type. When Himalayan and pure albino are crossed, however, all the F_1 offspring are Himalayan, and the F_2 yields 3 Himalayan to 1 pure albino; there is no reversion to the wild type. Obviously, Himalayan and albino are alleles of one another, and both are alleles of the wild color. Other instances of multiple alleles are known for coat color in mice, guinea pigs, and rats. In *Drosophila* at least 14 alleles for eye color have been found, from white and ivory through buff and apricot to the wild-type red. Several series are known in plants, especially snapdragons and maize. No more than two alleles of a series can occur in any particular individual.

Still more complex types of inheritance include modifying factors, multiple effects of a single gene, and those in which either the external environment or conditions within the animal change the manner in which a gene

mals are all sterile; the anterior lobe of the pituitary gland and the cortex of the adrenal are deficient. Continued implantation of anterior pituitary in such young causes resumption of growth, the animals may reach normal size, and males may become fertile. Thus hormones may exercise an influence on the manner in which genes act in the formation of characters.

12-13. Sex and heredity. No factor mentioned previously has any relation to sex; either the male or the female may carry one factor and the other parent its alternative. The situation is different for some other characters, including that of sex itself. Somatic and early germ cells in male animals contain a pair of homologous chromosomes in which one member is smaller than the other, and sometimes of different shape. These are the *sex chromosomes,* the larger being the *X chromosome* and the other the *Y chromosome;* in some species the latter is lacking. A pair of X chromosomes is present in females. Thus a male may be designated as XY (or XO) and a female as XX. All other pairs of strictly homologous chromosomes are termed *autosomes.*

Human cells, except gametes, contain 48 chromosomes—the 2 sex chromosomes, and 23 pairs of homologous autosomes (Fig. 3-9). During maturation the sex chromosomes segregate freely, like other chromosomes, so that an ovum contains 23 autosomes and an X chromosome, and a sperm has 23 autosomes and either an X or a Y chromosome.

If A is used to represent one haploid set of autosomes, then the genetics of sex in human beings can be diagramed as follows:

Any Parent Generation			Offspring	
sex	genotypes	gametes	genotypes	sex
male	$2A + XY$	$A + X$ / $A + Y$	$2A + XX$	female
female	$2A + XX$	$A + X$	$2A + XY$	male

regulates the development of a character. An instance of the last kind occurs with dwarfism in the house mouse, where a recessive gene halts growth at about two weeks of age and the ani-

Thus sex is evidently determined by the kind of sperm that fertilizes an egg. As approximately equal numbers of the two sexes appear in the offspring of most animals, it is reasonable to

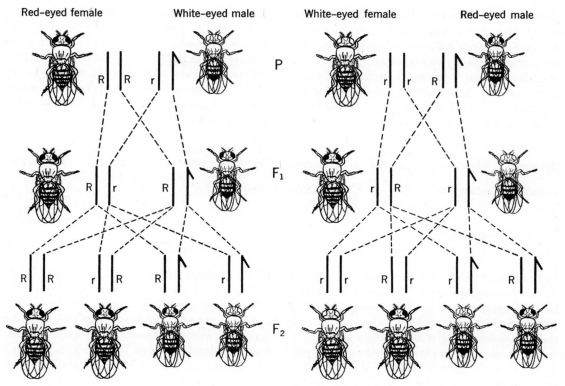

Red-eyed female   White-eyed male   White-eyed female   Red-eyed male

P

F₁

F₂

Fig. 12-7. Sex determination and sex-linked inheritance of eye color in *Drosophila*. The sex chromosomes are represented by vertical bars with symbols (*R, r*) for genes of eye color.

assume that X sperm and Y sperm are formed in equal numbers and that either kind has an equal chance of fertilizing an egg. The results are the same in species (many insects) that lack the Y chromosome, save that the female has an even number of chromosomes and the male one less. Among birds and moths the situation is reversed from that in other animals, there being two kinds of eggs and one of sperm; males are therefore XX (sometimes designated as ZZ), and females are XY (or ZW). The Y chromosome evidently carries no genes for sex or other characters; yet, in species where it normally occurs, males without a Y chromosome are sterile.

Prior to the discovery of sex chromosomes, many ingenious theories had been proposed to explain sex. Various schemes have been tried to control the sex of offspring, especially in domesticated animals and mankind, but none

is effective. In frogs and some invertebrates alteration of environmental conditions affects the sex ratio, which is the proportion of males to females among offspring (par. 11-15).

Some abnormalities of sex are known; occasional fruit flies, bees, and other insects are *gynandromorphs,* with one part of the body showing male and the other female characteristics. Intersexes have been seen in gypsy moths reared experimentally and also in pigs. In rare cases *sex reversal* has been seen among vertebrates, especially poultry, when an individual originally female has become a male.

12-14. Sex-linked inheritance. The X (or Z) chromosome has been found to carry genes for *sex-linked* characters, the inheritance of which is therefore related to sex determination. In the fruit fly, *Drosophila*, where eye color is sex-linked (Fig. 12-7), the normal red eye color is dominant to white eye. If a homozygous red-eyed female and a white-eyed male are mated, all the F_1 flies are red-eyed; when the latter are intercrossed, the F_2 yields an average of 2 red-eyed females to 1 red-eyed male to 1 white-eyed male. If X_R represents the gene for red eye and X_r that for white eye, the results of this cross may be diagramed thus:

About 150 sex-linked genes have been found in *Drosophila* (Fig. 12-9, chromosome I), and many sex-linked characters are known in other animals and in man; barred plumage in poultry and red-green color blindness in mankind (par. 12-25) are common examples. The latter occurs in about 8 per cent of men and only about 0.5 per cent of women.

P			F$_1$			F$_2$	
genotypes	phenotypes	gametes	genotypes	phenotypes	gametes	genotypes	phenotypes
$X_R X_R$	red-eyed ♀	X_R ⟶ $X_R X_r$	red-eyed ♀	X_R ⟶ $X_R X_R$	red-eyed ♀
		X_R			X_r ⟶ $X_R X_r$	red-eyed ♀
		X_r			X_R ⟶ $X_R Y$	red-eyed ♂
$X_r Y$	white-eyed ♂	Y ⟶ $X_R Y$	red-eyed ♂	Y ⟶ $X_r Y$	white-eyed ♂

In the P generation each matured ovum carries an X chromosome with the gene for red eye, half the sperm carry an X chromosome with a gene for white eye, and the other sperm contain a Y chromosome with no gene for eye color. In the F_1 generation two kinds of eggs are produced, with the gene for either red eye or white eye, and of the sperm half have a gene (on the X chromosome) for red eye and half have no gene for eye color (Y chromosome). Four kinds of zygotes are thus possible. In the F_2, half the females are homozygous for red eye and half are heterozygous, and the males are equally red- and white-eyed.

A somewhat different result is obtained in the opposite or *reciprocal cross* with a homozygous white-eyed female and a red-eyed male. In the F_1 the males are white-eyed, and the females red-eyed. In the F_2 there result approximately equal numbers of red-eyed females, white-eyed females, red-eyed males, and white-eyed males. Thus:

12-15. Linkage. Independent assortment (Mendel's second law) was evident in the examples discussed earlier in this chapter, and in the preceding paragraphs some types of sex-linked inheritance were described. Many other characters of animals tend to be inherited together. The number of pairs of Mendelian factors present in any animal far exceeds the number of chromosome pairs, and so each chromosome must carry several or many genes. Characters that tend to be inherited together are said to be *linked*. Studies of linkage relations in various animals and plants show that the genes occur in *linkage groups,* the members of each group being linked to one another in varying degree, while a pair in one linkage group assorts or combines independently with pairs in other linkage groups. When the linkage relations of many genes in a species are known, it is found that there are as many groups of linked genes as chromosome pairs. About 500 linked genes are known in *Drosophila melanogaster;* there are

P			F$_1$			F$_2$	
genotypes	phenotypes	gametes	genotypes	phenotypes	gametes	genotypes	phenotypes
$X_r X_r$	white-eyed ♀	X_r ⟶ $X_R X_r$	red-eyed ♀	X_R ⟶ $X_R X_r$	red-eyed ♀
		X_r			X_r ⟶ $X_r X_r$	white-eyed ♀
		X_R			X_r ⟶ $X_R Y$	red-eyed ♂
$X_R Y$	red-eyed ♂	Y ⟶ $X_r Y$	white-eyed ♂	Y ⟶ $X_r Y$	white-eyed ♂

Fig. 12-8. Diagrams of crossing over, the exchange of genes between homologous chromosomes. *A, a; B, b; C, c,* represent pairs of allelomorphic genes in homologous chromosomes that pair during synapsis.

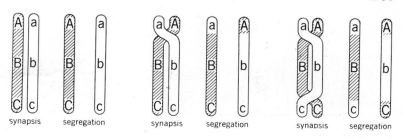

4 linkage groups (3 large, 1 small), and there are 4 pairs of chromosomes (3 long, 1 short). *D. willistoni* has 3 linkage groups and 3 chromosome pairs, and *D. virilis* has 6 of each. Among plants, maize has 10 of each, and the garden pea has 7 of each. This evidence is highly important in showing that the genes are contained in the chromosomes.

12-16. Crossing over. If the genes for two characters are in one chromosome and the latter remains intact through inheritance, their linkage will be complete, and the two characters will occur together; but such is not always the case (Fig. 12-8). The characters separate in a certain number of cases, the percentage of separations varying between different characters, although it is usually constant as between any two. Thus short ear and dilute coat color in mice are linked in over 99 per cent of individuals, but the percentage is variously lower with many other characteristics. Characters (genes) originally together that become separated are known as *crossovers*. During maturation the two chromosomes of a homologous pair are close together or intertwined at synapsis; ordinarily they separate as they come together, but at times they exchange homologous parts with one another, and this is the physical basis of crossing over.

If the genes in a chromosome are in linear arrangement, then two that are far apart will

Fig. 12-9. Chromosome maps for *Drosophila*. One chromosome of each pair is diagramed with the relative positions for some of the many genes "mapped" by linkage studies. Numbers indicate relative distance of each from "left" end of chromosome. Inset shows chromosomes of gonads.

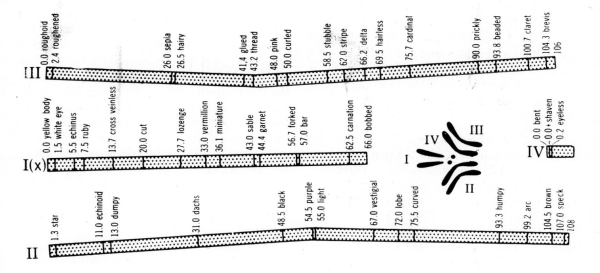

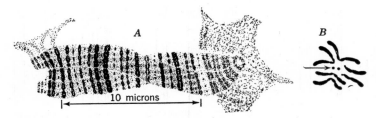

Fig. 12-10. *A*. One pair of giant chromosomes from salivary glands of *Drosophila*. Dark crossbands may be the location (loci) of genes. *B*. Chromosomes in gonads of *Drosophila* to the same scale. Arrow points to comparable (IVth) chromosomes shown in *A*. (*After Bridges, American Genetics Association.*)

have their linkage transposed by an exchange at any point between them, whereas if they are close together the chance of crossing over is much less. Assuming that the frequency of crossing over indicates the relative distance between genes on a chromosome, T. H. Morgan and his coworkers constructed "chromosome maps" for known genes in each linkage group of *Drosophila*. In a mating involving any two linked characters, 1 per cent of crossover is taken to represent 1 unit of distance between their respective genes.

Thus the three characters of yellow body, white eye, and ruby eye are all sex-linked and therefore pertain to chromosome I (X). In matings between yellow body and white eye, crossover occurs in 1.5 per cent of individuals, between white eye and ruby eye in 6.0 per cent, and between yellow body and ruby eye in 7.5 per cent; hence the sequence is yellow-white-ruby, with 1.5 units of space between the genes for yellow and white and 6.0 units between white and ruby (1.5 + 6.0 = 7.5). Many crosses between various linked characters provide data for constructing chromosome maps (Fig. 12-9).

12-17. Giant chromosomes. The relatively huge chromosomes in the salivary glands of *Drosophila* and other flies occur in permanent homologous pairs and, when stained, show many dark-colored transverse bands, some wide and others narrow (Fig. 12-10). The bands give clues to the location of genes, as in cases of deletion. Where a character has disappeared from a laboratory stock of *Drosophila*, part of

one chromosome is missing at the position for the gene of that character in the chromosome map. This is important evidence associating the genes with the chromosomes.

12-18. Mutations. At times, new characters appear in the offspring of animals and plants that upon test prove to be heritable; these are germinal variations, or **mutations,** caused by some change in the gene for the character concerned. A historic case was the sudden appearance in a true-breeding stock of red-eyed *Drosophila* of one white-eyed individual; when the latter was bred, this character proved to be heritable, and as it continued in succeeding generations the change was permanent. Over a thousand mutations have been observed in *Drosophila* (Fig. 12-11), and many in other animals and in plants. Most mutations in *Drosophila* are abnormalities, recessive defects, or lethals such as would not survive in nature. But distinctive mutations among domestic animals and plants have been preserved by selective breeding. Examples are the polled (hornless) Hereford cattle, the short-legged (Ancon) sheep, and the short-legged dachshund and the long-legged greyhound among dogs. The rate of mutation varies widely in different animals and for different genes; recent calculations indicate one mutation per 40,000 to 500,000 cell divisions. Thus, 14 or more mutations of one gene for eye color in *Drosophila* have been noted. Most mutant genes are recessive, but some dominants have appeared.

Only spontaneous natural mutations were found earlier, but certain chemicals and types

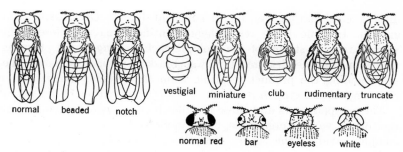

Fig. 12-11. Some mutations of wings and eyes in *Drosophila* used in study of crossing over and linkage. (*After Morgan and others.*)

of radiation have been found to induce mutations at increased rates. Mustard gas induces mutation, and colchicine causes duplication of chromosome sets (polyploidy) in plants. X rays applied to *Drosophila*, maize, and barley may increase the mutation rate two hundred fold in some cases, and in proportion to the dosage. These mutations prove heritable, like natural mutations, but most of them are lethal.

Because of the wider use and therefore greater exposure of people to high-frequency radiations, induced mutations are of practical importance. X-ray technicians, workers in atomic-energy plants, and others are endangered because the effects of radiation are cumulative; continued exposure to small amounts over several years may be as serious for an individual as receiving an equivalent dosage (same number of "roentgens") in a few minutes. Mutations due to irradiation may not be evident for several generations because they usually are masked by dominant alleles and only are seen as homozygous recessives. The general level of radioactivity is increasing throughout the world with the "atomic age." The social and biological implications of this situation are scarcely perceived, but knowledge is sorely needed.

12-19. Theory of the gene. The evidence on characters, genes, chromosomes, and linkage was summarized by T. H. Morgan [1] thus: (1) The characters of an individual are referable to paired genes in the germinal material, held together in a definite number of linkage groups; (2) at maturation each pair of genes separates (Mendel's first law), so that each gamete contains only one set; (3) the genes in different linkage groups assort independently (Mendel's second law); (4) orderly interchange or crossing over occurs at times between genes in corresponding (homologous) linkage groups; and (5) the frequency of crossing over furnishes evidence of the linear arrangement of genes in each linkage group and their relative position to one another.

The presence of a particular gene is recognized by some phenotypic characteristic that is produced in an organism, but the precise means by which the gene exerts its action is obscure. Evidence is accumulating, however, that at least some genes control particular biochemical reactions through their effects on specific enzymes.

A mold, *Neurospora*, provides some of the clearest of this information. The wild type of this organism will grow on a minimal medium including only a carbohydrate (sugar), a source of (inorganic) nitrogen, certain inorganic salts, and the vitamin biotin. From this simple mixture it can synthesize all the amino acids, vitamins, and other organic compounds essential to live, grow, and multiply. Beedle and Tatum assumed that the successive metabolic steps in these syntheses are controlled by a series of genes and that if one or more mutations were induced in the genes the requirements for successful growth would change. Wild-type *Neurospora* was irradiated to induce mutations. The mold would then grow on a "complete" medium (yeast and malt extracts, casein, various vitamins and amino acids, etc.), but irradiated strains (mutant) failed to grow on the "minimal" medium. One by one, vitamins, amino acids, etc., were added to the simple substrate

[1] Theory of the gene, New Haven, Conn., Yale University Press, 1926.

until a combination was found sufficient for growth. In time these researchers identified various mutant strains of the mold, in each of which one biochemical reaction was blocked; upon adding the product resulting from that reaction, normal growth resulted.

These experiments and those of other investigators on various organisms, both simple and complex, lead to the theory that there is an intimate association between genes and enzymes. Many enzymes are highly specific, each catalyzing a single kind of biochemical reaction; many genes likewise are specific in their effects. There could be a one gene–one enzyme pattern, and some geneticists have speculated that genes act directly as enzymes, but the situation may not be quite so simple.

12-20. Inbreeding and outbreeding. The mating of closely related individuals is called *inbreeding;* this may involve brother-sister matings or lesser degrees of relationship. Many races of domesticated animals and plants have been derived or improved by inbreeding, but practical breeders think that continued inbreeding leads to decline of vigor and the appearance of defects in offspring. Close marriages in human society, as between cousins, are usually banned for fear that defective children may result. Inbreeding tends to produce homozygous stocks. Since most genes for defects are recessive, it provides more opportunity for defective characters to appear. The results will depend on the genetic constitution of the stocks that are inbred. Guinea pigs carried through 23 generations of brother-sister matings by Sewall Wright and others ended with a stock reduced in size, fertility, and resistance to tuberculosis. Helen D. King, however, carried similar matings in white rats through 25 generations, using only the most vigorous individuals in each, and at the end the inbred animals compared favorably with cross-bred controls. Similar experiments through more generations with *Drosophila* have ended with normal stocks. Inbreeding with selection can produce satisfactory or improved stocks, combining desirable dominant characteristics in the homozygous condition.

Outcrossing, which is the mating of individuals not closely related, usually results in **hybrid vigor,** the offspring exceeding their parents in vigor and size. The mule is a familiar example, being larger and having more stamina than either of its parents, the mare and ass. Outcrossing tends to produce heterozygous individuals in which any defective features are masked by dominant normal characters. Most human marriages are outcrosses, the human population is heterozygous, and defects are relatively rare. People in an isolated community are more likely to be inbred and hence show more defects than in the general population.

12-21. Artificial selection. Selective breeding and the perpetuation of mutations have produced many breeds of domesticated animals that differ markedly in physical, physiological, and psychological characteristics from the wild ancestors. Choice among the resulting offspring and discarding those with unwanted features have yielded many useful forms.

The wild jungle fowl of India (*Gallus bankiva*) is small and slender, with variegated coloration, and the hens lay only 12 to 24 eggs per year. Continued selection has produced from it many domestic breeds of poultry that differ in size, coloration, and egg production. Bantams are only about 10 inches high and weigh about $1\frac{1}{2}$ pounds, whereas "meat fowls" such as the Cochins, Plymouth Rocks, and Rhode Island Reds are up to 16 inches tall and 6 to 8 pounds in weight. White Leghorn hens now average 120 eggs per year, and in some highly selected flocks each produces 200 or more.

Beef cattle, such as the Hereford, Shorthorn, and Aberdeen Angus breeds, are selected for shape (conformation) that yields desirable cuts of meat, and dairy breeds such as the Holstein-Friesian and Jersey have been developed for high milk production and high butterfat, respectively.

The greatest variety of characters perpetuated under domestication is among dogs (derived from wolves of Eurasia), over 100 breeds being recognized. These range from tiny Pekingese to great wolfhounds and from short-legged dachshunds and bulldogs to long-legged greyhounds. The coat color varies from white through shades of yellow, brown, and blue to black, and the character of the coat from nearly hairless in the Chihuahua to the dense sleek coat of the collie and curly hair of the Irish water spaniel.

Artificial selection has perpetuated peculiar mutations that would not survive long in nature, such as the pouters and fantails among pigeons or the bulldogs and Pekingese dogs. Indeed, few domesticated animals survive as such in the wild; if they persist at all, they generally revert to resemble the ancestral species. When domestic rabbits are released on islands the offspring soon are like the European gray rabbit whence they were derived. Specialized breeds of swine, such as the Poland China, similarly come to resemble the European wild boar from which they arose.

A reversal of artificial selection was tried by Lutz Heck of Berlin to reestablish the ancestral aurochs or ur (*Bos primigenius*) from which modern breeds of cattle were derived. By crossing several of the most primitive existing breeds of the Mediterranean region he obtained animals that resemble old paintings of the aurochs, which has been extinct as a species for several centuries.

12-22. Twins. Since the sum total of characteristics in any one individual results from the action and interaction of many genes, the various offspring from one pair of parents will differ. When a female produces more than one young at a birth, each usually develops from a separate egg, and the young are genetically different; but if the early blastomeres of one egg part and each gives rise to an individual, all the latter will have the same genetic make-up. The first condition produces *fraternal twins* (triplets, etc.) of the same or of different sex; they are no more alike than the other children of any one family. The second condition yields *identical twins,* always of the same sex, with like physical and physiological characteristics and showing practically the same mental traits and abilities. In the armadillo, four young of

identical kind result from partitioning a single egg. In various species a partial separation during cleavage or early embryonic development results in "double monsters," such as two-headed snakes or six-legged calves and Siamese twins in which two bodies are joined in varying degree.

12-23. Erroneous ideas about heredity. Formerly it was thought that *acquired characteristics,* which are those resulting from environmental influences during the lifetime of individuals, were heritable. No reliable evidence in support of the idea has ever been presented, and biologists now agree that such characters are not inherited. Environment ("nurture"), however, may play an important role as to the degree in which hereditary characters ("nature") develop in an individual.

Modification of the embryo by *maternal impressions,* or experiences of the mother during pregnancy, is another erroneous idea about heredity. The embryo is, of course, influenced by the health or nutrition of the mother, but that is quite another thing.

It was once thought that when a female animal was bred to a male the latter might influence the progeny from subsequent mating with other males; this notion of *telegony* was long held by animal breeders but is now largely discarded.

Breeders of domesticated animals sometimes refer to the *prepotency* of one parent, implying that it has ability to transmit characteristics more fully or to the exclusion of the other parent. Since the chromosome and genetic contribution of the two sexes is equivalent, this idea possibly arose from the greater attention given to one sex, usually the male, in efforts at improvement of a breed. Any actual difference results from dominance or heterozygosity in the animals mated.

HUMAN INHERITANCE

The genetic characteristics of human beings are passed from generation to generation like those of other animals. Details are difficult to

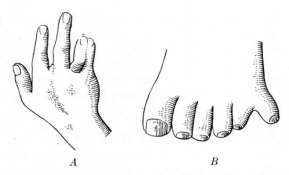

Fig. 12-12. Examples of two hereditary abnormalities known in man. *A*. Fused fingers (syndactyly). *B*. Extra digit (polydactyly).

work out for mankind because of the long intervals between generations and the scarcity of records that specify the characteristics of many individuals. By tracing backward through family histories in which the peculiarities of many members are listed, it has been possible to determine the manner of inheritance for some physical features, physiological characteristics, and mental traits (Figs. 12-12 to 12-14).

the iris, the color is hazel to dark brown. If pigment is lacking on both surfaces, the eyes appear pink (albino) because of the blood vessels in the iris. When both parents are blue-eyed, all their children have blue eyes; when one parent is heterozygous brown-eyed and one blue-eyed, the children are partly brown-eyed, partly blue-eyed. Marriage of two brown-eyed persons usually results only in brown-eyed children; yet blue-eyed ones may appear. These facts indicate that eye color is a simple Mendelian character; brown is dominant to blue, and blue-eyed individuals are homozygous recessives for eye color.

12-25. Color blindness. The inability to distinguish red from green is a sex-linked recessive character in mankind. Normal men neither have nor transmit the defect; "carrier" females enjoy normal vision but, being heterozygous for the character, may have color-blind children; color-blind males and females both transmit the defect (Table 12-1).

TABLE 12-1. Inheritance of Color Vision (Red-Green Discrimination) in Mankind

The gene for this factor, being sex-linked, is carried on the X chromosome. Color blindness (**X**) is recessive to normal vision (*X*). The heterozygous "carrier" female has normal vision.

Parents → ↓	gametes ↓ →	Normal ♂ *XY*		Color-blind ♂ **X**Y	
		X	Y	**X**	Y
		Children			
Normal ♀ *XX*	*X*	*XX* ♀ normal	*XY* ♂ normal	**X**X ♀ *carrier*	*XY* ♂ normal
Carrier ♀ **X***X*	*X*	*XX* ♀ normal	*XY* ♂ normal	**X**X ♀ *carrier*	*XY* ♂ normal
	X	**X**X ♀ *carrier*	**X**Y ♂ color-blind	**XX** ♀ color-blind	**X**Y ♂ color-blind
Color-blind ♀ **XX**	**X**	**X**X ♀ *carrier*	**X**Y ♂ color-blind	**XX** ♀ color-blind	**X**Y ♂ color-blind

12-24. Eye color. The iris of the human eye is brown or blue, rarely pink. Pigment on the back of the iris causes blue eyes of various shades; if there is also pigment on the front of

12-26. Blood groups. The importance of blood groups in transfusion was described in par. 6-8. The heredity of these groups is based on three genes for antigen production: antigen A, gene

A; antigen B, gene A^B; no antigen, gene a. Neither A nor A^B is dominant to the other, but both are dominant to a. The genotypes and blood groups of individuals are as follows:

Genotype....	aa	AA or Aa	$A^B A^B$ or $A^B a$	$A A^B$
Blood group..	O	A	B	AB

The relations possible between parents and off-spring are shown in Table 12-2. The blood group to which an individual belongs is useful in some but not all medicolegal cases involving parentage, as when two babies are accidentally interchanged in a hospital or when a woman claims a certain man as the father of a child. For example, if two parents, both of group O, are given a baby of group A, there obviously has been a mistake; likewise a couple of O $\times$ AB could not be parent to a group O baby. An A $\times$ B couple, however, could not make a valid claim for any particular baby.

have shown outstanding ability and leadership through successive generations, with many individuals distinguished in scholarship, the professions, the fine arts, business, statesmanship, and other fields of human endeavor. Conversely, other family lines include many degenerate individuals. The "Jukes" family, studied by Dugdale and Estabrook, is one of bad pedigree that was traced through several generations. From the marriage of a shiftless farmer's son and a prostitute, a total of 2,094 descendants was identified; these included 299 paupers, 118 criminals, 378 prostitutes, and 86 brothel keepers. There was a general record of intemperance and illegitimate births, and half the total were feeble-minded. The "Kallikak" family, analyzed by Goddard, presented an even more interesting situation. Martin Kallikak had a son by a feeble-minded girl, then married into a respectable family, and produced several children whose descendants became worthy members of society. The illegitimate feeble-minded

TABLE 12-2. Heredity of Human Blood Groups

Parents	Children		Child	One parent known to be	Other parent	
	Possible	Not possible			May be	Cannot be
O $\times$ O	O	A, B, AB	O	O A B	A, B O, B O, A	AB
O $\times$ A A $\times$ A	O, A	B, AB				
O $\times$ B B $\times$ B	O, B	A, AB	A	O B	A, AB	O, B
A $\times$ B	O, A B, AB	—	B	O A	B, AB	O, A
O $\times$ AB	A, B	O, AB	AB	A B AB	B, AB A, AB A, B, AB	O, A O, B O
A $\times$ AB B $\times$ AB AB $\times$ AB	A, B, AB	O				

12-27. Mental characteristics. Some traits, both good and bad, are inherited like other characteristics, although evidence about them may be difficult to interpret. Certain families

son, however, sired a degenerate line comparable with that of the "Jukes" family.

Practically every organ in the human body may be subject to hereditary defects in struc-

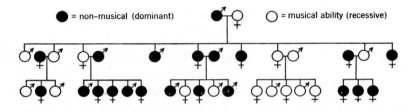

● = non-musical (dominant)   ○ = musical ability (recessive)

Fig. **12-13.** Inheritance of musical ability. (*After Hurst*, 1908.)

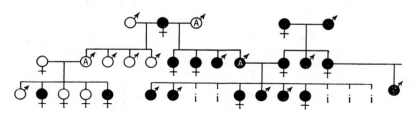

Fig. **12-14.** Inheritance of feeble-mindedness. Black, feeble-minded; white, normal; ♂, male; ♀, female; *A*, alcoholic; *i*, died in infancy. In the two cases where both parents were feeble-minded note that all children were also feeble-minded. (*After Holmes, Human genetics and its social import.*)

ture or function (Table 12-3), but mental defects, such as feeble-mindedness and insanity, are much more important. Furthermore it seems that such defects are increasing in frequency. Several million persons in the United States have an intelligence quotient of 70 or lower, from high-grade morons to imbeciles and idiots. More than 300,000 cases are of hereditary ori-

gin, but only about 11 per cent of them are thought to be the progeny of feeble-minded parents (Fig. 12-14). The remainder derive from normal persons who are heterozygous for this character. The feeble-minded become juvenile delinquents, problem children, and cases for public charity and relief. They breed early and often and so tend to increase their kind. Rela-

TABLE 12-3. Some Mendelian Hereditary Characteristics of Mankind

	Character	Dominant	Recessive
Normal	Hair form	Curly	Straight
	Hair color	Dark	Light
	Skin color	Dark	Light
	Skin pigmentation	Normal	Albinism (no pigment)
	Eye (iris) color	Brown	Blue
Abnormal	Fingers and toes	Short (brachydactyly)	Normal length
		"Webbed" (syndactyly)	Normal, not fused
		Extra digits (polydactyly)	Normal, 5 on each member
	Epidermis of skin	Thickened (keratosis)	Normal
	Hair and teeth	Absent (hypotrichosis)	Present
	Nervous function	Normal	Hereditary epilepsy
		Normal	Feeble-minded
		Normal	Insanity (also caused by organic disturbance, not genetic)
	Eye	Opaque lens (hereditary cataract)	Normal
		Internal swelling and pressure (glaucoma)	Normal
	Ear	Normal hearing	Deaf-mutism
Sex-linked	Color vision	Normal	Color-blind (cannot distinguish red and green)
	Clotting of blood	Normal	Hemophilia (clots slowly if at all)

tively few are in institutions, public or private. The end result is a rapidly mounting bill for their care and for dealing with the crimes that they commit. At least 28 states have laws that permit insane and feeble-minded persons to be sterilized, but only about 53,500 had been so dealt with up to 1952. This reduces the cost and difficulty of dealing with such defectives in institutions but does not affect the remainder.

The human race has evolved through a long series of progressive changes to its present state (Chaps. 14, 36) and can be further modified for better or worse. In primitive peoples many defective characters probably are weeded out by rigorous selective action of the environment. "Civilization" is mainly a control of man's environment, and it has increasingly tended to suspend such selection. Human races have crossed and recrossed, so that mankind has become the most variable of all animals and has accumulated many hereditary defects. The frequent outcrossing in human populations and the common bans on marriage between persons closely related tend to make the human germ plasm heterozygous and to mask recessive defects. Since there is little selective mating to rid the human population of such defects, these continue unabated. Modern medicine helps the individual to survive, but may actually be harming the race. In earlier centuries many defectives died before they became old enough to reproduce, whereas today such persons are repaired by medicine or surgery and survive to produce progeny that carry on their hereditary defects.

12-28. Eugenics. Many organizations and persons are now interested in *eugenics* (Gr. *eugenes*, well-born), a field of endeavor which seeks to improve the human race by applying the principles of genetics. If it were possible to control the matings between human beings, the race could be improved by eliminating certain serious defects and in many other ways, but this is not practical. Eugenists seek to determine the facts of human heredity, to educate the general public on the effects of good and bad matings, and to encourage legislation that will prevent matings between obviously defective persons. The further field of *euthenics* tries to improve the environmental conditions under which human beings develop and live so as to give the best possible expressions to the genetic constitution that each one has. No measurable aid in human genetics will be possible until much fuller records on human inheritance are available and until means are learned to recognize heterozygous individuals who carry genes of serious defects and to limit the mating of such persons.

REFERENCES

CASTLE, W. E. 1940. Mammalian genetics. Cambridge, Mass., Harvard University Press. ix + 169 pp., 131 figs.

DOBZHANSKY, T. 1951. Genetics and the origin of species. 3d ed. New York, Columbia University Press. xviii + 446 pp., 24 figs.

DUNN, L. C., and T. DOBZHANSKY. 1946. Heredity, race and society. Baltimore, Penguin Books, Inc. 115 pp.

GATES, R. R. 1946. Human genetics. New York, The Macmillan Co. 2 vols. xvi + 1,518 pp., 326 figs.

GOLDSCHMIDT, RICHARD. 1955. Theoretical genetics. Berkeley, Calif., University of California Press. x + 563 pp., illus.

LERNER, I. M. 1950. Population genetics and animal improvement. London, Cambridge University Press. xviii + 342 pp., 36 figs.

———. 1954. Genetic homeostasis. New York, John Wiley & Sons, Inc. vii + 134 pp., 12 figs.

LUSH, J. L. 1945. Animal breeding plans. Ames, Iowa, Iowa State College Press. viii + 443 pp., 50 figs.

MENDEL, G. 1866. Versuche an Pflanzen-Hybriden. *Verhandlungen der Naturf. Verein, Brünn*, vol. 4, pp. 3–47. Translated in Sinnott, Dunn, and Dobzhansky, 1950 (see below).

MULLER, H. J., C. C. LITTLE, and L. H. SNYDER. 1947. Genetics, medicine, and man. Ithaca, N.Y., Cornell University Press. ix + 158 pp., 29 figs.

SINNOTT, E. W., L. C. DUNN, and T. DOBZHANSKY. 1950. Principles of genetics. 4th ed. New York, McGraw-Hill Book Co., Inc. xiv + 505 pp., 202 figs.

SYNDER, L. H. 1951. The principles of heredity. 4th ed. Boston, D. C. Heath & Co. xi + 515 pp., 507 figs.

SRB, A. M., and R. D. OWEN. 1952. General genetics. San Francisco, W. H. Freeman & Co. x + 561 pp., 3 pls., 182 figs.

STERN, CURT. 1949. Principles of human genetics. San Francisco, W. H. Freeman & Co. xi + 617 pp., 198 figs.

WHITE, M. J. D. 1954. Animal cytology and evolution. 2d ed. London, Cambridge University Press. xiv + 454 pp., 147 figs.

13 ANIMAL ECOLOGY AND DISTRIBUTION

Every living organism from the simplest bacterium to the ponderous elephant has a distinctive mode of life that depends upon its structure and physiology and also upon the kind of environment that it occupies. Physical and biological factors act to make a wide variety of environments on different parts of the earth. The conditions are rather constant in some tropical lands and seas, but over much of the earth the temperature, moisture relations, and sunlight change with the seasons. Collectively these influences are known as *climate*. The life cycle of each species is closely adjusted to the climatic conditions of its environment. No animal lives entirely to itself; on the contrary, each is part of an integrated living *community* that includes others of its kind, many other sorts of animals, and plants of few or many types. The scientific study of organisms under natural conditions is termed *ecology* (Gr. *oikos*, house), and their occurrence in space and time is called *distribution.*

ECOLOGY

A. THE PHYSICAL ENVIRONMENT

Animals and plants are affected by various physical and chemical factors, the most important being (1) sunlight; (2) temperature; (3) water; (4) pressure; and (5) gases and minerals.

178

Each can be measured and its effects observed on animals, but all are interrelated and none acts independently. Sunlight provides the radiant energy used by plants in photosynthesis, but it also warms animal environments and raises the temperature of water, leading to evaporation (and eventually to precipitation of rain or snow). Temperature controls the speed of all chemical reactions, including the biochemical reactions in living organisms. Water is the solvent for soil minerals essential to plants, is a requirement in animal bodies, and is the medium in which many animals live.

13-1. Sunlight. All the energy used by organisms is derived from the sun (Fig. 13-1). Energy may be transformed from one type to another but is never created or destroyed (par. 3-3). Plants absorb the radiant energy in sunlight and, by the photosynthetic action of chlorophyll in their cells, produce carbohydrates from carbon dioxide and water; they also synthesize proteins and fats. The energy stored in these compounds is the ultimate source used by all animals. Energy relations underlie all physical and biotic processes on the earth and determine the activities of organisms.

13-2. Temperature. The degree of hotness or coldness of any object or body is called temperature and is measured on a scale, usually in

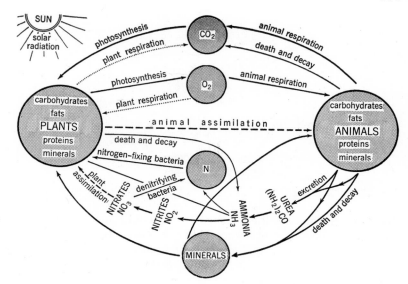

Fig. 13-1. The chemical cycles of carbon dioxide, oxygen, nitrogen, and minerals in nature. Arrows indicate the paths of movement of materials from the air (CO_2, O_2, N) and soil (minerals) to and from plants and animals.

degrees Fahrenheit or centigrade. Heat is a form of energy, and the amount in an animal or its environment is a factor of major importance, as can be seen in the lives of man, animals, and plants.

The range of temperatures in the universe covers thousands of degrees, but most life on earth can only exist within a range from zero to 60°C. or less. Heat tolerance is affected by moisture and really depends on the evaporating power of the air or the percentage of water vapor in relation to saturation at any given temperature. In the dry air on a desert, for example, a temperature of 32°C. (90°F.) is not uncomfortable to man, but the same temperature, coupled with high relative humidity, is difficult to tolerate in the tropics.

Temperature influences the growth, fruiting, and survival of the plants upon which various animals depend for food. A prolonged cold spring delays the development of grasses and leaves upon which many insects, rodents, and grazing animals forage and may determine their survival. Unseasonable weather at blossoming time may reduce the subsequent crops of berries or seeds on which various birds feed, forcing them to wander elsewhere for food or starve.

The cold-blooded animals—reptiles, amphibians, fishes, insects, and all other invertebrates

—have no internal regulation of body temperature and are practically always at that of their environment. The rate of chemical processes in their metabolism, hence their growth and activities, are influenced directly by environmental temperatures, being speeded up by warmth and delayed by cold. Each species has certain limits; any and all are killed by prolonged freezing or by excessive heat. If freezing weather occurs after their eggs or larvae have begun to develop, many are killed and their populations are reduced. Some insects have eggs, larvae, or pupae that overwinter as resting stages with lowered metabolism, either beneath the ground surface, within plants, or in the bottoms of ponds and streams, to escape being frozen. Certain insects trapped in ice may survive because the water in their bodies is so related to colloids that it does not freeze.

Reptiles and amphibians must hibernate in the ground or water to escape being frozen in regions that experience low winter temperatures. Some snakes of the arid West that are abroad by day in the spring become nocturnal in summer to avoid death by overheating. Most fresh-water fishes are inactive in cold weather, and each species has an upper limit of heat tolerance. Since temperature changes are slower and not so extreme in the ocean,

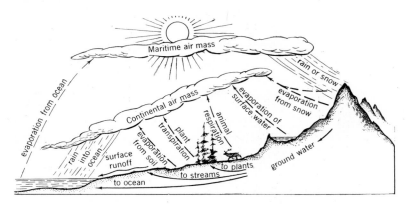

Fig. 13-2. The water cycle. Constant interchange of water between the air, land, and sea produces various daily and seasonal alterations in the environments of plants and animals.

marine organisms are less affected by seasonal changes of climate; yet many kinds of salt-water fishes migrate north and south seasonally.

The birds and mammals, having insulated bodies and regulated temperatures, are seldom affected directly by change of environmental temperature, but excessive winter cold or summer heat may alter their food supplies. Many birds that summer in Arctic and temperate regions travel, or *migrate,* to warmer regions for the winter to obtain appropriate food. Birds, elk, and deer that summer in high mountains, as in western North America, migrate to lower levels for the same reason.

Ground squirrels, bears, and some insectivorous bats enter a winter rest, or *hibernation,* when their food of the warmer seasons becomes unavailable. In hibernation the body temperature drops to about that of the animal's shelter, the heartbeat and respiration become very slow, and the reduced metabolism is supplied mostly by fat stored in the body before entering hibernation.

13-3. Water. There is a constant interchange of water between the air, land, and sea and between living organisms and their environments (pars. 3-11, 8-7). In addition, water profoundly influences the environments of organisms. The water cycle (Fig. 13-2) involves evaporation, cloud formation, precipitation, surface water runoff, and percolation through the soil. Water stores vast quantities of heat, and because its specific heat is so great (requiring 1 calorie to raise 1 gram of water 1°C. at 15°C.), any large

mass is slow to warm up in the spring and slow to cool in the fall. Water is heaviest at 4°C. (39.2°F.); it expands on cooling below this point and changes to ice at 0°C. (32°F.). The force of expansion is so great that rocks are split when water in crevices freezes; this is a process in soil formation. (The cracking of iron cylinders in an automobile when the jacket water freezes is a common example of this power.) The fact that ice floats, being lighter than water, is important to organisms. But for this, ice would form at the bottom of lakes and most large bodies of water would have permanent masses of ice in their depths. Instead, water sinks as it cools to 4°C. and warmer water rises, creating convection currents. These bring about a spring and autumn turnover in temperate lakes and protect organisms from temperature extremes, since those beneath the ice in deep lakes are never much below 4°C.

Many aquatic environments in eastern North America are relatively stable because water is retained by freezing in winter and that lost by evaporation in summer is replaced by frequent rains. In the western states, however, lakes fluctuate widely with changes in rainfall or snowfall. Many small ones and some of the larger dry out completely at times, killing all fishes and other strictly aquatic species. The margining marshes that shelter frogs, turtles, ducks, muskrats, and others also are destroyed. Abrupt changes in the flow of streams alter the conditions for their inhabitants. Severe floods modify the character of the bottom, covering gravel beds with silt; and the rushing waters may actually destroy many creatures. The reduction of a creek to scant flow or scattered pools exposes the aquatic animals to attack by predators of the land and also permits the waters to become overheated. Certain amphibians, insects, and invertebrates breed in transient rain pools; and if the rains are scant or unseasonal, the animals may lack for spawning places or the pools may dry out and kill the young before growth is completed.

Land animals are affected by the moisture content of the air, or *relative humidity* (percentage of water vapor in relation to saturation at any given temperature). Some are suited to deserts of low humidity, others exist only where the atmosphere is practically saturated, and many live at intermediate humidities. For small animals the *microclimate* of the little places where they feed or find shelter is all-important, usually having a lower temperature and higher humidity than the general climate of the region in which they occur. In arid regions many small animals remain in seclusion by day, else they would soon die of desiccation. They venture out at night when temperatures are lower and the humidity greater, especially close to the ground. In areas having frequent summer rains, or where fields and gardens are irrigated, the humidity near the ground is such that small invertebrates are active during the daytime.

All animals that inhabit soil are affected by change in its moisture content. Earthworms live close to the surface in damp soil during warm weather but go deeper as the surface layer dries, and the same occurs with many insect larvae. In turn, the moles that feed on such animals work in shallower or deeper layers as necessary.

13-4. Pressure. Animals of the land experience differences in atmospheric pressure at elevations above sea level because the density of the air (hence available oxygen) decreases with altitude. People living in high mountains have larger hearts and more red blood cells to compensate for the lesser oxygen supply; and mountain climbers from low altitudes use oxygen tanks to aid their breathing. Flight of some birds is thought to be less easy in highly rarefied air. At any one place, whatever its altitude, changes in air pressure (barometric reading) are associated with changes in weather. Strong winds—resulting from regional differences in pressure—affect animals variously; birds and insects fly less easily and may be blown to new places, and the rapid moving air has a drying effect on plants and many animals.

In deep lakes and the sea, water pressure increases regularly with depth (one "atmosphere," or 15 pounds per 10 meters), yet the Danish Galathea Expedition dredged nearly 100 invertebrates near the Philippine Islands at a depth of about 10,500 meters, where the pressure was about 1 ton per sq. cm. Such animals can live because the pressure within their bodies is the same as outside. Many plankton forms and some fishes are at depths of 400 meters by day but rise to the surface at night, gradually experiencing a 40-fold change in pressure. However, a deep-sea fish that has a closed swim bladder, if hauled up in a net, will literally explode in the low-pressure water near the surface. Human skin divers use air tanks both to supply oxygen and to keep up the pressure in their lungs when they are in the water.

13-5. Chemical cycles in nature. The elements that go to form the bodies of plants and animals are all derived from the environment, and there is a constant interchange of these, incident to the life and death of organisms (Fig. 13-3).

Carbon (C) is a constituent of all organic compounds in protoplasm (Chap. 3). From the carbon dioxide (CO_2) in air or water it is synthesized into the molecules of carbohydrates, and these, together with proteins and fats, make up the tissues of plants. The plants are eaten by certain animals, and after digestion and absorption in the latter (Chap. 5), the compounds of carbon become reorganized as animal protoplasm. In turn, these materials pass through other animals. Destructive metabolism in animals yields carbon dioxide as a

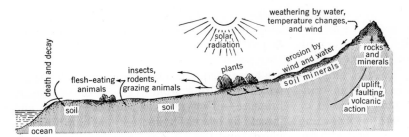

Fig. 13-3. The mineral cycle. Materials uplifted into mountains become disintegrated into soil minerals. By erosion and water or wind transport, these move gradually toward the lowlands and the sea; meanwhile, some pass once or many times through plants and animals.

respiratory waste that returns to the air or water.

Oxygen (O_2) is taken directly from the air or as dissolved in water (Fig. 13-1) to serve oxidative processes in animal bodies. It returns later to the environment, either combined with carbon as carbon dioxide or with hydrogen as water. From the carbon dioxide used by plants the oxygen is released to the environment, but plants also use some oxygen in respiration. A "balanced aquarium" contains animals and plants in such quantities that their mutual needs and outputs of oxygen and carbon dioxide are balanced.

Atmospheric *nitrogen* (N) can be used directly only by nitrogen-fixing bacteria in soil or in root nodules of some legumes, which combine it into nitrates (NO_3). Plants use nitrates to form vegetable proteins. These either return by decay to the soil or are eaten by animals and converted into animal proteins. In animal metabolism the latter are eventually broken into nitrogenous wastes, mostly urea, $(NH_2)_2CO$, and excreted. By action of other bacteria in soil or water, such wastes are converted to ammonia and to nitrites; by further bacterial action, either the nitrogen is returned to the air or the nitrites are converted into nitrates.

Certain *minerals,* or inorganic chemical substances, are essential for both plants and animals (pars. 3-10, 3-11, 5-13) in small but definite amounts that differ in various species. Plants obtain mineral constituents from the soil solution around their roots, and these return to the soil only by decay or burning of the plants. The supply for animals is taken partly from their food and partly from water, and in some cases directly from the soil. Minerals from animals return to the soil or water in ex-

cretions and feces and upon decay of their bodies (Fig. 13-4).

Phosphorus is an example of a "circulating" mineral needed in small amounts in protoplasm. Phosphates ($—PO_4$) are made available to plants through erosion from the great reservoirs of past ages in the rocks. Phosphorus normally is utilized by plants and animals and then returned to the soil through death and decay. Some is carried to the sea, and a part is lost in the deep sediments, but much of it is recaptured by fishes and marine birds. Man seeks the vast deposits of bird droppings (guano), such as occur on the coast of Peru and on Nauru Island in the South Pacific, for phosphate fertilizer to bring it back into the cycle.

B. THE BIOLOGICAL ENVIRONMENT AND INTERRELATIONS OF ANIMALS

Animals spend much of their time competing for food, shelter, and mates. In addition, there are various mutually beneficial relationships and many detrimental ones among animals and between plants and animals. Adverse effects of one species on another are usually obvious, whereas favorable effects are sometimes overlooked. Examples of the latter are man and his domesticated animals and cultivated crops. Within single species various degrees of interdependence occur, ranging from the initial provisioning of nests by wasps to the continuous care and long period of dependence of young seen in many birds and mammals, including man. A few animals, including termites, ants, bees, and man, have evolved genuinely cooperative societies with reproductives, workers, soldiers, nurses, etc.

13-6. Food. All plants compete for the same things—sunlight, soil minerals, and water—but animals are diverse in their needs. Animal food, of whatever kind, is derived ultimately from plants. Each species of animal has particular requirements, and every individual needs a certain amount of food of the right kinds. Human beings, rats, and house flies can subsist on a variety of foods and change from one to another as necessary. Many species, however, are more specialized and can exist only where and when their particular foods are available. The beaver eats only the inner bark of willows and poplars; the larva of the cabbage butterfly requires leaves of cruciferous plants; some leafhoppers subsist only on the juices of particular plants; and horse flies require mammalian blood. Some food supplies are seasonal, and the species depending upon them must, at other times of the year, shift to other foods, become dormant, migrate elsewhere, or perish.

The ocean, unlike the land, has few conspicuous plants; the sea hare (*Aplysia*), a mollusk, eats seaweed as a rabbit does lettuce, and some snails and limpets rasp off the dense short algae covering shore rocks. The foundation of ocean pasturage, however, is the *plankton,* composed mainly of microscopic plants (diatoms, algae) and animals (protozoans, larvae) that float and drift freely in the water. It varies in amount and species composition through the season (like the wild flowers in a field). Plankton is the food of innumerable small crustaceans, chaetognaths, and other animals and of the larvae of mollusks, annelids, and echinoderms.

Seaweeds are commonest in bays, estuaries, and shore waters, many of them being annuals. When they die and sink, they are reduced by a rich flora of bottom-dwelling bacteria. The resulting microscopic *detritus* (plant material plus bacteria) forms a bottom scum. This is the food of various worms and other invertebrates that secrete mucus nets or have special means to select fine particles from the water or mud. Sea cucumbers and some sea urchins ingest bottom mud in quantity to extract detritus for food. There is also a supply of larger

organic particles or *debris* derived mainly from animals that sink after death (from rough weather, killing by predators, etc.). Debris is the food of scavengers—certain shrimps, crabs, sea urchins, and others. In the ocean, however, above the microscopic level in size, animals are the principal food supply. Minute creatures that feed on plankton are eaten by other swimming invertebrates; these in turn are the food of larger crustaceans and small fishes which then are captured by larger fishes; and so on.

Plant-eating animals are the primary consumers in any animal community. They in turn serve as food for other animals (secondary consumers), which are eaten by still others. The energy originally derived from the sun by plants thus passes in material form through a *food chain;* all food chains in a community constitute a *food cycle* or *food web.*

Any food web or chain is essentially a system of energy transfers. Potential energy developed in plants passes through the successive animal consumer layers. Each gives off some as heat (of chemical transformation) to the environment, and the total declines progressively through the web. Decay of plants yields much heat (a mulch bed may become quite warm), and the decay of animals results in a lesser amount.

These relations are very complex (Figs. 13-4, 13-5), even in a small community, but may be illustrated by two simplified examples. In a pond the bacteria and diatoms synthesize materials, and then in sequence small organisms are eaten by larger ones, thus:

bacteria and diatoms → small protozoans → larger protozoans → rotifers, small crustaceans → aquatic insects → fishes

The large fishes, or any intermediate organisms, by death and decay become food for bacteria, thus completing the circuit. Or the fishes may be taken by herons, minks, or men and end up elsewhere. On land a food chain may include the following:

plants → plant-eating insects, rodents, or grazing mammals → predaceous insects or small carnivores → larger carnivores

184

SOURCES   PRODUCERS   PLANT FEEDERS   ANIMAL FEEDERS
(plants)   (herbivores)   (carnivores)

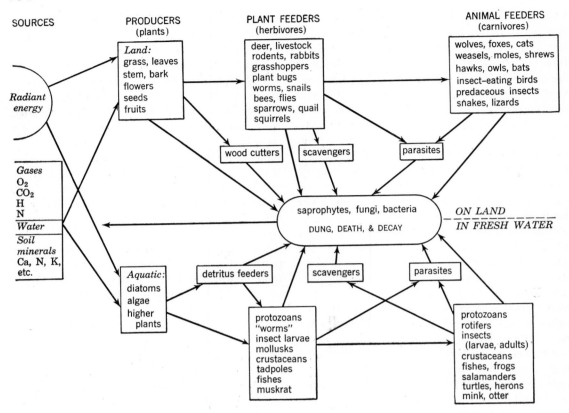

Fig. 13-4. Some interrelations between inorganic substances, plants, and animals in nature. Arrows indicate the path of materials from the primary (inorganic) sources through various organisms and back to the soil, water, or air. Any one circuit is a food chain.

This ends with death and decay as in the water. In any predator chain the successive members are larger in size but fewer in total numbers. Chains are not strictly linear but have many branches and alternative links. Any animal, above the smallest, takes food (prey) in relation to its size, neither so small that it cannot profitably gather enough nor too large for it to overcome successfully. Some food chains are long, but usually there are only about five successive links.

13-7. Pyramid of numbers. The food web in any community has been characterized by Charles Elton (English, 1900–   ) as a pyramid of numbers (Fig. 13-5). Animals at the base are small and abundant, whereas those at the apex are few but large; of those between, there is a progressive increase in individual size but decrease in numbers. In a deciduous woods, for example, aphids and other minute plant-feeding insects may be enormously abundant, spiders and carnivorous beetles are fairly common, insectivorous birds are fewer, and the hawks and weasels preying on the birds are numerically sparse. The smallest kinds, because of their size, can grow and multiply rapidly, whereas larger members of the chain reproduce more slowly. The largest predators at the apex are relatively so scarce that in turn they cannot serve profitably as prey for another species.

13-8. Shelter and breeding places. Animals that live in large bodies of water can avoid capture through superior ability in locomotion. Many species of the smaller waters and on the land live in various types of *cover* and use a retreat, or *shelter,* to avoid enemies and for other purposes. A rabbit, surprised in the open by a fox, darts for the first "briar patch." A white-footed mouse, when come upon, seeks the safety of a hole—in the ground, in a log, or under a rock; the same retreat may serve also as shelter from rain or excessive cold, as a storehouse for food, as sleeping quarters, and as a place to rear young.

Different mammals, birds, lizards, and insects live in cover such as grassland, shrubbery, trees, or rocks; various marine fishes and invertebrates dwell amid seaweeds, rocks, or coral in shore waters, and some fresh-water fishes inhabit stands of aquatic plants. Moles, pocket gophers, some snakes, certain insects, earthworms, and other invertebrates live more or less continually within the soil. In all these cases the animals find their food in the surroundings and are able to escape enemies and avoid extremes of weather.

Most animals also have special requirements for *breeding places* where the eggs or young are produced. For some the shelter serves, but others build special *nests,* as is done by many birds, some fishes, and various insects. Small animals breed wherever conditions are suitable. In many kinds of birds and some mammals, however, each pair establishes a *territory* to supply the food requirements of the parents and offspring for the breeding season; the territory is defended against invasion by others of the same species.

The availability of suitable cover, shelter, and breeding places is important in regulating the numbers of a species that can live in an area. If "housing" is in short supply, few can be accommodated and the others are exposed to weather and enemies. Man increases populations of game mammals, birds, and fishes by providing artificial cover or modifying natural conditions to provide better environment. Contrariwise, he may reduce objectionable species

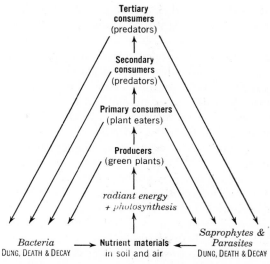

Fig. 13-5. The food cycle and pyramid of numbers. Going upward, the members of successive levels increase in size but decrease in numbers.

by destroying their cover: clearing the plants from the shallows of a reservoir eliminates mosquito breeding places.

13-9. Competition. The members of a species have the same requirements as to food (also shelter and mates) and compete with one another; representatives of different species that subsist on the same types of food are also in competition. Grasslands may be the common forage area of grasshoppers and other plant-eating insects, rodents, rabbits, deer, and domestic livestock. In times of food shortage, survival is determined by the quantities taken by each kind according to its population and the amount eaten by individuals. Species that have some latitude in choice of food may utilize other sources, whereas those restricted to but one type may be far reduced. In times of "crop failure," of either plant or animal materials, death by starvation is the lot of many animals; and if a species has built up to excessive numbers, it may come to the same end.

13-10. Enemies. Every animal that consumes another animal is called an *enemy,* or *predator,* and the animal eaten is its *prey.* Any that consumes members of its own species is termed *cannibalistic,* and one that eats dead animals is a *scavenger.* Any food chain, after the first plant-eating animal, is a succession of predations. Predation differs from parasitism in that a predator destroys its prey outright, but a parasite usually continues to feed on its living host. As Elton says, predators live on capital and parasites on income. In a food chain each predator is usually larger than its prey, whereas the parasite is always much smaller than its host.

The predator is commonly believed to "control" the numbers of its prey, but the relation is somewhat balanced. If a prey population increases, it will support more predators; if the latter then also increase, a heavier toll will be exacted of the prey, whereupon the latter will be reduced. In either type of change the numbers of the predator tend to lag behind those of the prey because the predator, being larger, has usually a slower rate of increase, although it lives longer. The amount of cover available in relation to the prey population also is a factor; more prey will escape the predators if there is much cover. When the prey population falls below a certain level it becomes unprofitable for the predator to pursue that particular kind; it must shift to some other source or suffer decline. The red fox preys variously on woodchucks, cottontail rabbits, squirrels, mice, birds, and insects but also eats fruits and berries; its "diet" changes with season and place according to the foods most readily available. Such a predator is likely to vary less in numbers than does the arctic fox, which lives mainly on lemmings or rabbits in the far North where the populations of both those rodents fluctuate widely.

13-11. Disease. Practically every animal species is subject to diseases produced by various types of organisms—viruses, rickettsias, bacteria, protozoans, parasitic worms, and arthropods. The disease organisms themselves must be considered as populations that in turn are affected by various factors in their respective environments, and they in turn influence the numbers and well-being of the animals on which

they live. Disease is probably one of the greatest agencies in regulation of animal numbers. Attention here will be confined to parasites.

A *parasite* is an organism that lives on or in another species, the *host,* obtaining food and shelter at the latter's expense. The host can live without the parasite, but the latter normally cannot exist without its host. The parasitic animals include many PROTOZOA, such as those causing malaria, amoebic dysentery, and other diseases; flukes, tapeworms, and other PLATYHELMINTHES; hookworms, root nematodes, and many other NEMATODA; all hairworms (NEMATOMORPHA) and spiny-headed worms (ACANTHOCEPHALA); various leeches (ANNELIDA); and many ARTHROPODA including fish lice, some barnacles, and other CRUSTACEA, the mosquitoes, flies, fleas, and various other INSECTA, and the ticks and many mites (ARACHNIDA).

A species of parasite either inhabits one host species, or a group of similar hosts, or alternates between two or more host species; each kind of parasite is usually restricted to a certain site in its host. *Ectoparasites* such as leeches and lice live on the skin, and *endoparasites* dwell within the body, in the gut cavity (many worms) or other organs, in muscles (trichina) or other tissues, in the blood (some worms and protozoans), or even in blood cells (malarial parasite). Some parasitic insects and ticks in turn are *intermediate hosts* for parasitic protozoans or other organisms that they transmit to other or *definitive hosts* (Chaps. 16, 19, 20, 21, 25–27).

Different parasites evidently arose separately in various phyla from free-living ancestors and have become variously specialized or degenerate for the parasitic mode of existence. Many have hooks or suckers for holding to their hosts; the gut is simplified (absent in tapeworms) because their fluid food is obtained directly by pumping or absorption from the host; and the reproductive organs are usually elaborated to produce enormous numbers of eggs or larvae to overcome successfully the hazards of reaching new hosts.

Some parasites have scant effect on their hosts, others injure the latter temporarily or permanently by the destruction of tissues or production of toxic secretions, and some kill their hosts. Harmful parasites are termed **pathogenic.** A host that recovers from the initial attack or damage often becomes a **carrier,** retaining some of the parasites, which continue to pass out eggs or larvae that may infect other hosts. Parasitism is the mode of life for many species; for survival as a species the parasite should not unduly injure its host. Parasitism, along with some diseases, is one factor in the regulation of populations of host animals. Some of the most notable instances of such control occur among insects where the matter is further complicated by secondary parasites, or **hyperparasites,** that parasitize the primary parasites (par. 26-26).

13-12. Symbiosis. Parasitism and some other kinds of special interrelations between two organisms of different species are termed **symbiosis** (Gr. living together). When one gains benefit by living with, on, or in another and without harm or benefit to the second, the case is called **commensalism.** The commensal "lives aboard his neighbor's vessel but does not eat his provisions"; some, however, do get scraps from the host's "table." In some cases the two are continuously associated with one another, such as the special types of barnacles that attach only to whales or sea turtles, the crabs that live regularly in the tubes of some annelid and echiurid worms, and the crabs that dwell in the mantle cavities of sea mussels. With others the association is not continuous—like the remora (Fig. 31-31) that attaches by its dorsal sucker to some other fish for transport, the fish (*Fierasfer*) that shelters in the cloaca of a sea cucumber, and the elf owl of the southwestern American desert that roosts and nests in holes made by the gilded flicker, another bird, in the giant sahuaro cactus.

More intimate is the relation of **mutualism,** where both parties are benefited. An example of "on and off" mutualism is seen in the birds that alight on large grazing mammals (cowbird or oxbird, on cattle, rhinoceros, etc.) to pick off ticks—the birds obtain food and the big beasts

are relieved of parasites; also the birds, by their behavior, warn the mammals of approaching enemies. Some marine fishes are similarly served by smaller fishes and crustaceans. Ants and aphids may feed separately, but certain ants keep aphids in their nests and put them on roots or stems of corn and other plants to feed. The aphids are protected, and the ants stroke them to obtain food, a sweet fluid from the hind-gut of the aphids.

In other cases two types of organisms are continuously associated. A striking example is that of certain termites and flagellate protozoans. The termites eat wood but cannot digest cellulose, but the flagellates in the termite gut can, so that food is available for both. Termites experimentally rid of the flagellates soon die of starvation, and the protozoans cannot live a free existence. Some species of sponges, hydroids, and sea anemones live regularly on shells of hermit and other crabs. The riders are carried to new feeding areas and are not stranded at low tide, whereas the crab is somewhat camouflaged and the riders protected in a degree from enemies. Animal-plant mutualism is seen in the green hydra (*Chlorohydra*) that has green algae (zoochlorellae) in its cells, the one producing carbon dioxide and the other oxygen as a by-product; sealed in a tube of water both live for some time by mutual aid. Various protozoans, sponges, sea anemones, corals, and flatworms have yellow or brown algae (zooxanthellae), and a similar O_2–CO_2 exchange occurs. Certain species of ants, beetles, and termites grow and tend "gardens" of peculiar types of fungi—that live only under such care—and the fungi serve those insects as their sole food. Even man has a mutualistic relation with his crops of wheat and maize that grow only with his aid.

The **cross-fertilization** or **pollination** of plant blossoms by insects (occasionally by birds) is a mutual relation of wide occurrence and great importance because many plants are self-sterile. Often both flower and insect are structurally and functionally specialized to achieve successful transfer of pollen from flower stamen to insect body to (another) flower pistil. Hive bees visit blossoms to obtain both nectar and pollen for their own needs (par. 26-14) and in so doing carry pollen between the flowers they visit. Many of man's staple food and forage crops depend on these flower-insect relationships.

13-13. Colonies and societies. All vertebrates, most arthropods, and many other invertebrates are *free-living* in that each individual gets about by its own efforts. By contrast, sponges, many hydroids, corals, bryozoans, tunicates, and others are *sessile,* in being fixed to some substratum of rocks, plants, or the shells of other animals. Among both categories, many species are *solitary* in that each individual is more or less independent, whereas others live in groups, or *colonies.* The many "individuals" of a colony among sponges, bryozoans, and tunicates are bound together structurally. In other cases the individuals in colonies of insects, schools of fishes, flocks of birds, and herds of hoofed mammals are structurally separate but may be integrated by behavior.

Solitary animals such as carnivores (mountain lions, minks, etc.), hawks, flycatchers, snakes, and predaceous insects forage best independently and pair up only for reproduction. Members of some other species assemble without reference to age or sex. In the winter flocks of robins, ducks, or starlings, many eyes and ears are of greater service when foraging or sleeping; groups of bats, rattlesnakes, or lady beetles gather for hibernation with some advantage. Among active groups of mammals or birds there is often a "leader," and a gradation in dominance, between individuals, known as the "peck order"; this may be seen among fowls of one sex in a barnyard flock. Sexual aggregations bring males and females together for mating, as with frogs, toads, gulls, and fur seals.

Societal organization occurs where many individuals of a species live together in an integrated manner so that each contributes in some specialized way to the welfare of all. The social habit has arisen independently in several orders of insects; it is highly developed among the termites and in many ants, bees, and wasps. The transition from solitary to social life apparently is correlated with lengthening of adult life and increasing parental care. Solitary bees provision their nests, lay eggs, and depart, never to see their offspring. Social bees, on the other hand, feed their young regularly during development. Distinct *castes* have developed to perform such tasks as feeding, guarding the colony, etc. Worker and soldier castes differ in structure and physiology and cannot live independently. Success with them is measured in terms of the colony and not of the individual (par. 26-31). Human society comprises integrated groups of like individuals that specialize in different trades or professions to the benefit of both the individual and the group.

13-14. Populations. All the animals of one species that occupy a given area comprise a *population.* Beyond the activities of its constituent members, a population has definite structure and organization. It grows and declines and has a certain composition as to ratio of the sexes and age groups that may change with circumstances. Population is stated in terms of density, numbers per unit of area. The rate of change—increase or decrease—is determined by the numbers of new individuals added (birth rate) versus the losses from all causes (death rate). When additions exceed losses the population increases, and vice versa. The course of a population with time can be expressed in a graph (Figs. 13-6, 13-7).

Few people realize the huge populations of animals and plants that exist. Diatoms and protozoans may exceed 1,000,000 per liter of sea water. Censuses of the upper half inch of topsoil near Washington, D.C., revealed small organisms at the rate of 1,200,000 animals and 2,100,000 seeds or fruits per acre of forest soil; meadow soil contained 13,600,000 animal items and 33,800,000 of plant materials. On croplands, grasshoppers sometimes number 20,000 to 200,000 per acre, and heavy infestations of eggs and larvae of the alfalfa weevil may total 8,000,000 to 22,000,000 per acre. The numbers of larger organisms are naturally much smaller —birds at 2 per acre over the United States,

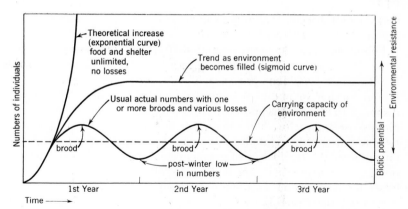

Fig. 13-6. Ideal curves of population growth.

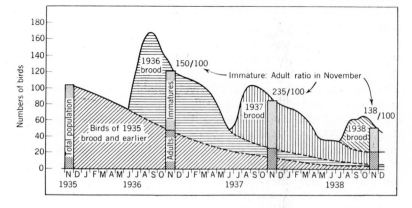

Fig. 13-7. Age composition and changes in numbers of a valley quail population at Davis, Calif., through several years, as determined from banded birds. Despite the large crop of young in 1936 the total population declined. (*After Emlen, 1940.*)

deer at 1 to 25 or 40 acres, and black bears at 1 per several square miles.

Some winter flocks of ducks have included more than 200,000 birds; the bison on the Great Plains originally numbered several millions, and of these about 3,000,000 were killed in 1872 to 1874 alone; in eastern North America, flocks of the now extinct passenger pigeon once darkened the skies for days during migration, and nearly 12,000,000 were killed and sold in one Michigan town in 40 days.

The potential rate of increase, or *biotic potential,* for all animals is very great, though slower in the larger forms. Any species would soon overrun the earth if it went unchecked, but *environmental resistance* in the form of competition, enemies, disease, and climatic limitations intervene. The characteristic growth curve for a population when introduced into a new area (or a population of fruit flies or flour

beetles in a laboratory culture) is sigmoid or $\int$-shaped (Fig. 13-6). Growth is slow at first because the few individuals do not readily meet for mating. After establishment, growth becomes very rapid, increasing in exponential fashion (like compound interest) but eventually levels off as (1) the population reaches the limit of its food supply, or (2) all suitable habitats are occupied, or (3) parasites and predators multiply seriously. Finally an *equilibrium* is reached and the population fluctuates around this level, depending on variations in climatic and biotic factors. The equilibrium is also known as the *saturation level* or *carrying capacity* for a given locality, assuming that environmental conditions remain relatively constant; actually conditions change from season to season, year to year, and over periods of years. The "balance of nature," therefore, is a dynamic one, ever changing with shifts in the many environmental factors, some of which are also subject to cyclical changes.

Following the season for production of young in any species there is a surplus of individuals resulting in a *population pressure.* The reaction is a reduction in numbers by several means: dispersal to other areas and losses by predation, disease, or starvation. The effects are *density-dependent,* that is, related to the numbers per unit of area. All the factors of loss operate more severely when numbers are high, their effects lessening as the population density declines.

Severe unseasonable weather (hurricanes, droughts, floods, excessive heat or cold) is *density-independent* in its effect on decline in a species; the kill is in proportion to the number of animals present, but there is no special effect related to the density of numbers when the calamity occurs.

Some populations remain relatively stable from year to year with only slight fluctuations; on an annual basis the numbers added balance those lost. There is, of course, seasonal change through the year, numbers being largest just after the production of young and then declining until the next breeding season (Fig. 13-7). In contrast, certain species show conspicuous cyclical fluctuations: Eurasian locusts, meadow mice, lemmings, ruffed grouse, snowshoe hares, and arctic lynx are a few examples. The numbers rise phenomenally in some years, then decline abruptly in others. The varying hare (*Lepus americanus*) in Canada has fluctuated over a 1 to 1,000 ratio, but more commonly in a 1 to 10 ratio. The cycle approximates 10 years. Meadow mice usually change less in numbers, and the cycle is about 4 years. Many theories have been proposed to explain the cycles, but none is yet adequate.

13-15. The biotic community. In any one place the populations of different animals (and plants) are interrelated to constitute a biotic community (ecosystem). Each member population has its ups and downs, and these changes influence other parts of the community. Some communities—a fallen log, a pond, a meadow, or a forest—are easy to visualize and define,

but others such as a lake shore or an ocean beach may merge with adjacent communities. Some large, free-ranging animals such as foxes or eagles have their headquarters in one kind of community but may forage in others.

Any community is a rather self-contained organic unit, the plants and animals living together in an interdependent manner. As in a human community the members are specialized for particular "jobs"—producers, consumers, and decomposers, organized into a complex food web (Fig. 13-5). In certain communities the members may have characteristic form and size: those in a fallen log are small and sometimes flattened, those in flowing water are streamlined. The larger communities of both land and water show *stratification.* A forest has characteristic animals of the treetops, the lower branches, the bark, the leaf litter, and the soil. A lake has surface dwellers (water striders, ducks), others in intermediate depths (plankton, fishes), and bottom inhabitants (snails, worms, insect larvae, etc.). In any community one or a few species are *dominant* over the others, either in numbers, physical characteristics, or both. In a pine forest the pine tree is dominant, exerting a controlling influence by shading other plants and the ground and by producing a carpet of needles (of acid reaction). Because of these conditions, the kinds and numbers of plants and animals that can live there are limited.

13-16. Ecological succession (Fig. 13-8). No community is permanent; some change abruptly, others persist for years or centuries. Typically, at any one place, there is a sequence or *succession* of communities: first a pioneer stage, then gradual change, and ultimately a relatively stable phase, the *climax.* The lake-pond-swamp-meadow succession is to be seen in many areas once glaciated, then gradually filled and covered with soil by inflowing streams. The glacial lake is low in dissolved nutrients, hence has poor plankton supply and few fish; the shallower pond has higher mineral content, more marginal plants, better plankton, and a variety of small crustaceans and in-

Fig. 13-8. Succession in plant cover and soil-making at the edge of a large lake —providing new habitats for animals. Over a period of several hundred years the shore line gradually moves out into the original lake area and succeeding plant types become established on the new land. The rock on the original beach is a "reference." (*Adapted from R. and M. Buchsbaum, Basic ecology, by permission of Boxwood Press, Pittsburgh, Pa.*)

sect larvae and more fish; the swamp has profuse rooted vegetation, few fish, and many aquatic invertebrates; finally the meadow has grasses and herbs and insects that forage on them, earthworms, toads and frogs, various birds, meadow mice, and shrews.

Cylindrical cores cut from the bottom of a Connecticut lake by Deevey showed a vertical succession of pollen types extending back 11,000 years (dated by radioactive carbon; par. 13-28). The climate, indicated by vegetational types, had varied from cold to warm (pine and spruce vs. deciduous hardwoods). Transition from deep clear waters to a shallow pond was indicated by remains of insect larvae: a freshwater midge (*Tanytarsus*) at the lower level and a stagnant-water type (*Chironomus*) higher up.

The principle of ecological succession is of practical importance in human affairs. Any field that is plowed and then left fallow has a changing sequence of plant growths. On range land the vegetational cover will be altered in a succession that depends on both the seasonal pattern and the intensity of grazing by livestock. In the eastern states when forest is removed trees soon grow, but the species composition may not resemble the original stand. In the arid West when a climax forest is cleared off—by lumbering or fire—the resulting excessive sunlight, erosion, and competition by herbs, shrubs, and rodents make for a long succession before the original pattern is reestablished.

13-17. Ecology and conservation. Any change in the physical or biological characteristics of an environment affects various species of plants and animals in different ways. To the natural forces that act upon wild populations, the influences of man have been added in many places and with increasing vigor in recent centuries and decades. Civilization is essentially an effort by man to manipulate and use the environment for his own advantage, usually immediate. In early stages man "lives off the land"; bison, elk, deer, waterfowl, and land game together with beaver and other fur bearers have been far reduced or completely eliminated in the zeal to obtain flesh and pelts. Later man's competitors, the wolf, coyote, mountain lion, and others that prey on livestock or game, and the rodents and insects that eat crops, have been subjected to extensive continuing control programs. More direct environmental manipulation has involved removal of forests, draining swamps, irrigating arid lands, and planting huge acreages of crops. Each ecological alteration has affected animals. Forest removal takes the food and shelter of tree-using species, but planting shrubs and trees in gardens and parks provides habitats for animals that previously could not occupy those sites. Draining swamps and lakes destroys living places for muskrats, beavers, ducks, some fishes, and others, whereas irrigation of once arid lands enables some aquatic and marsh-dwelling species to replace the rodents, reptiles, and other original denizens of those dry localities.

Agriculture, forestry, reclamation and irrigation, public health activities, and aid to game or fur species are all direct or indirect ecological manipulations. The perfection of heavy bulldozers, gang plows, and power saws, and of chemical poisons that can be distributed in quantity by airplane or from the ground to control insects or weeds has greatly multiplied man's ability to alter his surroundings. Much of this, however, is not constructive; accelerated erosion by wind and water after plowing up grass sod, stripping forests faster than they will regenerate, and various other effects are evident in many places. The disappearance of former large human civilizations that once flourished in the Near East and the decline in human "carrying capacity" of many other areas demonstrate that much human manipulation has been too hasty and ill-advised; it was largely exploitation with little regard for the future. A human civilization, like any plant or animal community, cannot long continue if its environment becomes damaged beyond recovery. Some current efforts at conservation of renewable (biological) natural resources are tending to correct the evils of former environmental manipulations.

DISTRIBUTION

No animal species occurs uniformly over the whole world, but each is restricted to a definite *range,* or area of *distribution.* The entire extent of land or water over which a species may occur is termed its *geographical range,* and the kind of environment in which it lives is its *ecological range.* The *geological range* of a species is its occurrence in the past (Figs. 13-9, 13-14). The study of animal distribution and of the factors controlling it is known as *zoogeography.* All the animals living in a particular area, large or small, are collectively termed the *fauna* (the equivalent term for plants is flora; the plants and animals together are the biota).

The beaver, for example, has a geographical range that embraces much of North America and Europe; its ecological range comprises fresh-water lakes and streams bordered by aspens, poplars, or willows that may be cut to serve for food and for building dams; and its geological range includes, besides the present or Recent geologic time, also the Pleistocene and Pliocene epochs when it had a wider geographical range. Some animals have large ranges: the harbor seal lives along most seacoasts of the world, and the sperm whale (formerly) occurred in most oceans between 56°N. and 50°S. Other species are local in occurrence, like the now extinct heath hen, until recently found only on an island of a few square miles (Martha's Vineyard off Massachusetts); some insects are known only from patches of plants covering but a few acres. The mallard duck inhabits fresh-water marshes through much of the Northern Hemisphere, the polar bear is restricted to Arctic shores and ice, and living elephants dwell in the forests of Africa, India, and nearby regions.

13-18. Factors regulating distribution. Since every species produces offspring in excess of the numbers that can survive within its normal range, there is a population pressure by which individuals tend to expand the boundaries of their range. Other factors such as competition,

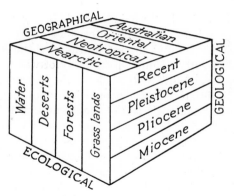

Fig. 13-9. Relations among the three types of animal distribution: geographical, ecological, and geological.

enemies, disease, shortage of food, adverse seasonal weather, and decrease in available shelter act to reduce the population. The distribution of all animals, from protozoans to mankind, is consequently dynamic rather than static and always subject to change. This is equally true of plants on which so many animals depend. Most plants, being rooted to the ground, cannot extend their range as individuals but only by dispersal of seeds.

The external factors that limit distribution are termed *barriers.* These include (1) *physical barriers* such as land for aquatic species and water for most terrestrial forms; (2) *climatic barriers* such as temperature (average, seasonal, or extreme), moisture (as rain, snow, air humidity, or soil moisture), amount of sunlight, and others; and (3) *biological barriers* such as absence of appropriate food or presence of effective competitors, enemies, or diseases. Many kinds of insects are limited to particular species of plants for their food, shelter, or breeding places, so that their distribution is controlled by factors that regulate these plants.

Every species of plant and animal has a limit of *tolerance*—maximum and minimum—to each factor in its environment. Tolerance to a poison in the soil or food may be narrow, whereas that to different wavelengths of light is wide. Changes in a factor beyond the tolerance limits result in migration, or death, or survival of only those individuals better suited (more tolerant) to the altered conditions. A species is limited in distribution by the sum total of external influences, many of which are interdependent. Nevertheless, the range and equilibrium level of a population is ultimately subject to Liebig's *law of the minimum,* being limited by the essential factor present in least amount or by some critical stage or condition for which the species has a narrow range of adaptability. Oysters, for example, can live in various saline waters but breed only if the temperature exceeds a certain minimum.

13-19. Methods of distribution. Free-living animals of some size become distributed by their own efforts. Birds, fishes, and others that migrate are quick to settle in any suitable new situation. Small aquatic animals and larvae and occasional large forms are carried about passively by water currents. Many small insects are wafted about in the air, mostly within a few hundred feet of the earth but some at higher levels, and thus may be deposited in new places. Rafts of trees, soil, and debris that carry animals pass down large rivers and occasionally are seen far at sea; oceanic islands may have been populated in part by such means. Violent hurricanes sometimes transport small living animals; some showers of organic matter in the United States have included earthworms deposited on a man's hat and on a buggy and many small fishes found after a heavy local rain in a previously dry cornfield in South Carolina. Parasites and commensal animals are transported by their hosts into new localities.

A species does not necessarily occur in all places suitable for it, but only in those to which it has access, and this depends on its own past history or that of its ancestors. Animal distribution of today is the joint result of barriers and environmental conditions in the past. The continents have persisted for long periods but have undergone many local alterations by elevation and erosion of mountain ranges, changes in the existence of lakes and streams, and the draining or flooding of lowlands. Some continents have been connected at times by *land*

bridges and separated by seas at other periods in earth history. Warm climates extended to the polar regions in some periods, whereas glaciers blanketed much of the Northern Hemisphere several times during the Pleistocene epoch preceding the present. All such changes have altered the distribution of plants and animals. Older areas of land or water have been reduced or eliminated, and new ones have become available. Living organisms have been forced to move about, many species have been exterminated, and new species or groups have evolved to take advantage of new areas or environments.

Many North American animals are more closely related to species of eastern Asia than to those in South America. From this we infer that the Aleutian Island chain now between Alaska and Siberia was a land bridge for terrestrial organisms in the late geological past (there are fossil remains of redwoods on those islands); the Isthmus of Panama is another bridge which has been interrupted at various times in the past, thus separating the Americas for considerable periods. Terrestrial species also need appropriate "ecologic bridges" of suitable environment through which to migrate. The bison could not pass from North to South America because no open grasslands existed in the areas between.

C. GEOGRAPHICAL DISTRIBUTION

13-20. Zoogeographic realms. These are the largest units in distribution and are defined by the land animals native to each (see front end papers). The realms are as follows:

1. **Australian.** Australia, Tasmania, New Guinea, New Zealand, and oceanic islands of the Pacific. All monotremes, most marsupials (no placental mammals but bats and rodents), emu, cassowaries, brush turkeys, lyre birds, birds of paradise, most cockatoos, Australian lungfish. New Zealand has sphenodon and kiwi.
2. **Oriental.** Asia south of The Himalayas: India, Ceylon, Malay Peninsula, Sumatra, Borneo, Java, Celebes, and the Philippines. Tarsiers, macaques, gibbons, orang-utan, Indian elephant and rhinoceros, jungle fowl, peacock.
3. **Ethiopian.** Africa including the Sahara Desert, Madagascar, and adjacent islands. Gorilla, chimpanzee, African elephant, rhinoceros and lion, hippopotamus,

zebra, giraffe, many horned antelopes, ostrich, guinea fowl, secretary bird. Many lemurs in Madagascar.

4. **Neotropical.** South and Central America, Mexican lowlands, and West Indies. Llama, alpaca, peccaries, arboreal sloths, armadillos, anteater, guinea pig, vampire bats, rheas, toucans, curassows and guans, most hummingbirds.

5. **Nearctic.** North America from the Mexican highlands to the Arctic islands and Greenland. Mountain goat, prong-horned antelope, caribou, muskrat.

6. **Palearctic.** Eurasia south to The Himalayas, Afghanistan, Persia, and Africa north of the Sahara. Hedgehog, wild boar, fallow and roe deer.

The limits of each realm and its fauna reflect the past history of animal groups and also of changes in the earth's surface that either permitted or prevented animal migrations. The Australian Realm has evidently been isolated longest and has many unique animals and plants. Its mammals include the egg-laying monotremes and many marsupials, the latter having "radiated" into a great variety of forms from huge jumping kangaroos to small burrowing marsupial moles (Chap. 35). There is much evidence to indicate that the great Asiatic land mass was for long a center whence various animal stocks originated and migrated to other regions. Thus the great flightless birds are now in southern realms, the emu and cassowaries in the Australian, the ostrich in the Ethiopian, and the rheas in the Neotropical. Such *discontinuous distribution* occurs also with the tapirs in Malaysia and Central America, the limbless amphibians (caecilians) in the tropics of the New and Old Worlds, and others. The Palearctic and Nearctic realms are least separated, and their faunas have much in common so that they are often combined as the *Holarctic Realm.* This is characterized by the elk (red deer), moose, bison, beaver, marmots, most bears and sheep, mallard duck, golden eagle, trouts, and salmons. Few or no species or groups occur throughout any single realm, but some range in parts of two. The tiger occurs from India to northern China, the opossum from South America into the United States, and the mountain lion and rattlesnake through both the Americas. Various subdivisions of each realm can be distinguished, each with a more or less distinct fauna.

13-21. Insular faunas. *Continental islands* stand in shallow waters close to the continents from which they were probably separated in the recent geologic past. The fauna of each resembles that of the nearby mainland, having identical species or closely related subspecies. It often includes various small mammals, reptiles, and amphibians probably resident on the area at the time of its separation from the continent, since they cannot travel through salt water. *Oceanic islands* arise by volcanic activity from great depths in the sea. The fauna lacks amphibians and small mammals save for bats and occasional rodents, the latter possibly transported in native boats. Wide-ranging fishes, sea birds, and marine mammals visit their shores. The land birds and insects are peculiar and often include wingless forms, which are less likely to be swept away by storms. The Galápagos Islands under the equator off Equador have bats and some land birds related to mainland species. The principal land birds (Family Geospizidae) comprise about 40 local forms, mostly finch-like but with some resembling warblers and woodpeckers. One of these employs a stick as a "tool" to probe for insects! The separate islands have various species of giant land tortoises, relatives of which occur only on certain islands in the Indian Ocean. The Hawaiian Islands, also oceanic, have one bat and one rat native. The bird family Drepanidae has "radiated" into various forms resembling finches, warblers, creepers, and other ecologic types. New Zealand is a continent with the characters of an oceanic island. It lacked native mammals but had flightless birds, the now extinct moas and the living kiwi. Its most distinctive reptile, *Sphenodon*, is the sole living species of an otherwise extinct order (par. 33-16), and its one "frog," *Liopelma*, likewise belongs to an ancient group.

13-22. Introduced animals. Many kinds of animals have been moved by man into regions where they were not native, some deliberately and others by accident. Many such *aliens* soon disappear, and some remain scarce, but others have become widespread and abundant. In each case the result depends on the suitability of the new environment, the degree of competition with native species, and the extent to which the alien is affected by predators and diseases in its new home. Fleas, lice, tapeworms, and other parasites of man and domestic animals have been accidentally spread with their hosts to new lands; some have then shifted to native hosts, as the sheep tapeworm into American deer. The European corn borer, Japanese beetle, cotton boll weevil, codling moth, Argentine ant, and garden nematode are conspicuous alien pests now important on crops in the United States. The domestic rats and mice, house fly, and bedbug are aliens that are common nuisances. Attempts have been made to restrict the further spread of many such pests by quarantine laws.

Some deliberate but harmful introductions include the European gray rabbit in Australia and New Zealand, where it competes for sheep pasturage, the Indian mongoose taken to Jamaica and Hawaii to control rats but which destroyed native birds instead, and the "English sparrow" brought into the United States in hope of controlling the introduced gypsy and brown-tail moths but which merely has become a nuisance.

Some introductions by man have been useful, such as the lady beetles imported for the "biological control" of various scale insects harmful to fruit trees, the ring-necked pheasant established in many states as an additional game bird, the trout transplanted into various waters, and the striped bass, shad, and other fishes placed in lowland waters of the Pacific coast to supplement the few native food and game fishes originally there.

In general, the practice of transplanting alien animals and plants has benefited the human race. Nearly all domesticated animals (the turkey is an exception) have been imported from other places, and most of our crop plants are likewise aliens. The practice, however, is dangerous. Parasites and diseases often are more destructive in their new homes. Plants and animals harmless in their native lands may become pests when transplanted; the prickly pear cactus and the European rabbit when introduced into Australia both ran wild, covering millions of acres. The prickly pear was finally controlled by introducing the insect enemies which kept it in check in its native home on the American desert, and the rabbit has been reduced by bringing in a disease, myxomatosis.

D. ECOLOGICAL DISTRIBUTION

That part of the earth containing living organisms is known as the *biosphere*. Within this relatively thin layer are many places, large and small, suitable for plants and animals (Fig. 13-11). The term *habitat* is loosely used to indicate the place where an animal lives. The immediate local situation that provides the essentials for its existence is called its *ecologic niche* —the habitat is the organism's "address," and the niche is its "profession." The most obvious major divisions of environments used by animals are the salt waters, fresh waters, and land, but even these grade into each other (Fig. 13-10). Water contains 7 cc. or less of oxygen per liter, its temperature changes slowly, it has less plant food than the land, and for animals the hazard of drying occurs only in temporary waters. The displacement support of water permits some active marine animals to be of huge size. On land, oxygen abounds (210 cc. per liter of air), temperatures may vary widely and change abruptly, and plant food usually is abundant. There is often a dearth of moisture so that land animals must adjust their habits to avoid desiccation or must have a drought-resistant body covering.

13-23. Salt waters. Oceans, seas, and bays cover about 71 per cent of the earth, providing habitats that are extensive and stable. Their physical features include:

(1) Temperatures from 32°C. (89°F.) in the tropics to −2.2°C. (28°F.) in some polar regions, but rarely with an annual variation more than 5°C. (9°F.) at any one place; (2) dissolved gases varying with temperature and depth; (3) salt content averaging 3.5 per cent (NaCl, 2.35; MgCl$_2$, 0.5; Na$_2$SO$_4$, 0.4; CaCl$_2$, 0.11; KCl, 0.07; NaHCO$_3$, 0.02; and others); (4) average depth of oceans about 12,500 feet, but 35,400 feet (6.7 miles) in the greatest "deep"; (5) pressure increasing

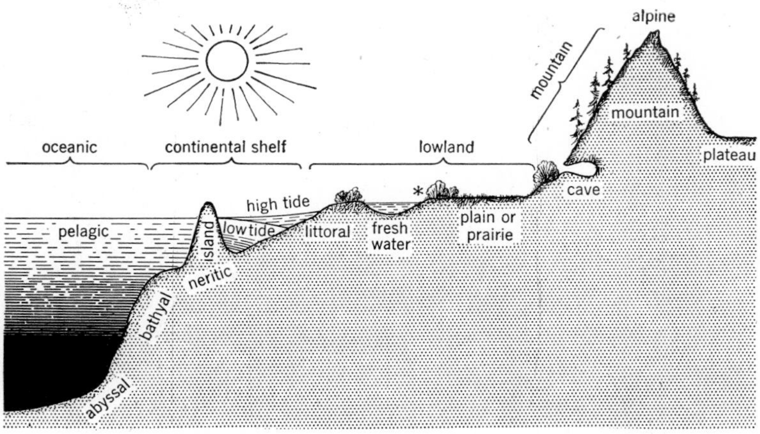

Fig. 13-10. An ideal section at the margin of a continent with indication of some common ecologic environments available to animals; the region marked with asterisk (*) is enlarged in Fig. 13-11.

about one atmosphere for each 10 meters (33 feet) of depth so that animals of deep waters live under enormous pressures, but these are equalized throughout their bodies; and (6) light penetrating decreasingly down to 600 feet, a trace to 3,000 feet, with complete permanent darkness below.

Marine animals include representatives of all phyla and of all classes except the centipedes, millipedes, ONYCHOPHORA, and amphibians. The ctenophores, brachiopods, chaetognaths, echinoderms, and lower chordates are exclusively marine. Species and individuals are most abundant near the surface and decrease with depth, but some occur down to the greatest depths. Dredgings by the English "Challenger" expedition gave the following results:

Depth, feet	Numbers of Species
0–200	4,400
200–1,000	2,050
1,000–2,000	710
2,000–3,000	600
3,000–4,000	500
4,000–5,000	340
Below 5,000	235

Marine animals are segregated ecologically as follows:

1. **Plankton.** Organisms that float and are moved passively by winds, waves, or currents; mostly of minute or microscopic size with surface large in relation to bulk, often with elongate body parts or ciliated; includes many protozoans and crustaceans, some mollusks, a few worms, and a host of larvae (sponges to tunicates) and microplants (diatoms, algae).

2. **Nekton.** Animals that swim freely by their own efforts; includes squids, fishes, sea snakes and turtles, sea birds, seals, whales, etc. Plankton and nekton animals of the open sea are termed *pelagic*.

3. **Benthos.** Strict bottom dwellers, segregated by depth and nature of the bottom.

a. LITTORAL or SHORE. Between the tide lines, alternately exposed to air and covered by water twice daily; strong wave action brings much food and oxygen; segregated according to nature of bottom (mud, sand, or rock) and zoned according to length of exposure between tides; population dense, protozoans to tunicates.

b. NERITIC. Below low-tide line to depths of about 600 feet (100 fathoms) on the "continental shelf"; water well oxygenated, some wave action; many animals, protozoans to fishes.

c. BATHYAL. At depths of 600 to 6,000 feet; water quiet, progressively colder, little to no light, fewer animals.

d. ABYSSAL. Below 6,000 feet; permanently cold quiet water, complete darkness, oxygen scant; animals scarce, usually small and dark-colored, eyes large or none, often with light-producing organs.

In the benthos, some worms, echinoderms, mollusks, and crustaceans *crawl* over the surface; many worms and some bivalve mollusks are *embedded* or *burrow*; and many sponges, hydroids, anemones, corals, bryozoans, mollusks, barnacles, and tunicates are *sessile*, or *attached* to various objects. The littoral and neritic vary in width according to the slope of the coast; the width of the littoral also varies with the height of the tides—12 inches at Galveston, Tex., and 18½ feet at Eastport, Maine.

13-24. Fresh waters. Unlike the sea, fresh waters are scattered, of lesser volume and depth, and more variable as to temperature, content of gases and salts, light penetration, turbidity, movement, and plant growth. "Pure" waters contain mere traces of salts, but some saline and alkaline waters have large amounts. Carbonates (especially $CaCO_3$) are usually commoner than other salts. Some fresh waters are nearly constant in volume, but those of arid

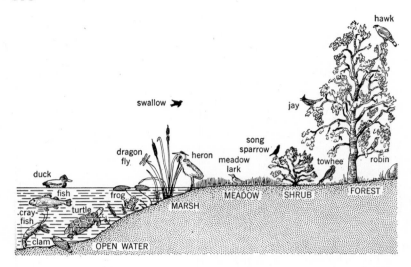

Fig. 13-11. Ecological distribution of some common animals of fresh water and land. In general, each keeps to a particular plant association or other subdivision of the environment.

regions often fluctuate from flood stages to small volume or dry up completely during a single season.

Fresh-water animals include many protozoans, a few sponges, coelenterates and bryozoans, many worms, rotifers and snails, various bivalve mollusks, crustaceans, larval and adult insects, and vertebrates from fishes to mammals. Many of the invertebrates produce eggs or other "resting" stages resistant to drying or freezing that may be blown about by winds or carried accidentally on the feet of waterfowl. They rarely have floating larvae, since these might be carried by streams to the sea and be lost. In any one place the kinds and numbers usually change markedly through the year.

The principal fresh-water habitats are:

1. **Running waters.** The cold mountain streams, spring-fed brooks, slower brooks and creeks, and rivers of various sizes contain mobile animals that are segregated according to the rate of water movement, temperature, oxygen content, and character of the bottom. Thus trout live only in cool well-oxygenated waters, whereas carp thrive in warm and even foul waters. Inhabitants of rapid waters often are flattened or have means for holding to the bottom.

2. **Standing waters.** These comprise lakes, swamps, marshes, and bogs (Fig. 13-11), either permanent or temporary, and occur in all regions from polar and alpine areas to the tropics. Lakes in cold climates may be frozen for a long time in winter, and those of temperate regions for shorter periods, but lakes of hot regions are always open. Large lakes afford more stable environments than flowing waters; they have littoral,

benthic, and pelagic divisions and a plankton fauna. Water in large temperate lakes undergoes circulation because of temperature differences and wind action. In spring and autumn this involves all depths; but in summer only the surface portion circulates, over a definite plane, or *thermocline,* separating it from the cold and often poorly oxygenated water below, where there are but few animals.

13-25. Land. The interaction of many physical, climatic, and biological factors produces a wide variety of ecologic conditions on the continents and islands.

Lands differ in (1) the *chemical nature* and *physical texture* of the soil, sand, and rocks exposed on the surface; (2) the *topography,* which includes plains, rolling lands, hills, valleys, and mountains; and (3) the *altitude* which varies from basins below sea level (Death Valley) to peaks exceeding 28,000 feet (Mount Everest). Some of the climatic variants are as follows: (1) *Air temperatures* at different places range from far below freezing (where soil also freezes) to 60° C. (140° F.) on some deserts; in many localities the temperature fluctuates widely, by day or through a season, but there is only slight change in many tropical areas. (2) *Moisture* as rainfall amounts to 500 inches annually in a few tropical places but only mere traces on some deserts; the moisture content of air and soil varies from complete saturation to slight amounts according to place and time of year. (3) *Winds* and *sunlight* affect both the temperature and the moisture content of the air and ground. The physical and climatic conditions influence the plant cover that may grow on any land area, and the plants in turn affect the animal population, particularly where the latter depends directly upon plants for food and cover.

The principal terrestrial animals are mammals, birds, reptiles, and insects, with lesser

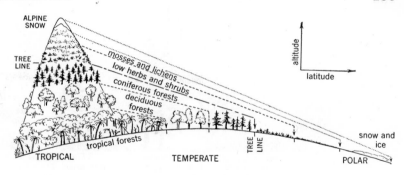

Fig. 13-12. Comparison of the latitudinal and altitudinal zones or associations of plants that provide the appropriate environments for various kinds of animals.

numbers of amphibians, crustaceans, mollusks, worms, and protozoans. They are all mobile save for some parasites and live on the land surface, on plants, or at shallow depths in the ground. The subterranean habitat affords more uniform conditions than the surface. All animals that fly or "live" in the air return to the ground or to trees or rocks.

Ecologic classifications of land habitats are based either upon climate (temperature, rainfall, relative humidity, etc.) or upon the various associations or communities (biomes) of terrestrial plants and animals that live in more or less interdependent relations.

13-26. Climatic zones.
It is a matter of common observation throughout the world that plants and animals are distributed according to more or less well defined zones, depending in a general way on the climate. Tropical rain forests occur near the equator, and treeless tundra covers wide areas in the Arctic. Between these extremes are deciduous forests, coniferous forests, grasslands, etc. This sequence of *life zones* is related to temperature as indicated by the correlation of latitudinal zones from the tropics to the polar regions with altitudinal zones from the bases to the tops of mountains (Fig. 13-12). Such zones are conspicuous on mountains in many parts of the world; in western North America distinct zones can be traversed within a few miles of travel or a few hundred feet of elevation.

Another ecological classification is by large and easily recognizable communities called *biomes* (see back end papers). The climax vegetation of a biome is of a uniform type or life form, though often of different species. Thus broad, thick leaves and heavy canopy are characteristic of the tropical rain-forest biome, whether in Panama, New Guinea, or equatorial Africa; the grassland biome is similar in growth form though different in species composition on each of the continents; and the great deserts of the world support a type of vegetation (the desert biome) characterized by thorny plants having adaptations for conserving water.

Biomes are determined by climate. The freezing temperatures and short growing season of the Arctic are favorable to the growth of sphagnum and dwarf vegetation of the tundra, whereas the dry conditions of deserts, caused by adjacent mountain ranges that deplete winds of their moisture, are habitable only by desert-type vegetation and associated animals. The biomes of North and Central America are as follows:

1. **Tundra.** Treeless Arctic region; only the surface soil thaws out in the short "60-day" summer; below is permafrost; drainage poor, many ponds, marshes, and bogs; principal plants are bog (peat) mosses, lichens, sedges, grasses, and low herbs; mammals include musk ox, Barren Ground caribou, wolf, arctic fox, weasels, lemmings, arctic hare; conspicuous resident birds are snowy owl and ptarmigan (snow grouse); many migratory waterfowl and shore birds nest here in summer but go south to winter; no reptiles.

2. **Coniferous forest** (evergreen). South of tundra to northern United States, with extensions southward along mountain systems (Sierra-Cascade, Rocky, and Appalachian) to Central America; winters bleak, summers cool, precipitation moderate; spruces, firs, pines, cedars; often includes shrubs and patches of grassland; mammals include moose and woodland caribou in the north and deer and elk toward the south, also the fur bearers—red fox, Canada lynx, pine marten, fisher, wolverine—with black bear and mountain lion, snow-

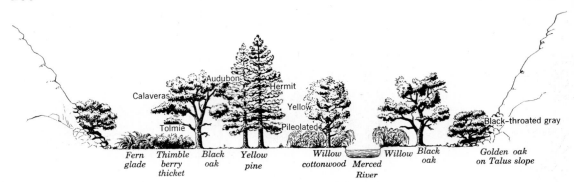

Fig. 13-13. Ecological segregation during the nesting season of seven species of birds, all members of one family (COMPSOTHLYPIDAE, wood warblers). Habitats are named below (fern glade, etc.) and the birds above (Tolmie warbler, etc.). Each has a separate forage niche and does not compete with the others. (*After Grinnell and Storer, 1924.*)

shoe rabbit, and some small rodents; birds are various grouse, warblers, chickadees, jays, etc.; few reptiles and amphibians; trout, grayling, etc., in waters.

3. **Broad-leaved deciduous forest** (summer-green). Especially from Mississippi Valley eastward; winters cold, summers warm and humid with rain; oaks, maples, beeches, elms, walnuts, many shrubs and herbs; white-tailed deer, gray fox, wildcat, raccoon, fox and flying squirrels; many warblers, vireos, and other small songbirds; snakes and amphibians common.

4. **Grassland** (prairies and Great Plains). Mississippi Valley westerly, Texas to Canada; winters of severe continental cold, summers hot, thundershowers. Great areas of hardy grasses (buffalo, bluestem, grama), trees locally along streams; formerly bison, prong-horned antelope, and wolf, now coyote, badger, skunk, jack rabbit (= prairie hare), cottontails in thickets, ground squirrels; prairie chicken, burrowing owl, soaring hawks, meadow larks; some snakes.

5. **Sagebrush.** Great Basin plateau between Rocky Mountains and Sierra-Cascade system. Dry, winters cold with limited rain or snow, summers hot. Sagebrush (*Artemisia tridentata*) and other bitter-flavored shrubs, bunch grasses, piñon (nut) pine, juniper. Prong-horned antelope, jack rabbit, ground squirrels, other burrowing rodents, coyote, badger, sage hen (largest American grouse), water birds in local ponds and marshes; many reptiles.

6. **Chaparral.** California hills and parts of mountains. Rainy (snowy) winters, warm to hot dry summers. Chamise, manzanita, and other shrubs with thickened evergreen leaves. Mule deer, woodrat, chipmunks, brush rabbit, California thrasher, wrentit, lizards.

7. **Deserts.** Southeastern California to western Texas and southward. Soil rocky or sandy. High summer temperatures, scant water at any time. Vegetation scattered, many herbs grow and flower soon after the occasional rains; cacti, yuccas. Smaller carnivorous mammals, many rodents active by night, few birds, many lizards, some snakes, few amphibians.

8. **Tropical rain forest.** Panama and parts of Central America. Sustained moderate temperatures, abundant rainfall. Forest of evergreen broad-leaved trees, many vines, orchids, etc. Marmosas, opossums, sloths, anteaters, bats, monkeys, great variety of birds and reptiles.

E. GEOLOGICAL DISTRIBUTION

13-27. Fossils. The animals living today are only part of a vast and continuing population that has inhabited the earth through millions of years (Figs. 13-14, 13-15). Evidence of former animals and plants is provided by *fossils.* A fossil (literally something dug up) is an organic relic preserved by natural means in rocks or softer sediments that affords information as to the character of the original organism.

Dead animals are usually destroyed by scavengers or by decay; but if soon covered by silt beneath water, by wind-blown soil, or by volcanic dust, decomposition will be slow and the hard parts may persist. If the surrounding material later becomes rock and is neither crushed nor heated, the remains will survive for long periods. A fossil may be (1) an **unaltered hard part** such as a skeleton, a tooth, or a shell; (2) a **mold,** where hard parts once present are dissolved away by percolating waters to leave a cavity showing the original form; (3) a **petrifaction** in which the original has been replaced particle by particle with other mineral substance to preserve all fine detail; or (4) a **cast** of mineral which fills a mold to show only exterior features. Even soft parts may leave im-

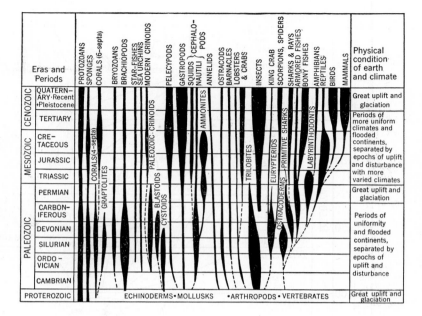

Fig. 13-14. Distribution of the major groups of animals through geological time (compare Fig. 13-15). Changes in width of the black areas suggest relative numbers of species in each group during different eras and periods; broken lines suggest possible sources and time of origin for certain groups. (*After a chart by W. D. Matthew, University of California Museum of Paleontology.*)

pressions in fine sediments. Some fossil records of animal activities survive as tracks, burrows, tubes, and droppings. Fossil plants are common as impressions, or casts. Special types of fossils are the carcasses (with flesh, hair, etc.) of the mammoth and woolly rhinoceros frozen in tundra soils of Siberia and Alaska; skin, hair, and dung of ground sloths in Nevada caves; skeletons of giant elk and other animals in peat bogs of Ireland and elsewhere; entire remains of insects and other small animals embedded in amber ("fossil resin") as along the Baltic Sea, arctic Alaska, and elsewhere; and skeletons of many species trapped in asphalt pits (former tar pools) of southern California.

Besides providing evidence of past life, fossils are used for identifying rock strata and for indicating a chronological or time sequence of such strata. They afford some information as to ancient environments and climates and as to the interrelations of bygone animals; and they furnish important data on the organic evolution of animals and plants down through time (Chap. 14). Many present-day species of animals occur also as fossils, showing that they lived in earlier geologic epochs. Fossils show that in the past various groups such as the di-

nosaurs came to great prominence and later perished completely, whereas others like the coelocanth fishes (par. 31-24) have a few living survivors. The fossil record is fragmentary at best. Remains are more complete and numerous in rocks of later geologic periods, whereas in the older formations they are scarcer and less perfect because the rocks have been disturbed and crushed by earth movements or changed by heat.

13-28. Geological time. Estimates of the age of fossils are derived mainly from study of radioactive minerals in fossil-bearing rocks.[1] The

[1] Uranium upon disintegration yields lead of atomic weight 206 (ordinary lead, atomic weight 207). Precise study shows that 1 per cent of uranium thus disintegrates in 66,000,000 years. Careful chemical analyses of the ratio of uranium to lead 206 in undisturbed rocks have provided an approximate time scale for the various strata of rocks containing fossils in the "geological column" and hence an estimate of the time when the animals there represented were living (Fig. 13-15).

More recent time scales are the chronology established by studying the number and spacing of tree rings (covering about 1,000 years) and the percentage of disintegration of radioactive carbon, carbon 14 (about 10,000 years). Carbon 14 is produced in minute amounts by bombardment of CO_2 by cosmic rays in the atmosphere. Some of this enters into plant tissues, and when analyzed, hundreds or thousands of years later, can be dated within fair limits of error.

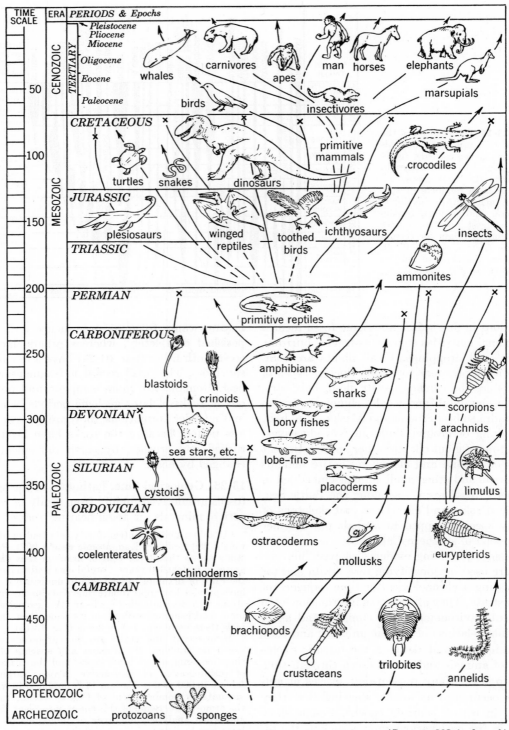

TIME SCALE | ERA | *PERIODS & Epochs*

Pleistocene
Pliocene
Miocene
Oligocene
Eocene
Paleocene

CENOZOIC — *TERTIARY*

whales — carnivores — apes — man — horses — elephants — marsupials — birds — insectivores — primitive mammals

CRETACEOUS

turtles — snakes — dinosaurs — crocodiles

MESOZOIC

JURASSIC

plesiosaurs — winged reptiles — toothed birds — ichthyosaurs — insects

TRIASSIC

ammonites

PERMIAN

primitive reptiles

CARBONIFEROUS

blastoids — crinoids — amphibians — sharks — scorpions — arachnids

DEVONIAN

bony fishes — sea stars, etc. — lobe-fins

PALEOZOIC

SILURIAN

cystoids — placoderms — limulus

ORDOVICIAN

coelenterates — echinoderms — ostracoderms — mollusks — eurypterids

CAMBRIAN

brachiopods — crustaceans — trilobites — annelids

PROTEROZOIC
ARCHEOZOIC

protozoans — sponges

50, 100, 150, 200, 250, 300, 350, 400, 450, 500

(See page 203 for legend.)

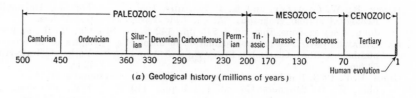

(a) Geological history (millions of years)

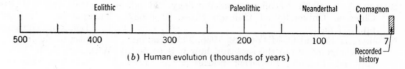

(b) Human evolution (thousands of years)

Fig. 13-16. Time scales of the paleontologist (a), archeologist (b), and historian (c); scales a and b are estimated.

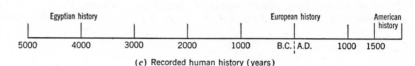

(c) Recorded human history (years)

oldest recognizable rocks (Archeozoic) are considered to be about 1,500,000,000 years old, and the oldest rocks (Cambrian) with numerous fossils 500,000,000 years old. The time since the Archeozoic may be visualized by comparing it to the distance from New York to San Francisco (about 3,300 miles). One year is represented by 0.133 inch (3.4 mm.), a human lifetime by 9.3 inches, the Christian era by 21.5 feet, and the time since early Pleistocene, when man appeared, by about 2.1 miles—but a short distance down the road of time (Fig. 13-16).

REFERENCES

ALLEE, W. C. 1931. Animal aggregations: a study in general sociology. Chicago, University of Chicago Press. ix + 431 pp., 35 figs.

———— and OTHERS. 1949. Principles of animal ecology. Philadelphia, W. B. Saunders Co. xii + 837 pp., 263 figs.

ANDREWARTHA, H. G., and L. C. BIRCH. 1954. The distribution and abundance of animals. Chicago, University of Chicago Press. xv + 782 pp., illus.

BAER, J. G. 1951. Ecology of animal parasites. Urbana, Ill., University of Illinois Press. x + 224 pp., 162 figs.

BARNETT, LINCOLN (editor). 1955. The world we live in. New York, Time, Inc. vi + 304 pp., many illus. in color.

CARSON, R. L. 1951. The sea around us. New York, Oxford University Press. 7 + 230 pp.

CAULLERY, MAURICE. 1952. Parasitism and symbiosis. Translated by A. M. Lysaght. London, Sidgwick & Jackson, Ltd. xii + 340 pp., 80 figs.

CLARKE, G. L. 1954. Elements of ecology. New York, John Wiley & Sons, Inc. xiv + 534 pp., illus.

DICE, L. R. 1952. Natural communities. Ann Arbor, Mich., University of Michigan Press. x + 547 pp., 52 figs.

EKMAN, SVEN. 1953. Zoogeography of the sea. London, Sidgwick & Jackson, Ltd. xiv + 417 pp., 121 figs.

ELTON, CHARLES. 1935. Animal ecology. Rev. ed. London, Sidgwick & Jackson, Ltd. xx + 207 pp., 8 pls., 13 figs.

Fig. 13-15. Time chart of animal life—the fossil record of some conspicuous animal groups. Heavy curving lines extend up from the time (period) when each group first appeared; those topped with arrows are of stocks surviving to the present (Recent time); an X indicates time at which other groups became extinct; broken lines show presumed earlier origins of some types. Each unit of time scale at left represents 10,000,000 years. Height of space for each period in the "geological column" is proportional to its duration in millions of years (e.g., Tertiary, 70; Pleistocene, 1; Proterozoic and Archeozoic not to scale). Recent time omitted. Compare Figs. 13-14, 13-16. (*Adapted in part from C. O. Dunbar, 1949, Historical geology, by permission of John Wiley & Sons, Inc.*)

Hesse, R., W. C. Allee, and K. P. Schmidt. 1951. Ecological animal geography. 2d ed. New York, John Wiley & Sons, Inc. xiii + 715 pp., 142 figs.

Lack, David. 1954. The natural regulation of animal numbers. Oxford, Clarendon Press. viii + 343 pp., 52 figs.

Odum, E. P. 1953. Fundamentals of ecology. Philadelphia, W. B. Saunders Co. xii + 384 pp., 119 figs.

Romer, A. S. 1945. Vertebrate paleontology. 2d ed. Chicago, University of Chicago Press. ix + 687 pp., 377 figs.

Russell, E. S., and C. M. Yonge. 1936. The seas: our knowledge of life in the seas and how it is gained. Rev. ed. London, Frederick Warne & Co., Ltd. xiii + 379 pp., 127 pls., some colored.

Ruttner, Franz. 1953. Fundamentals of limnology. Translated by D. G. Frey and F. E. J. Fry. Toronto, University of Toronto Press. xi + 242 pp., 51 figs.

Shrock, R. R., and W. H. Twenhofel. 1953. Principles of invertebrate paleontology. 2d ed. New York, McGraw-Hill Book Co., Inc., xx + 816 pp., illus.

Sverdrup, H. U., M. W. Johnson, and R. H. Fleming. 1942. The oceans: their physics, chemistry and general biology. Englewood Cliffs, N.J., Prentice-Hall, Inc. x + 1,087 pp., illus.

Tinbergen, N. 1953. Social behavior in animals. London, Methuen & Co., Ltd. xi + 150 pp., 8 pls., 67 figs.

Wallace, A. R. 1876. The geographical distribution of animals. New York, Harper & Bros. 2 vols., 1,108 pp., illus. and maps.

Welch, P. S. 1952. Limnology. 2d ed. New York, McGraw-Hill Book Co., Inc. xi + 538 pp., 50 figs.

14 ORGANIC EVOLUTION

Mankind has long sought to learn how, when, and where life originated and the ways in which the many kinds of animals and plants have come into being. This chapter considers some scientific theories on these subjects and the evidence on which they are based.

We have no knowledge of life except on the earth. Of the billion or more "heavenly bodies" in the universe, all but a few are gaseous stars at temperatures of 2000°C. or over, or accumulations of interstellar dust not conceivably habitable, or nebulae of star aggregates at such vast distances that little can be learned of them. The remainder are mostly planets (asteroids) too small to retain an atmosphere. Of the seven major planets besides the earth in the solar system, Neptune, Uranus, Saturn, and Jupiter have cloud-like surfaces and low temperatures (−100°C.?); Mercury lacks water and atmosphere and undergoes wide temperature fluctuations; and Venus lacks water and oxygen but has moderate temperatures (+60 to −20°C.?). Only Mars, 35,000,000 miles from the earth, possibly could support life as we know it, having oxygen, carbon dioxide, water, and temperatures from 10 or 15°C. to freezing. White caps (snow?) form at the poles in the Martian winter, and some surface areas change seasonally from green or blue-gray to yellow or brown; also lines (canals?) in geometric pattern on light-colored areas have been reported. To some persons the color changes imply the presence of plant life, and the "canals" are considered evidence of intelligent beings, but difficulties in observation leave the subject of life on Mars one for debate.

14-1. Environments for life. The earth may have originated from condensation of extremely hot gaseous material (nebular hypothesis) or as a molten mass (planetesimal hypothesis), in either case having been derived from some other heavenly body. It cooled slowly, decreasing in volume, and in time acquired an atmosphere that retained water on the surface. The water filled depressions on the surface to form the oceans, which originally may have been very hot. The oldest exposed rocks indicate great volcanic activity on the then exposed lands. Life as we know it could not have existed until the waters and lands had cooled.

14-2. How life originated. There are several principal theories on the origin of life:

1. SPONTANEOUS GENERATION. Earlier it was believed that life originated repeatedly from nonliving materials by spontaneous generation; this idea was discredited by experiments in the seventeenth and nineteenth centuries (Chap. 11).

2. SPECIAL CREATION. Until the middle of the nineteenth century life was generally presumed to have been created by some supernatural power either once, or at successive intervals, or

each species was presumed to have been created separately.

3. COSMOZOIC THEORY. Protoplasm in the form of resistant spores of simple living forms might have reached the earth accidentally from some other source in the universe. The extreme cold and dryness and the lethal radiations of interstellar space would not permit life to survive. And this theory provides no explanation as to the actual origin of life.

4. NATURALISTIC THEORY. At some time in the remote past, temperature and moisture conditions became suitable for life. The chemical elements had combined into complex but nonliving substances. From these, possibly under conditions not since duplicated, the vital step occurred to protein molecules capable of reproducing themselves. Such material (protoplasm) later became formed into units (cells) containing differentiated parts—the earliest plants or animals. The first living matter presumably utilized inorganic materials for food, like the autotrophic bacteria that make their own food. Then, with development of chlorophyll, plants such as one-celled green algae provided a means (photosynthesis) for using solar energy, and these became food for the first animals—simple protozoans. Once this stage was reached cells could begin to form aggregations, first of like units and later differentiated to form tissues with division of labor, as seen in higher organisms.

This concept of the origin of life receives support by recent studies on **viruses.** Low in the scale of living things, the viruses occur and multiply only within living cells. They are the causative agents of various diseases. Viruses are so small (about 10 to 300 mμ) they can pass through filters that stop most bacteria. They are invisible in ordinary microscopes, but images of them can be projected on the electron microscope. Viruses behave like living organisms—they multiply by genetic descent and show evidence of change (mutation) in virulence. Yet several viruses, including that of poliomyelitis, have been crystallized like inorganic substances (Fig. 1-4). The tobacco mosaic virus has now been separated into two non-

living portions, a protein and nucleic acid; when reunited, the combination again showed characteristics of life and caused infection in tobacco plants. As presently understood, however, viruses are not the ultimate link between living and nonliving matter since they can exist only in a special environment—within the cells of plants or animals—which is obviously not primitive.

14-3. Where life originated. Since many simpler and lower animals are aquatic and marine and since the cells and body fluids of all animals contain salts (NaCl and others), it is inferred that life began in the oceans. The earliest animal remains are all in rocks of marine origin. Various organisms later invaded the fresh waters and land. Some groups from the latter habitats have secondarily become marine, such as the early sharks and bony fishes, the plesiosaurs and other ancient reptiles, and the whales, seals, and sirenians among living mammals.

14-4. When life originated. One estimate places the beginning of the earth at 4,800,000,000 years ago. The oldest recognizable surface rocks (Archeozoic) are estimated to be 1,500,000,000 years old, and the first (Cambrian) that contain numerous animal remains were probably formed 500,000,000 years ago (Chap. 13). Since many groups of animals were then already differentiated, life may have begun fully 1,000,000,000 years ago. There is no conclusive evidence of any complete break in the record of life, so that conditions suitable for its existence must have prevailed somewhere on the earth throughout an enormous period of time.

14-5. Evolution. The data of astronomers indicate that the stars and the solar and other systems of the universe have undergone gradual change, or **cosmic evolution.** On the earth there is much evidence of gradual **geologic evolution** in the elevation and erosion of land masses, the transport of particles in water to form sediments, and the long-time changes in climates.

The animals now living and the many species of past times represented by fossils comprise a variety of forms progressively more complex, from the one-celled protozoans to the higher invertebrates and vertebrates. Biologists interpret the history of animals (and plants) on the earth to have been a continuing process of *organic evolution* (L. *evolvo*, unroll), which has produced the existing species. According to the doctrine of organic evolution, existing organisms are the modified but lineal descendants of other species that lived in former geological times. This is "descent with modification," the process termed "the origin of species" by Charles Darwin. The processes of evolution are considered to be still in operation and therefore capable of experimental study. Existing knowledge as to the pattern of evolution is summarized in the natural classification (Fig. 15-1; Chap. 15), which is a "genealogical tree" of the Animal Kingdom. Some similarities and differences between phyla and classes are summarized in Tables 15-1 and 28-1. Such characteristics are used in the classification of various groups at the ends of Chaps. 16 to 35.

Evidence for organic evolution is derived from comparative morphology, physiology, and embryology, from the study of fossils (paleontology), from animals and plants under domestication, from experimentation, and from other fields of biology. Scientists and many laymen

agree that there is abundant evidence for the *fact* that evolution has occurred, but there is difference of opinion as to the *processes,* or *methods,* by which evolution has taken place.

A. EVIDENCE OF EVOLUTION

14-6. Comparative morphology. All animals are alike in being composed of protoplasm organized as cells (Chap. 3). If each species had been created separately, animals might have been infinitely varied in structure with no consistent pattern and no correlation between organs of like function. Instead, we find that the larger groups of animals, although variously unlike in appearance, have similar organ systems for digestion, excretion, and other necessary functions. The members of any one group show greater structural resemblance; thus the insects have one pair of antennae, six legs, and many other features in common. Finally, the members of a species comprise animals of similar structure throughout.

In examining animals for structural evidences of evolution it is necessary to distinguish characters that are of common origin (homology), and hence indicative of common ancestry in descent, from purely adaptive fea-

Fig. 14-1. *Analogy* between wings of insects (no internal skeleton) and of vertebrates (with skeleton)—of like function but different origins. *Homology* in the wing bones of vertebrates, all derived from the common pattern of fore limb in land vertebrates, but variously modified. Pterodactyl (extinct reptile) with elongate 5th finger; bird with 1st and 5th lacking, 3d and 4th partly fused; bat with 2d to 5th fingers elongate.

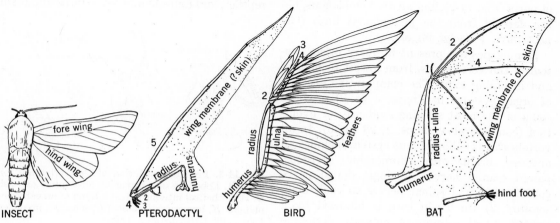

INSECT   PTERODACTYL   BIRD   BAT

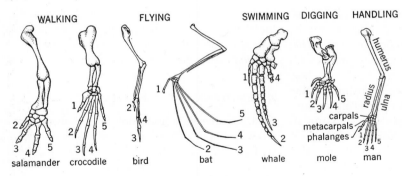

Fig. 14-2. Homology and adaptation in bones of the left fore limb in land vertebrates. The limbs are *homologous* in being composed of comparable bones (humerus, carpals, etc.), which in each kind of animal are *adapted* for special uses by differences in the length, shape, and bulk of the various bones; 1–5, digits or "fingers."

tures that are of similar function (analogy) but of unlike origin. Thus, the skeletal elements in the wings of bats, birds, and pterodactyls (extinct flying reptiles) are homologous in that all are modifications of the common pattern of fore limb in land vertebrates. The wings of insects, however, are only analogous to those of vertebrates; although used for flight, they are derived, not from limbs, but presumably as extensions of the body wall (Fig. 14-1).

Studies in comparative morphology, embryology, and paleontology make it possible to trace the derivation of appendages of vertebrates from lateral folds on the bodies of lower chordates (Figs. 28-12, 30-2) to the fins of sharks and bony fishes. The fins of some fossil fishes (CROSSOPTERYGII) furthermore contain skeletal elements that may be homologized with bones in the limbs of land vertebrates (Fig. 14-3). Limbs of the latter show a wide range in adaptive modifications for special uses by changes in length or by fusion or reduction of parts (Fig. 14-2). Yet all are homologous, being derived from the pentadactyl limb (Gr. *penta*, five + *dactyl*, finger).

Homologies are present in every organ system of the vertebrates, from lowest to highest and including man. The comparative account of organ systems in Chaps. 4 to 10 provides some of the most striking evidence for evolution (compare also Chaps. 2, 28 to 36). In all vertebrates (1) the nervous system includes an anterior brain with comparable divisions, paired cranial nerves, a single dorsal nerve cord, and paired spinal nerves to each body somite; (2) the brain case is followed by a jointed spinal column of separate vertebrae

that support the body and enclose the nerve cord; (3) the digestive tract is ventral to the vertebrae and always includes a liver and pancreas as the major digestive glands; (4) the ventrally placed heart connects to a closed system of vessels containing blood with both white and red corpuscles; and (5) the excretory and reproductive systems show many homologous features. In each system and organ there is agreement as to position in the body and general form and even in the microscopic structure of tissues. Consequently a frog, reptile, or mammal serves equally well for obtaining a basic knowledge of vertebrate anatomy.

The organ systems, however, are not exactly alike but show progressive changes from fishes to mammals. In the brain the trend (Fig. 10-3) is toward enlargement of the cerebral hemispheres, which are centers of higher mental activities, and also of the cerebellum, or center of coordination. The heart is two-chambered in fishes, three-chambered in amphibians and most reptiles, and four-chambered in birds and mam-

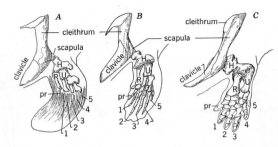

Fig. 14-3. Probable evolution of the vertebrate fore limb. *A.* Lobed fin of a Devonian crossopterygian fish. *B.* Hypothetical intermediate. *C.* Limb of an early amphibian. *H*, humerus; *R*, radius; *U*, ulna; *pr*, prepollex; 1–5, digits. (*After Gregory,* 1928.)

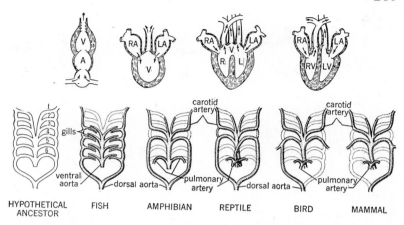

Fig. 14-4. Homology and embryonic sequence in the aortic arches and heart chambers of vertebrates. *Below.* Six pairs of arches develop in the embryos of all vertebrates, but parts indicated by dotted lines later disappear. In land vertebrates the third pair always forms the carotid arteries; the fourth becomes the systemic arches to the dorsal aorta, but only the right persists in birds and the left in mammals; the sixth arch always forms the pulmonary arteries. *Above.* The embryonic heart always begins with one auricle (*A*) and one ventricle (*V*); it remains thus in fishes; the auricle becomes divided (*RA, LA*) in amphibians; the ventricle becomes partly divided in reptiles and completely so (*RV, LV*) in birds and mammals. In embryos of higher forms the arches and chambers develop progressively through the succession of stages shown. Arrows indicate paths of blood flow. (Compare Fig. 6-6.)

mals, eventually separating completely the venous and arterial blood (Fig. 14-4). In the excretory organs, drainage of wastes is first from the coelom and later only from the blood (Fig. 8-3).

In like manner there are many homologies among invertebrates. All arthropods have segmented bodies with chitinous covering, a paired series of jointed appendages, a double ventral nerve cord, and many other features in common. A double ventral nerve cord is present also in annelid worms, primitive mollusks, and some other invertebrates.

14-7. Comparative physiology. Many basic similarities in physiological and chemical properties parallel the morphologic features of organisms.

1. A classification based on the structure of oxyhemoglobin crystals from vertebrate blood parallels the classification based on body structure. Crystals from each species are distinct, but all from a genus have some common characteristics. Furthermore, those of all birds have certain resemblances but differ from crystals obtained from blood of mammals or reptiles.

2. The precipitin tests are reactions of the blood serum. In such tests human serum is least distinct from that of anthropoid apes (gorilla, chimpanzee, etc.), more so from other primates (monkeys), and still more distinct from that of other mammals. Sera of mammals, in turn, are more sharply distinguished from those of other vertebrates.

3. Some hormones derived from endocrine glands show like reactions when injected into widely different animals. The thyroid gland in cattle controls their rate of metabolism; extracts of that gland may be fed to human beings deficient in their own thyroid secretion to speed up bodily metabolism. If beef or sheep thyroid is fed to frog tadpoles from which the thyroid gland has been removed, the tadpoles will grow normally and later metamorphose into frogs.

4. Many individual digestive enzymes present in different animals are essentially alike in physiological action. Trypsin, which acts upon proteins, occurs in many animals from protozoans to man; and amylase, which acts on starches, is present from sponges to mammals.

14-8. Comparative embryology. Except for a few specialized types of reproduction, every multicellular animal originates as a zygote, or fertilized egg (Chap. 11). The egg of each species has the distinctive ability to produce an individual of that species, but there are many features of embryonic development common to

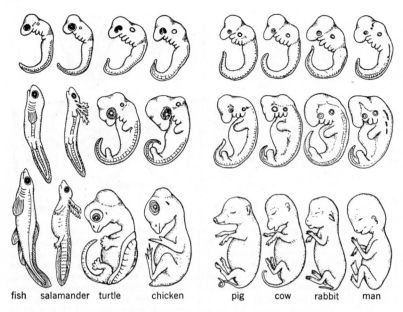

fish   salamander turtle   chicken   pig   cow   rabbit   man

Fig. 14-5. Series of vertebrate embryos in three successive and comparable stages of development. *Top.* All are much alike in the earliest stage. *Middle.* Differentiation is evident, but the four mammals (at right) are quite similar. *Bottom.* Later the distinctive characteristics of each become evident. (*After Haeckel,* 1891.)

members of any animal group. Fertilized eggs segment, pass through a blastula stage and a two-layered gastrula stage, then become variously differentiated. In many kinds of invertebrates the egg yields a trochophore larva (Fig. 15-5). Eggs of vertebrates differ somewhat in mode of cleavage according to the amount of yolk present (Fig. 11-10), but the early embryos of all are much alike; later, those of each class become recognizable, and still later family and species characters become evident (Fig. 14-5). The beginning embryo in a hen's egg (Fig. 11-13) has at first the vertebrate essentials of a notochord, dorsal nervous system, and somites; later, it acquires bird features such as a beak and wings; and, much later, there appear the characteristics of a chick instead of a pigeon or duck.

A fish embryo develops paired gill slits, gills, aortic arches, and a two-chambered heart; these all persist in the adult to serve in aquatic respiration. Comparable structures appear in a frog embryo and are necessary during the fish-like life of the frog larva in water. When the larva transforms into an air-breathing frog, however, the gills and gill slits disappear, lungs become functional for respiration in air, the aortic arches are altered to serve the adult structure,

and the heart is three-chambered for circulation of the blood both to the body and lungs. The amphibian thus begins with certain fish-like features necessary for an aquatic larva, and later these are altered for terrestrial life. Astonishingly, the early embryos of reptiles, birds, and mammals also develop a fish-like pattern of gill slits, aortic arches, and two-chambered heart (Fig. 14-6), although none of them has an aquatic larva and all respire only by lungs after birth. The embryonic gill slits soon close; the

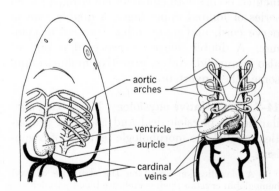

Fig. 14-6. Embryological evidence of evolution: The human embryo (3 mm. long) at right resembles adult shark at left in having a two-chambered heart, multiple aortic arches, and cardinal veins. (Compare Figs. 6-3, 6-6, 14-4, 30-4.)

multiple aortic arches become the carotids and other arteries (Fig. 14-4); and the heart soon becomes three-chambered, later having four chambers in birds and mammals.

The presence of gill slits and multiple aortic arches in embryos of reptiles, birds, and mammals is not explained by a theory of special creation, but under a theory of evolution they are obviously ancestral relics. The fossil record indicates that aquatic, gill-breathing vertebrates preceded the air-breathing land forms. In point of time their sequence of appearance was fishes, amphibians, reptiles, birds, and mammals (Fig. 13-15). The amphibians represent a transitional phase, through which each frog still passes from aquatic respiration to air breathing (Fig. 2-20).

Many other features in embryonic development and adult structure have a similar significance. In all land vertebrates the first embryonic gill pouch on each side is converted into a Eustachian tube connecting the pharynx and cavity of the middle ear. In a fish the gill region is supported by a series of visceral (branchial) arches (par. 31-5); and in higher vertebrates, including man, certain cartilages and bones of the jaws, middle ear, and larynx are derived from the embryonic "visceral arches" (Fig. 14-7).

The zoological position of some animals that are of degenerate form in the adult stages has been established only by study of their embryonic and larval stages. The larvae of barnacles (Fig. 25-14) show that these animals belong among the crustaceans, and the peculiar parasitic barnacle *Sacculina* (Fig. 25-16) can be recognized as a crustacean only during its larval existence. Likewise, the tunicates (Fig. 28-7) were found to be chordates only by a study of their larval characteristics; the degenerate form of the adults gives no clue to their real position among animals.

These and many other facts illustrate the "laws" of embryonic development stated by Von Baer (German, 1792–1876): (1) General characters appear before special characters. (2) From the more general the less general and finally the special characters develop. (3) An

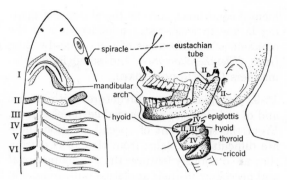

Fig. 14-7. Derivatives of embryonic visceral arches in man compared with the branchial arches (I–VI) supporting the gills in an adult shark. In man these become: I, lower jaw (only Meckel's cartilage) and malleus and incus of middle ear; II, styloid process of skull, stylohyoid ligament, lesser horn of hyoid, and stapes of middle ear; III, greater horn of hyoid; IV, thyroid cartilage of larynx and part of epiglottis; V, cricoid and arytenoid cartilages of larynx. Auditory ossicles shown in heavy black. The human maxilla (upper jaw) is a membrane bone of later origin.

animal during development departs progressively from the form of other animals. (4) The young stages of an animal are like the young (or embryonic) stages of other animals lower in the scale, but not like the adults of those animals. The oft-quoted "theory of recapitulation," or "biogenetic law," of Haeckel (German, 1834–1919) states that an individual organism in its development (ontogeny) tends to recapitulate the stages passed through by its ancestors (phylogeny). Haeckel's theory has been both stoutly defended and vigorously criticized by different biologists; Von Baer's "laws" provide a more accurate statement.

Many factors complicate the picture of embryonic development in its bearing on evolution. To the ancient (palingenetic) characters of embryos have been added other modern (cenogenetic) characters. Some of the latter appear early in the development of an individual, as, for example, the embryonic membranes of reptiles, birds, and mammals. These are "new" features, not present in the lower vertebrates, but essential for protecting embryos of land vertebrates (Fig. 11-15). Another complication is the omission or telescoping of developmental features in relation to special environmental conditions, such as the absence of float-ing larvae in fresh-water crustaceans and the omission of larval stages of some tree-dwelling frogs (*Eleutherodactylus*) and some land sala-manders (Plethodontidae).

14-9. Vestigial organs. Structures without use and of reduced size are termed *vestigial organs*. From the standpoint of special creation these are difficult to explain; from that of evolution they are obviously features that were functional and necessary in their ancestors but are now in process of disappearance from living organ-isms. Various cave-dwelling fishes, crayfishes, and insects have the eyes reduced or absent, whereas their respective relatives that live out in the open possess eyes. Traces of the pelvic girdle and hind limbs occur in boas (Fig. 33-8) and in whales. Whalebone whales lack teeth as adults, but tooth buds occur in their embryos. "Scarce as hens' teeth" does not apply to bird embryos, which have transient tooth buds; cer-tain fossil birds (Fig. 34-17) had teeth as adults. The flightless kiwi (Fig. 34-19) of New Zealand has degenerate wings with only rudimentary bones, and the great moas of that land lacked wings completely. The living horses have splint bones, which are vestiges of toes present in an-cestral horses (Fig. 14-13).

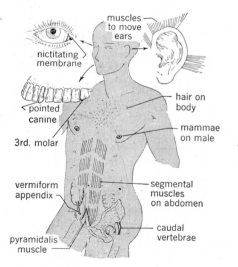

Fig. 14-8. Some vestigial structures in the human body. (*Partly after Kahn.*)

Fully 90 vestigial features are present in the human body; conspicuous examples are shown in Fig. 14-8. The horse, rodents, and some other mammals have a large caecum or appendix as an accessory digestive chamber. In man the appendix is a slender vestige about $2\frac{1}{2}$ inches long that serves no useful function and often is a site of infection requiring surgical removal. The external ears of mammals are moved by special muscles; lacking need for such move-ment in man the muscles are usually reduced and nonfunctional. In the inner angle of the human eye is a whitish membrane (plica semi-lunaris) representing the transparent nictitat-ing membrane, or third eyelid, to be seen in the cat, bird, frog, and other land vertebrates. The human "wisdom teeth," or posterior molars, are smaller and more variable than the other molars and irregular as to time or manner of eruption; this suggests that they are becoming useless and may eventually disappear.

14-10. The fossil record. Important evidence of evolution comes from the study of *fossils*.[1]

Leonardo da Vinci (Italian, 1452–1519) was the first to recognize that fossils were evidences of animal life in the past. The first important studies of fossils were made by the French com-parative anatomist, Georges Cuvier (1769–1832). In 1800 he published an account of fossil elephants, relating them to living forms; later, in a classification of fishes, he included both liv-ing and fossil species. Cuvier, however, believed in special creation, and it was Darwin who first showed that fossils were evidence of the conti-nuity and evolution of organisms. *Paleontology* (Gr. *palaios*, ancient), the study of fossils, is now an important science that links zoology and geology and provides many facts of evolu-tion.

The geological record of past life is variously imperfect. It is like the remnants of a book that lacks all the beginning chapters, contains only scattered pages or parts of pages in the central portion, and retains an increasing number of in-

[1] The nature of fossils, means for estimating their age, and their distribution in time are discussed in Chap. 13. Various fossils are discussed in Chaps. 16 to 35, and the fossil history of man is outlined in Chap. 36.

Fig. 14-9. A sample of the geological column: Succession of strata in north wall of the Grand Canyon, Ariz. (compare Fig. 13-15). Eras and periods are marked (names in parentheses are of local rock formations). One fault line is shown. Two unconformities (*Un*) mark long gaps in the record; below each the rocks were deformed, elevated, and finally far eroded before the layer next above was deposited. This site has no rocks of the Ordovician, Silurian, and Devonian periods or of the Mesozoic and Cenozoic eras. (*Photo by U.S. Geological Survey.*)

tact pages or parts of chapters toward the end. Records of past life result from a succession of accidental events: (1) The remains of a dead animal escape destruction and (2) become buried in sediment or ash that (3) survives undue heating, crushing, or folding such as would destroy the fossil. (4) The sediment or rock becomes elevated as a part of the land and (5) escapes destructive erosion by water or wind. Finally (6) the fossil becomes exposed or is dug out and comes to the attention of a paleontologist. Some fossil remains are complete, but many are fragmentary, and all the known fossils represent only a fraction of the many plant and animal species that lived in the past. Some species or groups may never have become fossils because they were soft-bodied or because

they lived where fossilization could not occur. Many fossils have been destroyed by alteration of the rocks or by erosion, and any now in rocks deep in the earth or under the sea are inaccessible.

14-11. Invertebrates. Rocks formed prior to Cambrian time have since been so folded and distorted that they now reveal few organic relics. Yet animals must then have been in existence for a long time, because the Cambrian rock strata, the oldest with many fossils, contain remains of numerous invertebrates. These include protozoans, sponges, jellyfishes, worms, brachiopods, echinoderms (sea cucumbers, crinoids), mollusks (gastropods, cephalopods), and arthropods (crustaceans, trilobites). The begin-

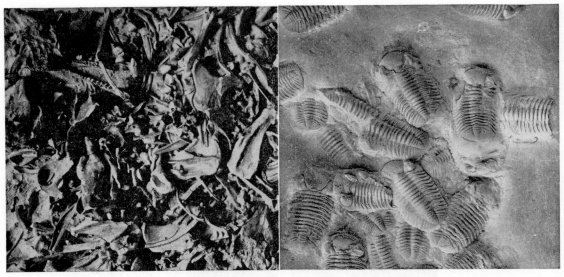

Fig. 14-10. Representative fossils; covering matrix of rock removed. *Left.* Fossil bone bed from the Miocene of Nebraska containing remains of rhinoceroses and other mammals. *Right.* Accumulation of Devonian trilobites. (*Left, from American Museum of Natural History; right, from U.S. National Museum.*)

nings of most invertebrate phyla and of some classes cannot be traced, but the rise, continuance, and decline or extinction of others are well recorded. The trilobites (Fig. 27-15) were dominant when the record opens in the Cambrian; they increased in numbers and variety, then

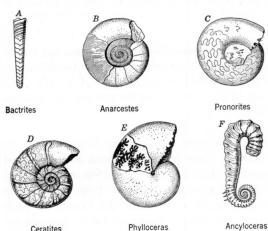

Fig. 14-11. Trends in evolution of the fossil ammonites (Phylum Mollusca, Class Cephalopoda), showing the coiling and later uncoiling of the shell and the changes in form of the sutures (shown by fine lines; black in *E*). All reduced, but not to same scale. (*From University of California Museum of Paleontology.*)

disappeared entirely in the Permian when there was continental elevation, greater aridity, and glaciation. The lamp shells (Brachiopoda, Fig. 21-14) were abundant throughout the Paleozoic era (456 genera) and less numerous in the Mesozoic (177 genera) but persist today with about 70 genera and 225 species. The living *Lingula* is much as it was in the Ordovician, 400,000,000 years ago, and is perhaps the oldest living genus of animals. The ammonites (Class Cephalopoda) began in the late Silurian. Like the pearly nautilus (par. 23-17) their shells comprise a succession of chambers, with the animal in the largest and terminal chamber. The gross form of the shell changed through time (Figs. 14-11, 14-12), and the sutures between successive chambers are simpler in the older stocks and more complex in those of later periods. The first chambers formed by some of the later ammonites were simple, like those of their ancestors. Then, surprisingly, some of the last of the ammonites had simpler sutures again and their shells were coiled in the young but straight in the adult parts. Finally the entire line of ammonites ended in the Cretaceous. The great Phylum Arthropoda was represented by aquatic crustaceans, trilobites, and king crabs in the Cambrian period. Scorpions, the first air-breathing and land animals, appeared in the Silurian. The winged insects appear suddenly in the Carboniferous, as several differentiated orders, and give no ready clue as to which arthropod type they stem from.

14-12. Vertebrates. The origins of the vertebrates are shrouded by imperfections in the geological record. Early stocks are thought to have been in fresh waters, from which no fossil-bearing strata have been found. The oldest vertebrate relics were evidently washed down to become embedded in marine deposits.

No vertebrate remains have been found in Cambrian rocks. Ordovician strata contain fragments possibly of ostracoderms, which were ancestral to cyclostomes, the lowest living vertebrates, without jaws or paired appendages. Silurian deposits have many ostracoderms and also spines and plates probably of placoderms, the earliest jawed vertebrates. By early Devonian time placoderms were abundant but ostracoderms less numerous. Further along in Devonian, however, both sharks and bony fishes appeared and then became abundant. Amphibians, with paired limbs, also are in the record of late Devonian. The reptiles undoubtedly began during the Carboniferous because by the end of that period there were already several specialized types. Thenceforth, from the Permian to the Cretaceous, they were the dominant animals of land, sea, and fresh waters. Many became large in size, such as the brontosaurs, dinosaurs, and plesiosaurs. All the great reptiles disappeared at the end of the Cretaceous. Meanwhile, the first small reptile-like mammals began in the Triassic, and the first known birds appeared in the Jurassic. Early in the Tertiary (Paleocene) the mammals blossomed into a great variety, including some existing orders and others since vanished. The early forms were replaced by more modern types, and the mammals reached a peak of diversity in the Miocene. Since then they have declined, a considerable number having become extinct at the end of the Pleistocene, just pre-

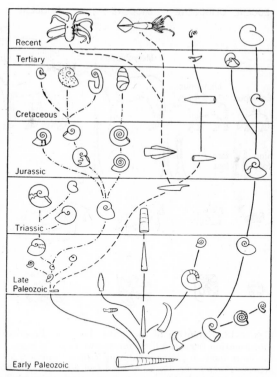

Fig. 14-12. An interpretation of evolution in the cephalopods. NAUTILOIDEA (solid lines), DIBRANCHIA (broken lines), and † AMMONOIDEA (dots and dashes). (Compare Figs. 14-11, 23-16.) (*After Raymond, Prehistoric life, reprinted by permission of the President and Fellows of Harvard College.*)

ceding the present or Recent period in which we live. Thus, despite the fragmentary nature of the early record, ascending the geological column the vertebrate types appear in an orderly time sequence that corresponds to the increasing structural complexity of the groups living today.

14-13. Horses. The Family EQUIDAE provides about the most complete record of evolution in an animal series (Fig. 14-13), leading to the existing horses, asses, and zebras of the Old World. Much of their ancestral development occurred in North America, but horses died out there late in the Pleistocene (or early in Recent time), for reasons unknown. The wild horses of the western states in the last five centuries all derived from stocks that were

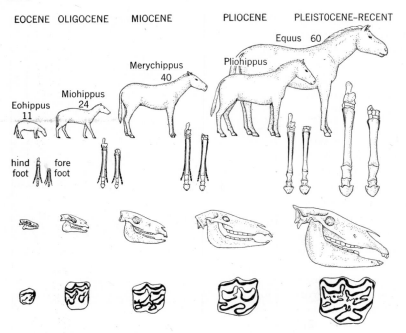

EOCENE OLIGOCENE   MIOCENE   PLIOCENE   PLEISTOCENE-RECENT

Equus 60

Merychippus   Pliohippus
40

Miohippus
24

Eohippus
11

hind   fore
foot   foot

Fig. 14-13. Evolution of the horse. *Top row.* Progressive change in size and conformation from the little forest-dwelling *Eohippus* of the Eocene epoch to the large modern plains-inhabiting *Equus* (numbers are height at shoulder in inches). *Second row.* Bones of hind feet and forefeet showing reduction in lateral toes (solid black), from *Eohippus* with three hind and four front toes to *Equus* with only the third toe functional on each foot; the second and fourth represented by splints. *Third row.* Skulls showing changes in size and outline, and closing of postorbital process. *Bottom row.* Grinding surfaces of second upper molar showing increasing complexity of enamel pattern (black). (*Top row adapted from R. S. Lull, Fossils, courtesy of The University Society, New York; others from W. D. Matthew, 1913, and R. A. Stirton, 1940.*)

brought in and escaped from early explorers and settlers.

The principal changes in the horses down through time include the following: (1) increase in size from that of a cat to some larger than existing horses; (2) enlargement and lengthening of the head anterior to the eyes; (3) increased length and mobility of the neck; (4) changes of the premolar and molar teeth from types suited for browsing to types suited for grazing (surface cusps, short crowns, and rooted vs. many enamel ridges, tall crowns, and rootless); (5) elongation of the limbs for speedy running, but with loss of rotational movement and fusion of bones in the foreleg to provide better hinge joints, together with support of the weight on the radius and tibia; and (6) reduc-

tion of the toes from five to one long toe (third) on each foot, which is covered by a hoof (claw); the lateral toes dwindle as "dew claws," and finally only small bones of the second and fourth toes persist as splints. By these changes the horse became a long-legged, swift-running mammal suited to live and feed on open grasslands, with tall teeth having many enamel edges to grind harsh grassy vegetation through a relatively long life.

The real origin of horses is unknown. The record begins with †*Eohippus* in the lower Eocene of North America and Europe. It was a browsing forest dweller, about 11 inches tall, with a short neck and head and a full set of 44 small short-crowned and rooted teeth that lacked cement. The front foot had four func-

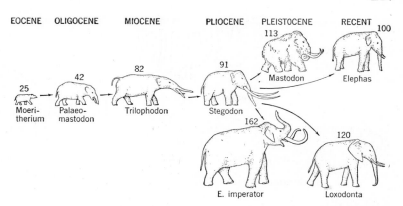

EOCENE   OLIGOCENE   MIOCENE   PLIOCENE   PLEISTOCENE   RECENT

Fig. 14-14. Phylogeny of the elephants, showing increase in size and in relative length of tusks and proboscis since Eocene time. Other lines of descent that later became extinct are omitted. Numbers indicate height at shoulder in inches. (*Adapted from Osborn, and from R. S. Lull, Fossils, The University Society, New York.*)

tional toes, but the hind foot only three, the first and fifth toes being represented by tiny splints. †*Mesohippus* of the Oligocene was the size of a sheep, with taller but rooted molars and three functional toes on each foot; the lateral toes were smaller and only one splint (fifth) persisted on the forefoot. By Miocene time, several lines (†*Parahippus*, †*Merychippus*) had developed, including both browsing and grazing types. During Pliocene there were several distinct groups of horses (†*Pliohippus*, etc.) grazing on the plains of North America. Some spread to Eurasia, and †*Hippidium* to South America, the latter giving rise to some short-limbed genera that did not survive the Pleistocene. The lateral toes were reduced to dew claws that did not touch the ground. The cheek teeth were longer, with short roots, more folding of the enamel, and cement between the folds. Finally the earliest one-toed horses developed, during the Pliocene in North America, and later they spread to all the continents except Australia. In Pleistocene, there were ten or more species (*Equus*) of various sizes in North America, all of which disappeared in prehistoric time. Evolution of the horses followed known changes in Tertiary landscapes from moist forest to dryish grasslands.

14-14. Elephants. The stout bones and teeth of elephants and their allies have left a well-documented story of evolution in the Order Proboscidea (Fig. 14-14). This begins in the late Eocene of northern Egypt with †*Moeritherium*, a creature about 2 feet high having a long narrow head that was elevated posteriorly and possibly a flexible snout since the nasal openings were behind the tip of the jaw. It had 36 teeth, the second incisors in each jaw were short tusks, and the molar teeth had crossrows of cusps. †*Palaeomastodon* of the Oligocene in Egypt was larger, with the skull and brain case more elevated and the nostrils farther back; there was probably a long snout or proboscis. The tusks were longer, other incisors and the canines had disappeared to leave 26 teeth, and all cheek teeth were functional at the same time. This and other forms (†*Phiomia*) spread to India and later to Eurasia. †*Trilophodon* of the Miocene reached North America. It had a long lower jaw and upper tusks, but only two molars in each jaw; these were bigger and had more transverse rows of cusps. Because of the length of its jaw, †*Trilophodon* may not have been a direct ancestor of later forms. Other collateral lines developed among the proboscidians but did not survive to later epochs. The long-faced †*Gomphotherium* of the Miocene and Pliocene was of wide occurrence and may have given rise to both elephants and mastodons.

No proboscidians are now native to the Americas, but four types inhabited North America during Pleistocene time, and mastodons lived in South America during the late Pliocene and Pleistocene. The mastodon (†*Mastodon americanus*) was about 9½ feet tall and had long coarse hair. It inhabited forests of Canada and the United States and probably was hunted by the earliest Indians. The mammoth (*Elephas* †*primigenius*) that ranged across

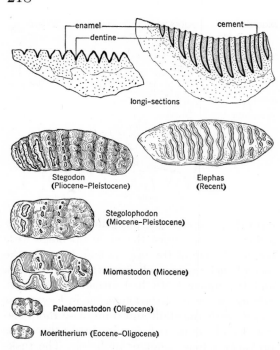

Fig. 14-15. Evolution of teeth in elephants (third lower left molar) through geological time, × ⅛. The progressive increase in size was accompanied by change of grinding surface from few rows of low conical cusps to many cross ridges of enamel, together with deepening of the enamel folds. The six lower figures show exposed grinding surface, the upper two are longitudinal sections of †*Stegodon* and *Elephas*.

the Northern Hemisphere was about 9 feet high and covered with dense wool. It was hunted by Paleolithic men in Europe who pictured it in cave drawings; fleshy remains of mammoths have been recovered in the frozen soil of Siberia and Alaska. The Columbian elephant (*E.* †*columbi*) was 11 feet high and had incurved tusks; in early Pleistocene it roamed the warmer parts of North America south to Florida and the Mexican tablelands. The huge imperial elephant (*E.* †*imperator*) grew to 13½ feet high and was probably a plains dweller from Pliocene to mid-Pleistocene. The living elephants of India and Africa (*Elephas, Loxodonta*) have two large tusks in the upper jaw and but one molar functional in each jaw at a time. The molars have many transverse ridges of enamel, between which the softer dentine and cement are worn down by the coarse foods (Fig. 14-15).

14-15. Human evolution. Many kinds of evidence (Chap. 36) indicate that man is a product of evolution. In both gross and microscopic *structure* the human body resembles closely that of the anthropoid apes, is like that of other primates, and has much in common with mammals generally (compare Figs. 4-5, 5-3, 36-2 to 36-4). Homologies with other vertebrates are present in every organ system; some vestigial organs of man have already been mentioned (Fig. 14-8). Strictly human characteristics such as the upright posture, opposable thumbs, flattened vertical face, scant body hair, and greatly increased brain are differences in degree and not in kind from other mammals. Many relationships in *function* (physiology) parallel those of structure; in both man and anthropoids there are comparable blood groups, human blood can be distinguished by immunological tests from all others except anthropoids, and some mouth protozoans are common to man and other primates. The earlier *embryonic development* of man is essentially as for other mammals (Fig. 14-5) and includes temporary gill slits and multiple aortic arches (Fig. 14-6). The *fossil record* of mankind includes a series of types (Fig. 36-8) that gradually approach the form of existing human races. Man's superior attainments over all other organisms are primarily matters of habits and behavior; these include social organization, modification of the environment to his own advantage, development of tools and of language, and the ability to transmit learning by teaching.

B. THEORIES OF EVOLUTION

Any effort to account for existing organisms and fossils should explain their origins, their likenesses and differences, their adaptations to various environments, and their distribution on the earth. Theories of special creation assume organisms to have been produced by a supernatural agency that provided for all such features. Theories of organic evolution postulate that since life began on the earth it has been continuous and that later organisms have been derived from earlier forms by the inheritance of variations, either large or small, and induced either by the environment or by processes within the animals. Evolutionary processes are considered to be slow in action and therefore difficult to test experimentally.

Primitive human races have various myths to "explain" the origin of man and animals by the creative acts of supernatural powers. Until the last century most persons, including such scientists as Linnaeus, Cuvier, Agassiz, and Owen, believed that species had been created separately. Cuvier thought the disappearance of fossil species had resulted from a series of catastrophes, the last being the Biblical flood, and that after each of these the earth had been repopulated by new creations of higher types. The belief in catastrophes was dispelled by the Scottish geologist Charles Lyell (1797–1875), who showed in his *Principles of Geology* (1830–1833) that the geological processes of sedimentation, uplift, and erosion are essentially continuous.

Some early Greek philosophers had vague notions of an evolutionary process, but Aristotle (384–322 B.C.), the first notable zoologist, thought that organisms were molded by a "perfecting principle," and his ideas prevailed for centuries (par. 1-7). Buffon (French, 1707–1788) was the first modern biologist to discard the concept of special creation. He believed that animals were plastic, that small variations produced by the environment were accumulated to make larger differences, and that each animal in the ascending series of types was transformed from some simpler ancestor. Erasmus Darwin (English, 1731–1802), grandfather of Charles Darwin, added the further idea that functional responses to external stimuli were inherited.

14-16. Lamarck and the inheritance of acquired characteristics. The first general theory of evolution was proposed by Jean Baptiste de Lamarck (French, 1744–1829), an anatomist and student of classification. His theory was outlined in 1801 and set forth fully in his *Philosophie zoologique* (1809). Lamarck recognized a fundamental continuity in the diverse kinds of animals and believed that there had been progressive development in form and structure.

His theory, briefed from his own words, is as follows: The environment affects the shape and organization of animals; frequent or continuous use develops and enlarges any organ, while by permanent disuse it weakens until it finally disappears; all acquisitions or losses wrought through influence of the environment, and hence through *use and disuse,* are preserved by reproduction.

The theory may be illustrated by two of his examples. Birds, he assumed correctly, were originally terrestrial. A land bird going to seek food in water would spread its toes to strike the water in moving about. The skin at the bases of the toes would be continually stretched, and muscular movements of the legs would promote an extra flow of blood to the feet. In consequence, the skin would become enlarged as webs between the toes, as seen in ducks, pelicans, and other water birds. Disuse Lamarck illustrated by the structure of a snake. In crawling through grass its body would be stretched repeatedly to pass through narrow spaces and the legs would not be used. Long legs would interfere with crawling, and four short legs could not move the body. Legs are characteristic of reptiles, and yet the snakes lost theirs. The eyes became lateral or dorsal the better to see when on the ground, and the tongue developed as a protrusible sensory organ to detect objects in front of the snake.

There is no reliable evidence for Lamarck's theory, and it has little support today. The muscles of an athlete increase in strength and bulk with extensive use but recede if exercise is discontinued; children never inherit such acquired characteristics of a father. The docking of tails in horses, sheep, and bulldogs for many generations has not made these mutilations hereditary. Pavlov trained mice to come for food at the sound of a bell and claimed that fewer and fewer trials were needed to teach mice of succeeding generations; and MacDougall has claimed similar results in the training of rats. Neither of these experiments nor many others designed to test this theory have produced convincing results. This conclusion is not surprising when it is recalled that a new organism develops from the germ cells of its parents, not from the somatic cells of the latter. The germ cells are set aside early in the growth of an individual and are subjected to little or no effect from the body cells or environment (Chap. 11). This was demonstrated by Castle and Phillips who replaced the ovaries of a white guinea pig with those from a black female. The former was then bred twice to a black male. All the six young produced were black and homozygous.

14-17. Darwin and the theory of natural selection. Charles Darwin (1809–1882) was a methodical painstaking English naturalist of broad vision. As a young man he served (1831–1835) as naturalist on the "Beagle," a vessel that explored South America, the Galápagos Islands, and other regions. From his detailed notes and studies he wrote excellent works on barnacles, mammalian fossils, geology, and coral reefs. The facts of animal distribution and the relations between living and fossil animals learned in his travels led him to consider the origin of species. He began taking notes on the subject in 1837, and the next year read Malthus's *Essay on Population,* wherein that author showed how populations increase in geometric ratio until checked by limiting factors. Darwin then recognized the struggle for existence within all populations and concluded that in such a struggle favorable variations would be preserved and unfavorable ones eliminated. In 1844 he wrote a summary of his theory but continued to gather data from original researches and observations by himself and many other persons. Meanwhile Alfred Russel Wallace (1823–1913), another English naturalist, while studying the rich fauna and flora of the Malay Archipelago, independently and rapidly arrived at similar conclusions. In 1858 he sent an essay on the subject to his friend Darwin. Through the interest of Charles Lyell and the botanist Joseph Hooker, Wallace's essay and a brief of Darwin's conclusions were published together in the same year. In 1859 Darwin issued his theory in a book entitled *On the Origin of Species by Means of Natural Selection, or the*

Preservation of Favoured Races in the Struggle for Life.

This was the most important book of the nineteenth century. It contains (1) overwhelming evidence of the fact of evolution and (2) arguments for natural selection as the process. The doctrine of evolution was not original with Darwin, but his convincing presentation quickly won the support of scientists and of many laymen. Unscientific attacks on "Darwinism," as the theory was called, continued until after his death. Meanwhile a great scientific search began for additional facts bearing on the theory, and there was much speculation on natural selection.

The essence of Darwin's theory is as follows:

1. *Variations* of all degrees are present among individuals and species in nature.
2. By the *geometric ratio of increase* the numbers of every species tend to become enormously large; yet the population of each remains approximately constant because many individuals are eliminated by enemies, disease, competition, climate, etc.
3. This involves a *struggle for existence;* individuals having variations unsuited to the particular conditions in nature are eliminated, whereas those whose variations are favorable will continue to exist and reproduce.
4. A *process of natural selection* therefore is operative, which results in:
5. The *survival of the fittest,* or "the preservation of favored races."

14-18. Variation. Among animals that reproduce sexually no two (save identical twins) are exactly alike. The individuals of every species vary in size, proportions, coloration, external and internal structure, physiology, and habits. Darwin recognized the widespread occurrence of variations; his theory assumes but does not explain their origins. In his day the laws of inheritance (Chap. 12) were unknown, and often he could not distinguish the heritable variations, which alone are important in evolution, from nonheritable variations produced by differences in food, temperature, or other environmental factors. Darwin saw that domesticated animals and plants are more variable in many ways than wild species. He knew that man has produced many domestic races by **artificial selection,** or breeding of individuals having heritable variations (characteristics) useful for human needs; also, that practical breeders have established and improved the many breeds of livestock and varieties of cultivated plants by gradually accumulating small but useful hereditary differences through many successive generations. He rightly believed that, in most cases, all the domestic breeds of a species had been derived from one wild ancestral species—all breeds of rabbits from the European gray rabbit, and all pouters, fantails, racers, tumblers, and other widely differing breeds of pigeons from the rock dove (pars. 34-23, 35-28). Many of these breeds now differ so greatly from one another in appearance that if they occurred in the wild any zoologist would classify them as distinct species and some as different genera! The domestic breeds of a species, however, all can mate with one another and produce fertile offspring. Having shown the wide diversity of domestic types produced from ancestral stocks by selection of small variations, Darwin assumed that small heritable variations in wild species were the materials of the evolutionary process in nature.

14-19. Geometric ratio of increase. All forms of life have the potentiality of rapid increase. The protozoan *Paramecium* (0.25 mm. long) can divide by fission about 600 times per year. If all survived and continued to divide, their total bulk after some months would exceed that of the earth. The fruit fly, *Drosophila*, completes its life cycle from egg to egg in 10 to 14 days, and each female may lay 200 or more eggs. In 40 to 50 days, if all survived and bred, they would number 200,000,000; during one summer their numbers would become astronomical. Darwin assumed the elephant to breed at 30 years and live to 100 years, each female producing but 6 young; in 750 years about 19,000,000 would be alive.

The brown rat, English sparrow, and European corn borer in the United States and the European rabbit in Australia are examples of pests that have multiplied somewhat in keeping with their theoretical possibilities when introduced into new and favorable environments. Plagues of native insects and of meadow mice result at times when abundant food supplies are suddenly available and enable individuals to reproduce and mature rapidly.

14-20. Struggle for existence. Under ordinary conditions, however, animals never increase to such numbers as just indicated. The populations of most species tend to remain more or less stationary because of various checks (pars. 13-6 to 13-11). There are limitations in the food supply, shelter, and breeding places; individuals of a species compete with one another for these necessities and also with other species having similar requirements; an enlarged population of any species soon is levied upon by its predators and is a fertile field for parasites and diseases. The "struggle for existence" is not always a spectacular battle, as of a rabbit trying to escape from a fox, but is a continuing process in nature involving many factors, each of which eliminates some individuals. It acts at any stage in the life cycle of a species, from the egg, which may fail of fertilization, through embryonic development, larval stages, and adult life. Any individual animal is "successful" in the struggle for existence if it survives long enough to reproduce its kind.

14-21. Natural selection. Darwin assumed that in the struggle for existence individuals with slightly favorable variations enabling them to meet the conditions of life more successfully would survive and propagate their kind; this process Herbert Spencer termed "the survival of the fittest." Under this sort of *natural selection* those lacking such variations would perish or fail to breed so that the characters which they possessed would be eliminated from the population. In succeeding generations the process would continue and result in gradually adapting animals more perfectly to their environments. With a change in environmental conditions there would be a change in the sort of characters surviving under natural selection. A species in a changing environment or one that had migrated to some new environment would be gradually altered to suit the new conditions. Animals failing to develop suitable new variations under any particular environmental conditions would soon be eliminated. In this manner, Darwin conceived the development of adaptations of whatever sort, the "origin of species" in changed or new environments, and also the disappearance of species in past geological time. Two portions of a species population having to meet slightly differing conditions would tend to diverge from one another and in time would be separated, first by small differences as varieties or subspecies, later when isolated from each other as species that could not interbreed. A continuation of such divergence would lead in time to the production of still other species and in turn to wider differences (at the level of genus, family, etc.). In this manner, he conceived the great number of species and larger categories of the Animal Kingdom to have been established through the long duration of geological time.

Most biologists accept Darwin's theory as the best general explanation of evolution. They differ mainly in their later and better understanding of some of the essential biological processes involved, which were unknown in his day, but which have been learned by later research. Modern interpretations, based on newer knowledge, are termed *Neo-Darwinism.*

14-22. Origin of heritable variations. Darwin realized clearly that heritable variations occur in both wild and domesticated animals, but he had no knowledge as to how they are produced or of the exact manner in which they are inherited. (Mendel's precise laws, although published in 1866, were not generally known until 1900.) Starting about 1875, however, biologists began to study the processes in germ cells and their relation to reproduction; a little later careful attention was given to experimental breeding. Soon there was a wealth of new knowledge that afforded a clear understanding of the manner of origin of heritable variations and of the ways they are passed from generation to generation. In recent years experimental breeding has been accompanied by study of the related changes in germ cells; these fields are combined as *cytogenetics.* The details of chro-

mosome behavior and of genetic processes are all-important for understanding certain evolutionary processes. The essential points are as follows:

1. Chromosomes in cell nuclei carry in linear arrangement the ultramicroscopic genes responsible for development of characteristics in an individual.
2. Meiosis segregates members of homologous chromosome pairs and halves the total number for each gamete (Chap. 11).
3. Fertilization, the random union of 2 gametes of unlike sex, brings together assortments of chromosomes (and therefore of genes) from 2 parents, resulting in production of individuals with different gene combinations (Chaps. 11, 12).
4. Mutations (changes) occur in genes (Chap. 12), and chromosome rearrangements take place; both result in altering the assortment of genes (hence characteristics) passed on to succeeding generations.

Many mutations first detected in laboratory stocks of *Drosophila* now are known to occur in wild populations. Conversely, the "black" and "silver" mutations of the red fox, first known in nature, are now found in captive foxes on fur farms, where still other mutations have been discovered. From these and many other records it now seems likely that new mutations are constantly appearing in nature and that species populations are highly heterozygous. These conditions then provide a wide range of hereditary variations in wild species. Whether any particular variation will become a persistent characteristic depends upon the size of the population, the degree of isolation or segregation of small groups of individuals, and other factors.

Different mutations may be beneficial, neutral, or harmful. The huge mass of experimental data (importantly from *Drosophila* and some plants) indicate that most of those found are harmful or neutral. Mutations useful to man are well known among domestic animals and crop plants. In wild species mutations with superior adaptive value seem scarce, but this is to be expected, since any that appear are probably soon incorporated in the gene complex of the species to its advantage. Many harmful genes are damaging, however, only when homozygous (such as those of lethal characters); in the heterozygous condition, paired with their normal alleles, the majority have no unfavorable effect. A characteristic that is harmful by itself or under one set of environmental conditions may be beneficial in combination with others or under different conditions. Indeed, some experimental data show that two characters, each harmful when alone, prove beneficial when combined.

14-23. Genic change and natural selection. Chromosome recombinations and mutations result in populations with altered assemblages of old and new characters, thus increasing the total variability. As opposed to this, natural selection works in the direction of narrowing species variability by weeding out characters that are nonadaptive or of no value for survival. The total effect that the physical and biological environment imposes on individuals is the "screen" of natural selection—it passes or permits those better suited to survive and eliminates all others. Sexual reproduction provides for abundant multiplication of individuals (geometric ratio of increase), and the cellular phenomena in gene mutations, chromosome rearrangements, and fertilization add to the supply of variability; then these abundant resources are screened by natural selection.

14-24. Adaptations. All animals and plants are fitted for existence in the environments they inhabit. The degree of adaptation differs in various groups, some being narrowly or closely adapted and others being quite generalized. Adaptations commonly involve a combination of characteristics—structure, physiology, behavior, and mode of life. The honeybee (Chap. 26) shows many adaptations such as sucking mouth parts for obtaining nectar, the ability to subsist on sugars, the hairs and brushes used to gather pollen, the production and molding of wax into shelters for food and young, and an intricate pattern of habits of three castes in a social colony. Man is a generalized species, able to do many things in various ways and to live in diverse environments. The brown rat, although specialized in being a rodent, is generalized enough to live successfully in a wide variety of conditions as to climate, shelter, and

food. The mole, by contrast, is narrowly adapted for life in the ground, with slender teeth to grasp worms, eyes covered and ears reduced, short fore limbs with huge palms bearing heavy claws to dig and "swim" through soil, and short reversible fur, which is not disarranged by moving forward or backward. Different mammals show adaptive modifications of teeth for various kinds of food (Fig. 35-11), and the bills of birds are adapted in relation to their food habits (Fig. 34-11). Other conspicuous examples are seen in the many parasites that can live in only a single host species and some, like the malarial parasite and liver fluke, that must alternate between two particular hosts to complete their life cycles (Chaps. 16, 19). *Adaptive radiation* is seen in the marsupial mammals of Australia that have "radiated" into diverse forms fitted to run, jump, climb, burrow, or glide. *Adaptive convergence* often occurs when animals of different groups come to live in a common habitat. Large vertebrates of the ocean, from sharks to mammals (Fig. 14-16), all have streamlined bodies and paddle-like fins or limbs, which enable them to swim more effectively. Such adaptive characters are superimposed on the fundamental ones that make the shark a cartilaginous fish and the seal a mammal.

Many adaptive features of animals are protective in a variety of ways—by structure, function, and coloration. The shells of armadillos, turtles, and most mollusks and the quill covering of porcupines are obvious structural adaptations that protect their owners. The stinging by bees and wasps and the use of venom by poisonous snakes are examples of functional adaptations serving a similar purpose.

Animal coloration is commonly considered another sort of protective adaptation inasmuch as very many animals more or less resemble the backgrounds against which they live. Among biologists many believe that coloration (and form) render animals less likely to attack by enemies, whereas some discount its purposiveness and hold that animals are taken as prey in proportion to their numbers. The coloration

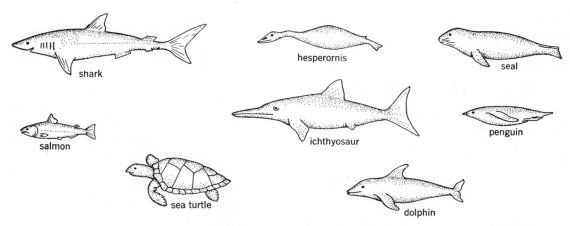

Fig. 14-16. Oceanic vertebrates, sharks to mammals, showing adaptive convergence for swimming—bodies streamlined and fins or limbs paddle-like.

of black crows and white herons obviously bears no relation to their respective environments, but by *protective coloration* many species harmonize more or less with their surroundings. Hares, weasels, and ptarmigan of the far North molt into white coats when snow covers their surroundings; the ruffed grouse has a variegated pattern that blends with the leafy backgrounds of its woods habitat. Many oceanic invertebrates and fish larvae are transparent. Bark-inhabiting insects are commonly flecked with colors of the backgrounds on which they live. These and many others are instances of camouflage, or *obliterative coloration,* whereby the outlines of the animal are obscured, save when it moves. *Warning coloration* is ascribed to some butterflies and other insects, considered to be distasteful to their enemies—they "advertise" their unpalatability. Bees and wasps with stout stings are often marked conspicuously with black and yellow.

In many instances harmless or palatable species resemble other stinging or unpalatable species. The viceroy butterfly is said to *mimic* the presumably unpalatable monarch butterfly (Fig. 14-17); and certain moths, beetles, and flies appear to have "copied" different species of wasps. Some long-horned beetles (CERAMBYCIDAE) resemble wasps in form and color and also hover about flowers in wasp fashion. One African butterfly (*Papilio dardanus*) corre-

sponds in color and form to three distasteful species of butterflies with which it occurs, three distinct types of females being produced by a single pair of parents.

Some insects show *protective resemblance* to objects in their surroundings by *both* form and color; a certain geometrid caterpillar rests in a position that resembles a twig of the tree on which it lives; a butterfly (*Kallima*) of India when resting with folded wings resembles a dead leaf; some walkingsticks (ORTHOPTERA) are like dead or green twigs and others like green leaves.

Recognition marks, or signals, are employed by some species of animals to aid in identification by others of their species and to warn the latter of danger. The white outer tail feathers of juncos, meadow larks, and other birds, the white rump patch on the American antelope, and the cottony-white tail of cottontail rabbits are all flashed into view when these animals are frightened.

Adaptations undoubtedly evolve over long periods of time, but there are some recent instances of rapid adjustment. For many years hydrocyanic acid gas proved successful in control of the red scale (Family COCCIDAE) on citrus trees in southern California; but by 1914 the standard fumigation dosage had become inadequate in one district, and later in adjacent localities. Investigation by Quayle and others

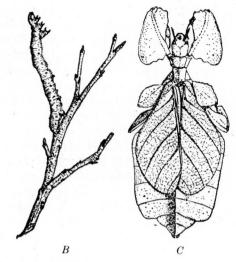

A

B   C

Fig. 14-17. Mimicry and protective resemblance. *A*. Viceroy butterfly (*Basilarchia archippus*) above, which mimics the monarch butterfly (*Danaus plexippus*) below. *B*. Moth larva in resting attitude resembling a twig. *C*. South American leaf insect, *Phyllium* (Order ORTHOPTERA). All × ⅔. (*B, C, after Wolcott, Animal biology.*)

showed that there were two races of the insect, one cyanide-resistant and the other not. At a certain concentration of the gas, 45 per cent of the former but only 4 per cent of the latter survived. Crossing the two races showed them to differ in one sex-linked gene of "HCN resistance." Similarly resistant stocks have appeared after years of spray control in other citrus pests and in larvae of the codling moth in apples. More recently among house fly populations sprayed with DDT, resistant stocks resulted after only a few generations. In these cases man has applied a new selective factor to the store of variability that included genes for both resistance and nonresistance.

Another rather quick adjustment was that of "industrial melanism" among moths in factory districts of England, Germany, and other European countries. With the increased outpouring of coal smoke that backened local vegetation, melanic variants of several species of moths appeared and spread. Over several dec-

ades they became more frequent and finally replaced the original paler stocks. Breeding experiments showed the darker moths to differ in one or a few genes and to have greater vigor. Darkish mutants were present but presumably did not survive in earlier times because they were not protectively colored (concealed from predators) on the clean vegetation then present.

14-25. Preadaptation. Within the store of variability of any species are many characters that are of no use in its immediate environment. Such characters may increase the potential adaptability of the species to new conditions. With a change to a colder climate, for example, a species with the potentiality to complete its life cycle during a shorter growing season will be able to survive or to invade areas beyond its original range. A species would be ***preadapted*** if able to survive under conditions to which it had not previously been exposed.

14-26. Orthogenesis. In some stocks of fossil and recent animals, evolution seems to have proceeded along rather direct courses. Examples are the progressive reduction of digits and the enlargement of teeth in horses; the increase in tusk length and size and the reduction in number of molar teeth in elephants; and the successive elaboration of horns from small "nubbins" to great unwieldy growths on titanotheres (fossil mammals). The term **orthogenesis** (Gr. *orthos,* straight) has been applied to this phenomenon, implying that evolution has been directed by some internal but unknown factor. The linear elaboration of a feature beyond the limits of apparent usefulness has been explained, on a Darwinian basis, by assuming that characteristics seemingly unfavorable may actually have a survival value at some short but critical period in the life of the species.

14-27. Isolation and speciation. Darwin's title for his book *The Origin of Species* indicates the level at which evolution takes place. Changes (mutations, chromosome rearrangements, etc.) occur in individual animals, and then by sexual reproduction are either preserved and spread through a population or are eliminated (natural selection). **Speciation,** the process by which new species are formed, is inseparably associated with isolation.

The number of individuals in many species is enormous—hundreds of thousands in common birds and mammals and millions or billions in widespread insects. The population of any one species, however, is not uniform in either distribution or characteristics. First, the individuals are not distributed evenly throughout the entire geographic range but are subdivided into smaller groups more or less isolated from one another. Each occupies a part of the range, and groups do not intermingle except along their boundaries because of limited powers of locomotion or various barriers. Second, the groups differ from one another qualitatively (size, color, etc.); these differences blend where representatives of different groups can interbreed (hybridize) along group boundaries. The term **race** or **subspecies** (Fig.

14-18) is applied to such local populations. In some species the population is not broken into distinguishable groups but shows gradual continuous change of characteristics along a gradient—north to south, lowlands to highlands, or dry to moist climate. Such cases, known as **clines,** are exemplified by species of birds and mammals that are larger in cooler climates or darker in warm humid regions. Evidence from several fields—taxonomy, migration, experimental breeding, cytology, serology—shows that many a "species" in the ordinary sense is actually composed of numerous biological strains, stocks, or races.

Isolation, the segregation of stocks into smaller units, may be brought about in several ways: (1) **geographical,** by physical separation in distance; (2) **ecological,** in different types of environments, although in the same general region; (3) **seasonal,** where two populations breed at different times of year; (4) **physiological,** where there is functional incompatibility in mating or in the production, fertilization, and survival of gametes; and (5) **behavioral,** where animals of two different groups will not mate with one another.

Species populations or subdivisions of a population separated by distance or other barriers are termed **allopatric.** Two or more different populations occupying the same area that maintain their distinctness are **sympatric.**

With random mating in a large and freely interbreeding population, the variability is usually high and constant. In small isolated populations, however, it is reduced rather rapidly and the genotype tends to become homozygous. Purely by chance, such populations tend to differ from one another in slight ways and become distinct stocks or races.

The effects of isolation on speciation are well shown by "Darwin's finches," birds of the subfamily Geospizinae on the Galápagos Islands 600 miles off Ecuador. This group of oceanic islands, the largest 80 miles long, probably originated as volcanoes. The plant cover is diverse, thorn and cactus in lowlands where the ground is of jagged lava, but changing to moist forest in rich black soil on the mountain tops

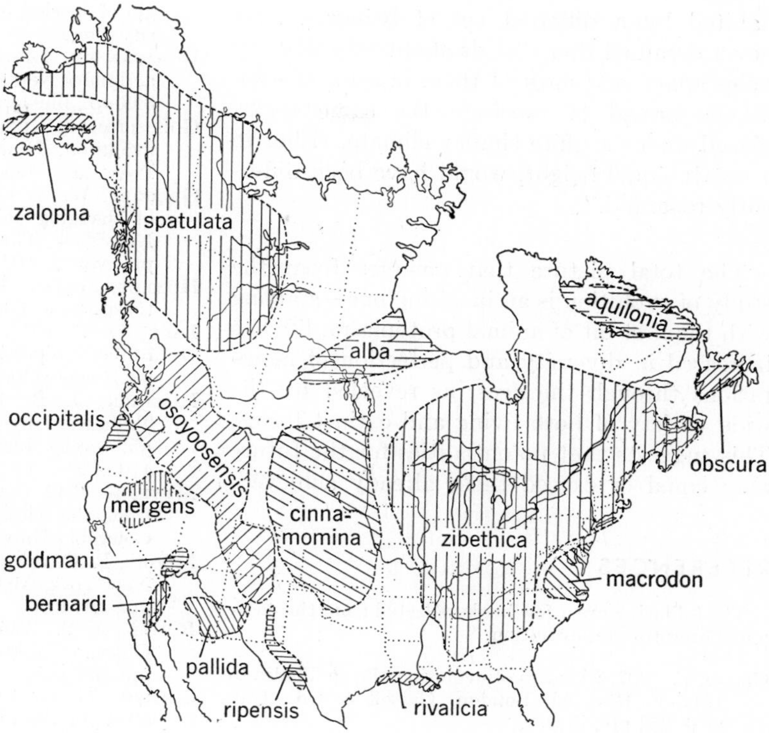

Fig. 14-18. Native geographical distribution of the muskrat (*Ondatra zibethica*), a species divided into geographic races or subspecies (*O. z. zibethica*, *O. z. alba*, etc.) that differ from one another in average characters of size, coloration, skull features, etc. Each subspecies occupies a distinct range (outlined by broken lines). Adjacent subspecies may intergrade along their boundaries; gaps between ranges of some subspecies indicate areas of unsuitable habitat where no muskrats live. (*From data supplied by the U.S. Fish and Wildlife Service.*)

of 2,000 to 4,000 feet. Giant land tortoises and iguanas are the only large animals. Most distinctive of the few resident land birds are the finches which have developed into 14 species. In turn, on separate islands, some have diverged further into subspecies or less distinct populations. In the Darwinian view small differences so produced lead to "incipient species" and speciation is regarded as complete when two such forms later meet and remain distinct. Thus, on Charles Island there are two closely related species of insectivorous tree finches that do not interbreed; presumably they evolved on adjacent islands and later came together.

These finches illustrate another aspect of evolution—*adaptive radiation.* Ancestors of the Galápagos plants and animals must have been transported there by accidental means (par. 13-19). When the original finch stock arrived, there were probably few or no competitors or enemies. Under such circumstances the new arrivals would increase in numbers to the limit of the food supply and would become extremely variable. Competition then would develop for food; individuals capable of eating different types of food would be more likely to survive and reproduce their kind. Under this competitive pressure diversity resulted. Some of the types among the "finches" are (1) seed eaters (*Geospiza*) with stout conical beak; (2) flower and nectar feeders (*Cactornis*) with long tapered beak; (3) bud, leaf, and fruit eaters (*Platyspiza*) with beak suggestive of a parrot; (4) insect eaters (*Certhidea*) with slender bill and habits of a warbler; and (5) a woodpecker type (*Camarhynchus*) with stout, straight beak for digging in tree trunks—lacking the long tongue of a true woodpecker, it uses a twig or cactus spine when probing.

These inconspicuous finches, on a group of remote tropical islands, have had an important part in evolutionary thought ever since the young Darwin (*Voyage of the Beagle*) wrote: "by far the most remarkable feature in the natural history of this archipelago . . . is, that the different islands to a considerable extent are inhabited by a different set of beings. . . . I never dreamed that islands about fifty or sixty miles apart, and most of them in sight of each other, formed of precisely the same rocks, placed under a quite similar climate, rising to a nearly equal height, would have been differently tenanted."

The total picture that emerges from the study of evolution is an inspiring one—starting with the first bit of animal protoplasm, life has increased in diversity and perfection of adaptations through the ages, as revealed by the wide variety of both living and extinct forms. This suggests that potentialities for the future may equal or exceed those already achieved.

REFERENCES

The following are a few books selected from the enormous literature on evolution.

CLODD, E. 1907. Pioneers of evolution: From Thales to Huxley. Rev. ed. London, Cassell & Co., Ltd. xi + 252 pp., illus.

DARWIN, CHARLES. 1859. On the origin of species by means of natural selection, or the preservation of favoured races in the struggle for life. London, John Murray. ix + 502 pp. Five subsequent editions by author; often reprinted.

DE VRIES, HUGO. 1909. The mutation theory, experiments and observations on the origin of species in the vegetable kingdom. La Salle, Ill., The Open Court Publishing Co. 2 vols., xv + 582 pp., 119 figs.; vii + 683 pp., 6 pls., 147 figs.

DOBZHANSKY, THEODOSIUS. 1951. Genetics and the origin of species. 3d ed. New York, Columbia University Press. x + 364 pp., illus.

DOBZHANSKY, THEODOSIUS. 1955. Evolution, genetics, and man. New York, John Wiley & Sons, Inc. 8 + 398 pp., illus.

GOLDSCHMIDT, RICHARD. 1940. The material basis of evolution. New Haven, Conn., Yale University Press. xi + 436 pp., 83 illus.

GREGORY, W. K. 1951. Evolution emerging: a survey of changing patterns from primeval life to man. New York, The Macmillan Co. Vol. 1, xxvi + 736 pp.; vol. 2, 1,013 pp. of illus.

HUXLEY, JULIAN. 1942. Evolution: the modern synthesis. New York, Harper & Brothers. 645 pp.

LACK, D. L. 1947. Darwin's finches. London, Cambridge University Press. x + 208 pp., 27 figs., 8 pls., some colored.

LAMARCK, J. B. 1809. La philosophie zoologique. Translated by Hugh Elliot, 1914, as Zoological philosophy. London, Macmillan & Co., Ltd. xcii + 410 pp.

MAYR, E. 1942. Systematics and the origin of species from the viewpoint of a zoologist. New York, Columbia University Press. xiv + 334 pp., 29 figs.

MOORE, R. C. 1949. Introduction to historical geology. New York, McGraw-Hill Book Co., Inc. ix + 582 pp., 364 figs.

ROMER, A. S. 1945. Vertebrate paleontology. 2d ed. Chicago, University of Chicago Press. ix + 687 pp., 377 figs.

SIMPSON, G. G. 1949. The meaning of evolution: a study of the history of life and of its significance for man. New Haven, Conn., Yale University Press. xv + 364 pp., 38 figs.

———. 1951. The meaning of evolution. Rev. and abridged ed. New York, Mentor Books, The New American Library. 192 pp., 22 figs.

———. 1953. The major features of evolution. New York, Columbia University Press. xx + 434 pp., 52 figs.

WEISMANN, AUGUST. 1904. The evolution theory. London, Edward Arnold & Co. 2 vols., xvi + 827 pp., 3 pls., 131 figs

Part II

THE ANIMAL KINGDOM

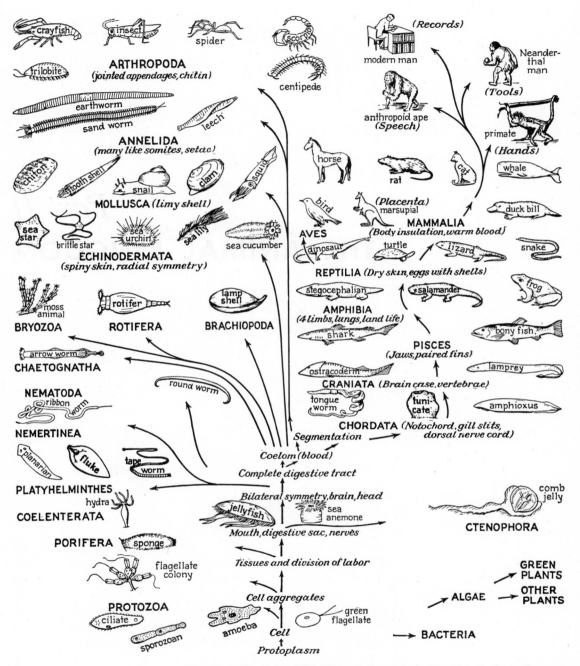

Fig. 15-1. The Animal Kingdom. A "genealogical tree" to indicate the probable relationships and relative position of the major groups (named in boldface type). All groups above a given characteristic (named in italics) possess that character. Figures not to same scale.

15 CLASSIFICATION AND NOMENCLATURE

One major objective of zoology is to obtain a perspective of the entire Animal Kingdom, yet no one person can become acquainted with more than a fraction of the known animals. Hence some means is necessary to group animals for study; this is one of the purposes of the science of *classification,* also known as *taxonomy* or *systematic zoology.*

15-1. Numbers of animals. Many kinds of animals now inhabit the earth, and many others have lived here during past geological time. The conspicuous kinds of land and sea are now well known, as are many lesser sorts in the more civilized regions; but of those living elsewhere our knowledge is imperfect.

The first clear-cut enumeration of all known animals was made by Linnaeus in 1758 and included 4,236 kinds. In 1859 Agassiz and Bronn counted 129,370, and by 1911 Pratt estimated that 522,400 had been named. The total now is nearly 1,000,000 (Fig. 15-2). New forms are still being named, and there may be several million kinds of living animals in the world today. For certain groups in particular regions there are more precise figures. Thus, in North America there are over 3,600 mammals from Panama northward, and the fishes of fresh and salt waters total 4,137; north of Mexico the birds number 1,420, the reptiles 438, and the amphibians 180. California contains 460 kinds of mammals, 644 birds, 104 reptiles, and 41 amphibians. Even small areas may have many kinds: Lake Maxinkukee, Ind. (1,854 acres), has 64 fishes, 18 amphibians, and 130 mollusks; and a suburban garden in New York, 75 by 200 feet, had 1,402 kinds of insects. The numbers for animal groups at the ends of chapters in Part II are mostly estimates by specialists.

A. CLASSIFICATION

15-2. Methods and purposes. Various degrees of resemblance and difference are easily seen in any mixed assemblage of animals. Of the domestic animals on a farm, the cow and sheep both have horns and cloven hoofs but differ in size, shape, color, and body covering. A horse agrees with the cow and sheep in having long legs and teeth of the grinding type, but lacks horns and has solid hoofs. A dog differs from all three in having nails and pads on its separate toes and having teeth of the stabbing and shearing types; it agrees in being covered with hair. The cat resembles the dog more closely than the hoofed animals. All these animals have hair and teeth, they produce living young which they suckle, and they show many other features in common. As a group they all differ from the chickens and ducks which are covered with feathers, lack teeth, and lay eggs —but these and all other birds have eyes, lungs, four limbs, and other characters like the four-footed animals named. So it is, by likenesses

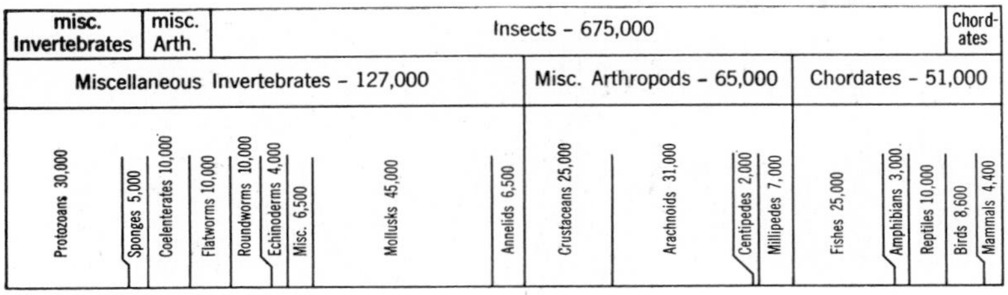

misc. Invertebrates	misc. Arth.	Insects – 675,000												Chordates
Miscellaneous Invertebrates – 127,000								Misc. Arthropods – 65,000					Chordates – 51,000	
Protozoans 30,000	Sponges 5,000 / Coelenterates 10,000 / Flatworms 10,000 / Roundworms 10,000 / Echinoderms 4,000 / Misc. 6,500	Mollusks 45,000	Annelids 6,500	Crustaceans 25,000	Arachnoids 31,000	Centipedes 2,000 / Millipedes 7,000	Fishes 25,000	Amphibians 3,000	Reptiles 10,000	Birds 8,600	Mammals 4,400			

Fig. **15-2.** Approximate numbers of species in major divisions of the Animal Kingdom.

and differences, that animals may be divided into minor and major groups.

The inherent peculiarities or **characters** of animals are the basis of classification. These include structural features, size, proportions, coloration, and others. A character is usually more significant if constantly associated with others; thus every bird has, besides feathers, a beak, wings, clawed feet, a four-chambered heart, and warm blood.

A first purpose of classification is convenience, but the more important one is to show relationships. Animals may be classified in various ways: as by grouping together all with shells, all of worm-like form, etc.; this was done by early zoologists. Increasing knowledge has shown that such arrangements bring together animals otherwise greatly different. The modern "natural system" of classification uses all available data as to structure, physiology, embryology, distribution, and other features; each group is distinguished by several to many characteristics. The natural classification is explained by the theory of evolution; it seeks to show "blood relationships" and the "genealogical tree" of the Animal Kingdom (Fig. 15-1).

For purposes of classification, characters that show **homology** or similarity of origin (and hence relationship) must be distinguished from those that exhibit **analogy** or similarity of use (but not necessarily of origin). The arms of man, forelegs of mammals and frogs, and wings of birds are homologous, being essentially similar as to structure of the bones, muscles, blood vessels, and nerves, although used for different purposes. By contrast, the wings of birds and butterflies are analogous, both serving for flight, but being unlike as to embryonic development and adult structure (Fig. 14-1).

15-3. Species. The basic unit or "building stone" in biological classification is the **species** (not specie; the plural is also *species*). A species is a group of individuals having many characteristics in common and differing from all other forms in one or more ways. The individuals of a species are all derived from a common ancestry, are related by "blood," and can breed with one another to produce fertile offspring that resemble the parents. As a general rule separate species do not interbreed, though hybrids between species do occur occasionally. Examples of common species are the house fly, yellow perch, bullfrog, and English sparrow. Often the total of individuals comprising a species can be subdivided into smaller groups known as **subspecies** that differ from one another in average rather than absolute characters. Each subspecies occupies a separate range, and specimens from the boundaries of range of two adjacent subspecies are usually intermediate in their characteristics (Fig. 14-12).

15-4. Higher groups. Two or more species with certain characters in common form a **genus** (pl. *genera*). In turn genera having common characters constitute a **family,** the families are combined into **orders,** the orders into **classes,** and the classes into **phyla** (sing. *phylum*). All the phyla together comprise the **Animal Kingdom,** which is comparable with the Plant Kingdom. The scheme of classification is like a tree having many leaves (species), with one to many on a fine stem (genus), several stems on a larger twig (family), two or more of these on a little branch (order), a number of these on a larger branch (class), and the latter borne on the main framework (phyla), the whole forming a tree (kingdom). Intermediate categories (sub-

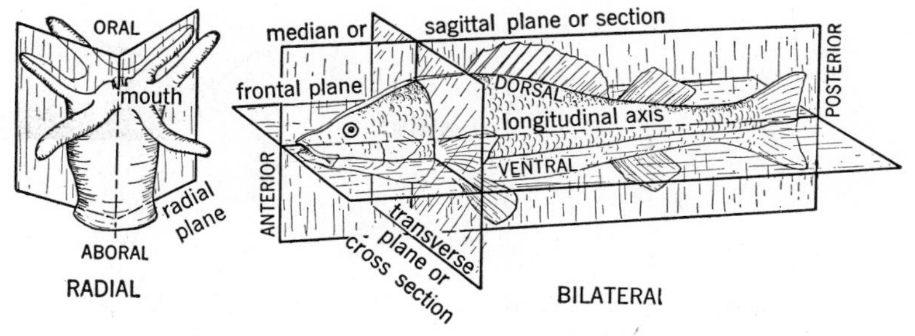

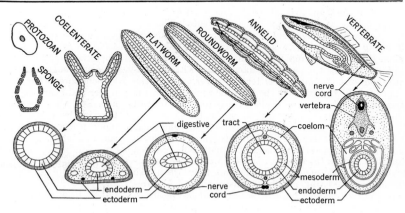

Fig. 15-3. Types of symmetry, and the axes, planes, and regions in animal bodies.

Fig. 15-4. Body structure in various types of animals (diagrammatic). *Above.* In median section. *Below.* In cross section, with indication of embryonic germ layers.

families, superclasses, subphyla, etc.) sometimes are needed to indicate properly the degrees of relationship. There are cases where a group—genus or higher—contains only one representative because it is distinct from all others; such a group is termed monotypic.

15-5. General characteristics. The wide occurrence of some characters makes possible the recognition of groups larger than phyla (see Classification, pp. 237–245). Animals of the Subkingdom Protozoa are of single cells or colonies of like cells, in contrast to those of Subkingdom Metazoa which are many-celled (tissue animals). Within the Metazoa, the sponges (Porifera) form the Branch Parazoa with no digestive cavity in contrast to the Branch Enterozoa (all higher animals) with such a cavity. The digestive tract is *incomplete* (mouth only) in the Coelenterata, Ctenophora, and Platyhelminthes, but *complete* (both mouth and anus) in all others. The Enterozoa are further divided according to the number of germ layers laid down in the embryo: two, or

diploblastic (Porifera, Coelenterata) vs. three or *triploblastic* (all others). The higher phyla (Bryozoa to Chordata) comprise the Eucoelomata, having the body cavity a *coelom* lined by peritoneum whence excretory and reproductive ducts lead to the exterior. In Mollusca and Arthropoda the coelom is far reduced, and the blood circulates in spaces between the internal organs which are known as a *hemocoel*. Body spaces in the Entoprocta and Aschelminthes are not lined and are called a *pseudocoel*. Still other lower phyla that lack body spaces are termed the Acoelomata. *Invertebrates* include all animals that lack a backbone, in contrast to the *Vertebrates* (Phylum Chordata: cyclostomes to mammals) that have a segmented vertebral column.

Besides the features just mentioned, some other characteristics are useful in classification (Figs. 15-3, 15-4).

1. Symmetry. Many Protozoa are *asymmetrical* because they are not divisible into equivalent parts; a few show *spherical symmetry*. The Coelenterata, Ctenophora, and Echinodermata are *radially symmetrical*

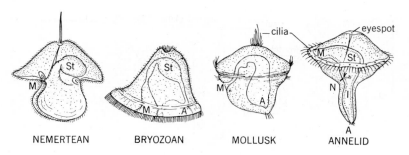

NEMERTEAN   BRYOZOAN   MOLLUSK   ANNELID

Fig. 15-5. Early larvae of some invertebrates: nemertean pilidium, bryozoan trochophore, molluscan trochophore (*Patella*), annelid trochophore (*Polygordius*). *M,* mouth; *St,* stomach; *I,* intestine; *A,* anus; *N,* nephridium. (*After various authors.*)

around a median axis through the mouth; planes through this axis will divide the animal into radial sectors (antimeres). Members of most other phyla are **bilaterally symmetrical;** a lengthwise vertical (sagittal) plane divides the animal into equal and opposite halves. In such animals the part that moves forward (and usually contains the mouth) is termed **anterior;** and the opposite end is **posterior;** the back or upper surface is termed **dorsal,** and the undersurface (usually toward the ground) is termed **ventral** (L. *venter,* belly).

2. SEGMENTATION. In the ANNELIDA, ARTHROPODA, and CHORDATA there is a linear repetition of body parts known as segmentation (metamerism); each repeated unit is a **somite** (metamere). In earthworms the successive somites are essentially alike, but they are unlike in different body regions of a crayfish or insect. Metamerism is conspicuous both externally and internally in annelids, is mostly external with arthropods, and mainly internal in man and other chordates (vertebrae, body muscles, some blood vessels, and nerves).

3. APPENDAGES. Protruding parts that serve in locomotion, feeding, and other ways are termed **appendages;** examples are the tentacles of sea anemones, minute setae of earthworms, antennae and legs of arthropods, and the fins, legs, and wings of vertebrates.

4. SKELETON. Most land dwellers and many aquatic animals have a skeleton for support or protection; it may be **internal** (frog, man, etc.) or **external** (coral, crab, insect) and may be of either inorganic or organic material.

5. SEX. An animal containing both **female** and **male** sex organs in one individual is termed **monoecious** (also hermaphroditic); members of most higher phyla are **dioecious,** each individual being either male or female.

6. EMBRYONIC DEVELOPMENT. Cleavage of the egg is complete or **holoblastic** in many invertebrates, amphioxus, amphibians, and mammals. In eggs with much yolk, cleavage is incomplete or **meroblastic,** confined to a limited portion, as in squids, insects, many fishes, reptiles, and birds. In most animals the blastopore becomes the anus, but in mollusks and annelids it gives rise to the mouth.

7. LARVAE. The young stages known as **larvae** (par. 14-8) often provide important information on relationships that is not evident in the adult animals. Many have features that are obviously adapted to particular environments (such as cilia for swimming), but their basic structure is usually characteristic for each group (phylum, class). Barnacles and tunicates, for example, were first placed properly in classification by study of their larvae.

A common larval pattern in many aquatic invertebrates is the minute, transparent, and free-swimming organism called a **trochophore** or trochosphere (Fig. 15-5). It is somewhat pear-shaped, with the large end uppermost, and encircled by two lines of cilia that beat so as to suggest a rotating wheel—hence the name "trochophore" (Gr. *trochos,* wheel + *phoros,* bear). The upper end bears an apical plate with a tuft of cilia and a sense organ (eyespot). With various modifications, this is the early larva of many marine flatworms, nemerteans, brachiopods, bryozoans, mollusks, and some annelids.

15-6. History of classification. Aristotle (Greek, 384–322 B.C.), the "father of zoology," indicated how animals might be grouped according to their characteristics, and from his writings other persons outlined the following classification that served for about 2,000 years:

I. Enaima (Vertebrates), with red blood.
   A. Viviparous.
      1. Man.
      2. Whales.
      3. Other mammals.
   B. Oviparous.
      1. Birds.
      2. Amphibians and most reptiles.
      3. Snakes.
      4. Fishes.
II. Anaima (Invertebrates), no red blood.
   A. Cephalopods.
   B. Crustaceans.
   C. Insects, spiders, etc.
   D. Other mollusks, echinoderms, etc.
   E. Sponges, coelenterates, etc.

John Ray (English, 1627–1705) was the first biologist to have a modern concept of species and to make some efforts to classify a few groups. It was Carolus Linnaeus (Swedish, 1707–1778) who laid the real basis for modern classification and nomenclature. He divided and subdivided the Animal Kingdom down to species on the basis of structural characters and gave each species a distinctive name. In his *Systema naturae* (10th edition, 1758) he recognized six "classes," as follows: Mammalia, Aves (birds), Amphibia (reptiles and amphibians), Pisces (fishes), Insecta, and Vermes (all other invertebrates). Linnaeus thus did not divide the invertebrates with as much discrimination as Aristotle had done long before him. Because of the limited knowledge then available, a Linnaean "genus" might include animals now divided among several orders or families or placed in different phyla. The principle of his system is, however, the basis for our present method of classification.

In 1829, Cuvier (French, 1769–1832) divided animals into four branches: Vertebrata (mammals to fishes), Mollusca (mollusks and barnacles), Articulata (annelids, crustaceans, insects, spiders, etc.), and Radiata (echinoderms, nematodes, coelenterates, rotifers, etc.). Anatomy and classification were of great interest through the nineteenth century, and many systems were proposed, a few of the important ones being by Lamarck (1801, 1812), Leuckart (1848), Owen (1855), Milne-Edwards (1855), and Agassiz (1859). Ernst Haeckel in 1864 and E. Ray Lankester in 1877 outlined the principal features of the zoological classification that is used today.

15-7. Difficulties in classification. All divisions in classification, from subspecies to phyla, are human concepts. Only individuals and populations of animals exist in nature. Whether a particular group shall be called a subspecies, species, genus, etc., is a matter of judgment based upon study of specimens. Biologists differ in appraising the relative importance of various characters and the amount of variation to be recognized in any group before subdividing it. Taxonomic "splitters" make many subdivisions, whereas conservative "lumpers" recognize fewer categories in the same material. Thus different recent authorities recognize 16 to 33 phyla, 20 to 40 orders of insects, and so on. As new facts are discovered, there is a tendency toward further subdivision. Zoologists are in fair agreement on much of animal classification, but no two may have exactly the same opinions on all details; as a result, different

books seldom contain identical schemes of classification.

Because animal groups differ in their evolutionary history, there is no uniformity in the content of groups above species. A certain genus may contain one or a few species, and another a hundred or more; different phyla have one to several classes. Attempts to indicate lines of descent by constructing "genealogical trees," especially in the higher units of classification (family, order, etc.), are difficult.

The sequence of phyla reflects in general the trend of evolution, from simple to complex— one cell to many, two germ layers to three, etc. It is impossible to represent the three-dimensional evolutionary tree on the successive pages of a book. Certain echinoderms, mollusks, insects, and vertebrates are recognized as the most advanced members of their respective lines, but it is a matter of opinion as to which of these phyla should be at the top. Some zoologists place the echinoderms and chaetognaths close below the chordates, whereas others give them a lower position. In this book the small phyla and some groups of uncertain position are, for convenience, assembled in a "miscellaneous" chapter (Chap. 21). The synopses of classification in chapters of Part II are analytic, dividing the Animal Kingdom into phyla, classes, and orders; some important families are listed in a few chapters.

B. NOMENCLATURE

15-8. Common or vernacular names. Each country has its own names for well-known animals. Thus a common sparrow of western Europe that is now established throughout the United States is known in different countries as follows:

> United States: English sparrow.
> England: House sparrow.
> France: Moineau domestique.
> Spain: Gorrion.
> Portugal: Pardal.
> Italy: Passera oltramontana.
> Germany: Haussperling.
> Holland: Musch.
> Denmark and Norway: Graaspurv.
> Sweden: Hussparf.

Within one country a species may have different local names; for example, in the United States, the mallard duck is also called wild duck, greenhead, gray duck, English duck, stock duck, and by some 30 other names. Still other names apply to the male (drake), female (duck, hen mallard), and young (ducklings). Thus confusion is likely between peoples of different nationalities or even within one country.

15-9. Scientific names. Until about the eighteenth century, manuscripts and most books were written or printed in Latin, the language of scholars. Few ordinary people then could read. When printed books began to appear in the languages of various countries, Latin was retained for the technical descriptions and names of animals, the names being long, descriptive "polynomials" that were useful but cumbersome. Thus in the first real natural history book in North America, Mark Catesby's *Natural History of Carolina, Florida . . .* (1731-1743), which had the text in parallel columns of English and French, the mockingbird was designated as

Turdus   minor   cinereo-albus   non   maculatus

meaning

Thrush   small   grayish-white   without   spots

When Linnaeus began his *Systema naturae*, which described and named all known animals (plants and minerals) with terse Latin descriptions of each, he started with Latin polynomials but later contracted these. In the tenth edition (1758) he consistently used but two names for each, a generic name and a specific name. This **binomial nomenclature** soon became a universal means in all countries for naming animals and plants scientifically. Linnaeus designated the mockingbird of America as *Mimus polyglottos*, the English sparrow (to him, "hussparf") as *Passer domesticus*, and the mallard as *Anas platyrhynchos*. When a species is divided into subspecies, the latter are designated by **trinomials;** thus *Passer domesticus domesticus* is the subspecies of continental Europe, and *Passer domesticus niloticus* (*P. d. niloticus*) is the slightly differing form of the Nile Valley.

15-10. Rules of scientific nomenclature. With so many kinds of animals and numerous taxonomists at work in naming and describing them in different countries, some confusion in nomenclature has arisen. Sometimes the same name has been given to different animals (homonyms) or different names to the same animal (synonyms). Some rules of nomenclature were used by Linnaeus and others proposed later. The International Congress of Zoology created a permanent Commission to prepare the International Rules of Zoological Nomenclature and to render decisions on difficult cases. The Rules (or Code) were adopted in 1901 and, with modifications, have helped to stabilize the names of animals. The Rules deal with all scientific names and provide in essence as follows:

(1) Zoological and botanical names are distinct (the same genus and species name may be used, but is not recommended, for both an animal and a plant); (2) no two genera in the Animal Kingdom may bear the same name, and the same applies to two species in a genus; (3) no names are recognized prior to those included by Linnaeus in the *Systema naturae*, 10th edition, 1758; (4) scientific names must be either Latin or latinized and preferably are printed in italics; (5) the genus name should be a single word (nominative singular) and begin with a capital letter; (6) the species name should be a single or compound word beginning with a small letter (usually an adjective agreeing grammatically with the genus name); (7) the author of a scientific name is the person who first publishes it in a generally accessible book or periodical, with a recognizable description of the animal; (8) when a new genus is proposed, the type species must be indicated; (9) a family name is formed by adding -IDAE to the stem of the name of the type genus, and a subfamily name by -INAE.

In publishing the description of a new species, it is now common practice to designate a particular or type specimen, to describe it, and to indicate the collection in which it is placed. Early authors often indicated no types and gave imperfect descriptions, so that confusion has arisen as to which of their species are actually distinct and as to who were their authors. If a genus or species has been described more than once, the earliest name and author, according to the above rules, is recognized under the **law of priority.** In technical works the name of the author, sometimes abbreviated, is written after the genus or species—thus, *Passer domesticus* Linnaeus (or as Linn. or L.).

TABLE 15-1. Some Characteristics of the Principal Groups of Animals

Cells	Germ layers	Symmetry	Digestive tract	Excretory organs	Coelom	Circulatory system	Respiratory organs	Segmentation	Phylum (Class)	Distinctive features (exceptions omitted)
1	..	v	..	..	..	..	..	..	I PROTOZOA	Microscopic; one-celled or colonies of like cells
Cells many, arranged in layers or tissues (METAZOA)	2, diploblastic	Radial	Incomplete	0	0	0	0	0	III PORIFERA	Body perforated by pores and canals
		Radial		0	0	0	0	0	IV COELENTERATA	Nematocysts; digestive tract sac-like
		Radial		0	0	0	0	0	V CTENOPHORA	Comb plates for locomotion
	3, triploblastic	Bilateral	Incomplete	+	0	0	0	0	VI PLATYHELMINTHES	Flat, soft; digestive tract branched or none
		Bilateral		+	0	+	0	0	VII NEMERTINEA	Slender, soft, ciliated; soft proboscis
		Bilateral	Complete (with anus)	+	ps	0	0	0	IX Cl. *ROTIFERA*	Microscopic, cilia on oral disc
		Bilateral		+	ps	0	0	0	IX Cl. *NEMATODA*	Cylindrical, tough cuticle; no cilia
		Bilateral		+	+	0	0	0	XI BRYOZOA	Grow as moss-like or encrusting colonies
		Bilateral		+	+	+	0	0	XIII BRACHIOPODA	Dorsal and ventral limy shell; a fleshy stalk
		Radial		0	+h	+	+	0	XIV ECHINODERMATA	Symmetry 5-part radial; tube feet; spiny endoskeleton
		Bilateral		+	+	0	0	0	XV CHAETOGNATHA	Small; arrow-shaped, transparent; lateral fins
		Bilateral		+	+h	+	+	0	XVI MOLLUSCA	External limy shell of 1, 2, or 8 parts, or none; body soft
		Bilateral		+	+	+	+0	+	XVII ANNELIDA	Slender, of many like segments; fine setae as appendages
		Bilateral		+	+h	+	+	+	XXI ARTHROPODA	Segmented, with jointed appendages; exoskeleton containing chitin
		Bilateral		+	+	+	+	+	XXII CHORDATA	Notochord, dorsal tubular nerve cord, gill slits; usually fins or limbs

+, present; 0, absent; *ps*, pseudocoel, not lined by peritoneum; *h*, coelom reduced, body spaces a hemocoel; *v*, symmetry various, or none.

CLASSIFICATION OF THE ANIMAL KINGDOM

The following outline of the Animal Kingdom will serve for identification of most specimens to phylum and class. Other characters for these groups and for the orders are given in the more detailed classifications ending Chaps. 16 to 35. A few minor groups are omitted here. Some alternative names, used in other books, are included in parentheses. Groups marked † are extinct. Names of a few representative genera are given in italics, followed by common names when available.

Subkingdom A. Protozoa. UNICELLULAR ANIMALS.

SARCODINA   MASTIGOPHORA   SPOROZOA   CILIATA   SUCTORIA

Fig. 15-6. Phylum PROTOZOA. Representatives of the five classes.

PHYLUM I. PROTOZOA. PROTOZOANS. Each individual one-celled or in colonies of similar cells; no tissues; size usually microscopic...(Chap. 16)

  SUBPHYLUM **A.** PLASMODROMA. Organelles for locomotion are flagella, pseudopodia, or none; nuclei of one kind.

   CLASS 1. *MASTIGOPHORA.* FLAGELLATES. One to many flagella for locomotion. *Ceratium, Euglena, Trypanosoma, Volvox.*

   CLASS 2. *SARCODINA* (Rhizopoda). Pseudopodia for locomotion. *Amoeba, Actinophrys, Globigerina, Badhamia.*

   CLASS 3. *SPOROZOA.* No locomotor organelles or contractile vacuoles; all parasitic. *Monocystis, Eimeria, Plasmodium.*

  SUBPHYLUM B. CILIOPHORA. Cilia at all or some stages in life history; nuclei of two kinds.

   CLASS 1. *CILIATA* (Infusoria). CILIATES. Cilia or cirri always present. *Opalina, Paramecium, Oxytricha, Vorticella.*

   CLASS 2. *SUCTORIA.* SUCTORIANS. Cilia in young, adults attached by stalk, with sucker-like tentacles. *Podophrya.*

Subkingdom B. Metazoa. MULTICELLULAR or TISSUE ANIMALS. Body of many cells, usually arranged in layers or tissues.

Branch 1. Mesozoa. Digestive cells few, external, ciliated.

PHYLUM II. MESOZOA. Symmetry radial; body slender, small; an external layer of ciliated digestive cells surrounding one or several reproductive cells; parasitic in cephalopods and other invertebrates. *Dicyema*...(Chap. 21)

Branch 2. Parazoa. Digestive cells many, internal, flagellated; no digestive cavity.

PHYLUM III. PORIFERA. SPONGES. Symmetry radial; body cylindrical, globose, branching, or irregular; skeleton internal, of minute spicules or of fibers (spongin); surface with many pores, connecting to canals and chambers lined by flagellated collar cells (choanocytes), and one or more large exits (oscula); aquatic, sessile..(Chap. 17)

   CLASS 1. *CALCAREA.* CALCAREOUS SPONGES. Spicules limy ($CaCO_3$), 1-, 3-, or 4-rayed; body surface bristly; marine, in shallow waters. *Leucosolenia, Scypha.*

   CLASS 2. *HEXACTINELLIDA.* GLASS SPONGES. Spicules siliceous, 6-rayed, and in definite arrangement; marine, at 300 feet or deeper. *Hyalonema; Euplectella,* Venus's flower-basket.

   CLASS 3. *DEMOSPONGIAE.* Skeleton siliceous, of spongin, of both, or none; canals complex; some large and brilliant; mostly marine. *Halisarca; Spongilla,* fresh-water sponge; *Spongia,* bath sponge; *Cliona,* boring sponge.

Branch 3. Enterozoa. A digestive cavity or tract.
Division *A*. Radiata. Symmetry radial.

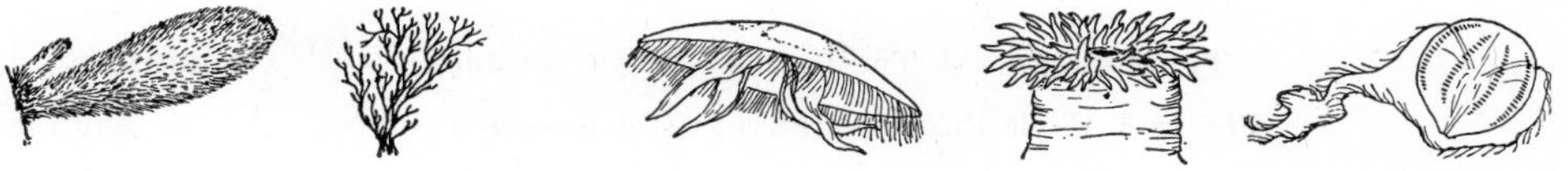

PORIFERA   HYDROZOA   SCYPHOZOA   ANTHOZOA   CTENOPHORA

Fig. 15-7. Phyla PORIFERA, COELENTERATA (three classes), and CTENOPHORA.

PHYLUM IV. COELENTERATA (Cnidaria). Symmetry radial; the individual a sessile cylindrical polyp often in colonies, or a bell-like free-floating medusa with much gelatinous mesoglea; stinging capsules (nematocysts) present; digestive cavity sac-like, sometimes branched; mouth surrounded by soft tentacles; no anus, head, or other organ systems; all aquatic, chiefly marine, attached or floating.
(Chap. 18)

CLASS 1. *HYDROZOA*. HYDROIDS (and some medusae). Mouth opens directly into a digestive cavity that lacks partitions; hydroid stage usually in colonies; medusa with velum. *Hydra*, fresh-water polyp; *Obelia*, colonial hydroid, marine; *Millepora*, "stinging coral"; *Physalia*, Portuguese man-of-war.

CLASS 2. *SCYPHOZOA* (Scyphomedusae). JELLYFISHES. Small to large medusae, chiefly of gelatinous mesoglea, and of bell or umbrella shape, margined with tentacles; digestive cavity with branched canals; polyp stage minute or none; medusae sexual, dioecious; all marine. *Aurelia*, common jellyfish.

CLASS 3. *ANTHOZOA* (Actinozoa). SEA ANEMONES, CORALS, etc. All polyps (no medusae); a flat oral disc with tentacles; mouth connects to stomodeum (gullet); digestive cavity divided by radial partitions; corals with limy exoskeleton; all marine and attached, some gregarious. *Metridium*, sea anemone; *Gorgonia*, sea fan (horny); *Astrangia*, *Orbicella*, stony corals; *Tubipora*, organ-pipe coral; *Pennatula*, sea pen.

PHYLUM V. CTENOPHORA. COMB JELLIES. Symmetry biradial; body subspherical with much mesoglea, or flat; 8 external rows of ciliated comb plates for locomotion; no nematocysts; digestive cavity with branched canals; no anus; marine; solitary. *Pleurobrachia; Cestum*, Venus's girdle; *Beroë*.
(Chap. 21)

Division *B*. Bilateria. Symmetry bilateral (secondarily radial in ECHINODERMATA); with organ systems and mostly with spaces between body wall and internal organs; digestive tract usually complete, with anus; mesoderm present.

Section a. Acoelomata. No body cavity; space between body wall and internal organs filled with parenchyma.

PHYLUM VI. PLATYHELMINTHES. FLATWORMS. Body depressed, thin and soft, leaf- or ribbon-like, digestive tract branched and without anus, or absent; parenchyma fills spaces between organs; a pair of anterior ganglia or a nerve ring and 1 to 3 pairs of longitudinal nerve cords; usually hermaphroditic. . . . .(Chap. 19)

CLASS 1. *TURBELLARIA*. FREE-LIVING FLATWORMS. Body ribbon-like to disc-like, epidermis ciliated, with many mucous glands, no hooks or suckers; often pigmented, some with brilliant markings; usually a digestive tract with ventral mouth; mostly free-living; marine, fresh-water, or terrestrial. *Euplanaria*, *Leptoplana*.

CLASS 2. *TREMATODA*. FLUKES. Body often leaf-like, with thick cuticle and no cilia; ventral suckers or hooks or both; mouth usually anterior, digestive tract 2-branched; all parasitic. *Fasciola*, liver fluke.

CLASS 3. *CESTOIDEA*. TAPEWORMS. Body narrow, flat, elongate, comprising a scolex, with suckers or hooks or both (for attachment), and a chain of few to many proglottids (pseudosegments), each with complete reproductive organs; cuticle thick, no cilia; no mouth or digestive tract; all parasitic. *Taenia*, *Dipylidium*.

TURBELLARIA   TREMATODA   CESTOIDEA   NEMERTINEA   NEMATODA

Fig. 15-8. Phyla PLATYHELMINTHES (three classes) and NEMERTINEA, and Class NEMATODA.

PHYLUM VII. NEMERTINEA (Rhynchocoela). RIBBON WORMS. Body slender, soft, very elastic, and covered with cilia; no segmentation; mouth anterior and with a long eversible proboscis; digestive tract complete, with anus; a blood vascular system; body spaces filled with parenchyma; no coelom; nervous system with anterior ganglia (brain) and 3 longitudinal nerve trunks; sexes separate; free-living, mostly marine, few fresh-water and terrestrial. *Cerebratulus, Stichostemma*. .(Chap. 21)

Section b. Pseudocoelomata. Spaces between body wall and internal organs not a coelom; anus present.

PHYLUM VIII. ENTOPROCTA. Individuals minute, solitary or colonial, each on a stalk, with calyx bearing single circle of many ciliated tentacles; digestive tract U-shaped, both mouth and anus within circle of tentacles; body spaces a pseudocoel filled with parenchyma; monoecious or dioecious; attached to objects or animals in salt or fresh waters. *Pedicellina, Urnatella*.........(Chap. 21)

NEMATOMORPHA ACANTHOCEPHALA   ROTIFERA   BRYOZOA   BRACHIOPODA

Fig. 15-9. Miscellaneous phyla and classes.

PHYLUM IX. ASCHELMINTHES. Size small or minute, body commonly slender; digestive tract complete, intestine usually straight, anus posterior; no anterior cilia (except rotifers).
  CLASS 1. *ROTIFERA* (Rotatoria). WHEEL ANIMALCULES. Body of trunk and tapering "tail," the latter often jointed and with "feet" having adhesive glands for attachment; anterior end with trochal disc bearing cilia, used for locomotion and feeding, that move so as to produce a wheel-like appearance; males minute. *Hydatina*... ....(Chap. 21)
  CLASS 2. *GASTROTRICHA.* To 0.54 mm. long; slender, flexible; ventral surface flat, with 2 lengthwise rows of cilia for locomotion; mouth anterior, surrounded by bristles; aquatic. *Chaetonotus.*
(Chap. 21)
  CLASS 3. *KINORHYNCHA* (Echinodera). To 1 mm. long, cylindrical, head of 2 rings, encircled by spines; mouth with spiny retractile proboscis; body of 11 (or 12) rings covered by stout cuticle and bearing spines; sexes separate; marine. *Echinodera*................................(Chap. 21)
  CLASS 4. *NEMATODA* (Nemathelminthes). ROUNDWORMS. Body rounded, slender, often tapered at ends; covered with tough cuticle; longitudinal muscles only, producing flexing motions but no elongation or contraction; an anterior nerve ring and 6 lengthwise nerve cords; sexes separate; free-living in soil or water, or parasitic. *Ascaris*, roundworm; *Necator*, hookworm.........(Chap. 20)
  CLASS 5. *NEMATOMORPHA* (Gordiacea). "HAIR SNAKES," or "HORSEHAIR WORMS." Body thread-like, not tapered, anterior end blunt; cuticle rough, opaque; body spaces lined with cells; sexes separate; larvae parasitic in insects, adults free-living in water. *Gordius*.................(Chap. 21)
PHYLUM X. ACANTHOCEPHALA. SPINY-HEADED WORMS. Body flat and rough in life, cylindrical and smooth when preserved; cuticle thin; anterior end with retractile proboscis bearing rows of recurved spines; no digestive tract; sexes separate; parasitic, larvae in arthropods, adults in vertebrates. *Echinorhynchus, Gigantorhynchus*..(Chap. 21)

Section c. Eucoelomata. With true coelom, usually lined with layer of cells.

PHYLUM XI. BRYOZOA. (Polyzoa). MOSS ANIMALS. Colonies branched and plant-like, or as low incrustations on rocks or shells, or as gelatinous masses; individuals many, minute, each in separate housing (zooecium); ciliated tentacles around mouth; digestive tract U-shaped, complete; coelom developed and lined; hermaphroditic; free-living in salt and fresh waters. *Bugula, Pectinatella.*

(Chap. 21)

PHYLUM XII. PHORONIDEA. Body worm-like, cylindrical, unsegmented, within a self-secreted membranous tube; anterior end bearing ciliated tentacles and a horseshoe-shaped lophophore; digestive tract complete, U-shaped, mouth and anus within lophophore; coelom of 6 compartments, with lining; blood vessels present, contractile; hermaphroditic; marine. *Phoronis*...............(Chap. 21)

PHYLUM XIII. BRACHIOPODA. LAMP SHELLS. External limy shell of dorsal and ventral valves, attached to rocks by a fleshy stalk; interior with 2 spiral arms (lophophores) bearing ciliated tentacles; digestive tract with or without anus; coelom well developed; heart small; sexes separate; marine. *Lingula, Terebratulina*..(Chap. 21)

ASTEROIDEA   OPHIUROIDEA   ECHINOIDEA   CRINOIDEA   HOLOTHURIOIDEA

Fig. 15-10. Phylum ECHINODERMATA. The five living classes.

PHYLUM XIV. ECHINODERMATA. ECHINODERMS. Symmetry radial, usually 5-parted, around an oral-aboral axis; no segmentation; body wall with calcareous plates, usually forming a rigid or flexible endoskeleton with external spines; digestive tract with (or without) anus; coelom includes water vascular system; with external tube feet for locomotion; sexes usually separate; all marine.

(Chap. 22)

CLASS 1. CRINOIDEA. SEA LILIES, FEATHER STARS. Body flower-like, a box-like calyx of many plates bearing slender branched arms; some species on aboral stalk. *Antedon.*

CLASS 2. ASTEROIDEA. STARFISHES or SEA STARS. Body star-shaped or pentagonal with 5 to 50 arms (rays) not sharply distinct from central disc; skeleton flexible, usually with short spines and pedicellariae; ambulacral grooves with 2 or 4 rows of tube feet. *Asterias, Pisaster.*

CLASS 3. OPHIUROIDEA. BRITTLE STARS. Body with central disc and 5 distinct slender jointed arms (sometimes branched); tube feet in 2 rows; no anus. *Ophiura,* brittle star; *Gorgonocephalus,* "basket fish."

CLASS 4. ECHINOIDEA. SEA URCHINS, SAND DOLLARS. Body hemispherical, disc- or egg-shaped, in shell (test) of fused plates that bear movable spines and pedicellariae; digestive tract elongate, coiled. *Arbacia, Strongylocentrotus,* sea urchins; *Dendraster,* sand dollar.

CLASS 5. HOLOTHURIOIDEA. SEA CUCUMBERS. Body elongate to worm-like, wall soft, fleshy; no arms, spines, or pedicellariae; mouth anterior, surrounded by retractile tentacles; digestive tract S-shaped, anus posterior. *Holothuria, Thyone.*

PHYLUM XV. CHAETOGNATHA. ARROW WORMS. Small, slender, transparent; body of head, trunk, and tail; bristles or hooks about mouth; paired fins on trunk and a terminal tail fin for locomotion; digestive tract complete; coelom of 3 paired cavities; hermaphroditic; free-living, marine. *Sagitta.*

(Chap. 21)

PHYLUM XVI. MOLLUSCA. MOLLUSKS. Symmetry bilateral (viscera and shell coiled in some); no segmentation; body soft, covered by a mantle that usually secretes a limy shell of 1, 2, or 8 parts; usually an anterior head and a ventral muscular foot for locomotion; digestive tract complete; a heart and blood vessels; respiration usually by gills; coelom reduced; nervous system of a few paired ganglia and connectives; sexes usually separate; in salt and fresh waters, some on land.

(Chap. 23)

AMPHINEURA   SCAPHOPODA   PELECYPODA   GASTROPODA   CEPHALOPODA

Fig. 15-11. Phylum MOLLUSCA. The five classes.

CLASS 1. *AMPHINEURA*. Chitons. Body usually elliptical, shell of 8 dorsal plates (or none); head reduced; no tentacles; marine. *Chiton.*

CLASS 2. *SCAPHOPODA*. Tooth Shells. Shell and mantle tubular, slenderly tapered; foot conical; no gills. *Dentalium.*

CLASS 3. *GASTROPODA*. Univalve Mollusks. Viscera usually asymmetrical in spirally coiled shell (shell in some reduced or absent); head distinct, with 1 or 2 pairs of tentacles; foot large, flat. *Helix*, snail; *Limax*, slug (shell internal), *Acmaea*, limpet (shell conical); *Haliotis*, abalone.

CLASS 4. *PELECYPODA*. Bivalve Mollusks. Body enclosed in shell of 2 lateral valves (right and left), with dorsal hinge; no head or jaws; foot often hatchet-shaped, extends between valves when moving. *Ostrea*, oyster; *Mya*, clam; *Teredo*, "shipworm."

CLASS 5. *CEPHALOPODA*. Squids, Octopuses, etc. Shell internal or external, or none; head large, with conspicuous complex eyes; mouth with horny jaws and surrounded by 8, 10, or many arms or tentacles; marine. *Loligo*, squid; *Octopus*, devilfish or octopus; *Nautilus*, pearly nautilus.

PHYLUM XVII. ANNELIDA. Segmented Worms. Body elongated, usually of many like segments with fine bristle-like setae for locomotion; cuticle thin; digestive tract complete, tubular; coelom usually large; blood vascular system closed; nervous system of dorsal "brain" and a ventral nerve cord having ganglia and lateral nerves in each somite; mostly free-living................(Chap. 24)

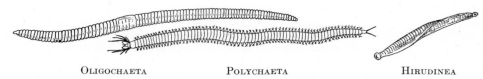

OLIGOCHAETA   POLYCHAETA   HIRUDINEA

Fig. 15-12. Phylum Annelida. The three commoner classes.

CLASS 1. *ARCHIANNELIDA*. Small; segmentation chiefly internal; no parapodia or setae; marine. *Polygordius.*

CLASS 2. *POLYCHAETA*. Sandworms, Tube Worms, etc. Segmentation conspicuous, with many somites having lateral projections (parapodia) that bear numerous setae; head region evident, with tentacles; sexes usually separate; chiefly marine. *Neanthes* (*Nereis*), clamworm, in sand; *Chaetopterus*, in tube.

CLASS 3. *OLIGOCHAETA*. Earthworms, etc. Segmentation conspicuous; no head or parapodia; setae usually few per somite; hermaphroditic; chiefly in fresh waters and moist soil. *Enchytraeus; Lumbricus*, common large earthworm.

CLASS 4. *HIRUDINEA*. Leeches. Body flattish; somites inconspicuous, each divided externally into several annuli; no setae or parapodia; a large posterior sucker, and often a smaller one at anterior end; coelom reduced; hermaphroditic; in salt and fresh waters or on land. *Hirudo, Macrobdella.*

PHYLUM XVIII. SIPUNCULOIDEA. "Peanut Worms." Body slenderly gourd-shaped, highly contractile; slender anterior end (introvert) retractile, with short hollow tentacles around mouth; no segmentation or setae; digestive tract slender, spiraled, anus dorsal at base of introvert; coelom large, undivided, ciliated, containing blood with corpuscles; anterior dorsal nerve ganglion and ventral nerve cord; sexes separate; marine. *Sipunculus, Phascolosoma*....................(Chap. 21)

PHYLUM XIX. PRIAPULOIDEA. Sausage-shaped; anterior end with swollen introvert bearing lengthwise rows of spines; body narrower, with transverse striations (not segmented); digestive tract straight, anus in posterior end surrounded by gill lobes; coelom large; adult lacks blood system, nephridia, and sense organs; sexes separate; marine. *Priapulus*............................(Chap. 21)

PHYLUM XX. ECHIUROIDEA. Body sausage-like; anterior end with trough-shaped elastic proboscis (nonretractile) leading to mouth; intestine spiraled, anus at posterior end, joined by 2 anal pouches; circulatory system of dorsal and ventral vessels; 1 to 3 pair of nephridia anteriorly; one pair of large ventral setae below mouth; adults unsegmented, larvae with 15 vestigial somites; monoecious; marine. *Echiurus, Urechis*....................................(Chap. 21)

PHYLUM XXI. ARTHROPODA. Joint-footed Animals. Body typically of head, thorax, and abdomen formed of segments and with body segments (somites) like or unlike, variously separate or fused; 4 or more pairs of jointed appendages; chitinous exoskeleton covering all parts, molted at intervals; digestive tract complete, straight; coelom reduced, body spaces a hemocoel; heart dorsal; respiration by gills, tracheae, or lung books; "brain" dorsal, nerve cord ventral and paired, with ganglia in each somite or concentrated anteriorly; sexes usually separate; terrestrial or aquatic, free-living, commensal, or parasitic..(Chap. 25)

SUBPHYLUM A. ONYCHOPHORA. Elongate; no head, but anterior end with paired short "antennae" and oral papillae; body somewhat cylindrical, unsegmented; 15 to 43 pairs of stumpy, un-jointed legs; terrestrial. *Peripatus*...(Chap. 27)

SUBPHYLUM B. †TRILOBITA. Body divided by 2 lengthwise furrows into 3 lobes; head distinct; abdomen of 2 to 29 somites and a fused caudal plate; all somites except last with biramous appendages; marine. Cambrian to Permian. †*Triarthrus*..(Chap. 27)

SUBPHYLUM C. CHELICERATA. No antennae; body of cephalothorax, with 6 pairs of appendages (chelicerae, pedipalpi, and 4 pairs of legs) and abdomen; chiefly terrestrial..............(Chap. 27)

   CLASS 1. *MEROSTOMATA*. Cephalothorax broadly joined to abdomen on which are 5 or 6 pairs of appendages; with compound lateral eyes; aquatic. *Limulus*, king crab; *Eurypterus*, eurypterid. (Chap. 27)

   CLASS 2. *PYCNOGONIDA* (Pantopoda). SEA SPIDERS. Mostly small to minute; body short, thin; mouth suctorial, on long proboscis; marine. *Pycnogonum*.................................(Chap. 27)

   CLASS 3. *ARACHNIDA*. SPIDERS, SCORPIONS, MITES, TICKS, etc. Abdomen lacks locomotor appendages; eyes all simple; no gills; terrestrial. *Epeira*, spider; *Sarcoptes*, itch mite; *Ornithodorus*, tick. (Chap. 27)

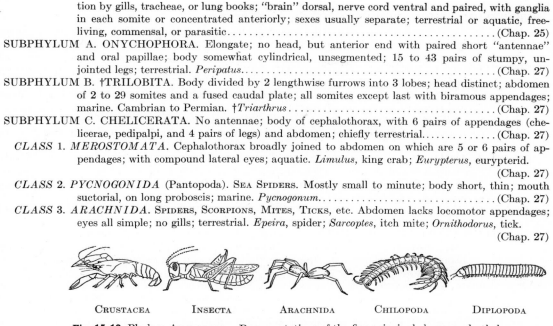

CRUSTACEA   INSECTA   ARACHNIDA   CHILOPODA   DIPLOPODA

Fig. 15-13. Phylum ARTHROPODA. Representatives of the five principal classes and subclasses.

SUBPHYLUM D. MANDIBULATA (Antennata). Body of 2 parts (head and trunk) or 3 parts (head, thorax with walking legs, and abdomen); 1 or 2 pairs of antennae; 1 pair of jaws (mandibles), 1 or more pairs of maxillae, and 3 or more pairs of walking legs.

   CLASS 1. *CRUSTACEA*. LOBSTERS, CRABS, WATER FLEAS, BARNACLES, etc. Two pairs of antennae, 1 pair of jaws, and 2 pairs of maxillae; some appendages biramous; respire mainly by gills; mostly aquatic. *Daphnia*, water flea; *Balanus*, barnacle; *Astacus*, *Cambarus*, crayfishes......(Chap. 25)

   CLASS 2. *INSECTA* (Hexapoda). INSECTS. One pair of antennae; head, thorax, and abdomen distinct; thorax typically with 3 pairs of legs and 2 pairs of wings; mainly terrestrial. *Melanoplus*, grasshopper; *Musca*, fly; *Apis*, bee..(Chap. 26)

   CLASS 3. *MYRIAPODA*. Body of 2 parts; head with 1 pair of antennae, 1 pair of mandibles, 1 or 2 pairs of maxillae; 1 or 2 pairs of legs per somite; terrestrial.

      SUBCLASS 1. CHILOPODA. CENTIPEDES. Body long, flattened, of 15 to 173 somites, each with a pair of legs; terrestrial. *Lithobius*, *Scolopendra*.......................................(Chap. 27)

      SUBCLASS 2. DIPLOPODA. MILLIPEDES. Body long, cylindrical; thorax of 4 somites, with 1 pair of legs on each; abdomen of 20 to more than 100 double somites, each with 2 pairs of legs; terrestrial. *Julus*...(Chap. 27)

      SUBCLASS 3. SYMPHYLA. To 6 mm. long; no eyes; adult with 12 pairs of legs; sex opening midventral between 4th pair of legs; terrestrial. *Scutigerella*, garden centipede..................(Chap. 27)

      SUBCLASS 4. PAUROPODA. Minute; no eyes; antennae 3-branched; body cylindrical, of 11 (12) somites and 9 (10) pairs of legs; sex opening midventral on 3d somite; terrestrial. *Pauropus*...(Chap. 27)

SUBPHYLUM E. PENTASTOMIDA (Linguatulida). Worm-like, soft, unsegmented, but abdomen ringed; 2 pairs of ventral hooks beside mouth; parasitic in vertebrates. *Linguatula*..........(Chap. 27)

SUBPHYLUM F. TARDIGRADA. WATER BEARS or BEAR ANIMALCULES. To 1 mm. long; body cylindrical, unsegmented; 4 pairs of stumpy unjointed legs with claws; in moss or fresh waters. *Echiniscus*. (Chap. 27)

PHYLUM XXII. CHORDATA. CHORDATES. Having, at some stage or throughout life, the following: an axial rod-like notochord for support of the body, a single dorsal tubular nerve cord, and paired gill slits between the pharynx and exterior; segmentation usually evident; tail behind anus.

(Chap. 28)

GROUP α. ACRANIA. No cranium, jaws, vertebrae, or paired appendages.

   SUBPHYLUM A. HEMICHORDATA (Enteropneusta, Stomochorda). Tongue Worms. Body worm-like, anterior end usually with fleshy proboscis and collar; notochord short, anterior; nerve tissues both dorsal and ventral in epidermis; many permanent gill slits; marine. *Balanoglossus, Saccoglossus, Cephalodiscus*...(Chap. 28)

   SUBPHYLUM B. TUNICATA (Urochordata). Tunicates. Larvae minute and tadpole-like with gill slits, and with both notochord and nerve cord in tail; adults tubular, globose, or irregular in form, covered with tunic or test, often transparent; with many gill slits, but notochord usually absent and nervous system reduced; marine...(Chap. 28)

      CLASS 1. *LARVACEA* (Appendicularia). Individuals are minute persistent larvae, separate and free-swimming, with notochord, "brain" and nerve cord, and 2 gill slits; test not permanent. *Appendicularia.*

      CLASS 2. *ASCIDIACEA.* Ascidians. Size and form various; solitary, colonial, or compound; usually sessile after metamorphosis when tail, nerve cord, and notochord are lost and "brain" is reduced to a ganglion, but many gill slits persist; test well developed, permanent. *Ciona, Molgula,* simple ascidians; *Botryllus,* compound ascidian.

      CLASS 3. *THALIACEA.* Chain Tunicates. Size various; adults free-living, with no tail or notochord; test permanent, with circular muscle bands. *Salpa, Doliolum.*

   SUBPHYLUM C. CEPHALOCHORDATA (Leptocardii). Lancelets. Body small, slender, elongate, "fish-like," distinctly segmented; notochord and nerve cord extending entire length of body, and many gill slits enclosed in an outer atrium, all permanent. *Branchiostoma,* amphioxus or lancelet. (Chap. 28)

GROUP β. CRANIATA. Vertebrates. With cranium (skull), visceral arches, and "spinal column" of segmental vertebrae, all cartilaginous in lower forms but bony in higher ones; notochord extends from tail to base of cranium; anterior end of nerve cord with enlarged brain of specialized parts; head region with paired special sense organs (smell, sight, hearing); paired semicircular canals for equilibration; circulatory system closed, with heart of 2 to 4 chambers, and red blood cells.

   SUBPHYLUM D. AGNATHA. Jawless Vertebrates. No true jaws or paired appendages.

      CLASS 1. †*OSTRACODERMI.* Extinct Armored Fishes. Head and body armored with large scales, often fused into a cephalothoracic shield. †*Cephalaspis,* †*Pterolepis.*

      CLASS 2. *CYCLOSTOMATA* (Marsipobranchii, Monorhina). Lampreys and Hagfishes. Body cylindrical, slender, with median fins only; skin smooth, no scales; heart 2-chambered; aquatic; mouth suctorial, with horny teeth; one nasal opening; 6 to 14 bag-like pairs of gill pouches opening on side of body. *Petromyzon,* lamprey; *Myxine,* hagfish............................(Chap. 29)

HEMICHORDATA   TUNICATA   CEPHALOCHORDATA   CYCLOSTOMATA   CHONDRICHTHYES

OSTEICHTHYES   AMPHIBIA   REPTILIA   AVES   MAMMALIA

Fig. 15-14. Phylum Chordata. Representatives of the three lower subphyla and of the seven classes of living vertebrates.

   SUBPHYLUM E. GNATHOSTOMATA. Jawed Vertebrates. One pair of visceral arches modified as biting jaws; 2 nasal capsules or tubes; 3 pairs of semicircular canals; usually with paired appendages (fins or limbs); sexes separate.

      SUPERCLASS **a.** PISCES. Fishes. With median fins supported by fin rays; paired fins usually present; skin usually with scales containing limy material; nasal capsules not connected to mouth cavity; heart with one auricle; respiration by gills; aquatic.

CLASS 1. †*PLACODERMI* (Aphetohyoidea). ANCIENT FISHES. Jaws primitive; hyoid unspecialized, followed by a complete gill slit, no spiracle; paired fins variable; body covering of bony scales or plates; skeleton bony. †*Climatius*, acanthodian; †*Dinichthys*, arthrodire; †*Pterichthyodes*, antiarch. (Chap. 30)

CLASS 2. *CHONDRICHTHYES*. CARTILAGINOUS FISHES. Skeleton cartilaginous, notochord persistent; skin covered with placoid scales; chiefly marine. *Squalus*, shark; *Raja*, ray; *Chimaera*, chimaera. (Chap. 30)

CLASS 3. *OSTEICHTHYES*. BONY FISHES. Skeleton more or less bony; mouth usually terminal; gills covered by opercula; scales usually cycloid. *Acipenser*, sturgeon; *Salmo*, trout, salmon; *Perca*, perch; *Neoceratodus*, lungfish...(Chap. 31)

SUPERCLASS **b.** TETRAPODA. FOUR-LEGGED "LAND" VERTEBRATES. Typically with two pairs of 5-toed limbs, variously modified, reduced, or absent; skeleton of bone; nasal capsules connect to mouth cavity; some with external auditory canals; heart with 2 auricles and double circulation of blood.

CLASS 1. *AMPHIBIA*. AMPHIBIANS. Living forms covered by a soft, moist, glandular skin; heart 3-chambered; larvae typically aquatic, respiring by gills; adults commonly terrestrial, usually respiring by lungs. *Ichthyophis*, caecilian; *Ambystoma*, salamander; *Bufo*, toad; *Rana*, frog....(Chap. 32)

CLASS 2. *REPTILIA*. REPTILES. Body covered with dry cornified skin, usually with scales, or scutes; toes usually ending in claws; feet and limbs reduced or absent in some; respire by lungs; heart imperfectly 4-chambered; mostly terrestrial, some aquatic. *Chrysemys*, turtle; *Sphenodon*, tuatara; *Sceloporus*, lizard; *Thamnophis*, garter snake; *Alligator*, alligator...................(Chap. 33)

CLASS 3. *AVES*. BIRDS. Body covered with feathers; fore limbs modified as wings for flight; respire by lungs; heart completely 4-chambered; "warm-blooded" (homoiothermous); terrestrial or aquatic. *Struthio*, ostrich; *Larus*, gull; *Anas*, duck; *Corvus*, crow; *Passer*, sparrow............(Chap. 34)

CLASS 4. *MAMMALIA*. MAMMALS. Body usually covered with hair; respire by lungs; heart as in birds; "warm-blooded"; females with mammary glands providing milk for nourishment of young. *Ornithorhynchus*, duckbill; *Macropus*, kangaroo; *Didelphis*, opossum; *Homo*, man; *Rattus*, rat; *Canis*, dog, wolf; *Equus*, horse...(Chaps. 35, 36)

REFERENCES

(See also the larger books and general works listed in Chap. 1.)

ARISTOTLE. The works of Aristotle. IV. Historia animalium. Translated by D'A. W. Thompson. 1910. Oxford, Clarendon Press. xv + about 300 pp.

LINNAEUS, CAROLUS. 1758. Systema naturae per regne tria naturae, secundum classes, ordines, genera, species cum characteribus, differenties, synonymis, locis. Editio decima, reformata. Tomus I. Holmiae [The system of nature of three natural kingdoms, classes, orders, genera, species with characters, differences, synonyms, distribution. 10th ed., rev. Vol. I. Stockholm], Laurentii Salvii. 8 + 5–824 pp. The starting point for scientific zoological nomenclature.

MAYR, ERNST, E. G. LINSLEY, and R. L. USINGER. 1953. Methods and principles of systematic zoology. New York, McGraw-Hill Book Co., Inc. ix + 328 pp., 45 figs. + appendix, pp. A–H. A general introduction to the subject.

SCHENCK, E. T., and J. H. McMASTERS. 1956. Procedure in taxonomy. 3d ed. Rev. by A. M. Keen and S. W. Muller. Stanford, Calif., Stanford University Press. vii + 119 pp. Includes International Code of Zoological Nomenclature.

16 PHYLUM PROTOZOA
One-celled Animals

The PROTOZOA (Gr. *protos*, first + *zoön*, animal) are mostly one-celled animals of microscopic size. In the Animal Kingdom they comprise the lowest of the great groups, or phyla, and stand in contrast to all the others, which are the multicellular tissue animals, or META-ZOA (Gr. *meta*, after). As to structure, a protozoan is comparable with one cell of a metazoan, but functionally it is an entire organism, physiologically balanced, and performs all the essential life processes of an animal. Some protozoans are very simple in structure and others are complex, with *organelles* (cell organs) that serve particular vital processes and that are functionally analogous to the organ systems of multicellular animals. Fully 30,000 kinds of PROTOZOA are known, and as individuals they far exceed all other animals in numbers. Each species lives in some particular moist habitat —in sea water or on the ocean bottom; in fresh, brackish, or foul waters inland; in soil or decaying organic matter. Many are free-living and free-swimming, whereas others are sessile, and some in both categories form colonies. Still others live on or in some plants and all sorts of animals from protozoans to man. In different cases the interrelationships vary from casual occurrence to strict parasitism. In turn, some kinds of bacteria live on or in certain protozoans as casuals, symbionts, or parasites. Many protozoans serve as food of other minute animals. Some are helpful in the purification of filter and sewage beds, but disease-producing species such as those causing amoebic dysentery, malaria, and African sleeping sickness are a scourge of mankind.

The PROTOZOA are divided, according to the structures they possess for locomotion (Fig. 16-1), into five Classes: (1) MASTIGOPHORA, or flagellates, with one or more whip-like flagella; (2) SARCODINA, or rhizopods, with pseudopodia; (3) SPOROZOA, with no locomotor organelles; (4) CILIATA, or ciliates, with cilia throughout life; and (5) SUCTORIA, with cilia in the young and tentacles in the adult stages. In this chapter each class is discussed separately and there is a classification of the phylum down to orders at the end.

16-1. Characteristics. 1. Small, usually one-celled, some in colonies of few to many similar individuals; symmetry none, bilateral, radial, or spherical.

2. Cell form usually constant, oval, elongate, spherical, or otherwise, varied in some species and changing with environment or age in many.

3. Nucleus distinct, single or multiple; other structural parts as organelles; no organs or tissues.

4. Locomotion by flagella, pseudopodia, cilia, or movements of the cell itself.

5. Some species with protective housings, or tests; many species produce resistant cysts or spores to survive unfavorable conditions and for dispersal.

6. Mode of life free-living, commensal, mutualistic, or parasitic.

7. Nutrition various: (*a*) *holozoic*, subsisting on other organisms (bacteria, yeasts, algae, other protozoans, etc.); (*b*) *saprophytic*, living on dissolved substances in

| *Amoeba* | *Euglena* | *Gregarina* | *Paramecium* | *Podophrya* |
| SARCODINA | MASTIGOPHORA | SPOROZOA | CILIATA | SUCTORIA |

Fig. 16-1. Common representatives of the Phylum PROTOZOA.

their surroundings; (*c*) *saprozoic*, subsisting on dead animal matter; (*d*) *holophytic*, or autotrophic, producing food by photosynthesis as in plants. Some combine two methods.

8. Asexual reproduction by binary fission, multiple fission, or budding; some with sexual reproduction by fusion of gametes, or by conjugation (in CILIATA).

The extreme age of the Phylum PROTOZOA is proved by finding the hard remains of RADIOLARIA and FORAMINIFERA in Pre-Cambrian rocks. Many of the flagellate Subclass PHYTOMASTIGINA have the cells embedded in a common gelatinous matrix and show physiological coordination between the individuals. Some are connected to one another by protoplasmic threads, and in *Volvox* there is differentiation into vegetative and reproductive cells. These conditions parallel the formation of tissues and the segregation of somatic and germ cells in METAZOA. Certain protozoans, ordinarily free-living, are occasionally found living within the bodies of other animals, thus affording a hint as to how strictly parasitic species may have been derived from free-living forms. Some chlorophyll-bearing flagellates resemble the green algae in structure and physiology and suggest common origin for plants and animals. The MASTIGOPHORA are probably the most primitive, the CILIATA the most specialized, and the SPOROZOA are probably simplified as a result of their strictly parasitic manner of life.

16-2. Size. Protozoans are mostly so small that they are measured in microns (one micron, μ, = 1/1,000 mm., or 1/25,400 inch). Some are only 2 or 3 μ in length. A dozen *Babesia* (sporozoan) may inhabit one red blood cell, or several hundred *Leishmania* (flagellate) a single tissue cell. Most species are less than 250 μ long; but

Spirostomum (ciliate) grows to 3 mm., and *Porospora gigantea* (sporozoan) to 16 mm.

CLASS SARCODINA. AMOEBAS, ETC.

The common amoeba (*Amoeba proteus*) of clean fresh waters that contain green vegetation serves as an introduction to the PROTOZOA and to the SARCODINA (Gr. *sarcodes*, fleshy). The amoeba (Fig. 16-2) appears to be about the simplest possible living animal, an independent cell with nucleus and cytoplasm but no permanent organelles. It has been studied intensively in the hope of discovering some of the fundamental features of life. Despite its seeming simplicity it can move, capture, digest, and assimilate complex food, egest indigestible residues, respire, produce secretions and excretions, respond to changes (stimuli) of various kinds in both its internal and external environment, grow, and reproduce itself in kind. It thus performs all essential animal activities and shows physiological specialization in various processes without having many structurally differentiated parts to perform these functions.

16-3 Structure. The living amoeba is a mass of clear, colorless, jelly-like protoplasm, up to 0.60 mm. long, that is flexible, of irregular

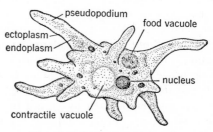

Fig. 16-2. Structure of *Amoeba*.

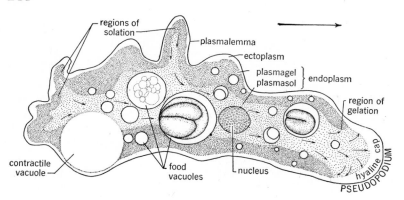

Fig. 16-3. Locomotion in *Amoeba*. The fluid inner plasmasol flows forward and is converted into plasmagel at the forward-moving pseudopod; the reverse process occurs in the opposite end and in pseudopodia that are being withdrawn. Large arrow indicates direction of movement of entire animal; small arrows that of endoplasm. (*After Mast*, 1926.)

shape, and undergoes frequent change of form. It consists of (1) a very thin elastic external cell membrane, or *plasmalemma,* and beneath this (2) a narrow zone of clear nongranular *ectoplasm* surrounding (3) the main body mass of granular *endoplasm.* The latter consists of (*a*) an outer stiffer *plasmagel* and (*b*) an inner *plasmasol* in which streaming movements are visible. Within the endoplasm are (4) a disc-like *nucleus,* not easily seen in the living animal; (5) a spherical fluid-filled *contractile vacuole,* which at intervals moves to the surface, contracts, discharges its contents into the surrounding water, and then re-forms; (6) one or more *food vacuoles* of various sizes, containing bits of food under digestion; and (7) various other *vacuoles, crystals, oil globules,* and other *cell inclusions* ranging downward in size to or below the limit of microscopic visibility.

Briefly, the functions of these parts are as follows: (1) The cell membrane retains protoplasm within the cell, but permits the passage of water, oxygen, and carbon dioxide; (2) the ectoplasm lends form to the cell body; (3) the endoplasm contains the other structures and serves in locomotion; (4) the nucleus controls vital processes of the organism; (5) the contractile vacuole regulates water content; (6) the food vacuoles contain food undergoing digestion; and (7) the other cell inclusions are reserve foods or other materials essential to metabolism. If the amoeba is cut in two, the cell membrane soon surrounds each piece and prevents loss of protoplasm; the part without a nucleus can still move and ingest food but is unable to

digest or assimilate the food and soon dies, whereas that with the nucleus will continue to grow and reproduce. An isolated nucleus, however, cannot survive. Thus the nucleus and cytoplasm are interdependent.

16-4. Locomotion. The amoeba moves by forming and extending temporary finger-like extensions, or *pseudopodia* (Gr. *pseudos,* false + *podos,* foot) at any place on its cell body (Fig. 16-3). This sort of irregular flowing is termed *amoeboid movement;* it occurs in many PROTOZOA and also in the amoebocytes of sponges and the white blood cells of vertebrates. Amoeboid movement is probably a basic characteristic of unspecialized protoplasm and, like most fundamental processes, is difficult to explain. Various theories have been offered to account for it. It can be imitated in part by some mixtures of nonliving materials, where differences in surface tension account for certain kinds of movement. S. O. Mast holds that movement in the amoeba is the result of changes within the colloidal protoplasm, from the fluid "sol" to the more solid "gel" condition, and vice versa. Three outstanding features of locomotion are (1) attachment to the substratum, possibly by a secretion; (2) transformation of plasmagel to plasmasol at the hinder end and the opposite process at the forward end of the animal; and (3) an increase in the elastic strength of the plasmagel as it passes backward. Attachment is best on rough surfaces but depends on the nature of the fluid about the animal and on the physiological condition of the amoeba.

Fig. 16-4. *Amoeba.* States in ingestion of food; total time 8 minutes. Arrows indicate movement of protoplasm in pseudopodia. (*After Schaeffer, 1917.*)

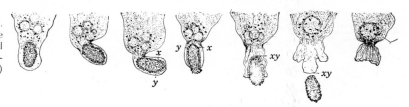

Fig. 16-5. *Amoeba verrucosa.* Stages in passing out a waste pellet; *xy*, ingrowth of new cell wall to prevent loss of endoplasm. (*After Howland, 1924.*)

16-5. Feeding. The amoeba eats other protozoans, algae, rotifers, and dead protoplasm, preferring small live flagellates and ciliates. It may eat several paramecia or several hundred small flagellates daily and exhibits choice in selecting food. The amoeba is attracted by movements of the intended prey or by substances diffusing from it; unwanted or indigestible materials are usually avoided, as are organisms that show intense activity. Food may be taken in at any part of the cell surface. The amoeba extends pseudopodia that encircle the food (Fig. 16-4), which, with some water, is taken into the endoplasm as a *food vacuole*. More water is included with an active item than with one that is quiet. The vacuoles are moved about by streaming movements in the endoplasm and thus come in contact with various parts of it. A recently formed vacuole gives an acid reaction (to litmus or neutral red), probably because of a secretion that kills the prey quickly. Later the reaction becomes alkaline, and the action of enzymes secreted by the endoplasm is evident. Food particles lose their sharp outlines, swell, become more transparent, and then lessen in amount as the products of digestion are absorbed by the surrounding protoplasm. Evidence is clear as to the digestion of proteins, but less certain as to fats, starches, and sugars. The absorbed materials serve for growth and reproduction as well as providing the energy for locomotion.

The vacuoles decrease in size as digestion proceeds, and undigested residues are passed to the outside (Fig. 16-5) at any place on the cell surface.

16-6. Respiration and excretion. The water in which the amoeba lives contains dissolved oxygen. This diffuses through the cell membrane, as in the internal respiration of cells in higher animals that derive their oxygen from the blood or other body fluids. Metabolism results in the production of waste products such as carbon dioxide and urea. For the well-being of the organism these must be eliminated; their disposal, mainly by diffusion through the cell membrane, is the process of excretion.

The contractile vacuole probably serves in part for excretion, but its principal function is to regulate the water content of the cell body. Water enters in food vacuoles, is a by-product of food oxidation, and also probably passes into the cell by osmosis, since the protoplasm contains a higher concentration of salts than the surrounding water. An amoeba placed in water with a higher salt content than usual forms a smaller vacuole that discharges less often than before; and some marine amoebas have no vacuole. The contractile vacuole forms gradually by fusion of smaller vacuoles that start from fine droplets. When filled, it is surrounded by a temporary "condensation membrane" that

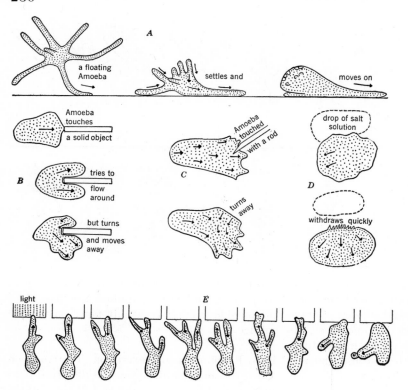

Fig. 16-6. *Amoeba. A–D.* Reactions to stimuli. Arrows indicate direction of movements. *E.* Successive stages at about 30-second intervals in reaction to strong light focused continuously on a microscope slide. (*A–D, after Jennings,* 1904; *E, after Mast,* 1910.)

vanishes as the vacuole discharges through the cell membrane into the surrounding water. In some amoebas, however, the vacuole may be dissected out under water with the membrane intact.

16-7. Behavior. The responses of an amoeba to stimuli, or changes in its environment, either internal or external, constitute its **behavior** (Fig. 16-6). Hunger is an internal stimulus to which the amoeba responds by searching for food. Contact with a food item is an external stimulus to which it responds by sending out pseudopodia to capture the food. The response to **touch** or **contact** is varied. A floating amoeba, with spread pseudopodia, responds positively to contact with a solid object by fastening to it; but a creeping amoeba, touched lightly with a needle, responds negatively by drawing back and moving away. Since the amoeba is exposed to **light** of varying intensity in nature, it does not respond to a gradual change in illumina-

tion. But if a strong beam is suddenly flashed on an individual in weak light, it responds negatively; the protoplasm streams away from the stimulus, and pseudopodia soon form to aid the withdrawal. Furthermore, if an amoeba comes repeatedly into a field of intense light (Fig. 16-6E), the number of attempts to continue in the original direction decreases as the number of trials increases—a change in behavior similar to the learning process of higher animals. Response to **temperature** is shown by changes in both locomotion and rate of feeding. These both lessen as the water temperature approaches freezing. Locomotion is speeded in higher temperatures but ceases above 30°C. To strong **chemicals,** the amoeba responds negatively (Fig. 16-6D), but to substances diffusing from food it responds positively. The responses by the amoeba to stimuli are such as to benefit the individual and the species, by avoiding unfavorable conditions and seeking those useful to it.

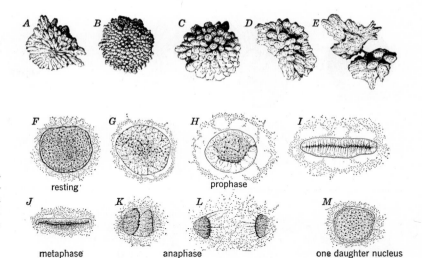

Fig. 16-7. *Amoeba.* Binary fission. *A–E.* External appearance, × 10. *F–M.* Mitosis in the nucleus during fission, × 118. (*After Chalkey and Daniel,* 1933.)

16-8. Reproduction. When the amoeba attains a certain size, it reproduces by **binary fission** (Fig. 16-7). The cell body becomes spherical and covered by short pseudopodia, then lengthens, and finally constricts into two parts; meanwhile, the nucleus has divided by mitosis. Under ordinary laboratory conditions, the amoeba divides every few days, and mitosis requires about 33 minutes at 24°C.

16-9. Other Sarcodina. The Genus *Amoeba* includes many species that differ from *A. proteus* in size, shape of pseudopodia, and other features. These and members of other genera of amoeba-like protozoans inhabit fresh, brackish, and salt waters. Still others produce a shell, or test, to enclose the cell body, examples being *Arcella*, which secretes a thick test, and *Difflugia* (Fig. 16-8), which cements together a test of sand grains or other foreign particles. Besides these free-living forms the Order AMOEBINA includes many commensal or parasitic amoebas. Species of the Genus *Endamoeba* inhabit the gut in cockroaches and termites, and those of the Genus *Entamoeba* live chiefly in the digestive tract of land vertebrates. Each is usually restricted to certain organs in a particular species of host animal. These amoebas may form resistant cysts by which they pass from an infected host to other individuals.

Six kinds of harmless amoebas may occur in man; of these, *Entamoeba gingivalis* lives in the mouth, and *E. coli* in the intestine. Another intestinal species, *E. histolytica*, however, is pathogenic and may produce the disease known as "amoebic dysentery" (Fig. 16-9). When food or water containing cysts of *E. histolytica* enters the digestive tract, the amoebas are soon liberated and may invade glands of the intestinal wall to feed on the blood and tissues and to multiply. They cause the formation of abscesses that rupture and discharge blood and mucus into the intestine, resulting in thin feces and diarrhea. After such an acute condition the patient may recover somewhat and become a carrier, with less severe symptoms but continuing to discharge thousands of encysted amoebas and so able to spread the disease. In some persons an intestinal infection never produces any severe symptoms, but in others the amoebas may invade the liver, spleen, or brain with fatal results. Microscopic examination of fecal smears for cysts of *E. histolytica* is the basis for diagnosis, and medical treatment with drugs is necessary for a cure. The intestinal abscesses heal very slowly. Fecal contamination of drinking water and raw vegetables or contamination by infected and careless food handlers are the means of spread. About 10 per cent of people in the United States are infected.

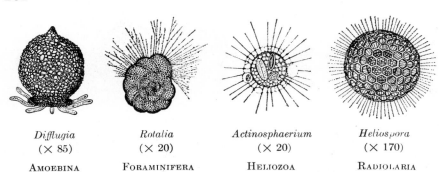

Difflugia
(× 85)
AMOEBINA

Rotalia
(× 20)
FORAMINIFERA

Actinosphaerium
(× 20)
HELIOZOA

Heliospora
(× 170)
RADIOLARIA

Fig. 16-8. Class SARCO-DINA. Representatives of four orders. (*After Wolcott, Animal biology.*)

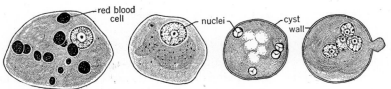

Trophozoite in feces   Precystic stage   Mature cyst   Excysting

Fig. 16-9. *Entamoeba histolytica*, the parasitic amoeba of man that causes amoebic dysentery. (*After Cleveland and Sanders, 1933.*)

The Order FORAMINIFERA (Fig. 16-10) includes about 18,000 species, mostly marine, that have a covering test through which the long thread-like reticulate pseudopodia stream out and in. Some fix to plants and hydroids or the sea bottom, others creep, and still others are pelagic, but all have some free-moving stage. The tests of various species are 0.01 to 190 mm. in diameter and of spherical, tubular, spiral, or other shapes. They are composed of gelatinous, chitinous, or limy material or of selected bits of sand, sponge spicules, or other debris. FORAMINIFERA have inhabited the seas since Pre-Cambrian time, and their tests have accumulated as bottom deposits that became rock strata. About 48,000,000 square miles (35 per cent) of the present ocean bottom is covered with "ooze" formed of tests of certain pelagic forms, particularly *Globigerina*. The great pyramids near Cairo, Egypt, were carved from limestone deposits made of tests of an Early Tertiary foraminiferan, †*Nummulites*. Petroleum geologists study the foraminiferans obtained in drilling test wells to identify oil-bearing strata.

Members of the Order HELIOZOA are spherical; the cell body may be naked, in a gelatinous matrix, or in a lattice-like test. The many fine radiating pseudopodia suggest the name "sun animalcules." Most of the species live in fresh waters. Protozoans of the Order RADIOLARIA somewhat resemble heliozoans, but the cyto-

Fig. 16-10. Shells of FORAMINIFERA, × 5. (*Specimens from G. Dallas Hanna.*)

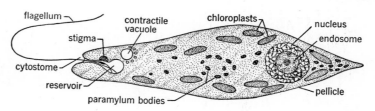

Fig. 16-11. Structure of *Euglena viridis*, a free-living flagellate (Class MASTIGOPHORA).

plasm is divided into outer and inner portions by a central capsule, and the skeleton is either of silica or of strontium sulfate. They are all marine and pelagic, from the ocean surface to depths of 15,000 feet, and very abundant as to species and individuals. About 2,000,000 square miles of ocean bottom, at depths of 12,000 to 24,000 feet, are covered with radiolarian ooze derived from empty skeletons of these animals. Many rock formations contain fossil radiolarians.

The Order MYCETOZOA (MYXOMYCETES of botanists) includes the slime molds. The species form masses of granular protoplasm (plasmodia), up to several inches in diameter, that contain thousands of nuclei and contractile vacuoles. They live on wood or other decaying vegetation in damp places on land.

Reproduction among the SARCODINA is varied. Besides binary fission, the parasitic amoebas undergo multiple division of the nucleus while in cysts. FORAMINIFERA multiply alternately by multiple fission and by "gametes," which are either flagellated or amoeboid. The HELIOZOA multiply by fission, as do the RADIOLARIA, and some of the latter may have flagellated swarmers. The MYCETOZOA produce multinucleate cysts to survive dry conditions.

CLASS MASTIGOPHORA. FLAGELLATES

The presence of one or more long slender *flagella* (sing. *flagellum*) at some or all stages in the life cycle is characteristic of the MASTIGOPHORA (Gr. *mastix*, whip + *phoros*, bearing). The flagella serve for locomotion and food capture and may be sense receptors. The cell body is usually of definite form—oval, long, or spherical—covered by a firm pellicle, and armored in certain groups of flagellates. Many species contain plastids with colored pigments; those with chlorophyll can synthesize food by the aid of sunlight and, as they seem akin to algae, are often classified as plants. Many flagellates are free-living and solitary, others are sessile, and some form colonies of a few to thousands of individuals. They abound in fresh and salt waters where, with diatoms, they are a major part of the food supply for minute aquatic animals. A number of species inhabit the soil. Many others are parasites of mankind and all sorts of animals, and some cause diseases of major importance. Reproduction usually is by longitudinal fission, but some undergo multiple fission, and there is sexual reproduction in one group. Free-living flagellates may encyst to avoid unfavorable conditions. Some SARCODINA also possess flagella at times, and certain MASTIGOPHORA have amoeboid stages; so these two classes are rather closely related.

16-10. Structure. *Euglena viridis* and *E. gracilis* are common, solitary, free-living flagellates that contain chlorophyll; they may be cultured and studied easily in the laboratory. The slender cell body is up to 0.1 mm. in length (Fig. 16-11). Euglena is of constant shape, with a blunt ***anterior end*** that habitually travels forward; the opposite or ***posterior end*** is pointed. The body shape is maintained by a thin flexible covering membrane, or ***pellicle,*** that is marked spirally by parallel striations or thickenings. Within is a thin layer of clear ***ectoplasm*** around the main mass of granular nonflowing ***endoplasm.*** The anterior end contains a funnel-like ***cytostome*** (cell mouth) that leads into a short tubular ***cytopharynx*** (cell gullet). A long ***flagellum*** extends out through the cytostome; it consists of a contractile axial filament surrounded by a delicate sheath and arises from a granule, the

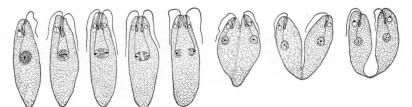

Fig. **16-12.** *Euglena viridis.* Stages in longitudinal fission. (*Modified from Tannreuther,* 1923.)

blepharoplast, within the anterior cytoplasm. Behind the cytopharynx is a permanent spherical **reservoir,** and near by a vacuole into which several minute **contractile vacuoles** empty. Fluid collected from the cytoplasm by the vacuoles passes into the reservoir and out the cytopharynx. Near the reservoir is a red **stigma** (eyespot) that is sensitive to light. The round **nucleus** is near the center of the cell. Euglena is of green color owing to the **chloroplasts** (chromatophores) containing chlorophyll that often crowd its cytoplasm. Other cell inclusions are the **paramylum bodies,** which consist of a carbohydrate allied to starch.

16-11. Movements. The flagellum beats back and forth to draw euglena through the water with a spiral rotation, so that it follows a straight course (see *Paramecium,* par. 16-19). The animal may also crawl by spiral movements of the cell body. At times it performs worm-like "euglenoid movements" by local expansions and contractions that suggest the peristalsis in a vertebrate's intestine. Euglena reacts positively to light by swimming toward a source of favorable intensity, as a green plant turns to the light, but it performs an avoiding reaction to direct sunlight.

16-12. Nutrition. Some free-living flagellates capture small organisms, which are taken into the cytopharynx and digested in food vacuoles in the cytoplasm, but such **holozoic nutrition** is rare or lacking in euglena. The latter utilizes **holophytic nutrition** whereby some food is synthesized within the body. This is done by photosynthesis, as in green plants, through the action of chlorophyll in the presence of light. Euglena commonly subsists by **saprophytic nutrition,** which is the absorption of nutrient

materials dissolved in the water where it lives. In rich nutrient solutions, cultures of some euglenas will persist and multiply rapidly in weak light or darkness.

16-13. Reproduction. In active cultures, euglena reproduces frequently by longitudinal **binary fission** (Fig. 16-12). The nucleus divides in two by mitosis, then the anterior organelles —flagellum, blepharoplast, cytopharynx, reservoir, and stigma—are duplicated, and the organism splits in two lengthwise. Euglena also has inactive stages when it becomes nonmotile and secretes a surrounding cyst. In hot weather, *E. gracilis* may do this temporarily as a protective measure, without undergoing any change while encysted. Euglena may also lose the flagellum, encyst, and then divide by longitudinal fission. There may be further multiplication by longitudinal fission, resulting in cysts that contain 16 or 32 small daughter euglenas. Encystment is stimulated by lack of food or by the presence of chlorophyll (as in strongly illuminated cultures).

16-14. Other Mastigophora. Many members of the group PHYTOMASTIGINA, to which the Genus

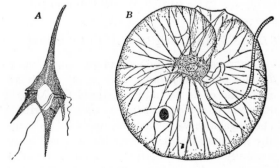

Fig. 16-13. Class MASTIGOPHORA. Two common marine flagellates. *A. Ceratium,* × 105. *B. Noctiluca,* × 27.

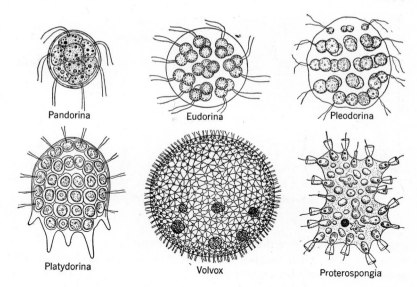

Pandorina Eudorina Pleodorina

Platydorina Volvox Proterospongia

Fig. 16-14. Class MASTIGO-
PHORA. Colonial flagellates.
(*After Hyman, The inverte-
brates.*)

Euglena belongs, are free-living, colored by chromatophores, and holophytic in nutrition. Species of the Order DINOFLAGELLATA are mostly marine and generally possess a cellulose-like armor of two to many plates (Fig. 16-13). *Ceratium* and *Peridinium*, along with diatoms, are important members of the microscopic plankton, or "ocean meadows," on which the minute larvae of crustaceans and other animals feed. Certain dinoflagellates sometimes become excessively abundant (20 to 40 million per liter) along North American coasts, causing "red water" on the sea by day and luminescence at night. A "flowering" of *Gymnodinium brevis* in 1947 on the west Florida coast killed billions of fishes and some sea turtles by the toxins it produced. *Gonyaulax catenella* on the California coast is fed on regularly by bivalves including sea mussels (*Mytilus*). It produces a substance, harmless to the mussels, but which causes "mussel poisoning" in a man if these mollusks are eaten in summer when they subsist largely on this protozoan. Upwards of 400 cases of illness and 36 human deaths have been recorded on the Pacific coast during recent years and a few in Nova Scotia.

The Order PHYTOMONADINA includes several green fresh-water flagellates (*Pandorina, Pleodorina, Volvox*, etc.) that form floating colonies (Fig. 16-14). *Volvox globator* is a hollow sphere (0.5 mm. in diameter), filled with watery jelly. Embedded in the gelatinous exterior wall are 8,000 to 17,000 minute (4 by 8 μ) individual cells, each with nucleus, contractile vacuole, red stigma, green chloroplast, and two flagella. Protoplasmic threads connect adjacent cells and provide physiological continuity between them. The flagella beat collectively to roll the colony through the water. Beginning in the spring, the first colonies develop from zygotes formed the previous season. Several asexual generations follow. In each colony a few cells (gonidia) lose flagella, enlarge, and divide to form hollow masses of small cells within the parent colony; the latter disintegrates, and each "embryo" mass grows asexually into a new colony. Then a sexual generation ensues. From 20 to 30 nonflagellated cells within a colony enlarge, each to become a *macrogamete* ("female sex cell," or "ovum"); a larger number of others divide repeatedly to form flat packets of 128 or more slender *microgametes* ("male sex cells," or "sperm"). Both types of gametes are discharged into the fluid interior of the colony, each "ovum" is penetrated by a "sperm," and the two fuse as a *zygote*. The latter secretes a cyst about itself and is released into the water when the parent colony disinte-

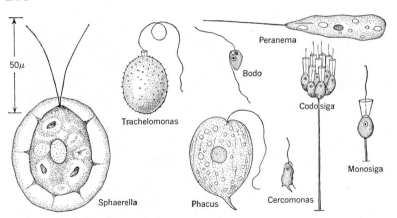

Peranema

Bodo

Codosiga

Trachelomonas

Monosiga

Sphaerella

Phacus

Cercomonas

50μ

Fig. 16-15. Class MASTIGO-PHORA. Representative free-living flagellates of fresh waters; all enlarged to about same scale.

grates. It remains in a dormant stage until the following year, then escapes from the cyst to start a new colony by asexual fission.

The volvox colony thus bears some resemblance to a multicellular animal. It is composed of cells of two kinds, unlike in structure and function. The **somatic cells** of the colony wall can synthesize food and cooperate in swimming but cannot reproduce and eventually die as does the body of a higher animal. The **germ cells** are unable to feed, are of two distinct kinds (sexes), and serve only to maintain the species by sexual reproduction.

The Subclass ZOOMASTIGINA comprises flagellates, lacking chloroplasts, that are simple to complex in structure. The free-living forms are holozoic in nutrition, and the many parasitic species are saprozoic. The Order PROTOMONADINA includes both types. *Bodo* (Fig. 16-15) and *Oicomonas* are common small solitary types in fresh waters and soil. *Codosiga, Proterospongia,* and some other colonial aquatic forms have

each flagellum surrounded by a collar, like the choanocytes of sponges.

All of the Family TRYPANOSOMIDAE are parasitic. *Phytomonas* lives in the latex cells of milkweeds and is carried from one plant to another by a bug (*Oncopeltus*). *Crithidia* and *Herpetomonas* are gut parasites of insects and spread by cysts. The Genus *Trypanosoma* (Fig. 16-16) is of slender leaf-like flagellates that inhabit the blood of vertebrates, form no cysts, and are carried from one host to another by bloodsucking invertebrates. Species in fishes, salamanders, frogs, and reptiles are transmitted by leeches. *T. lewisi* of the rat, spread by rat fleas (Fig. 16-17), usually does no harm to its host; but many other species are disease producers. *T. evansi* causes surra in domestic animals of the Orient and is carried by biting flies (*Tabanus*). *Trypanosoma brucei* occurs in antelope and other game mammals of Africa and is carried by native tsetse flies; in domestic livestock, it is the cause of nagana disease. *T. gambiense* and *T. rhodesiense* are the causative agents of two types of human sleeping sickness[1] in Africa, both carried by tsetse flies and both fatal unless treated in early stages. *T. cruzi* causes Chagas' disease in Central and South America, being transmitted by bugs (*Triatoma, Rhodnius*). The organism occurs in these insects and in wood rats (*Neotoma*) and other mammals in the southwestern United States,

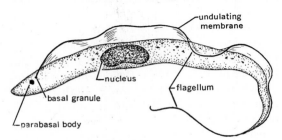

undulating membrane

nucleus

flagellum

basal granule

parabasal body

Fig. 16-16. Class MASTIGOPHORA. Structure of *Trypanosoma*. Greatly enlarged.

[1] Encephalitis, or "sleeping sickness," in the United States is caused by a virus.

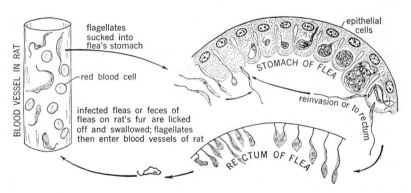

Fig. 16-17. Class MASTIGO-PHORA. Life cycle of the rat trypanosome, *Trypanosoma lewisi;* natural size, 25 μ long. (*Adapted from Minchin and Thompson,* 1915.)

where only one human case has been found. Flagellates of the Genus *Leishmania* attack the endothelial cells in blood vessels of man. *L. donovani* causes kala azar, and *L. tropica* the skin disease called Oriental sore; both occur in Asia, the Mediterranean region, and parts of South America. The related *L. brasiliensis* of Mexico and Central and South America also produces a skin disease. The spread of leishmanias is variously from rodents by blood-sucking flies (*Phlebotomus*), by direct contact between people, and by dogs.

Members of the Order POLYMASTIGINA have three or more flagella. *Tetramitus* and a few others are free-living, but many are intestinal parasites. *Hexamita* occurs in fishes and birds, *Eutrichomastix* in frogs, snakes, etc., *Devescovina, Oxymonas,* etc., in termites, and *Trichomonas* in both invertebrates and vertebrates.

The Order HYPERMASTIGINA comprises species with many flagella and complex internal structure. They abound in the gut of a cockroach (*Cryptocercus*) and in about one-fourth of the species of termites, where (with polymastigotes) they constitute an outstanding example of mutualism (Fig. 16-18). Termites (Chap. 26) eat wood, but many of them are unable to digest the cellulose that it contains. The flagellates that receive "lodging and board" are able to digest this material for themselves and their hosts. Termites experimentally defaunated (by exposure to an oxygen atmosphere or kept at 36°C. for 24 hours to kill the flagellates) will starve and die in 10 or more days, even when wood is eaten. If, however, they are reinfected with the flagellates, they can thenceforth utilize the wood and survive. The flagellates form pseudopodia to ingest the wood fragments in the termite's gut, the cellulose is digested, and the soluble products become available for absorption by the termites. Other nonsymbiotic protozoans occur in termites.

CLASS SPOROZOA. GREGARINES, COCCIDIA, HAEMOSPORIDIA, ETC.

The SPOROZOA (Gr. *spora*, seed + *zoön*, animal) are practically all parasites. The simple cell body is rounded or elongate, with one nucleus and no locomotor organelles or contractile vacuole. Some move by change in shape of the cell body. Food is absorbed directly from the host (saprozoic nutrition), and respiration and excretion are by simple diffusion. Most sporozoans increase rapidly by multiple asexual fission, or **schizogony;** the cell becomes multi-

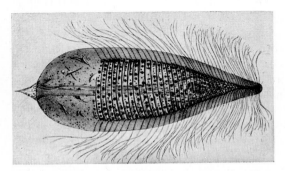

Fig. 16-18. Class MASTIGOPHORA. *Spirotrichonympha bispira,* a complex flagellate that lives only in the gut of termites. (*After Cleveland,* 1928.)

nucleate by repeated mitoses, and then the cytoplasm divides. They also produce sexual **macro-** and **microgametes;** these join in pairs of opposite kind to form **zygotes.** The latter, in many species, form seed-like **oöcysts** by **sporogony,** and in this stage the organisms are spread from one host individual to another. The typical coccidian life cycle is thus:

plasm so that many **gametes** of about equal size result. A pair of gametes, each from a different parent cell, then unite as a **zygote,** which secretes a thin hard spore case, or **oöcyst,** around itself while still within the cyst. The zygote nucleus inside divides successively into 2, 4, and 8 daughter nuclei, and each combines with part of the cytoplasm to become a sporozoite. The

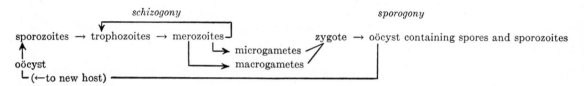

SPOROZOA are possibly the most widely occurring of animal parasites. Distinct species occur in various animals from protozoans to mammals. Some live within the host's cells, and others in its body fluids or cavities. They inhabit variously the digestive tract, muscles, blood, kidneys, or other organs. Malaria in man, coccidiosis in fowls and rabbits, certain fevers in cattle, and the pebrine disease of silkworms are examples of serious diseases caused by sporozoans.

16-15. Order Gregarinida. These are extra- or intra-cellular parasites of invertebrates (Fig. 16-19). A common example is *Monocystis,* which lives in the seminal vesicles of earthworms. The minute *spore* is a spindle-shaped case containing 8 *sporozoites.* Upon escaping from the spore, each sporozoite enters a clump of immature sperm cells and transforms into a *trophozoite* that consumes the cells. The trophozoites then become grouped as pairs of *gametocytes,* each pair being surrounded by a *cyst.* Sporulation follows, every nucleus dividing many times with later partitioning of the cyto-

manner by which spores are spread from one worm to another is unknown.

16-16. Order Coccidia. These parasites live in epithelial cells of many vertebrates, some myriapods, and a few other invertebrates. They occur chiefly in the lining of the intestine, but also in the bile duct, kidneys, testes, blood vessels, and coelom. The life cycles involve alternate schizogony and sporogony, with change of host by some species. Coccidia produce the disease coccidiosis, which may be serious and even fatal. Species of economic importance occur in poultry, domestic mammals, and many kinds of wild animals. *Eimeria stiedae* (Fig. 16-20) is common in both domestic and wild rabbits. When food contaminated with oöcysts is swallowed, the host's digestive juices dissolve the cysts and release the sporozoites. These enter epithelial cells in the bile duct and enlarge as feeding trophozoites that undergo rapid schizogony to produce many merozoites. In turn, the merozoites invade other cells to repeat the cycle. Epithelial tissue in the bile duct and liver may be destroyed, with consequent harm to the host. Later some merozoites develop into gametocytes, also within epithelial cells; some become enlarged macrogametes, and others divide to yield many microgametes. Union of a macrogamete and a microgamete forms a zygote that secretes an elliptical covering oöcyst. In this stage the coccidia pass out of the rabbit in the feces. Later the zygote

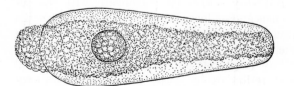

Fig. 16-19. Class SPOROZOA. A gregarine from the mealworm. Greatly enlarged.

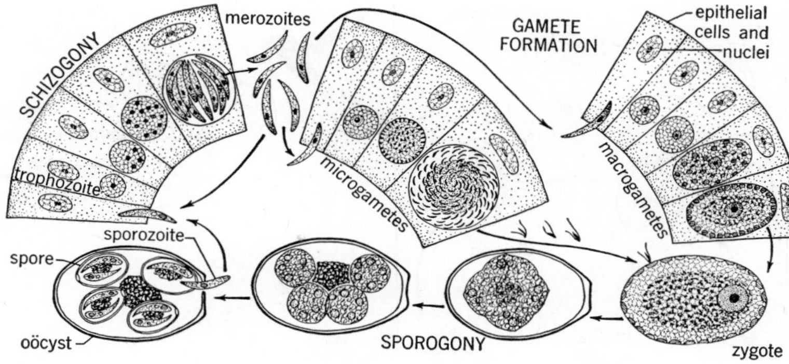

Fig. 16-20. Class SPOROZOA. Life cycle of *Eimeria stiedae*, a coccidium from the liver of the rabbit. (*Adapted from Wasielewski*, 1924.)

within divides into 4 spores, each enclosing 2 sporozoites, and this is the infective stage for a new host. Among domestic rabbits this parasite often causes severe epidemics with many deaths, particularly in young animals. Rearing rabbits in separate hutches, keeping their food off the floor, and cleaning the hutches frequently are practices essential to keep down losses from coccidiosis.

16-17. Order Haemosporidia. These SPOROZOA are parasites of blood cells and tissues in birds and mammals; they form no resistant spores but are transferred by bloodsucking arthropods as intermediate hosts. The most familiar example is *Plasmodium*, which causes malaria (Fig. 16-21). This disease, a scourge of man since ancient times, has caused an enormous amount of illness and innumerable deaths, especially in tropical and subtropical regions. Possibly it is the most important of all diseases. The parasites are transmitted to man by females of certain species of mosquitoes of the Genus *Anopheles* (Fig. 26-40). As the mosquito's mouth parts pierce the skin to obtain blood, the infective sporozoites pass from its salivary glands into the wound. The development immediately following injection is unknown, but after 3 days dividing **schizonts** are present in parenchyma cells of the liver. Infection then spreads into red blood cells where amoeba-like **trophozoites** develop. Each trophozoite in an individual blood cell grows to be a schizont, which by multiple fission (schizogony) divides into 6 to 36 daughter **merozoites,** according to the spe-

cies. By rupture of the corpuscle these escape into the blood plasma, to invade other red cells and repeat the cycle. After about 10 days the parasites are so numerous that the shock of their nearly simultaneous release produces a chill, followed by a violent fever in response to toxins from the liberated parasites. The chill-and-fever cycle thenceforth depends upon the species of parasite: every 48 hours in benign tertian malaria caused by *P. vivax;* and every 72 hours in quartan (fourth day) malaria caused by *P. malariae*. In aestivo-autumnal (malignant tertian) malaria caused by *P. falciparum*, the cycle is lacking or irregular. *P. ovale*, with a 48-hour cycle, produces a mild infection ending in about 15 days.

After a period of schizogony, some merozoites become **gametocytes** but do not change further in the human host. If taken with blood into the gut of an appropriate female *Anopheles*, the female gametocyte soon becomes a **macrogamete,** and the male gametocyte divides into 6 to 8 sperm-like **microgametes.** Two gametes of opposite sex fuse as a zygote. This becomes a worm-like **oökinete** that penetrates the gut wall to lie under the membrane surrounding the gut. It then absorbs nutrients from the insect and enlarges as a rounded **oöcyst.** A single mosquito may contain 50 to 500 oöcysts. In 6 or 7 days the contents of each cyst divide (sporogony) into thousands of slender sporozoites. The cysts burst, the sporozoites migrate through the body spaces, and many enter the salivary glands to await transfer to a human host. The sexual cycle in the

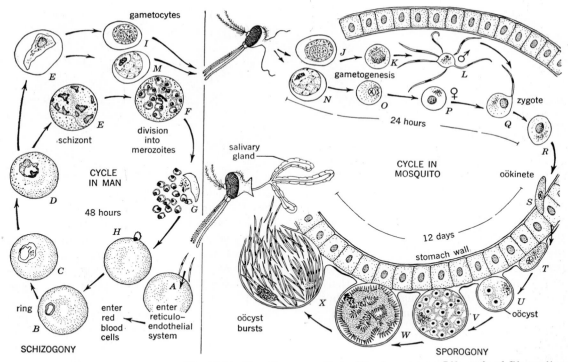

Fig. 16-21. Class SPOROZOA. Order HAEMOSPORIDIA. Life cycle of *Plasmodium vivax*, the tertian malarial parasite of man and anopheline mosquitoes. Sporozoites injected during the biting of the mosquito invade parenchyma cells of the liver (not shown in figure) and multiply asexually (schizogony); then the resulting parasites enter red blood cells and multiply further. Later gametocytes are produced; if drawn up by a biting mosquito they transform into gametes in the insect's stomach. The zygotes encyst externally on the gut wall and form large oöcysts. By asexual multiplication (sporogony) many sporozoites are produced that invade the salivary glands.

mosquito requires about 7 to 19 days until the insect becomes infective.

Acute symptoms of malaria in man usually continue for some days or weeks and then often subside as the body develops an **immunity** to the disease, but relapses may occur at irregular intervals. In different persons the infection disappears in time, or lingers and causes damage to other organs, or may result in death. Malaria patients are treated with primaquine. Healthy persons living in malarial regions often take small daily doses of daraprim or chloroquine as a prophylactic to kill any plasmodia received in mosquito bites. General reduction or control of malaria in a region requires (1) treating the human victims, (2) effectively screening dwellings to exclude mosquitoes, and (3) draining

off, oiling, or poisoning the water to reduce mosquitoes by killing the larvae. DDT and other new insecticides are highly effective in killing adult mosquitoes and larvae, thereby reducing the malarial hazard. Mosquito fish (*Gambusia affinis*) are planted in waters to eat mosquito larvae and pupae.

Other species of *Plasmodium* occur in mammals, birds, and reptiles; several in primates closely resemble the species in man.

Babesia bigemina, a minute parasite in the red blood cells of cattle, causes red water, or Texas cattle fever. The intermediate host is a tick, *Boöphilus annulatus* (Fig. 27-7*A*). Following asexual stages in the blood of cattle, the merozoites are withdrawn when the tick feeds. The sexual stages occur in the blind gut of the

Fig. 16-22. Structure of *Paramecium caudatum*, a ciliate of fresh waters (Class Ciliata). *A*. The entire animal. Lines of dots indicate rows of cilia over the surface. Arrows show path of food vacuoles in endoplasm. *B*. Enlarged sketch of a few cilia showing how they beat in coordinated waves to drive the paramecium forward (to the left). *C*. Outline of body form (cross sections) at different positions along its length.

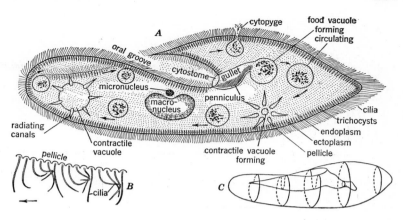

tick, and the zygotes then penetrate to the ovary and eggs. Later they multiply in the developing salivary glands of the embryo tick. When the latter hatches and feeds on a bovine animal, the sporozoites are injected into the new host individual. Control of this disease, which once ravaged herds in many southern states, has been accomplished by dipping the cattle to remove ticks and rotation of their pasturing so that clean herds have no chance to acquire infected ticks.

CLASS CILIATA. Ciliates, or "Infusoria"

The Ciliata (L. *cilium*, eyelid) possess cilia throughout life, which serve for locomotion and food getting. Each species is of constant and characteristic form, and most of them have one large macronucleus (or more) concerned with the routine or vegetative functions and one or more small micronuclei that are important in reproduction. Ciliates are the most specialized of protozoans in having various organelles to perform particular vital processes. This results in a division of labor between parts of the organism, analogous to that between organ systems in a multicellular animal. Ciliates abound in fresh and salt waters. Many are free-living; some are commensal or parasitic in other animals; and a few grow in colonies. They are much used in experimental studies because of their relatively large size and the ease with which they may be reared.

Paramecium (Fig. 16-22) is a ciliate common in fresh waters that contain some decaying vegetation. It multiplies rapidly in the laboratory in an "infusion" made by boiling a little hay or some wheat grains in water. The 8 or 9 species differ in size, shape, and structure. *P. aurelia* is 0.12 to 0.25 mm. long and *P. caudatum* measures 0.15 to 0.3 mm. in length. The following account deals mainly with *P. caudatum*.

16-18. Structure. The long cell body is blunt at the forward-moving or *anterior end,* widest behind the middle, and tapered at the *posterior end.* The exterior surface is covered by a distinct elastic membrane, the *pellicle,* with fine *cilia* arranged in lengthwise rows and of uniform length save for a posterior *caudal tuft* of longer cilia. Within the pellicle, the cell contents, as in *Amoeba,* consist of a thin clear external layer of dense *ectoplasm,* around the larger mass of more granular and fluid *endoplasm.* The ectoplasm contains many spindle-shaped *trichocysts,* alternating between the bases of the cilia, that may be discharged as long threads to serve perhaps in attachment or defense. From the anterior end a shallow furrow or *oral groove* extends diagonally back about halfway along the lower or *oral surface* and has the *cytostome* (cell mouth) at its posterior end. The cytostome opens into a short tubular *cytopharynx* (gullet), ending in the endoplasm. In the gullet cilia are fused to form two lengthwise dense bands (the penniculus). On

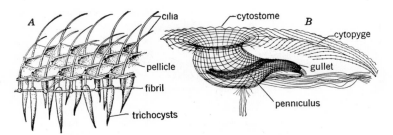

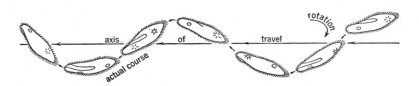

Fig. 16-23. *Paramecium multi-micronucleata.* *A.* Structure of the pellicle and associated organelles. *B.* The neuromotor system in part of the cell body. (*After Lund,* 1935.)

Fig. 16-24. *Paramecium.* Locomotion. The animal swims in a spiral manner so that the asymmetrical body progresses on a direct course. (*Adapted from Jennings, Behavior of the lower organisms, Columbia University Press.*)

one side, just behind the cytopharynx, is the **cytopyge** (cell anus), which can be seen only when particles are discharging through it. In the endoplasm are **food vacuoles** of various sizes that contain material undergoing digestion, and toward each end of the cell body is a large clear **contractile vacuole.** The small rounded **micronucleus** is partly surrounded by the larger **macronucleus.** *P. aurelia* has two micronuclei.

When specimens of *Paramecium* and similar ciliates are prepared by special methods (with nigrosin or silver salts) and studied under high magnification, the pellicle shows a hexagonal pattern of ridges, surrounding cup-like depressions with a cilium projecting from the center of each cup. Beneath the pellicle each cilium connects to a basal granule, and the granules are joined by longitudinal fibrils. Most ciliates have both transverse and longitudinal fibrils (Fig. 16-23), which in some are joined to a body (motorium) near the cytopharynx (Fig. 16-30). The granules and fibrils comprise a **fibrillar** or **neuromotor system,** probably sensory-motor in function, that coordinates ciliary action. Experimental destruction of the motorium in some ciliates (*Euplotes patella*) is followed by loss of coordination in movements of the membranelles and cirri. Contractile fibrils (myonemes) occur in ciliates such as *Stentor* and *Vorticella,* but not in *Paramecium.*

16-19. Locomotion. The cilia beat backward to carry the paramecium forward in the water, and, as their stroke is oblique, the animal rotates on its longitudinal axis. The cilia in the oral groove beat more vigorously than the others, so that the anterior end swerves aborally. The combined effect is to move the animal forward in a spiral course, counterclockwise as viewed from behind (Fig. 16-24). Thus the asymmetrical animal may travel in a direct path. To swim backward the ciliary beat is reversed, as is the path of rotation. If, when swimming forward, the paramecium meets some unfavorable chemical stimulus, it executes an **avoiding reaction** (Fig. 16-25): the ciliary beat reverses, the animal moves backward a short distance, and then rotates in a conical path by swerving the anterior end aborally while pivoting on the posterior tip. While doing this, cilia in the oral groove bring "samples" from the water immediately ahead; when these no longer contain the undesirable stimulus, the animal moves forward again. The reaction is similar upon encountering a solid object: it reverses, rotates, and goes forward, repeating the process if necessary until a clear path is found.

16-20. Feeding and digestion. Paramecium feeds on bacteria, small protozoans, algae, and yeasts. The constant beating of cilia in the oral groove sweeps a current of water containing food toward the cytostome, and movements of the penniculus gather the food at the posterior end of the cytopharynx in a watery vacuole. The vacuole becomes of a certain size, constricts off, and begins to circulate in the endoplasm as a *food vacuole;* another then begins to form in its place. Streaming movements (cyclosis) in the endoplasm carry the vacuoles in a definite route, first posteriorly, then forward and aborally and again posteriorly to near the oral groove. The contents of the vacuoles are acid at first and gradually become alkaline, as shown by use of congo red and other indicator dyes. As in amoeba, the food is digested by the action of enzymes secreted by the endoplasm. This process continues until digested material is absorbed by the surrounding protoplasm and either stored or used for vital activity and growth. The vacuoles gradually become smaller, and any indigestible residues are egested at the cell anus.

Paramecium caudatum will live and multiply in a bacteria-free suspension of liver extract, dead yeast, and kidney tissue that provides the necessary organic materials. *P. aurelia* requires certain salts and bacteria. *P. bursaria*, which contains spherical green algae (zoochlorellae) in its endoplasm, will multiply in a solution of salts alone if kept in the light—this is a case of mutualism where the organisms are interdependent. Carbon dioxide produced by the protozoan in respiration serves the algae with their chlorophyll to synthesize organic materials and produce oxygen, both of which are necessary for the paramecium.

16-21. Respiration and excretion. As with amoeba, respiration in paramecium corresponds to the internal respiration of cells in multicellular animals. Oxygen dissolved in the surrounding water diffuses through the pellicle and then throughout the organism; carbon dioxide and organic wastes resulting from metabolism are probably excreted by diffusing outward in the reverse direction.

The contractile vacuoles regulate the water content of the body and may serve also in excretion of nitrogenous wastes such as urea and ammonia. Liquid within the cytoplasm is gathered by a series of 6 to 11 *radiating canals* that converge toward and discharge into each vacuole. The canals are most conspicuous as a vacuole is forming. When each vacuole has swelled to a certain size, it contracts and discharges to the exterior, probably through a pore. The vacuoles contract alternately, at intervals of 10 to 20 seconds. If water containing a paramecium is densely filled with particles of carbon or carmine, the discharged contents from a vacuole will be evident momentarily as a clear spot in the surrounding clouded fluid before being dispersed by action of the cilia.

The rate of vacuole discharge varies with temperature, is higher in an inactive animal than in one that is swimming about, and is higher in water with a scant supply of dissolved salts than with stronger concentrations. Since the body of a paramecium contains dissolved substances, water tends to pass through the pellicle, which functions as a semipermeable membrane. The contractile vacuoles offset this tendency and maintain an optimum concentration of water in the body protoplasm by disposing of the excess.

16-22. Behavior. The responses of paramecium to various kinds of stimuli are learned by study of its avoiding reaction and of the grouping or scattering of individuals in a culture. The response is *positive* if the animal moves toward a stimulus and *negative* when it moves away. To an adverse stimulus the animal continues to give the avoiding reaction until it escapes. All adjustments are made by *trial and error*. The intensity of the reaction may differ according to the kind and intensity of the stimulus. Experiments indicate that the anterior end of the animal is more sensitive than other parts.

To *contact,* the response is varied; if the anterior end is lightly touched with a fine point, a strong avoiding reaction occurs, as when a swimming paramecium collides with some object in the water, but if touched elsewhere there may be no response. A slow-moving individual often responds positively to contact with an object by coming to rest upon it; since food or-

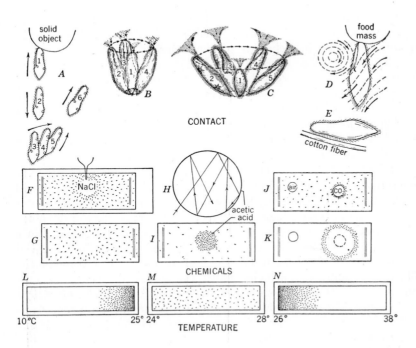

ganisms are common about masses of algae or plant stems, this response is advantageous, and individuals often concentrate about such materials. Paramecium seeks an optimum as to *temperature,* between 24 and 28°C.; in a temperature gradient the animals congregate in spots between these limits (Fig. 16-25). Greater heat stimulates rapid movement and avoiding reactions until the animals escape or are killed; in ice water, they also seek to escape but may be benumbed and sink. To *gravity,* there is generally a negative response, as seen in a deep culture where many individuals gather close under the surface film with their anterior ends uppermost. In a gentle *water current* the paramecia will mostly align with the flow, their anterior ends upstream. Likewise, to a constant or direct *electric current,* the animals "head"

toward the negative pole (cathode) from which electrons stream toward the positive pole (anode). To most *chemicals,* the response is negative. If a drop of weak salt solution (0.5 per cent) is introduced in a paramecium population on a microslide, the animals respond with the avoiding reaction and none enters the drop. To acids, however, the response is positive, even when the concentration is of sufficient strength to kill them. This latter phenomenon probably is related to the fact that, although paramecium often lives in alkaline waters, the local concentrations produce sufficient carbon dioxide to render the immediate environment acid, and it is to this condition that it is most adapted. The trichocysts of paramecium (Fig. 16-26) and certain other ciliates have been thought to be organelles of defense against enemies, but even when discharged they seldom save the animal from its predator.

Although paramecium is of almost universal occurrence in fresh waters, its means of dispersal is unknown. It has been reported to form cysts, but this observation lacks general confirmation.

16-23. Reproduction. Paramecium reproduces by fission and also undergoes several types of nuclear reorganization—conjugation, autogamy, and endomixis. In **binary fission** (Fig. 11-1) the micronucleus divides by mitosis into two micronuclei that move toward opposite ends of the cell, and the macronucleus divides transversely by amitosis; a second gullet forms, two new contractile vacuoles appear, and then a transverse furrow divides the cytoplasm into two parts. The resulting two "daughter" paramecia are of equal size, each containing a set of cell organelles. They grow to full size before another division occurs. Fission requires about 2 hours to complete and may occur one to four times per day, yielding 2 to 16 individuals. A single paramecium thus gives rise to 2, 4, 8, 16 . . . 2^n individuals; all individuals resulting by fission (uniparental reproduction) from a single individual are known collectively as a *clone.* Upward of 600 "generations" per year may be produced. The rate of multiplication depends upon external conditions of food, temperature, age of the culture, and population density; also on internal factors of heredity and physiology. If all descendants of one individual were to survive, they soon would equal the earth in volume. Stocks of *P. aurelia* have been maintained artificially for 25 years through 15,300 generations of fission without conjugation, by continually isolating daughter individuals in a fresh culture medium. In ordinary laboratory cultures with many individuals, the rate of fission gradually declines and some type of nuclear reorganization ensues.

16-24. Conjugation. In paramecium, other ciliates, and the SUCTORIA, there is, at intervals, a temporary union of individuals in pairs with mutual exchange of micronuclear materials that is known as **conjugation** (Fig. 16-27). The ani-

Fig. 16-26. *Paramecium* (below) discharging trichocysts upon attack by *Didinium*, another protozoan. (*After Mast*, 1909.)

mals become "sticky," adhering to one another by their oral surfaces, and a protoplasmic bridge forms between them. The pairs continue to swim about during this process. A sequence of nuclear changes then occurs in each animal. The macronucleus disintegrates and eventually disappears into the cytoplasm. The micronucleus enlarges, its chromatin forms long strands, a division spindle appears, and the micronucleus divides by mitosis; a second division of each follows at once, yielding four micronuclei. Three of the four micronuclei degenerate, and the remaining one divides again to yield two "pronuclei" in each animal. One from each then migrates through the protoplasmic bridge into the opposite individual, uniting there with the other pronucleus that has remained in place. Soon thereafter the two paramecia separate as exconjugants. In each the fused micronucleus or "zygote" divides successively into two, four, and eight micronuclei (the first two divisions are meiotic). Four of these enlarge to become macronuclei, and three of the others degenerate. Then the micronuclei and animals divide twice, so that from each exconjugant there are four paramecia, each with one macronucleus and one micronucleus. Thenceforth, the organisms multiply by binary fission as already described.

Conjugation differs from the sexual union of gametes in other PROTOZOA and in METAZOA because progeny are not a direct product of the fusion; after conjugation each individual continues asexual fission. The net result, however, is like the fusion of gametes (syngamy) in other animals. Conjugation is a process that provides

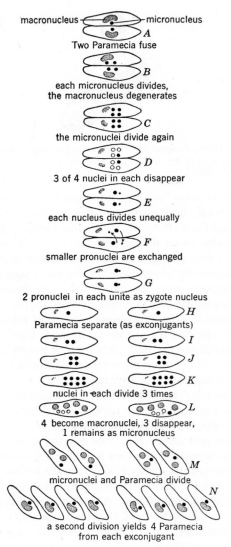

macronucleus — micronucleus
A
Two Paramecia fuse

B
each micronucleus divides,
the macronucleus degenerates

C
the micronuclei divide again

D
3 of 4 nuclei in each disappear

E
each nucleus divides unequally

F
smaller pronuclei are exchanged

G
2 pronuclei in each unite as zygote nucleus

H
Paramecia separate (as exconjugants)

I

J

K
nuclei in each divide 3 times

L
4 become macronuclei, 3 disappear,
1 remains as micronucleus

M
micronuclei and Paramecia divide

N
a second division yields 4 Paramecia
from each exconjugant

Fig. 16-27. *Paramecium caudatum.* Diagram of conjugation.

for hereditary transfer, as the two exconjugants are genetically altered by their exchange of micronuclear materials (chromosomes). The nuclear changes bear comparison with those of meiosis and fertilization in Metazoa, with divisions (reduction) of the micronucleus, the joining (fertilization) of one micronucleus (egg pronucleus) by a migrant micronucleus (sperm pronucleus) to form a fusion micronucleus (zygote). The macronucleus which directs the vegetative processes in a paramecium has been compared to the body (soma) of the multicellular animal, and its disintegration to the death of the body. The fusion micronucleus (zygote) then produces another macronucleus (soma) and continues as the reproductive component (germ plasm) of the exconjugant.

16-25. Mating types. For years no differences were detected between the two paramecia joining in conjugation. In 1937 Sonneborn reported stocks of *P. aurelia* containing two kinds ("sexes") of individuals; only members of opposite kinds would conjugate. These two categories were termed *mating types* I and II. By separating progeny of exconjugants that multiplied by binary fission, some clones produced only Type I, others only Type II, and still others both Types I and II. Later it was shown that the first two, so-called single-type clones, were not changed by endomixis, whereas the third or double-type clone, after endomixis, yielded all three sorts. By crossing and back-crossing (Chap. 6) the two types, Sonneborn further showed that mating types were determined by a single Mendelian factor. Single type clones were AA or aa, and double types Aa.

16-26. Autogamy. Nuclear reorganization resembling conjugation but occurring within one individual (hence one cell generation) is termed *autogamy* (Diller, 1936). In *Paramecium aurelia* (Fig. 16-28) which has 2 micronuclei, these divide twice (prezygotic) to yield 8. The macronucleus becomes skein-like, and later breaks up. Two of the 8 micronuclei, as gamete nuclei, enter a protoplasmic cone bulging near the cell mouth (the other 6 micronuclei disintegrate). The two fuse as a synkaryon (zygote), which then divides twice (postzygotic). Of the 4 resulting nuclei, 2 continue as micronuclei and 2 become macronuclei. The cell and micronuclei then divide to yield two daughter paramecia each with a (new) macronucleus and 2 micronuclei. Thereafter binary fission resumes.

Autogamy is a rhythmic process and one in which hereditary changes occur; lines homozygous as to mating type can be produced. There is decreased survival only when, as the result of a cross, the animals receive lethal genes.

16-27. Endomixis. At intervals, binary fission is interrupted by replacement of the macronucleus and a nuclear reorganization termed *endomixis*. In *P. aurelia* (with 2 micronuclei) the old macronucleus disintegrates and each micronucleus divides twice, but 6 of the 8 resulting micronuclei disappear. The paramecium divides, each daughter receiving a micronucleus. The latter divide twice, and 2 of the 4 in each animal become macronuclei. Then each paramecium and its micronucleus divide again, to yield 4 normal individuals. Endomixis in *P. aurelia* commonly occurs every 25 to 30 days, following some decline in rate of fission, and about every 50 to 60 days in *P. caudatum.* Some clones of *P. aurelia* and other species continue fission for years without either endomixis or conjugation.

16-28. Variation and heredity. A wild stock of *Paramecium* in nature will contain individuals that differ as to total length and other features. Such variations are of three kinds, as follows: (1) age variation; (2) random variations due to environmental factors; and (3) inherited variations due to genetic factors. From a wild stock, Jennings isolated eight "races," or biotypes, that differed in average size. Within each race the individual and random variations produced animals of various lengths, but the average of these was the same in successive generations by asexual fission because of their hereditary make-up.

DeGaris obtained conjugation between individuals of races that differed greatly in size, one (198 μ long) being twenty times the bulk of the other (73 μ long). After the exconjugants had separated, each produced a series of generations by fission. Those from the larger individual became successively smaller, and the opposite occurred with the smaller animal; after 24 days the offspring of both lines were alike. Before conjugation each race continued at its characteristic size; after conjugation the two individuals had like nuclear content but differed as to cytoplasm. The subsequent divisions show that for a period of days the size of descendants was affected by *both cytoplasm and nucleus*, but finally only by nuclear constitution. In other crosses the final size from both conjugants was not strictly intermediate but might be more nearly like either one or the other. Thus in these PROTOZOA, as in METAZOA, recombining the chromosomal materials produces different combinations in different cases.

In summary, paramecium shows (1) structural specialization in organelles; (2) physiological division of labor between parts to perform special functions; (3) a stereotyped avoiding reaction; (4) reproduction by binary fission; (5) nuclear reorganization by endomixis; (6) conjugation as a mechanism providing for exchange of hereditary factors; (7) segregation into many mating types that are mutually exclusive in conjugation; (8) pure lines that are genetically distinct in a wild population; and

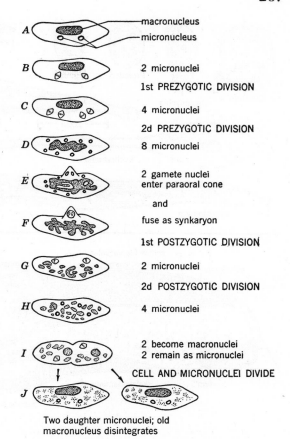

Fig. 16-28. *Paramecium aurelia*. Diagram of autogamy. (*Adapted from Diller*, 1936.)

(9) the relative influence of nuclear and cytoplasmic materials in inheritance.

16-29. Other Ciliata. Examination of a drop of water from any quiet fresh-, brackish-, or salt-water source will usually reveal one or more species of ciliates and testify to the wide occurrence of these protozoans (Fig. 16-29). Free-swimming species are commonly ellipsoidal to spherical in shape, whereas creeping forms are often flattened. Anterior-posterior and oral-aboral relations in structure and locomotion are usually evident. The cilia on some types are reduced in numbers and grouped to form membranelles or cirri, by which the animals move about. Some ciliates of both solitary (*Vorticella, Stentor*) and colonial habit (*Zoothamnium*) are

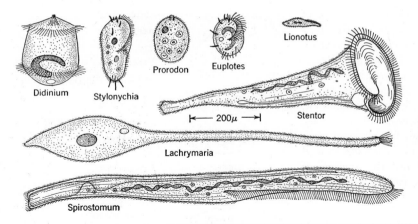

Fig. 16-29. Class CILIATA. Common fresh-water ciliates; all enlarged to about same scale. Macronucleus, heavy stipple; contractile vacuole, clear.

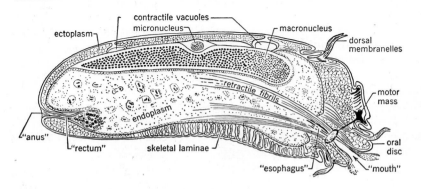

Fig. 16-30. Class CILIATA. *Epidinium (Diplodinium) ecaudatum*, a complex ciliate from the rumen of cattle, as seen in median section. (*After Sharp, 1914.*)

attached by stalks or other means. The ciliates as a group exhibit tremendous variety in configuration, placement of cilia, form of the macronucleus, and other features.

The Subclass PROTOCILIATA comprises intestinal inhabitants (*Opalina*, etc.), mostly in frogs and toads, that have two to hundreds of nuclei all alike and no cytostome; in "sexual reproduction" their gametes fuse permanently.

Each individual in the Subclass EUCILIATA has a macronucleus (some have more than one) and one or more micronuclei. Sexual reproduction (conjugation) involves only temporary union, as with *Paramecium*. The orders of ciliates are distinguished primarily by the arrangement of the cilia around the cytostome.

Members of the Order HOLOTRICHA, like *Paramecium*, are uniformly ciliated and have no adoral membranelles. They commonly encyst. The species are diverse in form and either

live in various kinds of water or are parasitic; those of the Suborder THIGMOTRICHA occur chiefly in the mantle cavities of bivalve mollusks.

The Order SPIROTRICHA contains, besides many free-living species, some of peculiar structure that inhabit parts of the digestive tract in herbivorous mammals—the caecum and colon of horses and the rumen and reticulum of sheep, cattle, deer, and other ruminants (Fig. 16-30). They may number up to 500,000 or 1,000,000 per cubic centimeter of gut contents so that a mature ox may contain 10,000,000,000 to 50,-000,000,000. These ciliates digest starches, fats, and proteins in the host's food. They probably are only messmates (commensals) without either benefit or harm to their hosts. *Balantidium coli* is a common ciliate parasite of the intestine in pigs that occurs rarely in man. Human infection probably is obtained by cysts carried into the mouth by the hands or with food. It sometimes invades the intestinal wall and produces ulcers.

The Order PERITRICHA is distinguished by a disc-like oral region that is conspicuously ciliated, with few or no cilia elsewhere; the opposite end of the cell has a structure for temporary or permanent attachment to objects in the water. Some species are colonial, and some secrete a case or lorica, into which the organism may withdraw.

CLASS SUCTORIA

16-30. Adult SUCTORIA are sessile protozoans that have delicate protoplasmic "tentacles" but neither cilia nor a cytostome (Fig. 16-1). Their young resemble the CILIATA in being ciliated and free-swimming. The cell body of suctorians is spherical, elongate, or branched in different species, usually attached by a stalk or disc to some object and covered by a pellicle. Some of the tentacles are tipped with rounded knobs that act as suckers to catch and hold the small ciliates used for food. Other tentacles are pointed and pierce the prey to take up its soft parts, which stream through these tentacles into the cell body. Reproduction is by fission or budding; the young swim for a time and then settle to lose their cilia and transform into the adult stage. Various species inhabit fresh, brackish, and salt waters and attach to inanimate objects, plants, and small aquatic animals; some are parasitic. *Podophrya* is a common, free-living, fresh-water representative; *Dendrosoma* is branched and up to 2.5 mm. tall. *Sphaerophrya* is spherical and parasitic in *Paramecium* and the ciliate *Stentor*; *Trichophrya micropteri* lives on the gills of bass; and *Allantosoma* attaches to ciliates in the colon of horses.

CLASSIFICATION

PHYLUM PROTOZOA. PROTOZOANS. Single-celled or in colonies of like cells (no tissues); symmetry spherical, bilateral, or none; size usually microscopic; Pre-Cambrian to Recent, 30,000 species.
  SUBPHYLUM 1. PLASMODROMA. Locomotor organs are pseudopodia, flagella, or none; nuclei of one kind.
    CLASS 1. *MASTIGOPHORA* (Flagellata). FLAGELLATES. With 1 to many flagella for locomotion; with or without pseudopodia.
      SUBCLASS 1. PHYTOMASTIGINA. Usually with chromatophores; mostly free-living.
        Order 1. Chrysomonadina. Small, solitary or colonial, often amoeboid; flagella 1 or 2 (or 3); chromatophores yellow, brown, or none; no gullet; nutrition holophytic or holozoic; produce endogenous cysts of silica. *Chromulina; Synura uvella* and *Uroglena americana*, both colonial, in fresh waters, causing bad flavor in water supplies.
        Order 2. Cryptomonadina. Small, oval, usually flattened, not amoeboid; flagella 2; chromatophores 1 or 2 yellow-brown, or none; usually with gullet; mostly holophytic; some live as zooxanthellae in other PROTOZOA and in METAZOA. *Chilomonas*, in foul waters, saprophytic.
        Order 3. Phytomonadina (Volvocales). Small, solitary or in swimming colonies; some enclosed in cellulose membrane; flagella 2 or 4 (or 8); no cytostome or gullet; chromatophores green or none; nutrition holophytic or saprophytic; reserve food is starch; mostly in fresh waters. Solitary forms: *Chlamydomonas nivalis*, on snow; *Haematococcus pluvialis*, appears suddenly, causing "red rain" in pools. Colonial forms (VOLVOCIDAE), in fresh waters: *Gonium*, as squares of 4 or 16 cells; *Pandorina*, globular, 16 cells; *Eudorina*, 32 cells near surface of gelatinous sphere; *Pleodorina*, 32, 64, or 128 cells in solid gelatinous ball; *Volvox*, to 15,000 cells on hollow gelatinous sphere, to 2 mm. in diameter (Fig. 16-14).
        Order 4. Euglenoidina. Form slender, usually definite; pellicle rigid or soft; flagella usually 1 or 2, in anterior gullet, near contractile vacuole; chromatophores green or none; nutrition holophytic, holozoic, or saprophytic; reserve food is paramylum; mostly in fresh waters. *Euglena*, some to 0.5 mm. long; *Astasia*, colorless; *Trachelomonas*, in shell; *Copromonas*, in feces of toads and frogs.
        Order 5. Chloromonadina. Flagella 2; chromatophores many if present; no stigma; reserve food stored as fat. *Gonyostomum.*

Order 6. Dinoflagellata. Flagella usually 2, in grooves, one in girdle around body, one trailing; body often of fixed form, in cellulose-like armor of 2 to many plates; chromatophores many, brown, yellow, or green; many species important in marine plankton, some in fresh water, some parasitic. *Gymnodinium*, unarmored; *Peridinium* and *Ceratium*, both "armored," in salt or fresh waters; *Noctiluca*, spherical, to 2 mm. in diameter, marine, luminescent; *Gonyaulax*, in ocean; *Blastodinium*, in intestine and eggs of copepods.

SUBCLASS 2. ZOOMASTIGINA. No chromatophores; free-living or parasitic.

Order 1. Rhizomastigina. Flagella 1 or more; pseudopodia varying in number. *Mastigiamoeba hylae*, in gut of tadpoles and frogs; *Histomonas meleagris*, cause of blackhead in turkeys and other fowls, transmitted by contact or by nematode (*Heterakis gallinae*).

Order 2. Protomonadina. Flagella 1 or 2; body plastic or amoeboid; in fresh or foul waters, in feces, or parasitic. Free-living and holozoic: *Oicomonas*, *Monas*, *Bodo*, all solitary; *Codosiga*, on stalks, and *Proterospongia*, in gelatinous matrix, both colonial. Parasitic and saprozoic: *Herpetomonas*, in gut of flies; *Protermonas*, in gut of amphibians and reptiles; *Phytomonas*, in milky juices of milkweeds, euphorbias, etc., transmitted by plant-sucking bugs; *Trypanoplasma*, in blood of fishes, transmitted by leeches; *Trypanosoma*, narrowly leaf-like, in blood of vertebrates, mostly transmitted by arthropods (by leeches to aquatic hosts).

Order 3. Polymastigina. Flagella 3 to 8 or more, one often trailing or bordering an undulating membrane; often with parabasal body and axostyle; holozoic or saprozoic; mostly commensal or parasitic, in gut and other organs of invertebrates and vertebrates. *Tetramitus*, in salt or fresh waters; *Chilomastix*, mainly in gut of vertebrates; *Devescovina*, in gut of termites; *Trichomonas*, in digestive and reproductive tracts of man and other animals; *T. foetus*, causes abortion in cows; *Hexamita*, *Giardia*, in intestines of vertebrates.

Order 4. Hypermastigina. Structure complex, many flagella and parabasal bodies; holozoic, mostly ingest wood; symbiotic in gut of termites and cockroaches and necessary for digestion of cellulose by these insects. *Trichonympha*, in termites and roaches; *Laphomonas*, in cockroaches; *Staurojoenina*, in termites.

CLASS 2. SARCODINA (Rhizopoda). With pseudopodia for locomotion and food capture; mostly free-living.

SUBCLASS 1. RHIZOPODA. Protoplasmic processes various but no central filament.

Order 1. Proteomyxa. Protoplasmic processes radiating, branched, tending to fuse. *Vampyrella*.

Order 2. Mycetozoa. SLIME MOLDS. Adult phase a sheet of multinucleate protoplasm with streaming movements; feed on decaying wood or leaves, or live fungi. *Ceratiomyxa*, on wood, masses to several feet long; *Badhamia*, on fungi.

Order 3. Amoebina (Lobosa). Pseudopodia short, lobose, changing; naked, in thin membrane, or in shell with 1 aperture; fresh and other waters or parasitic.
    Naked forms: *Amoeba*; *Chaos* (*Pelomyxa*), to 5 mm. long; *Naegleria*, with flagellate stage; *Hartmannella*, in foul waters, feeds on bacteria; *Entamoeba histolytica*, parasitic in intestine and tissues of man, causing amoebic dysentery; *E. gingivalis*, in human mouth, and *E. coli*, in intestine of man, apes, and monkeys, both harmless; others in frogs, cockroaches, etc. Shelled form: *Arcella*, with secreted shell.

Order 4. Testacea. In 1-chambered test of silicon or $CaCO_3$; mostly in fresh waters. *Difflugia*, test of sand grains over organic base.

Order 5. Foraminifera. Pseudopodia (myxopodia) slender, branched, sticky; with simple or chambered shell (test) of calcareous, chitinous, or foreign materials with 1 or many openings; shell 0.01 to 5 mm. (some 150 mm.) in diameter; reproduce asexually by multiple fission and sexually; mostly marine and bottom dwellers, some pelagic. Cambrian to Recent, 18,000 species living and fossil. *Allogromia*, no shell, in fresh waters; *Elphidium*; *Globigerina*, pelagic, its empty shells (in "globigerina ooze") cover about one-third the ocean floor at depths of 8,000 to 15,000 feet; †*Camerina* (†*Nummulites*), early Tertiary, European limestone.

SUBCLASS 2. ACTINOPODA. Many radiating axopodia, each with central filament.

Order 1. Heliozoa. SUN ANIMALCULES. Spherical, chiefly in fresh waters. *Actinophrys*; *Clathrulina*, in latticed sphere of silica.

Order 2. Radiolaria. RADIOLARIANS. Often spherical; protoplasm divided into inner and outer parts by porous spherical capsule of chitin; usually a skeleton of silica or strontium sulfate, with radiating spines; diameter microscopic to 6 cm. (colonies); marine, pelagic, surface to depths of 15,000 feet. Pre-Cambrian to Recent. *Acanthometron*, solitary; *Collosphaera*, colonial.

CLASS 3. *SPOROZOA.* SPOROZOANS. No locomotor organs or contractile vacuoles; reproduction by multiple asexual fission and sexual phases, usually producing spores; all internal parasites, usually with intracellular stages.

SUBCLASS 1. TELOSPORIDIA. Sporozoites elongate; no polar capsules in spores.

Order 1. Gregarinida. Mature trophozoite worm-like, 10 μ to 16 mm. long, extracellular; zygote producing 1-walled spore containing 8 sporozoites; in digestive, coelomic, and other cavities of invertebrates. *Ophryocystis*, in Malpighian tubules of beetles; *Monocystis*, in sperm balls of earthworms; *Gregarina*, in grasshoppers, meal worms, etc.

Order 2. Coccidia. Zygote nonmotile; spores with one to many walls; with alternate asexual schizogony followed by sporogony; intracellular, chiefly in epithelial tissues of mollusks, annelids, arthropods, and vertebrates. *Hepatozoon*, in liver, marrow, etc., of mammals; *Haemogregarina*, in red blood cells of turtles, frogs, and fishes; *Eimeria (Coccidium)*, chiefly in digestive epithelium of arthropods and vertebrates, especially domestic birds and mammals; *E. stiedae*, cause of coccidiosis in domestic rabbits.

Order 3. Haemosporidia. Zygote motile, producing naked sporozoites; reproduction alternately by schizogony, within red blood cells and blood system in vertebrates and by sporogony in bloodsucking intermediate arthropod host. *Plasmodium*, in mosquitoes (*Anopheles, Culex*), cause of malaria in birds, mammals, and man; *Haemoproteus*, in bloodsucking flies (HIPPOBOSCIDAE), birds, and reptiles; *Leucocytozoon*, in black flies (*Simulium*), causes disease in ducks; *Babesia bigemina*, carried by tick (*Boöphilus annulatus*) causes Texas fever of cattle in United States; *Theileria parva*, causes East coast fever of cattle in Africa.

SUBCLASS 2. ACNIDOSPORIDIA. Spore simple, no polar filaments.

Order 1. Haplosporidia. Spores few in cyst, small. *Haplosporidium*, chiefly in annelids.

Order 2. Sarcosporidia. Spores many in cyst to 50 mm. in diameter. *Sarcocystis*, in muscles of mammals and birds.

SUBCLASS 3. CNIDOSPORIDIA. Spore with 1 to 4 polar filaments for attaching to host.

Order 1. Myxosporidia. Spore large, bivalve; 1 to 4 polar filaments; parasitic in cavities and tissues of lower vertebrates, especially fishes, where heavy infections cause severe losses. *Sphaeromyxa*, *Myxidium*.

Order 2. Actinomyxidia. Spore with 3 valves, 3 polar filaments. In gut or coelom of aquatic annelids. *Triactinomyxon*.

Order 3. Microsporidia. Spore small, 1 or 2 polar filaments. Intracellular in arthropods and fishes. *Nosema bombycis*, causes pebrine diseases in silkworms; *N. apis*, causes nosema disease in honeybees.

Order 4. Helicosporidia. Spore barrel-shaped, 1 coiled filament. *Heliosporidium*, in fly and mite larvae.

SUBPHYLUM 2. CILIOPHORA. With cilia or sucking tentacles.

CLASS 1. *CILIATA.* CILIATES. Cilia usually present throughout life; no "tentacles."

SUBCLASS 1. PROTOCILIATA. OPALINIDS. No cytostome; nuclei 2 to many; no conjugation; parasitic. *Opalina, Cepedia*, in intestine of amphibians.

SUBCLASS 2. EUCILIATA. Cytostome usually present; usually with macro- and micro-nuclei; with conjugation; mostly free-living, some commensal or parasitic.

Order 1. Holotricha. Cilia simple, over all or part of cell body; no adoral cilia. *Didinium, Paramecium*, free-living; *Anoplophrya*, parasitic in invertebrates; *Ichthyophthirius*, parasitic on skin of fishes; *Isotricha*, commensal in digestive tract of cattle.

Order 2. Spirotricha. With adoral row of membranelles, beginning at right of peristome and passing around to left. *Stentor*, trumpet-shaped; *Spirostomum*, slender, to 3 mm. long; *Tintinnidium*, conical in a lorica; *Stylonychia, Euplotes, Oxytricha*, all with cirri on ventral surface; *Balantidium*, in intestines of various animals; *Diplodinium, Ophryoscolex*, of complex structure, commensal in digestive tract of ruminants.

Order 3. Peritricha. Adoral row of cilia beginning to left of peristome and passing around to right; few or no other cilia; body typically bell- or vase-like; mostly sessile, often colonial. *Vorticella*, solitary on stalk; *Epistylis, Zoothamnium, Opercularia*, in colonies; *Trichodina*, on aquatic animals.

Order 4. Chonotricha. Vase-like, cilia only on anterior funnel. *Spirochona*, on gills of amphipods.

CLASS 2. *SUCTORIA.* Cilia only in young stages; adults attached by stalk, with "tentacles" for feeding; no cytostome; mostly sessile; in salt or fresh waters. *Podophrya*, free-living; *Sphaerophrya*, spherical, parasitic in *Paramecium* and *Stentor*; *Trichophrya micropteri*, on gills of bass.

REFERENCES

BRUMPT, E. 1949. Précis de parasitologie. 6th ed. Paris, Masson et Cie. PROTOZOA, pp. 89–574, figs. 47–350.

CALKINS, G. N., and F. M. SUMMERS (editors). 1941. Protozoa in biological research. New York, Columbia University Press. xli + 1,148 pp., 4 pls., 226 figs. Modern summaries by leading American protozoologists.

CHANDLER, A. C. 1955. Introduction to parasitology. 9th ed. New York, John Wiley & Sons, Inc. PROTOZOA, pp. 31–235, figs. 1–56, especially human parasites.

CRAIG, C. F., and E. C. FAUST. 1951. Clinical parasitology. 5th ed. Philadelphia, Lea & Febiger. PROTOZOA, pp. 55–291, figs. 2–85.

CUSHMAN, J. A. 1948. Foraminifera, their classification and economic use. 4th ed. Cambridge, Mass., Harvard University Press. viii + 605 pp., 55 pls.

DOFLEIN, F., und E. REICHENOW. 1949–1953. Lehrbuch der Protozoenkunde. 6th ed. Jena, Germany, Gustav Fischer Verlagsbuchhandlung. viii + 1,213 pp., 1,151 figs.

GRASSÉ, PIERRE-P., and OTHERS. 1952–53. Traité de zoologie. Paris, Masson & Cie. Vol. 1, Protozoaires (except ciliates), pt. 1. xii + 1,071 pp., 829 figs.; pt. 2, 4 + 1,060 pp., 833 figs.

HAGELSTEIN, ROBERT. 1944. The Mycetozoa of North America. Mineola, N.Y., published by the author 5 + 306 pp., 16 pls.

HALL, R. P. 1953. Protozoology. Englewood Cliffs, N.J., Prentice-Hall, Inc. 6 + 682 pp., illus.

HUTNER, S. H., and ANDRÉ LWOFF. 1951; 1955. Biochemistry and physiology of Protozoa. New York, Academic Press, Inc. 2 vols.

HYMAN, LIBBIE H. 1940. Protozoa. *In* The invertebrates. New York, McGraw-Hill Book Co., Inc. Vol. 1, pp. 44–232, figs. 6–67.

JAHN, T. L., and F. F. JAHN. 1949. How to know the Protozoa. Dubuque, Iowa, William C. Brown Co. 6 + 234 pp., 394 figs.

JENNINGS, H. S. 1906. Behavior of the lower organisms. New York, Columbia University Press. xiv + 366 pp., 144 figs.

KUDO, R. R. 1954. Protozoology. 4th ed. Springfield, Ill., Charles C Thomas, Publisher. xiii + 966 pp., 336 figs. General account and classification.

KÜKENTHAL, W., and OTHERS. 1925. Handbuch der Zoologie. Berlin, Walter De Gruyter & Co. PROTOZOA, vol. 1, pt. 1, pp. 1–292, figs. 1–287.

WENYON, C. M. 1926. Protozoology, a manual for medical men, veterinarians and zoologists. Baltimore, William Wood & Co. 2 vols., xvi + ix + 1,563 pp., 20 pls., 565 figs. Emphasizes parasitic and disease-producing species.

17 PHYLUM PORIFERA

Sponges

The sponges are lowly multicellular animals, incapable of movement, that resemble various plants in appearance (Fig. 17-1). Different species are thin flat crusts, vase-like, branched, globular, or varied in form, and from 1 mm. to 2 meters in diameter. Many are gray or drab-colored, and others are brilliantly red, orange, yellow, blue, violet, or black. Most sponges are marine, living from the low-tide line to depths of 3½ miles; one family is widespread in fresh waters. All are attached to rocks, shells, and other solid objects in the water. The name PORIFERA (L. *porus*, pore + *ferre*, to bear) refers to the porous structure of the body, with many surface openings. The commercial "sponge," used in the bathroom or on an automobile, is the flexible skeleton of a marine sponge with all the once living protoplasm removed.

17-1. Characteristics. 1. Symmetry radial or none; multicellular; 2 germ layers; cells imperfectly arranged as tissues with mesenchyme between.

2. Body with many pores, canals, or chambers through which water flows.

3. Some or all interior surfaces lined with choanocytes (flagellated collar cells).

4. No organs, movable parts, or appendages; digestion intracellular.

5. Usually with an internal skeleton of separate crystalline spicules, or of irregular organic fibers, or both.

6. Reproduction asexual by buds or gemmules; also sexual by eggs and sperm; larva ciliated, free-swimming.

Sponges were once thought to be plants, and their proper place in the Animal Kingdom was not settled until about 1857. They resemble some colonial flagellate protozoans (*Proterospongia*) in having groups of flagellated collar cells and intracellular digestion but differ in having some cells arranged as tissues and a body with many pores. Sponges are multicellular, with some evidence of tissue formation, thus comparing in a degree with the METAZOA, but differ in having intracellular digestion and certain peculiarities of embryonic development. They are considered an aberrant stock, not on the direct line of evolution, and hence often are called the PARAZOA (Gr. *para*, beside).

17-2. Structure of a simple sponge. The simplest of sponges is represented by *Leucosolenia* (Fig. 17-2), which attaches to the seashore rocks just below the low-tide line. It consists of a small group of vase-like slender upright tubes united at their bases by irregular horizontal tubes. Each upright portion is a thin-walled sac, enclosing a central cavity, the **spongocoel,** with one large opening, or **osculum,** at the summit. The wall is made up of (1) an outer **epidermis** (dermal epithelium) of thin, flat cells and (2) a continuous inner lining of flagellated collar cells or **choanocytes,** in loose contact with one another; and between these

273

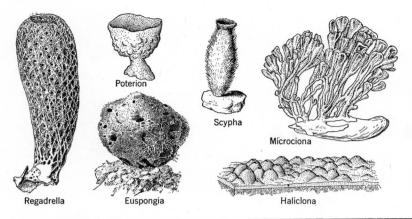

Fig. 17-1. Phylum PORIFERA. Class CALCAREA: *Scypha* (formerly called *Sycon*). Class HEXACTINELLIDA: *Regadrella*, glass sponge. Class DEMOSPONGIAE: *Poterion*, Neptune's goblet; *Euspongia*, bath sponge; *Microciona; Haliclona*, encrusting sponge. (*Regadrella and Scypha after Lankester, Treatise on zoology, A. & C. Black, Ltd.*)

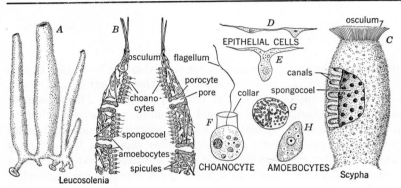

Fig. 17-2. Structure of simple sponges. *A. Leucosolenia*, a small colony. *B. Leucosolenia*, enlarged section at top of body. *C. Scypha*, entire individual with part of body wall cut away (compare Fig. 17-3). *D–H.* Cells of sponges. (*Adapted from Hyman.*)

two layers is (3) a gelatinous **mesenchyme,** which contains (4) free cells, or **amoebocytes,** of several kinds and (5) many minute crystal-like **spicules** of calcium carbonate supporting the soft wall. Some spicules are slender rods (monaxon), and others are three- or four-rayed (tri- or tetraxon). The wall is pierced by many minute incurrent openings, or **ostia,** that extend from the external surface to the central cavity, each pore being a canal through a tubular cell, or **porocyte,** of the epidermis.

The sponge cannot move, and contraction is slight at best, but the porocytes can open or close; in some sponges the osculum can close slowly. In life the amoebocytes move freely within the mesenchyme, which is soft, colloidal, or even watery in consistency. Each choanocyte is a rounded or oval cell, resting against the mesenchyme, its free end with a transparent contractile collar encircling the base of a single whip-like flagellum. The flagella beat back and

forth, producing a continual flow of water into the many ostia, through the central cavity, and out the single osculum. The water brings oxygen and food and removes wastes. A sponge only 4 inches tall is estimated to pass 25 gallons of water daily through its body. The food is of plankton—microscopic animals and plants —and bits of organic matter, captured and digested in food vacuoles of the choanocytes or passed to the amoebocytes. There are no special sensory or nerve cells, and stimuli are conducted slowly, presumably from cell to cell.

17-3. Other sponges. A somewhat more complex type is *Scypha* (formerly called *Sycon* or *Grantia*), a slender form rarely over an inch tall, with one tubular central cavity and a single osculum (Figs. 17-2, 17-3). The thick body wall is folded to form many short horizontal canals. The **incurrent canals** open from the exterior through small pores, or **ostia,** but end

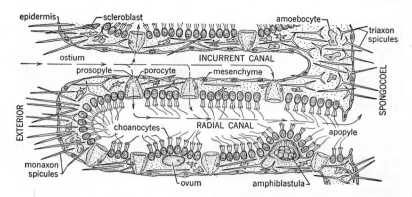

Fig. 17-3. Structure of the body wall of a *Scypha* sponge; diagrammatic section. Arrows indicate paths of water movements.

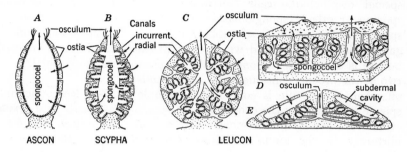

Fig. 17-4. Canal systems of sponges; diagrammatic sections; epithelium, light lines; mesenchyme, stippled; areas with collar cells, heavy black; arrows indicate water currents. *D*, portion of an encrusting sponge; *E*, fresh-water sponge.

blindly toward the inner surface, whereas the *radial canals* begin blindly near the outer surface and open by minute *apopyles* into the spongocoel. Other smaller canals, or *prosopyles,* connect the incurrent and radial canals. The exterior surface is covered by thin *dermal epithelium,* the spongocoel is lined with a thin *gastral epithelium,* and the radial canals are lined with *choanocytes.* The canal systems greatly increase the surface exposed to the water. The body substance between these layers and outside the canals is of gelatinous *mesenchyme* containing amoeboid cells as in *Leucosolenia.* The spicules supporting the body are chiefly of four kinds: long straight (monaxon) about the osculum, short straight (monaxon) surrounding the ostia, T-shaped (triradiate) lining the spongocoel, and three-branched (triradiate) in the body wall. Those about the osculum and incurrent pores protrude beyond the body surface, producing a bristly appearance.

17-4. Canal systems. In most sponges the structure is complex, with various kinds of canal systems (Fig. 17-4). (1) The simple *ascon* type (*Leucosolenia*) has a thin body wall perforated by short straight ostia leading directly to the spongocoel, which is lined with choanocytes. (2) The *sycon* type (*Scypha*) contains two types of canals, but only the radial canals are lined with choanocytes. (3) The *leucon* type has a body of thick dense mesenchyme penetrated by complexly branched canal systems, with choanocytes restricted to small spherical chambers.

17-5. Skeleton. The soft bodies of sponges are supported by many minute crystalline spicules or by organic fibers, forming a "skeleton" (Fig. 17-5). Calcareous sponges such as *Leucosolenia* and *Scypha* have spicules of calcium carbonate ($CaCO_3$), and those in "glass" sponges are of siliceous material (chiefly $H_2Si_3O_7$). Spicules are of many kinds, sizes, and shapes; some simple forms have been mentioned, but others are of complex types (polyaxon). Spicules of some deep-sea glass sponges become fused together in a framework. The bath sponges and some others contain fine interjoined and irregular

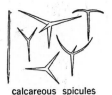

calcareous spicules

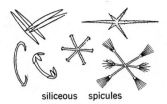

siliceous spicules

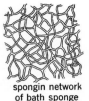

spongin network
of bath sponge

Fig. 17-5. Spicules and fibers of sponges. (*After Hyman, The invertebrates.*)

fibers of spongin. Like hair, nails, and feathers, this is a sulfur-containing scleroprotein, insoluble, inert chemically, and resistant to protein-digesting enzymes. Spicules are secreted by special mesenchyme cells (scleroblasts) and spongin by others (spongioblasts). A monaxon spicule begins within a scleroblast as an organic axial thread around which calcium carbonate is deposited, the one cell dividing into two as the process continues, and both wander off when the spicule is complete. A complex spicule is formed by the cooperation of several cells. The classification of sponges is based importantly on the kinds and arrangement of these skeletal materials.

17-6. Histology. The outer or dermal epithelium and the lining of the central cavity in complex sponges are both of thin flat cells. The choanocytes form a loose layer of cells wherever they occur. These are the organized cell layers of sponges. The amoeboid cells in the mesenchyme include (1) *scleroblasts;* (2) *spongioblasts;* (3) *collencytes,* or connective tissue cells of stellate form with thread-like pseudopodia; (4) *myocytes* or long contractile cells that form sphincters around pores and the osculum; and (5) *archeocytes* of amoeboid character and various functions; these last receive, digest, and circulate food and also give rise to the reproductive elements (ova, sperm, gemmules).

17-7. Individuality in sponges. Some cells in sponges are arranged in layers ("tissues"), but much of the vital activity is by separate cells. Food is engulfed in vacuoles by the choanocytes after the manner of protozoans and may be passed to the amoebocytes before being completely digested. Respiration and excretion are presumably performed by each cell independently. Sponges are thus cell aggregates without organs, and it is difficult or impossible to decide what is an "individual." Examples of *Leucosolenia* or *Scypha* each with a single osculum may be so designated, but in complex sponges with multiple canal systems and many oscula it is impossible to define the limits of an "individual."

17-8. Reproduction. Sponges multiply both asexually and sexually. Parts of a sponge lost by injury will be replaced by *regeneration,* an ability that is of value in the growing of bath sponges (par. 17-11). If a sponge is squeezed through fine meshed silk so that the cells are separated, they will come together by amoeboid movements, unite, and regenerate into a sponge like the original. Many kinds of sponges increase commonly by *budding,* the buds either separating from the original sponge as growth proceeds or else remaining attached and thus increasing the number of parts or the bulk of the mass.

All fresh-water sponges (and some others) form internal buds, or *gemmules,* to carry the species through unfavorable conditions such as cold or drought (Fig. 17-7). Groups of archeocytes (statocytes) enriched with food materials gather in the mesenchyme and are surrounded by a resistant covering, sometimes containing spicules. As the sponge dies and disintegrates, the minute gemmules drop out and survive. When conditions again become suitable, as in spring, the cell mass escapes from within the covering and starts growth as a new sponge.

In *sexual reproduction* some sponges are dioecious and others (e.g., *Scypha*) are monoecious. Ova and sperm develop from archeocytes, there being no special sex organs. The ovum

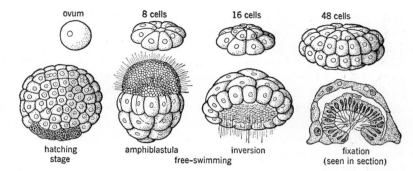

Fig. 17-6. Development of a calcareous sponge, *Sycandra*. (*After F. E. Schulze,* 1875, 1878.)

remains in the mesenchyme of the parent and is fertilized there by a sperm from another sponge. The first three cleavages are vertical and produce a disc of eight pyramidal cells (Fig. 17-6). A horizontal cleavage then yields eight large cells (future epidermis) and eight small (future choanocytes) arranged as a blastula. The latter increase rapidly and elongate, and each acquires a flagellum on its inner end facing the blastocoel. The few large cells become rounded and granular, and in their middle an opening forms that functions as a mouth to ingest adjacent maternal cells. The embryo then turns inside out (like a stage in the protozoan *Volvox*) through its mouth, bringing the flagellated cells outside. In this *amphiblastula* stage the oval larva escapes through the osculum of the parent to swim for some hours with the flagellated cells foremost. The flagellated half then invaginates into, or is overgrown by, the larger nonflagellated cells (= "gastrulation"). Soon the larva attaches to a solid object by the blastoporal end and begins growth as a young sponge (olynthus stage). Mesenchyme cells arise from both layers. Since the invaginated half seems to represent the animal hemisphere of the egg, the germ layers of a sponge are not comparable with those of metazoan embryos.

17-9. Fresh-water sponges. The Family SPONGILLIDAE includes about 15 genera and 150 species, of world-wide occurrence but restricted to fresh-water streams or ponds and lakes. They grow as tufts or irregular masses, up to the size of a person's fist, on sticks, stones, or plants (Fig. 17-7). Some are yellow or brown; others

are green when exposed to sunlight because of zoochlorellae (fresh-water algae) in the mesenchyme. *Spongilla lacustris* is common in sunlit running waters, whereas *S. fragilis* avoids the light.

17-10. Relations with other animals. Sponges are seldom attacked or eaten by other animals, probably because of their skeletons and the unpleasant secretions and odors that they produce. The interior cavities of many sponges are often inhabited by crustaceans, worms, mollusks, and other animals. In a sponge the size of a washtub, A. S. Pearse counted 17,128 animals, mostly one kind of shrimp, but with a considerable variety of others, including some slender fishes up to 5 inches long. Certain kinds of crabs tear off bits of living sponges, which are held against the shell until they attach;

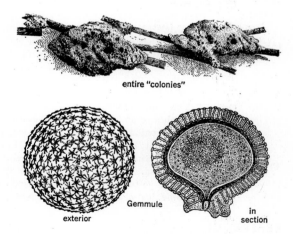

entire "colonies"

Gemmule

exterior   in section

Fig. 17-7. Fresh-water sponge (Family SPONGILLIDAE). Gemmules about 1 mm. in diameter. (*After Jammes; Wolcott; and Hyman.*)

continued growth provides the crab with a protective covering of sponge having a disagreeable odor and containing spiny spicules. The sponge *Suberites* commonly grows on snail shells inhabited by some hermit crabs, soon absorbing the shell so that the crab actually inhabits a cavity in the sponge. Another sponge, *Cliona*, grows on mollusk shells, boring into and eventually destroying the animal and its shell. Some sponges that grow on bivalve mollusks become competitors of the latter since both sponge and mollusk feed on plankton; these sponges may become a nuisance on oyster beds.

17-11. The sponge industry. Since the days of ancient Greece, mankind has used the fibrous skeletons of the bath sponge (*Spongia*) for washing and mopping (Fig. 17-1). The skeleton owes its water-holding capacity to capillary forces in the fine spaces of the irregular spongin network (Fig. 17-5). The best and principal supplies of these sponges occur on rocky bottoms in warm shallow waters of the Mediterranean Sea and the Gulf of Mexico, about Florida and the West Indies; over 2,000,000 pounds were formerly taken annually. A fungus infection reduced the total to 860,000 pounds by 1947. The living sponges are brought up by divers, by dredging or trawling, or by use of long-handled hooks. They are killed by treading to loosen the living protoplasm, which is allowed to decay, then washed and beaten to remove all but the flexible skeleton. The cleaned sponges are cut or trimmed, sometimes bleached, sorted, and marketed. Decline in the natural supply has encouraged sponge culture in Florida and Italy. Cut pieces of about 8 cubic inches are fastened to slabs of concrete or other supports on a shallow clean bottom where water currents provide abundant oxygen and food. Several years are needed for market size. The largest living bath sponges may be 50 years old.

CLASSIFICATION

PHYLUM PORIFERA. SPONGES. Form flat, vase-like, rounded, or branched; symmetry radial or none; color various; no organs; "body" with many pores; some or all inner cavities lined with choanocytes; an internal supporting skeleton of crystalline spicules, irregular spongin fibers, or both, rarely none; sessile and marine, one family in fresh water; about 5,000 species. Pre-Cambrian to Recent.

> *CLASS* 1. *CALCAREA* (Calcispongiae). CALCAREOUS SPONGES. Spicules calcareous, monaxon or 3- or 4-branched; surface of body bristly; dull-colored; mostly under 6 inches long.
>> **Order 1. Homocoela.** Body wall thin, interior not folded, lined continuously with choanocytes (asconoid). *Leucosolenia.*
>> **Order 2. Heterocoela.** Body wall thickened, folded internally; lining of choanocytes in radial canals not continuous (syconoid, leuconoid). *Scypha; Grantia.*
> *CLASS* 2. *HEXACTINELLIDA* (Hyalospongiae). GLASS SPONGES. Spicules siliceous and 6-rayed (hexactine), either separate or united in networks, some skeletons resembling spun glass; no surface epithelium; choanocytes only in finger-shaped chambers; body mass commonly cylindrical to funnel-shaped, some curved or flat or with basal stalk; length to 3 feet; exclusively marine, at depths of 300 feet to over 3 miles. *Hyalonema; Euplectella aspergillum,* Venus's flower-basket.
> *CLASS* 3. *DEMOSPONGIAE.* Skeleton of siliceous spicules, of spongin, of both, or none.
>> **Order 1. Tetractinellida.** Spicules tetraxon or none, no spongin; body mostly rounded or flattened, no branches or projections; in shallow waters. *Halisarca,* no skeleton; *Thenea; Geodea.*
>> **Order 2. Monaxonida.** Spicules monaxon; spongin in some; body form various; mostly in shore waters to 150 feet, but some to depths of $3\frac{1}{2}$ miles; abundant; most common of all sponges. *Suberites; Cliona,* boring sponge; *Spongilla,* fresh-water sponges; *Haliclona.*
>> **Order 3. Keratosa.** HORNY SPONGES. Skeleton a network of spongin fibers, no spicules; form usually rounded, often of considerable size; surface leathery, coloration dark, chiefly black. *Phyllospongia,* leaf-shaped; *Spongia (Euspongia),* bath sponge; *Hippospongia,* "horse" sponge.

REFERENCES

HYMAN, LIBBIE H. 1940. The invertebrates: Protozoa through Ctenophora. New York, McGraw-Hill Book Co., Inc. Sponges, pp. 284–364.

MOORE, H. F., and P. S. GALTSOFF. 1951. Sponges. *In* D. K. TRESSLER and J. McW. LEMON, Marine products of commerce. 2d ed. New York, Reinhold Publishing Corp. pp. 733–751, illus.

18 PHYLUM COELENTERATA
Coelenterates

The lowest animals with definite tissues are the COELENTERATA (Gr. *koilos,* hollow + *enteron,* intestine) or CNIDARIA (Gr. *knide,* nettle). The individuals are either separate or in colonies and of two types: (1) the *polyp,* with a tubular body having one end closed and attached and the other with a central mouth usually surrounded by soft tentacles, and (2) the free-swimming *medusa,* with a gelatinous body of umbrella shape, margined with tentacles, and having the mouth on a central projection of the concave surface. Both are variously modified, and both appear in the life cycle of many species (Fig. 18-1). Each individual has a digestive cavity, some muscle fibers, and many minute stinging capsules (nematocysts). All are aquatic, and nearly all are marine. The phylum includes the hydroids and hydromedusae, etc. (Class HYDROZOA), the jellyfishes (Class SCYPHOZOA), and the sea anemones and corals (Class ANTHOZOA). Many hydroids grow as small dense plant-like colonies, the jellyfishes and some hydroid medusae swim feebly, the flower-like anemones abound on rocky ocean coasts, and the corals with their limy skeletons form reefs on tropical shores. Anemones and corals are often brightly colored, some medusae are beautifully tinted, and many coelenterates are luminescent. Coelenterates are of slight economic importance; some coral is used for jewelry and decorative art, the stings of certain jellyfishes and siphonophores occasionally injure bathers, and natives on some Pacific islands eat jellyfishes.

18-1. Characteristics. 1. Symmetry radial about an oral-aboral axis (biradial in some ANTHOZOA); no head or segmentation.

2. Body of 2 layers of cells, an external epidermis and an inner gastrodermis, with little or much mesoglea between; nematocysts in either or both layers.

3. Skeleton limy, horny, or none; muscle fibers in epithelia.

4. Mouth surrounded by soft tentacles and connecting to a sac-like digestive cavity, or enteron, that may be branched or divided by septa; no anus.

5. No blood, respiratory, or excretory organs.

6. A diffuse network of unpolarized nerve cells in body wall, but no central nervous system; some with eyespots or statocysts.

7. Reproduction commonly by alternation of generations (metagenesis), with asexual budding in the attached (polyp) stage and with sexual reproduction by gametes in the free (medusa) stage; monoecious or dioecious; some with simple gonads, but no sex ducts; cleavage holoblastic; a ciliated planula larva; mouth forms from blastopore.

The stinging qualities of coelenterates were known to Aristotle, who considered these organisms as intermediate between plants and animals. They were long included in the Zoophyta (Gr., animal-plants) together with various forms from sponges to ascidians. When their animal nature was established in the eighteenth century, Linnaeus and others classed them with the echinoderms as Radiata because of their symmetry. Leuckart in 1847 grouped the sponges, coelenterates, and ctenophores as the COELENTERATA, and only in 1888 did Hat-

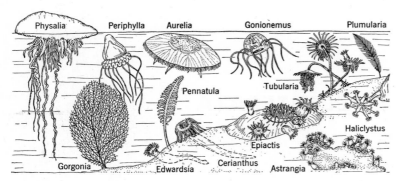

Fig. 18-1. Phylum Coelenterata. Some marine representatives in characteristic habitats, all reduced but not to same scale. Class Hydrozoa, Order Hydroida: *Tubularia, Plumularia;* Order Trachylina: *Gonionemus;* Order Siphonophora: *Physalia,* Portuguese man-of-war. Class Scyphozoa, Order Stauromedusae: *Haliclystus;* Order Coronatae: *Periphylla;* Order Discomedusae: *Aurelia,* common jellyfish. Class Anthozoa, Order Gorgonacea: *Gorgonia,* sea fan; Order Pennatulacea: *Pennatula,* sea pen; Order Actinaria: *Edwardsia, Epiactis,* sea anemones; Order Madreporaria: *Astrangia,* stony coral; Order Ceriantharia: *Cerianthus.*

schek separate these as distinct phyla, the Porifera, Cnidaria, and Ctenophora. The coelenterates, or Cnidaria, are distinguished from sponges in being "tissue animals" (Metazoa) that have a distinct digestive cavity. The coelenterates differ from ctenophores in being primarily radial in symmetry, in possessing nematocysts, in having a polyp stage, and in reproducing both asexually and sexually. The polyp has been considered an "arrested larva," and the medusa stage as the fullest expression of the phylum.

18-2. Size. Individual hydroid polyps are usually microscopic, but colonies of various species are a few millimeters to 2 meters in length. The jellyfishes are from 12 mm. to over 2 meters in diameter, the largest (*Cyanea arctica*) having tentacles up to 10 meters long. Anemones range from a few millimeters to a meter in diameter. The individual polyps on corals are minute, but their skeletons form massive growths in warm seas.

CLASS HYDROZOA. Hydroids

18-3. Hydra. The small solitary polyp known as hydra is one of the simplest of multicellular animals and serves well as an introduction to

both the Metazoa and the Coelenterata. It is slender and flexible, 10 to 30 mm. long, with several delicate tentacles at one end (Fig. 18-4). It lives in the cool, clean, and usually permanent fresh waters of lakes, ponds, and streams, attaching to stones, sticks, or aquatic vegetation. Of the eight species in the United States, the "white" hydra, *Hydra americana,* is gray or tan with short tentacles and no stalk; the brown hydra, *Pelmatohydra oligactis* (formerly *H. fusca*), has a slender base or stalk to the body and tentacles three or four times as long as the latter; and the green hydra, *Chlorohydra viridissima* (formerly *H. viridis*), has symbiotic algae (zoochlorellae) in its inner cells that make the body grass green. The following account will apply to any common species.

18-4. General features. The body (Fig. 18-2) is a cylindrical tube with the lower end closed to form a *basal disc,* or "foot," used for attaching to objects and for locomotion. The opposite and free oral end contains the *mouth* as a small opening on a conical *hypostome,* encircled by 6 to 10 slender hollow *tentacles.* The mouth leads into the digestive cavity, or *enteron,* which occupies the interior of the body and connects to the slender cavities in the tentacles. The number of tentacles differs between species and in-

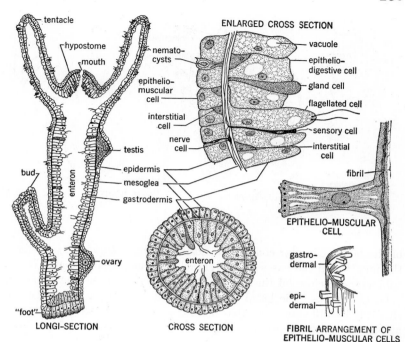

Fig. 18-2. Hydra. Structure as seen in microscopic sections. (*Epitheliomuscular cell after Hyman, The invertebrates.*)

ENLARGED CROSS SECTION

LONGI-SECTION   CROSS SECTION   FIBRIL ARRANGEMENT OF EPITHELIO-MUSCULAR CELLS

EPITHELIO-MUSCULAR CELL

creases with the age and size of an individual. The entire animal is very flexible. The body may extend as a slender tube, may bend in any direction, or may contract to a short spherical form. The tentacles move independently or together and may extend as long delicate threads or contract down to slight knobs. The side of the body may bear lateral **buds** that give rise to new individuals by asexual reproduction; at times it bears other rounded projections, the **ovaries** or **testes,** concerned with sexual reproduction.

18-5. Cellular structure and function. The wall of the body and tentacles consists of but two cell layers (Fig. 18-2), a thin external **epidermis,** of cuboidal cells, chiefly protective and sensory in function, and inside a thicker **gastrodermis,** of tall cells, serving mainly in digestion. Between the two is a thin noncellular **mesoglea,** or supporting lamella, secreted by and attached to both layers, that provides an elastic framework for both the body and the tentacles.

Both layers are composed of several cell types: (1) epitheliomuscular; (2) glandular; (3)

interstitial; and (4) sensory. A network of nerve cells lies in or against the mesoglea. The cells of each type are specialized in both structure and function to perform particular life processes; collectively, they are responsible for all the activities of the living hydra, as in all multicellular animals. Many of the cells in the gastrodermis bear one or two whip-like flagella, each arising from a blepharoplast within the cell.

EPITHELIOMUSCULAR CELLS. These cells are ⊥-shaped, having a bulbous outer portion and an elongate base containing a contractile fibril placed against the mesoglea. In the epidermis these cells are closely placed and collectively form the exterior surface of the body; their fibrils attach lengthwise to the mesoglea and act as longitudinal muscles that contract to shorten the body stalk and tentacles. The epitheliodigestive cells of the gastrodermis are the principal part of the lining of the enteron and function actively in the digestion of food. Their contractile fibrils attach transversely inside the mesoglea so that they act as circular muscles to reduce the diameter and extend the length

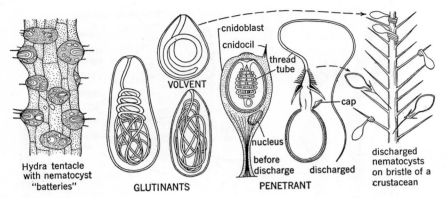

Hydra tentacle
with nematocyst
"batteries"

GLUTINANTS

VOLVENT

cnidoblast
cnidocil
thread
tube
nucleus
before
discharge   discharged

PENETRANT

cap

discharged
nematocysts
on bristle of a
crustacean

Fig. **18-3.** The nematocysts or stinging cap-
sules of hydra. (*After
Schulze.*)

of the body. Circular contractile fibrils around the mouth and the bases of the tentacles act as sphincters to close off these openings.

GLAND CELLS. The basal disc is covered exclusively by tall gland cells that secrete a sticky mucus by which the hydra attaches to objects in the water; these cells can also produce a gas bubble. Gland cells are uncommon elsewhere in the epidermis, but large ones occur about the mouth, and many others are scattered in the gastrodermis where they secrete the enzymes which digest the food.

INTERSTITIAL CELLS. These are small round undifferentiated cells, found between the bases of the epidermal cells, that give rise to nematocysts, buds, and sex cells; few occur in the gastrodermis.

NEMATOCYSTS. The *nematocyst* is a minute rounded capsule filled with fluid and containing a coiled *thread tube* that may be everted to aid in the capture of prey or in locomotion. Each nematocyst is included in an interstitial cell that has been modified as a *cnidoblast,* on the exterior of which is a trigger-like *cnidocil.* Some nematocysts occur singly, but often one large and several small ones are grouped in a single large epithelial cell to form a small surface tubercle, or "battery." Nematocysts are most abundant on the tentacles, but some occur throughout the epidermis, except on the basal disc.

Hydra (Fig. 18-3) has four kinds of nematocysts, as follows: (1) The large spherical *pene-*

trant (16 μ in diameter) has a long thread tube that is coiled transversely and bears at its base three long spines and three rows of small thorns; when discharged the thread tube shoots out to pierce the skin of small animals and "inject" a fluid (hypnotoxin) that paralyzes the prey. (2) The pear-shaped *volvent* (9 μ long) contains a short thick thread in a single loop; upon discharge this coils tightly around bristles or hairs of the prey. (3) The oval *streptoline glutinant* (9 μ) has a long thread, in three or four transverse coils, that bears minute thorns and may coil upon discharge. (4) The small *stereoline glutinant* (7 μ) discharges a straight unarmed thread. The first two types are of particular value in capturing prey; the others produce a sticky secretion possibly used in locomotion as well as food getting.

The cnidoblast is an independent effector in that discharge of the nematocyst is due, not to a nerve impulse, but to some stimulus affecting the cnidocil directly. It was formerly thought to act like a trigger, but direct mechanical stimulus, as by touching with a glass rod or by the protozoans that live and move about on the surface of hydra, is not ordinarily effective. Substances diffusing in the water from the small crustaceans, worms, and larvae on which the hydra feeds will usually provoke discharge, as will acetic acid added to the water. Eversion of the thread evidently is caused by increased osmotic pressure within the capsule.

The cnidoblast containing a nematocyst de-

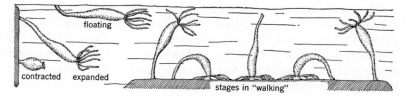

Fig. 18-4. Phylum COELENTER-ATA. Hydra, the fresh-water polyp; natural size to 30 mm. long. (*"Walking" after Wagner,* 1905.)

floating

contracted   expanded

stages in "walking"

velops in the body epidermis, whence it migrates into and through the fluid in the enteron and again passes through the body or tentacle wall to its final location in the epidermis; none originates in the tentacles. The thread tube when discharged cannot be withdrawn, and the cnidoblast cannot form another nematocyst; such parts return to the enteron and are digested, to be replaced by new cells and capsules arriving in the manner just described.

SENSORY AND NERVE CELLS. These require special staining methods for their demonstration. Scattered through the epidermis are many slender *sensory cells* of several kinds, with delicate tips. They are most numerous on the tentacles, about the mouth, and around the basal disc; a small number occur in the gastrodermis. The bases of the sensory cells connect to the *nerve cells* that form a network in the epidermis and adjacent to the mesoglea (Fig. 18-5). The nerve cells have slender processes of various kinds, but these are not differentiated into dendrites and axons as with higher animals. These processes join directly to sensory cells, between one nerve cell and another, and to contractile fibers of epitheliomuscular cells. The combination provides a *sensory-neuromotor mechanism;* the sensory cells *receive* stimuli, the nerve cells *conduct* impulses, and the contractile fibers *react* to the latter. Excluding the neuromotor organelles of some protozoans, this is the first and simplest neural mechanism to be seen among animals. It provides for coordination in movement of the body and tentacles. There is no central ganglion or brain such as occurs in flatworms and higher metazoan animals.

18-6. Locomotion. Hydra lives attached by its basal disc to objects in the water but is able to twist about, to perform movements for the capture of prey, and to change its location. It can move in several ways. Commonly it bends over, attaches the tentacles to the substratum by use of the glutinant nematocysts, releases and moves the basal disc to a new site, disengages the tentacles, and again assumes an upright position (Fig. 18-4). This "walking" resembles the looping action of a leech or measuring worm. Sometimes it travels inverted, using the tentacles as legs. Again, it may glide along the substratum by pseudopodia-like action of cells on the basal disc. Occasionally it uses a gas bubble secreted in mucus by the disc, to rise in the water and float at the surface. *P. oligactis* can "climb" by attaching its long tentacles to some object, releasing the basal disc, and then contracting the tentacles. The white and brown hydras often remain fixed for considerable periods, whereas green hydras move about often, especially when seeking food.

18-7. Feeding and digestion. Hydra feeds mainly on minute crustaceans, insect larvae, and similar animals; at times, it may swallow prey larger than itself. A hungry individual usually remains attached by its base with the body extended and the tentacles stretched to wave about in search of prey. When a tentacle touches any small animal, nematocysts are discharged into it at once. The penetrants puncture the victim and give off the paralyzing hypnotoxin, the volvents wrap about appendages or other parts, and the glutinants may fasten to its surface. Other tentacles may perform coordinated movements and discharge nematocysts to aid the capture. The tentacles bend inward and carry the food toward the mouth. The latter opens and moves around the food, which is swallowed and passed into the upper part of the enteron by contractions of the hypostome and body wall.

Gland cells in the gastrodermis then become active and discharge secretions containing enzymes that act upon the food. Expansion and contraction of the body wall and whipping movements of flagella on the digestive cells bring these secretions against all parts of the food. Soft parts of the latter soon become separated and liquefied, whereas harder portions (such as chitin) are unaffected. Some digestion is completed in the enteron, and the fully digested materials are absorbed by cells of the gastrodermis; this is *extracellular digestion* such as occurs in most multicellular animals. In addition, the free ends of epitheliomuscular cells in the gastrodermis send out pseudopodia that draw food particles into vacuoles within the cells, where *intracellular digestion* takes place as in protozoans and sponges. Hydra thus combines the digestive procedures of forms both lower and higher than itself. Indigestible residues pass out through the mouth, which thus functions also as an anus. Absorbed food (especially glycogen) is stored locally in cells of the gastrodermis, whence the needs of the epidermis are probably supplied by diffusion. There seems to be no general circulation of food in the gastrodermis or enteron. Stored materials tend to be concentrated where metabolism is active and where buds or gonads are forming.

18-8. Respiration and excretion. The oxygen necessary for respiration diffuses from the surrounding water directly into the cells of hydra, and metabolic wastes such as carbon dioxide and nitrogenous compounds are lost by diffusion, mainly from the epidermis.

18-9. Behavior. All movements result from action of the opposed sets of contractile fibers in

Fig. 18-5. Nerve cells in a young hydra. (*After Hadzi,* 1909.)

the body wall and tentacles and show an obvious coordination between the different parts of the organism that results from transmission of impulses through the nerve net (Fig. 18-5). The response of any individual hydra to stimuli from its environment will be conditioned by its physiological state at the time. A hungry individual usually responds more actively than one that has recently fed, and there are also differences in response between the species of hydra.

A slight touch, as with a needle, will cause the part touched to turn away, and a stronger stimulus such as jarring the dish containing the animal will usually result in sudden and complete contraction of both tentacles and body. Besides thus responding to external stimuli the hydra reacts also to internal stimuli; an undisturbed specimen will, from time to time, suddenly contract and then expand slowly. Such spontaneous movements probably are related to food getting, being more frequent with hungry individuals. Each species responds to a particular optimum of light intensity, the green hydra seeking a stronger intensity than other species. In the main, they avoid either very strong or very weak illumination and usually move about by trial and error until the most favorable condition is found. This probably also is related to feeding, since most of hydra's prey seeks well-lighted areas. Hydra prefers cool waters and in a temperature gradient will seek the colder portion. It endeavors to avoid injurious chemical substances. Under rich feeding, high temperature, foul water, and certain other conditions, hydra undergoes a lowered metabolic state known as "depression." There is a gradual shortening and loss of the tentacles and column, beginning at the distal end; this may proceed to disintegration or may be followed by recovery.

Hydra occurs in enormous numbers in some lakes, to depths of 180 feet, but commonly disappears from surface waters at 70°F. or higher. At times it infests fish nets in such numbers as to irritate the hands of fishermen and sometimes kills quantities of young fishes in hatcheries.

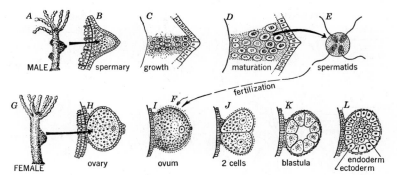

Fig. 18-6. Sexual reproduction of hydra. (*Adapted from Tannreuther*, 1908, 1909.)

18-10. Budding. Hydra produces new individuals either by asexual budding or by sexual means involving eggs and sperm. A ***bud*** forms as a projection about midway on the body wall; it contains epidermis, mesoglea, and gastrodermis with an outpocketing of the enteron (Fig. 18-2). This lengthens, acquires blunt tentacles and a mouth distally, and later is constricted and detached at the base, to become an independent hydra. Occasionally, several buds form on a single "parent," and these in turn may produce secondary buds, to form temporarily a group somewhat resembling a colonial hydroid. Prior to bud formation the gastroderm cells at the site become well supplied with food for the initial development; later, the bud receives food through the connection of its enteron with that of the parent individual. Budding may occur at almost any season.

18-11. Regeneration and grafting. The ability of certain animals to restore or ***regenerate*** lost parts was first reported in 1744 by Trembley, an English naturalist, from studies on hydra. If a living specimen is cut across into two or more pieces, each will regenerate into a complete but smaller hydra. The hypostome and tentacles alone will form a new individual, and a hydra split part way through the mouth will form a "two-headed" polyp, if the portions are held apart. Even minute fragments will regenerate completely, and pieces too small to grow independently may fuse and regenerate; but the "germ layers" will not mix. Epidermis joins only with epidermis and gastrodermis with gastrodermis, cells of the latter sending out proto-

plasmic processes that interweave with one another.

Parts of two hydras may be brought together and ***grafted*** in various arrangements. The parts usually retain their original polarity, that originally toward the oral end producing tentacles and the opposite end a basal disc, but an oral region grafted to an aboral end may ***induce*** an oral growth with tentacles in the latter.

18-12. Sexual reproduction. Most species of hydra are dioecious, any one individual producing only male or female sex organs and cells; a few species, however, are monoecious. The formation of gonads and sexual reproduction ordinarily occur in the autumn but may be induced at other seasons by reducing the water temperature. The ***gonads*** are the only reproductive organs (Fig. 18-6); these are temporary structures on the sides of the body, the ***ovaries*** producing eggs and the ***testes*** or spermaries producing sperm. Both the male and female gonads arise from interstitial cells in the epidermis.

Each of the several testes is a conical outgrowth containing (*A*, *B*) a number of elongate cysts. The interstitial cell (spermatogonium) at the base divides repeatedly to produce many spermatocytes (*C*). These migrate outward, and the cysts become rounded. As each cell goes through two maturation divisions (*D*), four nuclei are produced, but the cytoplasm does not separate until later. The spermatids (*E*) transform into sperm, which escape in numbers to the distal end of the cyst and emerge through a pore in the testis to swim in the water (*F*);

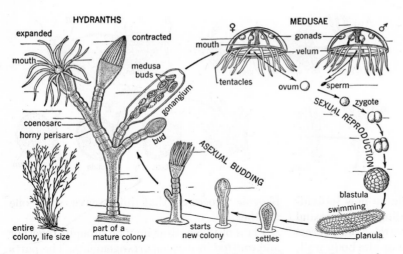

Fig. 18-7. Class HYDROZOA. Structure and life cycle of a colonial marine hydroid, *Obelia.* The colony comprises polyps of two types, the feeding hydranths and reproductive gonangia, both formed by asexual budding on branched stems attached to the substratum by a root-like hydrorhiza. Free-swimming medusae of separate sexes bud off from the gonangia and later produce ova and sperm. The zygote develops into a ciliated swimming planula larva; this soon attaches and forms a new colony by budding. The three kinds of individuals illustrate polymorphism, and the alternation of asexual and sexual generations is termed "metagenesis." (*Modified from Wolcott, Animal biology.*)

there they may remain active for a day or more.

The future egg forms from an interstitial cell under the epidermis (*G*); it enlarges and is joined by other interstitial cells, which become the yolk. Two maturation divisions ensue, with production of two polar bodies and reduction of the egg chromosomes from 12 to 6. The mature ovum (*H*) squeezes through a small opening in the epidermis covering the ovary to lie free on the surface of the latter (*I*). Fertilization then occurs with entrance of a sperm head, bringing 6 chromosomes.

The egg soon begins to divide (*J*), cleavage being total and equal. The blastula is a sphere formed of a single layer of cells, which enclose a small cavity. These cells shortly secrete a shell, or cyst, around the blastula (*K*). The outer ends of the blastula cells become the ectoderm, destined to form the epidermis, and their inner ends divide off to form the endoderm, which will produce the gastrodermis; the endoderm is solid (*L*) at first but later hollows out to make the enteron. Mesoglea is produced later be-

tween the two cell layers. The cyst containing the embryo soon hardens and drops into the water. After some time (10 to 70 days) the cyst softens and a young hydra with short tentacles hatches out. There is no larval stage.

18-13. Colonial hydroids. Unlike hydra, most other members of the Class HYDROZOA are marine and colonial. They include the hydroids, the stinging corals, some jellyfishes, and the free-floating siphonophores. *Obelia* (Fig. 18-7) is a typical hydroid, of mossy form, found on rocks or shells or piling in the shallow waters of seacoasts. The small whitish **colony** is fastened by a root-like base (hydrorhiza) bearing slender branched stems (hydrocauli) on which grow hundreds of microscopic polyps of two kinds. The feeding polyp, or **hydranth,** is hydra-like, with 20 or more solid tentacles, and is set in a transparent vase-shaped **hydrotheca** that affords it protection. These polyps capture minute animals by use of their nematocysts and tentacles. The reproductive polyp, or **gonangium,** is of cylindrical form, covered by a transparent gonotheca, and contains an axis or blastostyle on which lateral buds form that develop into medusae. The common stem supporting both kinds of polyps comprises an external transparent and noncellular **perisarc** that is continuous with the hydrotheca and gonotheca and an internal hollow **coenosarc** (common enteron) of cellular structure connecting the enterons of various polyps. Digested food circulates through the coenosarc. Both types of polyps are produced by buds on the stem.

The **medusa** is a minute jellyfish, shaped like an umbrella and rimmed with tentacles; on its concave side is a central projecting **manubrium**. This contains the mouth, which leads to an enteron in the middle of the bell, whence four **radial canals** extend to a **ring canal** in the bell margin. A gelatinous mesoglea fills the space between the epidermis over the bell, tentacles and manubrium, and the gastrodermis that lines the digestive tract and its branches. Although the feeding polyps and the medusae differ markedly in appearance, their basic structure is essentially the same (Fig. 18-11).

The medusae escape from the gonangia to float and feed in the sea. They are of separate sexes, and their gonads develop in the enteron, whence eggs and sperm are released into the water. There each zygote develops into a minute ciliated **planula** larva. This soon settles and attaches with its blastopore uppermost, then grows to be a small polyp, which by asexual budding begins a new colony. Such an alternation of sexual and asexual generations is termed **metagenesis.**

Hundreds of species of hydroids occur at various depths, a majority being found in shallow coastal waters. In HYDROZOA of the Order TRACHYLINA the polyp generation is reduced or lacking, and the medusa stage is a jellyfish of some size with a thin narrow velum around the inner margin of the umbrella; *Gonionemus* is a common representative in some localities along the Atlantic coast (Fig. 18-1).

18-14. Polymorphism. A wide range in the complexity of colony structure and polyp function is to be seen among various hydroids. *Hydra* is an individual polyp that performs all essential life functions, including reproduction. In colonial forms like *Obelia* the feeding hydranths perform all functions except that of reproduction, and the gonangia are solely reproductive, forming the medusae for dispersal. *Hydractinia*, which lives on shells of hermit crabs, has feeding, reproductive, and fighting polyps, the last being of slender form, with no mouth, and bearing spherical growths on which are many nematocysts. The greatest diversity is seen in members of the Order SIPHONOPHORA, which form floating or swimming colonies of specialized individuals. Thus, in *Physalia pelagica*, the Portuguese man-of-war, and in *Velella*, *Porpita*, and others, each colony includes at least four types of polyps, as follows: (1) the pneumatophore, or float, into which gas is secreted to render the colony buoyant; (2) feeding polyps; (3) defensive or fighting polyps with nematocysts; and (4) reproductive polyps. Some species also have sensitive or feeling polyps. In *Physalia* the float is used as a sail, attains to 8 or 10 inches in length, is crested, and may change in shape by contraction. Such diversity in form and function of a basic type (the polyp) is known as **polymorphism.**

CLASS SCYPHOZOA. JELLYFISHES

In the SCYPHOZOA (Gr. *skyphos*, cup + *zoon*, animal) the medusa stage is from an inch to 7 feet in diameter and consists largely of gelatinous mesoglea, or "jelly," the polyp being minute or lacking. *Aurelia aurita* is a common jellyfish of coastal waters, often seen singly or in companies.

18-15. Structure. The body (Fig. 18-8) is shallowly convex above and concave below and is fringed by a row of closely spaced delicate **marginal tentacles.** These are interrupted by eight equally spaced indentations, each with a **sense organ** between two small **lappets.** There is no velum. Circular muscle fibers are numerous in the bell margin. Central in the concave oral surface is the **mouth,** on a short **manu-**

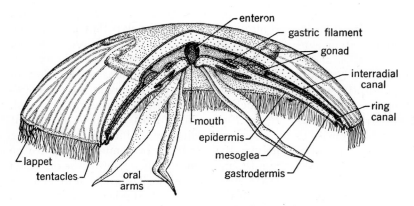

Fig. 18-8. Class SCYPHOZOA. Structure of a jellyfish, *Aurelia aurita;* one-quarter of the body cut away to show internal structure.

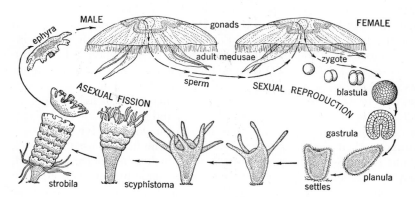

Fig. 18-9. Class SCYPHOZOA. Life cycle of the jellyfish, *Aurelia.* Adults of separate sexes produce eggs and sperm, and the zygotes develop on the oral arms of the female (but shown separately here). The ciliated planula larva swims and later attaches to become a small scyphistoma; this by transverse fission (strobilation) yields several ephyrae which grow to be adult jellyfishes. Medusae reduced, other stages enlarged. (*After Agassiz; and Wolcott, Animal biology.*)

brium, between four tapering **oral arms,** which are grooved and bear nematocysts along their edges. A short **gullet** through the manubrium connects to the **enteron,** or digestive cavity. Off the latter are four **gastric pouches** containing slender tentacle-like **gastric filaments** with nematocysts. Many **radial canals** extend through the mesoglea from the pouches to a **ring canal** in the bell margin. There are four U-shaped **gonads,** one in the floor of each gastric pouch. The **nerve net** is best developed about the bell margin. Each sense organ comprises (1) a pigmented **eyespot** sensitive to light; (2) a hollow **statocyst,** off the circular canal, that contains minute calcareous granules and gives direction for swimming movements; and (3) two **sense pits,** one lateral and one medial, probably chemoreceptors having to do with food recognition. The exterior surface is covered by epidermis; and the lining of the di-

gestive system and canals from the mouth inward, the gastric tentacles, and the gonads are of gastrodermis.

18-16. Natural history. Jellyfishes may occur singly or in great schools. They float quietly and can swim feebly by rhythmic contractions of the bell but are largely at the mercy of currents and waves. Great numbers are sometimes cast on shore during storms. The food is mainly of small invertebrates, seized and paralyzed by nematocysts on the oral arms, then carried into the mouth; further quieting of the prey may be accomplished by nematocysts on the gastric tentacles. Some of the food digested in the enteron passes to the radial and circular canals for absorption, and undigested parts are cast out the mouth. Respiration and excretion are presumably performed by the whole body surface. The nerve net serves to coordinate the

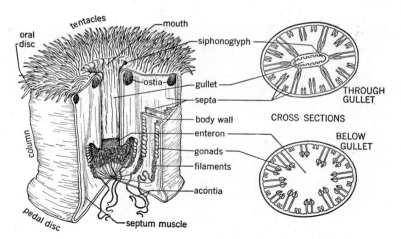

Fig. 18-10. Class ANTHOZOA. Structure of a sea anemone, *Metridium*. Part of the body has been cut away to show internal features. Cross sections through and below the gullet show the arrangement of the septa.

pumping contractions of the bell and action of the oral lobes.

The sexes are alike but separate (Fig. 18-9). Sperm from the gonads (testes) of a male pass out of its mouth and into the enteron of a female to fertilize the eggs produced in her gonads (ovaries). The zygotes emerge to lodge on her oral arms, where each develops into a ciliated planula larva. This escapes to swim for a while, then settles and attaches to the sea bottom. Losing the cilia, it becomes a minute trumpet-shaped polyp (scyphistoma) with basal disc, mouth, and tentacles. It feeds and grows to about 12 mm. long and may produce lateral buds that become separate polyps, as with hydra. In autumn and winter a type of transverse fission (strobilation) ensues; horizontal constrictions form around the body and deepen so that the organism somewhat resembles a pile of minute saucers with fluted borders, the edge of each being formed into eight double lobes. These flat eight-lobed ephyrae later separate, invert, and swim about, and each grows to be an adult jellyfish.

CLASS ANTHOZOA. SEA ANEMONES, CORALS, ETC.

The ANTHOZOA are marine polyps of flower-like form (Gr. *anthos*, flower + *zoon*, animal), of small to large size and rather firm texture, with a tendency toward biradial symmetry in arrangement of the gullet and internal septa. Besides the familiar sea anemones and stony corals, this class includes the soft, horny, and black corals, the colonial sea pens and sea pansies, and others, all of which lack a medusa stage. They abound in warm shallow waters, but some inhabit polar seas, and various species occur from the tide lines to depths of 17,400 feet.

18-17. Structure. A common sea anemone such as *Metridium* has a short cylindrical body (Fig. 18-10). On the upper and flat *oral disc* are many short hollow *tentacles* around a slit-like *mouth;* the base, or *pedal disc,* serves for attachment to solid objects in the sea. The *gullet,* or stomodeum, is a flat tube connecting the mouth and internal cavity, or *enteron.* Along one or both sides of the gullet is a smooth ciliated furrow, the *siphonoglyph,* in which water passes to the enteron. Internally the body is divided into radial compartments by six pairs of complete *septa,* or mesenteries, that extend vertically from the body wall to the gullet; between these are other, incomplete septa (secondary, tertiary) attached to the body wall but not reaching the gullet. In the septa, beneath the oral disc, are openings, or *ostia,* through which water can pass between the internal compartments. The free inner margin of each septum is a thick convoluted *septal filament,* continued below as a thread-like *acontium;* both parts

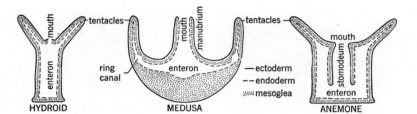

Fig. **18-11.** Phylum COELEN-TERATA. Comparison of the hydroid polyp, the medusa (inverted), and the anthozoan polyp.

bear nematocysts and gland cells. Other nematocysts occur on the tentacles. The acontia can be protruded through pores in the body wall or through the mouth, to aid in subduing prey. The **gonads** form along margins of the septa.

The exterior surface is covered completely by tough epidermis, with cilia on the oral disc, tentacles, and gullet, and the enteron is entirely lined by gastrodermis. Both these cell layers contain strong muscle fibers, arranged as in hydra, and there are additional longitudinal fibers in the septa. Between the epidermis and gastrodermis of the body wall and disc, and within the septa, there is mesoglea composed of cellular connective tissue. The epidermis contains a nerve net and nerves occur in the septa, but no localized sense organs are present.

18-18. Natural history. The sea anemone lives attached to some firm surface but can creep slowly on its pedal disc. When undisturbed and covered by water, the body and tentacles are widely extended. If irritated or if exposed by a receding tide, the oral disc may be completely inturned and the body closely contracted. Cilia on the tentacles and disc beat so as to keep these surfaces free of debris. A constant current of water moves down the siphonoglyph to circulate in the enteron for respiratory purposes and to keep the body turgid, and an outward current passes up elsewhere in the gullet.

The food is of mollusks, crustaceans, other invertebrates, and fishes, paralyzed by nematocysts and carried by the tentacles to the mouth; some prey is gripped directly by the mouth and gullet, both of which can gape widely. The food passes to the enteron, is digested by enzymes secreted from the filaments, and is absorbed by the gastrodermis. Undigested wastes are cast out the mouth.

The sexes are separate. Eggs and sperm leave the gonads through the mouth, and fertilization occurs in the water. The zygote develops into a slender ciliated gastrula; septa soon appear in the archenteron, the blastopore becomes a mouth, and long stiff cilia grow on the aboral end. This larva swims about, feeding on microorganisms, later creeps on the bottom, and then attaches by the aboral end. With growth of the tentacles, septa, and mesoglea, it becomes a miniature anemone.

Most kinds of anemones are attached to rocks, shells, or other surfaces, but some can move readily, a few minute forms (*Boloceroides*) can swim by lashing their tentacles, and some slender types (*Edwardsia, Cerianthus*) burrow in the bottom, leaving only the tentacles and oral disc exposed (Fig. 18-1). Anemones are eaten by fishes, crabs, other crustaceans, starfishes, and nudibranch mollusks; cod, flounders, and other fishes use them in some quantity. Some nudibranchs are immune to the toxins of anemones and even incorporate the undischarged nematocysts into their own bodies. Certain kinds of anemones reproduce asexually by fission, either longitudinal (*Sagartia*) or transverse (*Gonactinia*), and others (*Epiactis*) fragment pieces off the base to form new individuals. Some anemones regularly contain symbiotic algae (zooxanthellae) in the gastrodermis. Several instances of longevity in captive anemones are recorded, one of *Cereus pedunculatus* to over 65 years.

18-19. Corals. Members of the Order MADRE-PORARIA are the principal reef builders, growing as rigid masses able to resist the constant pounding of waves. Other coelenterates and invertebrates and marine algae also contribute to reef formation. Many kinds of animals live

Fig. 18-12. Types of corals (Class ANTHOZOA). *A.* Solitary, and *B–E*, parts of colonial stony corals (Order MADREPORARIA). *F.* Horny coral (Order GORGONACEA). (*After Wolcott, Animal biology.*)

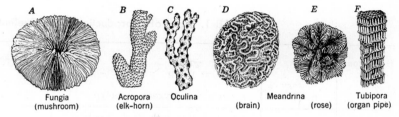

Fungia (mushroom)   Acropora (elk-horn)   Oculina   Meandrina (brain)   (rose)   Tubipora (organ pipe)

among or in corals; some commensal crabs become imprisoned in galls on corals, and in the cells of some shallow water corals are brown algae (zooxanthellae).

The coral organism is a small anemone-like polyp, with short tentacles, scant musculature, and no pedal disc, that lives in a stony cup with radial ridges in the bottom. Generations of such polyps in dense colonies produce the calcareous corals (Fig. 18-12) and coral reefs. They require waters at 20°C. or warmer and live from the surface to depths of about 120 feet between latitudes 28°N. and 28°S. They abound about Florida and the West Indies and in the Coral Sea from Hawaii and the Philippines to Australia and East Africa. A few stone corals (*Fungia,* etc.) are solitary, and some of these occur to depths of 25,000 feet.

Reef corals may form (1) a *fringing reef* extending out to a quarter mile from shore; (2) a *barrier reef* separated by a lagoon of some width and depth from a shore; and (3) an *atoll,* or circular reef, encircling a lagoon of water and not enclosing an island. Most famous is the Great Barrier Reef along northeast Australia, about 1,200 miles long and from a few to 90 miles off shore.

There are various theories as to the origin of coral reefs. Darwin inferred that growth began on a sloping shore and that, as the shore sank or was weathered away, this became a barrier reef and later an atoll when the land was completely submerged (Fig. 18-13). Daly's theory assumes that withdrawal of water to form the great icecaps of the last glacial period lowered the sea about 200 feet below its present level. Various terraces were then cut or islands leveled by wave action. Later, with rising temperatures, corals began growing and built up with the gradual rise in sea level as the ice melted. Recent borings on Bikini showed sand containing FORAMINIFERA of the Oligocene (about 30 million years ago) at a depth of 2,500 feet. Previous theories of atoll formation are inadequate to explain this finding. Present-day reefs grow 5 to 200 mm. per year, and it is estimated that all existing reefs could have been developed in 10,000 to 30,000 years.

18-20. Fossil coelenterates. Relics of the HYDROZOA and ANTHOZOA occur from Cambrian time onward, and scant impressions of the SCYPHOZOA appear in Cambrian, Permian, and Jurassic rocks. Fossil reefs of stony corals occur in Iowa, Kansas, Kentucky, and Europe, and a great reef surrounds the "Michigan basin," from Wisconsin to Ohio. The †TABULATA of Lower Ordovician to Permian times had colonies of many tubes with cross partitions, some pierced by pores; they are probably a subclass of ANTHOZOA. The †STROMATOPORIDEA (†*Stromatopora,* etc.) of Cambrian to Cretaceous times left masses of wavy calcareous plates that formed reefs in ancient oceans; they are considered to be related to the HYDROZOA. The †GRAPTOZOA of Middle Cambrian to carboniferous, formerly grouped with coelenterates, are now placed with hemichordates (par. 28-5).

Fig. 18-13. Formation of a coral reef. (*After Darwin.*)

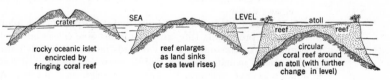

crater   SEA   LEVEL   atoll

reef   reef

rocky oceanic islet encircled by fringing coral reef   reef enlarges as land sinks (or sea level rises)   circular coral reef around an atoll (with further change in level)

TABLE 18-1. Types of Reproduction in the Coelenterates

Hydrozoa *Hydra*	small solitary polyp	→ bud → polyp → gametes → zygote → polyp
Obelia	polymorphic colony of minute polyps	→ bud → hydranth (feeding polyp) → bud → gonangium → bud → minute medusa → gametes → zygote → ciliated planula → polyp → buds → polyp colony
Scyphozoa *Aurelia*	large medusa	→ gametes → zygote → ciliated planula → minute polyp → bud → polyp → transverse fission → ephyra → medusa
Anthozoa *Metridium*	large solitary polyp	→ fission → polyp → fragmentation → polyp → gametes → zygote → ciliated larva → polyp

CLASSIFICATION

PHYLUM COELENTERATA (Cnidaria). COELENTERATES. Symmetry radial or biradial; the individual either a sessile cylindrical polyp, often in colonies, or a free-floating bell-like medusa with much mesoglea; with stinging nematocysts; digestive cavity (enteron) sac-like, sometimes branched; soft tentacles about mouth; no anus, no head, no other organ systems; nervous system diffuse; some with eye-spots, or statocysts; reproduction usually asexual in polyps and sexual in medusae; dioecious or monoecious; no sex ducts; all aquatic, chiefly marine, attached or floating; Lower Cambrian to Recent, 10,000 species.

CLASS 1. *HYDROZOA.* HYDROIDS (and some medusae). No stomodeum; enteron lacks partitions and nematocysts; mesoglea noncellular; medusa usually small and with velum (craspedote); chiefly in shallow salt waters; colonial or solitary; 3,700 species.

Order 1. Hydroidea. Polyp generation well developed, solitary or colonial, usually budding off small free medusae that bear ocelli and ectodermal statocysts.

SUBORDER 1. ANTHOMEDUSAE (Gymnoblastea). Hydranths lack hydrothecae; gonophores naked; gonads on manubrium; medusae tall, no statocysts. *Hydra, Pelmatohydra, Chlorohydra,* all in fresh water, solitary, no medusoid stage; *Cordylophora,* colonial, in rivers and brackish water; *Corymorpha,* solitary, marine; *Tubularia, Bougainvillia, Eudendrium,* sessile, colonial, and marine.

SUBORDER 2. LEPTOMEDUSAE (Calyptoblastea). Hydrothecae present; gonophores in gonothecae; gonads on radial canals; medusae flattish, usually with statocysts. *Obelia, Sertularia, Plumularia,* sessile, colonial, marine, and luminescent; *Polyorchis,* Pacific coast, no hydroid stage.

SUBORDER 3. LIMNOMEDUSAE. Polyps sessile; radial canals branched; gonads on walls of stomach or radial canals; medusae with statocysts. *Proboscidactyla,* commensal on tubes of sabellid polychaete worms.

Order 2. Hydrocorallina. Polyps minute and dimorphic (short, plump gastrozooids and slender dactylozooids) protruding through pores in massive calcareous skeleton. Triassic to Recent.

SUBORDER 1. MILLEPORINA. Dactylozooids hollow and with tentacles. *Millepora,* stinging coral, with powerful nematocysts, on Florida coast and on tropical reefs down to 100 feet.

SUBORDER 2. STYLASTERINA. Dactylozooids solid, no tentacles. *Stylantheca,* California.

Order 3. Trachylina. Polyp generation reduced or none; medusa of some size, with velum beneath bell margin and tentacles attached above margin; with statocysts and endodermal tentaculocysts; sexes separate.

SUBORDER 1. TRACHYMEDUSAE. Bell margin smooth, gonads on radial canals. *Liriope, Gonionemus, Aglantha,* all marine, warm seas, surface to depths of 10,000 feet; *Craspedacusta sowerbyi,* freshwater jellyfish, diameter to 20 mm., polyp stage 2 mm. tall, occasional in eastern North America.

SUBORDER 2. NARCOMEDUSAE. Bell margin scalloped by tentacle bases; gonads in floor of stomach. *Cunina, Aegina, Solmaris.*

SUBORDER 3. PTEROMEDUSAE. Body slender, like two pyramids; 4 swimming lobes at middle; gonads below velum, projecting inside and largely filling coelenteron. *Tetraplatia,* marine, in plankton.

Order 4. Siphonophora. SIPHONOPHORES. Swimming colonies comprising several kinds of polyps; no oral tentacles; upper end of colony usually a supporting float; nematocysts many, large, and powerful; medusae incomplete, attached to stem or disc, rarely free; marine, pelagic, especially in warm seas. *Physalia pelagica,* Portuguese man-of-war, float inflated; *Velella,* float thin, with erect sail; *Porpita,* float disc shaped.

CLASS 2. *SCYPHOZOA* (Scyphomedusae). JELLYFISHES. Chiefly free-swimming medusae of bell or umbrella form, with strong 4-part radial symmetry and much gelatinous mesoglea; no true velum; no stomodeum; gastric tentacles about mouth; central gastrovascular "stomach" with pouches; notches in bell margin with sense organs (tentaculocysts) having endodermal statoliths; medusae sexual, dioecious, with gonads in gastral cavity; polyp generation none or reduced (scyphistoma), producing medusae directly or by transverse fission; all marine; 200 species.

Order 1. Stauromedusae (Lucernariida). Goblet-shaped; marginal sense organs none or as modified tentacles; sessile, attached by oral stalk to seaweeds; bays and coastal waters of colder regions. *Haliclystus; Lucernaria.*

Order 2. Cubomedusae (Carydeida). Bell cubical and margin bent inward; tentacles 4 or in 4 groups; tropical and subtropical waters, shores, and open seas; feed mostly on fish. *Tamoya,* Atlantic coast.

Order 3. Coronatae (Peromedusae, part). Bell surrounded by circular furrow, above scalloped margin; chiefly in deep waters. *Periphylla; Nausithoë; Linuche.*

Order 4. Discomedusae. Corners of mouth prolonged as 4 grooved oral arms; chiefly in coastal waters, includes most jellyfishes.

SUBORDER 1. SEMAEOSTOMAE. Mouth central, corners prolonged as 4 frilly lobes; tentacles present. *Aurelia,* common jellyfish; *Cyanea,* to 7 feet in diameter, from Arctic waters south along both coasts of North America; *Pelagia,* in open ocean, no fixed scyphistoma stage.

SUBORDER 2. RHIZOSTOMAE. Oral arms fused and each doubled (8 in all); no central mouth, many small mouths in oral lobes; no tentacles. *Cassiopeia,* arms branched, Florida; *Rhizostoma,* arms with slender tips.

CLASS 3. *ANTHOZOA.* CORALS, SEA ANEMONES, etc. All polyps, and attached (no medusae); oral disc flat, with hollow tentacles; mouth leading into stomodeum (gullet), usually with siphonoglyph; enteron divided by vertical septa bearing nematocysts on inner margins; mesoglea a connective tissue; with or without skeleton; gonads (endodermal) in septa; all marine; solitary or colonial; 6,100 species.

SUBCLASS 1. ALCYONARIA (Octocorallia). With 8 pinnately branched tentacles and 8 single complete septa; one ventral siphonoglyph; an endoskeleton; colonial.

Order 1. Stolonifera. Polyps arising separately from common stolon or mat; skeleton of separate spicules, sometimes fused as tubes. *Clavularia,* California coast; *Tubipora musica,* organ-pipe coral, in warm waters on coral reefs.

Order 2. Telestacea. Colonies of stems, each an axial polyp with lateral polyps, on a slender base. *Telesto.*

Order 3. Alcyonacea. SOFT CORALS. Polyps with lower parts fused in a fleshy mass and only oral ends protruding; skeleton of separate limy spicules, not axial; mostly in warm shore waters. *Xenia; Alcyonium; Anthomastus.*

Order 4. Coenothecalia. Skeleton massive, of crystalline calcareous fibers. *Heliopora,* blue coral of Indo-Pacific region.

Order 5. Gorgonacea. HORNY CORALS. Colony usually of plant-like form; axial skeleton of calcareous spicules, of horn-like gorgonin, or both; polyps short; 1,000 species. *Corallium,* red coral, used for jewelry; *Gorgonia,* sea fan.

Order 6. Pennatulacea. Colony fleshy, of one long axial polyp, with many dimorphic polyps along sides, above bare stalk; skeleton of limy spicules; 300 species. *Pennatula*, sea pen, feather-like; *Renilla*, sea pansy, disc-shaped.

SUBCLASS 2. ZOANTHARIA (Hexacorallia). Tentacles few to many (never 8), sometimes branched; siphonoglyphs 2, 1, or none; skeleton solid, if present.

Order 1. Actiniaria. SEA ANEMONES. No skeleton; polyp of some size, columnar, with muscular wall and usually a pedal disc; stomodeum usually with siphonoglyphs; septa paired, often in multiples of 6; on rocks, on sand, or on invertebrates; sessile, but not fixed; essentially solitary, some closely grouped; 1,000 species.

SUBORDER 1. ACTINIARIA. Filaments with ciliated areas. *Metridium, Gonactinia; Anthopleura (Cribrina)*, Pacific coast, to 30 cm. tall; *Adamsia, Actininia*, on hermit crab shells; *Edwardsia*, in "burrows."

SUBORDER 2. PTYCHODACTIARIA. No ciliated areas on filaments; no capitate tentacles. *Ptychodactis, Dactylanthus*, Arctic and Antarctic waters.

SUBORDER 3. CORALLIMORPHARIA. No ciliated areas on filaments; with capitate tentacles, usually in radial series. *Corynactis*, central California.

Order 2. Madreporaria. STONY CORALS. Exoskeleton compact, calcareous; polyps small or minute, in cups on skeleton; tentacles in 6's usually; no siphonoglyph; muscles feeble; mostly colonial in warm seas; Pre-Cambrian to Recent; 2,500 living, 5,000 extinct species. *Fungia*, solitary; *Balanophyllia*, California coast; *Astrangia danae*, Atlantic coast; *A. insignifica*, southern California. Reef-building corals: *Orbicella*, in Florida and West Indies; *Acropora, Montipora, Meandra, Isophyllia, Siderastrea*, in the Coral Sea (Hawaii to Australia and Africa).

Order 3. Zoanthidea. No skeleton or pedal disc; polyps usually united by basal stolons, some solitary with stalked base; many species on exterior of various invertebrates. *Epizoanthus*, on hermit crab.

Order 4. Antipatharia. BLACK CORALS. Skeleton plant-like, of stems (some branched) composed of horny material and bearing small polyps; tentacles 6; in deeper tropical waters. *Antipathes*, West Indies, etc.

Order 5. Cerianthia. Slender, elongate, anemone-like; many tentacles in 2 circles; no pedal disc; one siphonoglyph; solitary. *Cerianthus*, inhabits slime-lined vertical tubes in sea bottom.

REFERENCES

DARWIN, C. 1842. The structure and distribution of coral reefs. 3d ed. 1896. New York, D. Appleton-Century Co., Inc. xx + 344 pp., illus.

FRASER, C. McL. 1937. Hydroids of the Pacific Coast of Canada and the United States. Toronto, University of Toronto Press. 207 pp., 44 pls.

———. 1944. Hydroids of the Atlantic Coast of North America. Toronto, University of Toronto Press. 451 pp., 94 pls.

HYMAN, LIBBIE H. 1928. Miscellaneous observations on *Hydra*, with special reference to reproduction. *Biological Bulletin*, vol. 54, pp. 65–108, pls. 1–6.

———. 1940. Cnidaria. *In* The invertebrates. New York, McGraw-Hill Book Co., Inc. Vol. 1, pp. 365–661, figs. 106–208.

KÜKENTHAL, W., and OTHERS. 1924. Handbuch der Zoologie. Berlin, Walter De Gruyter & Co. COELENTERATA (CNIDARIA), vol. 1, pp. 419–901, figs. 378–785.

MAYER, A. G. 1910. Medusae of the world. *Carnegie Institution of Washington, Pub.* No. 109, 3 vols., 735 pp., 76 pls.

SAVILLE-KENT, W. 1893. The Great Barrier Reef of Australia. . . . London, W. H. Allen & Co. xvii + 387 pp., illus.

STEPHENSON, T. A. 1928. The British sea anemones. London, Ray Society. I, xiv + 148 pp., 14 pls., 41 figs. 1935. II, xi + 426 pp., 33 pls.

YONGE, C. M. 1930. A year on the Great Barrier Reef. New York, G. P. Putnam's Sons. xx + 246 pp., illus.

19 PHYLUM PLATYHELMINTHES
Flatworms

In early classifications of animals all creatures with long slender bodies were called "worms" (Gr. *helminthes;* L. *vermes*). They differ from the radial sponges, coelenterates, and ctenophores in having an **anterior end** or head with sense organs that moves forward to "meet the environment" and a **posterior end** or tail behind; also, they travel or rest on a **ventral surface,** or undersurface, that remains downward against the ground or bottom, while the opposite **dorsal surface,** or back, is uppermost. Furthermore, they are **bilaterally symmetrical,** their external features and many internal parts being arranged symmetrically on either side of a median or sagittal plane. The worms share all these characteristics with most other higher animals. Among themselves the various kinds of worms differ in many structural and biological features so that they are separated into several phyla.

Lowest of the worms are the PLATYHELMINTHES (Gr. *platy,* flat), which have thin soft bodies. This phylum includes three Classes: the TURBELLARIA, or free-living flatworms, most of which inhabit fresh or salt water or moist places on land; the TREMATODA, or flukes, which are either external or internal parasites; and the CESTOIDEA, or tapeworms, which are intestinal parasites of vertebrates. Flukes and tapeworms are important parasites of man-

kind, livestock, and wild animals, some causing serious illness or death to these hosts.

19-1. Characteristics. 1. Symmetry bilateral; 3 germ layers; body usually flattened dorsoventrally; no true segmentation.

2. Epidermis soft and ciliated (TURBELLARIA) or covered by cuticle and with external suckers or hooks or both for attachment to host (TREMATODA, CESTOIDEA).

3. Digestive system incomplete, a mouth but no anus, and usually much branched; none in ACOELA or CESTOIDEA.

4. Muscle layers well developed; no body cavity; spaces between internal organs filled by loose parenchyma.

5. No skeletal, circulatory, or respiratory systems; excretory system with many flame cells connected to excretory ducts.

6. Nervous system a pair of anterior ganglia or a nerve ring connecting to 1 to 3 pairs of longitudinal nerve cords with transverse commissures.

7. Sexes usually united (monoecious); reproductive system of each sex with gonads, ducts, and accessory organs; fertilization internal; eggs microscopic, each enclosed with several yolk cells in a shell; development either direct (TURBELLARIA, monogenetic TREMATODA) or with one or more larval stages (digenetic TREMATODA, CESTOIDEA); asexual reproduction in some forms.

The PLATYHELMINTHES show many advances over the PORIFERA and COELENTERATA in having (1) bilateral symmetry, with anterior-posterior and dorsoventral relations; (2) a nervous system of enlarged anterior ganglia and nerve cords extending along the body; (3) mesoderm as a third germ layer (in place of mesoglea) pro-

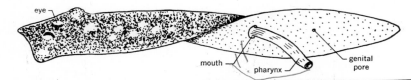

Fig. **19-1.** Class TURBELLARIA. Planaria. External features.

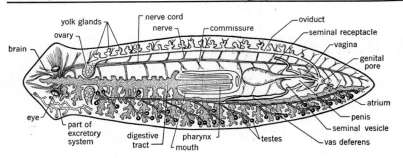

Fig. **19-2.** Planaria. General structure (somewhat diagrammatic). On the right (upper) side the testes, vas deferens, and parts of the digestive tract are omitted; on the left (lower) side the nerve cord, yolk glands, and oviduct are omitted; only a bit of the excretory system is shown on the left anteriorly.

ducing muscles and other organs between the ectoderm and endoderm; (4) layers and bundles of muscles making various movements possible; and (5) internal gonads with permanent reproductive ducts and copulatory organs. Flatworms differ from most higher animals in having (1) no body cavity; (2) the gut branched to various parts of the body; (3) usually no anus; and (4) the sexes united.

Most turbellarians are entirely free-living, a few dwell on the exterior of other animals, and a few are endoparasites. Flukes are either external or internal parasites, and all tapeworms are internal parasites. Structural and physiological specializations parallel this trend in habits. The turbellarians have a delicate ciliated epidermis, whereas both flukes and tapeworms are covered with cuticle resistant to digestion and have suckers and hooks for attaching to their hosts. Those which live internally lack sensory organs, and the tapeworms have no digestive tract. The species that are internal parasites produce enormous numbers of eggs, as is necessary for all organisms that have complex life histories.

19-2. Size. Turbellarians are mostly under 50 mm. long, and some ACOELA are microscopic, but a few land planarians become 500 mm. long. Various flukes are 0.5 to 75 mm. in length, and different species of tapeworms are 3 mm. to 12 meters (40 feet) in length.

CLASS TURBELLARIA
FREE-LIVING FLATWORMS

The common fresh-water planarians of North America, *Euplanaria maculata, E. agilis, E. dortocephala*, etc., are free-living animals. They inhabit cool, clear, and permanent waters, including streams, ponds, marshes, and springs, where they cling to the undersurfaces of submerged plants, rocks, and logs and avoid the light.

19-3. Structure. *Euplanaria (Dugesia)* is a thin, slender, and soft worm about 15 (5 to 25) mm. long, with a bluntly triangular anterior end, or "head," and a tapered body patterned with dark pigment (Fig. 19-1). The head region bears two black *eyespots* middorsally. The *mouth* is on the ventral surface near the middle of the body. Through it a tubular *pharynx* or *proboscis,* with muscular walls, can be extended to capture food. Minute *excretory openings* are present laterally on the dorsal surface but are difficult to see. Sexually mature worms have a small *genital pore* on the ventral surface behind the mouth.

The body (Fig. 19-4) is covered by *epidermis* of a single layer of cuboidal cells, resting on an elastic basement membrane. The epidermis contains small bodies called *rhabdites* of uncertain purpose and many deep-lying *unicellular glands* that open on the surface. The ventral

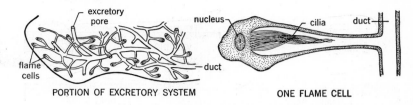

Fig. 19-3. Planaria. Part of the excretory system and one flame cell, both enlarged. (*Adapted from Lankester, Treatise on zoology, A. & C. Black, Ltd.*)

PORTION OF EXCRETORY SYSTEM   ONE FLAME CELL

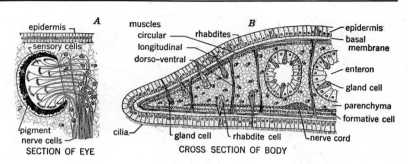

Fig. 19-4. Planaria. *A.* Section through eye. *B.* Cross section of the body (excretory structures omitted).

SECTION OF EYE   CROSS SECTION OF BODY

epidermis is largely covered with **cilia** that serve for locomotion. Beneath the basement membrane are layers of **muscle fibers,** circular, longitudinal, and diagonal, also dorsoventral fibers. Spaces between the muscles and internal organs are filled with **parenchyma,** a loose meshwork of cells lacking definite walls (syncytium); there is no body cavity. In the parenchyma are scattered free **formative cells,** which by mitosis produce new parts in regeneration.

The digestive system (Fig. 19-2) consists of the **mouth,** the **pharynx,** and the **intestine** of three main branches, one anterior and two posterior, with many smaller lateral subdivisions. It is composed of columnar epithelium, derived from endoderm.

There is no skeleton other than the elastic basement membrane, and no respiratory system. Oxygen–carbon dioxide exchange occurs through the epidermis, and thence to other tissues. The **excretory system** (Fig. 19-3) comprises two longitudinal ducts connecting to a network of tubules that branch throughout the body and end in many large **flame cells;** the latter are between various body cells, from which they collect excess water or fluid wastes. The central cavity within a flame cell contains a group of flickering cilia that drive the collected fluid into the tubules and to the canals

that open on the body surface. Flame cells can be seen in unpigmented worms or in preparations made by crushing living worms between two glass slides.

The **nervous system** of planarians is more highly organized than the diffuse nerve net of coelenterates. In the head region, beneath the eyes, are two **cerebral ganglia** joined to form a "brain," from which short nerves extend to the anterior end and the eyes, and two longitudinal **nerve cords** pass back, one along either side, with many **transverse connectives** and **peripheral nerves.** The **eyespots** (Fig. 19-4) are sensitive to light from certain directions but form no image. Auricular sense organs on the sides of the head region may be chemoreceptors of "taste" or "smell."

A sexually mature worm has both male and female reproductive systems and hence is monoecious, or hermaphroditic. Both testes and ovaries develop from formative cells of the parenchyma. The **male reproductive system** includes (1) several hundred small spherical **testes** along both sides of the body, each connected by (2) a minute **vas efferens** to (3) a larger **vas deferens,** which extends along each side; the two ducts enter (4) a median **seminal vesicle** for sperm storage, which connects to (5) the muscular **penis** opening into (6) the

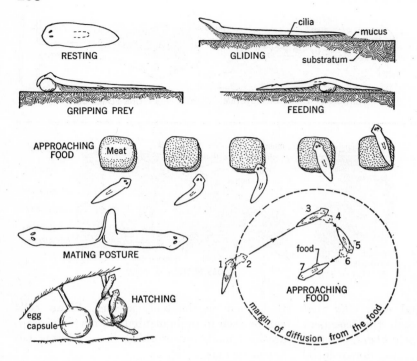

Fig. 19-5. Some activities of planarians. (*Mostly after Pearl, 1903; eggs and hatching redrawn from W. C. Curtis and M. J. Guthrie, Textbook of zoology, John Wiley & Sons, Inc.*)

genital atrium, just within the genital pore. The *female reproductive system* consists of (1) two rounded *ovaries* near the anterior end of the body, connecting to (2) two *oviducts* paralleling the nerve cords, and along each duct are (3) many *yolk* or *vitelline glands,* which supply yolk cells when eggs are produced; the two oviducts join (4) the median *vagina* opening into (5) the *genital atrium;* to the vagina is connected (6) the rounded *seminal receptacle* ("uterus").

19-4. Natural history (Fig. 19-5). Planarians avoid strong light and by day rest quietly on the undersurfaces of objects in water, often in groups of about 6 to 20. After dark, they crawl actively in laboratory aquaria and presumably do so in nature. They adhere to objects or surfaces by a sticky mucus secreted by the epidermal glands and do not swim independently in water. Locomotion is usually by *gliding* with the anterior end forward and slightly raised. This is accomplished by backward strokes of the cilia on the ventral surface, over a slime track produced by the glands. Less often a worm travels by *crawling.* This results from muscular movements; contraction of the circular and dorsoventral muscles elongates the body, the anterior end is then affixed by mucus, and the posterior part drawn up by contraction of the longitudinal muscles. Differential action of local muscle groups produces turning or twisting movements. A moving worm tests its environment by turning the head region from side to side.

On applying weak stimuli to the head, the worm turns toward the stimulus, but strong stimuli result in a negative reaction. The same is true in lesser degree upon stimulating the middle of the body; a strong stimulus at the posterior end causes the worm to move ahead. Compared with a coelenterate, the planarian shows much more coordination in the action of its parts. This results from the higher development of the nervous system, aided by sensory structures scattered in the epidermis, particularly in the head region. The complexity of muscular fibers under direction of the nervous system makes a greater variety of movements possible.

Planarians feed on other small animals, living or dead. When hungry, they travel about actively, gathering quickly on any edible material. They evidently feed on small crustaceans trapped in mucus that the worms secrete. When one planarian begins feeding, others are soon attracted, either by substances diffusing from the food or by digestive juices from the worm. The common method of collecting planarians is to place bits of meat in shallow water, when juices diffusing from the meat will soon attract them in numbers. A small food item may first be "gripped" by the head region (Fig. 19-5). Then the muscular pharynx is protruded on and into the food, bits of which are drawn into the mouth and enteron by suction of the pharynx. Digestion is almost all intracellular, within vacuoles of cells lining the enteron. Products of digestion gradually pass to other body tissues, probably in fluid in the parenchyma. Any undigested material must be disposed of through the mouth, since there is no anus. A planarian starved for several weeks will exhaust its stored food; then certain organs degenerate and are utilized, and the worm decreases markedly in size.

19-5. Reproduction. Asexual multiplication occurs by *transverse fission;* a worm constricts in two, usually behind the pharynx, and the missing parts on each piece then grow and differentiate. Planarians possess great powers of regeneration; when injured either naturally or experimentally, any part of the body can be replaced and entire small worms will result from artificial cutting of a larger individual into pieces (Fig. 11-2).

In sexual reproduction two planarians bring their posterior ventral surfaces together, and copulation is mutual, the penis of each being inserted into the genital atrium of the other; sperm from the seminal vesicle in the male system of each passes to the female seminal receptacle of the other. Such exchange of sex products between separate individuals is called *cross-fertilization,* and the direct transfer of sperm from male to female organs is termed *internal fertilization.* The worms separate after

mating, and sperm migrate up the oviducts to fertilize the eggs. Several zygotes and many yolk cells are later combined in a separate capsule, or egg shell; this is formed by the wall of the atrium and then passed outside. Development is direct, without a larval stage.

19-6. Other Turbellaria. The minute ACOELA are primitive marine worms with a mouth but no digestive cavity; food is digested in the solid mass of endoderm cells. They lack excretory organs, and the nervous system is diffuse. Many are free-living, and others live in the intestines of sea urchins and sea cucumbers. *Convoluta,* an acoele of tide pools, is colorless when hatched but soon becomes green by acquiring small green algae in its tissues.

The RHABDOCOELA have a straight unbranched digestive cavity. Many of them are free-living, some are commensals on the exterior of marine animals, and a few are true endoparasites in other turbellarians, mollusks, echinoderms, and crustaceans. The free-living *Microstomum* feeds on hydra, the nematocysts of which pass from the worm's gut to its own epidermis and serve for defense against other animals. This worm reproduces asexually like a planarian, but the parts may remain attached and form a chain of 8 or 16 individuals (Fig. 11-1C).

The Order TRICLADIDA, to which *Euplanaria* belongs, has other members in fresh waters, a few that are marine, and many land planarians in the humid tropics and subtropics. Some of the latter are large and brilliantly colored. They travel in damp places on slime paths and can descend from leaves or branches by hanging on slime threads. *Bipalium kewense* is a common land planarian in greenhouses around the world, having been transported widely with potted plants. Two species of *Geoplana* from South America are in California gardens.

The POLYCLADIDA are exclusively marine, living among rocks, sessile animals, or plants of the seashore. They are leaf-like, some quite broad, some with numerous eyespots, some with tentacles; the gut is many-branched. Some have a free-swimming larval stage.

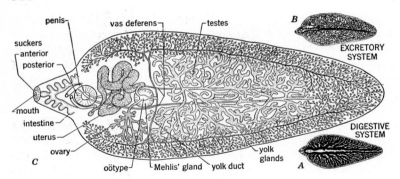

Fig. 19-6. Class TREMATODA. Liver fluke of sheep, *Fasciola hepatica*. *A*. Digestive system; *B*. Excretory system; both natural size. *C*. Reproductive system in ventral view and enlarged; digestive system shown only at anterior end. (*Modified from Sommer and Landois,* 1880.)

CLASS TREMATODA. FLUKES.

These flatworms are all parasitic, mostly in vertebrates. The body of a fluke is usually covered with cuticle secreted by cells beneath and lacks cilia save in some larval stages. There is usually a sucker about the mouth and one or more on the ventral surface. The mouth is anterior, and the digestive tract is usually somewhat λ-shaped with two main trunks having smaller branches. The food consists of the tissues or body fluids of the host, which are sucked in by action of the muscular pharynx. Complex muscle layers, excretory organs, and a nervous system are present as in the TURBELLARIA. Sensory organs such as dorsal eyespots occur in some larvae and in some flukes that are ectoparasites.

19-7. Order Monogenea. Members of this group inhabit only one host. They are chiefly ectoparasites of fishes, amphibians, and reptiles, but some inhabit the mouth cavities or urinary bladders. A monogenetic trematode has at the posterior end a well-developed adhesive organ with one or more suckers, and often with chitinous hooks or anchors as well. The reproductive organs resemble those of TURBELLARIA, and cross-fertilization is usual. Only one or a few eggs are produced at a time, either laid in water or attached to the host. A ciliated larva hatches from the egg to swim about and find a host or die. Development is direct to the adult form, so that each egg, if successful, yields one fluke. A common example is the minute *Gyrodactylus*, which lives on the fins, skin, and gills of carp, trout, and other fresh-water fishes. It

sometimes becomes abundant on fishes in hatcheries and kills many of them.

19-8. Order Digenea. These flukes are all internal parasites. Each species has a succession of stages that must live in certain organs of two or more host species to complete the life cycle, the larvae in a certain snail or other invertebrate and the adult in some vertebrate. Various species are peculiar to parts of the digestive tract, lungs, urinary bladder, or blood vessels. Some have about the most complex life cycles of any animals.

19-9. Sheep liver fluke. The common liver fluke of sheep, *Fasciola hepatica*, inhabits the bile ducts and sometimes invades other organs. It is commonest in sheep and cattle, sometimes in other mammals, and occasional in man, producing the disease known as "liver rot." Moderate infestations cause sheep to be unthrifty and subject to other diseases, and heavy infestations result in many deaths. Fluke disease thrives only on ranges or pastures with marshy areas where the appropriate snails occur, but is common in many parts of the United States, Europe, and other areas of the world.

The liver fluke has a leaf-shaped body up to 30 mm. long, rounded anteriorly and bluntly pointed behind (Fig. 19-6). The *anterior sucker* is terminal, surrounding the mouth; and close behind is the *ventral* (posterior) *sucker,* which serves for attachment in the host. Between them is the *genital opening*. The *digestive system* comprises the mouth, muscular pharynx, short esophagus, and two-branched enteron with many subdivisions throughout the body.

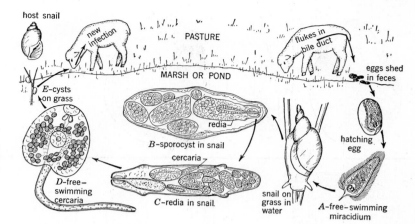

Fig. 19-7. Life history of the liver fluke of sheep, *Fasciola hepatica;* larval stages, about × 70; snail about natural size. (*Details from Thomas,* 1883.)

The **muscles** are complex, and parenchyma fills spaces between the internal organs. The **excretory system** has many flame cells joined to one main canal opening in a single posterior pore. The **nervous system** (visible when stained with methylene blue) includes a double ganglion near the esophagus, two lengthwise nerve cords, and various nerves. Both sex systems are highly developed in a mature worm. The **male reproductive system** has two much-branched testes along the middle of the body, each connected by a vas deferens to the single seminal vesicle, to which is also joined a prostate gland. The vesicle connects to the penis just within the genital opening. The **female reproductive system** comprises a branched ovary on the right side connected by an oviduct to the median oötype, which is surrounded by the Mehlis ("shell") glands. Off the oviduct is a seminal receptacle. Laurer's canal, of unknown function, extends dorsally from the receptacle. Along each side of the body are many yolk glands, joined to two lengthwise yolk ducts with a common entry into the oötype. From the latter an irregularly coiled uterus extends to the genital opening.

Each fertilized egg is combined with several yolk cells and surrounded by an egg shell in the oötype. Egg production is practically continuous; the uterus is crowded with eggs that are beginning to segment. The eggs (Fig. 19-9) emerge from the genital pore, pass through the bile duct and intestine of the sheep, and are voided with its feces (Fig. 19-7). At temperatures below 50°F. they remain undeveloped but viable for several months; in warmer damp surroundings they develop in 9 days or more. From each egg there emerges a microscopic larva, multicellular and ciliated, with a pointed anterior rostrum, two eyespots, a nerve ganglion, and two nephridia. If this **miracidium** (*A*) hatches in water, it swims about for not over 8 hours, to die unless it finds a certain kind of snail, *Lymnea* (*Galba*) *bulimoides,* or *L. columella* in the United States. In the latter event it burrows into the soft tissues and enters usually the pulmonary chamber or lymph vessels. Should many miracidia enter, the snail dies. The larva loses its outer cilia, enlarges, and becomes a sac-like **sporocyst** (*B*). Within the sporocyst are germ cells, each of which can develop by parthenogenesis (without fertilization) into another larval stage termed the **redia** (*C*). Each sporocyst produces 3 to 8 elongate sac-like rediae, with a mouth and short gut. Within about 8 days they burst from the sporocyst and migrate to another organ, usually the liver. There the rediae may produce other rediae parthenogenetically for one or two generations. Finally, each original or daughter redia yields several larvae of another type, known as a **cercaria** (*D*). This has a slender tail and disc-shaped body, with both oral and ventral suckers and a forked gut. The cercaria burrows out of the snail to swim through the water by use of its tail. After a few hours it settles on a grass blade or other

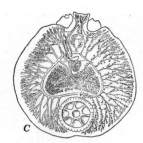
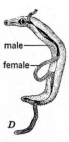

Fig. **19-8.** Class TREMATODA. Some representative flukes, variously enlarged. *A. Prosthogonimus macrorchis. B. Clonorchis sinensis. C. Tristoma coccineum. D. Schistosoma haematobium.* (*A, after Macy; B, D, after H. B. Ward; C, after Lameere.*)

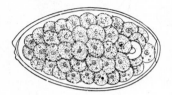

Fasciola hepatica   Dibothriocephalus   Taenia   Dipylidium

Fig. **19-9.** Eggs of the liver fluke and three species of tapeworms, × 250. (*After H. B. Ward.*)

vegetation near the water surface, loses the tail, and becomes a **metacercaria** (*E*), in a tough enclosing cyst. The encysted larvae remain viable for some weeks or months on grass or even on damp hay, if not subjected to high temperatures. When infested vegetation bearing cercariae is eaten by a sheep or other suitable host, the cysts are digested off and the larvae burrow through the intestinal wall to the body cavity to reach the liver. They burrow for several weeks and damage liver tissue before entering the bile duct to mature and live for several months.

Many chances of failure beset the path of a species that must complete such a life cycle. These include the dropping of eggs in dry places, failure of miracidia to find quickly a snail of the right kind, death of infected snails, drying of ponds, or encystment on vegetation where sheep do not happen to graze. As an offset of these hazards, each adult fluke may produce up to a half million eggs, and the parthenogenetic multiplication in the snail may yield up to 300 larvae from a single egg.

19-10. Other Trematoda. About 3,000 species of digenetic flukes (Fig. 19-8) have been described from various hosts—fishes to mammals—but the life histories of very few are known. Important parasitic flukes of mankind are:

INTESTINAL FLUKE, *Fasciolopsis buski.* China, to India and adjacent islands. Larval stages in snails. Cercariae encyst on water plants (water nuts, caltrop), used as raw vegetables in the Orient. In parts of China, over half the human population is infected. Also in pigs and dogs.

LIVER FLUKE, *Clonorchis sinensis.* Japan, China and adjacent islands, to Vietnam. Also in dogs and cats. Earlier larval stages in fresh-water snails and later ones (metacercariae) in muscles of many fresh-water minnows and carp. Human infections result from eating raw fish. Adult flukes inhabit bile ducts, and infections may last from 5 to 20 years (Fig. 19-8*B*).

LUNG FLUKE, *Paragonimus westermani.* In Japan, China, the Philippine Islands, New Guinea, India, Africa, Yucatán, and Peru; occasional in oriental immigrants in the United States. Also in cats, dogs, pigs, goats, rats, and various wild mammals of regions where human infections are present, the flukes showing little host specificity. Eggs discharged in host's sputum, larvae occur in snails, and cercariae encyst in fresh-water crabs and crayfish. By eating these crustaceans uncooked the final hosts become infected; young flukes occur in various organs, and mature flukes encyst near the surface of the lungs.

BLOOD FLUKES: *Schistosoma haematobium* about the Mediterranean, in Africa, Madagascar, and southwestern Asia; *S. mansoni* in Egypt, South Africa, South America, and the West Indies; and *S. japonicum* from Japan to the Philippines and Celebes, Rhodesia and the Belgian Congo; the last also parasitizes cats, dogs, rodents, pigs, and cattle. Adult flukes inhabit veins of abdomen. Sexes separate and unlike (Fig. 19-8*D*), male (9 to 22 mm. long) with widened and infolded body permanently enclosing the slender female (14 to 26 mm.). Eggs deposited in veins, migrate to bladder or rectum, and leave in urine or feces. Larvae in various snails, and cercariae with forked tails burrow through human skin or are taken in drinking water.

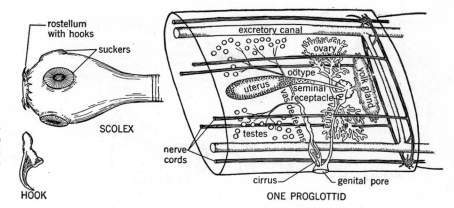

Fig. 19-10. Class Cestoidea. Scolex and one proglottid of the pork tapeworm, *Taenia solium.*

Cercariae of some nonhuman schistosome flukes burrow into the skin and produce a "swimmer's itch" on persons frequenting fresh-water lakes of the north-central states, Pacific coast, Canada, and Europe.

CLASS CESTOIDEA. Tapeworms

The cestodes (Gr. *cestus*, girdle + *oid*, like) are mostly slender and elongate, with a flat body usually of many short sections; hence the name "tapeworm." They lack cilia, are covered with cuticle, and have complex muscle layers, parenchyma, paired excretory ducts with flame cells, and a nerve ring with three pairs of nerve cords. There is no mouth or digestive tract; food is absorbed directly through the body wall. All are endoparasites, the adult worms in the intestines of vertebrates and the larvae (one exception) in tissues of some alternate host.

19-11. Subclass Cestodaria. This group includes a few species of small worms, each with a sucker for attachment, the body undivided, and one set of reproductive organs. *Gyrocotyle,* found in the ancient chimaeroid fishes, is an example.

19-12. Subclass Eucestoda. All other tapeworms belong to this group. A common example is *Taenia solium,* the pork tapeworm of man, known since ancient times, and from 6 to 25 feet long when mature (Fig. 19-10). It has a minute knob-like "head," or *scolex,* with four muscular *suckers* on the sides and a circle of *hooks* on the elevated tip, or *rostellum.* A short "neck," or budding zone, joins the scolex to the body, or *strobila,* which consists of a series of up to 1,000 sections, or *proglottids.* The suckers and hooks serve to fasten the scolex to the intestinal wall of the host, and the chain of proglottids lies free in the intestinal cavity. New proglottids are constantly forming by transverse budding in the neck and remain connected to be forced backward by growth of still others. As they move backward, the proglottids increase in size, mature, and finally become detached.

The scolex contains a nerve ring, with nerves to the suckers and rostellum and joined to three pairs of longitudinal nerves extending backward in the proglottids. In it also is an excretory structure connecting to a pair of excretory canals through the proglottids. Each proglottid contains muscles, parenchyma, sections of the excretory canals connected by a cross canal, many flame cells, and the nerves. A complete set of both male and female sex organs develops in every proglottid when some distance beyond the scolex. Those in any proglottid are comparable with the entire reproductive system in a turbellarian or trematode. The male system matures first. Self-fertilization between the systems in one proglottid, or in separate proglottids, or cross-fertilization between parts in two

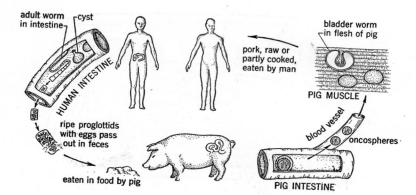

Fig. 19-11. Life cycle of the pork tapeworm, *Taenia solium.* (*Adapted from Buchsbaum, Animals without backbones, University of Chicago Press.*)

worms in one host are all possible. Eggs then develop in numbers, each including a fertilized ovum and several yolk cells enclosed in a resistant shell formed in the oötype. These pass into the uterus, which gradually becomes a branched sac crowded with thousands of eggs; other organs degenerate. Development of the eggs begins at once and continues as ripe proglottids are cast loose, pass out in the host's feces, and disintegrate (Fig. 19-11). In eggs thus scattered on the ground, development continues to the formation of a six-hooked embryo (oncosphere) in each and then stops.

If such eggs are eaten by a pig, the shells are digested off in the pig's intestine, and the six-hooked larvae burrow into blood or lymph vessels, to be carried finally to voluntary muscles where they encyst. The cyst enlarges, becomes filled with fluid, and is then called a "bladder worm" or **cysticercus.** One side of the inner wall thickens to form a hollow papilla projecting into the sac. In the cavity of the papilla a scolex develops, with suckers and hooks, but there is no further growth. When raw or imperfectly cooked pork containing such a cyst is eaten by man, the outer cyst wall is digested off, the papilla everts to form a scolex and "neck," and the bladder disappears. The scolex attaches to the host's intestine, and a new tapeworm begins to form. Larvae of this tapeworm may also occur in monkeys, dogs, cats, and sheep. In man larval infections may involve the central nervous system, with severe results.

The budding, gradual maturing, and freeing of proglottids by a tapeworm resembles some-

what the production of ephyrae by the strobila of a scyphozoan coelenterate (par. 18-19). The proglottids, however, degenerate to free the eggs, whereas each ephyra becomes a complete, free-living, and mature jellyfish that later reproduces sexually.

19-13. Adjustments to parasitic life. The tapeworm, as an internal parasite, has many special physiological adjustments in comparison with a free-living animal. (1) The cuticle protects against digestion by host alkaline digestive juices, but is freely permeable to water. Adults are resistant to alkaline pancreatic juice. (2) The internal osmotic pressure is lower than that of the surrounding host fluid or tissue. (3) The pH tolerance is high, 4 to 11 (see par. 3-6). (4) The tissues have a high glycogen content (to 60 per cent of dry weight) and much lipid,

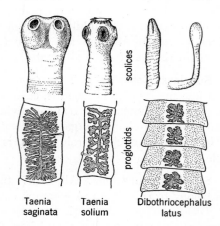

Fig. 19-12. Scolices and mature ("ripe") proglottids of three human tapeworms (beef, pork, and fish).

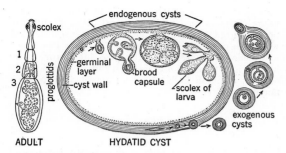

Fig. 19-13. Life cycle of the hydatid worm, *Echinococcus granulosus*. The adult, 3 to 6 mm. long, of 3 (or 4) proglottids, lives in carnivorous mammals; the larval stage is in various domestic and wild herbivorous mammals and man, forming multiple cysts.

but far less protein. (5) Oxygen is used in respiration if available, but anaerobic respiration predominates. (6) Eggs eaten by the intermediate host must experience both acid and alkali, hence are released only in the intestine. A cysticercus swallowed by the final host meets both acid and alkaline digestive juices, and its bladder is digested away, but the inverted scolex (exposed only to alkaline juice) does not; bile stimulates the scolex to evert.

19-14. Other cestodes. More than 1,500 species of tapeworms live in various vertebrates from fishes to mammals. The adult stage of each is usually in a final host that preys upon the intermediate host, consuming the flesh of the latter which contains the infective stages. Some tapeworms are harmless; others may produce severe symptoms but are rarely fatal. Human infections are decreasing in civilized countries because of a wider knowledge as to how infections may be avoided, because of the detection and treatment of persons harboring tapeworms, and because of the inspection and refrigeration of meat to eliminate any containing cysticerci. A few common tapeworms are:

Beef Tapeworm, *Taenia saginata*. Larvae in flesh of cattle, adult worm in man; 4 to 12 meters (even 25 meters) long, proglottids up to 2,000 (Fig. 19-12). About 1 per cent of cattle in the United States are infected; preference for rare beef may cause an increase in human infections.

Dog and Cat Tapeworm, *Taenia pisiformis*. Larvae in liver and mesenteries of rabbits, adults in dogs and cats.

Dog Tapeworm, *Dipylidium caninum*. Larvae in biting dog louse and fleas of dogs, cats, and man; adults in dogs and cats, occasional in man; 15 to 40 cm. long, not over 200 proglottids, each with 2 sets of reproductive organs.

Rat Tapeworm, *Hymenolepis diminuta*. Larvae in earwigs, flour beetles, fleas, other insects, and myriapods; adults common on rats and mice, occasional in man; 20 to 60 cm. long, 800 to 1,000 proglottids.

Dwarf Tapeworm, *Hymenolepis nana*. No intermediate host; larvae live in intestinal villi, and adults in intestine of man; 10 to 45 mm. long, to 200 proglottids; *H. fraterna*, in rats and mice.

Sheep Tapeworm, *Moniezia expansa*. Larvae in free-living mite (*Galumna*); adults in sheep, goats, etc.; up to 6 meters long.

Hydatid Worm, *Echinococcus granulosus* (Fig. 19-13). Adults in intestine of dog, wolf, and jackal, only 3 to 6 mm. long, 3 (or 4) proglottids; larvae in man, monkeys, cattle, sheep, pig, dog, cat, and other domestic and wild animals; larval cysts up to 50 mm. in diameter in pig,

Fig. 19-14. Life cycle of the broad tapeworm of fish, *Dibothriocephalus latus*. Adult worm and fish host much reduced, larval stages variously enlarged. (*Adapted partly from Kükenthal.*)

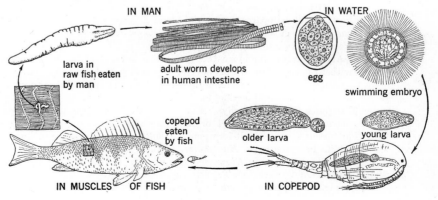

sometimes larger in man, and in various organs; delicate inner lining of cyst forms brood capsules each with 5 to 20 scolices; daughter or "exogenous" cysts also form and may scatter to secondary centers in body; dangerous and sometimes fatal to man; almost cosmopolitan; upward of 500 human cases reported in United States.

Fish Tapeworm, *Dibothriocephalus latus* (Fig. 19-13).

First larval stage (0.5 mm. long) in copepod crustaceans (*Diaptomus, Cyclops*), second (1 to 20 mm.) in perch, burbot, trout, and other fresh-water fishes; adult worms in man, pig, cat, dog, fox, or other fish-eating mammals; to 60 ft. long with up to 4,000 proglottids; human infections from eating fish raw or insufficiently cooked; common in Europe and Japan, increasing in northern United States.

CLASSIFICATION

PHYLUM PLATYHELMINTHES. FLATWORMS. Body soft, flattened dorsoventrally, often elongate, covered by ciliated epidermis or by cuticle; some with external suckers or hooks, or both; digestive tract incomplete or none; excretion by flame-bulb protonephridia with ducts; body spaces filled with parenchyma; nervous system with anterior ganglia or nerve ring and 1 to 3 pairs of longitudinal nerve cords; no skeletal, circulatory, or respiratory organs, or true segmentation; usually monoecious; fertilization internal; eggs microscopic, with shell and containing yolk cells; development direct (TURBELLARIA), or with larval stages; free-living, commensal, or parasitic; more than 10,000 species.

 CLASS 1. *TURBELLARIA.* FREE-LIVING FLATWORMS. Body undivided; epidermis with cilia, rod-like rhabdites, and many mucous glands; usually pigmented, some species brilliantly marked; usually with ventral mouth and intestine (except ACOELA); no suckers; development usually direct; asexual reproduction in some.

  Order 1. Acoela. Length 1 to 4 mm.; with mouth and pharynx but no intestine, protonephridia, oviducts, or definite gonads; marine. *Convoluta; Amphiscolops*, on sargassum weed; *Ectocotyla*, commensal on hermit crab.

  Order 2. Rhabdocoela. Length 0.3 to 15 mm., colorless or pale; digestive tract straight; nephridia 2 or 1; in salt, brackish, or fresh waters, some commensal or parasitic. *Stenostomum, Macrostomum, Mesostoma; Temnocephala*, 5 to 12 anterior tentacles, commensal on fresh-water invertebrates.

  Order 3. Alloeocoela. Length 1 to 40 mm., usually cylindroid; intestine straight or with short branches; mostly marine, some in fresh waters or damp places. *Prorhynchus, Plagiostomum.*

  Order 4. Tricladida. Usually small (2 or 3 mm. to 500 mm.); mouth midventral with proboscis; digestive cavity 3-branched. *Euplanaria* (*Dugesia*), pigmented, and *Protocotyla* and *Dendrocoelum*, milky white, all in fresh waters; *Bdelloura*, on gills of horseshoe crab; *Procerodes, Spalloplana*, white, eyeless, in Mammoth Cave, Ky.; *Bipalium*, common in greenhouses; *Geoplana*, terrestrial.

  Order 5. Polycladida. Small to 150 mm. long; usually thin and oval; eyes many; digestive cavity with many irregular branches; marine, a few pelagic. *Notoplana* (*Leptoplana*), *Planocera; Stylochus*, often feeds on oysters.

 CLASS 2. *TREMATODA.* FLUKES. Body undivided, covered by cuticle (no epidermis or cilia); one or more suckers for attachment; mouth usually anterior and digestive tract 2-branched; 1 ovary; all parasitic.

  Order 1. Monogenea (Heterocotylea). Oral sucker weak or none; posterior end with adhesive disc, usually with hooks; excretory pores 2, anterior, dorsal; eggs few; larva ciliated; no intermediate host; chiefly ectoparasites on cold-blooded vertebrates, few cephalopods and crustaceans. *Gyrodactylus*, on gills of fresh-water fishes; *Polystoma*, larva on gills of tadpole, adult in bladder of frog; *Sphyranura*, on gills of *Necturus*.

  Order 2. Aspidocotylea (Aspidogastraea). No oral sucker or anterior adhesive organs; ventral surface with 1 big sucker or row of suckers; excretory pore 1, posterior; endoparasitic, in 1 host. *Aspidogaster*, in pericardial and renal cavities of fresh-water bivalves (UNIONIDAE); *Stichocotyle*, slender, in spiral valve and bile duct of skates.

  Order 3. Digenea. Suckers usually 2, 1 around mouth, 1 ventral; no hooks; excretory pore 1, posterior; uterus long, eggs many; 1 or more larval stages reproducing in intermediate host(s) before metamorphosis to adult form; chiefly endoparasites, larvae in mollusks (also crustaceans, fishes), adults in vertebrates. *Bucephalus*, larvae in fresh-water or marine bivalves, adults in fishes; *Fasciola, Fasciolopsis, Clonorchis, Schistosoma.*

 CLASS 3. *CESTOIDEA* (Cestoda). TAPEWORMS. Body covered with cuticle, no epidermis or external cilia; unpigmented; no digestive tract or sense organs in adult; usually an anterior scolex for attachment, with adhesive grooves (bothria), or suckers, or hooks; body usually of few to many proglottids (segments), each containing 1 or 2 complete hermaphroditic reproductive systems; embryo hooked; all endoparasitic, usually with alternate hosts, adults in intestines of vertebrates.

SUBCLASS 1. CESTODARIA. Body undivided; no scolex; larva 10-hooked. *Amphilina*, in coelom of sturgeon; *Gyrocotyle*, in intestine of chimaeroid fishes.

SUBCLASS 2. EUCESTODA. Body long, ribbon-like, with 4 to 4,000 proglottids; a scolex with adhesive organs; embryo 6-hooked.

Order 1. Tetraphyllidea (Phyllobothrioidea). Scolex with 4 bothria, often with hooks. *Phyllobothrium*, in elasmobranchs.

Order 2. Lecanicephaloidea. Scolex of 2 parts, upper with disc or branches, lower with 4 suckers. *Polypocephalus*, in elasmobranchs.

Order 3. Proteocephaloidea. Scolex with 4 lateral suckers and terminal sucker or glandular organ. *Proteocephalus*, in fresh-water fishes, amphibians, and reptiles.

Order 4. Diphyllidea. Scolex large, lobed, with 2 bothria, neck with 8 rows of hooks. One genus, *Echinobothrium*, in elasmobranchs.

Order 5. Trypanorhyncha (Tetrarhynchoidea). Scolex with 4 bothria and 4 slender, protrusible spiny proboscides. *Tentacularia* (*Tetrarhynchus*), larvae in marine invertebrates or bony fishes, adults in elasmobranchs; *Haplobothrium*, larvae in *Cyclops*, adults in fresh-water fishes.

Order 6. Pseudophyllidea. Scolex not always distinct, bothria 2 to 6, some lack adhesive organs. *Triaenophorus, Caryophyllaeus*, larvae in copepods, adults in fresh-water fishes; *Dibothriocephalus latus*, fish tapeworm of man.

Order 7. Nippotaeniidea. Small; no scolex; 1 apical sucker. *Nippotaenia*, in fresh-water fishes of Japan.

Order 8. Taenoidea (Cyclophyllidea). Scolex with 4 deep suckers and often with hooks at tip; sex openings lateral; proglottids free or joined when mature; includes most tapeworms of higher animals and man. *Dipylidium, Echinococcus, Hymenolepis, Moniezia, Taenia*.

Order 9. Aporida. Scolex with 4 suckers, rostellum armed; no yolk glands, sex ducts, or pores. *Gastrotaenia*, in swans.

REFERENCES

BRUMPT, E. 1949. Précis de parasitologie. 6th ed. Paris, Masson et Cie. xii + 2,138 pp., 4 pls., 1,308 figs.

CAULLERY, MAURICE. 1952. Parasitism and symbiosis. Translated by A. M. Lysaught. London, Sidgwick & Jackson, Ltd. xii + 340 pp., 80 figs.

CHANDLER, A. C. 1955. Introduction to parasitology. 9th ed. New York, John Wiley & Sons, Inc. xii + 799 pp., 342 figs.

CRAIG, C. F., and E. C. FAUST. 1951. Clinical parasitology. 5th ed. Philadelphia, Lea & Febiger. 1,032 pp., 326 figs.

DAWES, BEN. 1946. The Trematoda with special reference to British and other European forms. Cambridge, England, Cambridge University Press. xvi + 644 pp., 81 figs.

FAUST, E. C. 1955. Animal agents and vectors of human disease. Philadelphia, Lea & Febiger. 660 pp., 9 pls., 216 figs.

HYMAN, L. H. 1951. Platyhelminthes. *In* The invertebrates. New York, McGraw-Hill Book Co., Inc. Vol. 2, pp. 52–458, figs. 13–173.

KÜKENTHAL, W., and OTHERS. 1928–1933. Handbuch der Zoologie. Berlin, Walter De Gruyter & Co. Platyhelminthes, vol. 2, pt. 1, secs. 1 and 2, xiii + 736 pp., 743 figs.

MONNIG, H. O. 1947. Veterinary helminthology and entomology. 3d ed. Baltimore, William Wood & Co. xviii + 427 pp., 275 figs.

NEVEU-LAMAIRE, M. 1936. Traité d'helminthologie médicale et vétérinaire. Paris, Vigot Frères. xxiii + 1,514 pp., 787 figs.

SPREHN, C. E. W. 1932. Lehrbuch der Helminthologie. Berlin, Verlagsbuchhandlung Gebrüder Borntraeger. xvi + 998 pp., 374 figs.

THOMAS, A. P. 1883. The life history of the liver-fluke (*Fasciola hepatica*). *Quarterly Journal of Microscopical Science*, ser. 2, vol. 23, pp. 99–133, pls. 2, 3.

WARDLE, R. A., and J. A. McLEOD. 1952. The zoology of tapeworms. Minneapolis, University of Minnesota Press. xxiv + 780 pp., 419 figs.

20 CLASS NEMATODA
Roundworms

The Class NEMATODA (Gr. *nematos*, thread) comprises the unsegmented roundworms with slender cylindrical bodies, resistant cuticle, and a complete and permanent digestive tract. Among multicellular animals they are probably second only to insects in numbers. Many are free-living in soil and water, and many others are parasites in the tissues or fluids of animals and plants. Still others are restricted to peculiar habitats: the roots of plants, seeds of wheat, gum of tree wounds, and the intestines, blood, and other organs in animal bodies. They are mostly small or minute, but a few grow to a meter in length. Their eggs are microscopic and resistant to adverse environmental conditions.

20-1. Characteristics. 1. Symmetry bilateral; 3 germ layers; no true segmentation, appendages, or proboscis.

2. Body slenderly cylindrical, covered with tough resistant cuticle; somatic cells few, of fixed number.

3. Digestive tract complete and permanent, a straight tube with mouth and anus at opposite ends of body.

4. Body wall with longitudinal muscle fibers only; space within body an unlined pseudocoel.

5. No circulatory or respiratory organs; excretory organs simple, 2, 1, or none.

6. Nerve ring around esophagus connecting to 6 anterior nerves and to 6 (or more) posterior nerves or cords.

7. Sexes usually separate, male smaller than female; gonads continuous with reproductive ducts, single (or double) in male, paired (or single) in female; fertilization internal; eggs microscopic, each covered by a chitinous shell; development direct, "larva" with several molts; no asexual reproduction.

The nematodes differ from flatworms in shape, in the absence of cilia and suckers, in the presence of a complete digestive tract and a body cavity, and in having separate sexes. Their muscles are all aligned with the body axis and permit only dorsoventral bending, thus are less complex than those in flatworms, nemerteans, and annelids. The body cavity compares with that of rotifers, gastrotrichs, and acanthocephalans in lacking a mesodermal lining; it is unlike the true coelom of annelids and vertebrates or the parenchyma-filled body of flatworms and nemerteans. Nematodes, rotifers, and gastrotrichs have a triradiate structure in the fore part of the gut. The complete digestive tract allows food to move along without mixing successive meals, and undigested residues pass out the anus. Digested food diffuses through the gut and is distributed to other tissues by fluid in the pseudocoel.

Zoological opinion has varied as to the proper place of nematodes in classification. They have often been designated as a separate phylum (NEMATHELMINTHES, either with or without the acanthocephs and nematomorphs), but recently have been made a class in the Phylum ASCHELMINTHES (Chap. 21).

20-2. Structure of Ascaris. The common intestinal roundworm of man and the pig (*Ascaris lumbricoides*) shows the general features of a nematode (Fig. 20-1). The female is 8 to 16 inches long and about ¼ inch in greatest diameter; the male is of lesser size, 6 to 10 inches

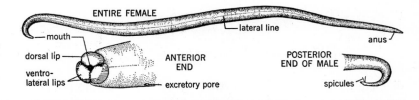

Fig. 20-1. Class NEMATODA. External features of the intestinal roundworm of the pig, *Ascaris lumbricoides*.

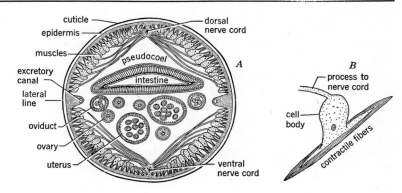

Fig. 20-2. *Ascaris*. *A*. Cross section of a female. *B*. One muscle cell. Both enlarged.

long. Fresh specimens are yellow to pink in color. The *body* is slender and round, tapering toward either end. It is covered with smooth, tough, and elastic *cuticle,* bearing minute striations. Four whitish *longitudinal lines* extend along the body, one dorsal, one ventral, and two lateral. The *mouth* opens at the anterior end, between three rounded *lips;* the dorsal lip bears two double papillae, and each ventrolateral lip has one double and two single papillae. The *anus* is a transverse slit close to the posterior end of the ventral surface. The *male* has a sharply curved posterior end, and two penial spicules project from the male genital pore just within the anus. The *female* is straighter, and the genital pore, or vulva, is midventral on the body at about one-third the distance from the anterior end.

The *body wall* (Fig. 20-2) is thin, consisting of (1) the *cuticle,* which is noncellular and secreted by the epidermis; (2) the *epidermis,* a thin protoplasmic layer that contains nuclei but no cell walls, hence is a syncytium; and (3) the *muscle layer,* of longitudinal fibers. Each muscle cell consists of a spindle-shaped fiber extending lengthwise beneath the epidermis and a club-shaped process that contains the nucleus and projects medially. The muscle layer is di-

vided into four lengthwise parts by the rib-like inner extensions of the four lateral lines. These lines and the muscle cells are the irregular outer boundary of the body space, or *pseudocoel,* in which the other internal organs lie free.

The straight *digestive tract* (Fig. 20-3) extends the length of the body and consists of (1) the *mouth;* (2) a small *buccal cavity;* (3) a muscular sucking *pharynx,* or esophagus, about $\frac{1}{2}$ inch long, that acts to draw in food; (4) a long narrow *intestine,* which is nonmuscular, composed of a single layer of tall endoderm cells that absorb the digested food, and covered externally by cuticle; and (5) a short *rectum* discharging through (6) the *anus.* No circulatory or respiratory organs are present. The inner part of each lateral line contains an *excretory canal,* both emptying through a minute midventral pore just behind the mouth. A *nerve ring* surrounds the esophagus; it connects to six short anterior nerves and to six posterior *nerve cords,* a larger dorsal and ventral cord each in the corresponding longitudinal line and others in the body wall, with various lateral branches and cross connectives. On the body surface are various papillae, probably sensory in function.

Each reproductive organ is a slender tube, closed at its inner end, of gradually increasing

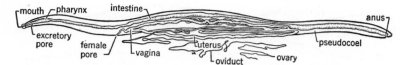

Fig. 20-3. *Ascaris.* Internal structure of a female.

diameter, coiled back and forth in the body space, and unattached save where connected to the genital pore. The gonad and reproductive duct are continuous. The **male reproductive system** is single; its parts are (1) the **testis** for sperm production; (2) the **vas deferens** for conduction; (3) the **seminal vesicle** for storing mature sperm; (4) the **ejaculatory duct** for ejecting sperm; and (5) a sac containing two **penial spicules,** which are inserted in the female's vulva to join the male and female during copulation. The **female reproductive system** is ≺-shaped; each branch is up to 125 cm. long and consists of (1) an **ovary,** (2) an **oviduct,** and (3) a **uterus.** The two uteri are joined in (4) a single short **vagina** opening at (5) the **vulva.**

20-3. Natural history. The adult ascaris lives as a parasite within the intestine of its host and has problems of existence somewhat different from those of a free-living animal. Locomotion and maintenance of position are accomplished chiefly by dorsoventral bendings of the body. The cuticle protects the living worm against the digestive juices of its host (antienzymes also may be a factor). Food is obtained from the semifluid materials in the host's intestine, being pumped in by the worm's muscular esophagus, and after digestion passes through its intestinal wall to be distributed by fluid in the body space to other tissues. Respiration is dependent upon the breakdown of glycogen within the worm's body, since the intestinal contents of its host contain little free oxygen. The sensory papillae probably are receptors for chemical and tactile stimuli.

20-4. Reproduction. Male and female worms copulate within the host's intestine. The eggs are fertilized in the oviducts of the female, and each (Fig. 20-6) becomes covered by a tough shell (measuring 45 to 75 by 35 to 50 μ). A large female may contain 27,000,000 eggs at one time

and lay 200,000 or more per day. The eggs pass out of the female, into the host's intestine, and leave with the feces. A period of development is necessary before they become infective for another host. In drought or cold they may lie dormant for many months, but in a warm, moist, shady site development requires 2 or 3 weeks. If such "embryonated" eggs (containing embryo worms) are swallowed by the proper host with food or water, they pass to the intestine. There the larvae (0.2 to 0.3 mm. long) hatch, burrow into veins or lymph vessels in the intestinal wall, travel through the heart, and on to pulmonary capillaries in the lungs, meanwhile growing in size. In a few days they break into the air passages and move via the trachea, esophagus, and stomach to the intestine again, where they grow to maturity.

No intermediate host is necessary to complete the life cycle (Fig. 20-4). Young pigs usually acquire larvae from infected soil in pig-

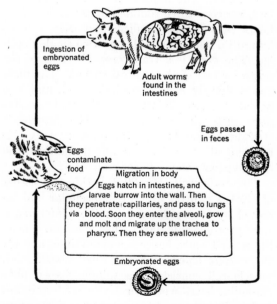

Fig. 20-4. *Ascaris.* Life cycle in the pig. (*From Koutz and Rebrassier, Ohio State University Press,* 1951.)

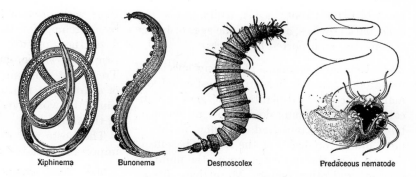

Fig. 20-5. Some free-living nematodes; all much enlarged. (*After Cobb*, 1915.)

Xiphinema   Bunonema   Desmoscolex   Predaceous nematode

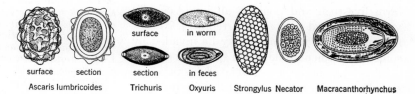

Fig. 20-6. Eggs of nematodes and an acanthocephalan (*Macracanthorhynchus*); all much enlarged. (*After H. B. Ward*, 1907.)

surface   section   surface   in worm   section   in feces

Ascaris lumbricoides   Trichuris   Oxyuris   Strongylus Necator   Macracanthorhynchus

yards or in dirt on the sow's udder when nursing. Adult pigs are rather immune to infection; therefore any worms they contain were probably acquired when young. Human infection with ascaris is not uncommon, and many persons in some rural localities are infected. Worms found in man and pigs are identical structurally, but differ physiologically in that infective eggs of the human ascaris do not ordinarily produce mature worms in pigs, and vice versa. Passage of many larvae through the lungs may cause local inflammation and even a pneumonia. Adult ascarids in the intestine may produce secretions toxic to the host, and the worms when numerous may obstruct the intestine. Worms sometimes migrate up to the mouth or nose, or even penetrate the intestinal wall and invade other organs, causing serious illness or death of the host. Some animals and people become sensitized or allergic to the secretions of ascarids.

20-5. Other nematodes. Many species, both parasitic and free-living, resemble *Ascaris* in general structure but differ in various details. Some parasitic forms have teeth, hooks, or cutting plates in the mouth for attachment and feeding; others that live on plant roots have a sharp hollow "spear" to puncture the cells and a muscular pharynx to withdraw cell sap. The cuticle on many free-living species bears minute bristles, spines, or transverse rows of scales that aid in crawling through soil. Some predatory nematodes have enlarged mouths margined with teeth or other projections that make them appear like "microscopic dragons" (Fig. 20-5). The orders of nematodes are diverse in structure of mouth and esophagus, with lesser differences in muscles, excretory organs, and reproductive structures. Males may have two, one, or no penial spicules, and some have the posterior end with an expanded caudal bursa to hold the female while mating. The vulva is variously located, and females of some species have a single ovary, oviduct, and uterus.

There is a great host of free-living nematodes, the life histories of which are practically unknown. They occur in moist soil and in some deserts, in the sand of ocean beaches, in fresh, stagnant, and salt waters, on the shores and bottoms of lakes and rivers, on the filter beds of waterworks, on mountain tops, in hot springs, and in polar seas and ice. The upper foot of an acre of alluvial soil may contain 3 billion nematodes, and the top 3 inches of beach sand a third as many. Other nematodes live in various

312   *Chapter 20*

parts of plants: roots, seeds, fruits, gums, leaf
axils, bark crevices, and galls; the eggs or larvae
of some are transported by insects.

20-6. Relations to man. The many species of
nematodes parasitic in man, domesticated animals, and cultivated plants are of great practical importance. Some do little or no damage,
but others cause impaired efficiency, unthriftiness, illness, or death of the host. The effects
depend upon the species of worm, the numbers
present, and other factors. More than 50 species are parasites of mankind. Others parasitize
farm livestock and poultry, all kinds of wild
vertebrates, and various invertebrates. Almost
any organ of a vertebrate may be invaded by
some kind of nematode. Each species is usually
confined to one or a few related hosts, occasionally invades others, and ordinarily occupies
a particular organ. Most parasitic nematodes
have a free-living egg or larval stage in soil or
water, and the filarial worms require an intermediate host. Occasionally a host contains enormous numbers, as a pint of stomach worms in
man, or 40,000 in a 50-pound mammal. Infec-

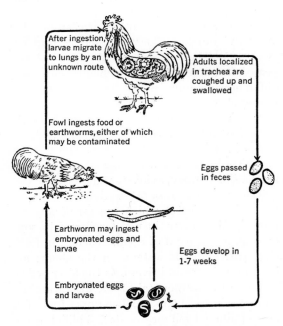

Fig. 20-7. Life cycle of the gapeworm, *Syngamus trachea. (From Koutz and Rebrassier, Ohio State University
Press, 1951.)*

After ingestion, larvae migrate to lungs by an unknown route

Adults localized in trachea are coughed up and swallowed

Fowl ingests food or earthworms, either of which may be contaminated

Eggs passed in feces

Earthworm may ingest embryonated eggs and larvae

Eggs develop in 1-7 weeks

Embryonated eggs and larvae

tions with intestinal worms can be diagnosed
by searching for the microscopic eggs in the
feces, those of most species being of characteristic size, shape, and structure (Fig. 20-6).
Treatment to eliminate nematodes requires use
of a drug, not too toxic for the host, that will
cause the worms to sicken and be carried out
in the feces.

The hosts and organs parasitized by some
important nematodes are as follows:

MAN. Small intestine: *Ancylostoma duodenale* and
Necator americanus, the hookworms; *Ascaris lumbricoides.* Caecum and appendix: *Trichuris (Trichocephalus) trichiura,* whipworm. Large intestine: *Enterobius
vermicularis,* pinworm, especially in children.
HORSE. Stomach: *Habronema megastoma.* Small intestine: *Parascaris equorum (= Ascaris megalocephala).*
Large intestine: *Oxyuris equi.* Caecum and large intestine: *Strongylus vulgaris.*
SHEEP. Air passages: *Dictyocaulus filaria,* lung thread-
worm. Stomach: *Haemonchus contortus; Trichostrongylus
axei.* Small intestine: *Bunostomum trigonocephalum.*
Large intestine: *Oesophagostomum columbianum,* nodu-
lar worm.
PIG. Air passages: *Metastrongylus apri,* and others.
Stomach: *Hyostrongylus rubidus.* Small intestine: *Ascaris lumbricoides.* Large intestine: *Oesophagostomum
dentatum.*
DOG. Small intestine: *Ancylostoma caninum,* hookworm; *Toxocara canis.* Caecum: *Trichuris vulpis,* whipworm.
CHICKEN. Air passages: *Syngamus trachea,* gapeworm
(Fig. 20-7). Gizzard: *Cheilospiura (Acuaria) hamulosa.*
Small intestine: *Ascaridea galli; Capillaria columbae.*
Caecum: *Heterakis gallinae,* caecum worm (also in turkey, where it carries the protozoan, *Histomonas mele-
agridis,* which causes the disease known as "blackhead").

20-7. Root nematodes. Many species of minute
to microscopic nematodes live in or about the
roots of plants. Some, such as the sugar beet
nematode, *Heterodera schachtii,* are restricted to
one or a few kinds of plants, but others are less
specialized. The common garden nematode, *H.
radicicola* or *marioni,* has been reported in over
1,000 varieties of plants and commonly infests
over 75 garden and field crops, fruit and shade
trees, shrubs and weeds (Fig. 20-8). Its eggs
are deposited in roots or soil, and the young
upon hatching penetrate rootlets to feed on the
tissues within. The roots react by forming small
galls of scar tissue—the "root knots"—about
the worms. The adult male is slender (1.2 to
1.5 mm. long), and the female becomes a whit-

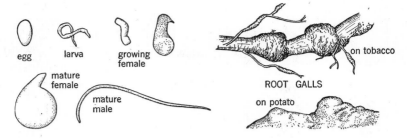

Fig. 20-8. The root knot nematode, *Heterodera marioni.* Eggs, larvae, and adults, all greatly enlarged. Root galls produced by the worms, about natural size. (*After Tyler,* 1933.)

egg   larva   growing female

mature female   mature male

ROOT GALLS

on tobacco

on potato

ish teardrop-like object (0.8 by 0.5 mm.) with a swollen body producing 500 to 1,000 eggs. Fertilization may occur but is unnecessary. The eggs are laid in a yellow gelatinous secretion. The life cycle requires nearly 3 months at 58°F. but less than a month in soil at 81°F. Several generations per year are thus possible in the warm southern and western states. The larvae within galls can withstand some drying and survive at 32°F. but die at lower temperatures. Root knot causes weakening or death of the plant, and soil infested with these worms often fails to yield profitable crops. The nematodes are carried into clean soils with plants, soil, manure, farm implements, or even irrigation water from infested lands. Once established, they are difficult to eradicate. Plant breeders have developed selected strains of some economic plants that are resistant to root nematodes. Certain chemicals (D-D, methyl bromide, etc.) are used to reduce the worms in infested soils.

20-8. Hookworm. This is one of the scourges of mankind in all moist tropical and subtropical regions. In populations of low economic level that go barefooted and use no sanitary toilets, from 50 to 95 per cent may be infected, and workmen in mines, tunnels, and brickyards often harbor hookworms. *Ancylostoma duodenale* and *Necator americanus* are both common in man, the latter especially in the United States.

The adult worm is 8 to 13 mm. long and has cutting plates or teeth in its mouth (Fig. 20-9). It attaches to the inner wall of the small intestine, where blood, lymph, and bits of mucous membrane are drawn into the worm's gut by action of the pumping pharynx. Feeding is aided by production of a secretion that prevents coagulation of the host's blood. The worm may pump more blood than it digests, and the wound it makes may bleed after the worm has moved elsewhere; the host, in consequence, loses blood into the intestine and becomes anemic.

Hookworms mate in the host's intestine, and each female produces several thousand fertile eggs daily, which pass out with the feces. In moist warm shady places these hatch in 24 to 48 hours (Fig. 20-10); the larvae feed on excre-

Fig. 20-9. Hookworms. *A.* Mouth of *Ancylostoma duodenale* in anterior view, showing the teeth. *B. Ancylostoma caninum* attached to intestinal wall in dog. Both enlarged. (*After Stiles; and Loess.*)

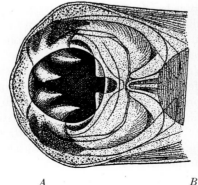

A

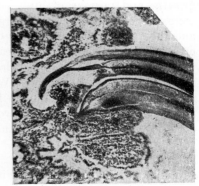

B

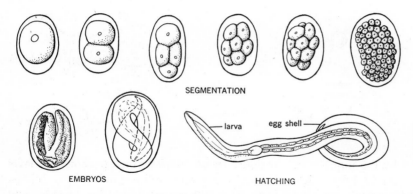

SEGMENTATION

EMBRYOS   HATCHING

Fig. 20-10. Development of the hookworm, *Ancylostoma duodenale.* (*After Stiles*, 1902.)

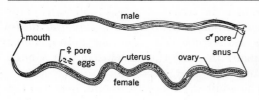

larva encysted in muscle

Fig. 20-11. The trichina worm, *Trichinella spiralis;* enlarged. Adults at left.

ment or other organic debris in the soil, later to undergo two molts. When about 0.5 mm. long, they become infective for man. Entry is usually by burrowing through the soft skin on the sides of the foot, causing "ground itch." The larvae travel in blood and lymph vessels, passing through the heart and to the lungs, from capillaries to air cavities, and thence up the trachea into the esophagus and to the intestine. With two further molts they soon mature and may live some months or even several years. Continued reinvasion of the host maintains the infection.

Children harboring a hundred or more hookworms are retarded in physical and mental growth, and persons of all ages with many worms become anemic; their energy is lessened, and their susceptibility to other diseases is increased. Treatment under medical supervision with tetrachlorethylene or hexylresorcinol will rid a person of these parasites. Wearing shoes and sanitary disposal of human feces prevent infection. Other species of hookworms occur in dogs, foxes, cats, cattle, sheep, and pigs.

20-9. Trichina worm. *Trichinella spiralis* occurs as a minute living larva encysted in the striated muscles (Fig. 20-11) of pigs, house rats, and

man, also in cats, dogs, and black bears. If an individual of any of these eats the flesh of another containing such larvae, the cysts are dissolved by the digestive juices and the larvae are liberated in the intestine of the new host. In about 2 days they become sexually mature and mate; male worms are then about 1.5 mm. long and females 3 to 4 mm. The females burrow into the intestinal wall to live for some time, each producing up to 1,500 living larvae about 0.1 mm. long. These enter lymph spaces, are carried in the blood stream, and burrow into skeletal muscles. They grow to about 1.0 mm. long, then coil up and become enclosed in cysts, which later may be calcified. Such larvae cannot mature unless the flesh containing them is eaten by another susceptible mammal, but they may live for months or years in man.

Mild infections cause no particular symptoms, and some encysted trichinae occur in about 16 per cent of people in the United States. Heavy infections cause the disease **trichinosis,** which may be severe and even fatal. Intestinal disturbances and abdominal pain occur first; with spread of the larvae there is fever, the muscles become swollen, hard, and painful, and there may be difficulty in swallowing and breathing. No specific treatment is

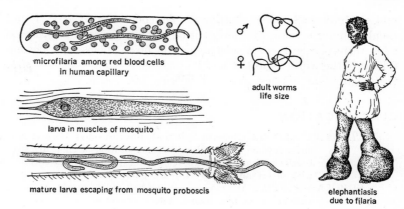

microfilaria among red blood cells
in human capillary

larva in muscles of mosquito

mature larva escaping from mosquito proboscis

adult worms
life size

elephantiasis
due to filaria

Fig. 20-12. Stages in the life cycle of the filaria worm, *Wuchereria bancrofti*. (*After Francis; Fulleborn; and Sambon.*)

known, and recovery is slow. Hogs, rats, and the other mammals become infected by eating slaughterhouse scraps, garbage, or animal carcasses that contain encysted larvae. Man receives infection by eating pork (occasionally bear meat) containing the microscopic cysts. Examination of pork in slaughterhouses for trichinae is economically impractical, and some infections may be missed. The only protection is to *cook pork thoroughly*, by heating all parts to at least 137°F. Pink color in freshly roasted pork is evidence of inadequate cooking. Salami, headcheese, and other pork products may be dangerous unless thoroughly cooked. Refrigeration at −10°F. for 3 days will usually kill all larvae, but cooking is safer.

20-10. Filarial worms. The filariae of man and various vertebrates are nematodes that require an intermediate arthropod host to complete the life cycle. One of these is *Wuchereria bancrofti* (Fig. 20-12), a human parasite in all warm regions of the world, formerly present about Charleston, S.C., where it was probably introduced with Negro slaves. The minute larvae, or microfilariae, are about 0.2 mm. long. They live by day chiefly in large blood vessels, passing at night to small vessels in the skin, but cause no trouble even if numerous. If taken up by certain kinds of nocturnal mosquitoes, the larvae pass to the insect's stomach, then to the thoracic muscles, undergo metamorphosis, and when about 1.4 mm. long move into the proboscis. At the mosquito's next meal, the larvae

crawl onto and presumably puncture the human skin, pass into lymph vessels, coil up in lymph glands, and later mature. The adult female grows to 80 mm. long, the male 40 mm., but neither is over 0.3 mm. in diameter. If both sexes are present, they mate, and each female produces perhaps 1,000 microfilariae. Adults obstruct the lymph circulation, and if present in numbers may, after some years, cause the disease **elephantiasis,** in which the limbs or other parts grow to enormous size. An amazing biological adjustment occurs in some localities where the microfilariae inhabit the deeper circulation by night and superficial vessels by day and are transferred by diurnal mosquitoes.

20-11. Guinea worm. *Dracunculus medinensis,* possibly the Biblical "fiery serpent" (Num. 21:6), is a human parasite in India, Arabia, Africa, South America, and the West Indies. It occurs in several Old World mammals and has been found in dogs, foxes, raccoons, and mink in the United States but not in man. The larvae occur in water fleas (*Cyclops*) which may be swallowed by the final host in drinking water. Upon reaching the host's stomach the larvae escape and burrow to subcutaneous tissues, occasionally to the heart or brain meninges. There a year or less of growth yields a female up to 1,200 mm. long by 1 or 2 mm. in diameter (males are practically unknown). The mature gravid female migrates, usually to the host's lower leg or ankle where an ulcer forms. Upon immersion of the limb in water, larvae escape to seek the intermediate host. Native peoples commonly remove a worm by winding it on a stick, a few turns per day; severe poisoning of the host follows if the worm is broken and its body contents enter the tissues. Another species (*D.*

ophidensis), found in Michigan, has the larval stage in *Cyclops viridis*, may occur in frog tadpoles, and becomes adult in the garter snake, *Thammophis sirtalis*, females growing to 250 mm. long.

CLASSIFICATION

CLASS NEMATODA (Nemathelminthes). ROUNDWORMS. Body slender, cylindrical, often tapered toward ends; covered with cuticle; no segmentation or cilia; digestive tract complete, straight; no proboscis; no circular muscles; body space (pseudocoel) usually not lined; sexes usually separate; male with cloaca, and usually 1 or 2 copulatory spicules; no cloaca in female; 12,000 species.

SUBCLASS 1. APHASMIDIA. No phasmids (caudal sensory organs); amphids (anterior sensory organs) various, rarely pore-like; excretory system often reduced or none; coelomocytes and mesenterial tissue well developed; males usually lack caudal alae.

Order 1. Chromadorida. Esophagus of 3 regions and not elongate; esophageal glands never duplicate, multinucleate, or opening anteriorly in esophagus.

SUBORDER 1. MONHYSTERINA. Esophago-intestinal valve not triradiate or vertically flattened; teeth none, 1 or 3 small, or 6 outward-acting; fresh or salt waters. *Monhystera, Plectus, Cylindrolaimus.*

SUBORDER 2. CHROMADORINA. Esophago-intestinal valve triradiate or vertically flattened; teeth 1 large, or 6 inward-acting, or 3 jaws; amphids spiral, circular, etc.; in salt and fresh waters. *Chromadora, Cyatholaimus, Desmoscolex.*

Order 2. Enoplida. Esophagus of 2 parts (anterior muscular, posterior glandular), often long, cylindrical or conoidal; amphids pocket-like, elongate, or pore-like.

SUBORDER 1. ENOPLINA. Intestine lacks muscles; no caudal sucker or stylet; male with 2 spicules; free-living in salt, brackish, or fresh waters or in soil. *Enoplus, Trilobus.*

SUBORDER 2. DORYLAIMINA (Trichurata). Intestine lacks muscles; no caudal sucker or glands; male with 2, 1, or no spicules. *Dorylaimus,* in soil and fresh or brackish water; *Trichinella spiralis; Trichuris (Trichocephalus) trichocephala,* whipworm; *Capillaria,* hair-like in liver, gut, and elsewhere in vertebrates; *Mermis,* larvae in insects, adults free-living but do not feed.

SUBORDER 3. DIOCTOPHYMATINA. Intestine with 4 rows of muscles; male with caudal sucker and 1 spicule. *Dioctophyma renale,* giant nematode, male to 450 mm. long, female to 900 by 15 mm., in body cavity of mammals; *Hystrichis,* in intestine of birds.

SUBCLASS 2. PHASMIDEA. With phasmids; amphids pore-like; excretory system with paired lateral canals; coelomocytes 4 to 6, mesenterial tissue scant; no caudal or lateral hypodermal glands.

Order 1. Rhabditida. Esophagus of 3 regions, especially in larvae.

SUBORDER 1. RHABDITINA. Lips 6, 3, 2, or 0; vagina short, transverse; caudal alae, if present, with papillae; no stylet; free-living and saprophagous in soil, or parasitic in plants or animals. *Rhabditis,* some free-living in soil, others parasitic; *Strongyloides, Rhabdias,* alternate generations of parasitic females and of free-living males and females.

SUBORDER 2. TYLENCHINA. Lips 8, 6, or 0; stylet present; lateral excretory canals only on 1 side; vagina short, usually transverse; feed on fluids of living cells or in body spaces of insects. *Tylenchus,* meadow nematode; *Heterodera,* root nematode (Fig. 20-8), in roots; *Anguina,* wheat eelworm; *Chondronema,* in insects.

SUBORDER 3. STRONGYLINA. Lips 6, 3, or 0, small; uterus heavily muscular, with ovejector; bursa with rays; parasitic in land vertebrates. *Oesophagostomum; Syngamus trachea,* gapeworm; *Ancylostoma, Necator,* hookworms; *Trichostrongylus,* hairworm; *Haemonchus,* stomachworm; *Metastrongylus,* lungworm.

SUBORDER 4. ASCARIDINA. Lips usually 3 large, or 6 small, or none; some with 2 lateral jaws; vagina and posterior uterus muscular; caudal alae with papillae (no muscles or rays); parasitic in land snails, insects, and vertebrates. *Ascaris; Enterobius,* pinworm; *Toxocara, Heterakis, Thelastoma.*

Order 2. Spirurida. Esophagus of 2 regions, anterior muscular and posterior glandular; adults in gut or tissues of vertebrates.

SUBORDER 1. SPIRURINA. Esophageal glands multinucleate; larval phasmids pore-like; intermediate stages usually in insects. *Gongylonema, Thelazia, Wuchereria, Filaria, Onchocerca; Loa,* "eyeworm"; *Tetrameres.*

SUBORDER 2. CAMALLANINA. Esophageal glands uninucleate; phasmids in larvae large, pocket-like; copepods are intermediate hosts. *Dracunculus medinensis*, Guinea worm; *Camallanus*, in turtles and fish.

REFERENCES

(*See works by Brumpt; Chandler; Craig and Faust; Faust; Monnig; Neveu-Lemaire; and Sprehn cited in References to Chap.* 19)

BAYLIS, H. A., and R. DAUBNEY. 1926. A synopsis of the families and genera of Nematoda. London, British Museum. xxxvi + 277 pp.

CHITWOOD, B. G., and OTHERS. 1937–   . An introduction to nematology. Baltimore, Monumental Publishing Co. 371 pp., 202 figs. 1950. Sec. 1, Anatomy. Rev. ed. viii + 213 pp., 145 figs. Technical; incomplete.

FILIPJEV, I. N., and J. H. SCHUURMANS STEKHOVEN, Jr. 1941. A manual of agricultural helminthology [nematology]. Leiden, Netherlands, E. J. Brill, N.V. xv + 878 pp., 460 figs.

GOODEY, T. 1933. Plant parasitic nematodes. New York, E. P. Dutton & Co., Inc. xx + 306 pp., illus.

————. 1951. Soil and freshwater nematodes. London, Methuen & Co., Ltd. xxvi + 390 pp., 190 figs.

HYMAN, L. H. 1951. Nematoda. *In* The invertebrates. New York, McGraw-Hill Book Co., Inc. Vol. 3, pp. 197–455, figs. 93–200.

KÜKENTHAL, W., and OTHERS. 1928–34. Handbuch der Zoologie. Berlin, Walter De Gruyter & Co. NEMATODA, vol. 2, pt. 1, sec. 4, pp. 249–402, figs. 267–426.

YORKE, W., and P. A. MAPLESTONE. 1926. The nematode parasites of vertebrates. Philadelphia, The Blakiston Co. xi + 536 pp., 307 figs.

21 MISCELLANEOUS PHYLA AND GROUPS

MESOZOA
CTENOPHORA
NEMERTINEA
ENTOPROCTA
ROTIFERA
GASTROTRICHA
KINORHYNCHA
NEMATOMORPHA
ACANTHOCEPHALA

BRYOZOA
BRACHIOPODA
PHORONIDEA
CHAETOGNATHA
SIPUNCULOIDEA
PRIAPULOIDEA
ECHIUROIDEA
BRACHIATA

Besides the major phyla described in other chapters, there are several additional groups of multicellular animals. While not often studied by beginners in zoology, they are described here to complete the account of the Animal Kingdom. All these animals are aquatic, in salt or fresh waters; some are abundant and of wide occurrence, and others uncommon.[1]

The status of several groups is uncertain, as are the relationships of most of them. Some have long been recognized as separate phyla, and others have been attached as special classes in certain well-established phyla. Several authorities now recognize a Phylum ASCHELMINTHES to include as classes the ROTIFERA, GASTROTRICHA, KINORHYNCHA, NEMATODA (Chap. 20), NEMATOMORPHA, and ACANTHOCEPHALA. Three other groups, the SIPUNCULOIDEA, PRIAPULOIDEA, and ECHIUROIDEA, often have been brought together as a Class GEPHYREA in the Phylum ANNELIDA; but each warrants being placed in a separate phylum.

[1] Some references in this chapter are to books more fully cited in the list at the end of Chap. 1.

The existence of small phyla is a logical consequence of evolution—various groups have originated and flourished in past geological time. Some died out completely, while others persist with smaller representation in Recent time. The bryozoans and brachiopods abounded in Paleozoic seas over 200,000,000 years ago and now are less abundant. The acanthocephs became highly modified for a parasitic life. Soft-bodied forms, such as rotifers, phoronids, or chaetognaths, have no fossil record to suggest their relationships to other existing classes or phyla. Studies in morphology and embryology have, as yet, failed to indicate the relative position, high or low, for many of these groups.

PHYLUM MESOZOA

21-1. The MESOZOA (Gr. *mesos*, middle + *zoön*, animal) are minute worm-like solid organisms with the simplest structure of any multicellular animals. *Dicyema* (Fig. 21-1), a common parasite in the nephridia of octopuses and squids, is up to 8 mm. long, composed of an outer layer of about 25 (16 to 42) ciliated somatic cells surrounding one or more long axial reproductive cells. The anterior 8 or 9 cells form a polar cap. Repeated fission of the axial cell yields cells (agametes, with no observed maturation) that develop asexually into new individuals and then escape from the parent; there is also a complex type of sexual reproduction. *Rhopalura* is a rare

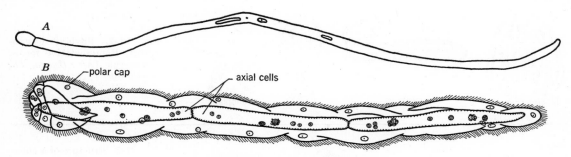

Fig. 21-1. Phylum MESOZOA. *Dicyema. A.* Outline of full-grown individual, 3 mm. long. *B.* Young nematogen stage, 0.4 mm. (*Adapted from McConnaughey*, 1949.)

parasite in tissues and cavities of flatworms, nemerteans, brittle stars, annelids, and a clam. About 43 species of mesozoans are known.

The MESOZOA resemble some colonial protozoans in having external cilia through much of the life cycle, in having intracellular digestion by the external cells, and in having special internal reproductive cells (as in *Volvox*). Their two cell layers are not comparable with the ectoderm and endoderm of METAZOA, and they have no internal digestive cavity. Either they are intermediate between unicellular and multicellular animals or else degenerate forms, possibly related to the PLATYHELMINTHES.

CLASSIFICATION

PHYLUM MESOZOA (see above).
> **Order 1. Dicyema.** Usual form (nematogen) to 8 mm. long; one internal cell. *Dicyema.*
> **Order 2. Orthonectida.** Sexual forms under 1 mm. long; an inner cell mass. *Rhopalura.*

References. HYMAN, L. H. 1940. Mesozoa. *In* The invertebrates. Vol. 1, pp. 233–247, figs. 68–71. McCONNAUGHEY, B. H. 1949. Mesozoa of the Family Dicyemidae from California. *University of California Publications in Zoology*, vol. 55, pp. 1–34, 7 pls. 1951. The life cycle of the Dicyemid Mesozoa. *Ibid.*, pp. 295–335, 13 figs.

PHYLUM CTENOPHORA. CTENOPHORES

21-2. The Phylum CTENOPHORA (Gr. *ktenos*, comb + *phoros*, bearing) comprises about 80 species of free-swimming marine animals with transparent gelatinous bodies. They are often called "comb jellies" because of the comb-like plates on the body; those with lengthwise ridges are known as "sea walnuts." Ctenophores show some resemblance to jellyfishes and formerly were classified with the coelenterates, but they are distinct in structure and biology (Fig. 21-2).

21-3. Characteristics. (1) Symmetry biradial (radial + bilateral), on an oral-aboral axis; 3 germ layers, with much mesoglea; no segmentation; (2) body more or less spherical (flat in some); usually with 8 external rows of comb plates; no nematocysts; (3) digestive system with mouth, "pharynx," stomach, and branched canals; (4) nervous system diffuse, with an aboral sense organ (statocyst); (5) sexes united; reproductive cells formed from endoderm in digestive canals; development direct; no asexual development or alternation of generations.

Ctenophores resemble coelenterates in having (1) basic radial symmetry; (2) parts arranged on an oral-aboral axis; (3) a gastrovascular cavity with branches; (4) gelatinous mesoglea; (5) no internal spaces except the digestive system; and (6) no other organ systems. They differ in possessing (1) eight rows of comb plates; (2) mesenchymal or mesodermal muscles; (3) higher organization of the digestive system; (4) an aboral sensory region; and (5) no nematocysts. The eight-part system of comb plates (with evidence for eight-part distribution of nervous elements) is, to some biologists, a foreshadow of the eight nerve strands in certain flatworms.

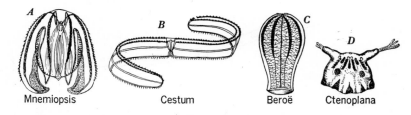

Fig. **21-2.** Phylum Cteno-phora. Representative forms; not to scale. (*After Hyman, The invertebrates.*)

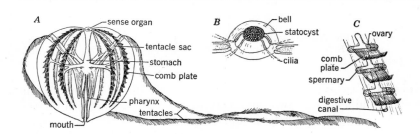

Fig. **21-3.** Structure of a cteno-phore. *A. Pleurobrachia*, entire specimen. *B*. Sense organ. (*Both after Hyman, The invertebrates.*) *C*. Reproductive cells in diges-tive canals under comb plates. (*From Bourne in Lankester, Treatise on zoology, A. & C. Black, Ltd.*)

21-4. Structure. *Pleurobrachia* is a common ctenophore along North American coasts (Fig. 21-3). Its highly transparent body is about ¾ inch in diameter and nearly spherical. The **mouth** is at the larger or oral end, and a **sense organ** at the opposite, or aboral end; these establish the radial axis. Eight equally spaced **comb plates** extend as meridians from pole to pole. Each plate is a slight ridge, bearing a succession of small transverse paddles or combs, formed of fused cilia. In life, these combs beat with quick strokes toward the aboral end, and a wave of beats progresses along each row from aboral to oral end. This propels the ctenophore with the mouth end forward. Near the aboral end, on opposite sides, are two blind sacs from each of which a long flexible **tentacle** protrudes. The tentacle is solid and contains muscle fibers; it may be trailed out to about 6 inches in length or contracted, but does not assist in locomotion. Its surface is covered with "lasso" or **glue cells** (colloblasts) that secrete an adhesive material to entangle small animals, which are then conveyed to the mouth. The position of the tentacles and some features of the digestive tract establish bilateral symmetry.

The **mouth** leads into the **pharynx** (stomodeum) where digestion begins and is extracellular. Beyond is the **stomach,** from which small **digestive canals** branch in definite pattern to beneath the comb plates, tentacle sacs, and elsewhere. The system is gastrovascular, serving for both the digestion and the distribution of food. From the stomach a canal runs aborally and gives off four branches, two of which open by "excretory pores" on opposite sides of the sense organ. Undigested wastes pass out through either the mouth or these pores.

The exterior surface, mouth, pharynx, and tentacles are covered with thin ciliated **epidermis,** and the stomach and canals are lined by ciliated **gastrodermis.** Gelatinous **mesoglea** fills all spaces between body structures and contains scattered muscle fibers, connective tissue cells, and amoebocytes of mesodermal origin. The animal is thus triploblastic.

The **sense organ** contains four elongated tufts of cilia that support a small rounded **statolith** of calcareous material, the whole in a covering like a bell jar. It is concerned in orientation with respect to gravity and in coordinating the beating of the comb plates. Beneath each comb plate is a nerve strand.

21-5. Natural history. Ctenophores abound in warm seas, and some occur in temperate or Arctic regions. They are mostly in surface waters, but a few live at various depths, even to 10,000 feet. They rest vertically in the water and can swim only feebly, so that currents or tides may concentrate them in large numbers. In the dark they emit a luminescence (light) from beneath the comb plates. Their food is of animals, including larvae of mollusks and crustaceans, fish eggs, and small fishes; digestion is rapid. Over oyster beds at spawning time they may consume numbers of oyster larvae. Ctenophores are eaten by some marine animals.

Ctenophores are monoecious, both eggs and sperm being produced by the endodermal lining in digestive canals beneath the comb plates. Mature sex cells pass out the mouth, fertilization occurs in the water, and development is usually direct to the adult form. Cleavage is determinate, the fate of parts of the blastula being determined so early that experimentally separated blastomeres yield only fractional embryos.

CLASSIFICATION

PHYLUM CTENOPHORA (see Characteristics).

> *CLASS 1. TENTACULA.* With tentacles.
>> **Order 1. Cydippida.** Body rounded; tentacles branched and retractile into sheaths. *Pleurobrachia; Hormiphora.*
>> **Order 2. Lobata.** Body laterally compressed; two large oral lobes; tentacles without sheaths. *Bolinopsis; Mnemiopsis leidyi,* Atlantic coast.
>> **Order 3. Cestida.** Body elongate, ribbon-like, compressed in plane of tentacles. *Cestum veneris,* Venus's girdle, to over 3 feet long and 2 inches wide, in tropical seas, travels by sinuous movements.
>> **Order 4. Platyctenea.** Body compressed on oral-aboral axis, to flattened creeping form, greatly modified. *Gastrodes,* early larva parasitic in tunicates (*Salpa*); *Coeloplana; Ctenoplana.*
> *CLASS 2. NUDA.* No tentacles. Body thimble-shaped; mouth wide, pharynx very large. *Beroë,* to 8 inches tall, often pink-colored, in colder waters.

References. HYMAN, LIBBIE H. 1940. Ctenophora. *In* The invertebrates. Vol. 1, pp. 662–696, figs. 209–221. Best recent account. MAYER, A. G. 1912. Ctenophores of the Atlantic coast of North America. *Carnegie Institution of Washington Pub.* No. 162, 58 pp., 17 pls., 12 figs.

PHYLUM NEMERTINEA. RIBBON WORMS

21-6. These are slender worms with soft, flat, and unsegmented bodies, capable of great elongation and contraction. A few are only 5 mm. long, many are a few inches in length, and one species may stretch to 80 feet. The 500 species are variously red, brown, yellow, green, or white, some solidly colored and others striped or cross-banded. Most nemerteans are marine, living closely coiled beneath stones, among algae, or in burrows between the tides, but some inhabit deep water. The genus *Prostoma* lives in fresh waters, the tropical *Geonemertes* in moist earth, *Malacobdella* in the mantle cavities of bivalve mollusks, and *Carcinonemertes* among the gills or egg masses of certain crabs.

21-7. Characteristics. (1) Symmetry bilateral, 3 germ layers; (2) body slender, soft, highly contractile, and unsegmented; (3) an eversible proboscis; (4) digestive tract straight and complete; (5) no coelom or respiratory organs; body spaces filled with parenchyma; (6) 3 longitudinal blood vessels, 2 lateral excretory canals, branched, with flame cells; (7) nervous system with paired anterior ganglia and a pair of lateral longitudinal nerves, some species also with middorsal and midventral nerve trunks; (8) sexes separate, with multiple pairs of gonads, and development direct or through a pilidium larva; asexual reproduction by fragmentation.

The NEMERTINEA (Rhynchocoela) are commonly placed near or with the PLATYHELMINTHES because of the character of the integument and nervous system, presence of flame cells, and lack of external segmentation or a coelom; they differ from flatworms in having a complete digestive tract and simplified reproductive system, and usually being dioecious. Some features parallel those of hemichordates and chordates—the nemertean dorsal nerve resembles the vertebrate spinal cord, the lateral nerves are placed like the lateral line nerves of fishes, the cephalic ganglia like the brain of vertebrates, the transverse nerves compare with spinal nerves, and the proboscis sheath suggests the notochord.

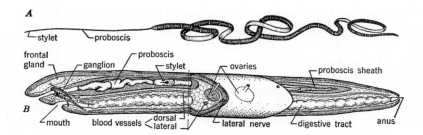

Fig. 21-4. Phylum NEMER-TINEA. *A.* External form with proboscis extended. *B.* Internal structure, diagrammatic. Left side removed except for part at middle of body and proboscis retracted into sheath.

21-8. Structure and natural history (Fig. 21-4). The soft *epidermis* is of columnar cells, ciliated, mucous, sensory, and others; beneath this are muscles, both circular and longitudinal. Loco-motion is by action of the external cilia and the muscles. At the anterior end, above the mouth, is a pore through which the soft *proboscis* may be extended far out or completely withdrawn, like inverting the finger of a glove; the probos-cis is contained in a *sheath* inside the body. It is thought to serve for offense and defense, be-ing armed with stylets or spines in some spe-cies. The *digestive tract* is a ciliated tube, ex-tending the entire length of the body, having both a mouth and an anus, and sometimes also paired lateral caeca; the food is of other ani-mals, both living and dead. The *circulatory sys-tem* includes a pair of lengthwise lateral vessels and usually a middorsal vessel, with cross con-nections at the head and about the digestive tract (Fig. 6-1). The blood is either red or color-less and circulates back and forth as a result of movements of the body. *Respiration* is by dif-fusion through the body wall. The *excretory system* comprises a pair of lateral canals with numerous branches, some with flame cells that lie close to blood vessels. There is no true body cavity, spaces between the body wall and in-ternal organs being filled with gelatinous paren-chyma. The *nervous system* includes two large cerebral ganglia in the head region, with cross connectives and with anterior nerves, especially to the proboscis. A large lateral nerve extends along each side of the body, with ganglion cells and cross connectives; some species have also a middorsal and a midventral nerve trunk with nerves under the epidermis or among the mus-cles. The *sense organs* include few to many ocelli and receptors in the integument of the head and along the sides of the body.

The sexes are usually separate (a few species are monoecious, some protandric). The *repro-ductive system* consists of pairs of simple sacs or multiple pairs of gonads between the intesti-nal pouches, developed within the parenchyma and opening directly on the body surface when the eggs or sperm are mature. Certain nemer-teans (LINEIDAE) have a free-swimming (pilid-ium) larval stage; development in others is direct, and some are viviparous. The adults have great powers of regeneration, and some reproduce regularly during warm weather by fragmentation of the body, each piece then growing into a complete worm.

CLASSIFICATION

PHYLUM NEMERTINEA (or Rhynchocoela; see Characteristics).
    CLASS 1. *ANOPLA.* Proboscis unarmed; mouth posterior to brain; nervous system under epidermis or among muscles.
        Order 1. Palaeonemertini. Muscles of body wall in 2 or 3 layers (innermost circular); dermis gelatinous. *Tubulanus.*
        Order 2. Heteronemertini. Muscles of body wall in 3 layers (innermost longitudinal); dermis fibrous. *Lineus, Cerebratulus.*
    CLASS 2. *ENOPLA.* Proboscis may be armed; mouth anterior to brain; nervous system inside muscles of body wall.

Order 3. Hoplonemertini. Proboscis with 1 or more stylets; intestine straight with paired diverticula. *Paranemertes; Carcinonemertes*, commensal on gills and eggs of crabs; *Prostoma*, in fresh waters; *Geonemertes*, terrestrial on shores; *Pelagonemertes*, in North Atlantic at depths of 1,000 meters or more.

Order 4. Bdellonemertini. Proboscis unarmed; intestine sinuous, no diverticula. *Malacobdella*, in mantle cavity of marine clams.

References. Böhmig, L. 1929. Nemertini. *In* W. Kükenthal and others, Handbuch der Zoologie. Vol. 2, pt. 1, sec. 3, pp. 1–110, figs. 1–75. Coe, W. R. 1935. Nemertea. *In* H. S. Pratt, Manual of the common invertebrate animals. pp. 230–241, figs. 325–335. Hyman, L. H. 1951. Rhynchocoela. *In* The invertebrates. Vol. 2, pp. 459–531, figs. 174–208.

PHYLUM ENTOPROCTA

21-9. The Entoprocta (Kamptozoa) are small creatures—microscopic to 5 mm. tall—solitary or colonial, that live attached to seaweed or other objects in shallow coastal waters. The body is a vase-like *calyx,* slightly flattened laterally, rimmed by a circle of ciliated *tentacles;* the base of the calyx joins a *stalk* serving for attachment. In some species the lower end of the stalk grows lateral extensions (stolons) attaching to the substrate. These animals formerly were included among the Bryozoa, which they resemble superficially, but their fundamental structure is quite different.

21-10. Characteristics. (1) Symmetry bilateral, no segmentation, 3 germ layers; (2) individual zooids minute, each with calyx, stalk, and enlarged base; (3) edge of retractile circular calyx surrounded by one row of many slender, active, ciliated tentacles; (4) both mouth and anus open within circle of tentacles; (5) digestive tract U-shaped, complete, ciliated, with esophagus, stomach, and rectum; (6) space within body a pseudocoel filled with gelatinous parenchyma; (7) retractor muscles present; (8) no circulatory or respiratory organs; (9) one pair of protonephridia for excretion; (10) nerve ganglia present; (11) monoecious or sexes separate, 2 gonads, with ducts; (12) eggs and larvae develop in ovary, then larvae swim freely in water before attaching to grow; (13) calyx often lost and regenerated from stalk.

Of the 60 or more species, *Urnatella gracilis*, usually found in pairs, is the only fresh-water form, living on the undersides of stones in running waters of the eastern and central states and in Lake Erie. *Loxosomella* and *Loxosoma* grow from buds that separate so each individual is distinct; large numbers live as commensals on marine annelid worms and less often on sponges or ascidians. Common colonial types are *Pedicellina* and *Barentsia*, which grow on shells or algae in shallow sea water. Entoprocts are ciliary feeders on microscopic animals and organic debris in the water.

CLASSIFICATION

PHYLUM ENTOPROCTA (see Characteristics).

Loxosomatidae. Solitary, stalk attached by simple adhesive disc; on sponges, polychaetes, ascidians, and other animals. *Loxosoma, Loxocalyx.*

Pedicellinidae. Colonial, with basal stolons. *Pedicellina, Barentsia.*

Urnatellidae. Small colony from a basal plate. One genus, *Urnatella*, fresh water.

References. Cori, C. J. 1930. Kamptozoa (Bryozoa entoprocta). *In* W. Kükenthal and others, Handbuch der Zoologie. Vol. 2, pt. 1, sec. 5, pp. 1–64, figs. 1–76. Hyman, L. H. 1951. Entoprocta. *In* The invertebrates. Vol. 3, pp. 521–554, figs. 209–223.

complete and usually straight, the anus posterior, and the space inside the body is a pseudocoel (Chap. 20, Nematoda). Except for the rotifers, none has anterior cilia.

PHYLUM ASCHELMINTHES

This phylum includes several groups of animals that are mostly of small to microscopic size and slender in form. The digestive tract is

CLASS ROTIFERA
Rotifers, or "Wheel Animalcules"

21-11. The rotifers are minute to microscopic (under 1 mm. long), attractive in form and

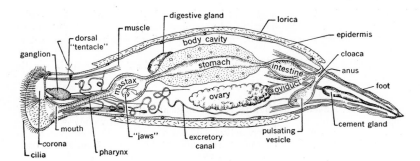

Fig. 21-5. Phylum Aschelmin-thes, Class Rotifera. Structure of a female rotifer, in section from the left side; much enlarged. (*After Delage and Herouard.*)

color, active in movements, and favorites of amateur microscopists. They abound in fresh-water lakes, ponds, and quiet streams, in muddy wayside ditches and eaves troughs, in street gutters and barnyard puddles, and occur even in the leaf axils of mosses. Most of the 1,300 species are free-living, but some are fixed in protective tubes, a few are external or internal parasites, and a few inhabit salt water. The class and common names refer to the beating cilia on the anterior end of the body, which suggest the rotation of microscopic wheels. This ciliated area, the absence of external cilia elsewhere, and movements of the chewing pharynx in life distinguish rotifers from all other minute aquatic animals.

21-12. Characteristics. (1) Symmetry bilateral, no true segmentation, 3 germ layers; (2) body somewhat cylindrical, with ciliated disc anteriorly and forked "foot" posteriorly; (3) body wall a syncytium covered with hardened cuticle (lorica); body cavity without special lining; (4) digestive tract complete or incomplete; (5) 2 nephridia, coiled and branched, with flame cells; (6) a dorsal nerve ganglion and various nerves (no cord), sense organs tuft-like or as eyespots; (7) sexes separate; males usually minute and degenerate or none; female with ovary, yolk gland, and oviduct; reproduction both parthenogenetic and sexual; usually oviparous; no larva.

The Rotifera resemble the Platyhel-minthes in having excretory organs with flame cells (protonephridia) and the Nematoda in being composed of relatively few cells and having a body cavity without special lining. Some adult rotifers resemble a trochophore larva. As a group, the rotifers display an amazing variety in structure, suggesting that they have had a long geologic history. Unfortunately, they are unknown as fossils, probably because of their minute size.

21-13. Structure and function. The typical rotifer (Fig. 21-5) is composed of an anterior **head** region, an expanded **trunk,** and a narrow tail-like posterior **foot,** usually movable and often ending in two slender **toes.** Each toe contains a **cement gland** providing a sticky secretion by which the animal may attach temporarily to some object. The **body wall** is a thin syncytium with nuclei, covered by a thin glassy chitin-like cuticle (lorica). On the anterior end is a retractile disc, or **corona** (often double), rimmed with cilia. These cilia beat with a whirling motion that draws water containing oxygen and food toward the head end, carries off wastes, and serves for locomotion. The digestive tract is lined by cilia, save in the pharynx, and includes (1) the **mouth** below the corona; (2) a rounded muscular pharynx, or **mastax,** that has a "dental mill" of chitin-like **jaws** with **teeth** used to grasp, cut, and grind the food; (3) a short **esophagus;** (4) a sizable **stomach,** of large cells and with a pair of digestive glands; (5) a short **intestine;** (6) the oval **cloaca;** and (7) the **anus,** which is dorsal at the end of the trunk. Some species lack digestive organs beyond the stomach. Between the body wall and digestive tract is a fluid-filled **body cavity,** without special lining and hence not a true coelom. Isolated **muscles,** chiefly longitudinal, serve to withdraw the corona and to move or contract the foot. Excretion is accomplished by two slender (proto) **nephridia** connected to an enlarged **pulsating vesicle** that discharges relatively large amounts of water into the cloaca; each nephridium is irregularly coiled and has several lateral branches beginning in flame cells. A large **nerve ganglion,** dorsal to the mouth, gives off nerves

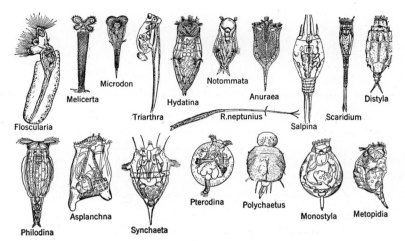

Floscularia   Melicerta   Microdon   Triarthra   Hydatina   Notommata   R.neptunius   Anuraea   Salpina   Scaridium   Distyla

Philodina   Asplanchna   Synchaeta   Pterodina   Polychaetus   Monostyla   Metopidia

Fig. 21-6. Phylum ASCHELMIN-THES, Class ROTIFERA. Various rotifers, all enlarged. (*After Jennings*, 1901.)

to various organs. There is usually a pair of short sensory tufts ("lateral antennae") on the sides of the body posteriorly; some rotifers have also a tuft (or two) above the brain, and one to three dorsal eyespots. Ectoderm provides the external covering, the nervous structures, and the lining at the ends of the digestive tract; the mid-gut is from endoderm; and the other structures grow from mesoderm.

The preceding account applies to a typical female, which has also a single **ovary** and **yolk gland** connected to an **oviduct** emptying into the cloaca. The male, in species where known, is much smaller than the female, and its body cavity contains one large **testis;** this opens by a duct, either in a **penis** that can be protruded dorsally or in the foot.

In various rotifers (Fig. 21-6) the body is slender (*R. neptunius*), broad (*Polychaetus*), sac-like (*Asplanchna*), flattened (*Ascomorpha*), or even spherical (*Trochosphaera*). The lorica may bear ridges, rings, or spines. The foot may be long, short, or absent; it serves for attachment and as a rudder in swimming, also in some as an organ for leaping. The corona may have one or two concentric wreaths of cilia; the jaws and teeth are of varied form. Many of these differences are used in classification.

21-14. Natural history. Rotifers are cosmopolitan; the same species may occur in America, Eurasia, and Australia, wherever conditions

are appropriate. Two lakes of like physical and biological characteristics, but hundreds of miles apart, may contain similar assemblages of rotifers; conversely, two others unlike but close together can have quite different kinds. The rotifer fauna of any body of water undergoes some change as to the constituent species during one summer season.

The great majority are free-living and solitary. They are commonest in quiet fresh waters with much aquatic vegetation. Some species swim in open water, but more live about or on fresh-water plants. Several species live attached, each in a self-constructed protective case either of its own secretions or of foreign particles; thus *Floscularia* (*Collotheca*) inhabits a transparent tube, and *Melicerta* (*Floscularia*) constructs a tube of microscopic "spherical bricks." Certain species are colonial, some free-swimming, and others fixed. The BDELLOIDEA can creep like leeches but also can swim. *Seison nebaliae* lives as a commensal on a crustacean (*Nebalia*), *Pleurotrocha parasitica* is an external parasite and *Alberta naidus* an internal parasite of fresh-water annelids, *Hertwigia* lives within colonies of the protozoan *Volvox*, and *Proales wernecki* forms microscopic galls in *Vaucheria*, an alga.

Rotifers that feed on unicellular algae have short broad teeth; those subsisting on the juices of larger plants have pointed teeth to pierce the plant cells and a muscular pharynx

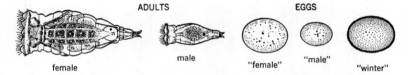

ADULTS   EGGS

female   male   "female"   "male"   "winter"

Fig. 21-7. Stages in the life cycle of a rotifer, *Hydatina senta;* all enlarged. (*After Whitney,* 1916.)

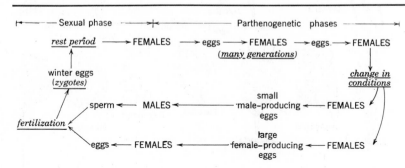

|←——— Sexual phase ———→|←——————— Parthenogenetic phases ———————→|

rest period ——→ FEMALES ——→ eggs ——→ FEMALES ——→ eggs ——→ FEMALES
                                      (*many generations*)

winter eggs
(*zygotes*)   *change in
                                                                             conditions*

sperm ←—— MALES ←—— small
                        male-producing ←—— FEMALES
fertilization   eggs

eggs ←—— FEMALES ←—— large
                        female-producing ←—— FEMALES
                             eggs

Fig. 21-8. Diagram of the life cycle of a rotifer, *Hydatina senta.*

that acts like a piston to suck out the juices; and those of predatory habit have slender jaws armed with teeth that can be projected through the mouth to grasp the protozoans, rotifers, and other animals used as food. Rotifers aid in keeping the water clean by feeding on bits of organic debris as well as on other organisms. In turn, various rotifers serve as food for small worms and crustaceans and are an important part of the "food chain" in the fresh waters.

21-15. Reproduction (Figs. 21-7, 21-8). The females, at different seasons, usually produce two kinds of eggs, "summer" and "winter." The first are thin-shelled, develop at once by parthenogenesis, and yield only females; in favorable waters a series of such generations may occur.

Then, with some change in environmental conditions not clearly understood, a generation is produced in which some females lay small eggs yielding only males and others lay larger eggs yielding only females, both by parthenogenesis. The males produce sperm to fertilize the females internally, and the latter lay "winter eggs" (zygotes) with thick and resistant shells, like protozoan cysts. These require a rest period and may remain dormant for long periods, can survive drought or freezing, and may be blown about by winds or carried on the feet or feathers of birds. Later, in favorable waters, they develop into females that resume the "summer" phase. Such means for surviving adverse conditions and for dispersal explain the universal distribution of rotifers.

CLASSIFICATION

CLASS ROTIFERA (see Characteristics).
    Order 1. Seisonacea. No lateral antennae or toes; 2 ovaries; males fully developed; only 2 species. *Seison,* commensal on a marine crustacean (*Nebalia*).
    Order 2. Bdelloidea. No lateral antennae; toes 0 to 4, foot glands numerous; 2 ovaries; males unknown. *Habotrocha, Philodina, Rotifer.*
    Order 3. Monogonata. Two lateral antennae on body; toes 0 to 2; one ovary; males usually present, but degenerate; includes most species of rotifers. *Proales, Salpina, Hydatina.*

References. HYMAN, L. H. 1951. Class Rotifera. *In* The invertebrates. Vol. 3, pp. 52–151, figs. 26–69. JENNINGS, H. S. 1918. The wheel animalcules (Rotatoria). *In* H. B. Ward and G. C. Whipple, Fresh-water biology. Pp. 553–620, figs. 856–962. PENNAK, R. W. 1953. Rotatoria. *In* Fresh-water invertebrates of the United States. Pp. 159–213, figs. 96–132. WESENBERG-LUND, C. 1929. Rotatoria. *In* W. Kükenthal and others, Handbuch der Zoologie. Vol. 2, pt. 1, sec. 4, pp. 8–120, figs. 2–131.

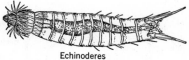

Chaetonotus   Echinoderes

Fig. 21-9. Phylum ASCHELMINTHES. *Left.* Class GASTROTRICHA, *Chaetonotus.*
Right. Class KINORHYNCHA, *Echinoderes.* Both enlarged. (*After Jennings; and*
Wolff and Krause.)

CLASS GASTROTRICHA

21-16. This group includes about 200 species
of microscopic forms (0.07 to 0.60 mm. long)
common among the algae and bottom debris of
quiet fresh and salt waters. In size and habits
they resemble some ciliate protozoans. A typical gastrotrich (*Chaetonotus maximus*) is slender and flexible; the posterior end is forked, and
each lobe contains a cement gland for temporary attachment (Fig. 21-9). The flat ventral
surface has two lengthwise bands of cilia used
for gliding locomotion, and on the arched dorsal
surface are many slender spines. The mouth is
anterior, surrounded by bristles and fine sensory hairs, the pharynx is muscular, the intestine straight, and the anus posterior. Unicellular algae are the chief food. The body cavity

has no special lining. Usually there are six pairs
of delicate lengthwise muscles. The two nephridia are coiled but unbranched, beginning
with flame cells and opening midventrally on
the body. In one group protonephridia are
lacking. A saddle-shaped nerve ganglion anteriorly connects to two longitudinal lateral
nerves and by fibers to the sensory hairs. In
fresh-water species only females are known;
the marine forms are hermaphroditic. The simple ovary fills much of the body cavity and
produces one to five large eggs, each in a tough
shell; some eggs have hooks that fasten to materials in the water. Development is direct. The
GASTROTRICHA (Gr. *gaster,* belly + *trichos,*
hair) are occasionally grouped with the NEM-
ATODA, from which they differ especially in
possessing cilia.

CLASSIFICATION

CLASS GASTROTRICHA

Order 1. Macrodasyoidea. Adhesive tubes anterior, lateral, and posterior; no protonephridia; hermaphroditic; marine shores, mostly in sand. *Cephalodasys, Macrodasys.*

Order 2. Chaetonotoidea. Adhesive tubes usually only on tail; 2 protonephridia; reproduction parthenogenetic (usually lacks male system); mainly in fresh waters on vegetation. *Chaetonotus, Lepido-
dermella; Neodasys,* marine.

References. BRUNSON, R. B. 1950. An introduction to
. . . the Gastrotricha. . . . *Transactions of the American Microscopical Society,* vol. 69, pp. 325–352, 56 figs.
PENNAK, R. W. 1953. Gastrotricha. *In* Fresh-water invertebrates of the United States. Pp. 148–158, 6 figs.
REMANE, ADOLPH. 1936. Gastrotricha. *In* Bronn,
Klassen und Ordnungen der Tier-reichs. Vol. 4, div. 2,
book 1, pt. 2, pp. 1–242, illus.

CLASS KINORHYNCHA (ECHINODERA)

21-17. This group consists of about 30 species
(Genus *Echinodera* and others) of marine
worms, up to 1 mm. long, found in bottom
mud and sand of shallow to deep seas. The

body is of 13 (or 14) rings; 2 rings form the
head, which is encircled by spines and has a
short retractile proboscis (Fig. 21-9). The trunk
is encased in 11 rings of chitinous cuticle bearing lateral spines. The mouth is at the proboscis tip, the stomach is expanded, and the anus
opens in the terminal, retractile ring. There are
two excretory tubes, each with a flame cell connected to a flagellated duct opening dorsally on
ring 9. The nervous system is in the epidermis,
beneath the cuticle, with a dorsal ganglion,
connectives around the pharynx, and a midventral cord having a ganglion in each segment.

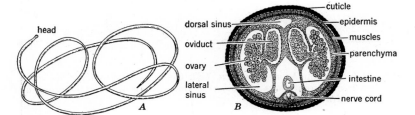

Fig. 21-10. Phylum Aschel-minthes, Class Nematomor-pha. The "horsehair worm," *Gordius*. A. Entire specimen. B. Cross section of female, en-larged. (*After Kükenthal.*)

The sexes are separate, each with a pair of tubular reproductive sacs opening ventrally beside the anus. *Echinodera* resembles the Nematoda but differs in having paired excretory organs, which are flagellated internally, and unfused sex organs. Development includes larval stages and a metamorphosis.

References. Remane, Adolph. 1936. Kinorhyncha. *In* Bronn. Klassen und Ordnungen der Tier-Reichs. Vol. 4, div. 2, bk. 1, pt. 1, pp. 243–372, figs. 210–297. Zelinka, Karl. 1928. Monographie der Echinodera. Leipzig, W. Engelmann. iv + 396 pp., 27 col. pls., 73 figs.

CLASS NEMATOMORPHA (Gordiacea). "Horsehair Worms"

21-18. The gordian worms are long and slender, with a uniformly cylindrical body and bluntly rounded anterior end (Fig. 21-10). Different species are from 10 to 300 or more millimeters long but only 0.3 to 2.5 mm. in diameter, females being longer than males. The exterior is opaque and yellow, gray, brown, or black. The body wall consists of (1) a thin cuticle bearing minute papillae; (2) the epidermis, which secretes the cuticle; (3) a single layer of longitudinal muscles, incomplete at the ends of the body; and (4) an epithelium lining the body cavity. The latter is nearly filled with loose parenchyma. The digestive tract is complete in young worms and ends posteriorly in a cloaca, but it becomes closed at both ends or degenerate in adults. No circulatory, respiratory, or excretory organs are present. A nerve ring surrounds the esophagus, connecting to one mid-ventral nerve cord; there may be one or two simple eyes and some sensory bristles. The sexes are separate, each with two gonads in the body cavity. The reproductive ducts are paired, not connected to the gonads, and empty into the cloaca. About 80 species are known.

Adult worms are often seen wriggling in the water of ponds, quiet streams, rain puddles, or drinking troughs. Their presence in such places, sometimes in numbers, is responsible for an old belief that they are long horsehairs that have "come to life" in water. The females deposit long swollen gelatinous strings (to 91 inches!) of minute eggs on aquatic vegetation.

The larva (to 0.25 mm. long) swims for a day in water, then is thought to encyst on damp vegetation. If the vegetation is eaten by a cricket, grasshopper, or certain beetles, the larva burrows into the insect's hemocoel, digests surrounding tissues, and in several weeks or months becomes an adult; if the host then falls into water, the worm emerges.

These animals have often been joined with the nematodes because of their body form, complete digestive tract, presence of a cuticle, simple musculature, and absence of segmentation. They differ from the latter in having the lined body cavity filled with parenchyma, a single nerve cord, and separate gonads and reproductive ducts.

CLASSIFICATION

CLASS NEMATOMORPHA

    Order 1. Gordioidea. No swimming bristles; pseudocoel filled with parenchyma; 2 gonads. *Paragordius*, to 300 mm. long, common; *Gordius robustus*, to 890 mm. long, 0.5 to 1 mm. in diameter.

    Order 2. Nectonematoidea. Two rows of swimming bristles; pseudocoel unfilled; 1 gonad. One genus, *Nectonema*, to 200 mm. long, marine, pelagic near coasts, larvae parasitic in crustaceans (*Palaemonetes*).

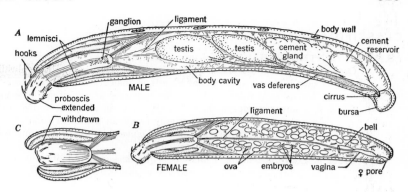

Fig. 21-11. Phylum ACANTHO-CEPHALA. Spiny-headed worm, enlarged and left side of body removed to show internal structure. *A.* Male. *B.* Female. *C.* Anterior end with proboscis withdrawn. (*Adapted from Lynch,* 1936.)

References. PENNAK, R. W. 1953. Fresh-water invertebrates of the United States. Nematomorpha. Chap. 10, pp. 232–239, 6 figs. RAUTHER, MAX. 1929. Nematomorpha. *In* W. Kükenthal and others, Handbuch der Zoologie. Vol. 2, pt. 1, sec. 4, pp. 403–448, figs. 427–480.

PHYLUM ACANTHOCEPHALA
SPINY-HEADED WORMS

21-19. These parasites of peculiar structure and function live as adults in the intestines of vertebrates and as larvae in arthropods. The distinctive feature for which the group is named (Gr. *acanthos*, spine + *kephale*, head) is the anterior cylindrical **proboscis** that bears rows of recurved spines serving to attach a worm to the host's gut (Fig. 21-11). The spines may be concentric or arranged in alternate radial rows. The proboscis is in a sheath into which it may be completely retracted by muscles. The body of most species is long, flattened, and rough in life (rounded and smoother in preserved specimens) and capable of extension and contraction. It is covered by a thin cuticle secreted by the epidermis, which is a syncytium with large nuclei and penetrated by minute fibers and canals. Beneath the epidermis is a layer of circular muscles, and within these a sheath of longitudinal muscles lining the fluid-filled body cavity. Neither the larva nor the adult has a digestive tract, food being absorbed directly from the host's intestine. There are no circulatory or respiratory structures. Two branched nephridia with cilia are connected to a common posterior excretory duct, but protonephridia are absent in two groups. A nerve ganglion in the proboscis sheath sends nerves to the proboscis and posteriorly. There are usually six to eight cement glands in the males.

The sexes are separate. The male contains a pair of testes developed in a cord-like ligament extending from the proboscis sheath to the posterior end, and the sperm pass out a duct, through the posterior bell-like bursa containing the genital pore. The female has no persistent ovary. Ova develop on the ligament, are set free in the body cavity and fertilized there, then surrounded usually by three membranes. They are generally advanced in development before escaping into the host's intestine to pass out with the feces. When eggs are eaten by the intermediate host, the larvae develop in the latter. Completion of the life cycle requires that the larval host in turn be eaten by the host of the adult worm.

The 300 or more species of acanthocephs are 1.5 to 650 mm. in length and parasitize different vertebrates from fishes to mammals. Larvae of those in terrestrial hosts usually develop in insects, and those of aquatic vertebrates in crustaceans. *Macracanthorhynchus hirudinaceus* is common in pigs and occasional in man; the male is 50 to 100 by 3 to 5 mm., and the female 100 to 650 by 4 to 10 mm. Its intermediate host is the "white grub," or larva of the June beetle (SCARABAEIDAE), which pigs often eat when in pastures.

The ACANTHOCEPHALA differ from NEMATODA in the presence of a proboscis, absence of a digestive tract, presence of circular muscles and ciliated excretory organs, and peculiarities of the reproductive organs. They show no closer relationships to other animals.

CLASSIFICATION

PHYLUM ACANTHOCEPHALA (see characteristics above).

    Order 1. Archiacanthocephala. Proboscis spines concentric; protonephridia present; 2 persistent ligament sacs in females; 8 cement glands in males; in terrestrial hosts. *Gigantorhynchus*, in anteaters; *Macracanthorhynchus*, in beetles and pigs; *Moniliformis*, in beetles or cockroaches and rodents.

    Order 2. Palaeacanthocephala. Proboscis spines in alternate radial rows; no protonephridia; ligament sacs transient in females; usually 6 cement glands in males; mostly in aquatic hosts. *Leptorhynchoides*, in amphipods and fishes; *Polymorphus*, in crustaceans and water birds; *Acanthocephalus*, in isopods and fishes and amphibians.

    Order 3. Eocanthocephala. Proboscis spines arranged radially; no protonephridia; persistent ligament sacs in females; cement gland syncytial with reservoir; in aquatic hosts. *Neoechinorhynchus*, in aquatic arthropods and fishes.

References. HYMAN, L. H. 1951. Acanthocephala. *In* The invertebrates. Vol. 3, pp. 1–52, figs. 1–25. MEYER, A. 1933. Acanthocephala. *In* Bronn, Klassen und Ordnungen der Tier-reichs. Vol. 4, pt. 2, book 2, sec. 2, pp. 333–582, illus. WARD, H. L. 1951; 1952. The species of Acanthocephala described since 1933. *Tennessee Academy of Sciences Journal*, vol. 26, pp. 282–311; vol. 27, pp. 131–149.

PHYLUM BRYOZOA. MOSS ANIMALS

21-20. Many of the bryozoans (Gr. *bryon,* moss + *zoon*, animal) are tufted or branched colonies, a few millimeters high, attached to objects in shallow sea water. Some resemble colonial hydroids and corals in appearance, but their internal structure is much more advanced. Their form suggested the names "moss animals" or "zoophytes" (plant-like animals), and the numbers of microscopic individuals in a colony suggested the name POLYZOA (Gr. *poly,*

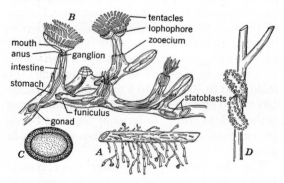

Fig. 21-12. Phylum BRYOZOA. Fresh-water bryozoans. *Plumatella. A.* Colony, natural size, on a twig. *B.* Part of colony much enlarged, showing both expanded and contracted individuals. *C.* Statoblast. *D. Cristatella*, entire colony is free-moving. (*After Allman*, 1856.)

many). They are often included among the "seaweeds" pressed and dried by amateurs at the seashore. Some bryozoans are mat-like, and others form thin incrustations on rocks, shells, or kelp. All members of the phylum are aquatic, and most of them are marine, but one order is restricted to fresh waters (Fig. 21-12).

Four of the five bryozoan orders appear in Ordovician rocks and were probably evolving in Cambrian time but then had no calcified structures and consequently left no fossil record.

More than 2,000 species are Paleozoic, 1,500 are Mesozoic, and about 2,500 are living. Their exoskeletons have aided in forming lime-bearing rocks of many strata. Many of the species had a short geologic (time) range but wide geographic distribution; they are thus useful in correlating geologic strata. For this purpose they are of economic importance in studying the cores brought up in drilling test wells for petroleum.

21-21. Characteristics. (1) Symmetry bilateral, no segmentation, 3 germ layers; (2) colonial, individuals minute, each in separate housing (zooecium); (3) digestive tract complete, U-shaped; mouth surrounded by a retractile lophophore bearing tentacles; anus opening outside lophophore; (4) coelom well developed, lined with peritoneum; no circulatory or respiratory organs; (5) no nephridia; (6) a nerve ganglion between mouth and anus; (7) usually monoecious with gonads developed from peritoneum; eggs fertilized in coelom and developed in a modified portion, or ooecium, serving as a brood pouch; larva a trochophore; colonies formed by asexual budding, also by statoblasts in fresh-water species.

The lophophore and tentacles of bryozoans suggest relationships with the brachiopods, and

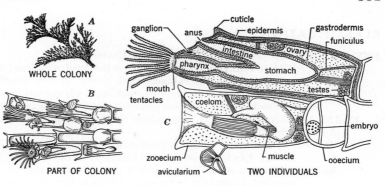

Fig. 21-13. Phylum BRYOZOA. Structure of *Bugula*. *A.* Whole colony, natural size. *B.* Part of colony, enlarged. *C.* Two individuals in longitudinal section, the upper expanded and the lower contracted.

the trochophore larva suggests ancient origin from some "worm" stock.

21-22. Structure and natural history. *Bugula* is a common bryozoan that grows as branched brown or purple tufts, 2 or 3 inches long, attached to objects in shallow sea water (Fig. 21-13). Each "stem" includes numerous individuals less than 1 mm. long, closely united in four longitudinal rows. An individual, or *zooid*, consists of a tubular chitinous housing, or *zooecium*, with the soft living parts, or *polypide*, inside. On the exterior of most zooids is an *avicularium* (modified zooid?) shaped like a bird's head, with jaws that open and snap shut to keep minute animals from settling on the surface. The anterior end, or *introvert*, of the living polypide is a rounded ridge, or *lophophore*, that bears a circle of slender, flexible, and ciliated *tentacles* around the mouth or a lip (epistome) that overhangs the mouth. The lophophore may be U-shaped or circular and is attached to an opening in the zooecium by a flexible chitinous collar. The tentacles sweep microscopic food organisms toward the mouth and also aid in respiration. The introvert may be completely withdrawn, like the tip of a glove finger, by *retractor muscles.*

The *digestive tract* is complete, with a ciliated lining, and includes the *mouth* between the tentacles, a wide *pharynx,* a slender *esophagus,* an enlarged *stomach* of U or V shape, and a slender *intestine* leading to the *anus,* which opens just outside the lophophore. The dorsal region is reduced so that the mouth and anus are close together. A retractor muscle (funicu-

lus) draws the stomach aborally. There are no circulatory, respiratory, or excretory organs. The body cavity is a true *coelom,* lined by thin peritoneum and filled with fluid containing corpuscles. Some bryozoans have a *nerve ganglion* just below the lophophore, with fibers to the tentacles and elsewhere. Ectoderm forms the epidermis of the body wall and secretes the zooecium, endoderm lines the digestive tract, and mesoderm provides the coelomic lining and muscles.

Bugula is monoecious; both ovaries and spermaries develop from the coelomic lining, the eggs in a portion of the coelom closed off as a brood pouch, or *ooecium.* Each egg becomes a ciliated trochophore larva which is liberated in the sea, soon to settle, apical end downward, and found a new colony by asexual budding.

21-23. Other bryozoans. The largest zooids are not over 3 mm. long by 1 mm. in diameter, and many are minute. In different species the zooecium is tubular, conical, or urn-like and is usually calcareous or chitinous. The fresh-water forms (PHYLACTOLAEMATA) produce gelatinous housings bearing zooids on the surface, and they have a special mode of asexual reproduction to survive unfavorable conditions. Internal buds called *statoblasts* form in the funiculus and are enclosed in a chitinous shell. Upon the death and decay of the parent colony these are set free in the water, either to float or to sink; they can survive freezing or drought and later produce new colonies. Fresh-water bryozoans may grow in water pipes, occasionally in such quantity as to obstruct the flow.

CLASSIFICATION

PHYLUM BRYOZOA (Polyzoa or Ectoprocta; see Characteristics).
    CLASS 1. *PHYLACTOLAEMATA.* Lophophore U-shaped; a lip (epistome) overhangs mouth; overwintering
        egg a statoblast with chitinous shell. Recent, in fresh waters. *Plumatella,* colony much branched
        or creeping, zooecium limy; *Pectinatella,* zooids exposed on surface of gelatinous mass of zooecia;
        Cristatella mucedo, creeping gelatinous mass to 10 inches long, in ponds.
    CLASS 2. *STENOLAEMATA.* Lophophore circular; no lip; zooids with membranous sac; zooecia cylin-
        drical, limy.
        Order 1. Cyclostomata. Zooecium tubular; no operculum; embryos in large ovicells. Upper Cambrian to
            Recent. †*Archaeotrypa,* Upper Cambrian; *Crisia, Idmonea, Tubulipora,* marine.
        Order 2. †Treptostomata. Zooecium of 2 parts, limy; operculum present; some colonies 24 inches in
            diameter. Ordovician to Permian. †*Amplexopora,* †*Hallopora.*
    CLASS 3. *GYMNOLAEMATA.* Lophophore circular; circle of tentacles around mouth; zooecia complex;
        mostly marine; includes many fossil and most living forms.
        Order 1. Ctenostomata. Colonies low, encrusting on rocks or shells; zooecium chitinous or gelatinous.
            Ordovician to Recent. *Alcyonidium, Serialaria,* marine; *Paludicella,* in fresh waters.
        Order 2. Cheilostomata. Zooecium chitinous or limy, box-like with avicularia. Jurassic to Recent. *Bugula,*
            Menipea, colonies tufted; *Membranipora,* colonies encrusting on kelp.
        Order 3. †Cryptostomata. Zooecia short, aperture at base of a vestibule. Ordovician to Permian. †*Fenes-*
            trellina, common in Indiana limestone.

References. BASSLER, R. S. 1922. The Bryozoa, or moss animals. *Smithsonian Institution Annual Report for 1920,* pp. 339–380, illus. HARMER, S. F. 1910. Polyzoa. *In* Cambridge natural history. Vol. 2, pp. 465–533, figs. 232–257. SHROCK, R. W., and W. H. TWENHOFEL. 1953. Principles of invertebrate paleontology. BRYOZOA, pp. 195–254, 45 figs.

PHYLUM BRACHIOPODA. LAMP SHELLS

21-24. The brachiopods bear a superficial resemblance to bivalve mollusks in having an external shell of two valves, but these are dorsal
and ventral, rather than lateral as in the mollusks. Brachiopods have inhabited the sea bottom since animal life was first common in
Cambrian time. Their shells are widespread
and abundant fossils in rock strata of marine
origin, and are useful for correlating such deposits. Some 456 genera are known from Paleozoic rocks and 177 in the Mesozoic; the 70
genera and 225 living species are but a remnant
of those now extinct. The living genus *Lingula*
is much as it was in Ordovician time—over
400,000,000 years ago—possibly the oldest living genus of animals. All living brachiopods are
marine, solitary, and usually attached; most of
them are in shallow waters, but a few go deeper,
even to 18,000 feet. The name of the phylum
(L. *brachio,* arm + Gr. *pod,* foot) refers to the

lophophore within the shell, and the term
"lamp shell" indicates the resemblance to an
old Roman oil lamp.

21-25. Characteristics. (1) Symmetry bilateral, no segmentation, 3 germ layers; (2) shell external, dorsal and
ventral valves unlike, with a fleshy peduncle for attachment; (3) mouth preceded by tentacles on a fleshy lophophore; digestive tract with or without anus; (4)
coelom well developed; a small heart; (5) excretion by
one or two pairs of nephridia, serving also as reproductive ducts; (6) a nerve ring about gullet; (7) sexes separate, each with paired gonads; eggs and sperm discharged into sea water; a free-swimming ciliated larva;
no asexual reproduction.

The form of the lophophore and its dorsal lip
in larval brachiopods resemble comparable
structures in the phoronids and bryozoans;
the larvae of BRYOZOA and BRACHIOPODA may
be considered as modified trochophores. These
groups formerly were placed as classes of a
Phylum MOLLUSCOIDEA, but they differ enough
to be placed as distinct phyla.

21-26. Structure and natural history (*Magellania*). The soft parts are contained between
two stout scoop-shaped calcareous **valves,** or
shells, which are covered externally with organic periostracum (Fig. 21-14). The larger
ventral valve has a posterior projecting **beak**
perforated for passage of the fleshy stalk, or

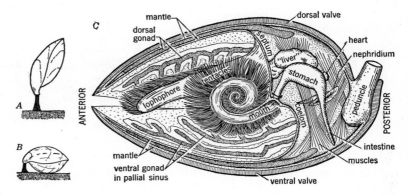

Fig. 21-14. Phylum BRACHIO-PODA. *A, B.* Typical positions of living lamp shells in life. *C. Magellania,* internal structure from left side; shells cut to midline, mantle and lophophore of left side removed. (*A, B, after Twenhofel and Shrock, Invertebrate paleontology.*)

peduncle, by which the animal attaches permanently to the sea bottom. The actual **body** occupies only the posterior part of the space between the shells. The body wall consists of an external epidermis, stout connective tissue, and a ciliated coelomic lining. Two double folds of this wall extend anteriorly as the dorsal and ventral **mantle lobes,** which line the interior surface of the respective shells and have fine papillae penetrating the shell substance. Within the dorsal valve a thin limy **shelly loop** supports a large W-shaped **lophophore** that attaches to the anterior surface of the body and lies in the space between the mantle lobes. The lophophore is fringed with long ciliated **tentacles** that circulate water in the mantle cavity for respiration and whip small food organisms into a groove leading to the **mouth.** The latter opens from the base of the lophophore into a short **gullet,** followed by the larger **stomach** (with paired **digestive glands**) and a blind **intestine.** Three pairs of **muscles** serve to close and open the valves, and two other pairs attaching to the peduncle and shell permit the animal to turn about. The large fluid-filled **coelom** contains the internal organs, which are supported on mesenteries; branches of it extend into the mantle lobes and lophophore. A small contractile **heart** and blood vessels are present. At each side of the intestine is a large **nephridium** for excretion, with a fringed nephrostome draining from the coelom and a small exit into the mantle cavity. A **nerve ring** surrounds the gullet, with nerves to various organs, but special sense organs are absent. The sexes are separate; in each are two **gonads,** dorsal and ventral, respectively, and the nephridia serve as reproductive ducts, discharging eggs and sperm to the exterior. The fertilized egg grows into a free-swimming larva of somewhat peculiar character, which later attaches by a structure that becomes the peduncle.

CLASSIFICATION

PHYLUM BRACHIOPODA (see Characteristics).

> CLASS 1. *INARTICULATA.* Two valves nearly alike, of chitinoid material containing calcareous spicules; no hinge, beak, or shelly loop; anus present.
>> **Order 1. Atremata.** Lower Cambrian to Recent. *Lingula,* Pacific and Indian Oceans, and *Glottidia,* both coasts of America, live between the tide lines and burrow in mud or sand with long contractile peduncle.
>> **Order 2. Neotremata.** Cambrian to Recent. *Crania,* ventral valve flat, fastened to rock, dorsal valve conical.
> CLASS 2. *ARTICULATA.* Dorsal and ventral valves unlike, densely formed of oblique calcareous prisms; with hinge, and usually with beak for peduncle and shelly loop for lophophore; no anus.
>> **Order 1. Palaeotremata.** Lower Cambrian. †*Rustella.*
>> **Order 2. Protremata.** Cambrian to Recent. *Rafinesquina.*
>> **Order 3. Telotremata.** Ordovician to Recent; includes many fossil and most living forms. *Rhynchotremata, Terebratulina, Magellania.*

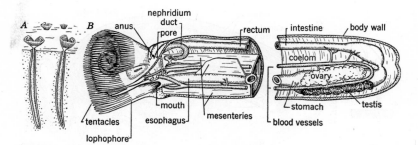

Fig. **21-15.** Phylum PHORONI-
DEA. *Phoronis.* A. Group of individuals as in life, in bottom
sand or mud under shallow water, each in a self-excavated
tube. B. Internal structure, enlarged and partly diagrammatic; left side of lophophore
and body wall removed; only
part of left lateral mesentery
shown. (*After Benham*, 1889.)

References. HELMCKE, J. G. 1939. Brachiopoda. *In* W. Kükenthal and others, Handbuch der Zoologie. Vol. 3, pt. 2, sec. 5, pp. 139–158, figs. 152–271. SCHROCK, R. R., and W. H. TWENHOFEL. 1953. Principles of invertebrate paleontology. Chap. 9, pp. 260–349, 60 figs.

PHYLUM PHORONIDEA

21-27. The phoronids are slender worm-like sedentary creatures of various sizes that inhabit the bottom under shallow seas. Some are scattered singly, and others are so densely placed as to fairly cover the sand for nearly an acre. Each is separately housed in a self-secreted tube of leathery, membranous, or limy texture from which its tentacles are extended to feed (Fig. 21-15). Some of the 15 or more species are less than 1 mm. long, but *Phoronopsis californica* grows to 12 or 15 inches and its tube may be 18 inches long.

21-28. Characteristics. (1) Symmetry bilateral, 3 germ layers, no segmentation; (2) body cylindrical, crowned by a double spiral of horseshoe shape (lophophore) bearing 60 to 300 hollow ciliated tentacles in 2 rows which are fused at their bases; (3) body wall of cuticle, epidermis, circular muscles (layer) and longitudinal muscles (bundles); (4) digestive tract U-shaped, mouth inside and anus outside lophophore, lining ciliated except in terminal part; (5) coelom throughout body and into tentacles, divided into compartments by transverse septum at base of lophophore and by 3 lengthwise mesenteries between body wall and gut; (6) circulatory system of 2 lengthwise trunks with lateral branches in body and vessels into bases of tentacles, blood with corpuscles containing hemoglobin; (7) no respiratory organs; (8) two ciliated nephridia opening near anus; (9) nervous tissue below epidermis, a ring surrounding mouth and fibers to parts of body; (10) monoecious, gonads (testis, ovary) develop beside blood vessels, gametes released through nephridia; (11) larva (actinotrocha) somewhat like a trochophore.

The systematic position of the phoronids is unsettled; once grouped with the GEPHYREA (sipunculids, etc.), they were later aligned with the bryozoans and brachiopods. A resemblance also is indicated to *Cephalanthus* in the hemichordates, particularly because of the coelomic spaces.

21-29. Natural history. Phoronids feed by extending the mucus-coated tentacles to lie on the bottom and take minute organisms from the water or in the surface debris. When uncovered by the receding tide or when disturbed, they withdraw to the shelter of their tubes. The lophophore, if torn off, can be regenerated. The bodies and tentacles of different species are red, orange, or green, and when numerous may give brilliant color to the sea floor. At Naples colonies of *P. kowalevskii* form a network of their intertwined tubes 2 or 3 inches thick on submerged piling.

References. BENHAM, W. B. 1889. The anatomy of *Phoronis australis. Quarterly Journal of Microscopical Science*, n.s., vol. 30, pp. 125–158, pls. 10–13. CORI, C. J. 1937. Phoronidea. *In* W. Kükenthal and others, Handbuch der Zoologie. Vol. 3, pt. 2, sec. 5, pp. 5–138, figs. 82–151.

PHYLUM CHAETOGNATHA
ARROW WORMS

21-30. These are little torpedo-shaped marine animals, from 20 to 70 mm. long, of which six genera and about 30 species are known. Some species are so abundant as to be important constituents of the ocean plankton. Many live at depths no greater than 100 feet and approach the surface at dusk and dawn when the light intensity is low. They feed actively on unicellular plants and animals, crustacean larvae, and other small marine life, darting about like ar-

Fig. 21-16. Phylum CHAETOG-NATHA. Arrow worm, *Sagitta*, ventral view; natural size 20 to 70 mm.

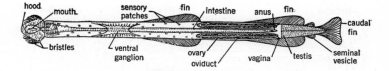

rows—hence the common name arrow worms and that of the principal genus, *Sagitta* (L., arrow); being transparent, they are also called glassworms. The phylum name refers to characteristic bristles about the mouth (Gr. *chaeton*, bristle + *gnathos*, jaw).

21-31. Characteristics. (1) Symmetry bilateral, 3 germ layers, no segmentation; (2) body slender, with lateral fins; (3) digestive tract complete, anus ventral; (4) coelom well developed as 3 pairs of cavities; (5) no circulatory, respiratory, or excretory organs; (6) nervous system with dorsal and ventral ganglia and sensory organs; (7) monoecious, development direct.

The chaetognaths show no obvious relation to other animals. They are not segmented, lack cilia on the epidermis and digestive tract, and the tail is postanal as in no other phylum except the chordates. Their embryonic development has some resemblance to that of many annelids and some chordates.

21-32. Structure and natural history. The body is cylindrical, with *head, trunk,* and *tail* regions (Fig. 21-16). There are two pairs of *lateral fins* at the middle and end of the trunk and a *caudal fin* across the tail. The *mouth* is a ventral slit on the broadened head, followed by the muscular *pharynx,* slender straight *intestine,* and *anus* at the end of the trunk. On either side of the mouth is a lobe bearing several sickle-shaped hooks, or *bristles,* of chitin; these are worked by muscles to serve as jaws in the capture of food, which is swallowed entire. The spacious *coelom* consists of three pairs of cavities separated by median *mesenteries* above and below the intestine and between the head, trunk, and tail. The *body wall* is made up of an *epidermis* with several layers of cells over a basement membrane, a thin layer of striated *muscles,* and the single-layered *coelomic lining.* Four lengthwise bands of muscles, two dorsolateral and two ventrolateral, provide for locomotion. The *intestinal wall* is of two cell layers,

digestive epithelium internally and coelomic lining outside. The *nervous system* is of ectodermal origin and includes a pair of cerebral ganglia dorsal to the pharynx, a pair of connectives around the latter, and a ventral ganglion midway of the trunk, with nerves to various parts. Dorsally on the head are two *eyes,* each with three lenses, and between the eyes a longitudinal *olfactory organ,* all with nerves to the cerebral ganglia. Small *tactile papillae* with stiff bristles occur over the body.

21-33. Reproduction. Chaetognaths are monoecious, and the sex cells are derived from the coelomic epithelium. In each trunk coelom is a long solid *ovary,* with a slender *oviduct* opening laterally at the end of the trunk. Each caudal coelom contains a narrow solid *testis* from which immature cells are released to mature as free sperm in the coelom, then collected by the ciliated funnel of a *sperm duct* opening laterally on the tail. Reproduction occurs through much or all of the year, and fertilization is internal. A typical gastrula is formed, with the coelom produced as lateral outgrowths of the gastrocoel. The young at hatching resembles an adult.

Reference. MICHAEL, E. L. 1911. Classification and vertical distribution of the Chaetognatha of the San Diego region. . . . *University of California Publications in Zoology,* vol. 8, pp. 21–186, 8 pls.

PHYLUM SIPUNCULOIDEA

21-34. Searchers at the seashore commonly find small unsegmented worms, yellowish or grayish in color, living shallowly in the sand or mud or sheltering in empty shells about rocks. When disturbed, the animals retract the anterior fringed end to assume the shape of a short club or even of a peanut kernel (Fig. 21-17). These are sipunculids, sometimes called peanut worms. About 250 species are known, a few being slender or even thread-like, but many

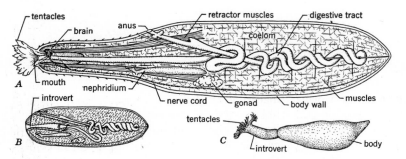

Fig. 21-17. Phylum SIPUNCULOIDEA. *Sipunculus*. *A*. Internal structure. *B*. Introvert retracted into body. *C*. External appearance, introvert and tentacles extended.

are chunkier; the larger forms are 10 to 18 inches long.

21-35. Characteristics. (1) Symmetry bilateral, 3 germ layers, no somites; (2) body usually bluntly cylindrical posteriorly, with narrow anterior retractile portion (introvert) bearing fine chitinous papillae and ending in a circle of short, hollow, fringe-like ciliated tentacles; (3) body wall includes a slightly roughened cuticle, epidermis, dermis with glands and sense organs, and 3 layers of muscle: circular, oblique, and longitudinal (the layers of lattice-like pattern interiorly); (4) mouth centered in tentacles, digestive tract slender, extending to posterior end and spiraled back on itself, anus dorsal near base of introvert; (5) coelom large, undivided but traversed by many strands of connective tissue and muscle attaching to gut; peritoneum ciliated, coelomic fluid with several kinds of corpuscles; (6) circulatory system of dorsal and ventral vessels with ring sinus below tentacles; (7) nephridia (brown tubes) 2 or 1, opening near anus; (8) nervous system of dorsal bilobed ganglion near tentacles with connectives to single ventral unsegmented nerve cord through body, and many lateral nerves; (9) sexes separate but alike, no permanent gonads, sex cells develop in tissues on retractor muscles of introvert, and gametes escape through nephridia; (10) larva usually a trochophore (no trace of somites).

21-36. Natural history. Some sipunculids make burrows in mud or sand that are lined with mucus but not so distinct as the homes of other types of tube-dwelling worms. When feeding, the tentacles are extended on the sea bottom and the beating cilia entrap microorganisms in mucus which is swallowed along with much mud or sand. Some sipunculids ingest sand as they burrow, then digest the adhering microorganisms. When a worm is disturbed, the introvert is drawn entirely into the anterior part of the body by retractor muscles but the tentacles are not inverted. Then the introvert can be extended by contraction of muscles in the wall of the fluid-filled body. Common widely distributed sipunculids include the genera *Sipunculus*,

Dendrostoma, and *Phascolosoma*. *Phascolion*, which lives at depths to 1,000 fathoms from the West Indies to the Arctic, inhabits a snail shell cemented full of sand to form a tube, which the worm carries about.

References. BALTZER, F. 1931. Sipunculida. *In* W. Kükenthal and others, Handbuch der Zoologie. Vol. 2, pt. 2, sec. 9, pp. 15–61, figs. 15–48. PEEBLES, FLORENCE, and D. L. FOX. 1933. The structure, functions and general reactions of the marine sipunculid worm Dendrostoma zostericola. *Scripps Institution of Oceanography, University of California, Bull., Tech. Ser.*, vol. 3, pp. 201–224, 11 figs.

PHYLUM PRIAPULOIDEA

21-37. The priapulids are cylindrical, worm-like creatures (Fig. 21-18), yellow or brown, and up to 80 mm. long, that inhabit mud or sand under shallow waters from Boston and

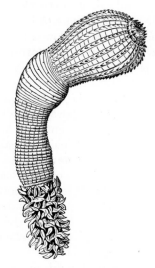

Fig. 21-18. Phylum PRIAPULOIDEA. *Priapulus*, external form. × 1½. (*From Wolcott, Animal biology*.)

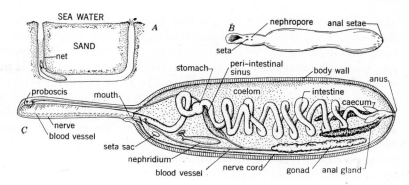

Fig. 21-19. Phylum ECHIUROI-DEA. *Urechis caupo. A.* The echiurid worm in its burrow with mucous net spread for food capture. *B.* Ventral view, proboscis partly retracted. (*Both after Fisher and Macginitie, 1928.*) *C.* Internal structure with left side of proboscis and body wall removed.

the Belgian coast northward and from Patagonia south to Antarctica. Recently they have been dredged from mud on the bottom of Tomales Bay, Calif., in 10-fathom water. They live in crevices of rocks or between sessile animals or in empty mollusk shells but can burrow to leave piles of castings on the bottom. Their food is of marine algae and bottom detritus. Only 3 species are known.

21-38. Characteristics. (1) Symmetry bilateral, 3 germ layers, no segmentation; (2) body cylindrical and fleshy, comprising an anterior retractile proboscis with lengthwise rows of spines and papillae, a trunk with superficial rings and folds, and usually 1 or 2 posterior processes with soft, hollow, gill-like outgrowths; (3) body wall soft, of cuticle, epidermis, circular and longitudinal muscles; (4) digestive tract straight, with muscular pharynx, thin-walled intestine, and cylindrical rectum; (5) coelom throughout body, large and undivided, connecting to caudal outgrowths; (6) two excretory organs (protonephridia) connecting to sex ducts; (7) nervous system subepithelial, with ring around mouth (no dorsal ganglion) and ventral nerve cord lacking ganglia; (8) sexes separate, 1 pair of gonads; (9) a larval stage.

Priapulids (*Priapulus, Halicryptus*) formerly were grouped with sipunculids and echiurids in the Phylum ANNELIDA despite their lack of setae, segmentation, and ganglia in the nervous system; but their characteristics indicate no immediate relationships to any of the living phyla.

Reference. BALTZER, F. 1931. Priapulida. *In* W. Kükenthal, Handbuch der Zoologie. Vol. 2, pt. 2, sec. 9, pp. 1–14, 14 figs.

PHYLUM ECHIUROIDEA

21-39. The echiurids comprise about 60 species of peculiar worms, of gray, reddish, or yellow-ish color, that inhabit the mud or sand between rocks under shallow coastal waters of all warm and temperate seas (Fig. 21-19). The commoner forms dig and live in widely U-shaped burrows in the bottom and have a narrow trough-like proboscis used in feeding. A few species dwell in empty shells. *Urechis caupo* of California grows to 450 mm. long, but others are smaller, down to 25 mm. or less.

21-40. Characteristics. (1) Symmetry bilateral, 3 germ layers, no segmentation in adult (but 15 vestigial somites in larva); (2) body commonly sausage-shaped, soft, with anterior proboscis either spatulate or thread-like and long, that is flexible and contractile but cannot be withdrawn into body; (3) body wall thick, fleshy, epidermis with rings of fine papillae; (4) one pair of ventral anterior setae, some (*Echiurus*) also with 1 or 2 rings of setae around anus; (5) digestive tract complete, mouth at base of proboscis, pharynx muscular, intestine long and much coiled, rectum with 2 long vesicles, anus posterior and terminal; (6) circulatory system of dorsal and ventral vessels joined anteriorly, but no lateral vessels; (7) coelom large, undivided, crossed by many muscle strands supporting intestine; (8) nephridia 1 to 3 pairs anteriorly or 1 large, all serve as gonoducts; (9) a midventral nerve cord in body with paired lateral nerves and a nerve trunk around edge of proboscis but no anterior or body ganglia and no sense organs; (10) sexes separate, dimorphic in some, gonad single, median and posterior; (11) larva a trochophore.

21-41. Natural history. The widely distributed *Echiurus* inhabits a burrow and feeds by extending the mucus-covered proboscis above the mud to trap plankton or debris. If disturbed the proboscis is cast off and then regenerated. *Urechis caupo* lives permanently in a tunnel dug by use of its setae and flushed with water expelled from the rectum. To feed, a band of epidermal cells behind the setae secrete a mucous cylinder (with pores only 0.004 μ in size) attaching to the burrow walls and fore part of the body. Then peristaltic contractions in the body wall draw water through the burrow. Microorganisms are sieved by the mucous net which later is swallowed. As commensals, a goby, a polychaete worm, and a small crab live also in the burrow. *Bonellia*, which uses deserted burrows on the sea bottom, is noted for sexual dimorphism. The female has a small green ovoid body and a thread-like proboscis, up to 1 meter long, forked at the tip. The male is minute and ciliated, like a turbellarian worm, but has no proboscis, mouth, or anus. Early in life it enters the female's gut, later to inhabit the nephridium as a "parasite." Large echiurids serve as bait for cod in Belgium and north Germany.

References. BALTZER, F. 1931. Echiurida. *In* W. Kükenthal and others, Handbuch der Zoologie. Vol. 2, pt. 2, sec. 9, pp. 63–168, figs. 49–132. FISHER, W. K., and G. E. MACGINITIE. 1928. The natural history of an Echiuroid worm. *Annals and Magazine of Natural History*, ser. 10, vol. 1, pp. 204–213. NEWBY, W. W. 1940. The embryology of the echiuroid worm, Urechis caupo. *Memoirs American Philosophical Society*, vol. 16, pp. xx + 219, 85 figs.

PHYLUM BRACHIATA

CLASS POGONOPHORA

21-42. Some sedentary worm-like creatures that live in long cylindrical tubes at depths of 3,500 meters in the Okhotsk Sea in the northwestern Pacific have been referred to a new phylum and class. The body has a short anterior section (2 segments) with a dorsal cephalic lobe and several complex ciliated tentacles; this portion is separated by a furrow (and transverse internal diaphragm) from the long unsegmented trunk on which are many external adhesive organs. The one-layered epithelium, rich in unicellular glands, is covered by cuticle. There is no digestive tract. The tentacles (each containing a loop of blood vessels in a slender coelom) are thought to take plankton and detritus for food and serve as respiratory organs. The closed circulatory system has a ventral vessel (blood flowing anteriorly) with a muscular heart at the base of the tentacles and a dorsal vessel (blood flowing posteriorly); there are cross connectives in the body and smaller vessels to the tentacles and brain. The coelom is of five parts, one in the "head" with extensions into the tentacles and a pair of compartments each in the anterior body and trunk. The excretory organs are two coelomoducts between the head coelom and exterior. The dorsal nervous system, embedded in the epidermis, includes a small brain in the cephalic lobe, nerves in the tentacles, and a median nerve down the body. The sexes are separate, each with two long gonads in the trunk coelom. The testes are posterior with long ciliated ducts opening ventrally at the anterior end of the trunk. The ovaries are anterior with ducts opening midway on the trunk. The group was originally described as the genus *Lamellisabella* and placed in the POLYCHAETA. Twelve species have been named. Relationships now appear to be with the HEMICHORDATA. The status of this animal group awaits the finding and study of more specimens.

References. JOHANSSON, K. 1937. Über Lamellisabella zachsi und ihre systematische Stellung. *Zoologischer Anzeiger*, vol. 117, pp. 23–26, 1 fig. IVANOV, A. V. 1956. On the systematic position of the Pogonophora. *Systematic Zoology*, vol. 5, pp. 165–173.

22 PHYLUM ECHINODERMATA
Echinoderms

The ECHINODERMATA (Gr. *echinos*, hedgehog + *derma*, skin) include the starfishes, or sea stars (Class ASTEROIDEA), brittle stars (OPHIUROIDEA), sea urchins and sand dollars (ECHINOIDEA), sea lilies (CRINOIDEA), and sea cucumbers (HOLOTHURIOIDEA), besides several extinct classes (Fig. 22-1). All are radially symmetrical, and most of them have a limy endoskeleton with protruding spines. They live on the seashore and sea bottom, from the tide lines down to over 12,000 feet, and are mostly free-living but slow-moving; a few are pelagic, but none is parasitic. Some are abundant, but they do not form colonies; some sea lilies are permanently attached, and many others swim in open water. A few echinoderms are used as human food, and their eggs serve in many experimental researches. Starfishes may damage commercial beds of oysters or clams.

22-1. Characteristics. 1. Symmetry radial, usually 5-parted in adults, bilateral in larvae; 3 germ layers; most organs ciliated; no head, brain, or segmentation.

2. Body surface of 5 symmetrical radiating areas or ambulacra, whence the tube feet project, and alternating between these 5 interambulacra (interradii).

3. Body covered by delicate epidermis over a firm mesodermal endoskeleton of movable or fixed calcareous plates usually in definite pattern; often with spines (skin leathery and plates usually microscopic in HOLOTHURIOIDEA).

4. Digestive tract simple, usually complete (some lack an anus).

5. Circulatory (hemal) system radiate, but reduced; coelom lined with ciliated peritoneum, usually large, its fluid containing free amoebocytes; part of larval coelom becomes a water vascular system usually with many tube feet serving for locomotion, food handling, or respiration.

6. Respiration by minute gills or papulae protruding from the coelom, by tube feet, and in HOLOTHURIOIDEA by cloacal respiratory trees.

7. Nervous system with circumoral ring and radial nerves.

8. Sexes separate (rare exceptions), alike externally; gonads large, with simple ducts; ova abundant, usually fertilized in the sea; larvae microscopic, ciliated, transparent, and usually free-swimming, with conspicuous metamorphosis. A few species are viviparous, a few reproduce also asexually by self-division, and many regenerate lost parts readily.

22-2. Relationships. The ECHINODERMATA were once joined with the COELENTERATA as the "Radiata," but belong well up among the invertebrates in a rather isolated position, being the only animals with complex organ systems that display conspicuous radial symmetry. Unique features such as the water vascular system, calcareous endoskeleton, and pedicellariae probably reflect their ancient origin, the echinoderms having been already differentiated in Cambrian time.

Some biologists believe that echinoderms have regressed from a type that once was more advanced and active, since the larvae are bilaterally symmetrical and free-living whereas the adults are radially symmetrical and of sedentary habit, with reduced blood and nervous systems. Radial symmetry and the lack of

339

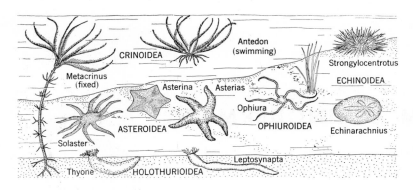

Fig. 22-1. Phylum Echinodermata. Representative forms as they live in the sea; all reduced, but not to same scale. Class Crinoidea: crinoids (*Metacrinus*, attached; *Antedon*, free-swimming). Class Asteroidea: common starfishes (*Asterias*, *Asterina*), sun star (*Solaster*). Class Ophiuroidea: brittle star (*Ophiura*). Class Echinoidea: sea urchin (*Strongylocentrotus*), sand dollar (*Echinarachnius*). Class Holothurioidea: sea cucumbers (*Thyone*, *Leptosynapta*).

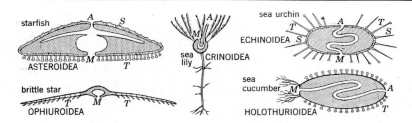

Fig. 22-2. Phylum Echinodermata. Diagrammatic sections showing for the five living classes the relations of the mouth (*M*), anus (*A*), tube feet (*T*), and spines (*S*). The digestive tract is outlined.

a "head" are adjustments enabling a sedentary animal "to meet the environment all around."

The Echinodermata show some chordate-like features such as (1) a mesodermal endoskeleton (not external and from ectoderm as in other invertebrates); (2) the embryonic blastopore becomes the adult anus (not the mouth as in annelids and mollusks); (3) the mouth forms from an ectodermal inpocketing (stomodeum) connecting to the endodermal esophagus; and (4) the mesoderm forms as outpocketings of the primitive gut (not from special mesoblast cells as in annelids and mollusks). Larvae of some echinoderms resemble those of the Hemichordata, which are variously included in or excluded from the Phylum Chordata (par. 28-2).

22-3. External appearance (Fig. 22-1). Most starfishes have 5 tapering arms, some 6, and some up to 50; others are pentagonal without distinct arms. Their colors are variously yellow, red, brown, or purple. Brittle stars have a small rounded central disc with 5 slender, jointed, and flexible arms, sometimes marked with crossbands of color. The sea urchins are hemispherical with long movable spines, and sand dollars

are disc-like with short spines; many species are purple or blue. Crinoids are flower-like with a cup-like disc bearing 5 branched arms and are of various colors. Sea cucumbers have soft sausage- or worm-shaped bodies covered by leathery skin, which may be white, red, brown, or black.

22-4. Size. Most echinoderms are of moderate size. The largest starfish (*Pycnopodia helianthoides*) spreads to about 32 inches. The largest deep-sea urchin (*Echinosoma hoplacantha*) has a shell about 12 inches across, and some tropical urchins (*Diadema*) have 12-inch spines. One sea cucumber (*Synapta maculata*) becomes 6 feet long and 2 inches in diameter. Some fossil sand dollars measure only $\frac{1}{4}$ inch, whereas the stem of a fossil crinoid was 70 feet long.

CLASS ASTEROIDEA. Starfishes

Starfishes abound on most seacoasts, especially on rocky shores and about wharf piling. Various species live from the tide lines to considerable depths on sand and mud. Common North American species are *Asterias forbesi* from the Gulf of Mexico to Maine, *A. vulgaris*

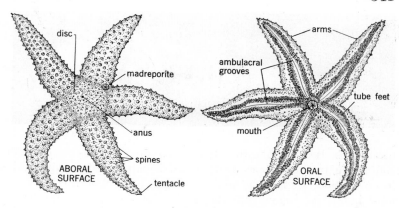

Fig. 22-3. Class ASTEROIDEA. Starfish, *Asterias forbesi.*

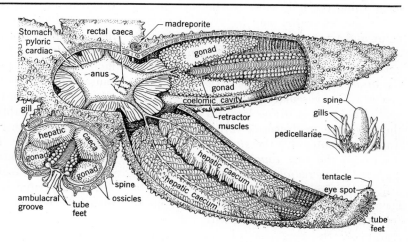

Fig. 22-4. Starfish, general structure. Three arms are cut off, one being shown in cross section at the left; the disc is cut away, and the aboral surface removed on two arms, and the hepatic caeca removed in the upper of these. Enlarged inset shows spine, gills, and pedicellariae.

from Cape Hatteras to Labrador, and *Pisaster ochraceus* along the Pacific coast.

22-5. Structure. The body (Figs. 22-3, 22-4) consists of a central *disc* and five tapering rays, or *arms.* The axes of the arms are termed "radii," and the spaces between them on the disc are "interradii." On the upper or *aboral surface* are many blunt calcareous *spines,* which are parts of the skeleton. Small soft *dermal branchiae* (papulae) project from the body cavity and between the spines to function as gills and for excretion. Around the spines and among the papulae are many minute pincer-like *pedicellariae.* Each pedicellaria has two jaws moved by muscles that open and snap shut when touched; they keep the body surface free of debris or small organisms and may help to capture food. The *anus* is a minute opening

near the center of the aboral surface, and nearby is the rounded *madreporite.* The *mouth* is in the middle of the lower or *oral surface,* surrounded by a soft peristomial membrane. A median *ambulacral groove,* bordered by large spines, extends along the oral surface of each arm, and from it many slender *tube feet* protrude in four (or two) rows. On the tip of each arm is a small soft tactile *tentacle* and a light-sensitive *eyespot.*

The entire body is covered by ciliated *epidermis.* Beneath is mesoderm that produces and contains the *endoskeleton,* a framework of many small calcareous *ossicles* of various but definite shapes and arranged in regular pattern (Fig. 22-5). The ossicles are bound together by connective tissue and joined by muscle fibers. Inside the skeleton is the large *coelom,* lined by ciliated epithelium, that contains the inter-

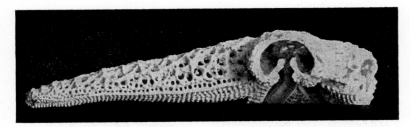

Fig. 22-5. Starfish, *Pisaster ochraceus*. Part of skeleton showing the framework of ossicles.

nal organs. It is filled with a lymph-like fluid containing free amoebocytes that participate in circulation, respiration, and excretion. Extensions of the coelom into the dermal branchiae bring the fluid close to the surrounding sea water, separated only by the thin peritoneum and external epidermis, where respiratory exchanges are easily made. The amoebocytes gather wastes in the fluid and then escape from the branchiae to the exterior.

The water vascular system (Fig. 22-6) is a specialized part of the coelom. Its parts are (1) the sieve-like *madreporite* through which sea water may enter; (2) the *stone canal* connecting to (3) the *ring canal* around the mouth, whence (4) five *radial canals* extend, one in each arm above the ambulacral groove. Each of the latter gives off (5) many *lateral canals,* one to (6) each of the *tube feet,* all with valves. The margin of the ring canal bears *Tiedemann bodies* that produce the free amoebocytes present in the fluid filling the system. Each tube foot is a closed cylinder with muscular walls, having a sucker at the outer or free end, and a

bulb-like *ampulla* at its inner end within the body cavity. When an ampulla contracts, the fluid it contains is forced into the tube foot and extends the latter as a slender flexible process that can be twisted about by muscles in its walls. If the tip touches an object, the muscles may contract and return the fluid to the ampulla so that the foot shortens. Withdrawal of fluid lessens the pressure within the tip and causes it to adhere to the object because of the greater pressure of the sea water or atmosphere outside; the foot thus acts as a suction cup. The tube feet act either independently or in a coordinated manner. They serve to hold the starfish to the substratum, for locomotion, and in the capture and handling of food.

The *digestive system* comprises (1) the *mouth;* (2) the sac-like *stomach* which is of two parts, a large lower or cardiac portion with thin folded muscular walls to which five pairs of retractor muscles attach, and a smaller aboral or pyloric portion joined by the ≺-shaped ducts of five pairs of *hepatic caeca* (digestive glands) located in the arms; and (3) a short minute *intestine* joined by two rectal caeca and leading to (4) the *anus*.

The hemal or *circulatory system* is reduced and difficult to see; it includes vessels encircling the mouth and five radial vessels, one in each arm under the canal of the water vascular system.

The *nervous system* includes a circumoral nerve ring and nerve cords in the arms. In each arm there is (1) a cord in the epidermis within the ambulacral groove, (2) a pair of deep nerves inside this epidermis, and (3) a cord in the peritoneum on the aboral side. Minute nerves extend to the tube feet, epidermis, and internal structures.

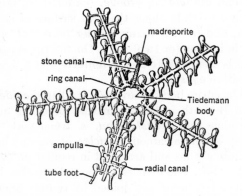

madreporite
stone canal
ring canal
Tiedemann body
ampulla
tube foot
radial canal

Fig. 22-6. Starfish. Diagram of the water vascular system. (*From Coe*, 1912.)

The sexes are separate. A pair of **gonads** lie in the coelom of every arm, and a minute duct from each opens aborally on the central disc.

22-6. Natural history. A starfish spends most of its time quietly attached to some clean solid object. The body seems stiff and rigid, and indeed can be broken in parts by rough treatment; yet the animal voluntarily bends or twists both the disc and arms when moving about or when its body is fitted into irregular spaces among rocks or other shelter. On a rough or upright surface the animal holds and travels by the tube feet, but on sand or a very smooth surface it does so by using action of the arms alone. To move, the ray or rays pointing in the given direction are raised slightly and the tube feet on them are stretched out an inch or so; these grip the new surface and then contract, pulling the body forward. There is no "head," and no one arm that habitually moves forward, although some experiments suggest that the part near the madreporite may often be carried forward. A starfish can be trained experimentally to use a particular arm, and the habit will persist for some time. The animal can progress in any direction over a surface, but once started shows coordinated action of the arms and tube feet. If turned upside down, the arms are twisted until some of the tube feet touch and attach to the substratum, and then the entire body slowly folds over so that the oral surface is again downward (Fig. 22-7).

The starfish feeds on mollusks, crustaceans, tube worms, and other invertebrates; deep-water species ingest mud. Small active animals, even fishes on occasion, may be caught by the tube feet, or pedicellariae, and passed to the mouth. With a bivalve, the starfish lies over the prey, which voluntarily opens its shells at intervals. The starfish can insert part of its stomach in a space only 1 mm. wide between the shells. Also, a starfish can grip the opposite valves with its tube feet and gradually pull them apart (maximum pull 1,300 versus 900 grams resistance by adductor muscles of bivalve). Then the starfish everts its stomach over the soft body of the bivalve. The stomach

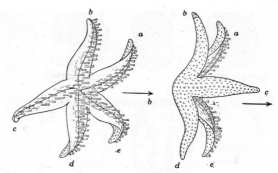

Fig. 22-7. Starfish. An inverted individual turning over (in direction of arrows); *a–e*, same arms in successive positions. (*After Coe*, 1913.)

secretes mucus, and the pylorus and caeca give off enzymes to digest the food which is taken into the stomach; then the stomach and contents are withdrawn into the body. Any large bits of waste are cast out the mouth since the small intestine serves mainly for excretion. Starfishes may feed voraciously but also can go for long periods without food. A month-old starfish in an aquarium devoured over 50 young clams in 6 days. On commercial oyster beds, starfishes may cause serious losses by eating the oysters. Owners of such beds use a rope drag to capture the starfishes, which are then killed in hot water or carried ashore; or they sprinkle lime on the beds to kill the starfishes.

22-7. Reproduction (Fig. 22-8). In early summer, eggs and sperm are shed into the sea water, where fertilization occurs. Cleavage is rapid, total, equal, and indeterminate, yielding on the second day a spherical ciliated **blastula** (0.2 mm. in diameter) that swims. Invagination produces an elongate **gastrula,** and the blastopore later becomes the anal end as in chordates. Mesenchyme forms from cells budded off the inner blind end of the gastrocoel, where also two outpocketings bud off to produce the coelom and its mesodermal lining. The mouth results from an ectodermal inpocketing (stomodeum) that connects to the esophagus, stomach, and intestine derived from the gastrocoel. Ciliated bands develop on the exterior that serve in locomotion and food capture. The bilaterally symmetrical larva swims

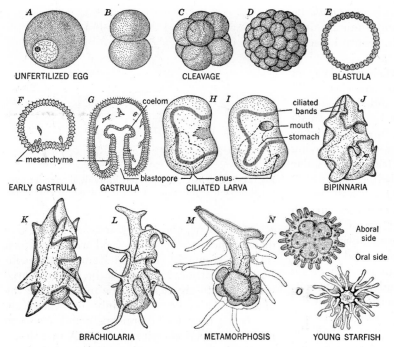

Fig. 22-8. Development of the starfish, *Asterias vulgaris*. The blastula (*E*) and gastrula (*F*, *G*) are sectioned; the latter shows migration of mesenchyme cells and budding of coelomic cavities off the gastrocoel. The blastopore becomes the anus (*H*), and the stomodeum invaginates to form the mouth (*I*). The bilaterally symmetrical bipinnaria larva (*J*) produces three pairs of lateral lobes that lengthen in the brachiolaria larva (*K*, *L*), as do others on the ventral surface. The starfish forms on the lower right side of the brachiolaria (*M*), the upper parts of which are absorbed. (*Adapted from Field; Goto; and Brooks.*)

anterior end foremost, with a clockwise rotation, feeding throughout its free existence. Later, three lobes form on each side of the body to produce the **bipinnaria** larval stage. Still later, these become modified as long ciliated processes that move and contract, when the larva is termed a **brachiolaria** (2 to 3 mm. long). After 6 or 7 weeks the larva settles to the bottom, the anterior end becomes a stalk by which it attaches, and the posterior end enlarges and bends to the left. Five lobes form on the right side of this posterior part, which becomes the aboral surface of the future starfish; the left side produces the oral surface. Skeletal elements appear as the first lobes (arms) become evident. Two pairs of outgrowths from the coelom (hydrocoele) in each lobe become the first tube feet and serve for attachment. A complex internal reorganization occurs during the metamorphosis, but no parts are cast off. Any bilateral symmetry in the adult is about a different plane than that in the larva. The female blood starfish (*Henricia*) produces few large-yolked eggs that are held beneath the disc by arching the rays; the larval stages are abbreviated, and young emerge as miniature adults.

Starfishes suffer injury in nature and may break off an arm (autotomy) if severely handled. The arms regenerate readily, and individuals often are seen with one or more of them growing out. Experimental removal of four or, exceptionally, all arms may be followed by complete regeneration.

CLASS OPHIUROIDEA. BRITTLE STARS AND SERPENT STARS

22-8. Structure. The brittle star has a small rounded disc with five distinct arms that are long, slender, jointed, and fragile (Fig. 22-1). An arm consists of many similar segments, each comprising two central fused ossicles covered by four plates, the laterals with spinelets and the dorsal and ventral spineless. The interior of a segment is almost filled by solid cylindrical ossicles ("vertebrae") excavated on the proximal face and convex distally so that the adjacent vertebrae articulate with one another by a complex ball-and-socket joint. Four mus-

Fig. 22-9. Class OPHIUROIDEA. Basket star, *Gorgonocephalus*. As illustrated by Rondelet, *De piscibus marinis*, 1551.

cles between each two vertebrae enable the arm to be bent readily. In the arm is a small tubular coelom, nerve cord, hemal space, and branch of the water vascular system. The small tube feet ("tentacles") are ventrolateral, without either suckers or ampullae; they are sensory, aid in respiration, and may pass food to the mouth. All digestive and reproductive organs are in the disc. The mouth is centered orally and surrounded by five groups of movable plates that serve as jaws. There is a sac-like stomach, but no caeca or anus; indigestible wastes are cast out the mouth. Five pairs of sac-like bursae open by narrow slits about the mouth; they function in respiration and receive the gonad ducts. The madreporite is on the oral surface. In the basket stars (*Gorgonocephalus*) the arms are repeatedly branched, with tendril-like tips (Fig. 22-9).

22-9. Natural history. Ophiurans live in shallow to deep water, hiding beneath stones or seaweed or burying themselves in the mud or sand, to become active at night. They move by rapid snake-like movements, holding to objects by one or more arms and pushing with the others so as to jerk the body along. They can swim by use of their arms much as a person

would do. Their food is of small crustaceans, mollusks, and other animals and of bottom debris; ophiurans in turn are eaten by fishes. The arms break or can be cast off easily, and some species can discard the disc except for the mouth framework, such parts being readily regenerated. The sexes are usually separate and release their sex cells into the sea. The resulting microscopic *pluteus* larva has long ciliated arms and after some days undergoes a metamorphosis resembling that of starfishes. Some ophiurans (*Ophioplocus*) rear their young, which have no free-swimming stage, in the bursae.

CLASS ECHINOIDEA. SEA URCHINS, SAND DOLLARS, AND HEART URCHINS

22-10. Structure. Members of this class have rounded bodies lacking free arms or rays but bristling with slender movable spines (Fig. 22-10). Sea urchins (*Arbacia, Strongylocentrotus*) are hemispherical in shape, heart urchins (*Spatangus*) are ovoid, and sand dollars, or "sea cakes" (*Echinarachnius, Dendraster*), are disc-like.

In a common urchin the viscera are enclosed in a test or **shell,** of 10 double rows of plates, usually firmly sutured together. Five areas (ambulacra), corresponding to the arms of starfishes, are perforated for a double series of long slender **tube feet,** and the other alternating areas (interambulacra) are wider but lack tube feet. On the plates are series of low

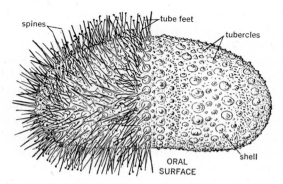

Fig. 22-10. Class ECHINOIDEA. Sea urchin, *Strongylocentrotus*. The tube feet and spines are in place on the left side of the figure, but removed on the right half.

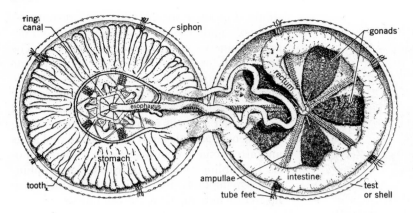

Fig. 22-11. Sea urchin, *Arbacia*, general structure. The test has been cut horizontally, and the oral half laid to the left; spines omitted. (*After Coe*, 1912.)

rounded *tubercles* over which the spines articulate. Each spine (a single crystal of calcite, $CaCO_3$) has a cup-shaped base fitting over the tubercle, and can be moved by muscles around the base. Among the spines are three-jawed *pedicellariae* on long flexible stalks; some echinoids have several kinds and a few bear poison glands. The pedicellariae keep the body clean and capture small prey. The *anus* is centered on the aboral surface, among large plates that contain the 5 (4 or 2) *genital openings.* The large *mouth* is on the oral surface, surrounded by five strong, sharp *teeth;* these are supported by a complex five-sided framework inside the shell that is known as "Aristotle's lantern."

The long *digestive tract* is looped around inside the test (Fig. 22-11). From the mouth a slender esophagus leads to a more expanded stomach that has sac-like pouches; the narrow intestine connects by the rectum to the anus. A slender tube-like *siphon,* lined with strong cilia, extends from the esophagus to the beginning of the intestine; presumably, it carries water directly to the latter and may aid in washing out indigestible residues. In sand dollars the mouth is central, but the anus is near the edge of the disc; in heart urchins both the mouth and anus are marginal, at opposite sides of the disc, providing a secondary bilateral symmetry. Ten *gills* protrude from the peristomial membrane about the mouth. The madreporite is aboral, a ring canal circles the esophagus, and five radial canals extend meridionally on the interior of the shell, connecting

to the tube feet. A *nerve ring* surrounds the mouth, and the five radial *nerves* accompany the radial canals. The *gonads* (5, 4, or 2) are attached by strong mesenteries to the inner aboral surface, and from each a fine duct leads to a genital opening. Eggs and sperm are discharged into the sea, and the minute fertilized egg becomes a *pluteus* that metamorphoses after 5 or 6 weeks. Some echinoids brood their eggs. When damaged, adult echinoids can regenerate parts of the test, spines, tube feet, and pedicellariae.

22-11. Natural history. The urchins live on rocks or mud of the seashore and bottom, some down to 5,000 meters. They move by joint use of the spines and tube feet, and the feet serve to grip objects on the sea floor. Some shore dwellers shift to tide pools or hide under seaweeds at low tide. Others live permanently in self-excavated depressions in hard clay or soft rock under shore waters. The sand dollars and heart urchins bury themselves shallowly in sand. All echinoids clean their bodies by movements of the spines and pedicellariae, and wastes from the anus are similarly moved off. They feed variously on seaweed, dead animal matter, and small organisms, and they also ingest sand or mud to extract the contained organic matter. Echinoids have many commensal ciliates in the digestive tract, and various other commensals and parasites live on or in their bodies. Fishes, sea stars, crabs, and predaceous birds and mammals are their chief enemies.

Gonads of echinoids, raw or roasted in the half shell, are eaten by people of the Mediterranean and South America, and formerly by American Indians.

CLASS HOLOTHURIOIDEA.
Sea Cucumbers

22-12. Structure. Unlike other echinoderms, sea cucumbers have slender bodies elongated on an oral-aboral axis. The body covering is leathery and contains only microscopic limy ossicles. *Cucumaria* and *Thyone* are common examples (Figs. 22-12, 22-13). The anterior mouth is surrounded by 10 to 30 retractile *tentacles,* comparable with the oral tube feet of other echinoderms. The holothurian lies usually with one side (dorsal) uppermost; this on some has two lengthwise zones of *tube feet* that are tactile and respiratory in function. The ventral side has typically three zones of tube feet, with suckers, that serve in locomotion. The body wall comprises a cuticle over a nonciliated epidermis, the dermis which contains ossicles, a layer of circular muscles, and then five double bands of powerful longitudinal muscles along the radii. The large, fluid-filled, and undivided coelom contains various amoebocytes. Action of the muscles over the fluid-filled body enables the holothurian to extend or contract its body and to perform worm-like movements.

The long digestive tract is slender and looped within the coelom. A short esophagus leads from the mouth to the enlarged stomach; the long intestine is supported by mesenteries and connects to a muscular cloaca ending at the posterior anus. Two much-branched tubes, the *respiratory trees*, extend forward from the cloaca into the coelom. Water pumped in and out of these tubes by action of the muscular cloaca serves for respiration and excretion; some water undoubtedly passes through the walls of the trees to keep the coelom turgid. The water vascular system includes a madreporite within the coelom, a ring canal around the esophagus, and five radial canals connecting to tube feet along each muscle band. The hemal system is more evident than in other echinoderms with vessels

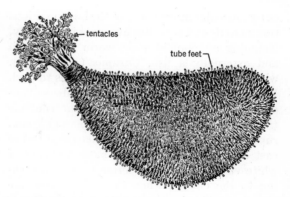

Fig. 22-12. Class Holothurioidea. Sea cucumber, *Thyone briareus.* External features. (*After Coe,* 1912.)

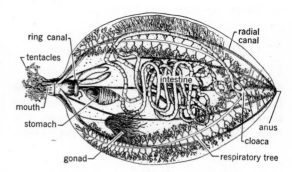

Fig. 22-13. Class Holothurioidea. Sea cucumber, *Thyone.* Internal structure; body wall cut lengthwise and laid open. (*After Coe,* 1912.)

along the intestine. A nerve ring circles the esophagus, and nerves extend along the radii. The sexes are separate (united in a few). The gonad is brush-like, with fine tubules joining a single duct that opens middorsally near the tentacles. Many holothurians extrude their eggs and sperm into the sea, and the resulting larva is an *auricularia.* Others brood the eggs either on or in the body.

22-13. Natural history. Sea cucumbers lie sluggishly on the sea bottom or burrow in the surface mud or sand to leave only the ends of the body exposed; when disturbed they contract slowly. The food is of organic material in the bottom debris that is pushed into the mouth or of plankton trapped in mucus on the tentacles. They travel slowly by use of the tube feet or by muscular movements of the body. Various commensals and parasites live on or in the body, including an annelid scale worm and a crab and externally a fish, *Carapus* (=*Fierasfer*), which dwells in the cloaca but emerges to feed. When strongly irritated, some cucumbers (*Synapta*) fragment the body by violent contractions into two or more pieces; others (*Thyone*) rupture the body wall, and various organs are cast out. Some holothurians have a cluster of white viscous tubes (Cuvierian organs) attaching to the cloaca; when disturbed, these are thrust out to entangle an enemy. In the Orient the body wall of some sea cucumbers is boiled and then dried in the sun to produce "trepang" or "bêche-de-mer" used for soup.

CLASS CRINOIDEA. Sea Lilies and Feather Stars

22-14. Structure and natural history. These flower-like echinoderms live from below the low-tide line to depths of over 12,000 feet. The body is a small cup-shaped *calyx* of limy plates

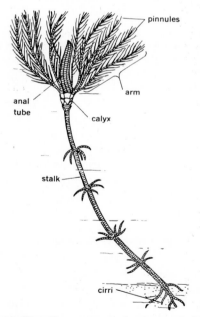

Fig. 22-14. Class Crinoidea. A simple attached crinoid.

to which are attached five flexible **arms** that fork to form 10 or more narrow appendages, each bearing many slender lateral **pinnules,** arranged like barbs on a feather. Sea lilies have a long jointed **stalk** from the lower or aboral surface of the calyx that attaches the crinoid to the sea bottom by root-like outgrowths; feather stars lack a stalk but have flexible **cirri** for gripping objects in the water (Figs. 22-1, 22-14). Both mouth and anus are on the upper or oral surface of the disc, the anus often on a raised cone. The oral surface of each arm has an open ambulacral groove, lined with cilia and containing the tentacle-like tube feet. The food is of microscopic plankton and detritus, caught by the tentacles and conveyed by the cilia to the mouth. There is no madreporite. The aboral nervous system has a central ring, and a nerve to each arm. The coelom is scant and the gonads are usually in the pinnules. Some crinoids shed the eggs directly into the water, but in other species they remain attached to the pinnules until hatched. The larva subsists on yolk in the egg, having no mouth. After a few days of free life, it attaches by the anterior end, and then the stem, disc, and arms are developed. Some crinoids brood the eggs inside the body. Crinoids have great powers of regeneration, casting off the arms or much of the calyx and then renewing these parts. No animals are reported to feed regularly on crinoids. There are many commensals and parasites, notably bizzare polychaetes (*Polynoe, Myzostomum*) on the arms and disc. Some small gastropods bore into crinoids to eat out the soft parts.

Crinoids were especially abundant in Paleozoic times, and many thick limestone beds over the world are mainly of fossil crinoids. Of living species about 80 are sea lilies that live attached to the bottom, on coral reefs, and elsewhere, forming extensive "gardens." The remainder are free-living feather stars like *Antedon* that can swim by using their long arms but commonly grip objects on the bottom with their cirri. Many living crinoids are brilliant—yellow, red, white, green, or brown in life.

CLASSIFICATION

PHYLUM ECHINODERMATA. Echinoderms. Symmetry radial, body usually of 5 ambulacra (radii) that bear tube feet alternating with 5 interambulacra (interradii), around an oral-aboral axis; no segmentation; body wall with epidermis over limy mesodermal plates that usually form a flexible or rigid box-like endoskeleton with projecting spines or low bosses (none in sea cucumbers); commonly with minute jawed pedicellariae; coelom large, lined with peritoneum; sexes usually separate but alike; larvae bilaterally symmetrical and free-living before metamorphosis; all marine; Cambrian to Recent; about 3,900 living species.

SUBPHYLUM 1. PELMATOZOA. Both mouth and anus on upper surface; body in cup- or calyx-shaped skeleton; usually attached by aboral stalk or by aboral surface.

CLASS 1. †*CARPOIDEA* (Heterostelea). Calyx laterally flattened, attached directly or by horizontal stalk; few arm extensions. Cambrian to Devonian. †*Trochocystites.*

CLASS 2. †*CYSTOIDEA.* Calyx upright, rigid, bud-like, usually not 5-parted. Ordovician to Devonian. †*Caryocrinites*, †*Pleurocystites.*

CLASS 3. †*BLASTOIDEA.* Calyx 5-parted, bud-like, of 13 major plates. Ordovician to Permian. †*Pentremites.*

CLASS 4. †*EDRIOASTEROIDEA.* Calyx globular or disc-shaped, many small plates. Cambrian to Carboniferous. †*Stromatocystites.*

CLASS 5. *CRINOIDEA.* Sea Lilies, Feather Stars. Calyx cup-like, symmetrical; arms branched, ambulacra open; tube feet lack suckers; no madreporite, spines, or pedicellariae. Cambrian to Recent; about 630 living and 5,000 fossil species. †*Platycrinites; Antedon tenella*, feather star, Chesapeake Bay to Newfoundland; *Bathycrinus.*

SUBPHYLUM 2. ELEUTHEROZOA. Mouth usually on lower surface; no stalk.

CLASS 6. *HOLOTHURIOIDEA.* Sea Cucumbers. Body long, sausage- or worm-shaped, wall leathery to thin; no arms, spines, or pedicellariae; skeleton usually only of microscopic plates in body wall; tube feet (podia) usually present; mouth anterior, ringed by retractile tentacles; gut long, anus posterior; cloaca usually with respiratory trees. Devonian to Recent; about 500 living species.

    Order 1. Aspidochirota. Tentacles usually 20 (15 to 30), each branched (peltate) from central stalk; tube feet many. *Holothuria, Stichopus, Bathyplotes.*

    Order 2. Elasipoda. Tentacles peltate; tube feet many; mouth usually ventral. Pelagic from surface down to 5,000 meters. *Pelagothuria.*

    Order 3. Dendrochirota. Tentacles with tree-like branches; tube feet many. *Cucumaria, Thyone; Psolus*, limy plates to ½ inch wide.

    Order 4. Molpadonia. Tentacles small, finger-shaped; tube feet only as anal papillae; posterior end of body usually tapered. *Molpadia, Caudina.*

    Order 5. Apoda. Tentacles pinnate; no tube feet or respiratory trees. *Leptosynapta, Chiridota.*

CLASS 7. *ECHINOIDEA.* Sea Urchins, Sand Dollars, etc. Skeleton (test) usually rigid and globular, disc-like, or heart-shaped; with movable spines, and 3-jawed pedicellariae; slender tube feet with suckers; gut long, slender, coiled; mouth and anus either central or lateral. Ordovician to Recent; about 860 living and 7,200 fossil species.

SUBCLASS 1. †BOTHRIOCIDAROIDA (Pseudoechinoidea). Madreporite ambulacral. Ordovician. †*Bothriocidaris.*

SUBCLASS 2. REGULARIA. Madreporite interambulacral; anus central on aboral surface; lantern present.

    Order 1. Lepidocentroida. Test flexible, plates overlapping; teeth grooved. Ordovician to Recent. †*Paleodiscus, Phorosoma.*

    Order 2. †Melonechinoida. Test high, rigid; no gills. Lower Carboniferous. †*Melonechinus.*

    Order 3. Cidaroida. Test globular, rigid or flexible; no gills; teeth grooved. Devonian to Recent. †*Archeocidaris, Cidaris.*

    Order 4. Aulodonta. Test usually rigid; external gills present; teeth grooved; spine tubercles perforated. Upper Triassic to Recent. †*Pedina; Diadema*, spines to 12 inches long.

    Order 5. Stirodonta. Test rigid; with external gills; teeth keeled; epiphyses of lantern unjoined. Lower Jurassic to Recent. †*Hemicidaris; Salenia.*

    Order 6. Camarodonta. Test rigid; with external gills; teeth keeled; epiphyses of lantern joined above pyramids. Cretaceous to Recent, includes most living forms. *Arbacia, Strongylocentrotus*, common sea urchins.

SUBCLASS 3. IRREGULARIA (Exocycloidea). Anus marginal, on aboral or oral surface; slight secondary bilateral symmetry.

    Order 7. Holectypoida. With lantern; teeth keeled, with lateral flanges. Lower Jurassic to Recent. †*Holectypus; Echinoneus.*

    Order 8. Cassiduloida. No lantern; ambulacral areas alike. Lower Jurassic to Recent. †*Galeropygus; Cassidulus, Echinolampas.*

    Order 9. Clypeasteroida. SAND DOLLARS. Test thin, round or oval; spines and tube feet short; with lantern; teeth keeled, no lateral flanges. Upper Cretaceous to Recent. †*Scutella; Clypeaster, Dendraster, Echinarachnius.*

    Order 10. Spatangoida. HEART URCHINS. Test mostly oval; no lantern. Lower Jurassic to Recent. *Echinocardium, Lovenia, Spatangus.*

CLASS 8. ASTEROIDEA. STARFISHES, or SEA STARS. Body flattened, star-shaped or pentagonal; arms 5 to 50, usually not sharply set off from disc; endoskeleton flexible, of separate ossicles; spines and pedicellariae short; ambulacral grooves open, with 2 or 4 rows of tube feet; madreporite aboral; oral surface downward; stomach large; mostly predaceous. Cambrian to Recent; 2,000 living and 300 fossil species.

    Order 1. †Platyasterida. Ambulacra widely open; arms with marginal plates. Ordovician to Devonian. †*Platanaster.*

    Order 2. †Hemizonida. Ambulacral grooves deep. Ordovician to mid-Carboniferous. †*Taeniactis.*

    Order 3. Phanerozonia. Arms with 2 rows of marginal plates; papulae all aboral; no crossed pedicellariae; tube feet in 2 rows. Ordovician to Recent. *Ctenodiscus,* mud star; *Astropecten; Luidia,* disc small, arms flexible; *Dermasterias,* leather star.

    Order 4. Spinulosa. Marginal plates small; pedicellariae rare. *Asterina; Patiria; Henricia,* arms slender, cylindrical; *Solaster,* sun star, 1 to 14 arms; *Pteraster,* cushion star, with brood chamber for young.

    Order 5. Forcipulata. Marginal plates inconspicuous; pedicellariae with crossed jaws. *Pycnopodia,* Pacific coast, large, rays 18 to 24, disc soft and flat; *Asterias, Pisaster,* common starfishes; *Leptasterias,* broods young; *Stephanasterias,* up to 9 arms.

CLASS 9. OPHIUROIDEA. BRITTLE STARS. Body a central disc and 5 slender, jointed flexible arms; tube feet in 2 rows, sensory, no suckers or pedicellariae; stomach sac-like, no caeca or anus; madreporite aboral; free-living, active. Carboniferous to Recent; about 1,800 living and 180 fossil species.

    Order 1. Ophiurae. Arms unbranched, cannot twist or turn to mouth; discs and arms usually covered with plates. *Ophiothrix.*

    Order 2. Euryalae. Arms often branched, can twist and turn to grip objects; disc and arms with thick skin. *Gorgonocephalus,* basket star.

CLASS 10. †OPHIOCISTIOIDEA. Discoidal, enclosed in plates except at mouth; 6 pairs of giant tubed feet in each ambulacrum. Ordovician to Devonian. †*Sollasina.*

REFERENCES

CLARK, A. H. 1921. Sea-lilies and feather stars. *Smithsonian Miscellaneous Collections*, vol. 72, no. 7, pp. 1–43, 16 pls., 63 figs.

———. 1915–1950. A monograph of the existing crinoids. Vol. 1. *U.S. National Museum Bulletin* 82, 4 + pts. Incomplete.

CUÉNOT, L. 1948. Échinodermes. *In* P.-P. Grassé, Traité de zoologie. Paris, Masson et Cie. Vol. 11, pp. 1–363, 399 figs.

FISHER, W. K. 1911–1930. Asteroidea of the North Pacific and adjacent waters. *U.S. National Museum Bulletin* 76, 3 pts., 1,020 pp., 296 pls.

GALTSOFF, P. S., and V. L. LOOSANOFF. 1950. Natural history and methods of controlling the starfish (*Asterias forbesi* Desor). *U.S. Bureau of Fisheries Bulletin*, vol. 49, pp. 75–132, 32 figs.

HYMAN, L. H. 1955. Echinodermata. *In* The invertebrates. New York, McGraw-Hill Book Co., Inc. Vol. 4, vii + 763 pp., 280 figs. Comprehensive, with bibliography.

JENNINGS, H. S. 1907. Behavior of the starfish *Asterias forreri* De Loriol. *University of California Publications in Zoology*, vol. 4, pp. 53–185, 19 figs.

MACBRIDE, E. W. 1896. The development of Asterina gibbosa. *Quarterly Journal of Microscopical Science*, n.s., vol. 38, pp. 339–411, pls. 18–29.

MORTENSEN, THEODORE. 1927. Handbook of the echinoderms of the British Isles. London, Oxford University Press. ix + 471 pp., 269 figs.

———. 1928–1951. Monograph of the Echinoidea. Copenhagen, C. A. Reitzel. "5" vols. (=16), 4,434 pp., 551 pls., 2,468 figs.

23 PHYLUM MOLLUSCA
Mollusks

Mollusks (L. *mollis*, soft) have soft unsegmented bodies, consisting typically of an anterior head, a ventral foot, and a dorsal visceral mass. The body is more or less surrounded by a thin fleshy mantle and is commonly sheltered in an external limy shell. The phylum comprises five classes of diverse appearance and habits: the chitons (Class AMPHINEURA), tooth shells (SCAPHOPODA), snails and slugs (GASTROPODA), clams, oysters, and other bivalves (PELECYPODA), and the nautili, squids, and octopuses (CEPHALOPODA). Mollusks are of wide distribution in both time and space, having a continuous record since Cambrian time with fully 45,000 living and nearly an equal number of fossil species; many are abundant as individuals. They are mostly marine, living along seashores or in shallow waters, but some occur down to 35,000 feet and others are pelagic. Various snails and some bivalves inhabit brackish and fresh waters, and other snails and the slugs are terrestrial. Most mollusks are free-living creatures that creep slowly. Some attach to rocks, shells, or wood, some burrow, others float, and the squids and octopuses can swim freely. Of major economic importance are the clams, oysters, squids, and others serving as human food; the shells of fresh-water clams that are cut into buttons; and a few bivalves that produce pearls. Some snails and slugs feed on cultivated plants, certain fresh-water snails are intermediate hosts for parasitic worms, and the teredos damage wooden ships and wharves. Conchology (malacology) is the study of shells, especially those of mollusks.

23-1. Characteristics. 1. Symmetry bilateral (viscera and shell coiled in GASTROPODA and some CEPHALOPODA); 3 germ layers; no segmentation; epithelium 1-layered, mostly ciliated and with mucous glands.

2. Body usually short, enclosed in a thin dorsal mantle that secretes a shell of 1, 2, or 8 parts (shell in some internal, reduced, or none); head region developed (except SCAPHOPODA, PELECYPODA); a ventral muscular foot variously modified for crawling, burrowing, or swimming.

3. Digestive tract complete, often U-shaped or coiled; mouth with a radula bearing transverse rows of minute chitinous teeth to rasp food (except PELECYPODA); anus opening in mantle cavity; a large digestive gland (liver) and often salivary glands.

4. Circulatory system includes a dorsal heart with 1 or 2 auricles and 1 ventricle, usually in a pericardial cavity, an anterior aorta, and other vessels.

5. Respiration by 1 to many gills (ctenidia) or a "lung" in the mantle cavity, by the mantle, or by the epidermis.

6. Excretion by kidneys (nephridia), either 1 or 2 pairs or 1, connecting to pericardial cavity and veins; coelom reduced to cavities of nephridia, gonads, and pericardium.

7. Nervous system typically of 3 pairs of ganglia (cerebral above mouth, pedal in foot, visceral in body), joined by longitudinal and cross connectives and nerves; many with organs for touch, smell, or taste, eyespots or complex eyes, and statocysts for equilibration.

8. Sexes usually separate (some hermaphroditic, a few protandric); gonads 2 or 1, with ducts; fertilization external or internal; mostly oviparous; egg cleavage determinate, unequal, and total (discoidal in CEPHALOPODA); a veliger (trochophore) larva, or parasitic stage (UNIONIDAE), or development direct (PULMONATA, CEPHALOPODA); no asexual reproduction.

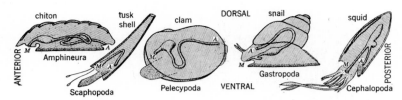

Fig. 23-1. Phylum MOLLUSCA. Relations in the five classes of the shell (heavy lines), foot (stippled), digestive tract (shaded), mouth (*M*), and anus (*A*).

23-2. Relationships. Invertebrates with limy shells such as brachiopods, barnacles, snails, clams, and others were confused in classification by early zoologists, as they may be by beginning students today. Study of both the shells and soft parts has shown the MOLLUSCA to be a large, well-defined, and homogeneous phylum. The type of cleavage in the egg and the resulting veliger larva in many marine snails, bivalves, and chitons resemble the cleavage and trochophore larva of marine annelids. Adult mollusks differ notably from annelids in the lack of segmentation and reduction of the coelom; the few ganglia in the nervous system and presence of one (or two) pairs of nephridia are possible relics of segmentation in mollusks. The chitons, most primitive of living mollusks, have lengthwise nerve cords, as in certain worms. The ANNELIDA and MOLLUSCA were probably differentiated in Pre-Cambrian time, and the classes of MOLLUSCA, including some groups now extinct, were separated soon afterward. Since then the MOLLUSCA have left a long and detailed fossil record by their shells.

23-3. General appearance. Mollusks are diverse in form (Fig. 23-1). Most AMPHINEURA are of elliptical outline, with a large flat foot and the body partly covered dorsally by eight overlapping calcareous plates. The SCAPHOPODA are lengthened dorsoventrally and encased in a slender tubular shell open at both ends. Most GASTROPODA have a long flat foot, a distinct head with eyes and tentacles, and the viscera usually housed in a spiral shell, coiled either to the right or to the left. The PELECYPODA are laterally compressed, have a small foot and no head, and the body is within a pair of lateral shells hinged dorsally. The CEPHALOPODA have a large head with conspicuous lateral eyes, and the mouth surrounded by 8, 10, or many fleshy arms; the shell is usually internal and reduced or lacking.

23-4. Size. Various chitons are ½ to 8 inches long, *Cryptochiton* of the Pacific coast being the largest. The tooth shells are mostly under 2½ inches long, but some grow to 6 inches. The gastropods range from minute snails under 1 mm. in diameter to the north Australian spindle shell (*Hemifusus*) 18 inches long; most species are less than 2 inches in diameter or height. The shells of bivalves are from ½ inch long up to 4½ feet in the "giant clam" (*Tridacna deresa*) of the tropical Pacific, which may grow to weigh 550 pounds. Some squids and octopuses are but 1 inch long, but the giant squid (*Architeuthis*) is recorded with a 20-foot body and 35-foot tentacles, far the largest invertebrate known (Fig. 1-2).

CLASS AMPHINEURA. CHITONS, ETC.

23-5. Structure. The chiton (Order POLYPLACOPHORA, Fig. 23-2) has an elliptical *body* with a convex dorsal surface bearing eight overlapping limy *plates* (valves); these are jointed to one another and covered at the sides (or entirely) by a thick fleshy *girdle* (part of the mantle) containing bristles or spines. The *mantle* covers the dorsal and lateral surfaces, and the flat *foot* occupies most of the ventral surface. Between the foot and mantle is a *pallial groove*. Under the anterior margin of the girdle is the small *head*, which contains the *mouth* but has no eyes or tentacles. The floor of the mouth cavity has a long *radula* with many crossrows of fine *teeth*. A short *pharynx* leads to the rounded *stomach*, to which the *digestive gland* (liver) connects. The long coiled *intestine* ends at the *anus* posteriorly in the pallial groove. The *heart* lies posterodorsally in a

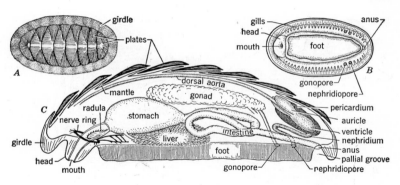

Fig. 23-2. Class AMPHINEURA. The chiton. *A.* Dorsal view. *B.* Ventral view. *C.* Internal structure from the left side, with the shell, mantle, and foot shown in median section.

pericardial cavity; it comprises two auricles and a ventricle connecting to an anterior aorta. Two slender *nephridia* drain wastes from the pericardial cavity. In each pallial groove are the *gills,* 6 to 80 in different species. The *nervous system* comprises a ring about the mouth thaa connects to two pairs of ventral longitudinal nerve cords, the pedal in the foot and pallial in the girdle; the cords have many cross connectives but no ganglia. Some chitons have eyespots or eyes in the integument over the shells. The sexes are separate, each having one fused *gonad* from which a duct extends on either side to a gonopore posterior in the pallial groove.

23-6. Natural history. Chitons are marine and live on rocks, mostly in shallow waters from the tide lines to moderate depths; some occur down to 13,800 feet. They cling tightly or creep slowly by use of the foot, but curl up, like a "pill bug," if dislodged. The dorsal plates protect them against most predaceous enemies. Their food is of seaweeds and microorganisms scraped from the rocks by use of the radula. Some part of the girdle is raised slightly to admit water about the gills for respiration. Fertilization is external, and the eggs (up to 200,-000 in some females) are discharged separately or in long strings. The larva is usually a trochophore. In the West Indies, chitons are eaten as "sea beef."

The Order SOLENOGASTRES comprises small worm-like forms in which the mantle covers the entire body and contains fine limy spicules as the only evidence of a shell. The foot is a cili-

ated ridge in a ventral groove or else is lacking. These animals live on corals or hydroids at considerable depths in the ocean.

CLASS SCAPHOPODA. TOOTH SHELLS OR TUSK SHELLS

23-7. Structure and natural history. In the SCAPHOPODA (Gr. *skaphe,* trough + *podos,* foot) the body is slender dorsoventrally, surrounded by the mantle that secretes a tubular shell, open at both ends, and slightly curved and tapered (Fig. 23-3). Scaphopods are all marine, in shallow waters to depths of 15,000 feet, and live partly buried obliquely in the mud or sand. The pointed foot protrudes from the larger ven-

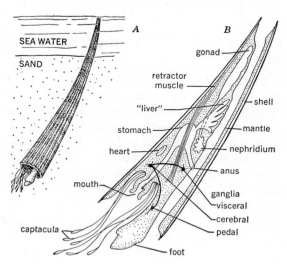

Fig. 23-3. Class SCAPHOPODA. The tooth shell, *Dentalium. A.* Position in life. *B.* Internal structure from the left side; diagrammatic.

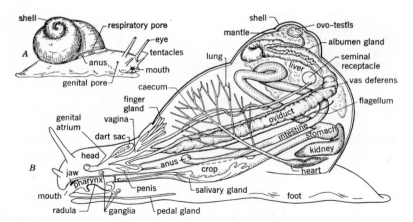

Fig. 23-4. Class Gastropoda. Brown garden snail, *Helix aspersa. A.* External features from the right side. *B.* Internal structure from the left side. The lung is indicated by the branching blood vessels of the mantle cavity that connect to the heart.

tral end of the shell for use in burrowing. About the mouth are several delicate ciliated and contractile tentacles (captacula) with expanded tips; these are sensory and prehensile, serving to capture the microplants and animals used as food. There is no head; lacking gills, the mantle serves for respiration. Scaphopods are dioecious; eggs are discharged separately, and after a short larval stage the young animals sink to the bottom. Scaphopod (*Dentalium*) shells kept on strings were the money of Indians on the Pacific coast, from California to Alaska; their early trade equivalent was 25 cents for 1⅞-inch shells to $5 for the rare 2½-inch shells.

CLASS GASTROPODA. Snails, Whelks, Conchs, Slugs, etc.

The conspicuous anterior head and long ventral foot of the Gastropoda (Gr. *gaster*, belly + *podos*, foot) are bilaterally symmetrical. The visceral mass is usually contained in a dorsal shell, both being spirally coiled and asymmetrical. The shell is unchambered, of one piece, and called a "univalve." Ancestral gastropods probably had bilateral symmetry throughout; but in living species the digestive tract, anus, heart, gills, kidneys, and some nervous structures have been rotated or coiled, to 180 degrees, and certain parts have disappeared (Fig. 23-5).

23-8. Structure. A common gastropod such as the "garden snail" (*Helix aspersa*, Fig. 23-4) has

a fleshy *head* bearing two pairs of retractile *tentacles,* a pair of *eyes* (on tentacles), and a *mouth.* The head joins directly to a muscular *foot,* on top of which is the *shell;* the latter is of calcium carbonate, covered externally by a horny periostracum. A mucous epithelium covers all exposed fleshy parts. On the right side, the *genital pore* opens beside the head, and the small *anus* and larger *respiratory pore* are in the soft mantle margin at the edge of the shell. The *mantle* is a thin membrane that secretes and lines the shell and surrounds the viscera within. All soft parts can be drawn entirely into the shell by the *columella muscle,* which extends internally to the spire at the top of the shell.

The *digestive system* includes (1) the mouth; (2) a muscular pharynx with a dorsal horny "jaw" and ventral radula; (3) a slender esophagus; (4) the large thin-walled crop; (5) a rounded stomach; (6) a long twisted intestine; and (7) the anus. Two flat salivary glands beside the crop send ducts to the pharynx, and a lobed liver high in the shell connects to the stomach. Replacing the gills of other gastropods and mollusks, the land snail has a *lung* and hence is a "pulmonate." The lung is a network of blood vessels on the outer wall of the mantle in the large *mantle cavity* within the shell; air enters and leaves by the respiratory pore. Blood collected from the body is aerated in the lung and then pumped by the heart through arteries to the head, foot, and viscera.

Fig. 23-5. Class GASTROPODA. Plan of organization in the 3 subclasses, showing rotation of the viscera and crossing of nerve commissures, with loss of the left ventricle, gill, and kidney in OPISTHOBRANCHIA, and a lung replacing the gill in PULMONATA. Shell and body outlined, mantle area shaded, nervous system black. *A*, auricle, *V*, ventricle; sex organs omitted. (*Modified from Stempell.*)

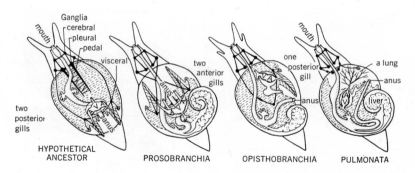

The *heart* has one auricle and a ventricle. A single *kidney* drains from the pericardial cavity around the heart and discharges into the mantle cavity. The *nerve ganglia* are condensed, the cerebral pair dorsal to the pharynx and the buccal, pedal, and visceral pairs close beneath it; nerves from the ganglia extend to all organs. The tip of each posterior tentacle has an *eye* with cornea, lens, and retina, and also probably an olfactory organ. Below the pedal ganglia lie a pair of *statocysts,* the organs of equilibrium, each containing calcareous bodies, cilia, and sensory cells. There are other sensory structures in the epidermis of the head and foot.

Each individual has a combined male and female *reproductive system.* High in the shell is the *ovotestis,* which produces both eggs and sperm. A *hermaphroditic duct* connects to the *albumen gland* of the female system. A slender *vas deferens* conducts sperm to the *penis,* which lies in a sac off the common *genital atrium;* the long *flagellum,* joined to the penis sac, presumably forms the spermatophore in which sperm are transferred at mating. The *oviduct* (larger than the vas deferens) leads from the albumen gland to the *vagina,* which in turn connects to the genital atrium. Joined to the vagina are the slender duct of the *seminal receptacle,* the *"finger" gland,* and the *dart sac.*

23-9. Natural history. *Helix* is most active at night and in damp weather. It glides slowly and smoothly by waves of muscular action on the ventral side of the foot, over a "slime track" of mucus secreted by the large pedal gland below the mouth. The food is of green vegetation, moistened by salivary secretions, held by the jaw, and rasped off in small bits by movements of the radula. Land snails, when present in numbers, may do severe damage to garden and field plants and even to trees. By day the snails hide beneath objects on the ground, in crevices, or in burrows; the soft head and foot are then drawn into the shell. In dry weather a temporary covering (epiphragm) of mucus and lime is secreted to cover the shell aperture and avoid desiccation.

Reproduction is preceded by a mating performance between two snails, during which a "dart" from each is discharged into the body of the other. Copulation is reciprocal, the penis of each being inserted into the vagina of the other for transfer of a spermatophore; the snails then separate. Each later deposits one or more batches of gelatinous-covered eggs in damp places or shallow slanting burrows. Development requires many days and is direct, the young emerging as minute snails.

23-10. Other Gastropoda. There is infinite variety in the shell and soft parts of gastropods. The shell may be tall or short, conical, turban-like, spindle-shaped, or cylindrical, white or variously colored, and plain or ornamented with ridges, spines, etc. Land slugs have the shell reduced and internal or lacking, and the nudibranchs have only a small coiled shell (protoconch) as larvae and none as adults. Most gastropods can withdraw completely into their shells, and many have a permanent plate (operculum) to cover the aperture. In most species the shell is right-handed (dextral), being coiled clockwise as seen from the spire, but some are left-handed (sinistral). In the HET-

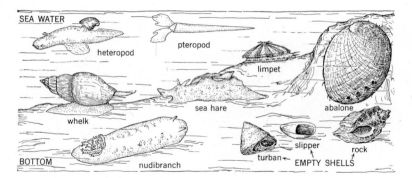

Fig. 23-6. Class GASTROPODA. Some marine forms in life and some empty shells. Subclass PROSOBRANCHIA: *Fissurella*, limpet; *Haliotis*, abalone; *Crepidula*, slipper shell; *Tegula*, turban shell; *Carinaria*, heteropod; *Murex*, rock shell; *Buccinum*, edible whelk. Subclass OPISTHOBRANCHIA: *Aplysia*, sea hare; *Clione*, pteropod; *Doris*, nudibranch.

EROPODA the foot is a vertically compressed fin, and the PTEROPODA have a pair of lateral fins near the head; both of these groups swim in the open sea (Fig. 23-6).

The more primitive gastropods (PROSOBRANCHIA) are chiefly marine and possess two gills; others (OPISTHOBRANCHIA) have but one gill, nephridium, and auricle, the left of each having disappeared and the true right organ being on the left side. The gastropods evidently developed in the sea, whence some forms in time migrated to fresh waters; some types invaded the land to become the PULMONATA. Certain of the latter have returned to fresh water where, having a lung instead of gills, they must come to the surface at intervals to respire. Some gastropods (limpets, nudibranchs) have regained an external bilateral symmetry, but the internal viscera are coiled, implying their derivation from coiled types.

Gastropods abound in salt and fresh waters and on land, occurring from the tropics to subpolar regions, to depths of 17,000 feet in the sea and up to 18,000 feet in The Himalayas. Land snails are found from moist tropical regions to arid deserts. A number of them and some slugs have been spread with cultivated plants to places where they were not native, and some marine snails have been transplanted with oyster "spat." Most marine gastropods produce large numbers of eggs that develop into a veliger larval stage before metamorphosing to the adult form.

The gastropods are mainly herbivorous, but some (*Buccinum*, *Urosalpinx*) are predators that bore into and feed on other mollusks. A few are predators on echinoderms. Many snails are the necessary intermediate hosts for trematode flatworms (par. 19-10). Gastropods are eaten by other invertebrates and by many kinds of vertebrates. For ancient man and primitive peoples univalves have served as food, and *Helix pomatia* is still eaten commonly in Europe. Shells of gastropods provided the "money" of various native races, including the wampum of American Indians.

CLASS PELECYPODA. BIVALVES: CLAMS, MUSSELS, OYSTERS, ETC.

Members of this class are bilaterally symmetrical and laterally compressed, with the soft body enclosed in a rigid shell of two parts —hence called "bivalves"; there is no head. The foot usually is wedge-shaped (Gr. *pelekys*, hatchet + *podos*, foot), and the gills are thin and plate-like (whence Lamellibranchiata, an earlier name for the class). Bivalves inhabit both salt and fresh waters. Some creep on the bottom, others attach to solid objects, and many burrow in sand or mud. A fresh-water clam or mussel, *Anodonta* or *Unio*, will illustrate the anatomy of a bivalve (Fig. 23-7).

23-11. Structure. The somewhat oval *shell* is a firm exoskeleton that protects the body and provides for muscle attachments. It is of symmetrical right and left *valves,* the thinner margins of which are ventral and the thicker dorsal. In the dorsal region are (1) the *hinge teeth* (none in *Anodonta*), which align the valves with each other and serve as a pivot when the

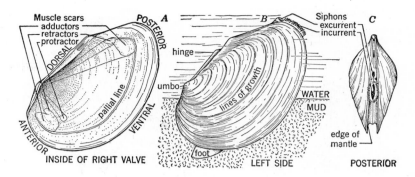

Fig. 23-7. Class PELECYPODA. Fresh-water clam, *Anodonta*. Shell and external features. Lines radiating from the umbo show the path of the muscle attachments as the shell grows in size.

shell opens or closes; (2) an elastic **hinge ligament** between the valves that tends to draw them together dorsally and separate their ventral margins; and (3) an anterior swollen **umbo** on each valve, representing its oldest portion. Around the umbo are many concentric **lines of growth** indicating intervals between successive growth stages, the annual lines being more conspicuous.

The shell (Fig. 23-8) is of three layers: (1) the external **periostracum,** a thin, colored, horny covering that protects parts beneath from being dissolved by carbonic acid in the water; the umbo on old shells is often corroded where this layer wears off; (2) a middle **prismatic layer** of crystalline calcium carbonate; and (3) the inner **nacre,** or "mother-of-pearl" lining, formed of many thin layers of calcium carbonate and having a slight iridescence. The outer two layers are produced by the edge of the mantle, and the nacre by the entire surface of that membrane. The shell grows in area by addition around the margin and in thickness by successive deposits of nacre, being thickest under the umbo.

The soft **body** within the shell (Fig. 23-9) consists of (1) a plump median **visceral mass,** attached dorsally and containing various organs; its anteroventral part forms (2) the muscular **foot.** On each side of these hang (3) a thin double **gill,** outside of which is (4) the **mantle lobe,** a thin sheet of tissue adhering to the inner surface of a valve. The free margins of the mantle are muscular and can be brought together to close the **mantle cavity** within. Posteriorly the mantle margins form two short tubes:

a ventral or **incurrent siphon** and a dorsal or **excurrent siphon.** Water moves in and out these openings by the action of cilia covering surfaces in the mantle cavity.

Scars on the inner surface of each valve indicate the attachments of **muscles** (Fig. 23-7*A*). These are the large **anterior** and **posterior adductors,** both transverse, which draw the valves together; the **anterior** and **posterior retractors,** which draw the foot into the shell, and the **anterior protractor,** which helps to extend the foot.

The **digestive system** includes (1) the small **mouth,** just behind the anterior adductor and between two thin fleshy **labial palps;** (2) a short **esophagus;** (3) a rounded **stomach** dorsally in the visceral mass, and joined by ducts from (4) the paired **digestive gland** (liver); (5) the slen-

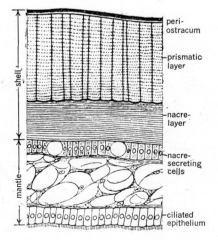

Fig. 23-8. Fresh-water clam. Enlarged cross section of shell and mantle.

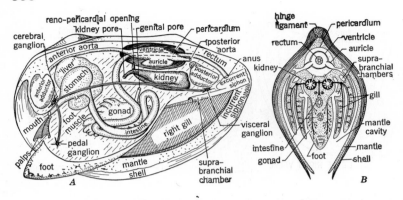

Fig. 23-9. Fresh-water clam, *Anodonta*. *A*. Internal structure as seen with shell, mantle, and gill of the left side removed. *B*. Cross section through the heart region. Both diagrammatic. (*B, after Stempell*.)

der *intestine* coiled in the visceral mass above the foot; (6) the dorsal *rectum* surrounded by the heart; and (7) the *anus* opening into the excurrent siphon. Off the stomach is a pouch (pyloric caecum), usually containing a transparent flexible rod, the *crystalline style,* that provides a starch-reducing enzyme useful in digesting plankton. The rectum has a longitudinal fold, or *typhlosole,* that increases its inner surface (as in earthworms). The mouth has no jaws or radula.

The *circulatory system* comprises a dorsal *heart,* of two auricles joining a muscular ventricle; the latter is around the rectum and within a *pericardial cavity.* The ventricle pumps blood forward in an *anterior aorta* supplying the foot and viscera (except the kidneys and gills) and backward in a *posterior aorta* delivering to the rectum and mantle. Blood oxygenated in the mantle returns directly to the auricles, but that which circulates through other organs is collected in a *vein* to the kidneys and thence passes to the gills for oxygenation before returning to the heart (Fig. 23-10). Some arterial blood enters vessels lined by epithelium, and some discharges into blood sinuses without cellular lining, as in the foot; some blood also diffuses to intercellular spaces. The blood carries oxygen and dissolved nutrients to all parts of the body; also it disposes of carbon dioxide in the gills and mantle and of organic wastes in the kidneys.

The function of respiration is performed jointly by the mantle and two double gills. The *gill* (ctenidium) is a W-shaped structure, each half of two thin plate-like *lamellae* completely joined at the ventral margin where there is a *food groove* (Fig. 23-11). Each lamella is made of many vertical *gill bars,* strengthened by chitinous rods and connected to one another by horizontal bars, with small pores (ostia) between. Cross partitions (interlamellar junctions), between the two lamellae, divide the interior of a gill into many vertical *water tubes.* Dorsally the water tubes of each gill join a common *suprabranchial chamber* that extends posteriorly to the exhalent siphon. There is a slit-like passage from the mantle cavity to the suprabranchial chamber of each inner gill. Blood from veins in the kidneys passes through fine afferent and efferent vessels in the interlamellar junctions for aeration before returning to the heart.

Just below the pericardium are two *kidneys,* which remove organic wastes from the blood and pericardial fluid. Each is a U-shaped tube

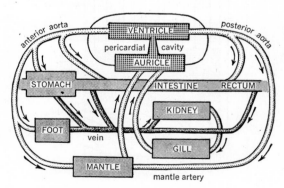

Fig. 23-10. Fresh-water clam. Diagram of the circulatory system and blood flow.

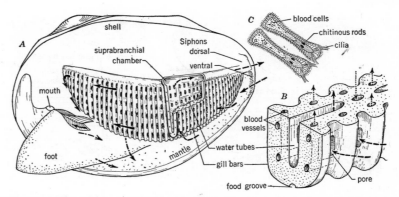

Fig. 23-11. Fresh-water clam. Diagrams of gill structure. *A*. Outer half of left gill partly cut away to show internal structure. ←----, path of water; ←, path of food particles caught in mucus and carried to mouth; ←·−·, path of rejected particles. *B*. Portion of gill enlarged. ←···, path of blood flow, down in afferent and up in efferent vessels. *C*. Cross section of two gill bars much enlarged to show ciliated surfaces and blood cells.

with a ciliated aperture draining from the pericardial cavity, a glandular region adjacent to the vein, and a bladder discharging through a ciliated opening into the suprabranchial chamber of the gill.

The *nervous system* includes three pairs of *ganglia,* the cerebral beside the esophagus, the pedal in the foot, and the visceral below the posterior adductor muscle. Each pair is joined by a commissure, and there are also cerebropedal and cerebrovisceral commissures besides nerves to various organs. The *sensory structures* include light-responsive devices in the siphon margins, tactile organs in the mantle edge, a pair of *statocysts* (for equilibration) in the foot, and an *osphradium* in the incurrent siphon over each visceral ganglion. The osphradia evidently test incoming water for silt, stimulating a reduction of intake when the silt content is high.

The sexes are separate but alike externally. In each are two much-branched *gonads* about the intestinal coils in the visceral mass, each discharging by a short *duct* near the kidney aperture.

23-12. Natural history. Fresh-water mussels live in ponds, lakes, and streams, some in quiet and others in flowing waters. They may migrate to shallows by night and retire to deeper places by day and may change their habitat with the seasons. They are usually embedded partly in sand or mud or are wedged between rocks, with the valves slightly spread, the mantle margins closed, and the siphons exposed (Fig. 23-7). They can travel slowly by extending the foot between the valves to expand or hook it into bottom materials and then draw the body along by contraction of the foot muscles. This action is aided by the filling and emptying of blood sinuses in the foot. Dragging the shell along leaves parallel furrows in the bottom. The siphons open and close in response to light, touch, and other stimuli. By the action of cilia covering the mantle and gills, water is drawn through the incurrent siphon into the mantle cavity. Organic particles and microorganisms (diatoms, protozoans, etc.), suspended in the water, constitute the food; this is trapped in mucus on the gills, carried ventrally by the beating cilia to the food groove along the ventral edge of the gill and to the labial palps and mouth. Food is digested in the stomach, by aid of "liver" secretions, and absorbed in the intestine; any residues pass out the anus. The water provides oxygen for aeration of blood in the gills; it passes through the pores, up the water tubes to the suprabranchial chambers, and out the exhalent siphon, carrying away carbon dioxide and feces, and sex products.

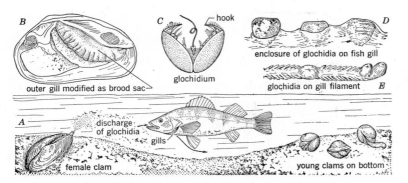

Fig. 23-12. Fresh-water clam. *A.* Diagram of the life cycle. *B.* The female's outer gill modified as a brood sac. *C.* One glochidium. *D.* Enclosure of glochidia by epithelium on gill of a fish. *E.* Glochidia on a gill filament. *C–E,* much enlarged. (*B–D, after Lefevre and Curtis,* 1910.)

23-13. Reproduction. Most mollusks set their eggs and sperm free, but the fresh-water bivalves of the Family UNIONIDAE have a peculiar mode of reproduction. In a female the ripe eggs pass from the ovaries to the suprabranchial chambers, and there are fertilized by sperm discharged from a male and brought in water entering the female. The eggs attach (by mucus) in the water tubes of her gills, which enlarge as **brood chambers** (marsupia); some species use all gill lamellae, others only the outer two (Fig. 23-12). Each egg, by total but unequal cleavage, develops into a minute larval **glochidium,** 0.1 to 0.4 mm. wide, with two valves closed by an adductor muscle and a long larval thread; in some (*Anodonta,* etc.) the valves have ventral hooks, but others (*Unio, Quadrula, Lampsilis*) lack hooks. The larvae are shed into the water through the female's exhalent siphon, then sink to the bottom or are scattered by water currents. They can open or close their shells but cannot move independently. Hooked glochidia attach to soft exterior parts of fresh-water fishes resting on the bottom; hookless forms clamp to the gill filaments of fishes, being carried in the respiratory water of the latter. In a few hours either type is covered with a capsule formed by migration and mitosis of cells of the host's epithelium. The parasitic larvae feed and grow by absorbing nutrients from the host's body fluids. Later the cyst weakens, the young mollusk opens and closes its valves, extends its foot, and escapes to the bottom to become free-living. In some clams (*Quadrula, Unio*) breeding occurs in summer (May to August), and the glochidial stages last

10 to 70 days depending on the species and water temperature. Others (*Anodonta, Lampsilis*) produce eggs in late summer, and the glochidia are retained in the female until the following spring. Individual fishes in nature may carry up to 20 glochidia, but a fish 3 or 4 inches long may be artificially infected with several hundred that will grow to metamorphosis. The glochidial stage serves to disperse the young over a wide area. At times glochidia in hatcheries cause losses among trout.

23-14. Other Pelecypoda. The bivalves are all aquatic, mostly marine, and chiefly sedentary bottom dwellers. They are commonest from the tide lines into shallow waters, but some occur down to 17,000 feet. A few creep slowly on the bottom, but most marine species, including various edible clams, burrow in the sand or mud and extend their siphons up to the water (Fig. 23-13). The sea mussel (*Mytilus*) attaches to solid objects by a "byssus" of threads secreted by glands in the reduced foot. Edible oysters (*Ostrea*) become attached permanently to rocks or shells by a secretion. Some bivalves (*Pholas*) can burrow in hard clay or soft rocks. The shipworms or teredos (*Teredo, Bankia*) are highly specialized with very slender bodies and small anterior shells; using the latter, they burrow in the wood of ships or wharves immersed in sea water. The scallop (*Pecten*) attaches by a byssus but can free itself and swim by clapping its shells together. In both *Pecten* and *Lima* the mantle edge is prolonged as filaments beyond the shell. Still other bivalves are commensals on echinoderms, some live in the bur-

Fig. 23-13. Class PELECYPODA. Positions of some marine forms in life; reduced but not to same scale. Order PROTOBRANCHIA: *Nucula; Yoldia.* Order FILOBRANCHIA: *Ostrea,* edible oyster; *Mytilus,* sea mussel with byssus; *Pecten,* scallop. Order EULAMELLIBRANCHIA: *Mya,* mud clam; *Venus,* quahog; *Tagelus,* jackknife clam; *Ensis,* razor clam; *Pholas,* rock borer; *Teredo,* pileworm or shipworm.

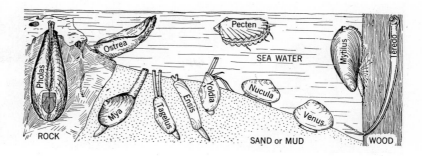

rows of worms and crustaceans, others are embedded in sponges and the tests of ascidians, and *Entovalva* is parasitic in holothurians.

Some bivalves are enormously abundant. An estimated 4,500,000,000 clams live on 700 square miles of the Dogger Bank, east of England. Shells of the fossil †*Exogyra* of Cretaceous time occur in rocks from New Jersey to Mexico, over 2,500 miles. Oysters, mussels, and others inhabit various coastal waters in large numbers.

In the great majority of PELECYPODA, both ova and sperm are discharged into the water where fertilization occurs, and the zygote develops into a ciliated ***veliger larva*** somewhat resembling the trochophore of annelids. This in time acquires a shell gland, sinks to the bottom, and becomes a miniature bivalve. Since the hazards in such reproduction are great, these mollusks produce vast numbers of eggs—from 16,000,000 to 60,000,000 may issue from a female oyster in one season.

In the common American oyster (*Crassostrea virginica*) of the Atlantic coast the sexes are separate. Eggs and sperm unite in the water, and within 48 hours the larva has a bivalved shell. It swims freely for about 2 weeks and grows, then goes to the bottom and moves around, using the foot. Finally it settles on the left valve and quickly becomes fixed to some solid object by a secretion from the mantle. The European oyster (*Ostrea edulis*) and the Pacific coast oyster (*O. lurida*) are both protandric, the gonad of an individual first producing sperm and then eggs, in rhythmic alternation. The eggs of *O. lurida* are fertilized and grow to bivalved larvae within the mantle cavity of the parent "female" and then have a brief free existence before attaching. Attached young oysters are called "spat."

23-15. Relations to man. Since man first visited the seashore, he has used bivalves as food. On many coasts are "shell mounds" where ancient peoples, for generations, ate mollusks and discarded the shells. An Indian shell mound on San Francisco Bay contained over 1,000,000 cubic feet of debris accumulated over an estimated 3,500 years. The United States annually takes more than 136,000,000 pounds of oysters, clams, scallops, and mussels, valued at about $47,000,000. Good natural oyster beds in shallow water are highly valued, some of the starfishes that prey on the oysters are removed, and spat is planted to replace the adult oysters that are harvested by tongs or dredges. Both the Atlantic oyster and the Japanese oyster (*C. gigas*) have been established on the Pacific coast. Man eats all of an oyster or clam, but only the single large adductor muscle of a "scallop" (*Pecten*). Oyster shell is used on roads and to supply lime for poultry and other needs. Various kinds of clams are dug by hand, and in many places a limit as to size, number, and season of take has been placed to conserve the stocks.

In the United States, "pearl" buttons for clothing are cut from shells of fresh-water bivalves (Fig. 23-14); no other material withstands repeated laundering so well. Originally these mollusks were more abundant in the upper Mississippi drainage than anywhere else in the world, but overfishing has seriously depleted them. Some species require several years to mature. The U.S. Fish and Wildlife Service

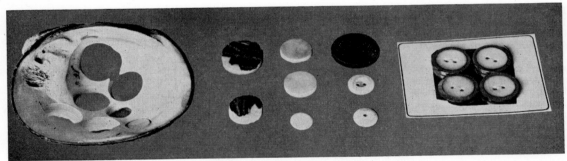

Fig. 23-14. The "pearl" button industry. Circular blanks cut from shells of fresh-water clams are ground and polished, sometimes dyed, and drilled to receive threads.

has made many experiments seeking to replenish the mollusks and place the industry on a sustained yield basis. The host fishes can be artificially infected with numbers of glochidia, and the latter have also been reared in an artificial nutrient medium, composed of the chemicals present in the blood serum of fishes.

Pearls are formed about foreign objects between the mantle and shell of bivalves. A bit of the mantle encloses the object and secretes successive layers of nacre about it, in the manner that the shell lining is produced. Some pearls form in fresh-water clams and in oysters, but the most valuable kinds come from marine pearl oysters (*Margaritifera*) of eastern Asia. The Japanese artificially introduce small particles in the mantle and then retain the bivalves (*Meleagrina*) in cages for several years until "culture" pearls are produced.

The burrowing of teredos in wooden marine structures sometimes causes serious damage, since the piles supporting wharves may be weakened and collapse. An estimated $25,000,-000 of such damage occurred in San Francisco Bay in 1917–1921. Wharves are now constructed of creosoted wood, concrete, or metal to avoid such troubles.

CLASS CEPHALOPODA. Nautili, Squids, and Octopuses

The Cephalopoda (Gr. *kephale*, head + *podos*, foot) are the most highly developed mollusks. A common example is the squid of

coastal waters, *Loligo pealei* along the Atlantic coast and *L. opalescens* on the Pacific coast.

23-16. Structure and natural history (Fig. 23-15). The large **head** bears two conspicuous **eyes** and a central **mouth**, which is surrounded by 10 fleshy **arms** bearing cup-like **suckers;** the fourth pair of arms are long retractile **tentacles.** The slender conical **body** has a fleshy triangular **fin** along either side of the tapered end. The head and body join by a **neck,** around which the free edge of the mantle forms a loose **collar.** Below the neck is a muscular funnel, or **siphon.** The skin contains many **chromatophores,** each with yellow or brown pigment in an elastic capsule surrounded by muscle cells. These expand and contract rhythmically, causing the animal to be alternately light and dark. The squid is elongated dorsoventrally, the head is morphologically ventral, and the arms and siphon represent the foot of other mollusks.

In the upper (anterior) wall of the body is a horny "pen," the shell, stiffening the body; a cartilage-like case surrounds the "brain"; there is a nuchal cartilage over the neck and similar support for the siphon and fins. The mantle, fins, siphon, and arms are all muscular. The **mantle** is a conical envelope surrounding the internal organs. By its alternate expansion and contraction, water is drawn into and expelled from the mantle cavity. For respiration alone the water passes into and out of the space between the neck and collar, but for "jet" locomotion the mantle closes around the base of the

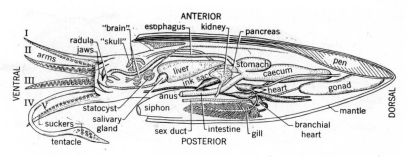

Fig. 23-15. Class CEPHALOP-
ODA. The squid, *Loligo*. Internal structure as seen with body
wall and arms removed on left
side.

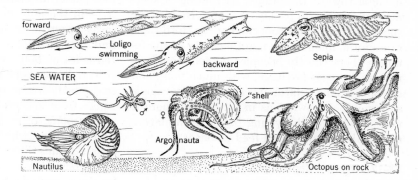

Fig. 23-16. Class CEPHALOP-
ODA. *Loligo*, squid; *Sepia*, cuttlefish; *Nautilus*, pearly nautilus; *Argonauta*, paper nautilus;
Octopus, octopus. Variously reduced.

siphon and water is forcibly ejected from the latter (Fig. 23-16). To swim "tail first," the siphon is directed toward the arms; to move head foremost the tip of the siphon is bent around to force the water tailward. The fins aid in steering and also serve in swimming.

The digestive system includes (1) the *mouth;* (2) a muscular *pharynx* (buccal mass) with a pair of horny *jaws,* like a parrot beak inverted, and a *radula;* (3) a slender *esophagus;* (4) the sac-like muscular *stomach,* joined by (5) a thin-walled *caecum* with a complex valve between; (6) the slender *intestine* and (7) *rectum* extend to (8) the *anus,* which opens into the mantle cavity. Two pairs of *salivary glands* connect to the pharynx, and the long *liver* and a small *"pancreas"* join by ducts to the stomach. The squid eats crustaceans, mollusks, and fishes. It swims forward with the arms together, then darts at the prey by suddenly ejecting water from the siphon; the arms are spread, the prey grasped and drawn to the mouth, bitten by the jaws, and swallowed. Small bottom animals are quietly covered by the spread arms and then gathered into the mouth.

Above the rectum is the glandular *ink sac,* with a duct opening near the anus; the ink is a dark pigment that can be forced out the siphon to produce an aquatic "smoke screen," under cover of which the squid can escape from an enemy. In each side of the mantle cavity there is an elongate *gill.* Blood in veins from body tissues is pumped by a *branchial heart* through capillaries in the gill filaments and then is collected in an auricle on each side; these two join the single ventricle of the *systemic heart,* which sends the blood through arteries to the gut, head, arms, and other organs. A pair of *kidneys* drain from the pericardial cavity around the heart into the mantle cavity. The pairs of *nerve ganglia* are concentrated in the "brain box" around the pharynx. The *eyes* are unique among invertebrates; each has a cornea, lens, anterior and posterior chambers, and retina with rods and can form a real image (Fig. 10-14*D*). They are structurally like those of vertebrates but differently derived. Below the brain are two *statocysts* serving for equilibration.

The sexes are separate, each with one *gonad* near the tip of the mantle cavity and a *duct*

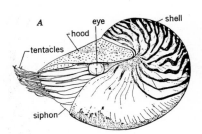
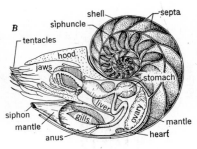

Fig. **23-17.** Class Cephalopoda. The pearly nautilus, *Nautilus pompilius*. *A.* External features. *B.* Internal structure; shell and mantle (except at siphon) cut away to mid-line; jaws, tongue, and radula shown in median section; two left gills removed.

opening toward the funnel. At mating, a spermatophore (sperm packet) is transferred by the specialized tip (heterocotylus) of the third right arm on the male to the mantle cavity of the female, where the tip becomes detached and remains. The eggs are large, with much yolk, and are laid in long gelatinous capsules. Cleavage is superficial, somewhat as in birds, and there is no larval stage; the young hatch as miniature adults able to swim and feed at once.

23-17. Other Cephalopoda. This class has swarmed the seas since Cambrian time and has a fossil record of 10,000 species (Figs. 14-11, 14-12). Nautiloids were dominant through Paleozoic times, the ammonites in the Mesozoic, and the dibranchiates (such as *Loligo*) abound today. Both of the earlier groups had external limy shells that varied in size, shape, and ornamentation, but were always divided into chambers by transverse septa. The animal probably lived in the outermost compartment, as does the living pearly nautilus. Early forms had slenderly conical shells, an inch to several feet in length. †*Endoceras* of Ordovician time was 15 feet long, the largest shelled invertebrate known; an ammonite, †*Pachydiscus*, of the Cretaceous had a coiled shell 6 feet 8 inches in diameter (Fig. 1-2). The only living relic of this great assemblage is the pearly nautilus (*Nautilus pompilius*) which inhabits the bottom at depths to 1,800 feet in the eastern Pacific and Indian Oceans (Fig. 23-17). Its spiral shell is up to 10 inches in diameter, closely coiled in one plane, and divided by septa. The animal lives in the outermost chamber, having previously occupied each of the others in turn as it and the shell grew. The head bears 60 to 90 tentacles without suckers.

The living cephalopods are all predaceous and mostly free-swimming (Fig. 23-16). Squids range from species an inch long to the giant *Architeuthis*, of cold depths off Newfoundland and elsewhere, which is eaten by sperm whales. Small squids like *Loligo* sometimes occur in enormous schools; they are eaten by fishes and marine mammals and are used as bait by fishermen, especially for cod. Squids are also an article of human food in many countries. The cuttlefish (*Sepia*) of Atlantic waters has a short oval body bordered by fins; its long tentacles are completely retractile. Its internal calcareous shell is the cuttlebone used as a bill sharpener for caged birds, and for centuries its ink has provided the sepia pigment of artists. The devilfishes, or octopuses, vary from 2 inches to 28 feet in spread. The flexible bulbous body lacks a shell and has eight long sucker-bearing tentacles. Octopuses crawl about rocks and tide pools along the seacoasts, but can swim by use of the siphon. Large squid and octopuses are feared more rightly for their dangerously powerful beaks than for their supposed ability to grip a person under water by their tentacles. In the paper nautilus (*Argonauta*) of temperate oceans, the female is up to 8 inches long and secretes a shell only as an egg case; the male is only about 1 inch long.

CLASSIFICATION

PHYLUM MOLLUSCA. MOLLUSKS. Symmetry bilateral (viscera and shell coiled in some); no segmentation; body soft, covered by thin mantle that commonly secretes limy shell of 1, 2, or 8 parts; usually an anterior head and ventral muscular foot; mouth with radula (except bivalves); heart dorsal with 1 or 2 auricles and 1 ventricle; respiration by gill-like ctenidia, secondary gills, or "lung"; nephridia, 2 or 1; nervous system with paired ganglia, connectives, and nerves; sexes separate or united; gonads 2 or 1, with ducts; mostly oviparous; with larval stages (trochophore, veliger, or glochidium) or development direct; mostly in salt or fresh waters, some GASTROPODA on land; 45,000 living, 40,000 fossil species.

CLASS 1. *AMPHINEURA.* Body elongate, shell of 8 plates or none; head reduced; nerve ring around mouth and 2 pairs of ventral nerve cords; no tentacles.

Order 1. Aplacophora (Solenogastres). Form worm-like; no shell or foot; integument thick, with minute calcareous spicules; foot vestigial; bottom dwellers at 60 to 6,000 feet, in ooze or on corals and hydroids; about 50 species. *Neomenia,* 20 to 30 mm. long, North Atlantic, hermaphroditic, 2 gonads; *Chaetoderma,* 2 by 25 mm., around North Atlantic to Maine, sexes separate, 1 fused gonad.

Order 2. Polyplacophora (Loricata). CHITONS. Body elliptical; shell a middorsal row of 8 broad plates, surrounded by fleshy girdle; foot large, flat; gills, 6 to 80 pairs, in groove around foot; sexes separate; 1 gonad; a trochophore larva; on rocks, chiefly in shallow coastal waters; 600 living, 150 fossil species; Ordovician to Recent. *Tonicella, Chaetopleura, Isnochiton, Chiton; Cryptochiton,* with integument over plates.

CLASS 2. *SCAPHOPODA.* TOOTH SHELLS or TUSK SHELLS. Shell and mantle slenderly tubular, slightly curved, open at both ends; foot conical; delicate "tentacles" around mouth; no gills; sexes separate; 1 gonad; a veliger larva; marine, in sand or mud, shallow water to 15,000 feet; 200 living, 300 fossil species; Devonian to Recent. *Dentalium, Siphonodentalium.*

CLASS 3. *GASTROPODA.* UNIVALVES: LIMPETS, WHELKS, SNAILS, SLUGS, etc. Shell usually spiral (uncoiled, reduced, or absent in some); head distinct, with scraping radula, commonly with tentacles and eyes; foot large, flat, for holdfast or creeping; visceral mass typically turned 180 degrees counterclockwise (torsion) on head and foot, and coiled in shell; ctenidia 2 or 1, or replaced by secondary gills or lung; nephridia 2 or 1; sexes separate or united; 1 gonad; mostly oviparous; larva with trochophore and veliger stages (except land forms); marine, fresh-water, or terrestrial. Upper Cambrian to Recent.

SUBCLASS 1. PROSOBRANCHIA (Streptoneura). Visceral torsion 180 degrees, nervous system a "figure 8"; tentacles 2; ctenidia anterior to heart; mantle cavity opens anteriorly; dioecious, 1 sex opening. Upper Cambrian to Recent, mostly marine, 25,000 living, 10,000 fossil species.

Order 1. Aspidobranchia. Nervous system little concentrated, pedal ganglia as long cords; ctenidia 1 or 2 (or none), plume-like with 2 rows of filaments; usually 2 auricles in heart; 2 nephridia. Upper Cambrian to Recent. *Acmaea, Patella, Lottia,* limpets, shell flatly conical; *Fissurella,* keyhole limpet; *Haliotis,* abalones, shell ear-shaped, aperture large; *Crepidula,* slipper or boat shells; *Littorina,* periwinkles; *Strombus gigas,* giant conch, southern Florida and West Indies, shell 250 mm. or more, largest univalve in United States.

Order 2. Pectinibranchia. Nervous system rather concentrated; ctenidia with filaments in 1 row; 1 auricle in heart; 1 nephridium, separated from gonad. *Cypraea,* cowries; *Atlanta, Carinaria,* heteropods, pelagic, transparent, foot used for swimming; *Murex,* rock shells; *Buccinum,* edible whelks; *Conus,* cone shells; *Urosalpinx,* oyster drill; *Bythinia, Viviparus (Paludina), Goniobasis,* all in fresh waters.

SUBCLASS 2. OPISTHOBRANCHIA. Shell reduced, internal, or none; viscera and nervous system secondarily "unwound"; opening of mantle cavity posterior; usually 1 nephridium, 1 auricle; ctenidium 1, posterior, or replaced by secondary gills; monoecious. Carboniferous to Recent, 3,000 living, 300 fossil species.

Order 1. Tectibranchia. Head large; usually with mantle, shell, and ctenidium; shell, if present, thin, in folds of mantle and foot. *Actaeon,* etc., bubble shells; *Gastropteron,* sea slugs, swim like rays; *Aplysia (Tethys),* sea hare, to 30 cm. long, shell internal, vestigial; *Cavolinia, Clione,* pteropods, pelagic, sides of foot expanded as fins.

Order 2. Nudibranchia. SEA SLUGS or NUDIBRANCHS. No shell or true ctenidium in adult; respire by skin or by secondary gills around anus, or in dorsal rows, or under lateral edge of mantle. *Polycera, Doris, Dendronotus, Hermissenda.*

SUBCLASS 3. PULMONATA. Fresh-water and Land Snails, and Slugs. Mostly small; shell a simple spiral (or none); head with 1 or 2 pairs of tentacles, 1 pair of eyes; mantle cavity anterior, its vascular lining an air-breathing lung, opens to a contractile pore on right side; no gills; monoecious; gonad single; mostly oviparous; development direct; chiefly terrestrial. Upper Carboniferous to Recent; more than 5,000 living, 1,000 fossil species. *Lymnaea, Helisoma (Planorbis), Physa,* all in fresh waters; *Polygyra, Zonites, Helminthoglypta,* all terrestrial, mostly in moist places; *Helix,* European "garden" snails, several introduced into the United States; *Testacella haliotidea,* greenhouse slug, with small terminal shell, in greenhouses, preys on earthworms; *Limax, Deroceras (Agriolimax), Ariolimax,* slugs with vestigial shell in mantle; *Arion,* slugs with no shell; *Achatina fulica,* giant African land snail, native to eastern Africa, widely introduced in islands of Pacific, causing much agricultural damage; *Gonaxis,* predaceous snail.

CLASS 4. *PELECYPODA* (Lamellibranchiata).[1] Bivalved Mollusks. Shell of 2 lateral valves, usually symmetrical, with dorsal hinge and ligament, and closed by 1 or 2 adductor muscles; mantle of flattened right and left lobes, the posterior margin commonly forming siphons to control flow of water in and out of mantle cavity; fleshy labial palps beside mouth; 1 (or 2)[2] pairs of gills (ctenidia or branchia), commonly plate-like; no head, jaws, or radula; usually dioecious, some protandric; gonad opening into mantle cavity; a veliger larva or glochidial stage; mostly marine, some in fresh waters. Ordovician to Recent, 11,000 living, 15,000 fossil species.

Order 1. **Protobranchia.** Gill with central axis bearing 2 divergent rows of short flat filaments; foot flat ventrally; 2 adductor muscles. *Nucula,* nut clam; *Solemyia,* awning clam; *Yoldia.*

Order 2. **Filobranchia.** Gill W-shaped with ciliary connections between lamellae of each half (demibranch), gill filaments long; adductor muscles 2, anterior reduced or absent in some. *Arca; Mytilus,* sea mussel, and *Ostrea,* edible oyster, both attached; *Pecten,* scallop, swims by clapping shells together.

Order 3. **Eulamellibranchia.** Gill W-shaped but lamellae of each half united by firm connections; 2 adductor muscles, equal-sized. *Anodonta, Unio (Elliptio), Lampsilis, Margaritana,* fresh-water mussels or clams, shells of some used for buttons; *Cardium,* cockle; *Mactra,* marine clam, to 15 cm. long; *Venus,* quahog or hard-shell clam; *Macoma; Solen; Ensis,* razor clam; *Mya arenaria,* mud clam, shell delicate; *Pholas,* burrows in clay or rock; *Teredo, Bankia,* shipworms, worm-like, burrow in wood in salt waters; *Pisidium, Sphaerium,* in fresh waters.

Order 4. **Septibranchia.** Gill reduced to horizontal muscular partition dividing mantle cavity. *Cuspidaria, Poromyia.*

CLASS 5. *CEPHALOPODA.* Nautili, Squids, and Octopuses. Shell external, internal, or none; head large, eyes conspicuous and complex; mouth with horny jaws and radula and surrounded by 8 or 10 arms, or many tentacles; a siphon; nerve ganglia grouped in head as "brain," in cartilage-like covering; eyes conspicuous; dioecious; development direct; all marine; 400 living, 10,000 fossil species.

Order 1. **Tetrabranchia.** Shell external, coiled in 1 plane, divided by internal septa; 2 pairs of gills and nephridia; siphon 2-lobed; no ink sac; tentacles many, no suckers; eyes without lens.

SUBORDER 1. †AMMONOIDEA. Ammonites. Silurian to Cretaceous. †*Ammonites.*

SUBORDER 2. NAUTILOIDEA. Nautili. Upper Cambrian to Recent. About 2,500 fossil species; 1 living genus of 2 or 4 species: *Nautilus pompilius,* pearly nautilus, eastern Pacific and Indian Oceans at depths to 1,800 feet.

Order 2. **Dibranchia.** Shell internal and reduced, or none; body cylindrical or globose, often with fins; arms 8 or 10, with suckers; one pair of gills and nephridia; siphon tubular; an ink sac; eyes with lens.

SUBORDER 1. DECAPODA. Ten arms. Triassic to Recent. (Belemnites of Carboniferous to Cretaceous with internal chambered shell. †*Belemnites.*) Living forms: *Spirula,* shell spiral, internal, deep

---

[1] Paleontologists and some zoologists use a classification emphasizing the teeth and muscle scars on valves: **Order 1. Taxodonta.** Shells with many similar teeth on hinge margin; usually 2 equal adductor muscles. *Arca, Nucula, Yoldia,* etc. **Order 2. Anisomyaria.** Anterior adductor small or none, posterior large; teeth various; mantle open, no siphons; gill lamellae flat and filaments similar, or plicate. *Ostrea, Pecten, Mytilus,* etc. **Order 3. Eulamellibranchia.** Hinge teeth few and unlike or none; adductor muscles equal or posterior larger; gill filaments fused into plates; usually with siphons. *Anodonta, Tridacna, Solen, Mya, Pholas, Teredo,* etc.

[2] Most American authors speak of 2 gills (ctenidia) on each side, and British authors of 1.

tropical seas, shells occasional on Atlantic coast; *Sepia*, cuttlefish, Atlantic waters; *Rossia*, body stubby, to 75 mm.; *Loligo*, squid; *Architeuthis*, giant squid.

SUBORDER 2. OCTOPODA. Eight arms. Cretaceous to Recent. *Argonauta*, paper nautilus; *Octopus*, octopus, or devilfish.

REFERENCES

ABBOTT, R. T. 1954. American sea shells. New York, D. Van Nostrand Co., Inc. xiv + 541 pp., 40 pls. (24 in color), 100 figs. Semipopular; describes 1,500 of 6,000 North American marine species.

HAAS, F. 1929–1935. Bivalvia [Pelecypoda]. *In* Bronn, Klassen und Ordnungen der Tier-reichs. Leipzig, Akademische Verlagsgesellshaft m.b.h. Vol. 3, div. 3, pt. 1, xii + 1,337 pp., 563 figs.

PELSENEER, P. 1906. Mollusca. *In* E. R. Lankester, Treatise on zoology. London, A. & C. Black, Ltd. Pt. 5, 5 + 355 pp., 301 figs.

PENNAK, R. W. 1953. Fresh-water invertebrates of the United States. New York, The Ronald Press Co. ix + 769 pp., 470 figs. MOLLUSCA, pp. 667–726, figs. 411–456.

PILSBRY, H. A. 1939–   . Land Mollusca of North America (north of Mexico). *Philadelphia Academy of Natural Sciences Monograph* 3, vol. 1, pts. 1, 2.

PRATT, H. S. 1935. Manual of the common invertebrate animals. . . . 2 ed. Philadelphia, The Blakiston Co. MOLLUSCA, pp. 556–604, figs. 740–921.

ROBSON, G. C. 1932. A monograph of the recent Cephalopoda. London, British Museum. 2 vols.

SHROCK, R. R., and W. H. TWENHOFEL. 1953. Principles of invertebrate paleontology. New York, McGraw-Hill Book Co., Inc. MOLLUSCA, pp. 350–502, figs. 10-1 to 10-86.

THIELE, G. 1924–1926. Solenogastres, Mollusca. *In* W. Kükenthal and others, Handbuch der Zoologie. Berlin, Walter De Gruyter & Co. Vol. 5, pp. 1–256, figs. 1–340.

TRESSLER, D. K. 1951. Marine products of commerce. 2d ed. New York, Reinhold Publishing Corp. xiii + 782 pp., illus. Oysters and clams, pp. 550–589.

24 PHYLUM ANNELIDA
Segmented Worms

In contrast to the various kinds of worms previously discussed, those of the Phylum ANNELIDA (L. *annelus*, little ring) have bodies composed of many essentially similar and ring-like segments, or somites. This segmentation usually shows in both external and internal features, including muscles, nerves, and circulatory, excretory, and reproductive organs. Most earthworms and their allies (Class OLIGOCHAETA) are inhabitants of damp soil and fresh waters, the marine worms (Class POLYCHAETA) are found chiefly along the seashore, and the leeches (Class HIRUDINEA) are mainly in fresh waters or on moist ground. Members of the small Class ARCHIANNELIDA are all marine. Some annelids are free-living, many inhabit burrows or dwell in tubes, some are commensals on other aquatic animals, a few are ecto- or endo-parasites, and many of the leeches attach to vertebrates.

24-1. Characteristics. 1. Symmetry bilateral; 3 germ layers; body elongate and usually conspicuously segmented both externally and internally.

2. Appendages are minute rod-like chitinous setae, few to many per somite; POLYCHAETA have fleshy tentacles on the head and the setae borne on lateral fleshy parapodia; most HIRUDINEA lack setae.

3. Body covered by thin moist cuticle over columnar epithelium containing unicellular gland cells and sensory cells.

4. Body wall and digestive tract both with layers of circular and longitudinal muscles; coelom well developed (except in HIRUDINEA), and divided by septa in OLIGOCHAETA and POLYCHAETA.

5. Digestive tract complete, tubular, extending length of body.

6. A closed circulatory system of longitudinal blood vessels with lateral branches in each somite; blood plasma contains dissolved hemoglobin and free amoebocytes.

7. Respiration by the epidermis, or by gills in some tube dwellers.

8. Excretory system typically of one pair of nephridia per somite, each removing wastes from the coelom and blood stream directly to the exterior.

9. Nervous system with pair of cerebral ganglia (brain) and connectives to a solid (double) midventral nerve cord extending length of body, with a ganglion and pairs of lateral nerves in each segment; sensory cells and organs for touch, taste, and light perception.

10. Sexes united and development direct (OLIGOCHAETA, HIRUDINEA), or sexes separate and with trochophore larval stage (POLYCHAETA, ARCHIANNELIDA); some OLIGOCHAETA and POLYCHAETA reproduce asexually by budding.

The ANNELIDA resemble the ARTHROPODA in having a segmented body covered by cuticle that is secreted by the epidermis, in the structure of the nervous system, and in forming mesoderm from special embryonic cells. They differ in having a large coelom, only simple unjointed appendages, little or no specialization of somites in different parts of the body, and no succession of larval stages, or molts. The Subphylum ONYCHOPHORA of the Phylum ARTHROPODA shows some annelid features (par. 27-17). The ANNELIDA resemble the MOLLUSCA in embryonic features of cleavage and mesoderm formation; and marine annelids have a trocho-

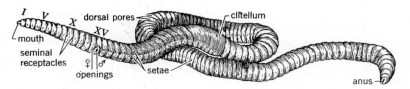

Fig. 24-1. Class OLIGOCHAETA. The earthworm, *Lumbricus terrestris*, external features. I, V, etc., somites.

phore larva (Fig. 15-5). The metameric animal may have arisen from an unsegmented stock in forming chains of individuals by asexual fission as occurs in some PLATYHELMINTHES and AN- NELIDA, but with the products of fission re- maining united and acquiring both structural and physiological unity. Another theory pre- sumes the segmental division of muscles, nerves, coelom, nephridia, etc., within a single individ- ual as seen in the formation of somites by both larvae and adults of some annelids.

24-2. Size. Some of the smallest OLIGOCHAETA (*Aeolosoma*, *Chaetogaster*) are under 1 mm. long, but the giant earthworms (*Rhinodrilus fafneri* of Ecuador and *Megascolides australis* of Australia) grow to over 7 feet long and 1 inch in diameter. Most earthworms are only a few inches in length. The smallest POLYCHAETA are minute, but *Neanthes brandti* of the Cali- fornia coast grows to 5½ feet and *Eunice gi- gantea* to nearly 10 feet. The leeches range from 10 to 200 mm., most of them being small.

CLASS OLIGOCHAETA. EARTHWORMS, ETC.

This class includes annelids with few setae per segment (L. *oligos*, few + *chaete*, spine). The large earthworm of Europe and eastern North America, *Lumbricus terrestris*, that may grow to 12 inches long and ⅜ inch in diameter, is the basis of the following account.

24-3. External features. The body (Fig. 24-1) is long and cylindrical, bluntly tapered at each end, and somewhat depressed posteriorly; the ventral side is flattened and paler than the dark dorsal surface. There is no distinct head. A mature worm is divided into from 115 to 200 ring-like segments, or **somites,** separated by transverse grooves. The **mouth** is in somite I, overhung by a fleshy lobe, the **prostomium,** and

the vertically oval **anus** is in the last somite. The **clitellum** (L., pack saddle) is a conspicuous glandular swelling over somites XXXII– XXXVII; it secretes material forming co- coons to contain eggs. On each somite except the first and last are four pairs of minute bristle-like **setae** that project slightly on the ventral and lateral surfaces. Each seta is a fine chitinous rod, contained in an epidermal seta sac within the body wall, and is secreted by a large cell in the sac. A seta can be moved in any direction and extended or withdrawn by protractor and retractor muscles attached to the sac. The setae serve as holdfast devices when a worm is in its burrow or moving over the ground.

Besides the mouth and anus there are many minute external openings on the body, includ- ing (1) a **dorsal pore,** connecting the body cav- ity and exterior, middorsally in the furrow at the anterior border of each somite from VIII or IX to the anal end; (2) a **nephridiopore,** or excretory opening, lateroventrally on either side of each somite except I–III and the last; (3) the four openings of the **seminal receptacles** laterally in the furrows between IX–X and X–XI; (4) the openings of the two **oviducts** ventrally on XIV; and (5) the openings of the paired **sperm ducts,** with swollen lips, ventrally on XV, from which two glandular ridges ex- tend to the clitellum.

24-4. Body wall. The exterior is covered (Fig. 24-2) by a thin transparent **cuticle,** marked with fine cross striations that produce a slight iridescence. This is secreted by the **epidermis** beneath, a single layer of columnar epithelium that includes many **unicellular glands** produc- ing mucus to pass through pores in the cuticle and keep the latter soft. The cuticle is also perforated by pores over many **sensory cells** in the epidermis. Both kinds of pores are seen

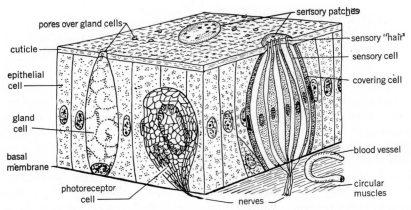

Fig. 24-2. Earthworm. Diagram of cuticle and epidermis in perspective. (*Adapted from Hess, 1925; and Langdon, 1895.*)

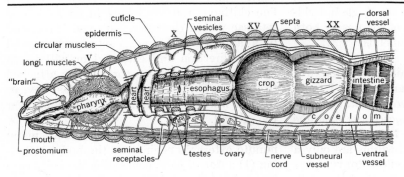

Fig. 24-3. Earthworm. Internal structure of anterior portion from the left side; body wall and digestive tract cut in median section. Two hearts shown in place; nephridia omitted; reproductive organs of right side included. I, X, XX, somites.

easily in pieces of cuticle stripped off and spread to dry on a glass slide. The epidermis rests on a basement membrane, beneath which is a thin layer of *circular muscles* and a thicker layer of *longitudinal muscles.* The inner surface of the body wall is covered by a thin smooth epithelium, the *peritoneum.* Pigment cells, connective tissue, and blood capillaries occur among the circular muscle fibers. There is no skeleton. The form of the animal is maintained by the elasticity of the body wall over the organs and fluids within. Contraction of the circular muscles elongates the body, contraction of the longitudinal muscles shortens it, and local or differential action of these same muscles produces the bending movements so characteristic of earthworms.

24-5. Internal structure (Fig. 24-3). If the body wall is slit middorsally and spread, the earthworm is seen to consist essentially of two concentric tubes, the outer *body wall* and the straight *digestive tract* within; the space between them is the body cavity, or *coelom.* It is divided into a succession of compartments by the *septa,* which are thin transverse partitions of connective tissue aligned with the grooves on the exterior surface; septa are absent between somites I and II and incomplete between III–IV and XVII–XVIII. The coelom and all organs within it are covered by peritoneum. The cavity contains watery coelomic fluid with free colorless amoebocytes. Small pores in the septa permit this fluid to pass from somite to somite in keeping with movements of the body, and some of it may pass out the dorsal pores to moisten the exterior surface.

24-6. Digestive system. This consists of (1) the *mouth,* followed by a short *buccal cavity* (somites I–III); (2) the *pharynx* (IV–V), with glands to lubricate the food and muscle fibers in its external walls; (3) the slender straight *esophagus* (VI–XIV) joined on either side by three pairs of *calciferous glands* (X–XIV); (4) a thin-walled and enlarged *crop,* or proventricu-

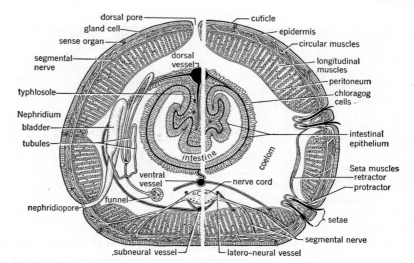

Fig. 24-4. Earthworm. Diagrammatic cross section. Left half shows an entire nephridium and a dorsal pore but omits setae; right half includes setae but no nephridium.

lus (XV–XVI) for storage; (5) the **gizzard** (XVII–XVIII), with thick firm muscular walls and lined with cuticle; and (6) the **intestine,** which continues to (7) the **anus.** The intestine is thin-walled and bulges laterally in each somite, and its dorsal wall carries an infolded **typhlosole;** the bulges and typhlosole afford increased surface for digestion and absorption of food. The internal lining is of columnar ciliated epithelium, containing many club-shaped gland cells; next are blood vessels, and then longitudinal and circular muscles; and the exterior of the intestine is covered by rounded yellowish **chloragog cells,** which are modified peritoneum. These cells may aid in fat distribution or elimination of wastes from the blood, and later become free in the coelom.

The food is chiefly of dead leaves, grasses, and other vegetation; it is moistened by saliva-like secretions from the mouth region and then drawn in by muscular action of the prostomium, "lips," and pharynx. Any organic acids present in the food are neutralized by calcium carbonate secreted by the calciferous glands of the esophagus, so that food undergoing digestion is alkaline in reaction. Food is stored temporarily in the crop and later ground up in the muscular gizzard by aid of sand grains present there. The digestive tract secretes enzymes including pepsin and trypsin acting on proteins, lipase on fats, cellulase on cellulose, and amylase on car-

bohydrates. Digested material is absorbed in the intestine, and residues are passed out the anus. Small animals on the ground may be eaten, and captive worms will eat bits of fat or meat and dead worms. Earthworms utilize any organic food contained in the earth taken while burrowing.

24-7. Circulatory system. The **blood** consists of a fluid **plasma** that contains free colorless **corpuscles** (amoebocytes). The plasma is colored red by **hemoglobin,** a respiratory pigment dissolved in it. Blood circulates to and from all parts of the body in a system of closed **blood vessels** with capillaries. There are five principal vessels extending lengthwise of the body and five pairs of "hearts" in somites VII–XI. Each somite from XII posteriorly has paired segmental vessels connecting between the longitudinal vessels and various organs; and special vessels serve structures in the anterior somites (Table 24-1; Fig. 24-5).

24-8. Respiration. There is no organized respiratory system. Blood circulating in capillaries close to the moist cuticle of the body wall receives oxygen there and gives up carbon dioxide. The oxygen combines with the hemoglobin in the plasma and is carried to various tissues. In an emergency an earthworm can survive for several hours without a fresh supply of oxygen.

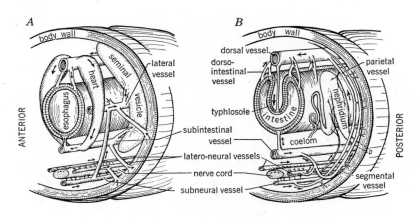

Fig. 24-5. Earthworm. Circulatory system. *A.* One pair of hearts and other vessels as in somite X. *B.* Relations of blood vessels in any somite behind the clitellum. Arrows indicate paths of blood flow. (*Adapted from Johnston and Johnson, 1902; and Bell, 1947.*)

TABLE 24-1. Blood Vessels and Paths of Circulation in the Earthworm

Vessels	Location	Receive blood from:	Direction of flow	Deliver blood to:
Dorsal (1)	Above gut, pharynx to anus	Dorsointestinals Parietals Lateral esophageals	Anteriorly	Typhlosole Hearts Pharynx wall
Hearts (5 pairs)	Somites VII–XI	Dorsal vessel	Ventrally	Subintestinal
Subintestinal or ventral (1)	Between gut and nerve cord	The hearts	Anteriorly from VII; posteriorly from XI	Ventral intestinals Nerve cord, I–XX Segmentals (and lateroneurals)
Lateroneural (2)	Sides of nerve cord, XX posteriorly	Segmentals	Posteriorly	Nerve cord
Subneural (1)	Under nerve cord	Nerve cord	Posteriorly	Parietals
Segmental	Body wall, 1 pair per somite (except first few)	Subintestinal	Dorsally	Body wall Nephridia Lateroneurals
Parietal	Body wall, 1 pair per somite, XII and posteriorly	Subneural Nephridia Body wall	Dorsally	Dorsal vessel
Lateral or esophageal (2)	Side of esophagus to X	Anterior end and gut wall	Posteriorly	Dorsal vessel in X and XII
Afferent (ventro-intestinal)	Gut wall, 2 per somite	Subintestinal	Dorsally	Gut wall
Efferent (dorso-intestinal)	Gut wall, 2 pairs per somite	Gut wall	Dorsally	Dorsal vessel
Typhlosolar	Median, 2 per somite	Dorsal vessel	Ventrally	Typhlosole Dorsal wall of gut

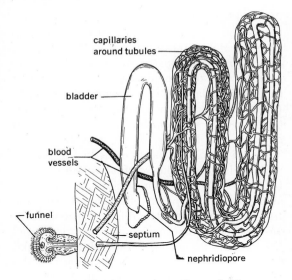

Fig. 24-6. Earthworm. An entire nephridium.

24-9. Excretory system. Every somite except the first three and the last has a pair of nephridia (Fig. 24-6) for excretion. Each *nephridium* begins as a ciliated funnel, or nephrostome, at the anterior base of the septum beside the nerve cord. It connects through the septum by a fine ciliated tubule to the main part of the nephridium in the somite behind. The tube there is of several loops of increasing size and a larger bladder that discharges to the exterior through a *nephridiopore* opening near the ventral pair of setae. Cilia of the funnel and tubule beat to draw wastes from the coelom, and other waste is received from blood vessels surrounding the nephridium. Excretory products (ammonia, urea, creatine) are formed in the body wall and gut wall and enter both the blood and coelomic fluid. The nephridia act much like tubules in a human kidney—by filtration, reabsorption, and tubular secretion they yield a protein-free urine and maintain the steady state in the body.

24-10. Nervous system. Above the pharynx (in somite III) is a pair of *suprapharyngeal* (cerebral) *ganglia,* the "brain" (Fig. 24-7*A*). Two *connectives* extend around the pharynx to the bilobed *subpharyngeal ganglia* (base of somite IV) whence the *ventral nerve cord* extends along the floor of the coelom to the anal somite. Several nerves connect to the prostomium and mouth region. The ventral nerve cord in each somite has an enlarged *ganglion* and gives off three pairs of *lateral nerves* (Fig. 24-7*B*). The cord and ganglia appear to be single but develop as paired structures. Each lateral nerve extends around half a somite between the two muscle layers of the body wall and includes both *sen-*

Fig. 24-7. Earthworm. *A.* Ganglia and larger nerves of the anterior end. (*After Hess,* 1925.) *B.* Stereogram of the ventral nerve cord and body wall to show a simple reflex arc. Sensory cells (receptors) in the epidermis connect to sensory fibers that pass in a lateral nerve to the nerve cord; the sensory axon joins through a synapse to a motor nerve that leads to the body muscles (effector). Arrows indicate the direction of nerve impulses.

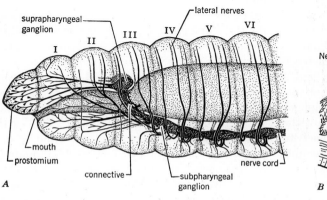

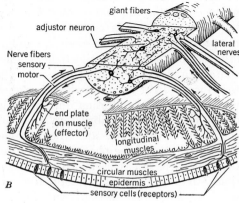

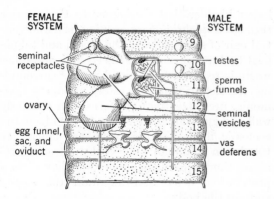

FEMALE SYSTEM

seminal receptacles

ovary

egg funnel, sac, and oviduct

MALE SYSTEM

9

10 testes

11 sperm funnels

12

13 seminal vesicles

14 vas deferens

15

Fig. 24-8. Reproductive system of earthworm in dorsal view, other organs omitted; seminal vesicles cut away on right side.

sory fibers, carrying impulses in from the epidermis to the nerve cord, and *motor fibers,* carrying directive impulses outward from the cord to muscles and epidermal cells. These nerves also include fibers of both types connecting to the nephridia, seta sacs, and other organs.

The epidermis has many *sense organs,* each a group of sensory cells surrounded by special supporting cells (Fig. 24-2). These abound on the anterior and posterior ends, on the swollen part of each somite, and in the buccal cavity— the parts of the body most likely to receive stimuli from the environment. Each sense cell has a hair-like tip projecting through a pore in the cuticle, and a sensory nerve fiber connects to the base of the cell. Free endings of nerve fibers also occur between cells of the epithelium. Special *photoreceptor cells* are present in the epidermis and on nerves at both ends of the body. These cells are most numerous on the prostomium, anterior somites, and anal somite, the parts most sensitive to light. Each cell contains a clear transparent organelle ("lens") that focuses light from any direction on a network of neurofibrils ("retina") in the periphery of the cell. The neurofibrils are probably the actual light receptors, and they connect to sensory nerves. These photoreceptors resemble the visual cells of leeches in structure and function. Stimuli on the light receptors enable the worm to distinguish daylight and dark.

24-11. Reproductive system. The earthworm is monoecious; both male and female sex organs are ventral and anterior (Figs. 24-3, 24-8). The *male reproductive system* includes (1) two pairs of minute *testes* (somites X, XI) and back of each (2) a ciliated *sperm funnel* connecting to (3) a short duct, the *vas efferens.* The two ducts on each side connect (in XII) to (4) a *vas deferens* that leads to (5) the *male pore* (XV). The testes and funnels are contained in (6) two pairs of large sac-like *seminal vesicles* (in IX to XIII) that extend dorsally around the esophagus. Immature sperm cells separate from the testes to complete their differentiation in the vesicles, and mature sperm are discharged through the funnels and ducts during copulation. The *female reproductive system* includes (1) a pair of *ovaries* (anterior in XIII) that discharge mature ova into the coelom, whence they are collected by (2) the two *oviducal funnels* (posterior in XIII), with egg sacs, connecting to (3) the *oviducts* opening on somite XIV. The female system also includes (4) two pairs of *seminal receptacles* (in IX, X) where sperm received in copulation are stored until needed to fertilize eggs in cocoons.

24-12. Natural history. Earthworms live in most lands of the world, including oceanic islands and subarctic regions. They are numerous in good soils, with much humus and abundant moisture, but scarce in poor, acid, sandy, or dry situations. They inhabit burrows for protection against enemies and unfavorable climatic conditions. The burrows are nearly vertical at the top, then wind about to various depths, some extending to 6 feet or more below the surface. In soft topsoil, a worm makes the burrow by using its slender anterior end as a wedge to enter any crevice and then forces the soil particles outward by swelling its pharynx region. In heavier or deeper soil the worm excavates by actually eating its way. The earth passes through its digestive tract and is deposited on the ground surface as small mounds of feces, or "castings," to be seen wherever worms are plentiful. The upper parts of a regular burrow may be smoothly lined with slime, earth from castings, leaves, or fine pebbles. Earthworms in cold climates retire below the frost line in winter and remain inactive; in arid regions they do likewise in summer to avoid the drought and heat, each rolling up in a close ball.

When the soil is moist and the temperature moderate, each worm lies by day in the upper part of its burrow, anterior end foremost. The entrance may be plugged with bits of leafy material. After dark this is pushed aside, and the worm extends its forward end out over the ground surface, to explore, forage, or mate; the posterior end remains in the burrow, holding by the setae, so that, if frightened, the entire animal can withdraw to safety by a quick contraction of its body. At times a worm will leave its burrow and travel on the surface, and a sudden flooding of the ground, as by a heavy rain, will cause many worms to emerge. This is the basis of an old notion that they "come down in rain"; however, on rare occasions worms have actually been carried by tornadoes!

Earthworms avoid all but the weakest of light, remaining hidden by day, and at night withdrawing quickly if a light is flashed on them; they tolerate a red light but avoid a blue one. They are sensitive to mechanical vibrations such as heavy footfalls but evidently do not "hear" mere sound vibrations in air. They react favorably to contact, being used to that of the ground surface or the surrounding burrow, and if turned up, as in the spading of a garden, will seek contact with the earth, thus also avoiding daylight. Tactile stimuli are all-important in retaining contact with the ground and burrow. Since respiration depends upon the cuticle being kept moist, they respond positively to a moist environment rather than to dryness. The chemical responses, comparable to taste and smell, are more difficult to study, but it is evident that they serve in the choice of food. Unpleasant or irritating chemical vapors in the air will cause withdrawal into the burrow.

24-13. Reproduction. Earthworms reproduce through much of the year, but most actively in warm moist weather. Mating occurs at night and requires 2 or 3 hours. Two worms stretch

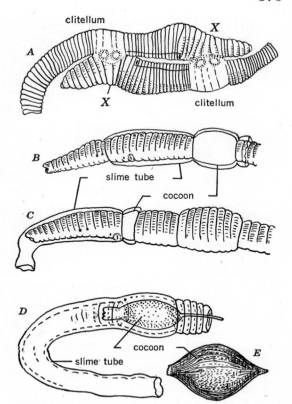

Fig. 24-9. *A*. Two earthworms in copulation (X = 10th somite). *B*. Secretion of slime tube and cocoon. *C*. Slime tube and cocoon slip forward. *D*. Free tube containing cocoon. *E*. Cocoon. (*A, after Grove*, 1925; *B–D, after Foot and Strobell*, 1902.)

out from their burrows and bring their ventral anterior surfaces together, with the anterior ends pointing in opposite directions (Fig. 24-9). The clitellum (XXXII–XXXVII) on each grips somites VII–XII of the other, and a lesser contact of somite XXVI on each is made with XV of the other. Special ventral setae (VI–X, clitellum) of each actually penetrate the body of the other to aid in holding the worms together. Each worm secretes a slime tube about itself, covering somites IX to XXXVI. On each worm a pair of seminal grooves forms (XV to clitellum), along which masses of sperm pass to enter the seminal receptacles of the other (between IX–X and X–XI); after this the worms separate. There is thus reciprocal fertilization and cross-fertilization.

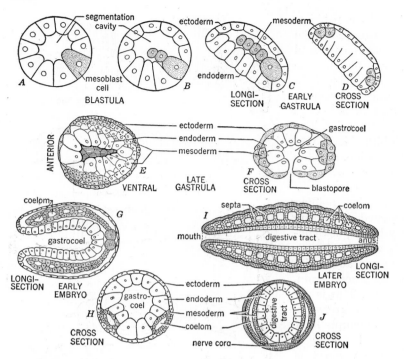

Fig. 24-10. Development of the earthworm; diagrammatic sections (except *E*). Blastula: *A.* Early, with mesoblast cell. *B.* Growth of mesoblast (mesoderm). Gastrula: *C.* Early longitudinal section. *D.* Early cross section. *E.* Later entire gastrula in ventral view. *F.* Cross section of later gastrula. *G, H.* Early embryo; two layers of mesoderm separate to yield coelom in somites. *I, J.* Later embryo; mouth derived from blastopore. (*Adapted from Wilson, 1889; and Sedgwick and Wilson, Introduction to general biology, Henry Holt and Co., Inc.*)

Each worm later produces cocoons containing eggs. In *Eisenia foetida*, each captive worm forms 2 to 10 cocoons at intervals of 3 to 5 days, containing 1 to 28 eggs, of which 10 to 12 develop. The cocoons of *Lumbricus terrestris* measure about 7 by 5 mm., and each has several eggs of which only 1 develops. For each cocoon a slime tube is secreted around the clitellum and anterior somites (X–XXXVI), and within this the cocoon forms as a separate secretion over the clitellum; eggs and albumen enter the cocoon while it is still on the clitellum. The tube and cocoon then slip forward, sperm to fertilize the eggs enter while passing over the seminal receptacles, and, as the worm withdraws from the tube, the cocoon closes into a lemon-shaped case that is deposited in damp earth.

Cleavage is holoblastic but unequal, making a hollow blastula of small ectoderm cells above and larger endoderm cells below (Fig. 24-10). Two large mesoblast cells develop on the future posterior surface and later pass inside to lie between the ectoderm and endoderm. The spherical blastula flattens and elongates as an oval plate, the endoderm cells become columnar,

and the ectoderm grows down marginally. In gastrulation the ventral surface becomes concave and the edges curl down, meeting first posteriorly. This closure proceeds forward, the endoderm thus invaginating as a tube (future gut) ending with the blastopore (future mouth) at the anterior end. The anus forms much later. Meanwhile two cords of mesoblast cells multiply from behind forward, between ectoderm and gut; they spread as two flat plates giving rise to a series of pockets (the somites) and the body muscles. After gastrulation albuminous material in the cocoon enters the primitive gut (gastrocoel) to nourish the embryo. Development requires several weeks, since young hatch in 2 to 3 weeks from cocoons kept in a laboratory.

The adult earthworm has some ability to regenerate somites removed at the ends of the body by accident or experiment. At the anterior end no more than 4 will form, and no "head" will form if 15 or more are cut off; regeneration at the anal end often follows loss of somites there. Experiments in grafting have produced worms with two tail ends, short

Fig. 24-11. Class POLYCHAETA. Clamworm, *Neanthes virens*. External features.

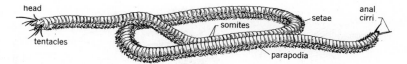

worms from two terminal portions, or extra-long worms by joining parts of three worms.

24-14. Relations to man. Earthworms are used as bait for fishing, and there is much commercial culture for this market. On lawns and golf greens worm castings can be a nuisance, and control by poison has been used. Ancient medical writers mention irrational uses of earthworms in human medicine, and some of these are still followed in parts of Japan and China.

In nature the long-time effects of earthworms have certain practical values. In many soils thousands are present per acre, and their burrowing during most of the year turns over much surface soil. According to Charles Darwin, in favorable locations they may bring up 18 tons of soil per acre in a year, and a layer of cinders or gravel may be completely covered by the castings over a period of years. In extreme instances, the burrows may cause water seepage through irrigation ditches or aid in soil erosion on sloping lands, but generally worm cultivation helps by turning over the top portion and allowing air and water to penetrate. Indeed, the depth of arable topsoil in less fertile areas may be gradually increased by the worms. Claims that adding cultures of earthworms to soil in gardens or orchards will give rapid increase in soil fertility are not true.

24-15. Other Oligochaeta. This class includes over 2,400 species, most of which are smaller than *Lumbricus terrestris*. The most common over North America is the small *Allolobophora caliginosa*. The brandling, or "stinking earthworm," *Eisenia foetida*, ringed with maroon and yellow, is a favorite fishworm that lives in piles of manure or compost. Earthworms are passive carriers of the gapeworm of fowls (*Syngamus*) and intermediate hosts for a cestode of fowls (*Amoebotaenia sphenoides*) and a lungworm of pigs (*Metastrongylus elongatus*); the latter parasite carries a virus that, in combina-

tion with a bacterium, causes swine influenza. Other oligochaetes inhabit damp banks of lakes and streams and either fresh or foul waters. Some live deep in lakes, some beneath stones or decaying seaweeds of the ocean shore, and a few are marine at shallow depths. Others occur in mountains to 12,500 feet (Kashmir), and some inhabit snow fields from Oregon to Alaska. Most oligochaetes feed on vegetation, but a few are probably carnivorous (*Chaetogaster*). The reddish *Tubifex* lives in tubes on the bottom of polluted waters, feeding on the bottom muck, and probably aids in purifying such places. Some oligochaetes are important in the diet of moles, various birds, amphibians, fishes, and predatory invertebrates.

Worms of the Families AEOLOSOMATIDAE and NAIDIDAE reproduce asexually by transverse fission, with several to many "generations" per year; in some genera no sexual individuals are known. Individuals of *Chaetogaster* and *Aeolosoma* form chains of zooids.

CLASS POLYCHAETA. SANDWORMS, TUBE WORMS, ETC.

The polychaetes (Gr., many bristles) are the segmented worms common along seacoasts. They differ from the OLIGOCHAETA in having (1) a differentiated head with sensory appendages; (2) each body somite with many setae borne on a pair of lateral parapodia; (3) the sexes usually separate and without permanent gonads; and (4) a free-swimming trochophore larval stage.

The clamworm, *Neanthes* (*Nereis*) *virens* (Fig. 24-11), is a representative polychaete that lives near the low-tide line. It hides by day beneath stones or in a temporary burrow, with only the head protruding; at night it reaches out, crawls over the sand, or swims by lateral wriggling of the body. Large individuals may be 450 mm. long.

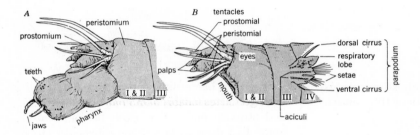

Fig. 24-12. Clamworm. Head region from left side. *A.* Pharynx extended. *B.* Pharynx retracted.

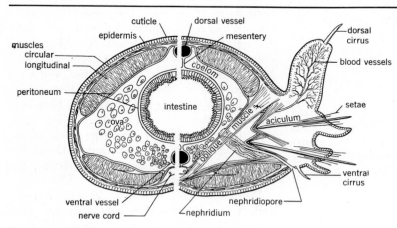

Fig. 24-13. Clamworm. Diagrammatic cross section. Left half with ova free in coelom, right half through the parapodium.

24-16. Structure and natural history. The long, slender, greenish *body* is rounded above and flattened ventrally and composed of 200 or more similar *somites.* A distinct *head* is formed by the prostomium and peristomium (somites I + II). The prostomium bears two short *prostomial tentacles* medially, a pair of stubby conical *palps* laterally, and two pairs of small *eyes* dorsally. The peristomium surrounds the ventral *mouth* and carries four pairs of *peristomial tentacles* dorsally (Fig. 24-12). These specialized sensory organs of touch, smell, and sight serve in finding food, avoiding enemies, and other activities. On either side of each somite there is a flat *parapodium* (Gr. *para,* beside + *podos,* foot) of two lobes (dorsal notopodium, ventral neuropodium), each bearing a *cirrus* and a bundle of bristle-like *setae.* Within are two needle-like chitinous *aciculi,* which extend into the body and serve to support and move the parapodium (Fig. 24-13). The parapodia serve for locomotion, in both creeping and swimming. The *anus* is in the last somite, on which are two soft sensory *anal cirri.*

The body is covered by *cuticle* over an *epidermis,* and beneath the latter are *muscles,* a thin layer of circular muscles and four large bundles of longitudinal muscles (2 dorsal, 2 ventral). The parapodia are moved by oblique muscles in each somite, and there are special muscles in the head. Within the body wall is the *coelomic cavity,* lined by peritoneum and divided by *septa* between most of the somites, as in the earthworm. There are also median dorsal and ventral *mesenteries* between the body wall and gut that divide the coelom of each somite into right and left compartments.

The *digestive tract* is a straight tube and includes (1) the *mouth;* (2) a protrusible *pharynx* with two horny-toothed jaws; (3) a short *esophagus* joined by two large digestive glands; and (4) the *stomach-intestine,* which extends from about somite XII to (5) the *anus.* The food is of small animals, grasped by the jaws.

The *circulatory system* comprises a dorsal vessel and a ventral vessel, both longitudinal, with transverse branches in each somite to the gut, nephridia, body wall, and parapodia. The blood plasma is red, containing dissolved hemoglobin and colorless corpuscles; circulation results from peristaltic contractions of the dorsal vessel. **Respiration** is effected by capillaries in the parapodia and body wall. **Excretion** is performed by paired nephridia that differ from those of the earthworm in being more compact and having much of the ducts ciliated. The **nervous system** includes a brain, nerves to the head and tentacles, connectives to the midventral nerve cord, and a pair of ganglia and lateral nerves in each somite.

The sexes are separate, and **gonads** are present only in the breeding season. Eggs and sperm form from cells of the coelomic peritoneum, and, when mature, pass out through the nephridia or burst through the body wall. Fertilization occurs in the sea, and the zygote develops into a ciliated trochophore larva (Fig. 15-5) which later transforms into a young worm.

24–17. Other Polychaeta. Most of the species live from the tide line down to about 120 feet, but a few go down to 18,000 feet. Some are brilliantly colored. Various species crawl on the bottom, hide beneath rocks or plants, dwell in temporary burrows, or live in permanent tubes. A few swim in the open sea, a few others inhabit fresh water, and the small oval MYZOSTOMARIA are ectoparasites on echinoderms. The free-ranging polychaetes are largely carnivorous, some burrowing forms feed on bottom muck, and tube dwellers subsist mainly on plankton.

The sea mouse, *Aphrodite*, has an oval body with pairs of large plates (elytra) dorsally and is covered by long hair-like setae. The lugworm, *Arenicola*, is a soft-bodied worm that burrows by ingesting sand or mud and produces castings like an earthworm. Other species plaster the sandy walls of their burrows with a mucous secretion that binds the sand grains against collapse and produces a smooth lining. *Terebella* builds a tube of selected sand grains, bits of shell, or other materials, set in mucus. *Pectinaria* cements a tapering tube of fine sand grains, open at both ends, which the worm

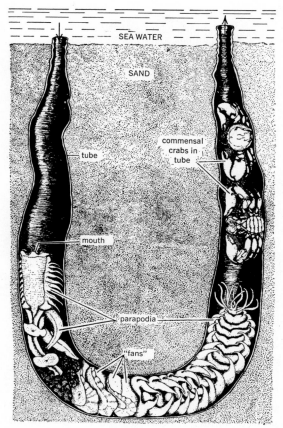

Fig. 24-14. Class POLYCHAETA. *Chaetopterus*, a specialized worm dwelling in a secreted tube in the sea bottom. The "fans" are modified parapodia that draw water through the tube. Commensal crabs (*Polyonyx*) also inhabit the tube. (*After Pearse, 1913.*)

may carry about. The minute *Spirorbis* secretes a spiral calcareous tube that is fastened to the surface of rocks or seaweed, and *Hydroides* forms a larger and irregular tube of the same sort. Some tube dwellers can burrow in rocks or shells. *Chaetopterus* is a specialized worm living permanently in a parchment-like U-shaped tube, up to ¾ inch in diameter, that is set with both openings just above the mud or sand (Fig. 24-14), at depths to 15 fathoms. Three pairs of modified parapodia on the middle of its body are modified as fans to draw in water containing oxygen and microscopic organisms. The mouth is a wide funnel. Other animals live as commensals in the tube. *Serpula*

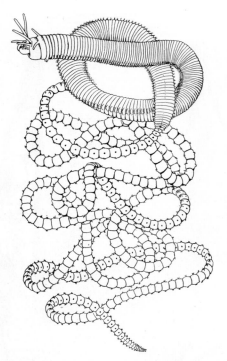

Fig. 24-15. *Eunice viridis,* the palolo worm. (*After Woodworth.*)

and other tube dwellers have a crown of many ciliated tentacles, derived from the prostomial palps, that collect microscopic food; the tentacles contain blood vessels and so serve also as gills for respiration. The tip of one filament is enlarged as an operculum to close the tube when the worm draws within. Some tube worms, such as *Sabellaria,* often occur in large closely set colonies. Other polychaetes have gills on the parapodia or, exceptionally, at the posterior end.

In some polychaetes the sexes are unlike at maturity, showing secondary sexual characters. The germ cells develop on the peritoneum or blood vessels, usually in the posterior somites, which become different in appearance from the anterior, or nonsexual, part. In *Syllis* the hinder sexual portion is budded off and develops a head, and the nonsexual part forms a new tail end. In *Autolytus,* regeneration of segments begins before such separation, and the sexual part may divide several times to produce a chain

of zooids. In *Syllis racemosa* there is lateral budding that yields branched chains of zooids.

The palolo worm, *Eunice viridis* (Fig. 24-15), of Samoa and Fiji, has its burrows in coral reefs and produces many posterior segments that become crowded with eggs or sperm. These are cast off as a unit by each worm to rise and swarm at the surface of the sea, when the water becomes milky with the millions of discharged gametes. Swarming occurs regularly on the first day of the last quarter of the October-November moon, continuing for 2 or 3 days. Another species (*Leodice fucata*) of the West Indies and Gulf of Mexico swarms in the third quarter of the June-July moon. Maturation of gametes possibly is stimulated by the light of the full moon and completed 8 or 9 days later when swarming ensues.

CLASS HIRUDINEA. LEECHES

The leeches are aquatic or terrestrial worms, of predatory or parasitic habits, that have enlarged terminal suckers for locomotion and attachment. Their annelid characteristics include a ventral nerve cord with segmental ganglia and the segmentally arranged nephridia and gonads in the reduced coelom. They resemble the OLIGOCHAETA in being monoecious with formed gonads in a few segments, in producing cocoons, and in lacking tentacles, parapodia, and a larval stage. They differ from other ANNELIDA in the lack of setae (except *Acanthobdella*) and in the presence of copulatory organs and of genital openings on the midventral line.

24-18. Structure (Fig. 24-16). The **body** of a leech at rest is long or oval in outline and usually flattened dorsoventrally, but is very flexible and may be greatly stretched, contracted, or dilated. It consists fundamentally of 34 **somites,** as shown by the nerve ganglia, but the exterior is marked by transverse furrows into many **annuli** (1 to 5 per somite). At the posterior end is a rounded **sucker,** formed from 7 somites; another sucker (of 2 somites) surrounds the mouth at the anterior end in many species.

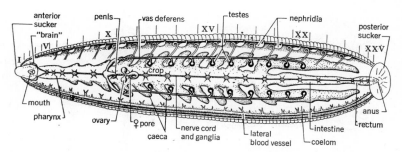

Fig. 24-16. Class HIRUDINEA. The medicinal leech, *Hirudo medicinalis*. Internal structure seen in dissection from the ventral side; I–XXV, somites.

The body is covered by **cuticle** secreted by a single-layered **epidermis,** and many unicellular mucous glands open on the surface. Beneath is a **dermis** with pigment cells and blood capillaries. The **muscular system** is elaborate and powerful, with circular, longitudinal, oblique, and dorsoventral bands of fibers. Mesenchyme between the muscles and internal organs reduces the **coelom** to a system of canals and sinuses, from which the nephridia drain and in which the gonads and major blood vessels are located.

The **digestive tract** includes (1) the mouth; (2) a muscular pharynx with unicellular salivary glands and usually either a proboscis or three horny-toothed jaws; (3) a short esophagus; (4) a long crop with up to 20 pairs of lateral pouches or caeca; (5) a slender intestine; (6) a short rectum; and (7) the anus opening before the posterior sucker. The **circulatory system** is of longitudinal vessels, dorsal, ventral, and lateral, with many cross connections; pulsations in some of these cause the blood to circulate. **Respiration** is by a network of capillaries beneath the epidermis. **Excretion** is by up to 17 pairs of peculiar nephridia that sometimes are branched and sometimes have closed nephrostomes. The **nervous system** resembles that of other annelids, with a pair of dorsal ganglia and paired connectives to the ventral nerve cord, which has segmental ganglia. Four of the anterior ganglia and seven at the posterior end are fused. Each ganglion gives off several pairs of nerves. The sensory structures include taste cells in the mouth, tactile organs on the lips and body, one to five pairs of eyes anteriorly, and other eye-like organs (sensillae) on several annuli.

The sexes are united. The **male reproductive system** includes 4 to 12 pairs of testes beneath the crop; those on each side join a vas deferens running anteriorly, and the two ducts enter a median penis to which accessory glands connect. The penis is within the male genital pore on the midventral surface and toward the anterior end of the body. The **female reproductive system** comprises two ovaries and oviducts joining a single albumen gland and median vagina that opens just behind the male pore.

24-19. Natural history. Most leeches inhabit fresh waters, a few occur on marine fishes, and some live in moist places on land (Fig. 24-17). They are largely nocturnal but may be attracted by food during the day. They travel by looping movements of the body—like a "measuring worm"—and use the suckers for attachment; some also swim by graceful undulations of the body. Leeches are either scavenging, predatory, or parasitic; some feed on dead animals, and others prey upon small worms,

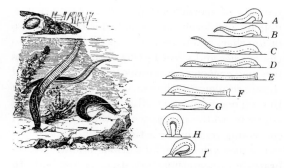

Fig. 24-17. Order HIRUDINEA. *Left.* Leeches in fresh water. (*After Schmeil.*) *Right.* Successive stages *A–I,* in locomotion of the medicinal leech. (*After Uexhull,* 1905.)

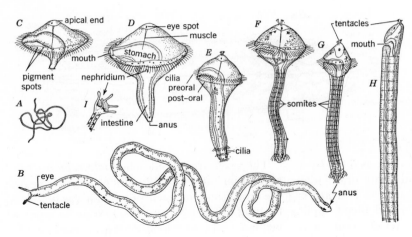

Krfwrthis

Fig. 24-18. Class ARCHIANNEL-IDA. *Polygordius*. *A*. Adult, natural size. *B*. Adult, enlarged. *C–H*. Successive stages in growth, beginning with trochophore and showing gradual increase in number of somites. *I*. Nephridium, enlarged. (*After Fraipont, 1887.*)

insects, larvae, mollusks, etc. The group is best known for the bloodsucking habits of some species. These attach to the exterior or mouth cavity of various vertebrates, from fish to man, some being restricted to one or a few host species. Such a leech fastens on by its suckers and pierces the skin; then blood is sucked out by action of the muscular pharynx and stored in the distensible crop. A salivary enzyme (hirudin) prevents coagulation of the blood. At one feeding a leech may ingest several times its own weight of blood. Much of the liquid is soon excreted, but the concentrated part of such a "full meal" remains fluid and is digested slowly over a period of several months.

Reproduction takes place in the warmer months. Copulation and reciprocal fertilization occur in some (Family HIRUDINIDAE); in others, packets of sperm (spermatophores) are deposited by one leech on the exterior body surface of another, whereupon the sperm penetrate to the ovaries and effect fertilization. Most leeches produce cocoons containing fertilized eggs, and these are placed either in water or in earth. In the GLOSSIPHONIIDAE the eggs are attached ventrally to the parent where they develop and the young remain for a time.

Leeches are eaten by various aquatic vertebrates and sometimes are used as fish bait. In North Temperate regions, they are a minor nuisance to persons wading or bathing in some waters, but they seldom produce serious effects

on mankind or large vertebrates. In some localities they may attach to the buccal cavity of people or mammals when drinking. The land leeches of southeastern Asia and neighboring islands are extremely abundant and sometimes cause severe injury to human beings. Most famous is the medicinal leech (*Hirudo medicinalis*) of Europe. It grows to 4 inches in length, can stretch 8 or 12 inches, and can ingest a large quantity of blood. Since ancient times, it has been used for "blood-letting." During the early nineteenth century this was a common, though erroneous, method of medical treatment. It was collected or reared in ponds in many parts of Europe. From 8,000,000 to 57,000,000 were annually imported into France from 1827 to 1854. Some use was made of them in England and also in the eastern United States

CLASS ARCHIANNELIDA

24-20. Archiannelids. This is a minor group of small worms that live along seashores. They show some features that resemble larval POLYCHAETA, and they may be either primitive or degenerate. *Polygordius* (Fig. 24-18) becomes 30 to 100 mm. long, having a slender body on which the somites are indistinct externally. The small prostomium bears two sensory tentacles. Most species have no setae or parapodia. The internal organs resemble those of polychaetes but are of simple form. Each segment of the coelom contains a pair of nephridia. The nervous system lies in the epidermis. The larva is a typical trochophore on which somites are produced posteriorly during metamorphosis.

CLASSIFICATION

PHYLUM ANNELIDA. SEGMENTED WORMS. Body long, usually segmented and with paired setae; cuticle thin, nonchitinous; digestive tract complete, usually tubular; coelom usually large; blood system closed; paired nephridia; a pair of dorsal cerebral ganglia connected to solid midventral nerve cord with ganglia and lateral nerves in each somite; world-wide, marine, fresh-water, and on or in soil; more than 6,500 species.

CLASS 1. *ARCHIANNELIDA.* Size small; segmentation chiefly internal; parapodia and setae usually absent; nervous system in epidermis; usually dioecious; gonads numerous; usually a trochophore larva; marine. *Polygordius; Dinophilus; Chaetogordius.*

CLASS 2. *POLYCHAETA.* SANDWORMS, TUBE WORMS, etc. Body segmented externally and internally, somites numerous, with lateral parapodia that bear many setae; a head region with tentacles; no clitellum; sexes usually separate; no permanent gonads; fertilization commonly external; a trochophore larval stage; asexual budding in some species; predominantly marine; 3,500 species.

Order 1. Errantia. Somites alike except in head and anal regions; parapodia alike along entire body; pharynx usually protrusible; free-living or in free or attached tubes; often predatory, some pelagic. *Neanthes* (*Nereis*), clamworm; *Aphrodite*, sea mouse; *Syllis*, with asexual budding; *Myzostomum*, ectoparasitic on echinoderms. Freshwater forms: *Manayunkia*, New Jersey and Great Lakes; *Nereis limnicola*, in Lake Merced, San Francisco.

Order 2. Sedentaria. Body of 2 or more regions with unlike somites and parapodia; prostomium indistinct, head appendages modified or none; pharynx without jaws, usually nonprotrusible; gills anterior or none; in burrows or tubes, feed on detritus or plankton. *Chaetopterus*, no gills; *Cirratulus, Amphitrite*, with long gills; *Arenicola*, with branched segmental gills and vestigial parapodia; *Hydroides, Spirorbis, Sabellaria, Serpula*, in tubes, with anterior gills.

CLASS 3. *OLIGOCHAETA.* EARTHWORMS, etc. Segmentation conspicuous externally and internally; no head or parapodia; setae usually few per somite; seldom with gills; monoecious, gonads few and anterior; with clitellum secreting cocoon for eggs; no larva, development direct; chiefly in fresh water and moist soil; 2,400 species. *Aeolosoma; Chaetogaster*, commensal on fresh-water sponges, bryozoans, and snails; *Tubifex*, often in delicate tubes in mud; *Enchytraeus*, in soil and on sea beaches; *Pontodrilus*, on seashores; *Bdellodrilus, Branchiobdella*, leech-like, commensal on gills of crayfishes; *Eisenia foetida*, the "brandling," in compost or manure piles; *Allolobophora, Lumbricus*, in soil.

CLASS 4. *HIRUDINEA.* LEECHES. Body pigmented, usually depressed; a large posterior sucker and often a smaller one at anterior end; no tentacles, parapodia, or setae (one exception); somites 34, subdivided externally into many annuli; coelom filled by connective tissue and muscles; monoecious; eggs usually in cocoons; no larva; in fresh or salt water or on land; 290 species.

Order 1. Acanthobdellida. No anterior sucker, proboscis, or jaws; 2 pairs of setae each on somites II–IV, coelom segmented. *Acanthobdella*, one species on salmon in Lake Baikal, Siberia.

Order 2. Rhynchobdellida. With or without anterior sucker; a protrusible proboscis; no jaws; blood colorless; usually 3 annuli per somite. *Branchellion*, with gills, marine, on rays and skates; *Piscicola*, on bony fishes; *Placobdella*, abundant on turtles and in fresh waters; *Glossiphonia*, in fresh waters.

Order 3. Gnathobdellida. An anterior sucker and usually 3 chitinous jaws, but no proboscis; blood red; includes most leeches. *Hirudo medicinalis*, European medicinal leech, introduced in eastern United States; *Haemopis marmoratis*, horseleech, in mud, usually feeds on invertebrates; *Macrobdella decora*, to 300 mm. long, in fresh waters of northern states, attacks man, cattle, frogs, and fish, eats invertebrates; *Herpobdella; Haemadipsa*, tropical land leech, southeastern Asia to Tasmania.

REFERENCES

BEDDARD, F. E. 1896. Oligochaeta (earthworms, etc.) and Hirudinea (leeches). *In* Cambridge natural history. London, Macmillan & Co., Ltd. Vol. 2, pp. 345–449, figs. 187–225.

BELL, A. W. 1947. The earthworm circulatory system. *Turtox News* (Chicago), vol. 25, no. 5, pp. 89–94, 4 figs.

BENHAM, W. B. 1896. Archiannelida, Polychaeta, and Myzostomaria. *In* Cambridge natural history. London, Macmillan & Co., Ltd. Vol. 2, pp. 239–344, figs. 121–186.

DARWIN, C. 1881. The formation of vegetable mould through the action of worms, with observations on their habits. London, John Murray. vi + 326 pp., 13 figs.

FOOT, K., and E. C. STROBELL. 1902. Further notes on the cocoons of Allolobophora foetida. *Biological Bulletin*, vol. 3, pp. 206–213, 3 figs.

GROVE, A. J. 1925. On the reproductive processes of the earthworm, Lumbricus terrestris. *Quarterly Journal of Microscopical Science*, vol. 69, pp. 245–290, pls. 16–17, 3 figs.

HESS, W. N. 1925. Nervous system of the earthworm, Lumbricus terrestris L. *Journal of Morphology and Physiology*, vol. 40, pp. 235–259, 7 figs.

———. 1925. Photoreceptors of Lumbricus terrestris, with special reference to their distribution, structure and function. *Journal of Morphology and Physiology*, vol. 41, pp. 63–93, 18 figs.

KÜKENTHAL, W., and OTHERS. 1928–1934. Handbuch der Zoologie. Berlin, Walter De Gruyter & Co. Vermes Polymera [= Annelida], vol. 2, pt. 2, xx + 874 pp., 806 figs.

LANGDON, F. E. 1895. The sense-organs of Lumbricus agricola, Hoffm. [= *L. terrestris*]. *Journal of Morphology*, vol. 11, pp. 193–234, 2 figs.

MICHAELSEN, W. 1900. Oligochaeta. *In* Das Tierreich. Berlin, Friedlander & Sohn. 10th Lieferung, xxiv + 575 pp., 13 figs.

MOORE, J. P. 1923. The control of blood-sucking leeches, with an account of the leeches of Palisades Interstate Park. *Roosevelt Wild Life Bulletin* (*Syracuse University*), vol. 2, no. 1, pp. 9–53, 1 pl., 17 figs.

NACHTRIEB, H. F., E. E. HEMINGWAY, and J. P. MOORE. 1912. The leeches of Minnesota. *Geological and Natural History Survey of Minnesota, Zoological Sciences*, no. 4, 150 pp., 6 pls.

PRATT, H. S. 1935. A manual of the common invertebrate animals. . . . 2d ed. Philadelphia, The Blakiston Co. Annelida, pp. 320–368, figs 443–502.

STEPHENSON, J. 1930. The Oligochaeta. Oxford, Clarendon Press. xv + 978 pp., 242 figs.

WILSON, E. B. 1889. The embryology of the earthworm. *Journal of Morphology*, vol. 3, pp. 387–462, pls. 16–22.

25 PHYLUM ARTHROPODA

Joint-footed Animals

Class Crustacea

Crustaceans

The Phylum ARTHROPODA (Gr. *arthros*, joint + *podos*, foot) contains most of the known animals, more than 775,000 species, and many of them are enormously abundant as individuals. It includes the crabs, shrimps, barnacles, and other crustaceans (Class CRUSTACEA), the insects (Class INSECTA), the spiders, scorpions, ticks, and their allies (Class ARACHNIDA), the centipedes (Class CHILOPODA), the millipedes (Class DIPLOPODA), and other less familiar and fossil forms. The body is segmented externally in varying degree, and the appendages are jointed, both being differentiated in form and function to serve special purposes (Fig. 25-1; Table 25-1). All exterior surfaces are covered by an organic exoskeleton containing chitin. The nervous system, eyes, and other sense organs are proportionately large and well developed, making for quick response to stimuli. This is the only major invertebrate phylum with many members adapted for life on land, apart from moist surroundings; and the insects are the only invertebrates capable of flight.

Arthropods occur at altitudes of over 20,000 feet on mountains and to depths of more than 18,000 feet in the sea. Different species are adapted for life in the air, on land, in soil, and in fresh, brackish, or salt waters. Others are parasites of plants and on or in the bodies of other animals. Some are gregarious, and several kinds of colonial insects have evolved social organizations with division of labor among members of different castes. Many arthropods are important economically. The larger crabs, lobsters, and shrimps are eaten by man, small crustaceans are staple foods for fishes, and insects and spiders are eaten by many land vertebrates. The insects are man's chief competitors, eating his crops, stored foods, household goods, or clothing. Some insects and ticks injure or carry diseases to mankind, his domestic animals, and his crops.

25-1. Characteristics. 1. Symmetry bilateral; 3 germ layers; body usually segmented and jointed externally; head, thorax, and abdomen variously distinct or fused (head somites always fused).

2. Appendages one pair per somite or less, each with few to many hinge joints and containing opposed sets of muscles; variously differentiated, sometimes reduced in number or parts, rarely lacking.

3. A hardened exoskeleton containing chitin, secreted by the epidermis, and molted at intervals.

4. Muscles striated, often complex, usually capable of rapid action.

5. Digestive tract complete; mouth parts with lateral jaws adapted for chewing or for sucking; anus terminal.

385

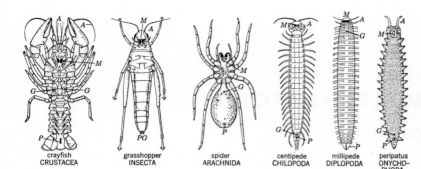

crayfish
CRUSTACEA

grasshopper
INSECTA

spider
ARACHNIDA

centipede
CHILOPODA

millipede
DIPLOPODA

peripatus
ONYCHO-
PHORA

Fig. 25-1. Phylum ARTHROP-ODA. Examples of six major groups in ventral view, showing body divisions, somites, appendages with their divisions, and the body openings. *A*, antennae; *M*, mouth; *P*, anus; *G*, genital opening(s).

TABLE 25-1. Phylum Arthropoda. General Characteristics of the Principal Groups

		Crustacea Crustaceans	Insecta Insects	Arachnida Spiders, etc.	Chilopoda Centipedes	Diplopoda Millipedes	Onychophora Peripatus
Body divisions		Usually cephalo-thorax and abdomen	Head, thorax, abdomen	Cephalo-thorax and abdomen	Head and long body	Head, short thorax, long abdomen	Head continuous with body
Paired appendages	Antennae	2 pairs	1 pair	None	1 pair	1 pair	1 pair
	Mouth parts	Mandibles Maxillae, 2 pairs Maxillipeds	Mandibles Maxillae, 1 pair Labium	Chelicerae Pedipalpi	Mandibles Maxillae, 2 pairs	Mandibles Maxillae, 1 pair	Jaws Oral papillae
	Legs	1 pair per somite, or less	3 pairs on thorax (+ wings)	4 pairs on cephalo-thorax	1 pair per somite	2 (or 1) pairs per somite	1 pair per somite
Respire by		Gills or body surface	Tracheae	Lung books, or tracheae	Tracheae	Tracheae	Tracheae
Sex openings		2, hind part of thorax	1, end of abdomen	1, second somite of abdomen	1, end of abdomen	1, third somite near head	1, end of body
Development		Usually with larval stages	Usually with larval stages	Direct, except mites and ticks	Direct	Direct	Direct
Principal habitat		Salt or fresh water, few on land	Mainly terrestrial	Mainly terrestrial	All terrestrial	All terrestrial	All terrestrial

6. Circulatory system open (lacunar); heart dorsal, distributing blood by arteries to organs and tissues, whence it returns through body spaces (hemocoel) to the heart; coelom reduced.

7. Respiration by gills, tracheae (air ducts), lung books, or body surface.

8. Excretion by coxal or green glands or by 2 to many Malpighian tubules joined to gut (segmental nephridia only in *Peripatus*).

9. Nervous system with paired dorsal ganglia over mouth and connectives to a pair of ventral nerve cords, with a ganglion in each somite or ganglia concentrated; sensory organs include antennae and sensory hairs (tactile and chemoreceptor), simple and compound eyes, auditory organs (INSECTA), and statocysts (CRUSTACEA).

10. Sexes usually separate, male and female often unlike; fertilization mostly internal; eggs with much yolk, in shells; either oviparous or ovoviviparous, cleavage superficial; usually with one to several larval stages and gradual or abrupt metamorphosis to adult form; parthenogenesis in some crustaceans and insects.

The ARTHROPODA and ANNELIDA are the only invertebrate phyla with conspicuous segmentation. Both show this in the body, muscles, and nervous system. The arthropods differ from the annelids in (1) the absence of cilia; (2) general lack of intersegmental septa; (3) reduction of the coelom; (4) presence of a lacunar blood system; (5) concentration of excretory organs and gonads; (6) separation of the sexes; (7) presence of an exoskeleton with chitin; (8) jointed appendages; and (9) compound eyes. Some primitive crustaceans (Subclass BRANCHIOPODA) are annelid-like in the structure of the heart and nervous system and grow by adding somites before the terminal part (telson) containing the anus. The peculiar worm-like *Peripatus* (Subphylum ONYCHOPHORA) has segmental nephridia recalling those in annelids, and its anterior end bears some resemblance to a polychaete annelid; but its body lacks internal septa, and its legs are not jointed.

Some zoologists divide the ARTHROPODA into subphyla, including the BRANCHIATA (crustaceans, trilobites), INSECTA or TRACHEATA (insects), CHELICERATA (spiders, etc.), CHILOPODA (centipedes), and PROGONEATA (millipedes, etc.), with several "appendices" for forms of uncertain status. Others recognize five to seven classes, and some join the centipedes and millipedes as the Class MYRIAPODA. Six subphyla and ten classes are recognized in this book (see

Classification, Chap. 27). The sequence of groups is mainly one of convenience, although the trilobites and crustaceans are probably the most ancient. These and some others originated in Pre-Cambrian time. The evidence from fossils and from the morphology of living forms is often conflicting, so that it is difficult to construct a genealogical tree for the arthropods.

25-2. Cuticle and chitin.

Arthropods are sheathed in an exoskeleton quite unlike either the soft epidermis or the limy shells of other invertebrate phyla. The body covering is a complex noncellular *cuticle* (of several layers) traversed by pore canals and is produced by the single-layered epidermis (hypodermis) immediately beneath. The best-known component of the cuticle is *chitin*,[1] a nitrogenous polysaccharide $(C_8H_{13}O_5N)_x$ that is insoluble in water, alcohol, alkalis, dilute acids, or the digestive juices of many animals. Formerly it was thought that the proportion of chitin determined the degree of rigidity in the exoskeleton (hence hard parts were said to be "heavily chitinized"), but later researches show more protein in the hard outer cuticle and more chitin (to 60 per cent) in the softer inner cuticle.

The cuticle covers all exterior parts, and lines the fore- and hind-gut, respiratory structures, and ducts of surface glands. Its texture varies from smooth to rough, often being sculptured with pits, ridges, or spines and perforated for sensory setae and gland exits (Fig. 26-4). In tracheal tubes and on gills the cuticle is microscopically thin and permeable, and at joints on appendages or between body parts it is soft to facilitate movements. As a general body covering it is commonly flexible and sometimes elastic (nymphs, larvae), but in other cases it is a thick rigid armor, hardened (sclerotized) by chemical substances (e.g., $CaCO_3$ in many crustaceans and millipeds). The exoskeleton protects the internal organs, provides attachments for muscles, and forms levers and fulcra

---

[1] Chitin also occurs in some sponges, hydroids, bryozoans, brachiopods, mollusks, and annelids, but not in protozoans, echinoderms, or vertebrates.

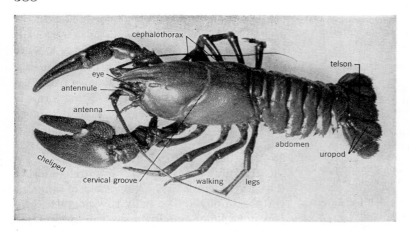

Fig. 25-2. Class Crustacea. External features of the crayfish

between movable parts. On terrestrial arthropods it prevents loss of water and body fluids from the tissues.

Such a jointed but fixed external armor necessarily limits the size of the animal inside. Molt, or ecdysis, is therefore necessary at intervals to permit an increase in size. Most arthropods have four to seven molts. Prior to molt, a new soft exoskeleton grows inside and the old layer becomes loosened. The latter then opens dorsally, the animal withdraws slowly and expands by swallowing air (or water). The new covering soon hardens by chemical change and not solely by exposure to the air or water.

25-3. Size. Because of the limiting weight of the exoskeleton, no arthropod is of great size. Some fossil eurypterids grew to be 9 feet long, and a living Japanese crab (*Macrocheira kämpferi*) spreads to 12 feet with its slender legs. The Atlantic lobster is recorded to 24 inches in length (weight to 34 pounds), and a living isopod (*Bathynomus giganteus*) to nearly 14 inches. No living insect exceeds 11 inches in length or spread. The smallest crustaceans, insects, and mites are under 1 mm. long.

CLASS CRUSTACEA. Crustaceans

The Crustacea (L. *crusta*, a hard shell) includes the fairy shrimps, water fleas, barnacles, crayfishes, crabs, and their kin. Most of them are marine, but many others live in inland

waters, and a few, like the sow bugs, are in moist places on land. Aquatic species inhabit variously the shore, rocks, submerged plants, or open waters; many larvae and some adults burrow, others are pelagic, and a few live deep in the sea. The great majority are free-living, and some gregarious species occur in vast "schools." The barnacles are either sessile or parasitic, and certain other crustaceans are commensal or parasitic on various aquatic animals, from hydroids to whales. Some parasitic species are so greatly modified that their status as crustaceans is shown only in their larval stages.

25-4. Characteristics. 1. Head of 5 fused somites with 2 pairs of antennae, 1 pair of lateral mandibles for chewing, and 2 pairs of maxillae; thorax of 2 to 60 somites, distinct or variously fused; abdominal somites usually distinct, with telson at end; often with a carapace over head and parts of thorax, as a dorsal shield or as 2 lateral valves; appendages variously modified, some usually biramous.

2. Respiration by gills (rarely by body surface); pseudotracheae on pleopods of some land isopods.

3. Excretion by 1 or 2 pairs of green glands; no Malpighian tubules.

4. Sexes separate (except in Cirripedia and some parasitic Isopoda); sex openings paired; eggs often carried by female; parthenogenesis in some Branchiopoda and Cladocera.

25-5. The crayfish. This animal (*Cambarus, Astacus*) serves well for an introduction to both the Arthropoda and the Crustacea (Fig. 25-2). It is up to 6 inches long and has appendages differentiated to serve special purposes.

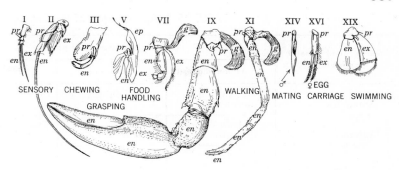

Fig. 25-3. Crayfish. Appendages of the right side in ventroposterior view (some omitted), showing structural differentiation to serve various functions. *pr,* protopodite; *en,* endopodite; *ex,* exopodite; *ep,* epipodite; *g,* gill.

The common English names of "crayfish" and "crawfish" (and even the American "crawdad") probably derive from the French word *écrevisse* (Old German *krebiz,* crab). Different crayfishes inhabit fresh-water streams, ponds, and lakes over much of the world. *Cambarus affinis* is common in the eastern states, *C. virilis* and others in the Mississippi Valley, and *Astacus nigrescens* occurs from San Francisco northward on the Pacific coast. *C. clarkii* of the Gulf states has become acclimatized in southern California. The lobster (*Homarus americanus*) of salt waters along the Atlantic coast is much larger, but resembles the crayfish closely in structure.

25-6. External features. An exoskeleton containing chitin covers the entire body and is hardened except at joints where it is thin and soft to permit of movements. The body comprises an anterior rigid *cephalothorax* (head + thorax) and a posterior jointed *abdomen.* It is composed of *somites* (head 5, thorax 8, abdomen 6), each with a pair of jointed *appendages* ventrally. The skeletal elements of a single somite, as in the abdomen, include a transverse dorsal plate, or *tergum,* and a ventral crossbar, or *sternum,* joined together at either side by a lateral *pleuron.* Somites of the cephalothorax are covered by a continuous *carapace* shielding the dorsal and lateral surfaces. On this a transverse *cervical groove* marks the division between the head and thorax, and at the anterior end is a median pointed *rostrum.*

Beneath the rostrum on either side is a *compound eye,* stalked and movable. The *mouth* is between the mandibles, and the *anus* opens ventrally in the broad median *telson* (not a somite) at the end of the abdomen. The *gills* are beneath either side of the carapace. The paired *female sex openings* are at the base of the third pair of walking legs on the thorax, and those of the *male* at the fifth pair.

25-7. Paired appendages (Table 25-2; Figs. 25-2, 25-3). Unlike the many simple and solid setae of the earthworm, the crayfish has one pair of jointed appendages on each somite; these contain opposed sets of muscles for their movement. The joints on the thoracic appendages are not all in the same plane, so that these members may be moved in various directions. The appendages on different somites are of parts that differ in number, structure, and function. They illustrate, however, the principle of serial homology in that all are referable to a common form, the two-branched or *biramous appendage;* this consists of a *protopodite,* typically of two joints (coxopodite, basipodite), that bears a medial *endopodite* and lateral *exopodite,* each of one to many segments.

The short *antennules* and long *antennae* are mobile sensory structures that test and receive stimuli from the environment. The stout *mandibles* crush the food, which is manipulated by the *maxillae* and *maxillipeds.* The large *chelae* (pincers) serve in offense and defense, and the other *walking legs* (pereiopods) are used for locomotion, handling food, and cleaning the body. The abdominal *swimmerets* (pleopods) aid in respiration and carry the eggs on females, and the wide *uropods,* with the telson, form a broad terminal paddle for swimming and for egg protection.

TABLE 25-2. Appendages of the Crayfish

Somite* and name of appendage	Number and structure of parts			Function
	Protopodite	Endopodite	Exopodite	
I Antennule	3, statocyst in dorsal base	Short jointed feeler	Short jointed feeler	Equilibrium, touch, taste
II Antenna	2, excretory pore in ventral base	Long feeler of many joints	Thin pointed blade	Touch, taste
III Mandible	2, heavy jaw + base of palp	2 distal parts of palp	0	Biting food
IV 1st maxilla	2, thin medial plates	1, small, unjointed	0	Food handling
V 2d maxilla	2, bilobed plates	1, narrow exopodite and epipodite form scoop (scaphognathite) to draw water over gills		
VI 1st maxilliped	2, broad medial plates + epipodite	2, slender, small	2, slender, minute	Touch, taste, food handling
VII 2d maxilliped	2, short, with gill	5, short, stout	2, slender	
VIII 3d maxilliped	2, with gill	5, larger	2, slender	
IX 1st "walking" leg	2, with gill	5, stout; heavy pincer at tip	0	Pincer for offense and defense
X 2d "walking" leg	2, with gill	5, slender, small pincer	0	Walking, grasping
XI 3d "walking" leg	2, with gill; sex opening in ♀	5, slender, small pincer	0	
XII 4th "walking" leg	2, with gill	5, slender, no pincer	0	Walking
XIII 5th "walking" leg	2, no gill; sex opening in ♂	5, slender, no pincer	0	
XIV 1st swimmeret	In ♀, reduced or none			Transfer sperm from ♂ to ♀
	In ♂: protopodite + endopodite fused, tubular			
XV 2d swimmeret	In ♂: 2 joints	Rolled, conical	Filamentous	
	In ♀: same as XVI			
XVI 3d swimmeret	2, short	Jointed filament	Jointed filament	Water circulation in both sexes; carry eggs and young in ♀
XVII 4th swimmeret	2, short	Jointed filament	Jointed filament	
XVIII 5th swimmeret	2, short	Jointed filament	Jointed filament	
XIX Uropod	1, short broad	1, flat oval plate	1, flat oval plate, with hinge	Swimming, ♂ and ♀; egg protection in ♀

* Some authorities consider that a somite without appendages precedes that bearing the antennule which would make 6 somites in the head and 20 in all.

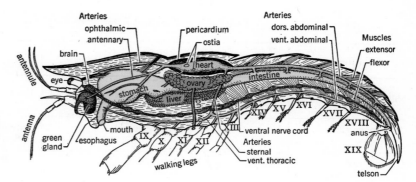

Fig. 25-4. Crayfish. Internal structure of a female. IX–XIX, somites.

25-8. Muscles. In the crayfish and other arthropods the muscles are complex, and all are contained within the exoskeleton, instead of being a part of the body wall as in coelenterates and annelids or external to the skeleton as in vertebrates. The muscles attaching to many parts are in opposed pairs: a *flexor* to draw the part toward the body or point of articulation and an *extensor* to straighten it out. The largest muscles are the flexors which bend the abdomen forward under the body when the crayfish swims backward.

25-9. Digestive system. This includes (1) the *mouth,* opening above the mandibles; (2) a short tubular *esophagus;* (3) the large thin-walled *stomach* in the thorax that is divided into a swollen anterior *cardiac chamber* and smaller *pyloric chamber* behind; (4) a short *mid-gut;* (5) the slender tubular *intestine* extending dorsally in the abdomen to (6) the *anus;* and (7) two large *digestive glands* (liver) beneath the stomach, each with a duct to the mid-gut (Fig. 25-4). Food is brought to the mouth by the chelate second and third pairs of legs, the soft parts being torn and crushed to small size by the mandibles, then passed through the esophagus to the cardiac chamber. Projecting into this are strongly calcified *teeth,* one median and two lateral, that are moved by muscles attached outside the stomach, forming a *gastric mill* for further grinding of the food. The entrance to the pyloric chamber bears many hair-like setae that permit only fine particles to enter. Each digestive gland is three-lobed and composed of many fine tubules that

secrete a pancreatic-like enzyme serving in digestion. Absorption of digested food occurs in the mid-gut, possibly also in the "liver." Hard particles are rejected by the mouth or cardiac mill, and undigested materials are formed as feces in the intestine to pass out the anus. The digestive tract, except for the mid-gut, is lined by delicate chitin, continuous at the mouth and anus with the external cuticle; the entire lining is shed at each molt. At some seasons the walls of the cardiac chamber have 2 calcareous gastroliths, thought to store lime salts for hardening the exoskeleton after a molt.

25-10. Circulatory system. The short muscular *heart* is of irregular shape and suspended in a large middorsal *pericardial sinus* of the thorax by 6 ligaments that attach to the sinus walls. Blood in the sinus enters the heart through 3 pairs of *valves* (ostia) and is pumped, by contraction of the heart, into 6 arteries that distribute to all parts of the body (Table 25-3).

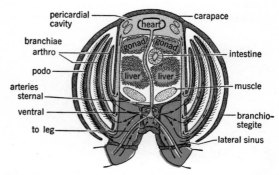

Fig. 25-5. Crayfish. Cross section of the body through the heart; arrows indicate the course of blood flow.

TABLE 25-3. Principal Arteries of the Crayfish

Artery	Origin	Direction of blood flow	Supplies
Ophthalmic (1) (anterior aorta)	Heart	Anterior to head	Eyes, antennules, brain
Antennary (2)	Heart	Anteroventral	Antennae, green glands, anterior muscles, stomach
Hepatic (2)	Heart	Ventral	"Liver," pyloric stomach, mid-gut
Dorsal abdominal (1) (posterior aorta)	Heart	Posterior, top of abdomen	Intestine, telson, abdominal muscles
Sternal (1)	Base of posterior aorta	Ventral (passes through nerve cord)	Ventral thoracic and abdominal arteries, gonads
Ventral thoracic (1)	Sternal artery	Anterior, floor of thorax	Mouth, esophagus, appendages III–XI *
Ventral abdominal (1)	Sternal artery	Posterior, floor of abdomen	Abdominal muscles, appendages XII–XIX *

* See Table 25-2.

The arteries contain valves that prevent a return flow. From the finer arteries the blood flows into open spaces, or *sinuses,* between body organs, whence it collects in a large *sternal sinus* in the floor of the thorax and passes in afferent channels leading to the gills. There the CO_2–O_2 exchange of respiration occurs, and the blood returns in efferent channels to the *branchiocardiac sinuses* that lead up the inner sides of the thoracic wall to the pericardial sinus. This *lacunar* or *open system,* distributing between the tissues and without veins, is characteristic of the arthropods and is in striking contrast to the closed circulatory systems of annelids and vertebrates. The nearly colorless *blood plasma* has a dissolved respiratory pigment (hemocyanin) that transports oxygen to the tissues; there are free *amoeboid corpuscles* in the plasma.

25-11. Respiratory system. The *gills* (Figs. 25-5, 25-6) are delicate plume-like projections of the body wall, containing blood channels and located along either side of the thorax in a *gill chamber.* The latter is covered by a lateral part (branchiostegite) of the carapace, but is open ventrally and at both ends. A paddle-like projection (scaphognathite) of the second maxilla moves back and forth in a channel under each side of the carapace to draw water containing dissolved oxygen over the gill filaments. The gills are arranged in lengthwise rows, the *podobranchiae* being attached to the coxopodites of appendages VII–XII, and the double row of *arthrobranchiae* (anterior VII–XII, posterior VIII–XII) to the membranes joining these appendages to the thorax, making 17 on each side. In the Genus *Astacus* there is one *pleurobranchia* on the thorax above appendage XIII.

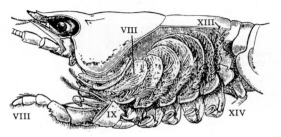

Fig. 25-6. Crayfish. The gills (podobranchiae) exposed by removal of the branchiostegite. (*After Huxley.*)

Fig. 25-7. Crayfish. Nervous system, dorsal view.

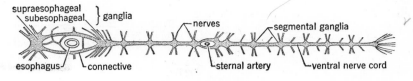

25-12. Excretory system.

Two large *green glands,* ventral in the head and anterior to the esophagus, serve to remove organic wastes from the blood and body fluids. Each consists of a glandular region, an expanded "bladder" with thin walls, and a duct opening ventrally on the basal segment of the antenna. The cavities in the excretory and genital organs comprise the only relics of the coelom in arthropods; the spaces within the body form a *hemocoel,* not comparable with the large coelom of annelids.

25-13. Nervous system.

In the crayfish, this system resembles that of the earthworm but is proportionately larger (Fig. 25-7). The *supraesophageal ganglia* ("brain") in the head send nerves to the eyes, antennules, and antennae, and a pair of *connectives* joins the *subesophageal ganglia,* behind the mouth, at the anterior end of the double *ventral nerve cord.* The fused subesophageal ganglia of the adult represent six (or five) pairs of ganglia that are separate in the embryo; nerves from these pass to the mouth appendages, esophagus, green glands, and anterior muscles. Along the nerve cord each somite from VIII to XIX contains a pair of joined ganglia sending nerves to the appendages, muscles, and other organs.

25-14. Sense organs.

These enable the crayfish to test its environment continually, to find shelter, food, and mates, and to avoid unfavorable surroundings and enemies. Much of the body is sensitive to *touch,* especially the chelae, chelipeds, mouth parts, underside of the abdomen, and edge of the telson. On these regions are many *tactile hairs,* which are delicate plume-like projections of the cuticle, containing fibers connected to sensory nerves. The *chemical sense* (taste + smell) resides in hairs on the antennules, tips of the antennae, mouth parts, and ends of the chelae. If meat juice is brought in a fine pipette to any of these, the animal vibrates its mouth parts, becomes excited, and turns toward the stimulus. Meat placed slightly away from a crayfish is "discovered" when juices diffusing from it through the water reach these sensory organs. The sense of *equilibrium* or orientation to gravity is served by a small chitin-lined sac, the *statocyst,* that opens dorsally under fine hairs on the basal segment of each antennule. It contains a ridge with many fine upright *sensory hairs* to which sand grains become attached by mucus and serve as *statoliths.* The action of gravity on the statoliths produces stimuli through the hairs, which are attached to an "auditory" nerve leading to the brain. Tilting or inverting the body alters the direction of gravitational pull on the statoliths and sets up a changed stimulus to the brain, which leads the animal to right itself. At a molt, the statolith lining and the sand grains are lost, but new grains are soon acquired from bottom debris. Proof of their function is had if a freshly molted crayfish is placed in filtered water containing no foreign particles so that no new statoliths can be acquired; its equilibrium will be disturbed. Should iron filings be placed in such water, some will enter the statocysts; if then a magnet is placed above or at the side of the crayfish, the latter will react by turning its ventral surface toward the magnet.

Each *compound eye* (Fig. 25-8) has an outer rounded surface covered by transparent cuticle, the *cornea,* which is divided into about 2,500 microscopic square *facets.* The facet is the outer end of a slender tapering visual unit, or *ommatidium.* Each of these consists of (1) the corneal facet, or *lens;* (2) two *corneagen cells,* which secrete the lens; (3) a *crystalline cone* of four cone cells; (4) *distal pigment cells* about the cone; (5) a long tapering *retinula* of eight cells, which form a central *rhabdom* where they meet; (6) *basal pigment cells* around the ret

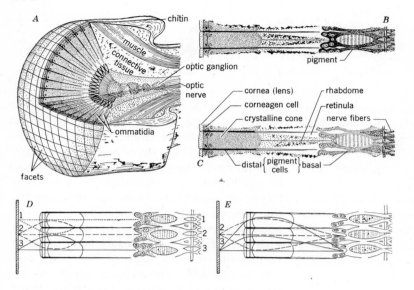

Fig. 25-8. Crayfish. The compound eye; diagrammatic. *A.* Entire eye sectioned to show its general structure. *B.* One ommatidium in the light, pigment extended. *C.* Ommatidium in the dark, pigment contracted. *D.* Apposition image formed of separate images on retinulae from points 1, 2, 3 on object. *E.* Superposition image, each retinula receives both oblique and direct rays from more than one point. (*Adapted in part from Imms, Textbook of entomology, E. P. Dutton & Co., Inc.*)

inula; and (7) a *tapetum cell* between the inner bases of the retinular cells. The inner ends of the retinular cells penetrate the *basement membrane* on which all the ommatidia rest, and each connects by a *nerve fiber* through four *optic ganglia* to the *optic nerve,* which joins the brain.

The eye forms images in two ways (Fig. 25-8*D, E*). In strong light the pigment is extended to isolate each ommatidium from those adjacent. Light from any small area on an object that passes axially through a lens will reach the light-sensitive retinula and stimulate its nerve fibers, but any rays entering at an angle are refracted into the pigment and absorbed. Of any object, the eye will form a *mosaic* or *apposition image,* the light from different parts registering on separate ommatidia. Any slight shift of the object will stimulate other ommatidia; hence, the compound eye is especially efficient in registering movement. In weak light the pigment recedes toward the distal and basal parts of the ommatidia, the light rays then spread to adjacent ommatidia, and there forms on the retinulae a continuous or *superposition image,* which is probably less distinct than the apposition image but provides a proportionately stronger stimulus in relation to the amount of light received.

25-15. Endocrine glands. The *sinus gland* on the eyestalk in various crustaceans produces a hormone that controls the spread of pigment granules in chromatophores of the body epidermis and in the compound eyes, regulates the molt, affects the deposit of lime salts in the exoskeleton, and is also necessary to the continuance of life. The hormone is evidently distributed by the blood stream, as in vertebrates.

25-16. Reproductive system. The sexes are separate in the crayfish, and the female has a proportionately broader abdomen than the male. The first two pairs of appendages on the male's abdomen are tubular, for sperm transfer. The gonads are hollow and three-lobed in both sexes. In the *male* the two soft white *testes* are fused and lie beneath the pericardial sinus. On each side a slender coiled *vas deferens* extends ventrally to open at the base of the fifth walking leg. In the female the two *ovaries* are of comparable form and location with the testes of the male. Eggs develop in follicles on the inner surface and are discharged through an *oviduct* opening near each third walking leg.

25-17. Natural history. The Genus *Astacus* includes 5 species in western North America and 10 in Europe and western Asia; *Cambarus* comprises about 70 species in North America east of the Rocky Mountains and in Central America. Other genera and species inhabit the Southern Hemisphere. The various species of *Cambarus* are segregated ecologically, some examples being (1) *C. affinis* in ponds, lakes, and slow rivers; (2) *C. acutus* in swifter streams; (3) *C. virilis* in large rivers; (4) *C. bartoni* in upland streams; (5) *C. diogenes* in marshes and meadows where it digs burrows 1 to 3 feet deep, down to the water, and topped by chimneys of mud; and (6) *C. pellucidus*, which is blind and lives in cave waters.

The crayfish is a solitary bottom dweller, hiding by day under stones or in crevices or burrows, where it keeps as much of its body as possible in contact with surrounding objects. The animal faces the entrance of its retreat, with the chelae extended, the antennae waving about, and the "scoops" and swimmerets performing respiratory movements; other appendages are moved at times to receive stimuli or detect food. It grasps any food that passes within reach and will emerge to seize prey and then go back into its retreat. It resists attack by use of the strong chelae and tries to avoid being drawn out of its shelter; if the latter is opened or removed, the animal darts off to a new hiding place. The crayfish can walk forward, sideways, obliquely, or backward with the fourth pair of legs bearing much of the weight. Through extension of the abdomen, uropods, and telson and sudden flexion of them under the body, the resistance offered these broad parts by the water enables the animal to "swim" or dart backward, and quick repetition of this action often enables it to escape danger. Crayfishes are most in evidence when feeding actively in spring and early summer; in cold weather they retire to burrows or other safe retreats below the water. During drought, the burrows are retreats for fishes and other aquatic animals that later emerge to reoccupy transient ponds.

The food includes live insect larvae, worms, crustaceans, small snails, fishes, and tadpoles, besides some dead animal matter. The burrowing species subsist extensively on stems and roots of plants, and other species use some such materials. The enemies of crayfishes, besides mankind, include certain fishes, large salamanders, turtles and water snakes, herons, kingfishers and other birds, and some aquatic mammals.

25-18. Molt. The living crayfish has an inelastic exoskeleton, and molt (ecdysis) is necessary for an increase in body size. The young molt several times per year, and adults less often. Prior to molt, some inorganic salts are withdrawn from the exoskeleton, a new soft exoskeleton grows beneath and separates from the older, and the muscles and other structures within the appendages soften and are reduced in bulk. The old cuticle then opens dorsally between the carapace and abdomen, and the animal slowly withdraws itself, leaving its former covering complete, even to such minor features as the gut lining, eye facets, and setae. Before the new cuticle hardens, an increase in bulk occurs, probably by taking in water. For some days the animal hides away to avoid enemies when in this defenseless condition.

25-19. Regeneration. The crayfish can replace lost parts, chiefly the appendages and eyes, but to a lesser extent than in lower animals such as coelenterates or earthworms. This ability of *regeneration* is greater in the young animals than in older ones. Upon loss or removal of an appendage, the new one is partly formed at the next molt and increases in size with successive molts until it may be fully restored. Removal of the tip of an eye may be followed by normal regeneration, but if the entire structure is cut away, an antenna-like replacement may result. Such regeneration of a part different from that which was removed is called *heteromorphosis.*

25-20. Autotomy. The crayfishes and other crustaceans, particularly crabs, possess the power of self-amputation, or *autotomy,* of the thoracic legs. If a cheliped or walking leg is broken or severely handled, the terminal five segments are cast off—sacrificed to the enemy. The fracture is at a definite breaking plane, marked by a fine encircling line on the basal segment of the endopodite on a cheliped and

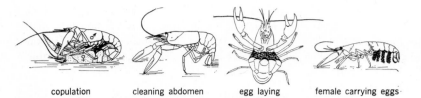

copulation   cleaning abdomen   egg laying   female carrying eggs

Fig. 25-9. Crayfish. Activities in reproduction. (*After Andrews*, 1904.)

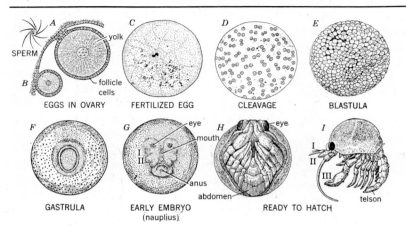

EGGS IN OVARY   FERTILIZED EGG   CLEAVAGE   BLASTULA

GASTRULA   EARLY EMBRYO (nauplius)   READY TO HATCH

Fig. 25-10. Development of the crayfish; figures variously enlarged. *B.* Eggs in ovary surrounded by follicle cells; when laid they become attached to swimmerets on female (Fig. 25-9). *D, E.* Cleavage is superficial. *F.* The shallow gastrula forms beneath the yolk. *F–H.* Ventral views. *I.* Young removed from egg just before hatching. (*A, B, from G. B. Howes, Atlas of zootomy, The Macmillan Co.; C–E, after Zehnder, 1934; F–I, after Huxley.*)

at the third joint on the others. This procedure is a precaution to avoid undue loss of blood. Across the inside of the appendage, on the proximal side of the breaking plane, there is a diaphragm with a small opening through which the nerves and arteries pass. The joint is fortified by interlocking external spines, and breaking is effected by a special muscle distal to the diaphragm. When the leg is cast off, the opening is quickly stopped by a blood clot and a small fold or valve; then it soon closes by cell growth. A miniature replacement of the limb begins growth, and at subsequent molts this increases toward normal size and complete replacement.

25-21. Reproduction. *Cambarus affinis* of the eastern states mates in March. The male grasps and inverts a female, stands over her, seizes all her walking legs with his two chelae, and flexes his telson tightly over the end of her abdomen, so that she is held motionless (Fig. 25-9). He uses one of his fifth walking legs to press the tips of the two modified pleopods on his somite XIV against the sperm receptacles (annuli) between somites XII and XIII on her thorax.

Sperm then pass in mucus along his pleopods to lodge in her receptacles, after which the animals separate. Some days or weeks later the female cleans her abdomen and pleopods thoroughly, lies upside down with her abdomen sharply flexed, and a slimy secretion issues from glands on the pleopods. Soon the 200 to 400 eggs (2 mm. in diameter) are extruded from the oviducts, fertilized by sperm from the seminal receptacles, and become affixed by the secretion to her pleopods. She later resumes normal position and backs into a shelter, when the eggs hang like berries and are aerated by movements of the pleopods. Five or more weeks ensue until hatching. Each young is a miniature crayfish (Fig. 25-10) about 4 mm. long, transparent, and attached to cuticle molted within the shell before hatching. Six or more additional molts occur during the first 2 months of life, the young enlarging at each. They remain attached to the female until the second stage, stay near her a few days more, and then become independent. By late autumn they are 35 to 50 mm. long and are colored and shaped like the adult. *Cambarus clarkii* in Louisiana mates in late spring and produces eggs late in summer that

Fig. 25-11. Class CRUSTACEA. Some marine forms in their respective habitats; mostly reduced, but not to same scale. Subclass CIRRIPEDIA, Order THORACICA: *Mitella*, goose barnacle; *Balanus*, acorn barnacle. Subclass MALACOSTRACA, Order NEBALIACEA: *Nebalia*. Order MYSIDACEA: *Mysis*, opossum shrimp. Order ISOPODA: *Ligia*. Order AMPHIPODA: *Gammarus*, sand hopper; *Caprella*, "skeleton shrimp." Order STOMATOPODA: *Squilla*. Order DECAPODA: *Crago*, shrimp; *Panulirus*, spiny rock lobster; *Pagurus*, hermit crab; *Cancer*, edible crab; *Uca*, fiddler crab.

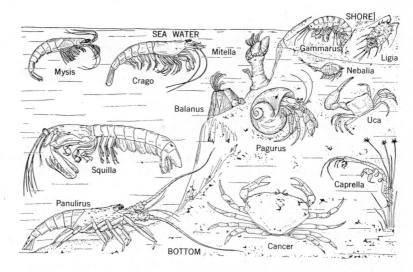

Fig. 25-12. Class CRUSTACEA. Some fresh-water inhabitants in their characteristic habitats. Subclass BRANCHIOPODA, Order ANOSTRACA: *Branchinecta*, fairy shrimp. Order NOTOSTRACA: *Lepidurus*. Order CLADOCERA: *Daphnia*, water flea. Subclass OSTRACODA, Order PODOCOPA: *Eucypris*. Subclass COPEPODA, Order EUCOPEPODA: *Cyclops*. Subclass MALACOSTRACA, Order ISOPODA: *Porcellio*, sow bug (on land); Order AMPHIPODA: *Hyalella*. Order DECAPODA: *Cambarus*, crayfish. Some enlarged (*Daphnia*, *Eucypris*, *Cyclops*) and others reduced, but not to same scale.

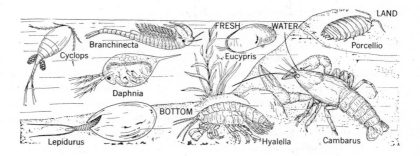

hatch in about 15 days. The young grow through the winter, and some are of market size (85 mm.) by February. In the cold waters of Europe, *Astacus fluviatilus* produces eggs in October or November that do not hatch until the following June.

25-22. Other Crustacea. The thousands of species present a wide variety in structure, coloration, habitat, and mode of life, as indicated under Classification and suggested in Figs. 25-11 and 25-12. The body is variously elongate or shortened, depressed in crabs, sow bugs, and others, and compressed in shrimps. The appendages of the more primitive BRANCHIOPODA are specialized only on the head region, and those elsewhere serve equally for locomotion, respiration, and egg transport. Strictly pelagic species have many long setae that help to bear them up in the water, and burrowing species have flattened appendages useful for digging. The coloration is varied—red, yellow, green, blue, brown, or black in different species. The pigment is contained in branched chromatophores, and some species change color in response to light intensity and the nature of the background. The nervous system varies from a ladder-like form (BRANCHIOPODA) with paired

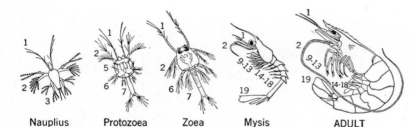

Nauplius   Protozoea   Zoea   Mysis   ADULT

Fig. 25-13. Larval stages and adult of a shrimp, *Penaeus*, showing the succession of changes in body form and in the appendages (1–19). (*After F. Müller; and Huxley.*)

ganglia in each somite as with annelids, to the crabs which have but a single posterior ganglion, and the parasitic barnacles in which there is but one ganglion serving the whole body. Some adults and many larvae have a simple median eye in addition to the pair of compound eyes. Most crustaceans are predaceous, subsisting on other animals of small size; but sow bugs use vegetation mainly, land crabs feed on coconuts, and some bottom dwellers swallow debris from which their food is extracted. In reproduction the females usually carry the eggs externally, but some have internal brood pouches, and others reproduce parthenogenetically. Eggs of a few fresh-water species are resistant to drought for 2 or more years and may be spread by winds.

Some small aquatic crustaceans ("Entomostraca") occur in enormous numbers. In lakes there may be thousands per cubic meter, when they give distinctive color to the water. Small marine forms often are so abundant, either as larvae or as adults, that whole schools of fishes or whales subsist chiefly on a single species. Crustaceans and some other members of the plankton occur in greatest numbers at certain depths and decrease above and below. They also fluctuate in numbers through the season, and many pelagic forms of both salt and fresh waters migrate up near the surface at night and descend during the day, presumably in response to the change in intensity of light.

Crabs may become covered with marine growths—algae, sponges, or barnacles—and some pick off and attach bits of sponge to the shell. In one type of hermit crab, living in a snail shell, a sponge (*Suberites*) grows over and dissolves the shell, leaving the crab encased in the sponge as a shelter.

25-23. Crustacean larvae. Like some other invertebrates of fresh waters, the young crayfish at hatching resembles the adult except for minor details. Many marine crustaceans, however, have several larval stages, the younger of which are quite unlike the parent animals. These minute larvae represent the means of dispersal, especially of sedentary forms. The first three larval stages of the lobster have exopodites on the thoracic legs, as in an adult schizopod, so that these are termed "schizopod" or "mysis" larvae.

Shrimps and prawns (*Penaeus*) begin as a minute *nauplius larva* (Fig. 25-13) with an unsegmented body, a simple median eye, and 3 pairs of appendages (the later antennules, antennae, and mandibles). With molt the *metanauplius* and *protozoea* stages appear, the latter with 7 pairs of appendages and beginning somites. Then follows the *zoea,* with distinct cephalothorax and abdomen, 8 pairs of appendages, and 6 more beginning. This molts into the *mysis* (schizopod) larva, having 13 pairs of appendages on the cephalothorax and those of the thorax bearing exopodites that serve in swimming. A further molt yields the adult, with 19 pairs of appendages. In a crab the first or *zoea* larva has a helmet-like carapace with long dorsal and anterior spines, and sessile eyes; the thorax bears 2 pairs of biramous swimming legs (maxillipeds), and the slender mobile abdomen lacks swimmerets. In the next or *megalops* larva the carapace is broad but lacks spines, the eyes are large and stalked, the thorax has 5 pairs of "walking" legs, and there are functional swimmerets on the abdomen. Both of these minute stages swim in surface waters. Later the megalops sinks to the bottom and molts into typical crab form, with a still

Fig. 25-14. Subclass CIRRIPE-DIA. Goose barnacle, *Lepas*. Adult with right side of mantle and shell removed. From the egg a free-swimming nauplius larva hatches that feeds and molts to become a cypris larva. The latter attaches by its antennules and cement gland, then transforms to the sessile adult stage. Egg and larvae much enlarged. *M*, mouth; *A*, anus; I, antennule; II, antenna; III, mandible; VI–XI, other appendages.

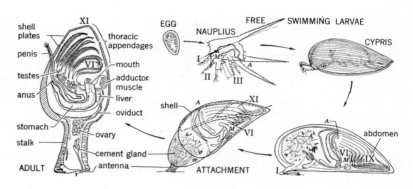

broader carapace, the abdomen folded beneath the carapace, and its swimmerets useless for locomotion.

Instances such as these among crustaceans, like comparable cases among the vertebrates, illustrate the **biogenetic law,** or **recapitulation theory,** of Haeckel. This states that "ontogeny recapitulates phylogeny," that the individual in its development passes through stages which represent those in the evolutionary history of the species or of the group to which it belongs. The progressive acquisition of appendages and their elaboration in successive larvae, the median "cyclops" eye before the paired compound eyes, the increase and segmentation of the thorax, and other features in the sequence of nauplius, zoea, and later larvae are suggestive of a possible course of evolution in the CRUSTACEA. Strict application of the theory is difficult because many ancestral features are abbreviated or omitted, but the concept has stimulated intense interest in embryological studies and has been fruitful in other ways.

25-24. Barnacles. These are highly modified crustaceans in which the adults are hermaphroditic as to sex, enclosed in a calcareous shell, and of sessile habit. The common goose barnacles (*Lepas, Mitella*) and rock or ship barnacles (*Balanus*) attach to fixed objects (Figs. 25-11, 25-14); other species fasten only to gorgonians, crabs, sharks, sea turtles, or whales, and still others are parasitic (Fig. 25-16). The egg develops in the parent's mantle cavity and hatches out a microscopic nauplius larva, which swims, feeds, and molts one to three times in a week or so, with slight changes in form. Another molt produces the very different **cypris larva,** with a bivalve shell and additional appendages and containing fat globules for buoyancy. This stage lasts for 4 days to 10 or 12 weeks in different species; the larva then settles to the bottom and hunts a place of attachment to which it adheres by the antennules, aided by secretion from a cement gland. In a rather complete metamorphosis the bivalve shell is lost, the body mass alters in form, and the valves of the adult shell appear. The barnacle thenceforth remains fixed, literally "standing on its head." When feeding, the long delicate thoracic appendages repeatedly fan out well above the shell opening, then curve and quickly withdraw, carrying food to the mouth.

25-25. Commensal and parasitic crustaceans. Most species of crustaceans are free-living, but many others are associated with various animals in relations ranging from casual attachment to full parasitism. Some crabs dwell in the tubes inhabited by annelid worms (Fig. 24-14), certain copepods, amphipods, and porcelain crabs are regular tenants of the snail shells used by hermit crabs, and other small crabs (*Pinnotheres*) live within the shells of oysters and mussels. Besides the many free-living isopods and copepods, others are ectoparasites on various fishes (Fig. 25-15); their anterior limbs are modified as hooks or suckers, and some (*Aega*) have mouth parts specialized to penetrate and suck blood from their hosts. Certain forms (such as *Cymnothoa*) are free-swimming as larvae but permanently attached

Fig. 25-15. Parasitic Crustacea (Subclass Copepoda) that live on fishes; enlarged. *A. Caligus,* second antennae hooked. *B. Argulus,* second maxillae become sucking discs.

as adults, and others are parasitic also as larvae. The copepod *Lernaea* is so far modified as to be of worm-like form. Isopods of the Suborder Epicarida are all parasitic on prawns and crabs. The most extreme of parasitic crustaceans are barnacles of the Order Rhizocephala, of which *Sacculina* is a common example (Fig. 25-16). Its earliest (nauplius) larva resembles that of other crustaceans and barnacles but lacks a digestive tract. The later (cypris) larva fastens to a "hair" on a crab, then discards its shell, and burrows into the host. It becomes a mere mass of cells that pass in the crab's blood stream, attach to the intestine, and grow. When next the crab molts, part of the parasite protrudes on the crab's abdomen as an ovary, later to be packed with eggs. The remaining internal parts become branched and root-like, penetrating all parts of the crab's body and absorbing nourishment from its tissues. The host thenceforth neither grows nor molts, and its sex organs degenerate so that it cannot breed.

25-26. Relations to man. Flesh of certain crustaceans is much esteemed as human food. In 1953 the commercial fisheries of the United States took 260,357,000 pounds of shrimp, 144,-147,000 pounds of crab, and 30,860,000 pounds

of lobster, valued at a total of $98,473,000. Some crayfishes are eaten in the Northwest and South. These and other crustaceans are also eaten in other parts of the world. Shrimps are captured with seines, but crabs, lobsters, and crayfishes are lured into baited traps (lobster "pots," etc.) of wire, wood, or net. The leg muscles of crabs and abdominal muscles of the others are either freshly boiled or canned. The blue crab (*Callinectes*) of the Atlantic coast is caught and held captive until it molts, then sold in the soft-shelled condition; after removal of the viscera the whole animal is cooked and eaten. The small crustaceans that abound in salt and fresh waters are important links in the food cycle for many fishes and other useful aquatic animals. Some copepods are the intermediate hosts for worm parasites of man and various vertebrates (par. 19-14). Crayfishes in the Gulf states often damage fields of cotton and corn by eating the young plants, and occasionally their burrows injure levees. Sow bugs sometimes eat plants in gardens and greenhouses, and the "gribble," a wood-boring isopod, burrows into and damages wharves in salt water.

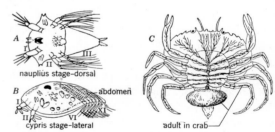

Fig. 25-16. Subclass Cirripedia. *Sacculina,* a barnacle parasitic in crabs; I–XI, appendages. Compare Fig. 25-14. (*After Stempell.*)

CLASSIFICATION

PHYLUM ARTHROPODA. Joint-footed Animals. (See Chap. 27.)

    CLASS 1. *CRUSTACEA.* Crustaceans. Head (of 5 fused somites) with 2 pairs of antennae, a pair of jaws, and 2 pairs of maxillae; body usually with a dorsal carapace and ending in a telson containing the anus; exoskeleton with lime deposits; appendages often biramous; respiration by gills (or body surface); excretion by antennal glands; sex openings paired, anterior; eggs usually carried by female; development usually with larval stages; mainly aquatic; 25,000 species.

        SUBCLASS 1. BRANCHIOPODA. Two pairs of 2d maxillae; more than 15 postcephalic segments; thoracic appendages 4 pairs or more, leaf-like, margined by gills; no abdominal appendages; parthenogenesis common; mostly in fresh waters; Cambrian to Recent, 800 species.

Order 1. Anostraca. Elongate, no carapace; eyes stalked; trunk appendages 11 to 19 pairs. *Artemia salina,* brine shrimp, 10 mm. long, in salty ponds, often cultured for fish food; *Branchinecta; Eubranchipus vernalis,* fairy shrimp, to 23 mm. long.

Order 2. Notostraca. Carapace low, oval; somites 40 to 60; eyes sessile. *Lepidurus; Apus,* to 30 mm. long.

Order 3. Conchostraca. Carapace bivalved, enclosing compressed body; somites 10 to 27; eyes sessile. Devonian to Recent. *Leptestheria,* Kansas to California; *Lynceus,* eastern states and southward.

Order 4. Cladocera. WATER FLEAS. Minute to microscopic; usually with bivalved carapace, which does not enclose head; paired eyes fused, median, and sessile; trunk appendages 4 to 6 pairs; 2d antennae enlarged for swimming jerkily. *Daphnia pulex,* water flea, 2 mm. long; *Alona; Leptodora,* 12–18 mm. long.

SUBCLASS 2. CEPHALOCARIDA. One pair of 2d maxillae; postcephalic segments 19 or 20; thoracic appendages 10, biramous and jointed, not leaf-like; no abdominal appendages; marine, central Atlantic coast and San Francisco Bay; 1 or 2 species. *Hutchinsoniella.*

SUBCLASS 3. OSTRACODA. Minute; carapace bivalved, compressed, enclosing all the poorly segmented body; only 2 pairs of trunk appendages; fresh or salt waters, mostly on or near bottom; 2,000 species. Ordovician to Recent.

Order 1. Myodocopa. Carapace notched; 2d antennae enlarged at base, alone used in swimming. *Cypridina, Chonchoecia,* northern oceans.

Order 2. Cladocopa. Carapace unnotched; both pairs of antennae used in swimming, 2d pair with 2 branches; marine. *Polycope.*

Order 3. Platycopa. Carapace unnotched; both pairs of antennae large, but not used for swimming, 2d pair flattened, biramous; marine. *Cytherella.*

Order 4. Podocopa. Carapace unnotched; 2d antennae leg-like, clawed at tips. *Eucypris, Darwinula,* both in fresh waters; *Entocythere,* on crayfish gills; *Cythereis,* marine.

SUBCLASS 4. COPEPODA. Mostly small to microscopic; form various; typically 9 free trunk somites with last 4 lacking appendages, but reduced in parasitic species; 3 ocelli often fused as median eye; eggs on abdomen of female in 1 or 2 egg sacs; fresh and salt waters, free-living, commensal, or parasitic.

Order 1. Eucopepoda. No paired compound eyes; genital opening on last thoracic somite. *Calanus finmarchicus,* "brit," 4 mm. long, northern oceans, important food of herring, mackerel, and whales; *Diaptomus, Cyclops,* both in fresh waters; *Asterocheres,* on invertebrates; *Monstrilla,* with intermediate larvae in polychaete worms; *Ascidicola,* male free, female worm-like and commensal in gut of ascidians and echinoderms; *Caligus,* marine, and *Lernaea,* fresh-water, both parasitic on fishes; *Choniostoma,* parasitic on crustaceans; *Salmincola,* dwarf male permanently attached to female that parasitizes gills of trout; *Rhizorhina,* adult female lacks appendages, parasitic on polychaete worms.

Order 2. Mystacocarida. Size microscopic; 4 eyespots, no compound eyes; genital opening on 1st thoracic somite. One species, *Derocheilocarus typicus,* damp intertidal sand near Woods Hole, Mass.

Order 3. Branchiura. Body flat, carapace disc-like, with compound eyes. *Argulus,* parasitic on fishes of fresh and salt waters.

SUBCLASS 5. CIRRIPEDIA. BARNACLES. Adults sessile and attached or parasitic; attach by cement gland on 1st antenna; carapace becomes mantle surrounding body, usually with limy plates; 6 pairs or less of slender and bristly biramous appendages behind mouth used in food gathering; abdomen vestigial; usually hermaphroditic; larvae free-swimming, marine; 800 species. Ordovician to Recent.

Order 1. Thoracica. Mantle and 6 pairs of trunk appendages. *Lepas, Mitella,* goose barnacles, body on fleshy stalk; *Balanus,* "acorn shell" or rock barnacle, body in irregular conical shell, no stalk.

Order 2. Acrothoracica. Mantle present; fewer appendages. *Trypetesa.*

Order 3. Apoda. No mantle or trunk appendages. *Proteolepas.*

Order 4. Rhizocephala. A mantle but no shell, appendages, or gut; body sac-like, with adsorptive "roots" penetrating host. *Sacculina,* parasitic on crabs.

Order 5. Ascothoracica. Digestive tract with branches into mantle; 6 pairs of trunk appendages. *Laura,* parasitic in black coral.

SUBCLASS 6. MALACOSTRACA. LOBSTERS, CRAYFISHES, CRABS, etc. Body typically of 19 somites (5 head, 8 thorax, 6 abdomen); head fused to one or more thoracic somites; commonly with carapace; abdomen with appendages.

Series 1. Leptostraca. Abdomen of 7 somites.

Order 1. Nebaliacea. Carapace bivalved; marine. Cambrian to Recent. *Nebalia*, to 12 mm. long.

Series 2. Eumalacostraca. Abdomen of 6 (or less) somites.

Division 1. *Syncarida.* No carapace.

Order 1. Anaspidacea. *Anaspides*, fresh waters of Australia.

Division 2. *Peracarida.* Carapace, when present, leaving 4 or more thoracic somites distinct; females with thoracic brood pouch where young develop.

Order 1. Mysidacea. OPOSSUM SHRIMPS. Carapace over much of thorax; uropods forming tail fan; mostly marine; 300 species. Carboniferous to Recent. *Mysis*, Great Lakes and Eurasia.

Order 2. Cumacea. Small; carapace with 2 anterior plates often joined over head; abdomen slender, mobile; uropods slender; mostly marine, burrowing in sand or mud. *Diastylis*, 10 mm. long.

Order 3. Tanaidacea. Mostly minute; carapace small; 2d thoracic appendage with chela; telson unjointed; marine, to depths of 12,000 feet, in mud or in tubes. *Apseudes, Tanais*.

Order 4. Isopoda. PILL BUGS, WOOD LICE, etc. Body usually depressed dorsoventrally; no carapace; abdomen short, partly or all fused; in salt or fresh waters among plants or under stones, some terrestrial, many parasitic on fish and crustaceans. Devonian to Recent. Marine: *Cirolana; Aega psora*, salve bug of fishermen; *Limnoria lignorum*, gribble, 3 mm. long, burrows in marine timbers, damaging wharves; *Idothea* and *Ligia*, free-living. Fresh-water: *Asellus communis*, to 15 mm. long. Land: *Oniscus asellus* and *Porcellio scaber*, sow bugs; *Armadillium vulgare*, pill bug, rolls up. Parasitic: *Hemioniscus*, on barnacles; *Hemiarthrus*, on decapod crustaceans.

Order 5. Amphipoda. SAND HOPPERS, etc. Body often laterally compressed; no carapace; abdomen flexed ventrally between 3d and 4th somites; telson usually distinct; mostly marine. Tertiary to Recent. *Orchestia*, beach flea, on sand or under seaweed; *Hyalella*, in fresh water; *Gammarus*, in both fresh and salt waters; *Caprella*, body cylindrical, abdomen vestigial, on seaweeds; *Cyamus*, "whale louse," on skin of whales, body narrow, legs with hooked claws, abdomen vestigial.

Division 3. *Hoplocarida.* Head with 2 movable anterior somites bearing eyes and antennules.

Order 1. Stomatopoda. MANTIS SHRIMPS. Marine, on bottom in sand or crevices; 200 species. Carboniferous to Recent. *Squilla; Chloridella empusa*, Florida to Cape Cod, to 250 mm. long, edible.

Division 4. *Eucarida.* Carapace large, fused to and covering all of thorax; eyes stalked; gills thoracic.

Order 1. Euphausiacea. Thoracic appendages all biramous; marine. *Euphausia*, "krill," to 25 mm. long, often abundant, an important whale food.

Order 2. Decapoda. Thoracic appendages mostly uniramous; "walking legs" 10 (5 pairs); mostly marine, some in fresh water, few terrestrial; many edible; Triassic to Recent, 8,000 species. Abdomen elongate: *Crago*, shrimp, and *Penaeus, Palaemonetes*, prawns; *Panulirus*, spiny rock lobster; *Homarus*, lobster, on Atlantic shores; *Astacus, Cambarus*, crayfishes, in fresh waters. Abdomen short (BRACHYURA, crabs): *Pagurus*, hermit crab, lives in snail shell; *Emerita (Hippa)*, sand crab; *Libinia*, spider crab, legs long; *Birgo latro*, coconut crab, to 12 inches long, terrestrial in tropics; *Cancer*, large edible rock crab; *Callinectes*, edible blue or "soft-shelled" crab of Atlantic coast; *Panopeus*, mud crab; *Uca*, fiddler crab; *Pinnotheres*, oyster or mussel crab, in mantle cavity of oysters and mussels.

REFERENCES

BORRADAILE, L. A., and F. A. POTTS. 1935. The invertebrata. 2d ed. New York, The Macmillan Co. ARTHROPODA, pp. 305–542; figs. 210–371.

CALMAN, W. T. 1909. Crustacea. *In* E. R. Lankester, Treatise on zoology. London, A. & C. Black, Ltd. Pt. 7, fascicle 3, viii + 346 pp., 194 figs.

———. 1911. The life of crustacea. London, Methuen & Co. xvi + 289 pp., 32 pls., 85 figs.

HUXLEY, T. H. 1880. The crayfish: an introduction to the study of zoology. London, Kegan Paul, Trench, Trubner & Co. xiv + 371 pp., 81 figs.

KÜKENTHAL, W., and OTHERS. 1927. Handbuch der Zoologie. Berlin, Walter De Gruyter & Co. Vol. 3, pt. 1, ARTHROPODA, pp. 211–276, figs. 182–215; CRUSTACEA, pp. 277–1,078, figs. 216–1,171.

PRATT, H. S. 1935. A manual of the common invertebrate animals. . . . 2d ed. New York, The Blakis-

ton Division, McGraw-Hill Book Co., Inc. CRUSTACEA, pp. 371–468, figs. 503–638.

SMITH, G., and W. F. R. WELDON. 1909. Crustacea. *In* Cambridge natural history. London, Macmillan & Co., Ltd. Vol. 4, xv + 217 pp., figs. 1–135.

SNODGRASS, R. E. 1938. Evolution of the Annelida, Onychophora, and Arthropoda. *Smithsonian Miscellaneous Collections*, vol. 97, no. 6, pp. 1–159, 54 figs.

———. 1952. A textbook of arthropod anatomy. Ithaca, Comstock Publishing Associates, Inc. viii + 363 pp., 88 figs.

SHROCK, R. R., and W. H. TWENHOFEL. 1953. Principles of invertebrate paleontology. 2d ed. New York, McGraw-Hill Book Co., Inc. ARTHROPODA, pp. 536–641, figs. 13-1 to 13-58.

WARD, H. B., and G. C. WHIPPLE. 1918. Fresh-water biology. New York, John Wiley & Sons, Inc. CRUSTACEA, pp. 661–850, figs. 1,011–1,318.

26 CLASS INSECTA
Insects

The grasshoppers, flies, lice, butterflies, beetles, bees, and a host of similar small creatures that comprise the Class INSECTA (L. incised, into distinct parts) number fully 675,000 species. They are the most abundant and widespread of all land animals, being the principal invertebrates that can live in dry environments and the only ones able to fly. These habits are made possible by the chitinous body covering that protects the internal organs against injury and loss of moisture, by the extensions of this covering that form the wings, and by the system of tracheal tubes that enable insects to breathe air. The ability to fly helps them to find food and mates and to escape enemies. Because their life cycles usually are short they can multiply rapidly under favorable conditions. Insects abound in all habitats except the sea; various kinds live in fresh and brackish waters, in soil, on and about plants of all kinds, and on or in other animals. Different species eat all sorts and parts of plants—roots, stems or leaves, sap or blossoms, seeds or fruits; many flower-visiting insects aid in pollination. Others utilize the tissues, fluids, and excretions of animals, and the scavenger insects consume dead animals and plants. Parasitic insects live in the eggs, larvae, or adults of other insects and on many other animals and plants. Some insects transmit diseases—virus, bacterial, protozoan, or others—to plants, animals, and man. Insects in turn are eaten by other insects, spiders, scorpions, and many vertebrates from fishes to mammals. The predaceous and parasitic species serve importantly to regulate the numbers of other insects.

Entomology (Gr. *entomon*, insect) is the science dealing with insects. Because of the numbers and many biological relations of insects, they are of great economic significance; some are useful and many are harmful to man's interests.

26-1. Characteristics.[1] 1. Head, thorax, and abdomen distinct; head with one pair of antennae, and mouth parts for chewing, sucking, or lapping; thorax (of 3 somites) with 3 pairs of jointed legs and usually 2 (1 or no) pairs of wings; abdomen of 11 or fewer somites with terminal parts modified as genitalia.

2. Digestive tract of fore-, mid-, and hind-gut; mouth with salivary glands.

3. Heart slender, with an anterior aorta; no capillaries or veins; body spaces a hemocoel (coelom reduced).

4. Respiration by branched cuticle-lined tracheae that carry oxygen from paired spiracles on sides of thorax and abdomen directly to the tissues; some with tracheal or blood gills.

5. Excretion by 2 to many fine Malpighian tubules attached to anterior end of hind-gut.

6. Nervous system of supra- and sub-esophageal ganglia connecting to double ventral nerve cord, with 1 pair or less of ganglia per somite; sense organs include simple and compound eyes, chemoreceptors for smell on the antennae and for taste about the mouth, and various tactile hairs; some with means for sound production and reception; no statocysts.

[1] Compare Phylum ARTHROPODA, Chap. 25, Table 25-1.

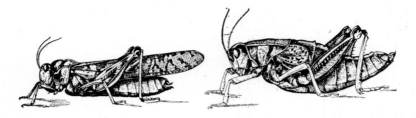

Fig. 26-1. Class INSECTA. *Left.* Long-winged grasshopper (*Dissosteira longipennis*), × 1⅓. *Right.* Short-winged, or lubber, grasshopper (*Brachystola magna*), × ¾. (*After Walton,* 1916.)

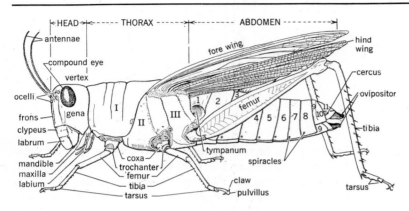

Fig. 26-2. External features of the grasshopper, a generalized insect. Female. I to III, somites of thorax; 1 to 11, somites of abdomen.

7. Sexes separate; gonads of multiple tubules with 1 median duct posteriorly; fertilization internal; ova with much yolk and protecting shells; cleavage superficial; development with several molts and direct, or with several nymphal stages and gradual metamorphosis, or with several larval stages and a complete metamorphosis to adult form; parthenogenesis in aphids, thrips, gall wasps, etc.

The earliest known fossil insects were fully winged and give no clue as to their origin. Several theories of insect origin have been proposed that would derive them variously from (1) forms resembling the zoea larvae of the higher CRUSTACEA with 3 pairs of appendages on both the head and thorax; (2) other CRUSTACEA that resemble the young of some THYSANURA; (3) the TRILOBITA; (4) the SYMPHYLA, which are like some DIPLURA; or (5) the polychaete worms (ANNELIDA) because of resemblances of the pleura and thoracic appendages of insects to the parapodia of polychaetes. Some authorities believe that winged insects arose from such wingless forms as the THYSANURA, and others consider that the winged forms were of separate origin. The wings may have arisen from thoracic gills or more probably as lateral extensions of the thoracic terga.

26-2. Size. Some insects are smaller than large protozoans, and others exceed the smallest of the vertebrates. Some beetles (TRICHOPTERYGIDAE) are but 0.25 mm. long, and a few egg parasites (MYMARIDAE) are even smaller. Most insects are 2 to 40 mm. long. The longest include *Pharnacia serratipes* (ORTHOPTERA), 260 mm.; a Venezuelan beetle, *Dynastes hercules*, 155 mm.; and a bug, *Lethocerus grandis*, 115 mm. The wingspread is greatest in some tropical moths, *Erebus agrippina*, 280 mm., and *Attacus atlas*, 240 mm.; some fossil insects (MEGANEURA) exceeded 700 mm. in wingspread.

THE GRASSHOPPER, OR LOCUST

To indicate some of the variety in the structure and function of insects, this chapter describes the grasshopper and includes a comparative account of the honeybee. The grasshopper is generalized as to anatomy, has chewing mouth parts, undergoes a gradual or incomplete metamorphosis from the young or nymph stages to the adult, and lives independently for a single season,

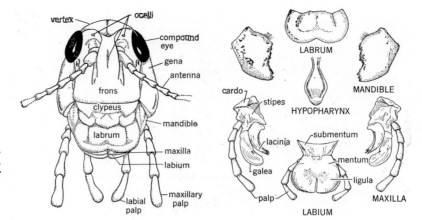

Fig. 26-3. The grasshopper. *Left.* Front view of the head. *Right.* Mouth parts in anterior view. Both enlarged.

Grasshoppers [1] occur over the world, mainly in open grasslands, where they eat leafy vegetation. The following description will serve for any common species such as the "Carolina locust" (*Dissosteira carolina*), the "American locust" (*Schistocerca americana*), or the short-winged lubber grasshopper (*Romalea microptera*)(Fig. 26-1).

26-3. External features. The body comprises a head of six fused somites, the thorax of three somites with legs and wings, and a long segmented abdomen ending with reproductive organs (Fig. 26-2). It is covered by a cuticular exoskeleton containing chitin, secreted by the epidermis beneath and molted periodically in the nymphs to permit of increase in size; adults do not molt. The exoskeleton is formed into hard plates, or *sclerites,* separated by *sutures* of soft cuticle that permit movement of the body segments and appendages. Pigment in and under the cuticle provides a protective coloration by which grasshoppers resemble their environments.

The *head* (Fig. 26-3) bears one pair of slender, jointed *antennae* with fine sensory bristles, two lateral *compound eyes* that are unstalked

but constructed like those of the crayfish, and three simple eyes, or *ocelli.* Much of the head is enclosed in a fused case or head capsule with a dorsal *vertex,* lateral cheeks or *genae,* and the anterior *frons.* Below the latter is a broad plate, the *clypeus.* The mouth parts are of the chewing or mandibulate type, ventral on the head, and include (1) a broad upper lip or *labrum,* hinged to the clypeus; (2) a median tongue-like *hypopharynx* behind the mouth; (3) two heavy blackish lateral jaws or *mandibles,* each with teeth along the inner margin for chewing food; (4) a pair of *maxillae* of several parts and with slender sensory palps at the sides; and (5) a broad median lower lip or *labium,* with two short palps.

The *thorax* consists of the large anterior *prothorax* (with a dorsal saddle-like pronotum), the *mesothorax,* and the posterior *metathorax;* each bears a pair of jointed legs, and the meso- and meta-thorax each a pair of wings. The sclerites on each somite form a dorsal *tergum* of four fused plates, a *pleuron* of two plates on each side, and a single ventral *sternum.* Each *leg* is a linear series of segments: (1) the short *coxa,* which articulates to the body; (2) a small *trochanter* fused to (3) the stout *femur;* (4) a slender spiny *tibia;* and (5) the *tarsus* of three parts, the proximal bearing four pairs of ventral *pads* and the distal having a fleshy *pulvillus* beyond two *claws.* The pulvilli enable the grasshopper to hold onto smooth surfaces, and the claws serve in rough places. All the legs are used

[1] Order ORTHOPTERA, Family ACRIDIDAE. A grasshopper is an essentially solitary and resident species, often abundant as to individuals, but which may occasionally migrate. The term locust applies properly to gregarious and migratory Old World forms (*Locusta*); the North American periodic cicada (*Magicicada*, Order HOMOPTERA), however, is also called "locust."

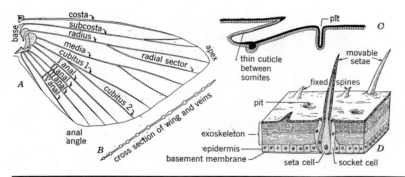

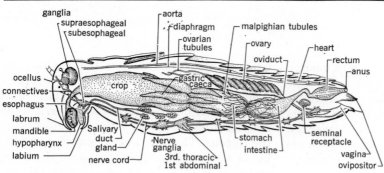

Fig. 26-4. The wings and body covering of insects; diagrammatic. *A.* Generalized wing showing the principal veins. *B.* Cross section of wing and veins. *C.* Section of body covering at junction of two somites. *D.* Structure of the body wall. (*A, B, after Metcalf and Flint; C, D, adapted from Snodgrass.*)

Fig. 26-5. The grasshopper. Internal structure as seen with left side of body wall removed; tracheae omitted. Compare Figs. 25-4, 27-3.

in walking and climbing. Each metathoracic leg has a large femur containing muscles and a long tibia that serve for leaping. The narrow *fore-wings* or *tegmina* are parchment-like. The **hind wings** are broad and membranous, with many veins, and fold under the forewings at rest. Each wing develops as a sac-like projection of the body covering and flattens to a thin double membrane that encloses tubular tracheae surrounded by blood sinuses. The cuticle thickens around the tracheae to form strengthening nervures, or **veins** (Fig. 26-4). When of full size, the wings become hard and dry but blood flow continues in some veins. The wing veins are of such constant pattern in species and higher groups of insects as to be useful in classification.

The slender cylindrical **abdomen** consists of 11 somites, the terminal ones being modified for copulation or egg laying. Along the lower sides of the thorax and abdomen are 10 pairs of small openings, the **spiracles** connecting to the respiratory system.

The first abdominal somite is divided about the insertions of the hind legs, with the sternum firmly united to the mesothorax; its tergum contains on either side an oval **tympanic membrane** over an organ of hearing. On somites 2 to 7 the tergum is ∩-shaped and joins the ⌣-shaped sternum by lateral membranes that permit the abdomen to pulsate in breathing. In a male, somite 8 resembles those preceding, the terga of 9–10 are fused, and the tergum of 11 forms the suranal plate over the anus; a small spine or **cercus** (relict appendage) projects behind 10, on either side, and the long ventral sternum of 9 encloses the male copulatory organ. In a female, the terga of 8 to 11 and cercus are as in the male, the sternum of 8 is apparently lacking, and that of 9 is elongate; a lateral plate of 10 is present, and the end of the abdomen bears 2 paired lobes forming the ovipositor (from somites 8–9).

26-4. Muscles. The head contains complex small muscles that move the antennae and mouth parts. In the thorax are large muscles that manipulate the wings and legs. Segmental muscles are most conspicuous in the abdomen but are small as compared with those of the crayfish; some perform the respiratory movements, and others control the reproductive structures.

26-5. Digestive system (Fig. 26-5). The mouth parts surround (1) the **mouth cavity,** from which (2) a slender **esophagus** extends to (3)

Fig. 26-6. The grasshopper. Respiratory system. Spiracles, tracheal trunks, and air sacs of the left side. (*Modified from Riley,* 1878.)

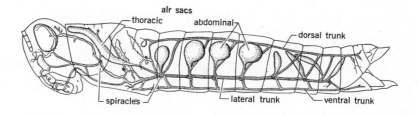

Fig. 26-7. The tracheae of insects. *A.* Large trunks and branches. *B.* Cellular wall of a tracheal tube and its internal spiral thread. *C.* Terminal branches around muscle fibers. *D.* Fine tracheoles distributed over muscle fibers. (*After Snodgrass.*)

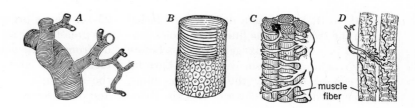

the large thin-walled **crop.** Below the crop are small branched salivary glands that discharge through ducts opening at the labium. Beyond the crop is (4) a small proventriculus or **gizzard,** lined by plates. The preceding parts comprise the fore-gut. Next is (5) the mid-gut, or **stomach** (ventriculus), joined by (6) a series of six double finger-shaped **gastric caeca.** The hindgut, or (7) **intestine,** consists of a tapered anterior part, slender middle portion, and enlarged **rectum** that opens at (8) the **anus.** Food is held by the forelegs, labrum, and labium, lubricated by the salivary secretion (which contains some enzymes), and chewed by the mandibles and maxillae; the palps bear organs of taste. Chewed food is stored in the crop, further reduced in the gizzard, and strained into the stomach. There it is digested by enzymes secreted by the gastric caeca and absorbed. In the rectum, excess water is withdrawn from the undigested material which is formed into slender fecal pellets and passed out the anus.

26-6. Circulatory system. The slender tubular **heart** lies against the dorsal wall of the abdomen in a shallow **pericardial cavity** formed by a delicate transverse **diaphragm.** Blood enters the heart through pairs of minute lateral openings or **ostia,** with valves, and is pumped forward by contractions of the heart into a dorsal **aorta** extending to the head. There it emerges into the body spaces or **hemocoel,** between the internal

organs, and moves slowly backward around these organs, finally to enter the pericardial sinus. Some blood circulates in the appendages and wing veins. The system is open, or lacunar, as in other arthropods, there being no capillaries or veins. The clear plasma contains colorless blood cells that act as phagocytes to remove foreign organisms. The blood serves mainly to transport food and wastes, as there is a separate respiratory system. The **fat body** is a loose network of tissue in spaces between the organs that stores food reserves, especially in young insects before metamorphosis.

26-7. Respiratory system (Figs. 26-6, 26-7). The paired **spiracles** connect to a system of elastic ectodermal air tubes, or **tracheae,** that branch to all parts of the body. The finest branches, or **tracheoles,** carry oxygen to and remove carbon dioxide directly from the tissue cells. The tracheal wall is a single layer of thin cells that secretes a lining of cuticle (cast off at molting), and the larger tubes are reinforced by a spiral thread to prevent their collapse; longitudinal air trunks connect to the spiracles. The grasshopper, unlike some insects, has several large thin-walled **air sacs** in the abdomen, where alternate contraction and relaxation of the body wall serve to pump air in and out of the tracheal system. At inspiration the first 4 pairs of spiracles are open and the posterior 6 are closed, and at expiration the arrangement is

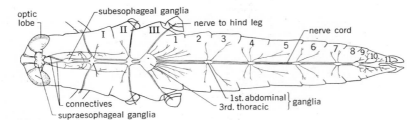

optic lobe — subesophageal ganglia — nerve to hind leg — nerve cord

I II III 1 2 3 4 5 6 7 8 9 10

connectives
supraesophageal ganglia

1st. abdominal
3rd. thoracic } ganglia

Fig. 26-8. The grasshopper. Nervous system in dorsal view; I–III, thoracic somites; 1–11, abdominal somites. (*After Riley,* 1878.)

reversed, so that there is a definite circulation of air in the tracheae. The finest tracheoles contain fluid in which the oxygen dissolves before actually reaching the tissue cells. Some harmful insects can be killed by the use of oil films, emulsions, or dusts that cover or clog the spiracles and stop respiration.

26-8. Excretory system. To the anterior end of the hind-gut are joined a number of thread-like *Malpighian tubules;* these lie in the hemocoel and have their free ends closed. The tubule wall is composed of a single layer of large cells that remove urea, urates, and salts from the blood and discharge into the intestine (Fig. 8-2).

26-9. Nervous system (Figs. 26-5, 26-8). The brain, or *supraesophageal ganglia,* in the head comprises 3 pairs of fused ganglia (optic, antennary, and intercalary) with nerves to the eyes, antennae, and other head organs. It joins by 2 *connectives* around the esophagus to the *subesophageal ganglia,* which are also of 3 pairs (mandibular, maxillary, and labial). From the latter, the ventral *nerve cord* extends posteriorly as a series of paired ganglia and longitudinal connectives. Each thoracic somite contains a pair of ganglia with nerves to the legs, wings, and internal organs. There are only 5 pairs of abdominal ganglia; some originally separate have become fused. These send nerves to various posterior organs. There is also a visceral or *sympathetic nervous system,* comprised of an esophageal portion with ganglia and nerves connecting to the brain, fore-gut, mid-gut, and heart, and a posterior portion from the last abdominal ganglion to the hind-gut and reproductive system. A fine pattern of peripheral nerves lies beneath the epidermis of the body wall.

26-10. Sense organs. The sensory receptors of the grasshopper are adapted for receiving stimuli from the air and the land. They include (1) *tactile hairs* on various body parts, especially the antennae, mouth palps, abdominal cerci, and distal leg segments; (2) *olfactory organs* on the antennae; (3) *organs of taste* on the palps and other mouth parts; (4) the *ocelli,* which are sensitive to light and shade and may form crude images at close range; (5) the *compound eyes,* which function essentially like those of the crayfish; and (6) the *organ of hearing.* The latter (Fig. 26-15) consists essentially of a stretched tympanic membrane that is set into movement by sound vibrations in the air; this affects a slender point beneath the membrane that is connected to sensory nerve fibers. The grasshopper produces sounds by rubbing the hind tibia, which has a row of minute pegs along the medial surface, against a wing vein to set the latter into vibration.

26-11. Reproductive system (Fig. 26-9). The sexes are separate and show secondary sexual characters in the terminal parts of the abdomen (par. 26-3). In a *male,* each of the two *testes* comprises a series of slender tubules or *follicles,* above the intestine, that are joined to a lengthwise *vas deferens.* The two vasa unite as a common median *ejaculatory duct,* which is joined by *accessory glands* and opens at the end of the large ventral male *copulatory organ* (edeagus). In a *female,* each *ovary* is composed of several tapering egg tubes or *ovarioles,* in which the ova are produced, and is joined to an *oviduct.* The two oviducts unite as a median *vagina* that leads posteriorly and is joined by a small *seminal receptacle* (spermatheca) where sperm received at copulation are stored. The

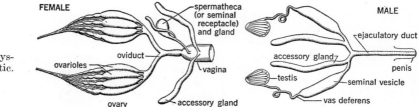

Fig. 26-9. Reproductive systems of insects; diagrammatic. (*After Snodgrass.*)

FEMALE
spermatheca (or seminal receptacle) and gland
MALE
ejaculatory duct
oviduct
accessory gland
ovarioles
penis
vagina
testis
seminal vesicle
ovary
accessory gland
vas deferens

female tract opens close to the ventral *egg guide.*

26-12. Natural history. In the warm days of early spring the nymphs hatch from eggs laid in the soil the previous autumn. They resemble adults but differ in proportions and have no wings or reproductive organs (Fig. 26-11). They feed on tender vegetation and hide under plants or in crevices to avoid enemies and desiccation. After a few days the cuticle softens and is molted; the emerging nymph swallows air and increases in volume, and then its fresh cuticle hardens and darkens. Each individual has 5 (or 6) nymphal stages, and its entire growth period requires 30 to 50 or more days. The wings first appear as small pads, which become larger at successive molts and unfold to full size after the last molt into the adult stage.

Both nymphs and adults eat many kinds of vegetation, especially succulent types; they often migrate into new feeding grounds and may damage or ruin farm and garden plantings. Feeding is most active in the midmorning hours of quiet sunny days. When food is scarce, these insects will eat cotton or woolen fabrics, wood, and disabled grasshoppers. Adults of some species, under conditions of crowding, sometimes perform long migrations. Many were marked with red lacquer in North Dakota one summer and later recaptured 86 to 215 miles away in the direction of prevailing winds.

Grasshopper eggs are eaten by some beetles, bee flies, moles, skunks, and mice, the nymphs by robber flies and digger wasps, and both nymphs and adults by large predatory insects and by frogs, reptiles, birds, and mammals. One-tenth of all insects found in bird stomachs examined by the U.S. Biological Survey were grasshoppers and their close allies. Eggs of

grasshoppers are parasitized by certain insects (Fig. 26-39). Flesh flies (*Sarcophaga*) lay living maggots on adults, and tachinid flies deposit their eggs on grasshoppers in flight; the larvae of both burrow into their hosts and consume the fat tissues. Parasitized grasshoppers become logy and fail to reproduce, or die. The parasitic insects thus constitute a factor in grasshopper control. Both fungus and bacterial diseases also destroy numbers of grasshoppers at times. Man practices control by using chemical sprays and poisoned baits on fields where nymphs and adults feed and also by plowing weed or stubble fields to expose the egg masses.

26-13. Reproduction. Some days after the adult stage is reached in late summer, the grasshop-

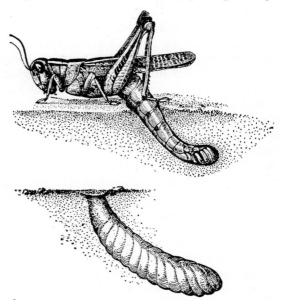

Fig. 26-10. A female grasshopper, with greatly extended abdomen, depositing eggs in ground; below, a complete "pod," or packet of eggs. (*After Walton*, 1916.)

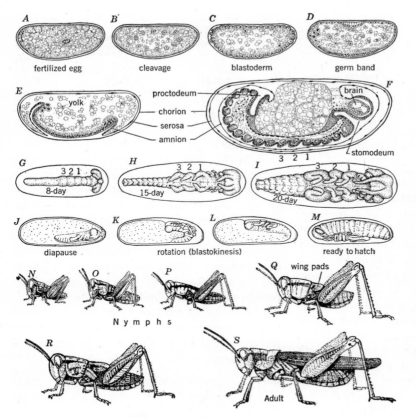

Fig. 26-11. Development of the grasshopper. *A*. Fertilized egg surrounded by chorion. *B*. Cleavage, nuclei scattered. *C*. Blastoderm cells surround yolk. *D*. Germ band formed. *E*. Early embryo, serosa, and amnion forming. *F*. Later embryo with somites. *G*. 8-day embryo. *H*. 15-day embryo. *I*. 20-day embryo, ready for diapause; 1, 2, 3, thoracic somites. *J*. Embryo in diapause. *K, L*. Blastokinesis, or rotation of the embryo. *M*. Embryo before hatching. *N–R*. The five nymphal stages with gradual increase in size and development of wing pads. *S*. Adult with wings. (*A–F, generalized sagittal sections, after Johannsen and Butt; G, H, ventral views, after Slifer, 1932; K–M, lateral views, after Burkholder, 1934; N–S, modified from Emerton in Riley, 1878.*)

pers begin to mate and do so several times. The male clings to the female's back, inserts his genitalia into her vagina, and transfers spermatozoa. After a further interval, egg laying (Fig. 26-10) begins and continues into the autumn. The eggs are 3 to 5 mm. long. About 20 are laid at a time, and one female may lay up to 10 lots. The adults die some days after breeding is ended. In the ovary, each egg is enclosed by a delicate inner *vitelline membrane* and a brownish flexible shell, or *chorion,* that contains a minute pore, or *micropyle,* through which sperm enter during laying. The female uses her ovipositor to form a short tunnel in the ground in which the eggs are placed, surrounded by a sticky secretion that fastens them together as an egg pod. Development (Fig. 26-11) begins at once and continues for about 3 weeks until the embryo is well formed. Then a rest, or *diapause,* ensues until spring, when growth is resumed, and the young soon hatch and crawl to

the ground surface. The diapause is a means to survive the adverse conditions of cold and lack of food in winter.

The fertilization nucleus within the egg yolk divides into scattered cleavage nuclei. These migrate to the periphery of the yolk where each is surrounded by cytoplasm and a cell wall, and the cells form an epithelium, or blastoderm, around the yolk. Those of a limited ventral area thicken as a *germ band* that will produce the *embryo,* and the lateral and dorsal cells become the embryonic envelope, or *serosa.* At the ends and sides of the germ band, folds then form; their outer layers, inside the serosa, become the *amnion,* which encloses the embryo in an amniotic cavity. A lengthwise ventral furrow along the germ band folds up to form a layer (mesoderm + ?endoderm) above the germ band. The latter then divides by cross furrows, from before backward, into a linear series of somites that give rise to the head and its appendages,

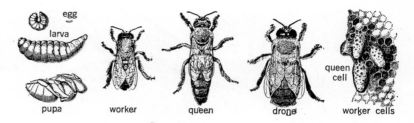

Fig. 26-12. The honeybee, *Apis mellifera* (Order HYMENOPTERA); growth stages and three adult castes slightly enlarged; portion of comb reduced. (*After Phillips*, 1911.)

egg
larva
pupa
worker
queen
drone
queen cell
worker cells

the thorax and its legs, and the segmented abdomen. The future fore-gut, or stomodeum, forms as a pit at the anterior end, and the hind-gut, or proctodeum, similarly at the posterior end. Later the mid-gut forms from endoderm cells, and the gut becomes a continuous tube. The tracheae develop as paired lateral invaginations of ectoderm. The nervous system arises as an infolding of ventral ectoderm into two lengthwise strands of cells that later produce the nerve cords, ganglia, and brain.

The embryo shows six primitive head somites, as follows: (1) preoral, with compound eyes; (2) antennal, and (3) intercalary, respectively homologous with the antennule and antennal somites of the crayfish; (4) mandibular, behind the mouth; (5) maxillary; and (6) labial, with a pair of embryonic appendages that provide the fused labium of the adult. There are six pairs of nerve ganglia in the head, three preoral pairs forming the supraesophageal ganglia and three postoral forming the subesophageal ganglia. Rudiments of abdominal appendages appear but later disappear except posteriorly where they form parts of the external genitalia.

THE HONEYBEE

26-14. A social insect. The honeybee, *Apis mellifera* (Order HYMENOPTERA), resembles the grasshopper in general structure but is specialized in many features. It has mouth parts suited for both sucking and chewing, undergoes complete metamorphosis from the worm-like larva through a pupal stage to the flying adult, feeds on nectar and pollen, and lives socially in a permanent colony comprising many individuals of three *castes* (Fig. 26-12). The *queen* lays the eggs; the males, or *drones,* serve only

to fertilize new queens; and the thousands of sterile females, or *workers,* build and guard the hive, provide the food for all castes, attend the queen, and rear the young. Wild honeybees live in natural cavities of trees or rocks, but man has partly domesticated this species and houses it in hives of wood. Each colony lives amid vertical *combs* of wax that contain small lateral cells used to store honey or pollen and rear the young. Workers collect fluid *nectar* from flowers; this is chemically altered and stored as the sirupy carbohydrate solution that we call *honey.* They collect *pollen* ("bee bread") to provide proteins for growth of the larvae. Bees also gather resins from plant buds which, as *propolis,* serve to cement and varnish crevices in the hive against wind and water. The workers have *stings* to protect the colony and its honey against robbery by other animals, from bees to bears.

26-15. Structure and function. The body of a bee (Fig. 26-13) is densely covered by hairs having short lateral barbs where pollen grains lodge easily. Unbranched hairs occur on the compound eyes and legs. On each foreleg, the tibia is margined by an *eye brush* of stiff hairs for cleaning the compound eyes, and its distal end bears a flat movable spine, or *velum.* The latter closes over a bristle-lined notch on the proximal end of the tarsus to form an *antenna comb,* through which the antenna is drawn to remove pollen or other foreign material. Long hairs on the large first segment of the tarsus form a cylindrical *pollen brush* to gather pollen from the fore parts of the body. On each middle leg, the flat tarsus has a *pollen brush* to remove pollen from the forelegs and nearby body parts; and the inner distal end of the tibia bears a *spur*

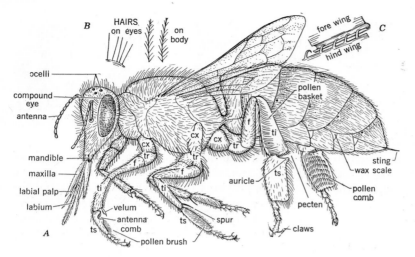

HAIRS on eyes / on body

fore wing / hind wing / C

ocelli

compound eye

antenna

pollen basket

mandible

maxilla

labial palp

labium

velum

antenna comb

pollen brush

auricle

pecten

sting

wax scale

pollen comb

claws

B

A

Fig. 26-13. The honeybee worker. *A.* Mouth parts, pollen-collecting structures, and sting. *B.* The hairs. *C.* The wing-locking mechanism. Leg segments: *cx,* coxa; *tr,* trochanter; *f,* femur; *ti,* tibia; *ts,* tarsus. (*Adapted in part from Casteel,* 1912.)

used to pick up wax. On the hind leg, the wide tibia is slightly concave externally and margined by incurving hairs to form a *pollen basket* (corbicula). This has a comb of stiff hairs, the *pecten,* at its distal end, and just below is a flat plate, or *auricle,* on the proximal end of the tarsus. The outer surface of the tarsus has a *pollen brush* for cleaning the body posteriorly, and on its inner surface are about 10 rows of stiff downward-pointing spines that form a *pollen comb.*

The thin delicate *wings* (Gr. *hymen,* membrane + *pteron,* wing) lie flat over the back at rest. In flight the two on each side are locked together by fine hooks bordering the hind wing that catch to a groove along the rear margin of the forewing (Fig. 26-13C). The wings may vibrate up to 400 times per second with the tips moving in an ∞-shaped path. Workers are capable of long flights, even to 8 miles.

The smooth *mandibles* of workers serve to gather pollen and also to mold wax in making combs. The maxillae and labial palps form a tube around the slender *tongue,* or labium; by movements of the ligula and a pumping action of the pharynx, fluid nectar is drawn into the large crop, or *honey stomach.* Behind the latter are four triangular lips that form a *valve* (honey stopper) to prevent nectar or honey from entering the stomach except when wanted for food. The slender *intestine* is joined by about

100 *Malpighian tubules,* and the large rectum serves to accumulate feces for discharge through the anus after a bee leaves the hive.

The *sting* is a modified ovipositor and hence is present only in workers and queens. It comprises (1) a hollow dorsal *sheath* and (2) two *darts* grooved along their inner surfaces so that they may slide along each other by the action of muscles at their inner bases, (3) at either side a sensory *sting palpus,* and (4) a large median *poison sac* supplied by two acid glands and a slender alkaline gland. The fluid is pumped into the wound made by the darts. A worker dies about 2 days after using its sting, as all the poison apparatus and some adjacent parts pull off in the process. The queen's slender sting serves to combat rival queens and can be used more than once.

Among the numerous adaptive features, each short *antenna* has many olfactory pits that provide a keen sense of smell (1,600 on queen, 2,400 on worker, 18,900 on drone). Each *compound eye* has many ommatidia (4,900 on queen, 6,300 on worker, 13,000 on drone). The brain is proportionately large. Bees evidently find their way about and seek food by both scent and sight. They can be trained to visit a food supply having a particular scent or associated with certain colors, except red which they cannot distinguish from black. Glands on the abdomen produce a scent when bees are

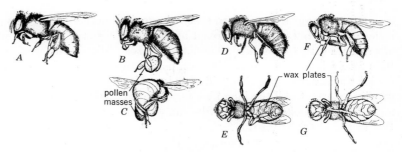

Fig. 26-14. The honeybee. *Pollen gathering* (during flight). *A.* The forelegs remove wet pollen from the head and mouth parts; this is passed to the middle legs which are then drawn between the pollen combs on the hind legs. *B.* Middle legs pat down pollen masses in "baskets" on hind legs. *C.* Pollen from comb on right hind leg is scraped onto the pecten of the left hind leg. *Wax manipulation* (while bee stands on its midlegs). *D, E.* Wax scale is removed from gland pocket by hind leg. *F, G.* Wax scale is carried forward to the mandibles. (*After Casteel*, 1912.)

disturbed and may serve to "mark" new sources of food afield. Honeybees have a good sense of orientation, and each returns to its own hive. If a hive is moved, the absent workers return to the old site; but if confined within during the moving, they take account of the new location upon leaving and will return to it.

26-16. Food. A worker bee, upon discovering a food supply in the field, fills her nectar stomach, returns to the hive, and either deposits the gathered nectar or feeds young bees. Then she executes a "dance" that informs other bees as to the direction and distance of the source. She walks a semicircle, returns to the original point, and makes a semicircle in the opposite direction, a pattern like a compressed ∞, repeating several times. Experiments by von Fritsch show that the location is indicated in relation to the sun's position. Clinging to the upright comb, if the supply is directly toward the sun, the axis is vertically upward; if at an angle to the sun, the axis of the dance is at that angle. The distance is indicated by the number of turns in a given interval (e.g., in 15 seconds). The nature of the food supply is communicated by odor from the plant source on her body or in the nectar brought. Other bees keep their antennae touching the scout during her dance.

When the bee visits a flower, (1) pollen taken by the mandibles is moistened with honey and (2) mixed with that gathered on the pollen brushes of the forelegs; (3) it is then taken by the pollen brushes on the middle legs, which in turn are (4) drawn between the pollen combs of the hind tarsi; (5) each of the latter is then scraped over the opposite leg to deposit pollen on the pecten or outer surface of the auricle, and (6) by flexing the tarsus on the tibia, the pollen is pushed upward and packed into the pollen basket. The bee thus (Fig. 26-14) accumulates a bulging load of sticky pollen in both baskets, returns to the hive, and pushes her load into a cell, to be tamped down by the heads of young workers. Propolis is carried similarly but is removed by other workers.

Nectar held in the honey stomach is acted upon by salivary enzymes, cane sugar being inverted to dextrose and levulose. Upon returning to its hive, a worker regurgitates this fluid into a cell of the comb, where the young "house bees" work it over in their mouths, causing further chemical changes; they evaporate the excess water by fanning with their wings and then seal the cell with wax. Honey averages 17 per cent of water and 77.5 per cent sugars, with small amounts of minerals, enzymes, and pollen; its color is water-white to dark, and the flavor varies according to the nectar source.

26-17. Reproduction. The reproductive system is vestigial in workers but highly developed in queens. About 7 days after emerging, a young queen mates with a drone high in the air; his copulatory organs then are torn away to remain in her genital bursa until removed by workers after her return to the hive. The spermatozoa thus received into her spermatheca must serve for all the fertilized eggs she will ever lay. Her ovaries enlarge to fill the long abdomen, and in a day or two she begins to lay. She can control the process of fertilization. Unfertilized eggs produce drones, or males (genetically haploid, 16 chromosomes), and fertilized eggs yield females (diploid, 32 chromosomes). In the season of nectar flow, a queen lays up to 1,000 eggs per day, gluing each to the bottom of a cell. The tiny worm-like *larva* has no legs or eyes. For 2 days all larvae are fed on "royal jelly" produced by pharyngeal glands of young workers. Thereafter, drone and worker larvae receive mainly honey and pollen, but queen larvae continue chiefly on royal jelly, which causes them to develop differently and to become larger. Each larva has several molts and grows; then its cell is capped with wax, and the larva within spins a thin *cocoon.* There, as a *pupa,* it undergoes complete metamorphosis and finally cuts the cell cap with its mandibles to emerge as a young bee. The time of development for each caste is standardized because of the temperature regulation in the hive:

    Queen: egg, 3; larva, 5½; pupa, 7½ = 16 days
    Worker: egg, 3; larva, 6; pupa, 12   = 21 days
    Drone: egg, 3; larva, 6½; pupa, 14½ = 24 days

To mankind, the honeybee is a symbol of industry and cooperation, gathering food in time of plenty against the needs of winter. When the warmth of spring brings early flowers, the workers gather nectar and pollen, the queen lays rapidly, and new workers soon swell the colony population. Overcrowding leads to *swarming;* the queen and several thousand workers emerge as a dense swarm and fly to a new site previously located by worker scouts. Prior to this, some queen larvae are started in the old colony. One of the queens emerges, usually stings the other queen larvae, is fertilized in a mating flight, and returns to serve the old hive in egg laying. A queen may live for 3 to 5 seasons and lay a million eggs. Drones are produced during

active nectar flow; but when brood production ceases, they are mostly driven out to starve and die. Many workers hatched in autumn survive until spring, but those born earlier in the year use up their energy more rapidly—like a battery—and live only 6 to 8 weeks.

26-18. The hive. Each comb (Fig. 26-12) in a hive is a vertical sheet of wax, fastened to the top (and sides) of a cavity. The *worker cells* where workers are reared and honey or pollen is stored are about 5 mm. across, and the *drone cells,* 6 mm. across, serve to rear drones and for storage. Large vertical peanut-like *queen cells,* open below, are built along the lower comb margins for queen rearing. The wax is secreted as small flakes by glands in pockets under the abdomen on workers. Once formed, the combs are used for years, the cells being cleaned and polished for re-use.

Honeybees are about the only animals that achieve "air conditioning." In summer they fan their wings vigorously to ventilate the hive, to keep the temperature inside at about 33°C. for brood rearing, and to evaporate excess water from honey in open cells. In hot dry weather they carry in water to humidify the colony and to dilute the honey if necessary. During winter, when the stored honey is used as food, they form a compact cluster and produce heat by active body and wing movements. Clusters form at 14°C. (57°F.) or below and can raise the hive temperature to 24 or 30°C., even when the outside air is at or below freezing.

Bee colonies are reduced by dearth of nectar or pollen and by exhaustion of honey stores in winter. Adult bees are eaten by toads, skunks, and bears, the latter having a proverbial liking for honey as well. Two serious "foul brood" diseases cause heavy losses in colonies if unchecked.

OTHER INSECTS

26-19. Form and function. Except for a few degenerate forms, the adults of all insects are alike in having one pair each of antennae and compound eyes, a fused head, a thorax of three somites with six legs (hence sometimes called Hexapoda), and a distinct abdomen. Within these limits members of the various orders, families, and species show great diversity in details of structure and habits. Many features are adaptive modifications to particular modes of life.

The *coloration* is produced by pigments (chemical), or by surface structure (physical), or by a combination of these. Some pigments are deposited in the exoskeleton, and others in the epidermis or deeper. The iridescent colors of some beetles, butterflies, and others are produced by differential interference of light falling upon microscopically fine surface ridges or parallel plates of chitin.

The exterior *cuticle* is often waxy and not easily wetted; this is of advantage to the insects but causes some difficulty in attempts to control harmful species by sprays. The *body* is adaptively streamlined in many aquatic bugs and beetles, depressed in cockroaches and others that live in crevices, and fusilage-shaped in the fast-flying dragon-flies. In other insects it shows no obvious adaptation to habits. The hairy covering on some nocturnal moths may help to insulate them against chilling, and the hairs on many flies and bees serve in the gathering of pollen.

All insects have *eyes* except some larvae that live concealed from the light, some adults that inhabit caves or nests of termites or ants, some biting lice, and the nonsexual castes of some ants and most termites. The *mouth parts* are of two main types—chewing or sucking—as in the grasshopper and bee, respectively. Many species with sucking mouth parts have means for piercing tissues, such as the mosquitoes and fleas that "bite" other animals and the aphids that puncture plants.

The *legs* are modified for running in tiger beetles, jumping in fleas, swimming in water bugs and beetles, skating in water striders, burrowing in mole crickets, and spinning in embiids. The *wings* are commonly thin and membranous. The forewings are hardened as elytra in beetles; they are leathery in the ORTHOPTERA, and the forward half is thickened in

the HEMIPTERA. Flies (DIPTERA) and male coccids have the hind pair represented by minute knobbed halteres (balancing organs), and the fore pair is reduced on male stylopids. Primitive insects (PROTURA to THYSANURA) and lice, fleas, and some other parasitic forms lack wings; ants and termites are also wingless save for the sexual castes. The embryo in many insects has abdominal appendages, but there are rarely any on adults except for the cerci and copulatory organs. The *muscles* are numerous and complex; about 2,000 are present in a caterpillar. Many insects are disproportionately powerful as compared with larger animals; a honeybee, for example, can pull twenty times its own weight and can lift a load equal to four-fifths its weight in flight.

The *digestive system* shows modifications in relation to food habits. The salivary glands of bloodsucking insects produce anticoagulants that keep the blood fluid during ingestion and digestion. *Respiration* is performed by a tracheal system in most insects, but through the thin body covering in COLLEMBOLA, some PROTURA, and some endoparasitic larvae. Adult aquatic insects that dive carry along a film of air on the exterior of their nonwettable bodies or beneath their wings to serve for respiration. Some aquatic larvae, such as those of mosquitoes, must extend their spiracles above the water to breathe, but the larvae of caddis-flies and others have thin *gills*—tracheal, anal, or blood—that take up oxygen dissolved in water (Fig. 7-2). None of these is homologous with the gills of CRUSTACEA.

The *nervous system* is annelid-like in the lowest insects and in many larvae of higher forms, with paired ganglia in each body somite, but in the adults of some flies and others the (posterior) ganglia are concentrated forward in the body. *Sound production* is possible in many ORTHOPTERA (Fig. 26-15), HEMIPTERA, cicadas, certain moths, some mosquitoes and other flies, and some beetles and bees. The mechanism of production varies and in some may be merely incidental to their manner of flight. *Light* is produced by glow-worms, fireflies (LAMPYRIDAE) and a few others.

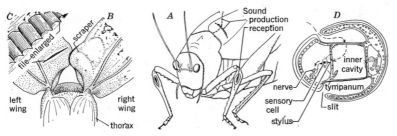

Fig. 26-15. *A.* Fore parts of a katydid showing the location of structures for sound production and reception. *B.* Undersurface of the forewings with file and scraper that are rubbed together to produce sounds. *C.* Enlarged detail of the file. *D.* Cross section of foreleg showing the sound receptor or "ear," with paths of sound waves (broken line) and nerve impulses (solid arrow). (*Partly after Dahlgren, 1925.*)

26-20. Distribution. Some insects are of wide occurrence, over a continent or more, whereas other species are limited to a few acres. Insects occur from sea level to well above 20,000 feet on the highest mountains. Surveys by airplanes show that many insects inhabit the air, especially by day in summer; they are mostly below 1,000 feet, but some have been taken up to 14,000 feet. By such means, species are constantly being carried to new localities. Some beetles and COLLEMBOLA live on seabeaches between the tide lines, and a few water striders (*Halobates*) on the ocean surface; there are few submerged marine insects.

26-21. Seasonal occurrence. Life on land exposes insects to greater extremes of environmental conditions than are experienced by most inhabitants of the sea and fresh waters. They have to withstand changes in temperature and food supply, as between the summer and winter and in the abundance or scarcity of plants. Different species are adapted to these problems in various ways. Many are abundant in warm seasons and far reduced at other times. Some, such as yellowjackets, overwinter as adults that hide away to hibernate in shelters where their bodily metabolism is far reduced. Others survive as pupae or larvae. In many species all individuals die at the close of the warm season and then are represented only by eggs that will develop and hatch the following spring.

26-22. Sensory perceptions and behavior. Insects respond to many stimuli that provoke sensations in man, including light, chemical stimuli (smell, taste), touch, and sound, but their perceptions differ in both kind and magnitude. They detect chemical stimuli far too delicate for the human nose or tongue, and some react to ultraviolet rays but not to red or infrared.

The simplest response is a *reflex* such as the action of a bee's sting, which operates if touched, even when severed from the body. The invariable type of response by which an animal orients itself to or away from a stimulus is known as a *taxis*. A *Drosophila* is guided by its olfactory organs to overripe fruit that bears the yeast upon which the fly feeds by a *positive chemotaxis* to certain alcohols and organic acids in the fermenting fruit. Many insects find mates by a similar taxis to the delicate scents emitted by the opposite sex. The moth that flies directly to (and even into) a flame shows *positive phototaxis;* and the cockroach that runs for cover when suddenly exposed to a lamp, a *negative phototaxis.* Aquatic larvae of caddis-flies often show *positive rheotaxis* by aligning themselves head foremost in a current of water. The term *kinesis* is used to describe undirected locomotor reactions where the speed of movement or frequency of turning depends on the intensity of stimulation. The cockroach, besides avoiding light, seeks shelter in crevices where its body is in contact with the shelter—this is thigmokinesis. Taxes and kineses, and some other types of reactions, enable insects and many other animals to find and inhabit

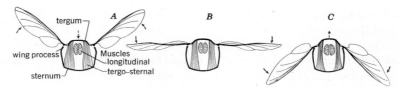

Fig. 26-16. Wing movements in the flight of an insect. *A. Upstroke:* Contractions of the tergosternal muscles depress the tergum and carry the wing bases downward, each acting over a wing process as a fulcrum. Rotation of the wings is produced by still other muscles. *C. Downstroke:* Contraction of the longitudinal (and other) muscles causes the tergum to bulge upward and forces the wing tips downward. (*After Snodgrass.*)

the small environmental niche or microclimate in which each kind is most successful.

Many details of behavior in insects are based on *instincts* (par. 10-8)—series or chains of coordinated reflexes by the whole organism. The complex sequence of events by which a solitary wasp constructs a nest, deposits an egg, provisions it with paralyzed insects, and skillfully closes the cell is an example of chain instincts. Other features of insect behavior are plastic, or modifiable, and bring to bear some features of experiences of an individual that are registered as organic memory. An example here is the hive bee, which is trained to associate color with a food supply.

26-23. Flight. Insects, birds, and bats are the only animals capable of true flight. The wings of insects (Figs. 26-4, 26-16) are unique structures in being derived as extensions of the body integument quite unlike the limb-wings of the vertebrates (Fig. 14-1). The ability to fly enables insects to extend their feeding ranges and to disperse and occupy new territory.

26-24. Water conservation. When the ancestors of insects left the water and moved to the land and air, they experienced changes analogous to those of amphibians and reptiles as compared with fishes. The sense organs became adapted to function in air, the chitinous body covering served to resist the loss of body fluids by evaporation, and the tracheae provided a means for breathing air. All insects, save those in humid environments, have a problem in the conservation of body water that does not beset aquatic animals, since moisture may be lost in respira-

tion and in evacuating food residues. The valves in the spiracles may limit the amount of air (and moisture) exhaled under some conditions, but the more vigorous respiratory movements during flight serve incidentally to deplete the supply of fluids. Insects in dry situations extract water from food residues in the rectum, and they probably gain some metabolic water as a by-product of the oxidation of food materials within the body.

26-25. Food. Fully half the known species of insects are *phytophagous,* feeding on the tissues or juices of plants. The grasshopper eats a great variety of plants, the potato beetle uses only those of the Family SOLANACEAE, the larva of the monarch butterfly eats only the milkweeds (Genus *Asclepias*), and that of a common copper butterfly is restricted to a single species of sorrel (*Rumex acetosella*). Most termites and certain beetles subsist on wood, but some of them and certain ants eat fungi exclusively; among such insects are some that produce their own food by planting, fertilizing, and tending "fungus gardens." The *saprophagous* insects include beetles, fly larvae, and others which eat dead animals, and the *carnivorous* species are those which capture and devour insects or other living animals.

26-26. Enemies. Because of their abundance, the insects are preyed upon by a great variety of other insects and vertebrates of the land and fresh waters. Insects are subject to many diseases that act to reduce their numbers.

The larvae of tachinid flies (DIPTERA) and of the ichneumonid, braconid, and chalcid wasps

(HYMENOPTERA) are *parasites* of other insects, and the scelionids (HYMENOPTERA) are egg parasites. The parasites weaken or kill their hosts or destroy the eggs and thus serve to control the populations of the latter; but as the supply of host individuals declines, so must that of the parasites, which fluctuate in numbers with their hosts. This matter is further complicated by *hyperparasitism,* wherein parasites in turn are themselves parasitized by other species. A tussock moth caterpillar (*Hemerocampa leucostigma*) studied by L. O. Howard was found to have 23 primary parasites (6 DIPTERA, 17 HYMENOPTERA), which in turn had 13 secondary parasites, or hyperparasites; the latter were subject to 2 (or 5) tertiary parasites—such are the complexities in the "balance of nature"!

26-27. Reproduction. Fertilization is always internal. Most species are *oviparous* and lay their eggs singly or in clusters, either on or in the ground, on the plants or animals where their larvae feed, or in plant tissues. Those with aquatic larvae oviposit in or near water. The eggs of some hatch in a few hours, but those of some ORTHOPTERA and LEPIDOPTERA require many months before doing so. The aphids and several DIPTERA are *viviparous,* producing living young. Eggs of tachinid flies, which are deposited on other insects, will hatch almost as soon as laid. The living young of tsetse and hippoboscid flies develop within the "uterus" of the female parent where they are nourished by special secretions. *Parthenogenesis,* or reproduction from eggs without fertilization, occurs in aphids, thrips, gall wasps, saw-flies and others (par. 26-17). The generations of aphids in spring and summer consist only of females that reproduce by parthenogenesis, but later both sexes are produced in the same manner. These mate, and the fertilized females then lay eggs that remain quiescent over winter to produce females for the next spring. A special type of parthenogenesis known as *paedogenesis* occurs in the fly *Miastor* (CECIDOMYIDAE) and a few other insects. Each larva produces 7 to 30 larvae, and these in turn yield others. Some later larvae pupate to become male and female

flies. The chalcid wasps that parasitize eggs of LEPIDOPTERA exhibit *polyembryony;* a chalcid egg begins development, then divides into 100 or more masses, each of which grows to be a larva that transforms into a wasp.

26-28. Gall insects. The cynipid or gall wasps (HYMENOPTERA) and the cecidomyids or gall flies (DIPTERA) are small insects that oviposit in plant tissues. Some substance then injected or resulting from growth of the larvae causes the plant to produce a characteristic swelling, or *gall.* These are of distinctive form and location (stem or leaf) according to the host plant and the kind of insect involved. Galls are also produced by some aphids and psyllids (HOMOPTERA) and by certain gall mites (ACARINA).

26-29. Number of offspring. This varies in different insects from the single larva hatched at a time by some viviparous flies to the million eggs, more or less, laid by a queen bee. The actual number from any one female is less important than the rate of increase; in some species with short life cycles this is very rapid. The pomace fly (*Drosophila*) lays up to 200 eggs per female, and the entire cycle requires only 10 days at about 80°F. The house fly may complete its cycle in 8 to 10 days during hot weather. Parthenogenesis in aphids and others likewise leads to extremely rapid multiplication of the population under optimum conditions of temperature, moisture, and food supply. The offspring of a single aphid could cover the earth in one season if all survived!

26-30. Growth and metamorphosis. Since an insect lives in an armor-like exoskeleton, it can change form or increase in size only after a molt, and none molts after attaining the adult stage. The increase in linear dimensions at each successive molt is about $\sqrt[3]{2} = 1.26$. The primitive Orders PROTURA to THYSANURA attain adult form and size by slightly graded changes and hence are called the AMETABOLA (Gr. *a,* not + *metabola,* change; Table 26-2). The HEMIMETABOLA (ODONATA to THYSANOPTERA) undergo a gradual or incomplete metamorphosis, as with the grasshopper. The young hatches as a small *nymph,* crudely resembling the adult, with compound eyes. In successive stages, or *instars,* the wings appear externally as small wing pads that enlarge at successive molts to become functional in the *adult,* or *imago.* In the HOLOMETABOLA (MECOPTERA to HYMENOPTERA), the young emerges as a small worm-like segmented *larva* having the head, thorax, and abdomen much alike and with short legs but no wings or compound eyes. The successive larval instars increase in size through several molts. Each then enters a "resting" stage as a *pupa,* within the last larval skin, in a special puparium, or in a cocoon. Many larval organs then break down and are reabsorbed by phagocytic cells, while new structures for the adult arise concurrently. These profound changes occur before the adult, or *imago,* hatches out. This is complete metamorphosis as seen in the honeybee.

Experimental evidence indicates that both molt and metamorphosis are controlled by *hormones,* probably produced by the *corpus allatum* (par. 9-2). This gland originates from ectoderm behind the mandibles and comes to lie behind the brain. Its removal at certain critical stages in nymphs of the bug *Rhodnius* will prevent them from molting. Conversely, if removed in early nymphs at certain other times, they will acquire some adult characteristics upon molting. The presence of a hormone is deemed essential for molt, and removal of the gland evidently takes out some substance that inhibits the appearance of adult characteristics. Like vertebrate hormones, this substance is nonspecific and if transplanted will exercise its influence in insects of other genera and orders.

26-31. Social insects. Most insects are *solitary,* each individual living unto itself; the sexes associate only to mate, and the female deserts her eggs or dies after laying. *Gregarious* species assemble in large numbers, as in swarms of locusts and hibernating ladybird beetles. With all such insects the parents usually never see or live coincidently with their offspring. About 6,000 species of insects, however, exhibit social

instincts, the female or both parents living cooperatively with their offspring in a common shelter. These conditions begin with *subsocial relations,* as of a female earwig (Order DERMAPTERA), which guards her eggs and later the young. Cockroaches and crickets, some beetles and bugs, the EMBIOPTERA, and the ZORAPTERA do likewise. A solitary wasp provisions individual egg cells with insects as food for her larvae, which later hatch out and grow independently. True *social life* occurs with all termites, all ants, and certain wasps and bees. The female lives, according to her species, protected within the soil, in cavities in wood, or in a manufactured nest, often in darkness under a lowered temperature and regulated humidity where her muscular movements and catabolism are lessened. She has a lengthened life span, possibly because of these favorable conditions. Queens of some termites and ants may live for several years. In the simpler cases, the female merely remains with successive broods or feeds them daily. From this condition there is a graded series to the complex colonial life of termites, ants, and hive bees, which have a division of labor between several castes. The constant association of many individuals in a colony evidently leads to formation of useful new reflexes and instincts; with different kinds of food and possibly by the action of hormones, these may have led to the origin of castes. The larger populations with social life require an enhanced food supply. The ants show a progression in food habits such as probably occurred in man's history. The lowest kinds hunt insects or flesh. Pastoral ants attend and shelter aphids ("ant cows") from which they obtain honeydew as food, and harvester ants gather and store seeds in summer to tide them through the winter. Finally, the fungus ants (*Atta*) grow their own pure crops of certain fungi in underground gardens fertilized with organic debris; each young queen upon setting out to found a new colony carries a seed stock of fungal hyphae in a pouch below the mouth.

26-32. Relations to man. Practically every person is affected by some insects, from the apartment dweller who eats honey, wears silk, and swats flies to the poor Indian who is plagued by lice, fleas, and flies and in extremity eats grasshoppers. Economic entomology deals with the several thousand species of insects of importance to agriculture, forestry, and the food industries, and medical entomology with those affecting the health of man and domestic animals.

There are many **beneficial insects.** The bees and others that go from flower to flower to gather pollen are essential in cross-fertilizing blossoms of apples, cherries, blackberries, clover, and other crops, which otherwise will not set fruit or seed. Hives of bees are placed in orchards or fields to ensure such fertilization. The Smyrna fig, which is grown in California, produces only female flowers; to set good fruit, these need "caprification" (pollination) by a small wasp (*Blastophaga*) that develops only in the small nonedible capri-fig whence it brings pollen. Hive bees of the United States produce about 100,000 tons of honey annually, which serves as human food; they also yield over 1,000 tons of beeswax, used in polishes, church candles, and modeling and to wax thread. Raw silk is obtained in the Orient and Europe from the silkworm (*Bombyx mori*). The larvae are reared in domestication on a diet of white mulberry leaves, and each spins a cocoon of silk from its salivary secretions. A cocoon yields about 1,000 feet of fiber, and about 25,000 cocoons are unwound to spin 1 pound of silk thread. The shellac of commerce is obtained from waxy secretions of certain lac or scale insects (Cocci-dae) of India, and the dyes known as "cochineal" and "crimson lake" are derived from the dried bodies of some tropical scale insects of cactus.

Many harmful plant-eating insects are devoured by a host of **predaceous insects** —ground beetles, syrphid flies, and wasps. Scale insects that feed on and damage citrus and other trees are eaten by larvae of lady beetles (Coccinellidae); certain species of these beetles have been imported, reared, and liberated in orchards to control scale insects. The parasitic insects that oviposit in eggs or young of plant-feeding insects and whose larvae destroy the latter are another useful group; some are reared artificially and liberated to serve in "biological control" of harmful species. Such parasites are in turn subject to hyperparasites, which reduces their effectiveness.

Other useful insects are the scavenger beetles and flies that clean up the dung and dead bodies of animals. Flesh flies lay quantities of eggs in animal carcasses, which their voracious larvae soon reduce to skin and bone. Ants, termites, and beetles slowly reduce the remains of dead trees and other plants, but termites also do much damage to buildings and other wooden structures. Finally, many insects are indirectly useful as the food for fishes, game birds, fur mammals, and other wild vertebrates and at times for poultry and turkeys.

Many species of **harmful insects** injure farm crops, forests, flower and truck gardens, stored foods, and other property; and others affect the comfort and health of wild and domestic animals and man. The aggregate damage by such insects is estimated at over $1,325,000,000 annually in the United States. Every cultivated plant has more than one insect pest, and each important crop, such as corn, cotton, wheat, and tobacco, has a hundred or more. These levy a steady toll in damage or loss of crops and in expenditures for control by poison sprays, dusts, and parasites. Some major **native pests** are the potato beetle, chinch bug, and grasshoppers; among the many **introduced pests** are the hessian fly of wheat, European corn borer, cotton boll weevil, and codling moth of apples. Federal and state quarantines are maintained to limit the spread of some of these insects.

Human foods are eaten or ruined by ants, cockroaches, and weevils and are dirtied by house flies; stored cereals are damaged by grain weevils and moths; woolen clothing, carpets, furs, and feathers are riddled by clothes moths and carpet beetles; and books are damaged by silverfish, beetle larvae, and termites. Bedbugs, stable flies, mosquitoes, and gnats bite man and his animals; attacks of biting lice cause poultry and livestock to become unthrifty; bloodsucking tabanid flies annoy horses, and horn flies do the same to cattle; larvae of bot flies are a source of irritation in the stomachs of horses; and larvae of ox warble flies burrow in the backs of cattle, causing them to lose flesh and damaging the hides for leather.

Many insects and some ticks act as intermediate hosts for various diseases of man and the larger animals and plants; a few important examples are given in Table 26-1.

flies, and some (†*Meganeura*) had a wingspread up to 29 inches! Six existing orders date from the Permian, and others appeared in the Mesozoic. The rising land, colder climates, and appearance of seasonal seed plants of those times evidently favored the evolution of pupae to withstand adverse conditions, since the earliest scorpion flies (MECOPTERA) are so much like existing species as to suggest that complete met-

TABLE 26-1. Examples of Diseases Transmitted by Insects and Ticks

Disease	Causative organism	Carried by:	Order
Dutch elm disease........	*Ceratostomella* (fungus)	Bark beetles (*Scolytus*)	COLEOPTERA
Cucumber wilt..........	*Bacillus tracheiphilus*	Cucumber beetles (*Diabrotica*)	COLEOPTERA
Curly top of sugar beets...	Virus	Beet leafhopper (*Circulifer*)	HOMOPTERA
Human yellow fever......	Virus	Mosquito (*Aëdes aegypti*)	DIPTERA
Bubonic plague of rats and man..............	*Pasteurella pestis*	Fleas (*Xenopsylla* and others)	SIPHONAPTERA
Tularemia..............	*Pasteurella tularensis*	Deer fly (*Chrysops*) and others	DIPTERA
Human typhus fever.....	*Rickettsia*	Body louse (*Pediculus*)	ANOPLURA
Human malaria..........	*Plasmodium* (protozoan)	Mosquito (*Anopheles*)	DIPTERA
Chagas' disease..........	*Trypanosoma cruzi*	Bug (*Triatoma*)	HEMIPTERA
Filariasis..............	*Wuchereria bancrofti* (nematode)	Mosquitoes (*Culex* and others)	DIPTERA
Dog tapeworm..........	*Dipylidium caninum*	Louse (*Trichodectes*) and fleas	MALLOPHAGA SIPHONAPTERA
Rocky Mountain spotted fever of man..........	*Dermacentroxinus rickettsi*	Tick (*Dermacentor andersoni*)	ACARINA
Texas cattle fever........	*Babesia bigemina*.............	Tick (*Boophilus annulatus*)	ACARINA

Control of injurious insects has become more efficient with recent development of many new organic poisons, of which DDT and benzene hexachloride are conspicuous examples. Unfortunately, some populations of insects develop immunity to the poisons after a few generations (see also par. 14-24).

26-33. Fossil insects. Despite their fragile nature, remains of insects as fossils have been found in Australia, China, Russia, Europe, and the United States, and over 10,000 species have been described. The oldest are in Upper Carboniferous rocks, about 250,000,000 years old, and include the primitive †PALEODICTYOPTERA, which lasted into Permian time; others (BLATTARIA) are closely related to living cockroaches. The †PROTODONATA resembled dragon-

amorphosis was an early achievement. The oldest fossil forms were fully winged and specialized along lines that distinguish the orders to which they belong. The fossil remains indicate that the orders differed, however, in relative abundance, as the beetles (COLEOPTERA) comprise only 1 per cent of known Permian insects but nearly 40 per cent of all insect species today. The flies (DIPTERA) make up 0.3 per cent in the Permian, 5 per cent in Mesozoic, 27 per cent in Tertiary, and 10 per cent of Recent species.

The transparent Baltic amber (fossil resin) of Oligocene, found along the coast at Königsberg, U.S.S.R., contains many insects with all external details beautifully preserved and easily seen. Existing families and genera are common, but extinct species also occur. Eight

TABLE 26-2. Orders of the Class Insecta

(Characters of adults; exceptions as to wings or other features omitted)

Subclass	Metamorphosis	Orders and common names	Chewing	Sucking	Fore	Hind	Distinctive features
APTERYGOTA	AMETABOLA: no metamorphosis	1. **Protura**	C		None		No antennae
		2. **Collembola:** springtails	C		None		Spring (furcula) on abdomen
		3. **Diplura:** japygids	C		None		2 pincers or cerci on abdomen
		4. **Thysanura:** bristletails	C		None		Body fine-scaled; 3 cerci on abdomen
PTERYGOTA typically winged; wings reduced or absent in some	HEMIMETABOLA: young are *nymphs* with compound eyes, and wings grow externally; metamorphosis gradual (incomplete)	5. **Orthoptera:** roaches, grasshoppers	C		4 or none Leathery	Thin	Usually with cerci
		6. **Dermaptera:** earwigs	C		Hard, short	Thin, fan-like	Forceps at end of abdomen
		7. **Plecoptera:** stone-flies	C		Filmy, narrower	Pleated, broader	2 long cerci
		8. **Isoptera:** termites	C		Sexual forms with like wings; others wingless		Sexual forms pigmented; others pale, uncolored
		9. **Embioptera:** embiids	C		♂ winged; ♀ wingless		Tarsi of forelegs enlarged for spinning
		10. **Odonata:** dragon-flies	C		Filmy, not folded, nearly alike		Large; eyes big; no cerci
		11. **Ephemeroptera:** May-flies	C		Filmy, not folded Larger	Smaller	Mouth parts vestigial, cerci 2 or 3
		12. **Mallophaga:** biting lice	C		None		Minute, flat; head wide
		13. **Anoplura:** sucking lice		S	None		Minute, flat; mouth parts retractile; head narrow
		14. **Corrodentia:** book lice	C		4, folded, roofed, or none		A maxillary "pick"
		15. **Hemiptera:** true bugs		S	Half leathery	Filmy	A triangular scutellum; base of beak far forward on head
		16. **Homoptera:** aphids, scale insects		S	Texture uniform; 4, 2, or none		Base of beak close to thorax
		17. **Thysanoptera:** thrips		S	Fringed with hairs		Tarsi bladder-like
	HOLOMETABOLA: young are *larvae* with no compound eyes; wings grow internally; metamorphosis complex (complete)	18. **Mecoptera:** scorpion flies	C		Filmy, roofed, nearly alike		Head elongate as a beak; cerci short
		19. **Neuroptera:** ant lions, dobson flies	C		Filmy, roofed, nearly alike		No cerci
		20. **Trichoptera:** caddis flies	C		Filmy, roofed		Wings hairy-coated
		21. **Lepidoptera:** moths, butterflies		S	Covered by fine over-lapped scales		Maxillae as coiled proboscis for feeding
		22. **Diptera:** true flies		S	No hind wings		Halteres ("balancers") replace hind wings
		23. **Siphonaptera:** fleas		S	None		Small; body laterally com-pressed
		24. **Coleoptera:** beetles, weevils	C		Hard, veinless	Filmy, folded	Prothorax large, mesothorax reduced
		25. **Strepsiptera:** stylops	C		Hind wings only in ♂; none in ♀		♀ maggot-like, having head and thorax fused
		26. **Hymenoptera:** ants, wasps, and bees	C	S	Filmy; 2 pairs or none		Base of abdomen usually con-stricted

♂ = male; ♀ = female; filmy = membranous; roofed = wings at rest over abdomen, thus / \.

kinds of ants are structurally identical with living species, implying survival for 30,000,000 years. The ants show polymorphism, and some had learned to attend plant lice. Older amber deposits are known from Canada and the Arctic slope of Alaska north of the Brooks Range. Arctic amber is of Cretaceous age (60,000,000 years old) and the insects found thus far differ from modern genera but belong to present-day families. In contrast to the Baltic amber fauna, no ants have been found in the Canadian or Arctic amber. One of the richest known fossil insect faunas is preserved at Florissant, Colo., near Pikes Peak, in Oligocene lake deposits of volcanic sand and ash that later became shale. Most of the genera of insects of Tertiary time (Fig. 26-17) still survive, others have disappeared, and some are now less widely distributed. The tsetse fly, *Glossina*, for example, is known as a fossil in Florissant shales but is restricted to parts of Africa at the present time.

Fig. 26-17. Examples of fossil insects. *Above.* Weevil (*Epicaerus;* Family Curculionidae), × 7, in shale rock at Florissant, Colo. *Below.* Fungus gnat (*Bradysia*, Family Sciaridae), × 3½, in amber—fossil resin—from Simajoval, Chiapas, Mexico. Both Oligocene.

CLASSIFICATION

(Lengths are given for body, not including wings)

    CLASS 2. INSECTA (Hexapoda). Insects. Head, thorax, and abdomen distinct; 1 pair of antennae; mouth parts for chewing, sucking or lapping; thorax typically with 3 pairs of jointed legs and 2 pairs of wings, variously modified, reduced, or absent; a slender mid-dorsal heart and aorta; respiration by branched tracheal tubes conveying air from spiracles directly to tissues; excretion by Malpighian tubules joined to hind-gut; brain of fused ganglia, double ventral nerve cord with segmental ganglia, often concentrated anteriorly; eyes both simple and compound; sexes separate; sex opening usually single, at end of abdomen; usually oviparous; development after hatching with gradual or abrupt metamorphosis; in all habitats, few in ocean; fully 675,000 species.

    SUBCLASS 1. APTERYGOTA (Ametabola). Primitively wingless; little or no metamorphosis; abdomen with ventral appendages (styli) besides cerci.

    Order 1. Protura. Minute (0.6 to 1.5 mm.), primitive, mouth parts insect-like; no antennae, true eyes, or wings; 3 pairs of 5-jointed legs; abdomen of 12 somites, each of first 3 with pair of minute appendages; first nymphal stage with 9 abdominal somites, 1 added at each molt by division of terminal somite; no metamorphosis; in damp places between decaying leaves, under bark on logs or twigs, or in moss; 90 species. *Acerentulus* (Fig. 26-18*A*).

    Order 2. Collembola. Springtails. Minute to 5 mm., colored or white; antennae 4-jointed; chewing mouth parts; no wings, compound eyes, or Malpighian tubules, usually no tracheae; abdomen of 6 somites; animal leaps by action of ventral springing organ (furcula) on 4th abdominal somite, when released by hook (hamula) on 3d somite; a ventral tube on 1st somite receives sticky secretion from gland behind labium by which animal adheres to smooth surfaces; no metamorphosis; in damp places under leaves, moss, bark, or stones; food of decaying matter; 2,000 species; Devonian? to Recent (Fig. 26-18*B*). *Papirius fuscus; Sminthurus hortensis,* "garden flea," damages young vegetables; *Achorutes armatum,* in manure, damages mushrooms; *A. nivicola,* "snow flea," sometimes gets into sap at maple-sugar camps.

Order 3. Diplura (Entotrophi). JAPYGIDS. Size to 50 mm.; antennae long; no eyes; chewing mouth parts sunk within head; no wings; abdomen of 11 somites, with 2 slender jointed cerci or a pair of pincers; no metamorphosis; 200 species. *Campodea*, in rotten wood or under leaves or stones; *Japyx* (Fig. 26-18*C*), cerci pincer-like, under stones.

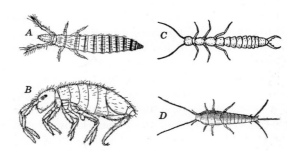

Fig. 26-18. *A.* Order PROTURA. *Acerentulus barberi,* 1.0 mm. long. *B.* Order COLLEMBOLA. Springtail (*Entomobrya laguna*), 2 mm. *C.* Order DIPLURA. Japygid (*Japyx*), to 25 mm. long. *D.* Order THYSANURA. Silverfish (*Lepisma*), 10 mm. (*After various authors.*)

Order 4. Thysanura. BRISTLETAILS. Minute to 30 mm.; antennae long; chewing mouth parts; no wings; body scaly; abdomen of 11 somites, with 2 or 3 slender jointed cerci at end; run swiftly, avoiding light; no metamorphosis; 700 species; Oligocene to Recent. *Lepisma saccharina,* "silverfish" (Fig. 26-18*D*), in buildings, eats starch in books, glazed paper, and clothing, often harmful; *Thermobia domestica,* firebrat, about fireplaces and bake ovens.

SUBCLASS 2. PTERYGOTA. WINGED INSECTS. Wings usually present, sometimes reduced or absent; no abdominal appendages except cerci and genitalia.

Division 1. *Hemimetabola* (Exopterygota). Young stages are nymphs with compound eyes; wings develop externally; metamorphosis gradual to adult form.

Order 5. Orthoptera. GRASSHOPPERS (LOCUSTS), CRICKETS, etc. Size medium to large; chewing mouth parts; forewings (tegmina) narrow, parchment-like, and veined; hind wings membranous, broad, many-veined, folding fan-like beneath forewings; some wingless; abdomen usually with cerci and ovipositor; mostly plant feeders; 23,000 species; Carboniferous to Recent (Fig. 26-19).

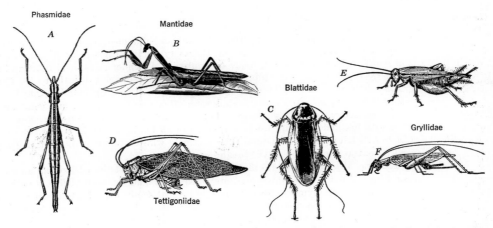

Fig. 26-19. Order ORTHOPTERA. *A.* Walkingstick (*Anisomorpha*), 75–100 mm. long. *B.* Praying mantis (*Paratenodera*), 70 mm. *C.* American cockroach (*Periplaneta americana*), 45 mm. *D.* Katydid (*Microcentrum*), 70 mm. *E.* Field and house cricket (*Gryllus*), 30 mm. *F.* Tree cricket (*Oecanthus*), 19 mm. (*After various authors.*) See also Fig. 26-1.

BLATTIDAE. COCKROACHES. Body depressed, head partly under prothorax; antennae long; dark-colored, foul-smelling; hide in crevices, run rapidly in dark; omnivorous, spoil foods, clothing, leather, and books. *Periplaneta americana,* American cockroach; *Blatta orientalis,* oriental cockroach; *Blattella germanica,* croton bug or European cockroach; all in United States.

MANTIDAE. PRAYING MANTIS. Head free, prothorax long; forelegs enlarged to grasp insects used as food; movements stealthy; mostly tropical. *Stagmomantis carolina*, praying mantis, north to Ohio and New Jersey, 60 mm. long.

PHASMIDAE. WALKINGSTICKS. Form stick-like, mimicking twigs on which insect rests; wings small or none; meso- and meta-thorax and legs long; slow-moving; feed on foliage; mostly tropical, some to 330 mm. long, some mimic leaves. *Anisomorpha (Diapheromera) femorata*, north to Canada, wingless.

ACRIDIDAE (Locustidae). GRASSHOPPERS, LOCUSTS. Body deeper than wide, head and eyes large, antennae short; tarsi 3-jointed; hind legs elongate for jumping; males produce sounds; diurnal; feed on green plants, often damage crops. *Melanoplus femur-rubrum*, red-legged grasshopper; *M. spretus*, Rocky Mountain grasshopper; *Dissosteira carolina*, "Carolina locust," and *Schistocerca americana*, "American locust," both of wide distribution; *Romalea microptera*, lubber grasshopper, almost wingless, in southern states; *Locusta migratoria*, winged migratory locust of Old World, cause of Biblical locust plagues.

TETTIGONIIDAE (Locustidae). LONG-HORNED GRASSHOPPERS, KATYDIDS, etc. Form delicate; often green; antennae often longer than body; tarsi 4-jointed; hind legs long for jumping; nocturnal; males produce sounds. *Microcentrum*, katydid; *Anabrus simplex*, "Mormon cricket," wingless, a crop pest.

GRYLLIDAE. CRICKETS. Short, dark-colored; antennae long; tarsi 4-jointed; some wingless; often leap on long hind legs; males produce chirps. *Gryllus*, field and house crickets; *Gryllotalpa*, mole cricket, burrows in ground; *Oecanthus*, tree crickets, small, greenish white, puncture twigs and berry canes to lay eggs.

Order 6. Dermaptera. EARWIGS. Elongate; chewing mouth parts; forewings short, leathery, no veins; hind wings large, semicircular, membranous, veins radial, fold beneath forewings at rest; some wingless; tarsi 3-jointed; cerci form stout horny forceps at end of abdomen; metamorphosis

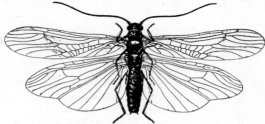

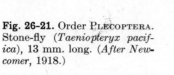
Fig. 26-20. Order DERMAPTERA. European earwig (*Forficula auricularia*), 11–15 mm. long. (*From W. B. Herms.*)

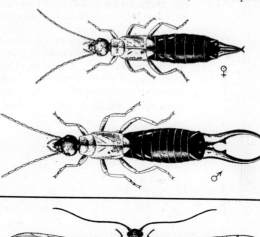
Fig. 26-21. Order PLECOPTERA. Stone-fly (*Taeniopteryx pacifica*), 13 mm. long. (*After Newcomer, 1918.*)

gradual; feed on green plants and on other insects; hide in crevices, sometimes in buildings; 1,100 species; Jurassic to Recent. *Labia minor*, 6 mm. long, common; *Forficula auricularia* (Fig. 26-20), European earwig, now a local garden nuisance in eastern states and on Pacific coast; *Anisolabis maritima*, wingless, acclimatized from Europe on beaches of Atlantic coast.

Order 7. Plecoptera. STONE-FLIES. Size moderate to large; body soft; mouth parts for chewing, but often absent in adults; antennae long, with setae; wings 4, membranous, held pleated but flat on back at rest, hind pair larger; tarsi 3-jointed; end of abdomen usually with 2 long many-jointed cerci; nymphs aquatic, often with a tufted tracheal gill behind each leg; live under stones, eat small insects; used as fish bait; adults of weak flight; metamorphosis gradual; 1,500 species; Permian to Recent. *Pteronarcys; Taeniopteryx pacifica*, "salmon fly," occasionally damages fruit-tree buds in Washington (Fig. 26-21).

Order 8. Isoptera. TERMITES. Body soft; thorax joins broadly to abdomen; chewing mouth parts; workers and soldiers wingless, sterile, blind, colorless (hence, "white ants"); sexual males and females pigmented, with 2 pairs of similar, narrow, membranous wings, carried flat on back at rest and detached after nuptial flight; metamorphosis gradual; 1,800 species, mostly in tropics; Eocene to Recent (Figs. 26-22, 26-23). *Reticulitermes*, subterranean termites, in earth and into dry

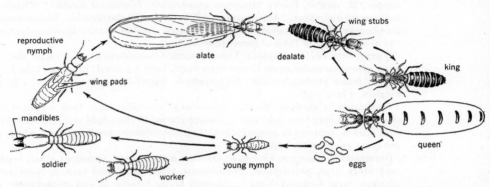

Fig. 26-22. Order ISOPTERA. Castes and life cycle of a termite. (*Modified from Kofoid and others, Termites and termite control, University of California Press.*)

wood, Mexico to southern Canada; *Kalotermes*, dry-wood termites, in wood, north to Virginia and California; *Zootermopsis*, damp-wood termites, western Canada to Virginia and southward; *Amitermes*, in earth of deserts, Texas to California; *Macrotermes*, in tropics, constructs firm aboveground nests (termitaria) to 30 feet tall, of earth particles cemented by salivary secretions; *Nasutitermes*, in tropics, builds aboveground nests of "carton" (paper-like wood debris); some with "fungus gardens" for food.

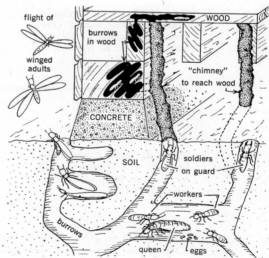

Fig. 26-23. Activities of the subterranean termite (*Reticulitermes*). (*Adapted from Light, 1929.*)

Primitive, social, live in closed tunnels within earth, wood, or nests, in colonies of few to thousands of individuals comprising 3 or more castes: (1) *sexuals* (kings and queens), swarm out in flights for dispersal, then settle in pairs, remove wings at preformed breaking joint near base, excavate new nest, mate, and produce colorless, wingless, and sterile young; (2) **soldiers,** heads and mandibles large, used to defend colony (some produce poisonous spray); (3) **workers,** excavate tunnels and build nests, collect food and feed other castes and rear young with aid of older nymphs. **Supplementary reproductives** derived from certain nymphs may become sexually mature and replace king and queen. Feed on cellulose, which in some termites is digested by symbiotic flagellates (par. 16-14); termites help to reduce stumps, downed logs, etc., and form humus, but do serious economic damage, especially in tropics, by tunneling in wooden buildings, bridges, posts, and lumber, also in furniture, books, and papers; some attack living trees, and some distribute wood-destroying fungi.

Order 9. Embioptera. EMBIIDS. Small; body long, straight-sided, and soft; chewing mouth parts; forelegs with first segment of tarsi inflated, containing spinning organs; cerci 2-jointed; males usually winged, females all wingless; in grass or under objects on ground, construct silk-lined tunnels

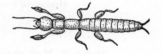

Fig. 26-24. Order EMBIOPTERA. *Embia major,* × 1½.

joined to underground nests; colonial; eat decayed plant matter; tropical and subtropical; 200 species; Oligocene to Recent. *Anisembia texana,* Texas; *Gynembia tarsalis,* California (Fig. 26-24); *Oligotoma,* Africa, eastern Asia, etc., introduced in United States.

Order 10. Odonata. DRAGON-FLIES, DAMSEL-FLIES. Large; body often brightly colored; chewing mouth parts; eyes huge, prominent, with up to 30,000 ommatidia; 2 pairs of transparent membranous wings with complex cross veins, a strong cross vein and notch, or nodus, in anterior margin of each; abdomen slender, elongate; adults strong-flying, predaceous; legs used to capture other insects in flight but not for locomotion; mate in air; eggs dropped in water or inserted in aquatic plants; nymphs (naiades) aquatic, capture prey with extensible labium having hook-like "jaws" at end; 11 to 15 molts, 3 months to 5 years in water with gradual metamorphosis, climbing out for final molt to winged adult stage; 5,000 species; Permian to Recent (Fig. 26-25).

Fig. 26-25. Order ODONATA. Dragon-flies. *Aeshna: A.* Nymph capturing prey, with labium extended. *B.* Nymphal skin. *Libellula: C.* Nymph. *D.* Nymphal skin. *E.* Adult at rest with wings extended. (*After Brehm.*)

SUBORDER 1. ANISOPTERA. DRAGON-FLIES. Hind wings wider at base than forewings; wings held laterally in repose; nymphs with gills in rectum, water for aeration drawn in and expelled, aiding also in locomotion. *Gomphus, Anax, Aeshna, Libellula, Sympetrum.*

SUBORDER 2. ZYGOPTERA. DAMSEL-FLIES. Wings alike, held vertically over back in repose; nymphs with 3 external leaf-like caudal gills. *Hetaerina,* ruby spot; *Lestes, Argia.*

Order 11. Ephemeroptera. MAY-FLIES. To 25 mm. long; body soft; mouth parts for chewing, but vestigial; antennae short; wings 4, membranous, forewings much larger, all held vertically above body at rest; end of abdomen with 2 or 3 long, many-jointed cerci; nymphs aquatic, with lateral tracheal gills; feed on plant materials; up to 21 molts, few months to 3 years in water; finally float at surface, and flying subimago emerges and soon molts to imago that lives but a few hours or days, reproduces, and dies without feeding; 1,500 species; Permian to Recent. *Ephemera; Leptophlebia; Callibaetis* (Fig. 26-26).

Fig. 26-26. Order Ephemerop-
tera. May-flies. (*From General Biological Supply House.*)

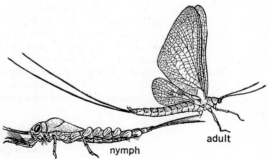

Order 12. Mallophaga. Biting Lice. Small, to 6 mm. long; body depressed, flat; wingless; head broad; mouth parts highly modified for chewing (biting); antennae short, 3- to 5-jointed; eyes reduced or none; thorax short, more or less fused; legs short; tarsi 1- or 2-jointed, clawed for clinging to host; no cerci; metamorphosis slight; exclusively ectoparasitic on birds and a few mammals; feed on fragments of feathers, hair, or epidermis; eggs glued to host; 2,700 species, none fossil. *Menopon, Philopterus, Colpocephalum,* various species on different wild birds; *M. gallinae* and *M. stramineum,* common "hen lice" of poultry (Fig. 26-27 *A, B*); *Goniodes, Lipeurus,* on various domestic fowls; *Trichodectes,* various species on wild and domestic mammals; *T. bovis,* on cattle; *T. canis,* on dogs, intermediate host of tapeworm (*Dipylidium caninum*).

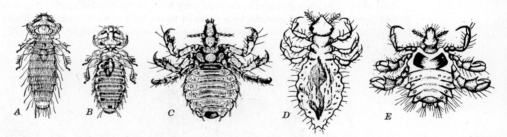

Fig. 26-27. Order Mallophaga. Hen louse (*Menopon stramineum*), 2–2.5 mm. long: *A.* Male. *B.* Female. Order Anoplura. *C.* Hog louse (*Haematopinus suis*), 5–6 mm. *D.* Human body louse (*Pediculus humanus*), 3 mm. *E.* Crab or pubic louse (*Phthirius pubis*), 2 mm. (*After U.S. Department of Agriculture.*)

Order 13. Anoplura. Sucking Lice. Small, to 6 mm. long; body depressed, flat; wingless; head narrow; mouth parts modified for puncturing skin and sucking blood, can be withdrawn into head when not in use; eyes reduced or none; antennae short, 5-jointed; thorax fused; tarsi 1-jointed, each with single claw; metamorphosis slight; exclusively ectoparasitic on mammals; feed on blood and transmit various diseases; 225 species, none fossil (Fig. 26-27*C–E*). *Pediculus humanus* (or *corporis*), human louse, or "cootie," on head and body, eggs, or nits, on hair or clothing; adults transmit typhus fever, trench fever, European relapsing fever, and other diseases of mankind; related species on apes and monkeys; *Haematopinus suis,* hog louse, on domestic swine; *Polyplax spinulosa,* spiny rat louse; *Echinophthirius horridus,* on harbor seals; others on sea lions, walrus, and fur seals.

Order 14. Corrodentia (Psocoptera). Book Lice, etc. Small to minute; antennae slender; chewing mouth parts; prothorax small; wings 4 (or none), veined, membranous, roofed over abdomen at rest; no ovipositor; metamorphosis gradual; 1,100 species; Permian to Recent.

    Suborder 1. zoraptera. Antennae 9-jointed; tarsi 2-jointed; cerci short. *Zorotypus,* 6 species, under 3 mm. long, Texas, Florida, etc., under bark, in humus, near termite nests, etc.

SUBORDER 2. PSOCIDA. Antennae 13- to 50-jointed; a maxillary "pick"; tarsi 2- or 3-jointed; no cerci; feed on starches, cereals, paste, and decaying materials; under bark, in bird nests, among fungi and carry spores. *Psocus*, bark lice, winged, some under silken tents; *Troctes divinatorius*, book louse, wingless (Fig. 26-28); others winged on trees, etc.

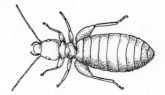

Fig. 26-28. Order CORRODENTIA. Book louse (*Troctes divinatorius*). 1.0 mm. long. (*After U.S. Dept. Agr. Farmer's Bull. 1104.*)

Order 15. Hemiptera. TRUE BUGS. Mostly large; mouth parts piercing-sucking; jointed beak attached far forward on head, composed of labrum with piercing mandibles and maxillae; pronotum large; triangular scutellum between wing bases; wings 4 (or none), forewings thick and horny at bases, membranous behind, crossed at rest; hind wings membranous, fold under forewings; aquatic or terrestrial; food of plant sap or animal body fluids; many important economically; 40,000 species; Triassic to Recent (Fig. 26-29).

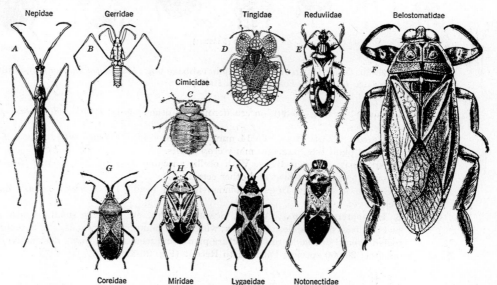

Fig. 26-29. Order HEMIPTERA. *A.* Water scorpion (*Ranatra*), 50 mm. long. *B.* Water strider (*Gerris*), 20 mm. *C.* Bedbug (*Cimex*), 5 mm. *D.* Lacebug (*Corythucha*), 3 mm. *E.* Corsair bug (*Rasahus*), 18 mm. *F.* Giant water bug (*Lethocerus*), 60 mm. *G.* Squash bug (*Anasa*), 16 mm. *H.* Plant bug (*Lygus*), 6 mm. *I.* Milkweed bug (*Lygaeus*), 12 mm. *J.* Back swimmer (*Notonecta*), 12 mm. (*After various authors.*)

SUBORDER 1. CRYPTOCERATA. Antennae short, under head; aquatic; mostly predaceous.

CORIXIDAE. WATER BOATMEN. Swim upright by fringed oar-like hind legs; eat microplants. *Corixa.*

NOTONECTIDAE. BACK SWIMMERS. Swim by long hind legs, with convex dorsal surface downward; bloodsucking; may bite man. *Notonecta.*

NEPIDAE. WATER SCORPIONS. Usually slender, stick-like, 25 to 50 mm. long; long anal breathing tubes; crawl in shallow waters. *Ranatra*, slender; *Nepa*, broad.

BELOSTOMATIDAE. GIANT WATER BUGS. To 115 mm. long; beak short but stout, bite severely if handled; often under lights; some females glue eggs to back of male. *Lethocerus*, "electric-light bug," or "toe-biter"; *Abedus, Belostoma.*

SUBORDER 2. GYMNOCERATA. Antennae long, visible from above; mostly terrestrial or on water surface.

GERRIDAE. WATER STRIDERS. Delicate, long-legged, walk on surface film of water; predaceous. *Gerris*, on fresh waters; *Halobates*, on warm oceans even far from land.

REDUVIIDAE. ASSASSIN BUGS. Head narrow, beak stout, curved under head into groove of prosternum; predaceous. *Rasahus*, corsair bug, sucks juices of insects, also bites man severely; *Rhodnius* and *Triatoma*, cone noses, suck blood of mammals; *T. protracta*, to 22 mm. long, Texas to California, in nests of wood rats (*Neotoma*) and human dwellings, often infected with *Trypanosoma cruzi*, which causes Chagas' disease in South America (par. 16-14).

CIMICIDAE. BEDBUGS. Depressed, oval; wing pads only; nocturnal, bad-smelling, bloodsucking. *Cimex lectularius*, common bedbug of man; other species on bats, poultry, and swallows.

PENTATOMIDAE. STINK BUGS. Body oval or shield-shaped; antennae 5-jointed; scutellum over part or all of abdomen; bad-smelling; some predaceous, many plant feeders. *Murgantia histrionica*,

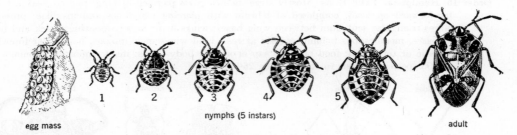

egg mass   nymphs (5 instars)   adult

Fig. 26-30. Order HEMIPTERA. Harlequin cabbage bug (*Murgantia histrionica*), adult 10 mm. long. (*After U.S. Dept. Agr. Farmer's Bull. 1061.*)

harlequin bug (Fig. 26-30), on cruciferous and other plants; *Perillus bioculatus*, eats caterpillars and beetles.

MIRIDAE. PLANT BUGS. To 14 mm. long; no ocelli; forewings with fracture. *Lygus pratensis*, tarnished plant bug, damages many crop plants.

LYGAEIDAE. CHINCH BUGS. With ocelli; antennae below center of eye. *Blissus leucopterus*, seriously harmful to wheat and other cereals.

COREIDAE. SQUASH BUGS. Antennae high on head. *Anasa tristis*, squash bug, harmful to melons, etc.

Order 16. Homoptera. CICADAS, APHIDS, SCALE INSECTS, etc. Mostly small; mouth parts piercing-sucking; base of beak close to thorax; wings 4 (or none), membranous, of like texture throughout, roofed over abdomen at rest; puncture plants and feed on sap, many destructive, some transmit diseases; 20,000 species; Permian to Recent (Fig. 26-31).

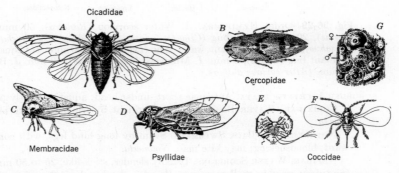

Fig. 26-31. Order HOMOPTERA. *A.* Periodic cicada (*Magicicada septendecem*), 25 mm. long. *B.* Spittle bug (*Aphrophora*), 10 mm. *C.* Treehopper (*Platycotis*), 10 mm. *D.* Psyllid (*Paratrioza*), 1.4 mm. *E–G.* San José scale (*Aspidiotus perniciosus*): *E.* female, 1.0 mm.; *F.* male; *G.* scales on tree bark. (*After various authors.*)

SUBORDER 1. AUCHENORHYNCHA. Rostrum (free) on head; antennae short, a bristle at end; tarsi 3-jointed; active.

CICADIDAE. CICADAS or "LOCUSTS." Usually large; femur of foreleg enlarged; males "sing" loudly, by 2 sets of vibrating plates on fore part of abdomen. *Magicicada septemdecem*, periodical cicada, or "seventeen-year locust," nymph grows 13 or 17 years in ground, sucks sap from tree roots, then emerges as flying adult; eggs laid by chisel-like ovipositor, damaging fruit trees.

CERCOPIDAE. SPITTLE BUGS, FROGHOPPERS. To 12 mm. long; ocelli 2 or none; tibiae usually spined; brown; nymphs hide in whipped-up white froth. *Aphrophora*.

CICADELLIDAE (Jassidae). LEAFHOPPERS. Small; antennae bristle-like, between eyes; can run sidewise. *Circulifer (Eutettix) tenella*, beet leafhopper, transmits virus causing curly-top disease in sugar beets.

MEMBRACIDAE. TREEHOPPERS. To 10 mm. long; prothorax variously enlarged and projecting in grotesque shapes. *Ceresa bubalus*, buffalo treehopper, on various trees.

SUBORDER 2. STERNORHYNCHA. Small; rostrum apparently arising on thorax; antennae longer, no bristle.

PSYLLIDAE. JUMPING PLANT LICE. To 6 mm. long; leap by enlarged hind legs. *Psylla pyricola*, on pears; *P. mali*, on apples.

APHIDIDAE. APHIDS or PLANT LICE. Small to minute, delicate; 2 honeydew tubes (cornicles) dorsal on abdomen; mostly wingless, but males and some females winged; parthenogenesis common (Fig. 26-32); suck sap from plants, much of which is secreted as "honeydew" and often

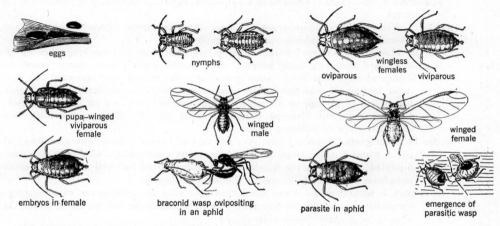

Fig. 26-32. Order HOMOPTERA. Family APHIDIDAE. Spring grain aphid (*Toxoptera graminum*), adult male 1.5 mm. long. Braconid wasp (*Lysiphlebus testaceipes*). (*After U.S. Bur. Entomology Bull.* 110.)

eaten by ants. *Phylloxera*, grape phylloxera, damages roots; *Anuraphis maidi-radicis*, corn root aphid, harmful to roots; *Aphis gossypii*, cotton or melon aphid, on various vegetables.

ALEYRODIDAE. WHITE-FLIES. 1 to 3 mm. long, body and wings covered by white powder; nymphs flat, scale-like, sessile; all adults winged. *Trialeurodes vaporariorum*, greenhouse white-fly.

COCCIDAE. SCALE INSECTS and MEALYBUGS. Small to minute; males with one pair of wings; females lack eyes, legs, and wings, covered by secreted wax or shell-like scale; many harmful to crop and garden plants. *Saissetia oleae*, black scale, on many host plants, causes great damage; *Aspidiotus perniciosus*, San José scale, quite harmful (Fig. 26-31*E–G*); *Pseudococcus citri*, citrus mealybug, damages various plants; *Tachardia lacca*, lac insect of southeastern Asia, secretion used to make shellac.

Order 17. Thysanoptera. THRIPS. Mostly minute (0.5 to 8 mm.), slender; mouth parts conical, rasping-sucking; antennae 6- to 9-jointed; wings 4, alike, narrow, few veins, fringed by many long hairs, and laid flat on body at rest; some wingless; tarsi 1- or 2-jointed, ending in protrusible "bladder"; no cerci; parthenogenesis common, males unknown in some species; larvae often gregarious; metamorphosis gradual to complete; 1 to 10 generations per year in different species; both larvae and adults scrape epidermis on flowers, leaves, and fruits to suck out juices of plants and leave whitened scars; many species injurious to crops, and some transmit virus diseases of plants; 3,200 species; Jurassic to Recent.

SUBORDER 1. TEREBRANTIA. Females with saw-like ovipositor to deposit eggs in epidermis of plants. *Thrips tabaci*, onion thrips, world-wide on hundreds of plant hosts; *Hercothrips fasciatus*, bean thrips (Fig. 26-33), on many cultivated crops; *H. haemorrhoidalis*, greenhouse thrips, on roses, tomatoes; *Scirtothrips citri*, citrus thrips, 0.75 mm. long, damages oranges and lemons.

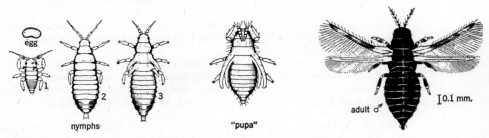

Fig. 26-33. Order THYSANOPTERA. Bean thrips (*Hercothrips fasciatus*). (*From Stanley F. Bailey.*)

SUBORDER 2. TUBULIFERA. Females lack ovipositor, eggs laid on surface of plants; less harmful. *Leptothrips.*

Division 2. *Holometabola* (Endopterygota). Young stages are larvae without compound eyes; wings grow internally; metamorphosis complete (complex).

Order 18. Mecoptera. SCORPION FLIES. Small to large; antennae and legs long; chewing mouth parts on downward-projecting beak; wings 4, alike, slender, membranous, many-veined, roofed over abdomen at rest; cerci small; some males carry end of abdomen upcurved like scorpion; inhabit dense herbage; larvae and adults carnivorous; larvae caterpillar-like with 3 pairs of thoracic legs and 8 of prolegs on abdomen, live in burrows and feed on ground surface; 350 species; Permian to Recent. *Panorpa*, scorpion fly (Fig. 26-35*G*); *Bittacus*, resembles crane fly; *Boreus*, on winter snow in northern states.

Order 19. Neuroptera. DOBSON FLIES, ANT LIONS, etc. Large to small; antennae long; chewing mouth parts; wings 4, alike, large, membranous, many cross veins, roofed over abdomen at rest; tarsi 5-jointed; no cerci; larvae spindle-shaped with grooved suctorial mandibles, carnivorous; metamorphosis complete; 4,700 species; Permian to Recent.

SUBORDER 1. MEGALOPTERA. Veins not forked near wing margins; larvae with chewing mouth parts. *Corydalis cornuta*, dobson fly, male with huge mandibles but harmless, larvae (hellgrammites) aquatic for 3 years; *Sialis*, alder fly.

SUBORDER 2. PLANIPENNIA. Veins forked near wing margins; larvae with sucking mouth parts.

CHRYSOPIDAE. LACEWINGS or GOLDENEYES. Small; wings delicate, green; eggs on stalks attached to plants; larvae (aphid lions) predaceous, beneficial, feed on aphids. *Chrysopa* (Fig. 26-34).

eggs   larva eating an insect   cocoon   adult

Fig. 26-34. Order NEUROPTERA. Green lacewing-fly (*Chrysopa oculata*), adult 12 mm. long. (*After U.S. Bur. Entomology Bull.* 110.)

MYRMELEONIDAE. ANT LIONS. Adults resemble damsel-flies but have knobbed antennae; eggs laid in sand or loose earth; larva, or "doodle bug," makes a conical crater to trap ants, aphids, etc., which fall in and from which it sucks the body fluids. *Myrmeleon, Hesperoleon.*

Order 20. Trichoptera. CADDIS FLIES. Adults 3 to 25 mm. long, soft-bodied; mouth parts rudimentary; antennae and legs long; wings 4, membranous, many longitudinal and few cross veins, roofed over abdomen at rest; body and wings clothed with hairs, scale-like on some; larvae carnivorous, aquatic, each species living in distinctive movable case of leaves, plant stems. sand, or gravel, bound by lining of silk secreted by glands opening near mouth; some in rapid water construct nets and funnels to capture prey; often used as fish bait; 4,500 species; Jurassic to Recent. *Limnophilus; Hydropsyche* (Fig. 26-35A–F).

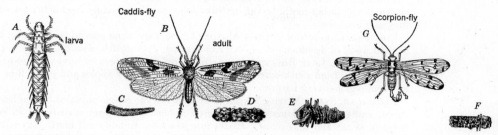

Fig. 26-35. Order TRICHOPTERA. Caddis-fly: *A.* Larva, 15 mm. long. *B.* Adult (*Phryganea*), 10 mm. *C–F.* Cases of various larvae. *G.* Order MECOPTERA. Scorpion-fly (*Panorpa*). (*A–F, after Furneaux, Life in ponds and streams, Longmans, Green & Co., Inc.; G, Riverside natural history, Houghton Mifflin Co.*)

Order 21. Lepidoptera. MOTHS and BUTTERFLIES. Size various, spread 3 to 250 mm.; mouth parts for chewing in larvae, for sucking in adult; usually no mandibles; maxillae joined as coiled tube (proboscis) for sucking fluids; antennae long; eyes large; wings, 4, membranous, usually broad with few cross veins and covered by microscopic overlapping scales; body scaly or hairy; coloration brilliant to obscure; larvae (caterpillar, cutworm, etc.) worm-like with 3 pairs of legs plus prolegs on abdomen; 2 silk glands on labium used to spin cocoon to contain pupa; 112,000 species; Jurassic to Recent.

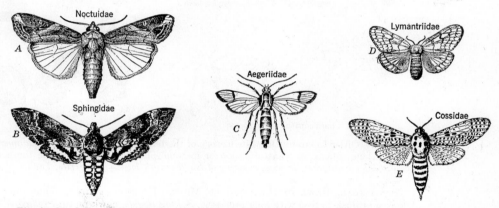

Fig. 26-36. Order LEPIDOPTERA. Moths. *A.* Fall army worm (*Laphygma frugiperda*), spread 25 to 30 mm. *B.* Tomato-worm moth (*Protoparce sexta*), spread 100–125 mm. *C.* Plum-tree borer (*Aegeria*), spread 30 mm. *D.* Gypsy moth (*Porthetria dispar*), spread 50 to 60 mm. *E.* Leopard moth (*Zeuzera pyrina*), spread 60 mm. (*After various authors.*)

SUBORDER 1. JUGATAE. No coiled proboscis; veins alike on all wings; process of forewing hooked to hind wing in flight.

    MICROPTERYGIDAE. Small; mandibles functional. *Micropteryx.*

    HEPIALIDAE. Mouth parts vestigial. *Hepialus.*

SUBORDER 2. FRENATAE. MOTHS and MILLERS. Mouth with siphoning proboscis; antennae not enlarged at tip; often with ocelli; veins unlike in fore and hind wings; hind wing with one or more strong bristles holding to forewing in flight; mostly nocturnal (Fig. 26-36).

    AEGERIIDAE (Sesiidae). CLEAR-WINGED MOTHS. Wings mostly scaleless, transparent; adults resemble wasps but sluggish; larvae bore in wood of trees and shrubs. *Aegeria exitiosa*, peach-tree borer; *Ae. tipuliformis*, currant borer, from Europe.

GELECHIIDAE. Small; larvae burrow in seeds, tubers, twigs, or leaves. *Sitotroga cerealella*, angoumois grain moth, 12 mm. wide, larvae in grains and corn; *Pectinophora gossypiella*, pink bollworm, larvae in cotton bolls, 4 to 6 generations per year.

TINEIDAE. CLOTHES MOTHS. Small, native to Europe, widely naturalized. *Tinea pellionella*, case-making clothes moth, larvae in "silk"-lined case, covered by food debris; destroys woolens, furs, and feathers.

COSSIDAE. CARPENTER or GOAT MOTHS. Adults large, some spread to 180 mm.; larvae burrow in solid wood of deciduous trees, live 2 or 3 years. *Prinoxystus robiniae*.

TORTRICIDAE. LEAF ROLLERS. Larvae often roll up and feed in leaves. *Carpocapsa pomonella*, codling moth, from southeastern Europe, larvae in fruits of apples and pears, 2 or 3 generations in warm regions, very harmful.

PYRALIDAE. SNOUT MOTHS. Spread to 25 mm.; larvae often concealed, roll in leaves or bore in stems, fruits, or stored materials. *Pyrausta nubilalis*, European corn borer, in eastern states, bores in stems and kills plants; *Plodia interpunctella*, Indian-meal moth, damages dried foods; *Galleria mellonella*, bee moth, larva (wax-worm) eats combs of hive bees; *Nymphula*, etc., larva aquatic.

PSYCHIDAE. BAGWORM MOTHS. Larvae in cases of silk and foliage scraps, females wingless, remain in cases. *Thyridopteryx ephemeraeformis*.

LASIOCAMPIDAE. TENT CATERPILLARS. Adults with proboscis atrophied, cannot feed; larvae spin community web among branches of trees and forage outside. *Malacosoma americana*, tent caterpillar (Fig. 26-37), may defoliate trees.

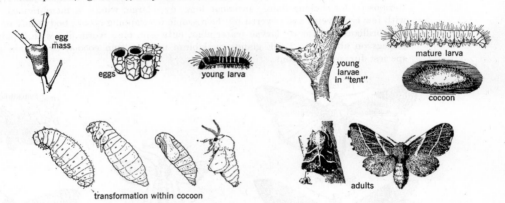

Fig. 26-37. Order LEPIDOPTERA. Life history of the tent caterpillar (*Malacosoma americana*); adult 20 mm. long. Stages in transformation or metamorphosis take place inside the cocoon. Not to scale. (*After Snodgrass, Insects, courtesy of Smithsonian Institution Series, Inc.*)

SPHINGIDAE. HAWK or HUMMINGBIRD MOTHS. Forewings narrow, flight rapid, hover over flowers at dusk to feed with long proboscis. *Sphinx chersis*, hawk moth; *Protoparce sexta*, tomato worm moth, and *P. quinquemaculata*, tobacco worm moth, both with naked larvae to 100 mm. long, adults spread to 125 mm.

GEOMETRIDAE. MEASURING- and CANKER-WORM MOTHS. Many resemble butterflies, some females wingless; larvae naked, feed on exposed foliage, and walk by looping body that has legs only near ends, hence called "loopers" or "measuring worms." *Palecrita vernata*, spring canker-worm, on trees.

SATURNIIDAE. GIANT SILKWORM MOTHS. Some yield silk from cocoons. *Samia cecropia*, cecropia moth, North America, wingspread to 165 mm.; *Telea polyphemus*, polyphemus moth, spread to 120 mm.; *Attacus*, in tropics, females spread to 240 mm.

BOMBYCIDAE. *Bombyx mori*, silkworm moth, native to China, entirely domesticated; larvae feed on mulberry leaves and spin dense cocoons that yield the genuine white and yellow silk of commerce—a most valuable insect; larvae subject to pebrine disease (caused by *Nosema bombycis*, a sporozoan) studied by Louis Pasteur.

ARCTIIDAE. TIGER MOTHS. Adults bright-colored; larvae densely hairy, the "woolly bears." *Hyphantia cunea*, fall webworm.

NOCTUIDAE. OWLET MOTHS. Colors somber, some adults spread to 150 mm.; larvae feed variously, some in ground as cutworms. *Heliothis obsoleta*, corn ear worm; *Cirphis unipuncta*, armyworm of North America, larvae sometimes "march" across country in great numbers; *Erebus agrippina*, largest moth.

LYMANTRIIDAE. TUSSOCK MOTHS. Larvae thickly covered with hairs. *Porthetria dispar*, gypsy moth, and *Nygmia phaeorrhoea*, brown-tail moth, both of Europe and now in northeastern states, defoliate and kill shade trees.

SUBORDER 3. RHOPALOCERA. SKIPPERS and BUTTERFLIES. Mouth with siphoning proboscis; antennae enlarged at tip (hooks only in skippers); no ocelli; veins unlike in fore and hind wings; wings on each side held together by expanded membrane near base of hind wing; wings vertical above body at rest, upper surfaces in contact; diurnal.

HESPERIIDAE. SKIPPERS. Antennae with hooked tips, abdomen heavy; larvae with constriction behind head. *Atalopedes campestris*, field skipper.

PAPILIONIDAE. SWALLOWTAILS. Spread to 125 mm.; bright-colored; usually a tail-like projection on each hind wing; larvae mostly naked; pupae angular, not in cocoons. *Papilio* (Fig. 26-38).

larva   pupa   resting adult   spread adult

Fig. 26-38. Order LEPIDOPTERA. Black swallowtail butterfly (*Papilio polyxenes*); reduced. (*After Webster.*)

PIERIDAE. WHITE and SULPHUR BUTTERFLIES. Abdomen slender. *Pieris rapae*, cabbage butterfly, wings white, on cabbage, etc. *Eurymus philodice*, wings yellow, on clovers.

NYMPHALIDAE. FOUR-FOOTED BUTTERFLIES. Forelegs reduced, not functional, folded under body; tibiae hairy. *Danaus plexippus*, milkweed or monarch butterfly, tawny and black; *Aglais antiopa*, mourning-cloak butterfly, blackish; *A. californica*, tortoise-shell butterfly, occasionally irrupts and migrates in great numbers; *Vanessa cardui*, painted lady; *Basilarchia archippus*, viceroy, coloration mimics that of monarch (Fig. 14-17).

LYCAENIDAE. BLUES, HAIRSTREAKS, and GOSSAMERS. Mostly small, delicate, often brown, eyes white-rimmed; front tarsi reduced on males; larvae slug-like. *Lycaena hypophloeas*, the copper; *Feniseca tarquinius*, larvae prey on woolly aphids; *Lycaenophilus*, wings blue, polymorphic; *Strymon melinus*, wings gray.

Order 22. Diptera. TRUE FLIES. Forewings transparent, few veins; hind wings represented by short knobbed halteres; some wingless; mouth parts piercing-sucking, or "sponging," often forming a proboscis; body divisions distinct, abdomen of 4 to 9 visible somites; larvae usually footless; metamorphosis complete; mostly diurnal; 85,000 species; Upper Permian to Recent (Fig. 26-39).

SUBORDER 1. ORTHORRHAPHA. No frontal lunule (⌒-shaped sclerite) over antennae; larva often with distinct head; pupa naked, emerges from pupa case through T-shaped dorsal opening.

TRIBE 1. NEMATOCERA. Antennae long, 6- to 39-jointed.

TIPULIDAE. CRANE FLIES. Slender, like enlarged mosquitoes, legs long and fragile, wings narrow; a V-shaped mark on back; larvae are "leather worms," living about grass roots, or semiaquatic. *Tipula*.

PSYCHODIDAE. MOTH FLIES and SAND FLIES. To 4 mm. long, woolly, wings velvety; larvae and adults in sewers or damp organic wastes, some larvae in water. *Psychoda; Phlebotomus*, sucks blood of vertebrates, carries human "three-day" fever in Mediterranean region and verruga peruana in Peruvian Andes.

CULICIDAE. MOSQUITOES. Slender, delicate; proboscis long and piercing in females; body humped; wings fringed by scales; larvae ("wrigglers") with large head, long abdomen, and

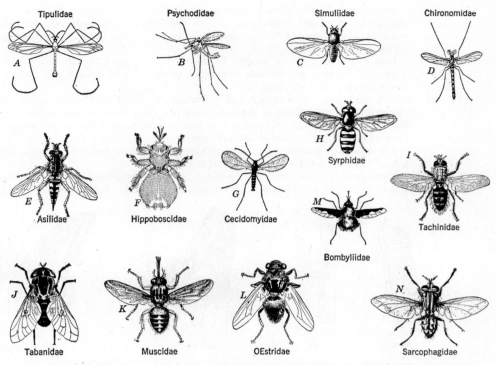

Fig. 26-39. Order DIPTERA. Flies. *A.* Crane fly (*Tipula*), 10–25 mm. long. *B.* Sand fly (*Phlebotomus*), 1.5 mm. *C.* Black fly (*Simulium*), 2 mm. *D.* Midge (*Tendipes* = *Chironomus*), 3 to 10 mm. *E.* Robber fly (*Erax*), 25 mm. *F.* Sheep ked (*Melophagus ovinus*), 6 mm. *G.* Hessian fly (*Phytophaga*), 2.5 mm. *H.* Hover fly (*Syrphus*), 10 mm. *I.* Tachinid fly (*Tachina*), 8 mm. *J.* Horse fly (*Tabanus*), 25 mm. *K.* Tsetse fly (*Glossina*), 13 mm. *L.* Bot fly (*Hypoderma bovis*), 12 mm. *M.* Bee fly (*Bombylius*), 10 mm. *N.* Flesh fly (*Sarcophaga*), 7 mm. (*After various authors.*)

breathing siphon, in various waters; adult males suck plant juices; adult females chiefly blood-suckers, on birds, mammals, and man; abundant, annoying, some transmit serious diseases (Fig. 26-40); 1,500 species. *Culex*, many species; *C. pipiens*, common house mosquito, transmits bird malaria; *Anopheles*, some species transmit *Plasmodium* (SPOROZOA) of human malaria (Fig. 16-21); *Aëdes*, different species in salt marshes, swamps, tree holes, and snow waters; *Aëdes* (*Stegomyia*) *aegypti*, tropics and subtropics, transmitter of human dengue fever and yellow fever.

CHIRONOMIDAE. MIDGES, GNATS, and PUNKIES. Mostly minute, delicate, mosquito-like, mouth parts short, wings scaleless; larvae in water or damp places; adults often "dance" as swarms in air at end of day; few marine; a few reproduce parthenogenetically. *Chironomus*, larvae are "bloodworms," important as fish food.

CECIDOMYIDAE. GALL GNATS. Minute, mosquito-like, antennae with whorled hairs; many produce galls on plants, in which larvae are reared; others are predaceous or parasitic or feed on decaying matter or on plants. *Phytophaga destructor*, hessian fly, feeds in stems of wheat, very harmful; *Diarthronomyia hypogaea*, chrysanthemum gall fly, produces galls; *Miastor*, reproduces by paedogenesis in larvae.

MYCETOPHILIDAE. FUNGUS GNATS. Small, delicate, mosquito-like; antennae and coxae long; in damp woods, basements, etc.; larvae feed on fungus, some gregarious. *Mycetophila mutica*, in mushrooms and toadstools.

SIMULIIDAE. BLACK FLIES. Short, chunky, wings broad; first tarsal joint dilated; larvae attach by anal end to rocks in running water. *Simulium*, females suck blood of domestic birds and mammals and of man; *S. pecuarum*, buffalo gnat.

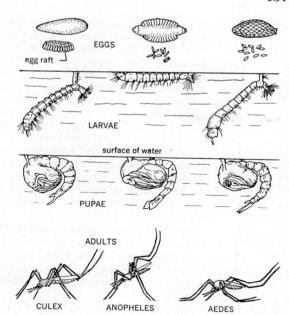

Fig. 26-40. Order DIPTERA. Family CULICIDAE. Stages in the life cycles of three important types of mosquitoes. Larvae and pupae in typical postures in the water; adults posed as when resting or biting.

TRIBE 2. BRACHYCERA. Antennae short, 3-jointed.

TABANIDAE. HORSE FLIES. Stout; eyes large, lateral, often banded; proboscis projecting; eggs and larvae in water or damp places; male flies suck plant juices and honeydew, females blood-sucking. *Tabanus*, horse fly, buzzes about and bites horses and cattle; *Chrysops*, deer (and horse) fly; *C. discalis* transmits tularemia from rodents to man.

ASILIDAE. ROBBER FLIES. Large, robust; body bristly; hairy "beard" about mouth; catch insects in air and suck out their juices. *Erax; Asilus.*

BOMBYLIIDAE. BEE FLIES. Densely haired, resembling bees; legs and proboscis long, slender; larvae parasitic or prey on other insects; adults hover and feed in flowers, harmless. *Bombylius.*

SUBORDER 2. CYCLORRHAPHA. Adults with frontal lunule over antennae; antennae usually 3-jointed with bristle (arista) at end; last larval skin a hard puparium around pupa, opening by circular lid.

TRIBE 1. ASCHIZA. No frontal suture around antenna base.

SYRPHIDAE. HOVER FLIES. Bright-colored, no bristles, mimic wasps or bees; larvae prey on aphids or on small insects or (rat-tail maggots) scavenge in filth; adults hover over and feed in flowers. *Syrphus*, hover fly; *Merodon, Eumerus*, bulb flies, larvae damage narcissus, onions, etc.

TRIBE 2. SCHIZOPHORA. A seam around antenna base.

TRYPETIDAE. FRUIT FLIES. Tip of abdomen narrow. *Ceratitis capitata*, Mediterranean fruit fly, and *Dacus dorsalis*, Oriental fruit fly, boring larvae of both injure fleshy fruits.

DROSOPHILIDAE. POMACE FLIES. Eyes usually red. *Drosophila melanogaster*, about decaying fruit; much used in genetics (Fig. 12-1).

ANTHOMYIDAE. ROOT MAGGOT FLIES. Larvae on roots or decaying materials, some carnivorous. *Hylemyia brassicae*, cabbage maggot, and *H. antiqua*, onion maggot, both damage crops.

MUSCIDAE. HOUSE FLIES, etc. Arista usually plumed to tip; larvae grow in decomposing organic materials; adults about wild and domestic mammals and man, obnoxious and harmful;

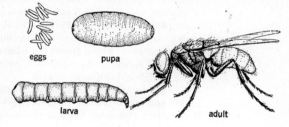

Fig. 26-41. Order DIPTERA. House fly (*Musca domestica*), 4 to 6 mm. long. (*After W. B. Herms.*)

Musca domestica, common house fly (Fig. 26-41), with sponging mouth parts, may contaminate food with filth and spread disease; *Calliphora vomitoria*, bluebottle, and *Lucilia caesar*, greenbottle, both "blow" (oviposit on) flesh; *Stomoxys calcitrans*, stable fly, and *Haematobia irritans*, horn fly, both bite domestic mammals; *Cochliomyia macellaria*, screwworm, maggots in wounds, nose, or navel of domestic mammals, cause injury and death; *Glossina*, tsetse fly, carries trypanosomes of African sleeping sickness (Fig. 16-16).

SARCOPHAGIDAE. FLESH FLIES. Larvae consume dead animals, feces, garbage, etc., or live in insects. *Sarcophaga*.

TACHINIDAE. TACHINID FLIES. Eggs or larvae deposited on insects and destroy the latter; adults feed in flowers. *Gonia*, in cutworms.

OESTRIDAE. BOT FLIES. Adults large, bee-like, hairy, about domestic animals. *Gastrophilus intestinalis*, horse bot, eggs, or "nits," laid on hairs, removed by tongue; larvae burrow from mouth to stomach, pupae emerge in feces; *Hypoderma bovis*, larvae live as warbles under skin on back of cattle, hosts become unthrifty, and hides are damaged for leather; *Oestrus ovis*, in sheep, living larvae deposited about nose, live as head maggots in nasal region; *Cuterebra*, under skin of rodents.

TRIBE 3. PUPIPARA. Abdomen indistinctly segmented; feet clawed; ovoviviparous, 1 larva at a time.

HIPPOBOSCIDAE. LOUSE FLIES. Body flat, louse-like; winged or wingless; abdomen rubbery, expanded; deposit pupae on hosts; ectoparasitic, bloodsucking. *Melophagus ovinus*, "sheep tick," or "ked," 6 mm. long, on domestic sheep, harmful; *Lynchia*, on domestic pigeons; *Ornithoica*, on wild birds.

BRAULIDAE. BEE LOUSE. *Braula coeca*, minute, wingless, on queens and drones of honeybees.

Order 23. Siphonaptera. FLEAS. Body laterally compressed, tough; no wings; mouth parts piercing-sucking; antennae short, in grooves; eyes simple or none; legs long, adapted for leaping, coxae enlarged, tarsi 5-jointed; eggs laid in habitat of or on host; larvae minute, legless, feed on organic debris; pupae in cocoons; adults periodically ectoparasitic and bloodsucking on birds and mammals, avoid light and seek warmth; metamorphosis complete; 1,100 species; Oligocene to Recent. *Pulex irritans*, human flea, also on rats, etc.; *Ctenocephalides canis*, dog flea, and *C. felis*, cat flea (Fig. 26-42), both on dogs, cats, and man; *Xenopsylla cheopis*, Indian rat flea, transmits *Pasteurella*

egg   larva   pupa   adult
                                                                           female

Fig. 26-42. Order SIPHONAPTERA. Cat flea (*Ctenocephalides felis*), 2.5 mm. long. (*After W. B. Herms.*)

pestis, that causes bubonic plague; also transmits murine typhus in southern states; *Ceratophyllus*, various species on wild birds and mammals; *Echidnophaga gallinacea*, sticktight flea of poultry, often harmful; *Tunga (Dermatophilus) penetrans*, chigoe, or jigger, on feet of man and mammals, female burrows in skin, abdomen distends to size of small pea; *Hystricopsylla gigas*, largest flea, 5 mm. long, on some California rodents.

Order 24. Coleoptera. BEETLES, WEEVILS. Minute to large, cuticle heavy; chewing mouth parts, some snout-like; forewings (elytra) thick, leathery, veinless, meet along middorsal line; hind wings membranous, few veins, fold forward under forewings at rest; some wingless; antennae usually 11-jointed; prothorax enlarged, movable; meso- and meta-thorax united to abdomen; larvae worm-like, usually with 3 pairs of legs; pupae rarely in cocoons; metamorphosis complete; more than 280,000 species; late Permian to Recent (Fig. 26-43).

SUBORDER 1. ADEPHAGA. Antennae filiform; hind wings with 1 or 2 cross veins.

CICINDELIDAE. TIGER BEETLES. Adults long-legged, bright-colored, run actively in open places, flight fast; larvae in deep burrows, catch insects at surface. *Cicindela*, in sandy places; *Omus*, black, wingless, nocturnal.

CARABIDAE. GROUND BEETLES. Mostly blackish, long-legged, and terrestrial; tarsi 5-jointed; adults and larvae mainly carnivorous; some burrow, some blind in caves, some emit foul spray if disturbed. *Calosoma*, large, preys on caterpillars and cutworms.

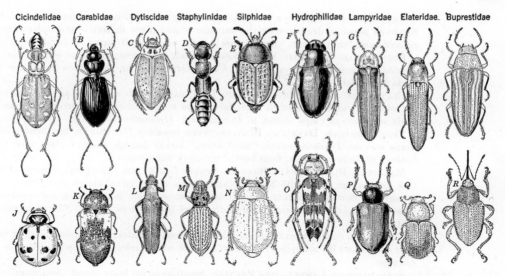

Cicindelidae Carabidae Dytiscidae Staphylinidae Silphidae Hydrophilidae Lampyridae Elateridae Buprestidae

Coccinellidae Dermestidae Meloidae Tenebrionidae Scarabaeidae Cerambycidae Chrysomelidae Scolytidae Curculionidae

Fig. 26-43. Order COLEOPTERA. Beetles. Not to scale. *A.* Tiger beetle (*Cicindela*), 14 to 16 mm. long. *B.* Ground beetle (*Pterostichus*), 8 to 17 mm. *C.* Predaceous water beetle (*Rhantus*), 10 to 12 mm. *D.* Rove beetle (*Staphylinus*), 12 to 25 mm. *E.* Carrion beetle (*Silpha*), 11 to 18 mm. *F.* Water scavenger beetle (*Tropisternus*), 8 to 11 mm. *G.* "Firefly" (*Photinus*), 6 to 14 mm. *H.* Click beetle (*Limonius*), 5 to 12 mm. *I.* Flat-headed borer (*Buprestis*), 14 to 19 mm. *J.* Lady beetle (*Hippodamia*), 6 to 8 mm. *K.* Larder beetle (*Dermestes*), 6 to 7 mm. *L.* Blister beetle (*Epicauta*), 7 to 14 mm. *M.* Darkling ground beetle (*Nyctoporis*), 11 to 15 mm. *N.* June beetle (*Phyllophaga*), 13 to 24 mm. *O.* Long-horned beetle (*Megacyllene*), 13 to 23 mm. *P.* Leaf beetle (*Chrysochus*), 9 to 11 mm. *Q.* Bark beetle (*Dendroctonus*), 5 to 8 mm. *R.* Acorn weevil (*Balaninus*), 5 to 9 mm. (*Drawn by Frieda L. Abernathy.*)

DYTISCIDAE. PREDACEOUS DIVING BEETLES. To 37 mm. long; oval, smooth, shiny; hind legs flat, fringed with hairs, serve as oars in swimming; air stored under elytra when diving; adults and larvae aquatic and predaceous; food of larvae digested externally. *Dytiscus.*

GYRINIDAE. WHIRLIGIG BEETLES. Small, oval, lustrous, eyes divided horizontally; skate rapidly on water surface, gregarious; predaceous. *Gyrinus.*

SUBORDER 2. POLYPHAGA. Antennae various; hind wings lack cross veins.

STAPHYLINIDAE. ROVE BEETLES. Slender; elytra short; scavengers or predators. *Creophilus,* preys on carrion fly maggots; *Myrmedonia,* resembles ants and lives in ant nests; *Termitomimus,* in termite nests, ovoviviparous.

SILPHIDAE. CARRION BEETLES. Minute to 37 mm. long; many flattened; eat carrion, fungi, or decaying plant material. *Necrophorus,* burying beetle, buries small animals as food for larvae; *Silpha,* some feed on crop plants.

PLATYPSYLLIDAE. One species, *Platypsyllus castoris,* on beaver; flat, blind, and wingless.

HYDROPHILIDAE. WATER SCAVENGERS. Resemble DYTISCIDAE; black, a lengthwise keel under body; eat decaying material in water or damp places. *Hydroustriangularis,* to 27 mm. long.

COCCINELLIDAE. LADYBIRD BEETLES. Many 3 to 6 mm. long, rounded, convex, elytra cover abdomen; bright-colored, spotted; head turned down in notch of prothorax; larvae soft, spiny; both larvae and adults beneficial, preying on aphids and scale insects. *Coccinella* and *Hippodamia,* predaceous; *Epilachna corrupta,* bean ladybird, eats beans and other crops, harmful.

DERMESTIDAE. SKIN BEETLES. Small, dark, hairy; both adults and larvae destructive, eating furs, woolens, meat, and hides. *Anthrenus scrophulariae,* buffalo or carpet beetle, 3 mm. long, very injurious.

LAMPYRIDAE. GLOW-WORMS, FIRE-FLIES. To 12 mm. long, straight-sided; prothorax semicircular over downturned head; nocturnal; with light-producing organs on abdomen. *Lampyris, Photinus.*

ANOBIIDAE. POWDER-POST BEETLES, etc. Length 3 to 8 mm.; cylindrical or globular, dark. *Sitodrepa panacea*, drugstore beetle, damages stored plant materials and upholstery; *Xestobium rufovillosum*, "deathwatch," larva bores in solid wood, adult taps with head.

BUPRESTIDAE. METALLIC WOOD BORERS. Body iridescent, antennae serrate; larvae with expanded flat prothorax, head minute. *Chrysbothris femorata*, flatheaded apple-tree borer, larva feeds under bark.

ELATERIDAE. CLICK BEETLES. Adults hard, narrow; can snap into air when placed on back, by releasing catch on ventral keel; larvae are tough-skinned "wireworms," some harmful to seeds and roots of crops. *Alaus*, to 45 mm. long; *Melanotus*.

TENEBRIONIDAE. DARKLING BEETLES. Some resemble CARABIDAE, but tarsi 4-jointed; body shape various. *Tenebrio molitor*, "meal worm," larvae damage stored cereals, used to feed caged birds; *Tribolium confusum*, flour beetle, larvae in flour, etc.

MELOIDAE. BLISTER or OIL BEETLES. Length 7 to 30 mm.; prothorax narrow, neck-like; some lack hind wings, some with hypermetamorphosis (extra larval stages and prepupa); adults eat foliage and flowers. *Epicauta*, larvae damage crops; *Lytta*, larvae eat grasshopper eggs, *L. vesicatoria*, "Spanish fly," yields cantharidin, used in poultices; *Meloë*, *Sitaris*, larvae in nests of solitary bees.

LUCANIDAE. STAG BEETLES. Mandibles enormous in males; front tibiae enlarged for digging in soil; adults feed on honeydew; larvae in roots or wood under ground, some live 4 or more years. *Lucanus*.

SCARABAEIDAE. LAMELLICORN BEETLES. Small to large; body broad, deep, convex; legs spiny; antennae oval, clubbed, of 3 to 7 plates; nocturnal. *Phyllophaga*, larvae, or "white grubs," on grass roots, etc., adults on foliage; *Popillia japonica*, Japanese beetle, destructive, introduced in eastern states; *Macrodactylus*, rose chafer, adults eat leaves of cultivated trees and shrubs; *Scarabaeus sacer*, Egyptian sacred scarab or dung beetle, adults roll up balls of dung for food of larvae.

CHRYSOMELIDAE. LEAF BEETLES. To 12 mm. long; color brilliant, often metallic; adults eat leaves; larvae often in ground, feed on roots; many destructive. *Leptinotarsa decemlineata*, Colorado potato beetle, widespread; *Diabrotica*, cucumber beetles; *Donacia*, larva aquatic, obtains oxygen by piercing plants.

CERAMBYCIDAE. LONG-HORNED BEETLES. Slender, to 75 mm. long; colors often bright; antennae often exceed body in length; adults eat foliage or soft bark; larvae are roundheaded borers in solid wood. *Saperda candida*, roundheaded apple borer; *Ergates*, "pine sawyer."

CURCULIONIDAE. WEEVILS or SNOUT BEETLES. Small to 50 mm.; hard-shelled, often rough-surfaced; snout prolonged; femora often swollen; adults feign death when disturbed; larvae legless, feed within seeds, fruits, stems, or roots; many very destructive to crops. *Anthonomus grandis*, cotton boll weevil; *Conotrachelus nenuphar*, plum curculio; *Sitophilus granarius*, granary weevil; *Phytonomus posticus*, alfalfa weevil (Fig. 26-44).

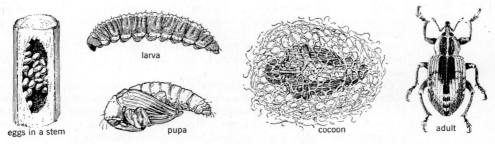

eggs in a stem   larva   pupa   cocoon   adult

Fig. 26-44. Order COLEOPTERA. The alfalfa weevil (*Phytonomus posticus*); adult 3 to 5 mm. long. (*After U.S. Bur. Entomology Circ.* 137.)

SCOLYTIDAE. BARK BEETLES. Short, cylindrical; antennae clubbed; adults and larvae feed under bark, "engraving" branched channels. *Scolytus rugulosus*, shot-hole borer, in various trees; *Dendroctonus*, pine beetle, in various conifers; *Xyleborus*, ambrosia beetle, grows fungus ("ambrosia") for food.

Order 25. Strepsiptera. STYLOPS. Minute; metathorax enlarged; mouth parts for chewing, but small (or none); males with fan-shaped hind wings but forewings reduced to clubbed halteres; mobile, live 1 or 2 days; females larva-like, no antennae, eyes, wings, or legs; head and thorax fused; females and larvae permanently parasitic in body spaces of bees, wasps, HOMOPTERA, etc.; absorb nutriment from host and modify structure of ("stylopize") latter; a hypermetamorphosis; 300 species; Oligocene and Recent (Fig. 26-45). *Stylops*, in bee (*Andrena*); *Xenos*, in wasp (*Polistes*).

Fig. 26-45. Order STREPSIP-TERA. *Stylops*, male 2 mm. long. (*After Bohart*, 1941.)

Order 26. Hymenoptera. WASPS, ANTS, and BEES, etc. Mouth parts chewing or chewing-lapping; wings 4 (or none), small, membranous, few veins, interlocked in flight; female with ovipositor for sawing, piercing, or stinging; larvae caterpillar-like or legless; pupae commonly in cocoons; metamorphosis complete; most species solitary, but some social in colonies, others parasitic as larvae; 103,000 species; Jurassic to Recent (Fig. 26-46).

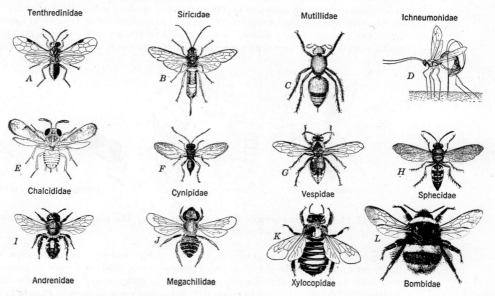

Fig. 26-46. Order HYMENOPTERA. *A*. Saw-fly or rose slug (*Endelomyia*), 15 mm. long. *B*. Horntail (*Sirex*), 30 mm. *C*. "Velvet ant" (*Sphaerophthalma*), 12 mm. *D*. Ichneumon-fly (*Megarhyssa*), to 37 mm. *E*. Chalcid wasp (*Aphytis*), 0.8 mm. *F*. Rose-gall wasp (*Rhodites*), 3 mm. *G*. White-faced hornet (*Vespa maculata*), 12 to 19 mm. *H*. Mud dauber wasp (*Sphecius*), 12 to 20 mm. *I*. Mining bee (*Andrena*), 6 to 18 mm. *J*. Leafcutter bee (*Megachile*), 12 mm. *K*. Carpenter bee (*Xylocopa*), 12 to 20 mm. *L*. Bumblebee (*Bombus*), 10 to 20 mm. (*After various authors.*)

SUBORDER 1. CHALASTROGASTRA. Abdomen broadly joined to thorax; larvae caterpillar-like, with legs, feed on plants.

SIRICIDAE. HORN-TAILS, WOOD WASPS. Body straight-sided; abdomen with spine at end; female with projecting ovipositor for boring; larvae in wood of trees or shrubs. *Sirex; Tremex*, to 50 mm. long.

TENTHREDINIDAE. SAW-FLIES. Body robust; female with ovipositor concealed and saw-like; parthenogenesis common; larvae eat foliage or bore in stems, etc. *Cimbex americanus*, American saw-fly, wingspread to 50 mm.; *Eriocampoides limacina*, larva—pear or cherry "slug,"—eats epidermis of tree leaves.

SUBORDER 2. CLISTOGASTRA. Base of abdomen a narrow "waist" behind thorax; larvae legless.

ICHNEUMONIDAE. ICHNEUMON WASPS or "FLIES." Length 4 to 38 mm.; ovipositor very long (to 150 mm. in *Thalessa*); larvae parasitize caterpillars and other insects, live and pupate in host. *Therion*; *Ephialtes*.

BRACONIDAE. BRACONID WASPS. Mostly under 3 mm.; like ichneumonids in form and habits, but usually pupate outside of host. *Apanteles congregatus*, on larvae of sphingid moths; *Lysiphlebus testaceipes*, in aphids (Fig. 26-32).

CHALCIDIDAE. CHALCID WASPS. Mostly minute; antennae elbowed; some larvae in seeds or stems, others parasitic, some in other parasites. *Bruchophagus funebris*, larvae in clover seed; *Harmoleta grandis*, larvae in wheat stems, harmful; *Blastophaga psenses*, fig wasp, male wingless, breeds in wild capri figs and serves to pollinate Smyrna figs; *Trichogramma minutum*, millions reared and released for control of pest insects such as European corn borer.

CYNIPIDAE. GALL WASPS. Small to minute; abdomen laterally compressed; eggs laid in plant tissues, mainly on oaks, which form swollen galls around the developing larvae; males rare, parthenogenesis common. *Andricus*, on oaks; *Diplolepis*, on rose roots.

FORMICIDAE. ANTS. Length 2 to 18 mm.; pronotum enlarged; abdominal pedicle narrow; polymorphic, with sexual females (queens), males, and wingless (female) workers; other secondary castes in some species; social, in colonies of few to 100,000; queen removes wings after nuptial flight; she starts colony, later only lays eggs, and is fed liquids from mouths of workers; most species are scavengers and useful in cleaning up dead materials; few predaceous; many eat seeds, often are harmful; some colonize aphids and cause much trouble to agriculture. *Ponera*, primitive, few in colony; *Eciton*, legionary ants of tropics and southern states, no permanent nests, march in large companies, predaceous; *Monomorium*, small black ant (Fig. 26-47), nests

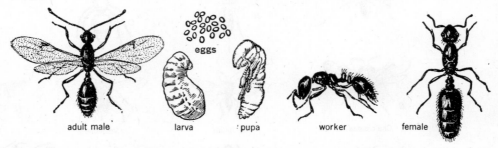

adult male   larva   pupa   worker   female

Fig. 26-47. Order HYMENOPTERA. Family FORMICIDAE. The black ant (*Monomorium*); worker 4.5 mm. long. (*From General Biological Supply House.*)

in soil or wood; *Solenopsis geminata*, fire ant, stings severely, damages crops; *Pogonomyrmex*, harvester ant, eats seeds and often clears ground about entrance to nest in ground; *Atta*, fungus ant, feeds on fungus cultured on organic debris in underground galleries; *Formica*, builds large "anthills" of debris over nest in ground; *F. sanguinea* rears workers of *F. rufa* to serve as slaves; *Iridomyrmex humilis*, Argentine ant, a great household and agricultural pest, colonizes and attends aphids and scale insects to obtain honeydew as food; *Camponotus*, carpenter ant, large, in dead wood or ground. Many beetles and other insects inhabit ant nests, including (1) scavengers or predators; (2) indifferent guests; (3) true guests, which are fed and even reared by ants; and (4) parasites.

MUTILLIDAE. "VELVET ANTS." Body black, densely covered with colored hair; males winged, females wingless; larvae parasitic in cocoons of solitary wasps and bees. *Mutilla*.

SCOLIIDAE. VESPOID WASPS. Large, black, hairy; larvae parasitic in white grubs or larvae of other scarabaeid beetles. *Tiphia*.

CHRYSIDIDAE. CUCKOO WASPS. Integument hard; colors metallic; abdomen flat beneath, curled under body when attacked; larvae in nest cells of solitary wasps and bees. *Chrysis*.

EUMENIDAE. SOLITARY TRUE WASPS. Make solitary nests, of mud or in plant stems, each with one egg stocked with prey that is stung but not killed to feed larva. *Eumenes*.

VESPIDAE. COLONIAL WASPS. Sting powerful; young females overwinter, and each starts colony that lasts 1 season; nest of paper (chewed wood) with horizontal combs of cells to contain larvae;

many small females or workers; males produced in late summer from unfertilized eggs; adults feed on nectar, honeydew, or fruit juices; young carnivorous. *Polistes*, nest flat and open below, 1 female; *Vespa diabolica*, yellow jacket, nest in or above ground, combs enclosed by paper walls; *V. maculata*, white-faced hornet, 12 to 19 mm. long, nests large, enclosed, in trees.

SPHECIDAE. MUD-DAUBER WASPS. Abdomen slender, long, enlarged at end; nests in ground or mud cells provisioned with stung prey for food of larvae. *Sphex; Sceliphron*.

BEMBICIDAE. BEE-LIKE WASPS. Live in separate nests but close together; larvae in unsealed cells, fed daily by adults. *Bembix*.

ANDRENIDAE. MINING BEES. Each female prepares a nest, lays eggs, and feeds nectar and pollen to larvae; nests close together, some with common entrance guarded by a sentinel bee. *Andrena*.

MEGACHILIDAE. LEAF-CUTTING and MASON BEES. Resemble hive bees, head broad, tongue long, mandibles sharp; nests in plant stems, wood, or earth, and provisioned with nectar and pollen. *Megachile*, leaf-cutter bee, nests lined with discs cut from leaves; *Anthidium*, mason bee, nests of mud, cells lined with plant down, etc.

XYLOCOPIDAE. CARPENTER BEES. Large, black, resemble bumblebees but less hairy; powerful mandibles used to tunnel in solid wood for nest cells. *Xylocopa*.

BOMBIDAE (Bremidae). BUMBLEBEES (HUMBLEBEES). Medium to large, densely haired; tongue long, hence useful in pollinating clover and many other crop plants; overwintering young queens establish new colonies that last 1 season, with queen, many worker females, and drones (males); colonies in mouse nests or rodent burrows surrounded by grass, with wax cells to contain larvae and open cells ("honeypots") for food storage. *Bombus (Bremus)*.

APIDAE. HONEYBEES. Eyes hairy; workers with pollen baskets on hind legs; native to Old World, probably Asia. *Apis mellifera*, hive bee (Figs. 26-12 to 26-14).

REFERENCES

The literature of entomology comprises a great number and variety of books, pamphlets, and periodicals. Besides the many works on general entomology, others are devoted to individual orders, families, or species and to the insect faunas of particular regions, large or small. The *Journal of Economic Entomology* and the *Annals of the Entomological Society of America* are two of the principal periodicals in the United States; others deal with special groups or regions. The *Annual Review of Entomology* summarizes recent research in selected fields. Many bulletins, circulars, and reports of the Federal government and of the state agricultural experiment stations contain the results of new investigations and provide information for controlling species of economic importance to agriculture, domestic animals, and the public health.

BISHOPP, F. C., and OTHERS. 1952. Insects, The Yearbook of Agriculture. Washington, D.C., Government Printing Office. xviii + 780 pp., 72 col. pls., many figs.

BRUES, C. T., A. L. MELANDER, and F. M. CARPENTER. 1954. Classification of insects. Rev. ed. Cambridge, Mass., *Museum of Comparative Zoology Bulletin*, vol. 108, v + 917 pp., 1,219 figs.

CHU, H. F. 1949. How to know the immature insects. Dubuque, Iowa, William C. Brown Co. 234 pp., 631 figs.

ESSIG, E. O. 1926. Insects of western North America. New York, The Macmillan Co. xi + 1,035 pp., 766 figs.

FOLSOM, J. W., and R. A. WARDLE. 1934. Entomology with special reference to its ecological aspects. 4th ed. Philadelphia, The Blakiston Co. ix + 605 pp., 5 pls., 308 figs.

GRASSÉ, PIERRE-P., and OTHERS. 1949. Traité de zoologie. Paris, Masson et Cie. Insects, vol. 9, 1,117 pp., 752 figs.; vol. 10 (2 pts.), 1,948 pp., 1,648 figs. Incomplete.

HERMS, W. B. 1950. Medical entomology . . . man and animals. 4th ed. New York, The Macmillan Co. xvi + 643 pp., 191 figs.

HOWARD, L. O. 1930. A history of applied entomology (somewhat anecdotal). *Smithsonian Miscellaneous Collections*, vol. 84, viii + 564 pp., 51 pls.

IMMS, A. D. 1947. Insect natural history. London, William Collins Sons & Co. xviii + 317 pp., 72 pls., 40 figs.

———. 1957. A general textbook of entomology. 9th ed. London, Methuen & Co. Ltd. xii + 876 pp., 609 figs. Rev. by O. W. Richards and R. G. Davies.

JAQUES, H. E. 1947. How to know the insects. 2d ed. Dubuque, Iowa, William C. Brown Co. 205 pp., 411 figs.

JOHANNSEN, O. A., and F. H. BUTT. 1941. Embryology of the insects and myriapods. New York, McGraw-Hill Book Co., Inc. 462 pp., illus.

METCALF, C. L., and W. P. FLINT. 1951. Destructive and useful insects. 3d ed., rev. by R. L. Metcalf. New York, McGraw-Hill Book Co., Inc. xiv + 1,071 pp., 584 figs.

ROEDER, K. D. (editor). 1953. Insect physiology. New York, John Wiley & Sons, Inc. xiv + 1,100 pp., 257 figs.

ROSS, H. H. 1956. A textbook of entomology. 2d ed. New York, John Wiley & Sons, Inc. xi + 519 pp., 402 figs.

SNODGRASS, R. E. 1935. Principles of insect morphology. New York, McGraw-Hill Book Co., Inc. ix + 667 pp., 319 figs.

STEINHAUS, E. A. 1946. Insect microbiology. Ithaca, Comstock Publishing Associates, Inc. xi + 763 pp., 256 figs. Microbes associated with insects and ticks.

———. 1949. Principles of insect pathology. New York, McGraw-Hill Book Co., Inc. xi + 757 pp., 219 figs. Diseases of insects.

VON FRITSCH, KARL. 1950. Bees: their vision, chemical senses, and language. Ithaca, Cornell University Press. xiii + 119 pp., 61 figs.

WHEELER, W. M. 1928. The social insects, their origin and evolution. New York, Harcourt, Brace & Co. xviii + 378 pp., 79 figs.

WIGGLESWORTH, V. B. 1950. The principles of insect physiology. 4th ed. London, Methuen & Co., Ltd. viii + 544 pp., illus.

27 PHYLUM ARTHROPODA
Miscellaneous

This chapter deals with arthropods other than the Classes CRUSTACEA and INSECTA. It includes the spiders and their allies (Subphylum CHELICERATA), the centipedes and millipedes (Subphylum MANDIBULATA in part), the peculiar worm-like *Peripatus* (Subphylum ONYCHOPHORA), and some groups of uncertain position as to relationships and classification. Figure 25-1 and Table 25-1 show some features of likeness and difference between the major subdivisions of the ARTHROPODA; other characteristics are given in the classification ending the present chapter.

SUBPHYLUM CHELICERATA. SPIDERS AND THEIR ALLIES

The CHELICERATA (Gr. *chele*, claw + *keros*, horn) is a varied assemblage comprising the spiders, mites, ticks, harvestmen, scorpions, whip scorpions, pseudoscorpions, king crabs, and others (Figs. 27-1, 27-2). Members of this group differ in body form and the nature of their appendages. They are mostly free-living terrestrial animals of small size, and the great majority are more numerous in warm dry regions than elsewhere. Many possess poison glands and poison claws or "fangs" by which they kill insects and other small animals, whose fluids and soft tissues they suck as food. The spiders and some other arachnids have also spe-

cial glands that secrete fine threads of silk. This material is used to build nests, shelters, and egg cases and for other purposes.

Some members of this subphylum, because of their peculiar appearance, are feared by many persons, although the great majority are quite harmless. Spiders and some others are actually beneficial to man because they feed upon various kinds of insects. A few spiders and scorpions, however, do have bites or stings that may cause man serious illness and even death. Some mites injure plants, and certain mites and ticks which parasitize man and animals produce injury, sickness, and death. Several kinds of ticks are the intermediate hosts for protozoans and viruses that cause particular diseases (par. 16-17; Table 26-1).

There is an age-old belief in southern Europe that the bite of a "tarantula" (lycosid spider?) will be followed by melancholy and death unless cured by dancing, especially to the lively music of a "tarantella," whereby the poison will be eliminated by perspiration!

27-1. Characteristics.[1] 1. Body usually of distinct cephalothorax and abdomen (except ACARINA); typically with six pairs of jointed [2] appendages: chelicerae, pedipalpi, and four pairs of legs, all on cephalothorax; no antennae or mandibles.

2. Mouth parts and digestive tract mainly suited for sucking; some with poison glands.

[1] Compare ARTHROPODA, Table 25-1.
[2] For brevity the divisions or segments of appendages are referred to as "joints"—three-jointed, etc.

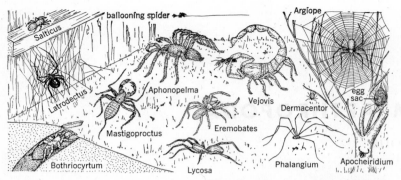

Fig. 27-1. Class ARACHNIDA. Some common types in their characteristic habitats; not to scale. Order SCORPIONIDA: *Vejovis*, scorpion. Order PEDIPALPI: *Mastigoproctus*, whip scorpion. Order SOLPUGIDA: *Eremobates*, sun spider. Order PSEUDOSCORPIONIDA: *Apocheiridium*, false scorpion. Order PHALANGIDA: *Phalangium*, "harvestman." Order ACARINA: *Dermacentor*, tick. Order ARA-NEAE: *Bothriocyrtum*, trap-door spider; *Aphonopelma*, American "tarantula"; *Lycosa*, wolf spider; *Latrodectus*, black widow spider; *Argiope*, orb-weaving spider with egg case; *Salticus*, jumping spider.

3. Respiration by lung books, tracheae, or gill books.

4. Excretion by paired Malpighian tubules, or coxal glands, or both.

5. Nervous system with dorsal ganglia (brain) and ventral nerve cord having paired ganglia, or else concentrated anteriorly; eyes usually simple and in pairs; tactile hairs or bristles on body.

6. Sexes mostly separate; sex opening single and anterior on abdomen; fertilization usually internal; mainly oviparous; development direct or through a larval stage.

7. Chiefly terrestrial and solitary; either free-living and predaceous, or parasitic.

The CHELICERATA are of ancient origin, some stocks having been developed in Cambrian time. The lack of antennae and mandibles is a distinctive characteristic. The trilobites of the Paleozoic differed in having biramous append-

ages and one pair of antennae. The ONYCHOPH-ORA have a slender body with one pair of unjointed legs per somite and a pair of sensory "preantennae." Among the MANDIBULATA (with mandibles) the CRUSTACEA have biramous appendages and usually two pairs of antennae, the INSECTA have wings (absent in some) and three pairs of legs; and the MYRI-APODA are slender with one or two pairs of jointed legs on each segment. None of the other small arthropod groups can be confused with the CHELICERATA.

27-2. Size. The king crab (*Limulus*) grows to 500 mm. in length. Most spiders are under 25 mm. long, the extremes being *Microlinypheus*,

Fig. 27-2. Subphylum CHELICERATA. Representatives of eight groups in ventral view (not to scale), showing general form, division between cephalothorax and abdomen (broken line), chelicerae (black), pedipalpi (outlined), and legs (stippled), with joints in each. (Compare Fig. 25-1.)

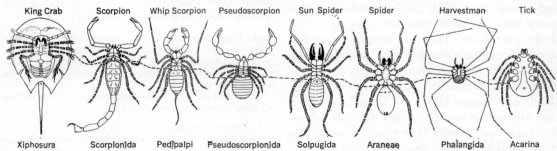

King Crab   Scorpion   Whip Scorpion   Pseudoscorpion   Sun Spider   Spider   Harvestman   Tick

Xiphosura   Scorpionida   Pedipalpi   Pseudoscorpionida   Solpugida   Araneae   Phalangida   Acarina

which is under 1.0 mm., and *Theraphosa lebondii,* which grows to 90 mm. long. The smallest scorpion (*Microbuthus pusillus*) is 13 mm. long and the largest (*Pandinus dictator*) 160 mm. The SOLPUGIDA are 8 to 70 mm. long, *Galeodes caspius* being the largest. The smallest mites are under 0.5 mm. long, and the largest tick (*Amblyomma*) is only 30 mm. in length.

CLASS ARACHNIDA

The arachnids (Gr. *arachne,* spider) include spiders, scorpions, pseudoscorpions, whip scorpions, solpugids, ticks, mites, and a few obscure groups. In general, they are terrestrial, with two pairs of mouth parts (chelicerae and pedipalps), and four pairs of legs, thus differing from the other chelicerate classes—the MEROSTOMATA, EURYPTERIDA, and PYCNOGONIDA.

27-3. Order Araneae, the spiders. More than 20,000 species of spiders are known. They live in various habitats, from sea level to the highest mountains, from the seashore and fresh-water swamps to the driest of deserts, among rocks, in or on sandy or other soils, in forests, bushes, and grasses, and about buildings. The following general account will apply to most common species.

27-4. External features.[1] The body consists of a distinct *cephalothorax* and an *abdomen,* both rounded and unsegmented and joined by a slender "waist," or *peduncle.* The cephalothorax commonly has eight simple *eyes* anteriorly, and its ventral surface bears six pairs of appendages. Each of the two *chelicerae* has a basal segment and a terminal claw-like fang with a duct near its tip, connecting to a poison gland within the cephalothorax. The pair of *pedipalpi* are short, six-jointed, and leg-like, with enlarged bases that form "maxillae" used to squeeze and chew the food; in mature males the tip becomes a specialized container for the transfer of sperm. There are four pairs of *walking legs,* each of seven joints (coxa, trochanter, femur, patella, tibia, metatarsus, and tarsus) and ending in two or three toothed claws; on some spiders the tip bears a pad of "hairs" (scopula) by which the animal may cling to a wall or similar surface. All external parts are covered by cuticle bearing many bristles and hairs, some of sensory nature.

The external openings are as follows: (1) The minute **mouth,** between the maxillae; all others are ventral on the abdomen and include (2) the **genital opening** anteriorly in the mid-line and covered by a plate, or epigynum; (3) the slit-like entrances to the two or four **lung books,** or respiratory organs, at each side of the epigynum; (4) a **spiracle** anterior to the anus and connecting to short tracheae; (5) the two or three pairs of bluntly conical **spinnerets,** sometimes jointed, each with many fine tubes through which the "silk" for webs and other purposes is secreted from glands within the abdomen; and (6) the terminal **anus.**

27-5. Internal structure (Fig. 27-3). The **digestive system** comprises (1) the mouth; (2) a slender esophagus connecting to (3) a sucking stomach operated by muscles extending from its dorsal surface to the cephalothorax; (4) the main stomach in the cephalothorax, with five pairs of caeca, or pouches, one dorsal and one toward each leg; (5) the straight intestine in the abdomen, which is joined by ducts of (6) the much-branched digestive gland ("liver") and extends to (7) the rectum where (8) an enlarged stercoral pocket connects just before (9) the anus.

The **circulatory system** is somewhat like that of insects; the heart is a slender, muscular, and contractile tube dorsally placed in the abdomen, with three pairs of openings, or ostia, and surrounded by a tubular pericardium. From the heart a caudal aorta extends backward, and an anterior aorta sends paired arteries to the stomach, legs, eyes, and poison glands. The colorless blood contains amoeboid corpuscles and dissolved hemocyanin as a respiratory pigment. The heart pumps blood through the aortae and into sinuses among the tissues;

[1] Details of structure may be examined closely on a live spider enclosed in a petri dish under a binocular microscope.

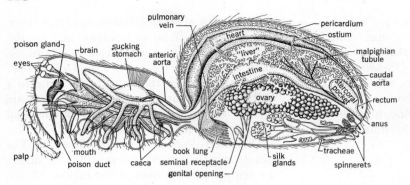

Fig. 27-3. Class ARACHNIDA. Structure of a spider as seen with left side of body removed. (*Modified from Leuckart.*)

thence it passes to the lung books for aeration and returns by "pulmonary veins" to the pericardial cavity to reenter the heart through the ostia.

Respiration is accomplished mainly by the **lung books**, which are peculiar to arachnids; each is of 15 to 20 leaf-like horizontal plates containing fine blood vessels. Air entering the external slit on the abdomen circulates between the plates, where the O_2–CO_2 exchange occurs. The **tracheae**, if present, are like those of insects but restricted to the abdomen. **Excretion** is performed by paired **Malpighian tubules** connected posteriorly to the intestine and by a pair or two of **coxal glands** in the floor of the cephalothorax that empty by ducts between the legs. These glands are considered homologous with the green glands in crustaceans.

The **nervous system** is concentrated, comprising a bilobed ganglion above the esophagus that joins by two thick connectives to a large ventral ganglionic mass, whence nerves radiate to all organs. Paired ganglia occur in the abdomen of young spiders, but not in adults. The **eyes** are simple, with a chitinous lens, epithelial layer, optic rods, and retinal cells; vision is keener in some spiders than in others. The pedipalpi and many of the external hairs are evidently sensitive to touch. The response to sound is uncertain, although some spiders have sound-producing mechanisms. The sense of smell seems well developed and may reside in minute "lyriform organs" on the body and appendages.

The sexes are separate and often unlike in markings and size, females being larger. The **male** has two testes below the intestine that join by coiled vasa efferentia to a single seminal vesicle leading to the genital opening. In the **female** the two ovaries are large and hollow, each with an oviduct joining the single vagina; two lateral seminal receptacles attach to the vagina.

27-6. Natural history. Spiders are free-living, solitary, and predaceous creatures that feed mainly on insects. Hunting spiders either wait for or wander in search of food, run it down (*Lycosa*), or jump on it (*Salticus*). Other spiders entrap their prey in webs. Small prey is grasped, killed by a quick stroke of the poison-bearing fangs, and "eaten" (sucked out). Larger items of food may first be bound in silk shroud or fastened to the web and then killed. The poison kills invertebrates quickly, and that of some large spiders (*Eurypelma*) will overcome small vertebrates. When food is available, spiders feed often, but in captivity some may fast for many weeks. In the majority of species, individuals live only about a year. The enemies of spiders are mainly birds, lizards, and certain wasps; some ichneumonids (HYMENOPTERA) oviposit in spider cocoons where their larvae hatch quickly and consume many spider eggs.

Spider silk is a proteid secretion of special abdominal glands that passes out the many microscopic tubes in the spinnerets and solidifies into a thread upon contact with the air (Fig. 27-4); it serves many purposes. Terrestrial hunting spiders pay out a "dragline" as they travel. Spiderlings are dispersed by climbing to some height and spinning a long thread

Fig. 27-4. Structural details of spiders. Ctenid spider: *A.* Front of head. *B.* Spinnerets on abdomen. Black widow spider: *C.* Front of head with enlarged pedipalpi of male. *D.* End of leg with claws hooked on web.

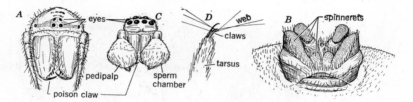

on which they are carried by the wind; trees sometimes become covered by such gossamer, and numbers of "ballooning" young spiders are occasionally seen by ships at sea. The most primitive webs are scarcely more than many draglines radiating from a spider's retreat (*Segistra*). Some (*Amaurobius*) add a sheet of fine silk "carded" by a plate (cribellum) anterior to the spinnerets, and others form a hammock-like sheet over a definite framework (*Tegenaria*). Some webs are irregular networks of silk (*Latrodectus*). The orb weavers (*Argiope, Epeira, Miranda*) outline a flat rectangular framework within which radial threads are neatly spaced; and then a spiral of silk, bearing sticky droplets, is attached for the capture of prey. The webs are repaired or renewed at frequent intervals. Snares, shelters, nests for hibernating or mating, and egg cocoons are spun with various kinds of silk by different species.

27-7. Reproduction. The male, when mature, spins a small web on which a droplet of fluid containing sperm is deposited and then taken into cavities in his pedipalps (Fig. 27-4). He then seeks a female and may go through a nuptial performance with her before transferring the sperm by inserting his pedipalps in her genital opening. The female may kill and eat the male after mating, but this is not his invariable end. Later she spins a padded cocoon in which the eggs are laid. Females of some species fasten the cocoon to or near the web, and others carry it about; the female *Lycosa* carries the young on her abdomen for some days after they hatch. The black widow (*Latrodectus mactans*), for example, lays 25 to over 900 eggs in a cocoon and produces one to nine cocoons per season. Her eggs hatch in 10 to 14 days, and the young remain in the sac for 2 to 6 weeks, leaving after the first molt. Males undergo

about five molts before becoming sexually mature, and females seven or eight. At successive molts the spiders increase in size and change in form, proportions, and color pattern.

27-8. Other Arachnida (Figs. 27-1, 27-2). The scorpions (SCORPIONIDA) are elongate, with big pincer-ended pedipalpi and a long 12-segmented abdomen bearing a terminal sharp poison claw. They inhabit warm dry regions (to 45°N. in North America), hiding under stones or in shallow burrows by day and running actively at night to catch the insects, spiders, and scorpions used for food. Prey is grasped by the chelicerae and torn slowly apart by the pedipalpi, larger animals first being paralyzed by the sting. The comb-like pectines, ventral on the abdomen, are evidently tactile organs. Mating is preceded by a courtship dance, and the female produces living young, which ride for some days on her abdomen.

Whip scorpions or vinegaroons (PEDIPALPI) somewhat resemble scorpions but lack poison; their large pedipalpi have pincers, and the first legs are tactile; some have a slender abdominal whip. They live in warm countries, are nocturnal, and prey on insects. The pseudoscorpions (PSEUDOSCORPIONIDA) are like miniature scorpions but lack a sting. Silk from glands near the chelicerae is spun into nests for molt and hibernation. They live under stones, moss, or bark, and some in books or furniture; their food is of minute insects. Sometimes they are abundant—150,000 per acre in North Carolina. The sun spiders (SOLPUGIDA) are of spider-like form but lack a "waist"; the pedipalpi are leg-like, and the enlarged chelicerae give them an undeserved reputation as dangerous. They lack both poison and silk glands. Their habitat is in warm dry regions. Harvestmen, or daddy longlegs (PHALANGIDA), have compact ovoid bodies

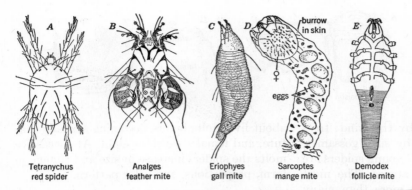

Tetranychus
red spider

Analges
feather mite

Eriophyes
gall mite

Sarcoptes
mange mite

Demodex
follicle mite

Fig. 27-5. Order ACARINA. Some representative mites. All enlarged, not to same scale. (*After Banks, 1905.*)

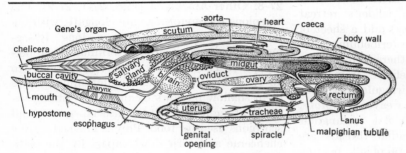

Fig. 27-6. Order ACARINA. Female Rocky Mountain spotted fever tick (*Dermacentor andersoni*); internal structure, from the left side. (*After J. R. Douglas.*)

and extremely long legs by which they run readily. They lack poison but have "stink" glands for protection. They are common in temperate regions, and their food includes small insects.

The mites and ticks (Order ACARINA) are small to microscopic, with the head, thorax, and abdomen fused closely and unsegmented. The integument is membranous or leathery, sometimes with hard plates or shields. A slender anterior region, often jointed to the body, bears the mouth parts. The eight legs are laterally placed and often bear bristles. The sexes are separate. In most species there hatches from the *egg* a six-legged *larva* that feeds and molts into an eight-legged *nymph* having no genital opening. With further feeding and molt, this transforms into the *adult* sexual stage.

Mites (Fig. 27-5) abound as to species and individuals in soil, humus, stored foods, fresh and salt waters, on plants, and as parasites of both plants and animals. Some feed on fresh or decaying plant and animal materials, others suck plant juices, and still others subsist on

the skin, blood, or other tissues of land vertebrates.

The ticks (Figs. 27-6, 27-7) feed on the blood of reptiles, birds, and mammals. Upon finding a host, the tick's mouth parts pierce the skin, and the sucking pharynx draws in blood, which is kept fluid by a salivary anticoagulant; its stomach expands until "as full as a tick." In spring the female tick deposits her eggs under shelter on the ground, and hatching occurs a month or so later. The larvae climb on bushes to wait for appropriate hosts, to which they fasten; then they drop off after feeding and to molt. In turn, the nymphs and then the adults do likewise. Ticks can survive long periods without feeding, some for a year or more if they fail to find a host animal. The spotted fever tick normally requires 2 years to complete its life cycle. Adults of the soft or argasine ticks hide by day and emerge at night to feed briefly, whereas all stages of ixodine ticks remain in place on their hosts for some time. In the latter the males are smaller, with a scutum covering the whole dorsal surface; the scutum on females is smaller and anterior.

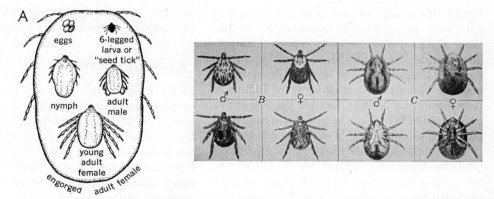

Fig. 27-7. Order Acarina. Ticks. *A*. Texas cattle-fever tick (*Boöphilus annulatus*), × 5. Smaller stages inside the outline of an engorged female. (*After U.S. Department of Agriculture.*) *B*. Rocky Mountain spotted fever tick (*Dermacentor andersoni*, Family Ixodidae). *C*. Relapsing fever tick (*Ornithodorus hermsi*, Family Argasidae). Upper row, dorsal; lower row, ventral. (*From W. B. Herms.*)

27-9. Relations to man. The bite of most spiders is harmless to mankind. Even the large American "tarantulas" (*Eurypelma*) cause no more injury than a wasp. Females of the Genus *Latrodectus*, however, are distinctly dangerous. Of four species in various parts of the world, the black widow spider (*L. mactans*) occurs from southern Canada to South America and the Hawaiian Islands, living in cliffs, piles of rock and lumber, and in outdoor privies and other buildings. The adult female is shiny black, with an hourglass mark of red beneath the abdomen. Upward of 400 human cases of poisoning by this spider have been recorded in the United States, with about 5 per cent of mortality; most of these are in California, where the black widow causes more poisonings than rattlesnakes. Severe pain, muscle spasms in the abdomen, and restlessness are common symptoms. Serum from previous cases and antivenin are used in treatment, with magnesium chloride injections to relieve the muscle spasms.

Some scorpions in the southwestern states and in the tropics have powerful venom. The state of Durango, Mexico, between 1890 and 1931 reported over 1,700 deaths, chiefly of children, from scorpions. Treatment by antivenin and bounties for destruction of scorpions decreased the danger in later years. The hairy scorpion (*Hadrurus hirsutus*) of the southwestern United States often stings people, causing severe but transient pain.

Of the mites that suck plant juices, the red spider (*Tetranychus telarius*) causes blisters and injures leaves of orchard trees; the blister mite (*Eriophyes*) injures buds and fruits of pears, apples, grapes, and other crops; and the bulb mite (*Rhizoglyphus hyacinthi*) tunnels in bulbs and roots, whereby fungi and bacteria are able to enter. The itch mite (*Sarcoptes scabei*) burrows in and irritates human skin; related species cause mange in hogs, dogs, and other mammals; the scab mite (*Psoroptes communis*) produces serious damage to sheep; and the chicken mite (*Dermanyssus gallinae*) causes unthriftiness in fowls.

Ticks, when numerous, may make the host anemic and liable to various diseases or may cause its death. Common species are the fowl tick (*Argas persicus*) on poultry, and the spinose ear tick (*Ornithodorus megnini*) and dog or "wood" ticks (*Dermacentor variabilis* and *D. occidentalis*), which infest both wild and domestic mammals and man. The salivary secretions injected in the biting of some ticks produce severe, slow-healing wounds; certain ticks are intermediate hosts of disease. *D. andersoni* transmits the rickettsia organism causing

Rocky Mountain spotted fever, a disease of native rodents and larger mammals in the arid West (Montana to eastern Oregon) that produces serious illness and high mortality in man. Since 1931 spotted fever has also been recognized in various eastern states from Illinois to New Jersey and North Carolina. Vaccine grown on incubated hen's eggs is now made to protect persons exposed to tick bite. Texas cattle fever of the southern states is due to a sporozoan (*Babesia bigemina*) carried by a cattle tick (*Boophilus annulatus*). In both these diseases the infective agent passes from the female tick to her eggs. Texas cattle fever was the first disease in which an arthropod vector was proved to be the essential agent transmitting the causative organism from infected to healthy hosts.

CLASS MEROSTOMATA

27-10. King crabs.[1] The Subclass XIPHOSURA includes many fossil forms and four living species of king or horseshoe crabs. Of these, *Limulus polyphemus* (Fig. 27-8) inhabits shallow quiet waters of the Atlantic coast from Nova Scotia to Yucatán. Over its body is a shiny dark-brown unsegmented carapace that is arched and of horseshoe shape and joined to a broad hexagonal abdomen with lateral movable spines and a bayonet-like telson. Besides the six pairs of appendages on the cephalothorax, as in other arachnids, the abdomen bears six pairs of broad thin appendages joined medially. On the hind surface of the last five pairs are exposed gill books, each of 150 to 200 leaves containing blood vessels for respiration. A pair of coxal glands in the cephalothorax serves for excretion. The nerve ring about the mouth connects to a ventral nerve cord with ganglia. On the carapace are two lateral compound eyes and two medial simple eyes.

The king crab burrows by shoving its carapace into the sand and pushing with its telson and appendages. It can walk on the bottom, can swim by flapping the abdominal plates, and may hop by aid of the telson. It is active by night and feeds on nereid worms and soft mollusks, which are grasped by the chelicerae, aided by the pincers on other appendages, and chewed by the bases of the legs (gnathobases) which serve as jaws. In early summer the smaller male mounts the female, and groups of small eggs, fertilized externally, are deposited shallowly in sand between the tide lines. The larva at hatching resembles a trilobite in having a segmented abdomen without appendages

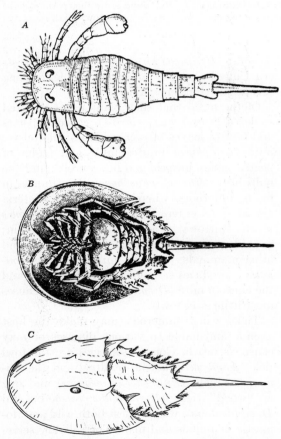

Fig. 27-8. Class MEROSTOMATA. *A.* Extinct eurypterid (†*Eurypterus,* Subclass †EURYPTERIDA), in dorsal view. *B, C.* The living king crab (*Limulus polyphemus,* Subclass XIPHOSURA). *B,* ventral view; *C,* laterodorsal view; length to 18 inches.

[1] Aquatic members of the CHELICERATA, living and fossil, are variously grouped. Class MEROSTOMATA includes the king crabs (Subclass XIPHOSURA) and eurypterids (Subclass †EURYPTERIDA), but these groups are sometimes recognized as separate classes and the name MEROSTOMATA has been used for the king crabs alone. Sea spiders (Class PYCNOGONIDA) sometimes are separated from the CHELICERATA.

or telson, but these features change at the first molt. The XIPHOSURA date from the Cambrian, and the Genus *Limulus* from Triassic time.

27-11. Eurypterids. Subclass †EURYPTERIDA (Fig. 27-8) was a dominant group in seas of Paleozoic times, before the rise of the cephalopods. In form they were somewhat scorpionlike, some being up to 9 feet long. They probably swam or crawled on the bottom of salt and brackish waters.

CLASS PYCNOGONIDA

27-12. Sea spiders (Fig. 27-9). These marine animals are spider-like in appearance but remotely related to other arthropods. The body is small, with 4 (rarely 5 or 6) pairs of legs, the mouth at the end of a slender proboscis, and typically there are three pairs of anterior appendages. Sea spiders occur from the shore to depths of 12,000 feet and are most abundant in polar waters. They feed on fluids and soft parts of hydroid colonies and other fleshy animals. Males carry the eggs during early stages of development.

SUBPHYLUM MANDIBULATA

This is far the largest subdivision of the arthropods, including the CRUSTACEA (Chap. 25), INSECTA (Chap. 26), together with centi-

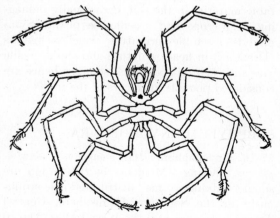

Fig. 27-9. A sea spider (*Nymphon*, Subclass PYCNOGONIDA).

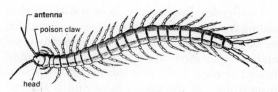

Fig. 27-10. A centipede (Subclass CHILOPODA).

pedes, millipedes, and their allies. All are alike in having the first pair of jaws as mandibles, although these structures are variously modified.

CLASS MYRIAPODA

Myriapods have a long slender body of two parts: the head with one pair each of antennae and mandibles, and one or two pairs of maxillae; the trunk has one or two pairs of legs per somite. The group is sometimes divided according to the position of the sex opening—posterior in centipedes (CHILOPODA) but anterior in the millipedes and others (DIPLOPODA, SYMPHYLA, PAUROPODA).

SUBCLASS CHILOPODA. CENTIPEDES

27-13. Structure and habits. The centipedes (Fig. 27-10) are of slender, elongate, segmented form and are flattened dorsoventrally. The head bears a pair of long antennae with 12 or more joints, a pair of mandibles, and two pairs of maxillae. In different species, the body is of 15 to 173 somites. The first somite bears a pair of four-jointed poison claws, and on each of the other somites except the last two is a pair of small seven-jointed walking legs. The digestive tract is straight, with two or three pairs of salivary glands at the mouth and two long Malpighian tubules posteriorly for excretion. The heart extends the length of the body, surrounded by pericardium, with a pair of ostia and of lateral arteries in each somite. In some somites there are spiracles joining a fused system of tracheal tubes that serve for respiration. The sexes are separate, each having one dorsal gonad and paired accessory glands connected to a ventral genital opening near the posterior end.

Centipedes live mainly in warm countries, hiding by day under stones or logs and running swiftly about at night to prey on earthworms and insects; large species may capture small lizards or mice. Prey is killed quickly by poison from a duct in the poison claw and is chewed by the mandibles. Some centipedes lay eggs, and others are viviparous. The young resemble adults, with the same or a lesser number of somites. Some tropical species are 6 to 8 inches long, and their bites are painful to man. The small agile house centipedes (*Cermatia*) have 15 pairs of extremely long fragile legs. They eat insects and are harmless to man.

SUBCLASS DIPLOPODA. MILLIPEDES, OR "THOUSAND-LEGGED WORMS"

27-14. Structure and habits. The millipedes have cylindrical bodies of many somites and the body wall includes deposits of lime salts (Fig. 27-11). Many are brightly colored. The head bears two clumps of many simple eyes and a pair each of short antennae, jaws, and maxillae. The thorax is short, of four single somites, each with one pair of legs. The long abdomen has 20 to over 100 double somites, each containing two pairs of spiracles, ostia, and nerve ganglia and bearing two pairs of seven-jointed legs. The digestive and circulatory systems are somewhat as in centipedes. There are many separate tracheae, each a tufted pouch connected to a spiracle in front of a leg. The gonad is single and ventral, with a duct opening on the third somite. The male has modified appendages (gonopods) on the seventh somite. Fertilization is internal, and each egg is enclosed in a covering of regurgitated food.

Millipedes live in humid dark places under stones or beneath or within rotting logs and shun the light. They travel slowly, with the body extended, and test the route of travel

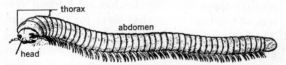

Fig. 27-11. A millipede (*Spirobolus*, Subclass DIPLOPODA). (*From Haupt.*)

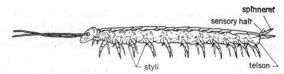

Fig. 27-12. The garden centipede (*Scutigerella*, Subclass SYMPHYLA), to 6 mm. long. (*After Michelbacher.*)

with the antennae. The many legs seemingly move in a series of waves from behind forward. Their food is of dead plant materials, but they also will eat animal matter. Some species roll up in a spiral when disturbed. From some enemies they are protected by a series of "stink" glands that secrete an objectionable fluid. The young at hatching have but six somites and three pairs of legs, others being added in front of the anal somite at the successive molts (up to 10) during growth.

27-15. Other Mandibulata. Two other subclasses are commonly recognized among the MYRIAPODA. The PAUROPODA are minute soft-bodied creatures, usually with 11 trunk segments and 9 pairs of legs. They live in moist soil or among decaying leaves and are thought to feed on fungi. The SYMPHYLA (Fig. 27-12) includes the "garden centipedes" (*Scutigerella*) that have small slender pale-colored bodies with one pair of antennae, a pair of unjointed posterior appendages, and 12 pairs of jointed legs ending with double claws. The sex opening is on the third body somite. They live on vegetable material in the soil, occasionally damaging field crops and greenhouse plants. Symphylids resemble primitive wingless insects (DIPLURA) in head structure and the eversible sacs and styli on abdominal somites, hence are considered possible ancestors of the insects.

SUBPHYLUM ONYCHOPHORA

27-16. Onychophora (Gr. *onychus*, claw + *phorus*, bearing). Members of this group are small "walking worms" distributed discontinuously in the Southern Hemisphere, Central America, Mexico, and the West Indies. The 70 species live in dark moist places, in rock crev-

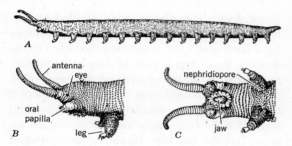

Fig. 27-13. Subphylum ONYCHOPHORA. *Peripatus*. *A*. Entire animal, slightly enlarged. *B*, *C*. Anterior end in lateral and ventral views. (*After Snodgrass*, 1938.)

ices, under stones, or beneath bark on rotting logs.

Peripatus capensis, a representative species, is about 50 mm. long, with a cylindrical body but no distinct head (Figs. 27-13, 27-14). The anterior end bears (1) two short *antennae;* (2) a pair of small *eyes* dorsally; (3) a midventral *mouth* rimmed by a fleshy fold and containing two small horny *jaws* used to tear or grind food; and (4) two blunt *oral papillae,* one at each side of the mouth. The *skin* is thin and lightly chitinized, with many transverse rings of fine papillae, each with a spine. The only features of segmentation are 15 to 43 pairs of short stumpy *legs,* each ending in two claws. At the inner base of each leg is a *nephridial opening.* The *anus* opens at the bluntly conical posterior end, preceded by the single ventral *genital opening.*

The *body wall* includes a thin cuticle, an epidermis, and a thin but complex series of muscle layers, circular, longitudinal, and transverse. Special muscles operate the legs and parts at the anterior end. Within the body is an undivided cavity, or *hemocoel,* containing the internal organs. At either side is a large and

much-branched *slime gland,* one opening through each oral papilla. These produce slimy mucus that can be squirted several inches and adheres to any object; it serves for defense and to capture insects and other small animals used as food. The *digestive system* is a straight tube, from mouth to anus, with a buccal cavity, two large salivary glands, muscular pharynx, short esophagus, long stomach-intestine, and rectum. The *circulatory system* consists of a single mid-dorsal vessel having muscle fibers in its walls and a pair of openings, or ostia, in each segment. Many delicate tubular ingrowths of the body wall, termed *tracheae,* presumably serve for respiration. The *excretory organs* are pairs of nephridia-like structures; each has a sac closed at its inner end, a ciliated funnel and duct, a slightly expanded bladder, and a nephridiopore. The *nervous system* comprises a pair of oval cerebral ganglia (the brain) above the mouth, several anterior nerves, two circumpharyngeal connectives, and a pair of separate ventral nerve cords without true ganglia that extend the length of the body and have many transverse connections. The eyes resemble those of annelids.

The sexes are separate, and the reproductive organs are paired, but with a single external opening. The *male* system includes paired testes, seminal vesicles, vasa deferentia, accessory glands, and an ejaculatory duct. In the *female* the paired ovaries and oviducts join to a common atrium at the genital opening. Most species of ONYCHOPHORA are viviparous, and part of each oviduct is specialized as a uterus where the embryos develop. In some forms a placenta-like trophoblast develops by which the embryo obtains nourishment from the uterine wall. A large female may produce 30 to 40

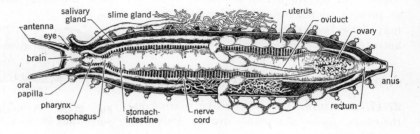

Fig. 27-14. *Peripatus*. Internal structure in dorsal view. (*After Snodgrass*, 1938.)

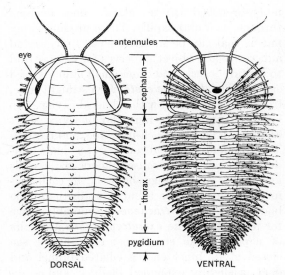

Fig. 27-15. Class †TRILOBITA. A trilobite (†*Triarthrus becki*) of Ordovician time. (*After Beecher.*)

young per year, which at birth resemble adults except in size and color.

The ONYCHOPHORA resemble annelids in the structure of the eyes, the segmental nephridia, the ciliated reproductive ducts, and the simple gut. Some of their arthropod characteristics comprise the jaws that are derived from appendages; the body cavity's being a hemocoel; the dorsal "heart" with ostia; the coelom reduced to the cavities of the nephridia and reproductive ducts; and the general structure of the reproductive organs. Their tracheae somewhat resemble those of insects. Features peculiar to the ONYCHOPHORA are the single pair of jaws, scant metamerism, arrangement of the tracheal apertures, nature of the skin, and separate nerve cords with no true ganglia. *Peripatus* is evidently of an ancient stock, as indicated by its relationship to certain Pre-Cambrian fossils and by its discontinuous distribution at present; it suggests that the ARTHROPODA may have been derived from an annelid-like ancestor.

SUBPHYLUM †TRILOBITA. TRILOBITES

27-17. Structure. These primitive marine arthropods, quite abundant during Paleozoic times, had a three-lobed body divided by two lengthwise dorsal furrows. They were covered by a hard shell that could be rolled up. On the distinct head was a pair of slender antennae, four pairs of biramous appendages, and often a pair of compound eyes. The thorax was of 2 to 29 short separate somites, and the abdominal somites were fused in a caudal plate. All somites but the last bore biramous limbs fringed by setae. The larva began as a pronauplius (protaspis) that gained somites in successive molts. Details of structure and growth have been learned from many entire and sectioned specimens, especially of †*Triarthrus becki* from the Ordovician shale near Rome, N.Y. (Figs. 14-10, 27-15).

Trilobites were differentiated in Pre-Cambrian time, were at a peak in the Cambrian and Ordovician, and died out in the Carboniferous save for one Permian genus. The adults were usually 50 to 75 mm. long, but different species were from 10 to 675 mm. in length. Many evidently burrowed or pushed through the bottom mud and sand of ancient seas; the larvae and some adults probably swam. Some species were local in occurrence, and others were cosmopolitan.

SUBPHYLUM PENTASTOMIDA

27-18. Pentastomida or Linguatulids (Fig. 27-16). These are worm-like, unsegmented parasites that live in the lungs and nasal cavities and elsewhere in vertebrates. They have two pairs of ventral hooks near the mouth. There are no special circulatory, respiratory, or excretory organs. Although highly specialized for parasitic life, these animals show affinities to the arthropods, having a chitinous cuticle, striated muscles, and a segmentally organized

Fig. 27-16. A linguatulid "worm" (*Porocephalus*, Subphylum PENTASTOMIDA).

nerve cord. The two pairs of "legs" in one group are like those of tardigrades and *Peripatus*.

SUBPHYLUM TARDIGRADA

27-19. Tardigrada (Fig. 27-17). The water bears or bear animalcules are creatures up to 1 mm. long with soft unsegmented bodies, a slightly constricted anterior region, and four pairs of short unjointed legs, each with two or four claws. The cuticle lacks true chitin. Some live in damp moss, others in water. Lacking seg-

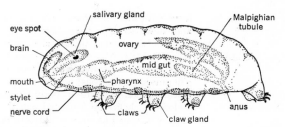

Fig. 27-17. A water bear (Subphylum TARDIGRADA); length to 1 mm.

mentation, they are doubtfully placed among the arthropods.

CLASSIFICATION

PHYLUM ARTHROPODA. JOINT-FOOTED ANIMALS. Body with head, thorax, and abdomen, of like or unlike somites, variously fused, and each typically with a pair of jointed appendages; exoskeleton containing chitin, molted entire at intervals; digestive tract complete, of fore-, mid-, and hind-gut; coelom reduced, body spaces a hemocoel; circulatory system lacunar, heart dorsal; respiration by gills, tracheae, lung books, or body surface; excretion by Malpighian tubules or coxal glands (nephridia rare); brain dorsal, nerve cord ventral, and paired ganglia in each somite or concentrated anteriorly; with simple and compound eyes, antennae, sensory hairs (and statocysts); sexes usually separate, gonads paired, and fertilization internal; cleavage superficial; commonly with larval stages and metamorphosis; some parthenogenesis; terrestrial or aquatic; free-living, sessile, commensal, or parasitic; fully 775,000 living species.

SUBPHYLUM 1. ONYCHOPHORA. Form slender, to 200 mm. long; anterior end (no head) with a pair each of eyes, short antennae, and blunt oral papillae; body somewhat cylindrical, unsegmented, with many crossrows of fine papillae and 15 to 43 pairs of stumpy legs; sex opening midventral before anus; terrestrial in moist places; Pre-Cambrian, Recent; 70 species. *Peripatus.*

SUBPHYLUM 2. †TRILOBITA. Body 10 to 675 mm. long, divided by 2 lengthwise furrows into 3 lobes; head distinct; abdomen of 2 to 29 somites and a fused caudal plate; all somites except last with biramous appendages fringed by setae; development with larval stages; marine. Cambrian to Permian; over 2,000 species. †*Triarthrus.*

SUBPHYLUM 3. CHELICERATA. Body usually of 2 parts (except ACARINA); cephalothorax unsegmented (except SOLPUGIDA), with 2 chelicerae bearing chelae or claws, 2 pedipalpi variously modified, and 4 pairs of legs; no antennae or true jaws; abdomen either of 6 to 14 somites or undivided and with no locomotor appendages (except MEROSTOMATA); respiration by gills, lung books, or tracheae; excretion by Malpighian tubules or coxal glands; sexes usually separate, male often smaller; sex opening anterior on abdomen; mostly oviparous; some with larval stages; mostly predaceous; chiefly terrestrial, some in fresh or salt waters.

CLASS 1. *MEROSTOMATA.* Cephalothorax with compound lateral eyes and broadly joined to abdomen on which are 5 or 6 pairs of appendages bearing exposed gills and a terminal bayonet-like telson; aquatic.

SUBCLASS 1. XIPHOSURA. KING CRABS. Cephalothorax an arched, horseshoe-shaped carapace; abdomen wide, unsegmented; chelicerae 3-jointed, pedipalpi and legs 6-jointed; marine, in shallow waters; Cambrian to Recent. *Limulus polyphemus*, Nova Scotia to Yucatán; *Tachypleus*, Japan to Malaysia and India.

SUBCLASS 2. †EURYPTERIDA (Gigantostraca). EURYPTERIDS. Carapace not expanded; abdomen of 12 somites, narrowed behind; Ordovician to Carboniferous. †*Eurypterus*, †*Pterygotus.*

CLASS 2. *PYCNOGONIDA* (Pantopoda). SEA SPIDERS. Mostly small to minute; body short, thin, of 1 cephalic and 3 or 4 trunk somites (or all fused in a disc), abdomen vestigial; 4 eyes; mouth suctorial, on long proboscis (homology with CHELICERATA doubtful); usually 3 pairs of head appendages, 1 pair being 10-jointed ovigerous (egg-bearing) legs; 4 (5 or 6) pairs of long thin walking legs, 8- or 9-jointed; sexes usually separate, eggs carried by male; development direct, or a 4-legged larva with metamorphosis; marine, on hydroids, anemones, or algae, or under stones, from tide lines down to more than 12,000 feet; Devonian, Recent; 500 species. *Pycnogonum; Nymphon; Colossendeis*, spreads to 24 inches; *Achelia*.

CLASS 3. *ARACHNIDA*. Abdomen lacks locomotor appendages; eyes all simple; cuticle often with sensory hairs or scales; pedipalpi usually sensory, modified in male for transfer of sperm to female; no gills; mostly oviparous; no metamorphosis (except ACARINA); chiefly terrestrial.

Order 1. Scorpionida. SCORPIONS. Body elongate; cephalothorax (prosoma) compact, broadly joined to abdomen; chelicerae 3-jointed, small; pedipalpi large, 6-jointed, with stout pincers; abdomen long, of 12 ring-like somites, 2d with pair of comb-like and tactile pectines; last 6 somites (metasoma) narrow, with a sharp poison claw at end; 4 pairs of lung books; viviparous; nocturnal, in warm regions; Silurian to Recent; 600 species. *Hadrurus hirsutus*, hairy scorpion, and *Vejovis spinigerus*, both to 100 mm. long, Texas to California; *V. boreus*, small, Nebraska to Nevada; *Centrurus*.

Order 2. Pedipalpi. WHIP SCORPIONS. Cephalothorax narrowly joined to flat abdomen of 12 somites; 8 eyes; chelicerae small, 2-jointed, chelate; pedipalpi strong, 6-jointed, tarsus of 1st leg a long, many-jointed feeler; nocturnal; Carboniferous to Recent; 150 species.

SUBORDER 1. UROPYGI. Abdomen with slender terminal whip-like flagellum; odoriferous glands. *Mastigoproctus giganteus*, to 130 mm. long, Florida to Arizona.

SUBORDER 2. AMBLYPYGI. Abdomen without a whip; no odoriferous glands. *Tarantula* (not a tarantula!), 20 mm. long, Florida, Texas, and California.

Order 3. Palpigrada. Size minute; chelicerae stout, 3-jointed, pedipalpi like walking legs; no eyes; abdomen oval, of 11 somites, with slender "tail" of 15 segments; live under stones. *Prokoenenia*, 2.5 mm. long, Texas, California.

Order 4. Araneae (Araneida). SPIDERS. Cephalothorax and abdomen both unsegmented, joined by narrow "waist"; chelicerae small, 2-jointed, a poison duct in terminal claw; pedipalpi short, 6-jointed, leg-like, the basal joint on each an enlarged "maxilla" for chewing; legs 7-jointed; eyes 8 to none; lung books 2 to 4, some with tracheae; tubercle-like spinnerets on abdomen extrude silk; oviparous, eggs commonly in cocoons; chiefly terrestrial; Carboniferous to Recent; 20,000 species. Some common families and members are (Fig. 27-1):

SUBORDER 1. ORTHOGNATHA (Mygalomorphae). Chelicerae horizontal.

CTENIZIDAE. TRAP-DOOR SPIDERS. Tarsal claws 3. *Pachylomerus* (southeastern United States) and *Bothriocyrtum* (California), nest hole in ground closed by hinged door of earth and silk.

THERAPHOSIDAE. BIRD SPIDERS. Tarsal claws 2; body size to 4 inches; live to 20 years. *Dugesiella, Aphonopelma* (*Eurypelma*), American "tarantula," to 48 mm. long, Arkansas and Texas to California; on ground or in trees; bite painful but not dangerous to man.

SUBORDER 2. LABIDOGNATHA (Araneomorphae). Chelicerae vertical.

THERIDIIDAE. Tarsal claws 3; legs without spines. *Latrodectus mactans*, black widow spider, web irregular, bite dangerous and sometimes fatal; *Theridion tepidariorum*, house spider, web flat, in corners.

AGELENIDAE, FUNNEL-WEB SPIDERS. Tarsal claws 3; legs with spines; eyes almost equal in size. *Agelena naevia*, grass spider, web flat with funnel at side, in grass and in houses; *Tegenaria derhami*, house spider, naturalized from Europe, webs in corners.

LYCOSIDAE. HUNTING SPIDERS. Tarsal claws 3; legs with spines; eyes unequal in size. *Lycosa*, wolf spider, to 25 mm. long; active on ground, hunts prey or builds turrets to watch for prey; female carries egg cocoon and young.

ARGIOPIDAE. ORB WEAVERS. Tarsal claws 3; webs of geometrical design. *Miranda aurantia*, orange garden spider, web to 2 feet across, with zigzag band, in grass or bushes; *Epeira marmorea*, with "nest" of leaves at side of web, where spider sits holding a thread to web.

THOMISIDAE. CRAB SPIDERS. Tarsal claws 2; front pair of eyes not larger than others; body short, wide, appearance and gait crab-like, no web. *Misumena*, bright- or white-colored, lives in flowers and mimics colors; *Philodromus*, mottled; *Xysticus*, under bark or leaves.

SALTICIDAE (Attidae). JUMPING SPIDERS. Tarsal claws 2; front pair of eyes much larger than others; run and jump in all directions, no web. *Salticus scenicus*, on fences and houses; *Phidippus*, on plants, nest bag-like, among leaves.

Order 5. Solpugida (Solifugae). SUN SPIDERS. Cephalothorax of 6 somites, 1st to 3d a "head," eyes 4 or 6; chelicerae swollen, 2-jointed, with chelae, and joined to carapace; pedipalpi leg-like, 6-jointed; 1st legs tactile, not locomotory; no "waist"; abdomen of 10 somites; no spinning organs; in warm dry regions; Carboniferous to Recent; 570 species. *Eremobates*, southwestern United States; *Ammotreca; Galeodes*, "tarantula" of Egypt.

Order 6. Pseudoscorpionida (Chelonethida). FALSE SCORPIONS. Length 1 to 7.5 mm.; unsegmented cephalothorax broadly joined to abdomen of 11 somites; no sting; eyes 2, 4, or none; chelicerae 2-jointed, with comb-like serrula handling silk for nests from 2 glands in cephalothorax; pedipalpi large, 6-jointed, chelate; under moss or stones, in trees, or about buildings; Tertiary to Recent; 1,000 species. *Garypus*, California seacoast, to 7.5 mm. long; *Chthonius; Chelifer cancroides*, house or book scorpion, 3.5 mm. long, about buildings.

Order 7. Podogona (Ricinulei). Small; movable hood on cephalothorax over small chelicerae; no eyes; abdomen of 6 somites, 1st and 2d forming a "waist"; tropical; Carboniferous to Recent. *Cryptostemma*, *Cryptocellus*, few specimens known.

Order 8. Phalangida (Opiliones). HARVESTMEN, "DADDY LONGLEGS." Body short, ovoid, cephalothorax broadly fused to faintly segmented abdomen; chelicerae 3-jointed, slender; pedipalpi 6-jointed, not chelate; legs 7-jointed, very long and delicate, tarsi many-jointed; stink glands on cephalothorax; no lung books or silk glands; sexes much alike; in fields, woods, and buildings; Carboniferous to Recent; 2,200 species. *Phalangium, Liobunum*.

Order 9. Acarina (Acari). MITES and TICKS. Small to microscopic; body compact, ovoid, cephalothorax and abdomen fused; no segmentation; chelicerae and pedipalpi various; legs widely separated, 6- or 7-jointed; respire by tracheae or body surface; with larval and nymph stages; free-living or parasitic; world-wide; Oligocene to Recent; 6,000 species. (Figs. 27-5 to 27-7.)

SUBORDER 1. MESOSTIGMATA. One pair of stigmata with a slender tube, lateral to legs; free-living, predaceous, or commensal. *Parasitus*, on insects; *Laelaps*, on rodents; *Spinturnix*, on bats; *Halarachne*, in bronchi of seals; *Pneumonyssus*, in lungs of Old World monkeys; *Liponyssus bacoti*, tropical rat mite, common on alien rats (*Rattus*); *Dermanyssus gallinae*, chicken mite, attacks poultry and poultrymen; *Allodermanyssus sanguineus*, on house mouse (*Mus*), transmits *Rickettsia akari*, cause of rickettsialpox in man.

SUBORDER 2. IXODIDES. TICKS. One pair of stigmata, with stigmal plate, posterior or lateral to legs.

ARGASINE TICKS. No dorsal shield. *Argus persicus*, fowl tick, 8 to 10 mm., on poultry, quail, pigeons; *Ornithodorus megnini*, spinose ear tick, in ears of horses, cattle, sheep, and man; *O. turicata*, 6 to 7 mm., on hogs, cattle, and man; *O. moubata*, carries African tick fever; *O. hermsi*, on wild rodents, transmits *Spirochaeta recurrentis*, cause of relapsing fever in man.

IXODINE TICKS. A dorsal shield (Fig. 27-7). *Ixodes ricinus*, castor-bean tick, 3 to 10 mm., on various mammals; *Dermacentor variabilis* and *D. occidentalis*, dog ticks, to 15 mm. long, on domestic mammals and man, common in woods and brush; *D. andersoni*, on domestic and wild mammals and man—this and other species transmit *Dermacentroxenus rickettsi* causing spotted fever in man; *Boophilus* (*Margaropus*) *annulatus*, on cattle, transmits *Babesia bigemina* (SPOROZOA), causing Texas cattle fever (Table 26-1).

SUBORDER 3. TROMBIDIFORMES. One pair of stigmata on or near mouth, or stigmata absent; chelicerae usually modified for piercing; palpi as pincer-like clasping organs or as sensory organs.

RED SPIDER MITES. *Tetranychus*, 0.4 mm., red or yellow, suck leaves of plants making pinpoint lesions; female spins silken web.

CHIGGERS. *Trombicula alfreddugesi* (*irritans*), larvae puncture and irritate the skin. Oriental species transmit a rickettsial disease, scrub typhus.

WATER MITES. Length 0.5 to 8 mm., colored, in fresh or salt waters to 3,500 feet deep in the ocean. *Hydrachna, Halacarus*.

GALL MITES. Body slender, legs 4, anterior; suck juices from plants, stimulating formation of open-ended galls. *Eriophyes*, blister mite, damages buds, leaves, and fruits of trees and shrubs.

FOLLICLE MITES. Slender, ringed, 8 legs, 3-jointed. *Demodex folliculorum*, 0.4 mm., in hair follicles and sebaceous glands of man and domestic mammals.

SUBORDER 4. SARCOPTIFORMES. No stigmata or with tracheae opening on various parts of body; chelicerae modified for chewing; palpi simple. *Galumna*, horny or beetle mite, cuticle hard, in moss or tree bark, eats decaying matter; *Acarus siro*, cheese mite; *Rhizoglyphus echinopus*, bulb mite, in bulbs and roots; *Analgopsis megninia*, feather mite, in bird feathers and quills, not harmful.

ITCH and MANGE MITES. Body ovoid, legs 8, with suckers, claws, or bristles. *Sarcoptes scabei*, female burrows and oviposits in skin, causing itch in man and mange in domestic animals; *Psoroptes*, scab mites of domestic animals; *Knemidokoptes*, itch and scaly-leg mites of poultry.

SUBPHYLUM 4. MANDIBULATA (Antennata). Body of 2 parts (head and trunk) or 3 parts (head, thorax with walking legs, and abdomen); 1 or 2 pairs of antennae, 1 pair of jaws (mandibles), 1 or more pairs of maxillae, and 3 or more pairs of walking legs; respiration by gills or tracheae; excretion by Malpighian tubules or antennal glands; sexes usually separate; oviparous or ovoviviparous; usually with larval stages; terrestrial or aquatic, in fresh or salt waters.

CLASS 1. *CRUSTACEA*. Crustaceans. (See Chap. 25.)

CLASS 2. *INSECTA* (Hexapoda). Insects. (See Chap. 26.)

CLASS 3. *MYRIAPODA*. Myriapods. Body of 2 parts; head with 1 pair of antennae, 1 pair of mandibles, 1 or 2 pairs of maxillae; 1 or 2 pairs of legs per somite; respiration by tracheae; excretion by Malpighian tubules; development direct; terrestrial (Figs. 27-10, 27-11).

SUBCLASS 1. CHILOPODA. Centipedes. Body long, flattened dorsoventrally; head with 1 pair of jointed antennae, 1 pair of jaws, and 2 pairs of maxillae; body somites, 15 to 181, each with 1 pair of legs; 1st pair of body appendages 4-jointed, hook-like, with poison duct opening in terminal claws; sex opening midventral on next to last somite; terrestrial; nocturnal; Tertiary to Recent; 2,000 species.

Order 1. **Scutigeromorpha.** Legs long, 15 pairs; spiracles middorsal. *Cermatia (Scutigera) forceps*, house centipede, to 25 mm. long, in buildings, swift moving, eats insects.

Order 2. **Lithobiomorpha.** Legs short, 15 pairs; spiracles lateral; includes smallest centipedes, from 3 mm. long. *Lithobius*, to 30 mm.

Order 3. **Scolopendromorpha.** Legs, 21 or 23 pairs; some species to 265 mm. long. *Scolopendra*, to 100 mm. long, 21 pairs of legs, widely distributed.

Order 4. **Geophilomorpha.** Legs 31 to 181 pairs. *Geophilus*, legs 31 to 93 pairs, body thin.

SUBCLASS 2. DIPLOPODA. Millipedes. Body long, usually cylindrical; head with 1 pair each of short, 7-segmented antennae, jaws, and maxillae; thorax of 4 somites, the 1st legless, the 2d to 4th each with 1 pair of legs; abdomen of 9 to over 100 segments (double somites) closely spaced, each with 2 pairs of legs; sex opening midventral on 3d somite; terrestrial in moist places; Eocene to Recent; 7,000 species.

Order 1. **Pselaphognatha.** Body somites 13; back and sides with large tufts of hair. World-wide. *Polyxenus*, 2.5 to 3 mm. long.

Order 2. **Limacomorpha.** Body somites 22; male gonopods (clasping organs) are 1 or 2 pairs of legs on last somite. Old and New World tropics. *Glomeridesmus*, 10 mm.

Order 3. **Oniscomorpha.** Body somites 14 to 16; male gonopods, 1 or 2 pairs on last somite. Old World. *Glomeris*, 10 to 15 mm.

Order 4. **Polydesmoidea.** Body somites 19 to 22; male gonopods, 1 or 2 pairs on 7th somite; no spinning glands. *Polydesmus*, flattened, to 28 mm., Texas.

Order 5. **Nematomorpha.** Body somites 26 to 60; male gonopods, 1 or 2 pairs on 7th somite; end of body with 2 or 3 pairs of spinning glands and bristles. *Striaria*, 30 body somites.

Order 6. **Juliformia.** Body somites 40 or more; male gonopods, 1 or 2 pairs on 7th somite; no spinning glands. *Julus virgatus*, 12 mm. long, body somites, 30 to 35; *Narceus (Spirobolus)*, to 100 mm. long, to 100 pairs of legs (50 somites), North America, China.

Order 7. **Colobognatha.** Body somites 30 to 60; male gonopods are 2d pair of legs on 7th somite and 1st pair on 8th somite; head conical. *Platydesmus*, southeastern states and California.

SUBCLASS 3. SYMPHYLA. Garden Centipede. To 6 mm. long; white; no eyes; with antennae, jaws, and 2 pairs of maxillae; adult with 12 pairs of legs; sex opening midventral between 4th pair of legs; terrestrial, in damp places with humus. *Scutigerella immaculata*, garden centipede (Fig. 27-12), often injures seeds and young shoots of sugar beets, asparagus, and other crops.

SUBCLASS 4. PAUROPODA. Length 0.5-1.8 mm.; antennae 3-branched; no eyes; body cylindrical, of 11 (12) somites, with 6 dorsal plates and 9 (10) pairs of legs; sex opening midventral on 3d somite; 4 larval instars; in dark damp places under logs, stones, or leaves, and in soil; about 300 species. *Pauropus huxleyi*, eastern states and Europe; others in California.

SUBPHYLUM 5. PENTASTOMIDA (Linguatulida). Form worm-like, soft, unsegmented; cephalothorax short, 2 pairs of ventral retractile hooks beside mouth; abdomen elongate, ringed; no circulatory, respiratory, or excretory organs; sexes separate; parasitic.

Order 1. **Cephalobaenida.** Mouth hooks without a basal arm (fulcrum); sex opening anterior; development direct, no intermediate host. *Cephalobaena tetrapoda*, in South American snakes; *Reighardia sternae*, in gulls and terns.

Order 2. Porocephalida. Mouth hooks with a basal arm; sex opening anterior in male, posterior in female, development indirect, larvae in a different host than adult. *Linguatula serrata*, larva 5 mm. long, in liver, lung, etc., of rabbit, horse, goat, etc.; adult female to 130 mm. long, male to 20 mm., in nasal cavities of fox, wolf, and dog, occasional in horse and goat, rare in man; *Sibekia*, in crocodiles; *Kiricephalus*, in water snakes; *Porocephalus crotali*, larva in rodents, adult in rattlesnakes; other species in boas and pythons (Fig. 27-16).

SUBPHYLUM 6. TARDIGRADA. WATER BEARS or BEAR ANIMALCULES. To 1 mm. long; body cylindrical, rounded at ends, no somites; 4 pairs of stumpy unjointed legs ending in 2 or more claws, last pair at hind end of body; anterior end with retractile snout and teeth; mouth with stylet; no circulatory or respiratory organs; rectal glands for excretion; sexes separate; 1 gonad; some have larval stages; about 280 species (Fig. 27-17). *Echiniscus*, 0.2 mm. long, in moss on damp roofs, but can resist desiccation; *Macrobiotus*, 0.7 mm., in fresh waters; others marine and terrestrial.

REFERENCES

BAKER, E. W., and G. W. WHARTON. 1952. An introduction to acarology. New York, The Macmillan Co. xiii + 465 pp., 377 figs.

COMSTOCK, J. H., and W. J. GERTSCH. 1940. The spider book. 2d ed. New York, Doubleday & Co., Inc. xi + 729 pp., 766 + figs. Includes other ARACHNIDA in brief.

FABRE, J. H. 1919. The life of the spider. New York, Dodd, Mead & Co., Inc. 404 pp., illus.

GERTSCH, W. J. 1949. American spiders. New York, D. Van Nostrand Co., Inc. xiii + 285 pp., 32 pls., some colored.

GRASSÉ, P-P. 1949. Traité de zoologie. Paris, Masson et Cie. Vol. 4, Onychophores, Tardigrades, Arthropodes, Trilobitomorphes, Chelicerates. Pp. 1–979, 719 figs.

HEDGPETH, J. W. 1954. On the phylogeny of the Pycnogonida. *Acta Zoologica*, vol. 35, pp. 193–213, 9 figs.

HELFER, H., and E. SCHLOTTKE. 1935. Pantopoda. *In* Bronn, Klassen und Ordnungen des Tier-reichs. Vol. 5, pt. 4, book 2, pp. 1–314, 223 figs.

HERMS, W. B. 1950. Medical entomology . . . man and animals. 4th ed. New York, The Macmillan Co. xvi + 643 pp., 191 figs.

HEYMONS, R. 1935. Pentastomida. *In* Bronn, Klassen und Ordnungen des Tier-reichs. Vol. 5, pt. 4, book 1, pp. 1–268, 148 text figs.

KASTON, B. J., and E. KASTON. 1953. How to know the spiders. Dubuque, Iowa, William C. Brown Co. vi + 220 pp., 552 figs.

KÜKENTHAL, W., and OTHERS. 1926–   . Handbuch der Zoologie. Berlin, Walter De Gruyter & Co. Vol. 3, pt. 2, ARACHNOIDEA, ONYCHOPHORA; vol. 4, pt. 1, DIPLOPODA, CHILOPODA, etc. About 1,400 pp., 1,800 figs.

MARCUS, E. 1929. Tardigrada. *In* Bronn, Klassen und Ordnungen des Tier-reichs. Vol. 5, pt. 4, book 3, viii + 608 pp., 1 pl., 397 figs.

PETRUNKEVITCH, A. 1933. . . . The natural classification of spiders based on a study of their internal anatomy. *Connecticut Academy of Sciences Transactions*, vol. 31, pp. 299–389.

——. 1939. Catalogue of American spiders. *Idem*, vol. 33, pp. 133–338.

PRATT, H. S. 1935. Manual of the common invertebrate animals exclusive of insects. 2d ed. Philadelphia, The Blakiston Co. ARACHNOIDEA, etc., pp. 468–555, figs. 639–739.

SAVORY, T. H. 1928. The biology of spiders. London, Sidgwick & Jackson, Ltd. xx + 376 pp., 16 pls., 121 figs.

——. 1935. The Arachnida. London, Edward Arnold & Co., Ltd. xi + 218 pp., 8 pls., 99 figs.

VERHOEFF, K. W. 1934. Symphyla and Pauropoda. *In* Bronn, Klassen und Ordnungen des Tier-reichs. Vol. 5, pt. 2, book 3, pp. 1–200, 136 figs.

28 PHYLUM CHORDATA
Lower Chordates

The Phylum CHORDATA (Gr. *chorda*, string) comprises the lowly tongue worms, tunicates, and lancelets and the "vertebrates"—the lampreys, sharks and rays, bony fishes, amphibians, reptiles, birds, and mammals (Table 28-1). The lower chordates are mostly of small size, all are marine, and most tunicates are sessile. All other chordates are free-living, and none is strictly parasitic. The vertebrates include practically all living animals of medium to large size, including some huge sharks and whales (Fig. 1-2). This chapter describes the general features of the Phylum CHORDATA (Fig. 28-1) and the structure and natural history of the lower chordates.

28-1. Characteristics. The chordates are bilaterally symmetrical, with three germ layers, a segmented body, complete digestive tract, and well-developed coelom. Three outstanding characteristics distinguish them from all other animals—a single dorsal tubular nerve cord, the notochord, and gill slits in the pharynx (Fig. 28-2). These features all form in the early embryo of a chordate, and they persist, are altered, or may disappear in the adult.

The *notochord* is the first supporting structure of the chordate body. In the early embryo it forms above the primitive gut as a slender rod of cells that contain a gelatinous matrix and is sheathed in fibrous connective tissue.

In tunicates, it is present in the tail and only during the larval stages. In the lancelets and higher forms, it extends almost the length of the body. It persists throughout life as the main axial support in lancelets and lampreys, but in the fishes to mammals is later surrounded or replaced by the vertebral column.

The *nerve cord* forms on the dorsal surface of the early embryo soon after the gastrula stage. Infolding of the ectoderm produces the hollow tubular cord that lies above the notochord. The anterior end becomes enlarged as a simple "cerebral vesicle" in tunicate larvae and in lancelets, but in all vertebrates it thickens and differentiates as the brain, to become progressively more complex in higher forms. In tunicates the cord and vesicle degenerate to a ganglion at metamorphosis. From the lampreys onward the nerve cord later becomes surrounded by neural arches of the vertebrae that protect it from injury, and the brain is enclosed by a brain box, or cranium.

Paired *gill slits* develop on the sides of the embryonic pharynx (digestive tract). Each is formed by an outpocketing of endoderm in the pharynx and a corresponding inpocketing of ectoderm on the outside of the body; the intervening wall breaks through to form a gill slit. The characteristic development is seen in a shark or fish in which each slit is margined by many slender filaments containing blood ves-

462

TABLE 28-1. Major Divisions of the Phylum Chordata

(For other details, see Classification in Chaps. 15 and 29 to 35.)

	Subphyla	Classes and their principal characteristics	See chap.
ACRANIA. No cranium or brain, etc.	HEMICHORDATA Notochord short, anterior; nerve tissues in epidermis	*ENTEROPNEUSTA.* TONGUE WORMS. Worm-like; gill slits many	28
		PTEROBRANCHIA. Minute; gill slits 2 or none	
		†*GRAPTOZOA.* GRAPTOLITES. Colonial, branched, with chitinous covering.	
	TUNICATA Notochord and nerve cord only in larva; adult contained in secreted tunic	*LARVACEA.* Minute, tadpole-like; tunic temporary; 2 gill slits	
		ASCIDIACEA. ASCIDIANS. Tunic with scattered muscles; many gill slits	
		THALIACEA. CHAIN TUNICATES. Tunic with circular muscle bands	
	CEPHALOCHORDATA Notochord and nerve cord along entire body and persistent, as are the gill slits	*LEPTOCARDII.* LANCELETS. Slender, fish-like, segmented; epidermis 1-layered, no scales; many gill slits	
CRANIATA (vertebrates). With cranium, visceral arches, vertebrae, and brain	AGNATHA No true jaws or paired appendages	†*OSTRACODERMI.* ANCIENT ARMORED FISHES. Scales large, often fused as cephalothoracic shield	29
		CYCLOSTOMATA. CYCLOSTOMES. Skin without scales; mouth suctorial; gills 6 to 14 pairs	
	GNATHOSTOMATA With jaws and, usually, paired appendages — Superclass *PISCES* Paired fins, gills, and skin with scales	†*PLACODERMI.* ANCIENT FISHES. Jaws primitive; complete gill slit before hyoid	
		CHONDRICHTHYES. SHARKS and RAYS. Skin with placoid scales; skeleton of cartilage; 5 to 7 pairs of gills in separate clefts	30
		OSTEICHTHYES. BONY FISHES. Skin with cycloid or ctenoid scales; 4 pairs of gills in common cavity under opercula	31
	Superclass *TETRAPODA* Paired limbs, lungs, cornified skin, and bony skeleton	*AMPHIBIA.* AMPHIBIANS. Skin moist, soft, no external scales	32
		REPTILIA. REPTILES. Skin dry, with scales or scutes	33
		AVES. BIRDS. Skin with feathers; fore limbs are wings; warm-blooded	34
		MAMMALIA. MAMMALS. Skin with hair; warm-blooded; suckle young	35

Fig. 28-1. Basic differences between (*A*) a nonchordate (insect) and (*B*) a chordate (salamander) as to location of the nervous system, digestive tract, and heart; diagrammatic.

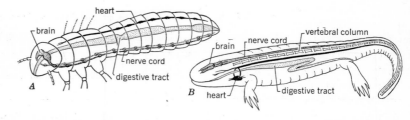

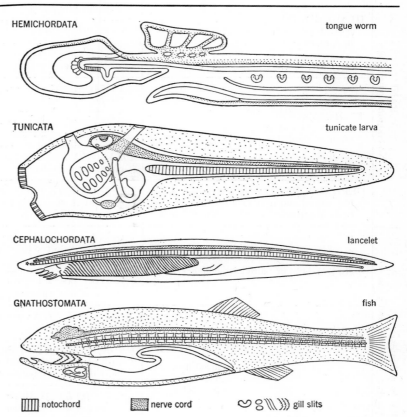

Fig. 28-2. Phylum CHORDATA. Basic features of four subphyla; diagrammatic.

sels, to form a gill. Water containing dissolved oxygen passes into the mouth and pharynx and out over the filaments, where the blood gives up its carbon dioxide and acquires oxygen, so that the gill serves the process of external respiration. All aquatic chordates from tongue worms to amphibians respire by gills. In amphibians which transform from aquatic larvae to air-breathing adults, the gills are lost at metamorphosis. The reptiles, birds, and mammals all develop several pairs of gill slits during early embryonic life, but they are never func-

tional and soon close; all these animals later acquire lungs for breathing air when they hatch or are born.

28-2. Origin of chordates. There is no reliable clue as to the origin of the chordates. No remains of them have been found in Cambrian rocks where animal fossils first are common. The earliest were probably soft-bodied, without hard skeletal elements likely to be preserved. The first vertebrates are several groups of fishes in Silurian and Ordovician time (Fig.

13-15). Thenceforth vertebrates are common and often dominant elements in the record of animals of the past and show a progressive series of developments toward the living types of the present day. The earliest sharks and bony fishes appear in fresh-water deposits, and later both groups invaded the seas. The amphibians probably derived from crossopterygian fishes. They appear first in Devonian rocks and were differentiated into three orders by Carboniferous times. The first salamanders (Cretaceous) and frogs (Jurassic) are distinct, like their modern successors. Reptiles appeared in Permian time and expanded widely into a great variety of dominant types in the Mesozoic era; then most of the orders died out at the end of the Cretaceous. The first bird (†*Archaeopteryx*) appeared in the Upper Jurassic. The mammals arose from the reptiles, beginning in the Triassic, and differentiated widely in the early Tertiary period. The study of fossils has contributed importantly to the classification of vertebrates and has indicated the probable origins of most of the larger groups.

Resemblances between the lower chordates and some invertebrates have been the basis for several theories of chordate origins, of which a few may be mentioned.

ANNELID THEORY. Annelids and chordates are both bilaterally symmetrical and segmented, with segmental excretory organs, a well-developed coelom, a nerve cord, and longitudinal blood vessels. Inverting an annelid would place its nerve cord dorsal to the digestive tract, and the path of blood flow would resemble that of chordates; however, the mouth would then be dorsal, unlike a chordate, and other dorsoventral relations would be altered. Annelids, moreover, have no structures suggestive of the notochord or gill slits.

ARACHNID THEORY. Resemblances are seen between Paleozoic eurypterids (arthropods) and early ostracoderms (chordates), both armored with dorsal exoskeletons. Chordates, however, have no arthropod-like appendages, their nerve cord is dorsal and that of arthropods is ventral, and there are other important differences.

ECHINODERM THEORY. The tornaria larva of tongue worms and the bipinnaria larva of echinoderms are both minute and transparent, with almost identical external ciliated bands and a like number of coelomic cavities; both have a dorsal pore. Indeed, the first known tongue worm (hemichordate) larva was identified as that of a starfish by a famous zoologist! A hypothetical sequence of ancestry might be:

echinoderm (auricularia) larva → hemichordate larva → tunicate larva → amphioxus → ostracoderm

If chordate ancestry is involved in such small soft larvae, the chance of finding any conclusive fossil record is remote.

SUBPHYLUM HEMICHORDATA. TONGUE WORMS, ETC.

Living hemichordates are small soft-bodied animals, of sandy or muddy sea bottoms. They possess paired gill slits, both dorsal and ventral nervous tissue, and a short anterior structure considered to be a "notochord"—termed a stomocord by recent authorities (Fig. 28-4). Hemichordates have commonly been considered the lowest of chordates. Zoologists who regard the stomocord as not a true notochord recognize this group as a separate phylum.

28-3. Class Enteropneusta. The acorn or tongue worms are slender and 25 to 2,500 mm. long. Most of them live under shallow water; but a few go deeper, and one was dredged at 2,500 fathoms off West Africa. They burrow shallowly by means of a soft proboscis, and a sticky mucus secreted by glands in the skin causes formation of a tubular case of sand and other debris in which each animal lives. About 12 genera and 60 species are known. *Balanoglossus* is world-wide in distribution, and *Ptychodera* occurs in the Pacific. *Saccoglossus* (= *Dolichoglossus*) inhabits both coasts of North America; *S. kowalevskii* occurs from Beaufort, N.C., to Massachusetts Bay and grows to about 175 mm. long. *S. pusillus* of southern California becomes 75 mm. in length and is brilliantly orange; in *S. kowalevskii* the proboscis is yel-

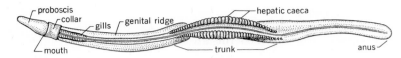

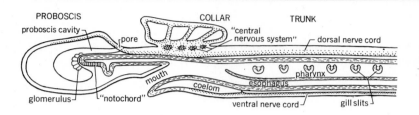

Fig. 28-3. Subphylum HEMI-CHORDATA. The tongue worm, *Saccoglossus*, dorsal view. (*After Spengel.*)

Fig. 28-4. Subphylum HEMI-CHORDATA. The tongue worm, *Saccoglossus*. Median section of anterior portion; diagrammatic.

lowish white, the collar red-orange, and the trunk orange-yellow to green-yellow posteriorly. Some tongue worms have persistent and often unpleasant odors.

The body (Fig. 28-3) comprises a *proboscis,* a *collar,* and a long *trunk*. Behind the collar are many *gill slits* on either side. Ventral to these is a lateral ridge marking the presence of the gonads. Some species have paired transverse ridges, dorsally behind the gills, that indicate the hepatic caeca. The *mouth* opens widely at the anterior ventral margin of the collar, behind the proboscis; a dilated *buccal cavity* follows, then the *pharynx,* with U-shaped openings high on either side that connect to the gill pouches. The straight *intestine,* with dorsal *hepatic caeca* (liver sacs), leads to the terminal *anus*.

In life the cavities in the proboscis and collar (Fig. 28-4) are believed to fill with water through pores on the dorsal surface; when these parts become turgid, the animal burrows through the sand or mud, aided by muscular movements of the trunk. The mouth remains open so that a mixture of water and sand containing organic debris is forced into the buccal cavity. The water passes through the gill slits for respiration, the organic material serves as food, and the sand passes out the anus.

The *circulatory system* includes a middorsal vessel, in which colorless blood flows anteriorly (as in annelids), and a midventral vessel. The two are joined to a "heart," dorsal to the notochord, and there are other branches near the

gill slits. A pulsating vessel has been described in the larva, but its presence in the adult is debatable; contractions of the larger vessels probably cause the blood to circulate. A small unpaired glomerulus (proboscis gland) is thought to be the *excretory organ*.

In the *body wall* (Fig. 28-5), the thick unicellular epidermis contains many mucus-secreting cells; it rests on a basement membrane, beneath which are muscle layers. The *nervous system* consists of cells and fibers in the base of the epidermis. Concentrations of these provide a middorsal and a midventral nerve "cord" of small size, with a ring-like connective between the two posteriorly in the collar. A thickened cord, hollow in some species, lies in the collar dorsal to the mouth cavity, and has many nerve fibers in the epidermis of the proboscis.

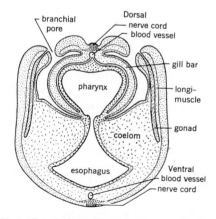

Fig. 28-5. Subphylum HEMICHORDATA. Cross section through pharynx. (*Modified from Sedgwick, Textbook of zoology, George Allen & Unwin, Ltd.*)

The "notochord," or stomocord, is a short anterior outpocketing of the digestive tract in the hind part of the proboscis. There is also a small proboscis skeleton of firm material. The **coelom** is represented by five cavities, one in the proboscis and a pair each in the collar and the trunk.

The sexes are separate, with multiple **gonads** in two dorsolateral rows from behind the collar to the hepatic caeca; each, when mature, releases its contents immediately to the exterior through a separate pore, and fertilization is external. In some species the egg produces a small ovoid tornaria larva, quite transparent, and with surface bands of cilia (Fig. 28-6); at metamorphosis the proboscis and collar become evident. The American species of *Saccoglossus* develop directly without a larval stage. Tongue worms can regenerate the trunk region, proboscis, and collar.

28-4. Class Pterobranchia. These small forms resemble the Enteropneusta in basic features. They live in both deep and shallow seas. The Order Rhabdopleuridea (*Rhabdopleura*) are colonial, without gill openings, have a lophophore with one pair of arms, and one gonad. The Cephalodiscidea (*Cephalodiscus*) live free, not in colonies, have one pair of gill openings, many pairs of lophophore arms, and two gonads. Fossil forms occur in the Ordovician period, and from the Cretaceous onward. *Cephalodiscus* secretes a "housing" that harbors many individuals, each with a U-shaped digestive tract having the mouth and anus close together. Pterobranchs reproduce both by budding and sexually.

28-5. Class †Graptozoa. The graptolites (†*Dictyonema*, etc.) of middle Cambrian to Carboniferous were colonial marine forms, either fixed or floating, with simple, branched, or bush-like stems of chitinous material that housed individuals in separate pits. Formerly, these were placed in the Coelenterata, but the chitinous test and the presence of a stolon suggest that their true affinities are with *Rhabdopleura* in the Pterobranchia.

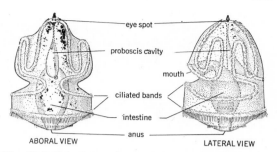

Fig. 28-6. Subphylum Hemichordata. Tornaria larva. (*After Spengel.*)

SUBPHYLUM TUNICATA. Tunicates

Tunicates inhabit the sea, from the polar oceans to the tropics and from shallow beach waters to depths of 3 miles. Some are free-living, and others become fixed or sessile after a short free larval stage. Tunicates may be solitary, colonial, or with many individuals grouped under a common covering. They vary in size from nearly microscopic forms to others a foot in diameter. About 2,000 species are known, of which 100 are pelagic. Their methods of reproduction are varied, some sexual, some asexual by budding. The group name refers to the self-secreted "tunic," or sac-like covering, over the body. The best-known tunicates are the "sea squirts" or ascidians, which suddenly squirt water from openings in the body covering when touched.

Aristotle (384–322 B.C.) described a simple ascidian as Tethyum, but not until early in the nineteenth century were many species described in detail. Cuvier then gave the name Tunicata to the group and placed it between the "Radiata" and "Vermes"; later, its members were classified as mollusks. In 1866 Kowalevsky, by careful study of the developmental stages of a larval ascidian, brilliantly demonstrated the true position of the group to be among the chordates.

The tunicates are best understood by considering first the free-living larva of an ascidian and then the adult. The larva shows chordate characteristics; but some of these are absent in the adult, and others are obscured by adaptations to the sessile mode of life.

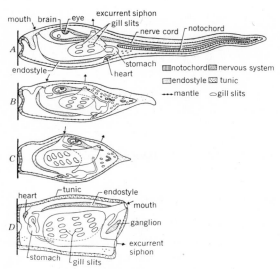

mouth brain   eye   excurrent siphon
                      gill slits
                         nerve cord   notochord

A

endostyle
                      stomach   notochord   nervous system
                      heart   endostyle   tunic
                                 mantle   gill slits

B

C

     heart   tunic   endostyle
                           mouth
D   ganglion
                           excurrent
                           siphon
     stomach gill slits

Fig. 28-7. Subphylum TUNICATA. Stages in the metamorphosis of a simple ascidian from the free-swimming larva to the sessile adult. Arrows indicate entrance and exit paths of water currents. (*Adapted from Kowalewsky; and Herdman.*)

A. Larva attaches to a solid object by anterior mucous suckers.

B. Tail reabsorbed, notochord and nerve cord reduced.

C. Notochord disappears, internal organs begin to rotate.

D. Metamorphosis complete, with rotation (90 to 180 degrees) of internal organs and external apertures; branchial sac enlarges, tunic (or test) is secreted, and nervous system reduced to a ganglion. (See Fig. 28-8.)

28-6. The larval ascidian. The small fertilized egg segments to form a blastula and then a gastrula; the embryo elongates and soon hatches as a transparent free-swimming larva, somewhat resembling a frog tadpole (Fig. 28-7*A*). Its tail contains a supporting *notochord* (whence the earlier name Urochordata), a dorsal tubular *nerve cord,* and serial pairs of lateral, segmental muscles. The other organs are confined to the anterior and larger head + body region. The anterior end bears three mucous or *adhesive glands.* The *digestive tract* is complete, with mouth, perforate *gill slits,* endostyle, intestine, and anus; there is a *circulatory system* with blood vessels, and a *coelom.* The *nervous system* (continuous with the nerve cord in the tail) and sensory structures include (1) a *"brain"* and posterior to it (2) a *trunk ganglion,* (3) a median *eye* with retina, lens,

pigment, and cornea, and (4) a pigmented *otolith,* or ear, attached to delicate hair cells.

28-7. Metamorphosis. After a few hours or days of free life, the small larva attaches vertically by its adhesive glands to a rock or wharf pile (Fig. 28-7). A rapid transformation (retrograde metamorphosis) ensues in which most of the chordate features disappear. The tail is partly absorbed and partly cast off, its notochord, nerve cord, and muscles being withdrawn into the body and absorbed. Of the nervous system only the trunk ganglion persists. The branchial or gill sac enlarges, develops many apertures, and is invaded by blood vessels. The stomach and intestine grow. That portion of the body between the point of attachment and the mouth grows rapidly, causing the body within to rotate dorsoposteriorly nearly 180 degrees, so that the mouth is at the upper nonattached end. Finally the gonads and ducts form in mesoderm between the stomach and intestine. The adhesive glands disappear, and the tunic grows upward to enclose the entire animal.

28-8. The adult ascidian. A simple ascidian (*Ciona, Molgula,* etc.) is cylindrical or globose, attached by a *base* or stalk (Fig. 28-8). It is covered with a tough elastic layer, the *test* or *tunic,* of cellulose (a material rare in animals). The test is lined by a membranous *mantle* containing muscle fibers and blood vessels. There are two external openings, the *incurrent siphon* (branchial aperture) at the top and the *excurrent siphon* (atrial aperture) at one side. Water drawn into the incurrent siphon brings minute organisms that serve for food and oxygen for respiration; that passed out the excurrent siphon removes wastes and the sex cells. Within the test and mantle is the *atrial cavity,* in which is a dilated *branchial sac* having many pores.

The digestive system begins with the incurrent siphon followed by a circle of hair-like sensory tentacles at the entrance to the branchial sac. Along the midventral wall of the latter is the *endostyle,* a vertical groove lined with both ciliated and mucous cells where food from the entering water becomes entangled and moved downward. Feeding only on plankton, the ascidian needs no large appendages to handle food. From the base of the branchial sac a short *esophagus* leads to the dilated *stomach,* which connects to the *intestine;* the latter two organs are outside the branchial sac. The intestine curves to end at the *anus* below the excurrent siphon. A *digestive gland* (liver) connects to the stomach.

The wall of the branchial sac has many pores margined by ciliated cells that beat to move water from within the sac to the atrial cavity, whence it flows to the excurrent siphon.

The circulatory system includes a tubular heart in the *visceral cavity* near the stomach. To each end is connected a large vessel or *aorta,* one distributing to the stomach, test wall, and one side of the branchial sac, the other to the opposite side of the branchial sac. In the walls of the latter an intercommunicating series of small vessels surrounds the pores, to constitute the respiratory mechanism. These "vessels," however, are spaces within the tissues and lack an endothelial lining. The tunicate is unique in that the path of blood flow reverses at short intervals; the heart and vessels lack valves. The blood cells may be colorless or blue, red, etc.

Near the intestine is a structure, without a duct, considered to be excretory in function. The only relic of the nervous system is a long *trunk ganglion* in the mantle between the two siphons, with nerves to various parts. Nearby is a *neural gland,* possibly of endocrine nature, and somewhat like a pituitary structure.

The ascidians are hermaphroditic, but self-sterile. The *ovary* is a large hollow gland, on the intestinal loop, with an *oviduct* paralleling the intestine and opening in the atrial cavity near the anus. The *testes* comprise numerous branched tubules, on the surface of the ovary and intestine, that discharge into a *vas deferens* paralleling the oviduct. Some tunicates also reproduce asexually, by budding.

28-9. Class Larvacea.
These small organisms (*Oikopleura, Appendicularia*) are up to 5 mm.

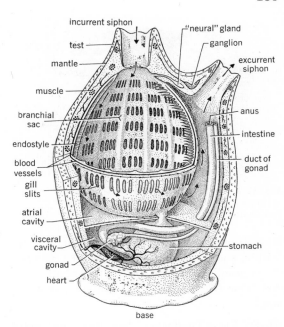

Fig. 28-8. Subphylum TUNICATA. Structure of an adult simple ascidian; diagrammatic. Tunic, mantle, and upper half of branchial sac removed on left side. Arrows indicate path of water currents through the animal.

long, larva-like in appearance, with a persistent notochord. They live in upper levels of the sea and swim by contractions of the bent or curved tail. Some are brilliantly pigmented with orange or violet and, when abundant, may color the water by their numbers. Each individual at times secretes a large gelatinous housing or tunic.

28-10. Class Ascidiacea.
In the simple ascidians the individuals are "solitary," that is, each has a distinct and separate test. Many inhabit shallow waters, but some occur down to 2,900 fathoms. The compound ascidians (Fig. 28-9) are those in which the "individuals" are buried in a common covering mass or housing and do not have separate tests. In many of this group, each "individual" possesses a separate incurrent siphon, but several or many (to several hundred) have a common external aperture ("cloaca") into which their respective excurrent siphons discharge. Compound ascidians reproduce asexually by gemmation and also produce eggs and sperm for sexual reproduction. With most spe-

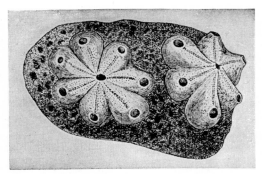

Fig. 28-9. Subphylum Tunicata. A compound tunicate (*Botryllus*); individuals with separate incurrent siphons, but common excurrent siphon. (*After M. Edwards.*)

cies, development proceeds to the larval stage within the atrium, then the young emerge. Most ascidians (*Ciona, Botryllus*) are attached, but some (*Polycarpa*) are free-living in sand or mud.

28-11. Class Thaliacea. The salpians are highly modified tunicates of peculiar form that live in the open sea and have specialized modes of reproduction. The body is cask-shaped, surrounded by complete bands of circular muscles, and has the incurrent and excurrent openings at opposite ends. Some swim by contracting the ring-like muscles so as to force water out the posterior end, and others are wafted about by water currents. In *Doliolum* (Fig. 28-10), the fertilized egg develops into a free-swimming tailed larva, somewhat like that of an ascidian. This metamorphoses into a barrel-shaped adult "nurse" stage that by asexual reproduction gives rise to many individuals. Some of the latter eventually produce eggs and sperm. *Salpa* is another type in which, by asexual means, a solitary adult produces long chains of individuals, sometimes several hundred connected to one another. Fragments of such a chain, comprising several animals, may break loose from the parent structure. Later these, while still connected or further separated, reproduce sexually. Each gives rise to one or several eggs that remain attached to the parent by a placenta-like structure, analogous to that of higher chordates, where the maternal and embryonic blood circulations are closely related

during development. The young that hatch out become the asexual form.

SUBPHYLUM CEPHALOCHORDATA.
Lancelets

28-12. Amphioxus. This group (Class Lepto-cardii) comprises about 30 species of fish-like animals (*Branchiostoma*, etc.), commonly called amphioxus, that inhabit tropical and temperate seacoasts. *Branchiostoma virginiae* occurs from Chesapeake Bay to Florida, and *B. californiense* from San Diego Bay southward. The latter grows to 100 mm. long, but most species are smaller. Amphioxus burrows in clean shifting sand of shallow shore waters, leaving only its anterior end protruding. At times it emerges to swim by rapid lateral movements of the body. Amphioxus is of especial zoological interest because it shows the three distinctive characteristics of the Phylum Chordata in simple form and is considered to resemble some ancient ancestor of this phylum.

The **body** is slender, long, and laterally compressed, pointed at both ends, and has no distinct head (Fig. 28-11). The low median **dorsal fin** along most of the body and the **preanal fin**

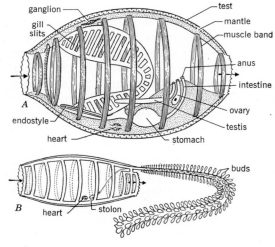

Fig. 28-10. Subphylum Tunicata. A chain tunicate (*Doliolum*). *A.* Adult of sexual generation. *B.* Asexual adult ("nurse" stage) with attached chain bearing many buds. Arrows indicate path of water through the animal. (*Modified from Stempell.*)

Fig. 28-11. Subphylum CEPHALOCHORDATA. The lancelet or amphioxus (*Branchiostoma*). Adult partly dissected from left side. Natural size about 2 inches long.

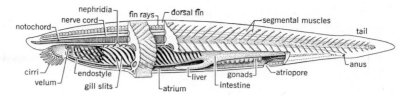

from atriopore to anus are made of fin-ray chambers containing short *fin rays* of connective tissue. The *tail* has a membranous fin. Anterior to the ventral fin, the body is flattened ventrally with a *metapleural fold* along each side. The *mouth* is ventral at the anterior end, the *anus* is on the left side near the base of the tail fin, and the *atriopore* is an additional ventral opening forward of the anus.

The body covering is a single layer of soft *epidermis* in which some cells bear sensory processes; beneath this is a soft connective tissue. The *notochord* is the chief support of the body. It is a slender rod of tall cells containing gelatinous material and is surrounded by a continuous sheath of connective tissue. Other supportive structures include a circular cartilage-like reinforcement in the oral hood, the fin rays, and delicate rods with cross connections in the gill bars. Along each side of the body and tail, different species have 50 to 85 <-shaped muscles, or *myomeres,* each of lengthwise muscle fibers and separated from one another by thin septa of connective tissue. Those on the two sides alternate in position— a unique feature. These muscles contract to produce the lateral bending for burrowing and swimming. Transverse muscles in the floor of the atrial cavity, between the metapleural folds, serve to compress the cavity and force water to the exterior.

The straight and simple *digestive tract* begins with the anterior *oral hood* (vestibule) which is surrounded by about 22 delicate fleshy *buccal cirri;* behind the latter are several ciliated bars. The *mouth* proper is a circular opening in a membrane, or *velum,* posterior in the oral hood. It is guarded by 12 *velar tentacles,* which exclude large particles. Cilia in the hood, during life, produce a rotating effect and are called the "wheel organ." On the cirri and tentacles and

within the hood are sensory structures. Behind the mouth is the large compressed *pharynx,* with many diagonal *gill slits* at the sides. There follows the narrow straight *intestine,* which ends at the *anus.* A slender sac-like *liver,* thought to secrete digestive fluid, attaches ventrally to the anterior part of the intestine.

The pharynx is suspended dorsally, beneath the notochord, but hangs free in a cavity, the *atrium,* within the muscles of the body wall. The atrium is an external cavity, lined by ectoderm (hence not a coelom), and connects to the atriopore. The pharynx contains a middorsal furrow, the *hyperbranchial groove,* lined with ciliated cells, and midventrally is a corresponding groove, the *endostyle,* having both ciliated and gland cells (Fig. 28-12). Water, containing minute organisms, is drawn into the mouth by action of the cilia; the food is trapped

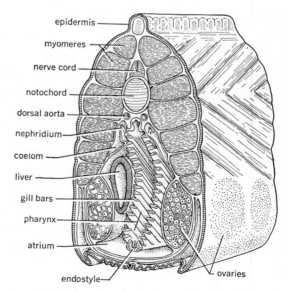

Fig. 28-12. Subphylum CEPHALOCHORDATA. Amphioxus. Enlarged section through pharynx. (*Adapted from Kükenthal.*)

by mucus in the endostyle and carried posteriorly to the intestine, while the water passes between the gill bars to the atrium and thence to the exterior through the atriopore.

The *circulatory system* is somewhat on the plan of that in higher chordates, but lacks a heart. Besides the definite blood vessels, there are open spaces where the colorless blood escapes into the tissues. Blood from the digestive tract flows anteriorly in a *subintestinal vein* to the *hepatic portal vein* entering the liver; thence it collects in a *hepatic vein,* and with other blood from the posterior part of the body passes forward in a *ventral aorta* below the endostyle and into branches at each primary gill bar. Each branch has a small pulsating bulb, and together these function as a heart, forcing blood upward in the gill bars where it is aerated and then collects in the paired *dorsal aortas.* The latter join behind the pharynx to form a single *dorsal aorta* in which the blood moves posteriorly to supply the body and intestine and finally through capillaries to the venous side. Some oxygenated blood passes forward in the right dorsal aorta to the anterior end of the body. The general course of blood movement in amphioxus is thus like that in higher chordates and opposite to that in invertebrates such as annelids.

Respiration results from passage of water containing oxygen from the pharynx through 100 or more *gill slits* on each side, past the *gill bars* that contain blood vessels, and into the atrium. This water current is aided by cilia in cells on the gill bars. The gill system of amphioxus is like that of higher chordates during early larval life, its inner surface being of endoderm and the exterior of ectoderm. Later the exterior surface of the gill region of amphioxus is enclosed by growth of the covering wall that forms the atrial cavity outside the gills.

During development, the *coelom* is formed of five embryonic pouches as in hemichordates; in the adult amphioxus it becomes reduced and complicated except around the intestine. The *excretory system* comprises about 100 pairs of small ciliated *nephridia* in dorsal relics of the coelom above the pharynx; they connect the coelom to the atrial cavity and show some structural resemblance to the nephridia of certain annelid (polychaete) worms. A pair of larger structures, the *"brown bodies,"* dorsal to the intestine, may also be excretory in function.

The *nervous system* lies above the notochord; it consists of a single dorsal *nerve cord* with a small central canal. The anterior end is slightly enlarged to form a median *cerebral vesicle,* with a middorsal *olfactory pit,* a small nonsensory *eyespot* of black pigment, and two pairs of "cranial" *nerves.* The cord gives off to each myomere alternately a pair of *nerves,* the dorsal root being both sensory and motor, the ventral only motor in function. In the skin and the mouth region are ciliated cells thought to be sensory in function.

The sexes are separate; about 25 pairs of *gonads* (in 2 rows) bulge into the atrium. Eggs and sperm break into the atrial cavity to pass out through the atriopore, and fertilization is external. The egg is about 0.1 mm. in diameter, with little yolk, and segmentation is holoblastic (Fig. 11-10*A*). During the breeding season, egg deposition usually occurs about sunset, and by morning a free-swimming ciliated larva is hatched; this feeds and grows for up to 3 months, gradually assuming the adult form, and then takes to burrowing in the sand.

Lancelets of the Genus *Asymmetron* have gonads only on the right side.

Amphioxus is usually of purely zoological interest, but in Fukien Province near Amoy, in southern China, a local fishery for these animals has existed for hundreds of years. On a small area of sand where the animals are abundant, the catch amounts to over 1 ton per day; and an estimated one billion individuals are taken from August to April each year, to be used, either fresh or dried, as human food.

THE CRANIATA. Vertebrates

28-13. Characteristics. The Classes Cyclostomata to Mammalia comprise the major part of the Phylum Chordata. They all have an enlarged brain enclosed in a brain case or cra-

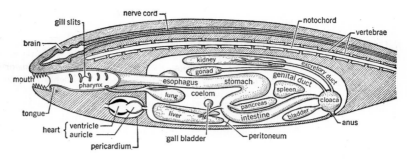

Fig. 28-13. Diagram of the principal structures in a craniate or vertebrate (both lungs and gills are indicated but rarely occur together).

nium, and a segmental spinal column of vertebrae that becomes the axial support of the body. Typically the body comprises a head, neck, trunk, and tail. These classes show a progressive series of structural and functional advances in all organ systems besides the features of the notochord, nerve cord, and gill slits mentioned earlier in this chapter under Characteristics (Fig. 28-13; see also Chaps. 4 to 10).

1. The *body covering* is a stratified epithelium, of epidermis and dermis, with many mucous glands in aquatic species; most fishes are covered with protective scales; the exterior is cornified on land dwellers, with scales on reptiles, feathers on birds, and hair on mammals; feathers and hair form insulated body coverings.

2. The internal and jointed *skeleton* is of cartilage in lower vertebrates and of bone in higher groups; it supports and protects various organs; the cranium shelters the brain and has paired capsules to contain organs of special sense; a series of visceral arches supports the gill region, and certain arches become the jaws and other structures of the head region; the vertebral column extends from the base of the cranium to the end of the tail and has neural arches dorsally to house the nerve cord. Two pairs of appendages, the fins of fishes and limbs of tetrapods, with jointed skeletal supports, are articulated with the vertebral column through limb girdles.

3. On the skeleton are *muscles* that move its parts and provide for locomotion.

4. The elongate *digestive tract* is ventral to the vertebral column; the mouth contains a tongue and usually teeth; the anus opens at the end of the trunk; the liver and pancreas are 2 large digestive glands that pour their secretions through ducts joined to the intestine.

5. The *circulatory system* includes a well-developed muscular heart of 2, 3, or 4 chambers, located ventral to the digestive tract; its contractions propel the blood through a closed system of arteries, capillaries, and veins, the flow being anteriorly on the ventral side and posteriorly in the dorsal arteries; the blood plasma contains both white and red corpuscles, the latter with hemoglobin as a respiratory pigment; a system of lymph vessels is present; paired aortic arches transport blood from the heart to the gills in lower vertebrates; progressive separation of the respiratory (pulmonary) and systemic blood paths through the heart leads to realization of regulated body temperature in the "warmblooded" (homoiothermous) birds and mammals.

6. *Respiration* in the lower forms is by paired gills; terrestrial species have lungs developed from outpocketings of the digestive tract.

7. The paired *excretory organs,* or kidneys, discharge through ducts opening near or through the anus; in lower forms, they are of segmental nature and drain wastes from both the coelom and the blood; in higher forms, they are nonsegmental and drain only from the blood; a bladder for storage of urine occurs in many.

8. The *brain* becomes regionally differentiated as to structure and function; the cerebral hemispheres and cerebellum enlarge, especially in higher forms; there are 10 or 12 pairs of cranial nerves in the head that serve both motor and sensory function, including the paired organs of special sense (smell, sight, and hearing plus equilibration); from the *nerve cord* a pair of spinal nerves serves each primitive body somite; an autonomic nervous system regulates involuntary functions of internal organs.

9. A series of *endocrine glands* (thyroid, pituitary, etc.) provide internal secretions, or hormones, transported by the blood stream, that regulate bodily processes, growth, and reproduction.

10. With rare exceptions the *sexes* are separate, and each has a pair of *gonads* that discharge sex cells through ducts opening into or near the anus.

CLASSIFICATION

PHYLUM CHORDATA. Chordates. At some stage or throughout life with notochord, dorsal nerve cord, and paired gill slits; segmentation and coelom usually evident; tail behind anus.

GROUP α. ACRANIA. Lower Chordates. No cranium, jaws, vertebrae, or paired appendages; all marine.

SUBPHYLUM A. HEMICHORDATA (Stomochorda). "Notochord" (stomocord) short, anterior; nerve tissues both dorsal and ventral in epidermis; marine, mostly in shallow waters, tropics to Arctic.

CLASS 1. *ENTEROPNEUSTA.* Tongue Worms. Body 25 to 2,500 mm. long, fleshy, contractile, comprising proboscis, collar, and trunk; paired gill slits 10 to 80 or more; digestive tract straight; coelom distinct, 3-parted. About 63 Recent species. *Ptychodera*, tropical coral reefs; *Balanoglossus*, *Saccoglossus*, worldwide.

CLASS 2. *PTEROBRANCHIA.* To 5 mm. long; body vase-like; digestive tract U-shaped; gill slits 2 or none; collar with lophophore of hollow branched ciliated arms; reproduce sexually or by buds.

Order 1. Rhabdopleuridea. Lophophore 2-armed; no gill slits; gonad 1; colonial; Cretaceous to Recent. *Rhabdopleura.*

Order 2. Cephalodiscidea. Lophophore of several arms; 2 gill slits; gonads 2; solitary; Ordovician, Recent. *Cephalodiscus.*

CLASS 3. *†GRAPTOZOA.* Graptolites. Colonial, each individual in a chitinous housing; Middle Cambrian to Carboniferous; marine, attached or free-floating.

Order 1. †Dendroidea. Form bush-like. *†Dendrograptus.*

Order 2. †Graptoloidea. Individuals on stalk in 1, 2, or 4 rows with common axial canal, or a compound colony with float. *†Tetragraptus*, *†Glossograptus.*

SUBPHYLUM B. TUNICATA (Urochordata). Tunicates. Larva free-living, minute, tadpole-like, with notochord and nerve cord in tail and with gill slits; adult tubular, globose, or irregular in form, covered with tunic (test), often transparent; usually no notochord, nerve cord reduced to ganglion; no coelom, segmentation, or nephridia.

CLASS 1. *LARVACEA* (Appendicularia). To 5 mm. long; larva-like in form and structure; notochord, "brain," and nerve cord persistent; 2 gill slits; tunic not persistent; free-swimming, pelagic. *Oikopleura*, *Appendicularia.*

CLASS 2. *ASCIDIACEA.* Ascidians. Size and form various; solitary, colonial, or compound; usually sessile after metamorphosis when notochord, nerve cord, and tail are lost and brain reduced to a ganglion; gill slits many, persistent; tunic well developed, permanent; atrium opens dorsally; stolon simple or none.

Order 1. Enterogona. Body sometimes divided (thorax, abdomen); neural gland usually ventral to ganglion; gonad 1, in or behind intestinal loop; larva with 2 sense organs on "head." *Clavelina*, *Ciona*, *Ascidia.*

Order 2. Pleurogona. Body undivided; neural gland usually dorsal or lateral to ganglion; gonads 2 or more, in lateral walls of mantle; larva usually with 1 sense organ on "head." *Styela*, *Molgula*, simple; *Botryllus*, compound.

CLASS 3. *THALLIACEA.* Chain Tunicates. Size various; adults lack notochord and tail; gill slits various; tunic permanent, with circular muscle bands; atrium opens posteriorly; stolon complex; adults free-living, pelagic.

Order 1. Pyrosomida. A compact, tubular colony; muscle bands at ends of body only; gill slits tall, numerous, to 50; phosphorescent in life; no larva. All oceans, at surface to depths of 9,000 feet. One genus, *Pyrosoma.*

Order 2. Salpida. Salps. Cylindrical or prism-shaped; muscle bands incomplete below, convergent above; 1st gill slit in adult a single large opening; transparent in life; no larva. Widespread in coastal and deeper waters to 4,500 feet. *Salpa.*

Order 3. Doliolida. Barrel-shaped; muscle bands complete, with 8 regular rings; gill slits few or many, short; a tailed larva. In warm and temperate oceans, widely distributed. *Doliolum.*

SUBPHYLUM C. CEPHALOCHORDATA (Leptocardii). Lancelets, "Amphioxus." Slender, body fish-like, segmented; epidermis 1-layered, no scales; notochord and nerve cord along entire body and persistent as are the many gill slits. Widely distributed in shallow waters. Only 2 genera: *Branchiostoma*, gonads paired; *Asymmetron*, gonads unpaired.

GROUP β. CRANIATA. Vertebrates. With cranium, visceral arches, vertebrae, and brain. See Classification in Chaps. 29 to 36.

REFERENCES

Lower Chordates

BIGELOW, H. B., and I. P. FARFANTE. 1948. Lancelets. *In* Fishes of the western North Atlantic. New Haven, Yale University, Sears Foundation for Marine Research. Pt. I, pp. 1–28.

BERRILL, N. J. 1950. The Tunicata, with an account of the British species. London, The Ray Society. iii + 354 pp., 120 figs.

GRASSÉ, PIERRE-P., and OTHERS. 1948. Echinodermes-Stomocordés-Procordés. *In* Traité de zoologie. Paris, Masson & Cie. Vol. 11, pp. 367–1,040, figs. 1–460.

HATSCHEK, B. 1881. Studien ueber der Entwickelung des Amphioxus. *Arbeiten des zoologische Institute zu Wien,* vol. 4.

HUUS, J., and OTHERS. 1933. Tunicata. *In* W. Kükenthal and others, Handbuch der zoologie. Vol. 5, pt. 2, secs. 1–7, pp. 1–768, 581 figs.

MORGAN, T. H. 1894. The development of Balanoglossus. *Journal of Morphology,* vol. 9, pp. 1–86, illus.

VAN DER HORST, C. J. 1927–1935. Hemichordata. *In* H. G. Bronn, Klassen und Ordnungen der Tierreichs. Vol. 4, pt. IV, book 2, pp. 1–514, 588 figs.

VAN NAME, W. G. 1945. The North and South American ascidians. *American Museum of Natural History Bull.,* vol. 84, pp. 1–476, 31 pls., 327 figs. A manual with keys to species.

WILLEY, A. 1894. Amphioxus and the ancestry of the vertebrates. New York, Columbia University Press. xiv + 316 pp., illus.

Vertebrates (See also Chaps. 29 to 35)

BERRILL, N. J. 1955. The origin of vertebrates. Oxford, Clarendon Press. viii + 257 pp., 31 figs.

BOLK, LOUIS, and OTHERS. 1931–1939. Handbuch der vergleichenden Anatomie der Wirbeltiere. Berlin, Urban & Schwartzenberg. 6 vols.

DE BEER, G. R. 1951. Vertebrate zoology. New ed. London, Sidgwick & Jackson, Ltd. xv + 435 pp., 185 figs.

COLBERT, E. H. 1955. Evolution of the vertebrates. New York, John Wiley & Sons, Inc. xiii + 479 pp., 122 figs.

GOODRICH, E. S. 1930. Studies on the structure and development of vertebrates. London, Macmillan & Co., Ltd. xxx + 837 pp., 754 figs.

HYMAN, L. H. 1942. Comparative vertebrate anatomy. Chicago, University of Chicago Press. xx + 544 pp., 136 figs.

PARKER, T. J., and W. A. HASWELL. 1941. A textbook of zoology. 6th ed. London, Macmillan & Co., Ltd. Vol. 2 on chordates revised by C. Forster-Cooper. xxiii + 758 pp., illus.

RAND, H. W. 1950. The chordates. Philadelphia, The Blakiston Co. xi + 862 pp., 609 figs.

ROMER, A. S. 1941. Man and the vertebrates. 3d ed. Chicago, University of Chicago Press. viii + 405 pp., 106 pls., 135 figs.

———. 1955. The vertebrate body. 2d ed. Philadelphia, W. B. Saunders Co. viii + 644 pp., 390 figs.

YOUNG, J. Z. 1950. The life of vertebrates. Oxford, Clarendon Press. xvi + 767 pp., 496 figs.

29 CLASS CYCLOSTOMATA
Cyclostomes

The CYCLOSTOMATA (Gr. *cyklos*, circular + *stoma*, mouth) include the lampreys, hagfishes, and slime eels (Fig. 29-1), all of which live in salt and fresh waters. These lowest of living vertebrates are jawless, and their nearest allies are the ancient, armored fish-like ostracoderms of Silurian and Devonian times.

29-1. Characteristics. 1. Body long, slender, and rounded, tail region compressed; median fins supported by cartilaginous fin rays; skin soft and smooth, with many unicellular mucous glands; no scales, jaws, or paired fins.
  2. Mouth ventroanterior and suctorial, margined by fleshy papillae or tentacles; nasal sac single and median.
  3. Skull and visceral arches (branchial basket) cartilaginous; notochord persistent; vertebrae represented by small imperfect neural arches (arcualia) over notochord.
  4. Heart 2-chambered, with auricle and ventricle; multiple aortic arches in gill region; blood with leucocytes and nucleated circular erythrocytes.
  5. Six to 14 pairs of gills, in lateral sac-like pouches off pharynx.
  6. Two kidneys with ducts to urogenital papilla.
  7. Brain differentiated, with 10 (or 8) pairs of cranial nerves; each auditory organ with 1 or 2 semicircular canals.
  8. Body temperature variable (poikilothermous).
  9. Gonad single, large, without duct; fertilization external; development direct (hagfishes and slime eels) or with long larval stage (lampreys).

The vertebrate features of cyclostomes include the differentiated brain and paired cranial nerves, eyes, and internal ears, beginnings of segmental vertebrae, characteristic organ

systems, and presence of both red and white blood cells. Cyclostomes differ from other vertebrates in having no differentiated head, jaws, paired appendages, limb girdles, ribs, or reproductive ducts, a single nasal sac and gonad, and but one or two semicircular canals in each "ear."

29-2. Structure of a lamprey (Figs. 29-2, 29-3[1]). The combined head-and-trunk or *body* is cylindrical, and the *tail* is laterally compressed. On the posterior dorsal region and tail are *median fins*. Ventrally on the head is a large cup-like *buccal funnel,* margined by soft papillae and lined within by conical yellow horny *teeth.* The single *nostril* is middorsal on the head, followed by thin skin over the pineal organ. The two large *eyes* are lateral and covered by transparent skin, but lack lids. Behind each are seven rounded *gill slits.* A row of small lateral *sense pits* extends segmentally along each side of the body and tail. The *anus* opens ventrally at the base of the tail, and close behind is a small *urogenital papilla,* pierced by a duct. The whole animal is covered by smooth epithelium containing many mucous glands but no scales.

29-3. Skeleton. The *notochord* persists throughout life as the axial skeleton; it is a slender gelatinous rod sheathed in tough connective tis-

[1] See color Fig. 29-3, p. 484.

Fig. 29-1. Class CYCLOSTO-
MATA. *Above.* California hagfish (*Polistotrema stouti*), with
soft suctorial mouth, 4 pairs of
tentacles, and 12 pairs of gill
slits. *Below.* Sea lamprey (*Petromyzon marinus*), with buccal
funnel, eyes, and **7** pairs of
gill slits. (*Modified from Wolcott, Animal biology.*)

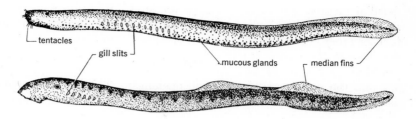

sue. The other principal **skeletal elements,** all
cartilaginous, include (1) the complex skull
(cranium and sense capsules); (2) the stout
lingual cartilage of the tongue, and a ring of
annular cartilage surrounding the buccal funnel; (3) the elaborate paired visceral arches, or
"branchial basket," supporting the gill region;
and (4) small slender rod-like arcualia dorsal
to the notochord, two pairs to most body segments, that represent the neural arches of
higher vertebrates.

29-4. Muscular system. The trunk and tail
regions are walled by short segmental muscles,
in ⋛-shaped arrangement, as in other fishes.
Radial muscles operate the buccal funnel, and
the tongue is moved by stout retractor and
smaller protractor muscles.

29-5. Digestive system. The small **mouth** is
centered in the buccal funnel and closed or
opened by the fore-and-aft piston-like movement of the **tongue.** On the latter are horny
teeth like those in the funnel (Fig. 29-5*A*). A
short **pharynx** follows, then the tract divides
into a dorsal **esophagus** and ventral **respiratory
tube;** the entrance to the latter is guarded by a
flexible transverse plate, the **velum.** There is no
stomach. The posterior end of the esophagus
opens, by a valve, into the straight **intestine.**

Within the latter is a spiral longitudinal fold
(typhlosole), or spiral valve. The intestine ends
at the small **anus.** The **liver** is usually without
a bile duct; it is uncertain whether a "pancreas" is present.

29-6. Circulatory system. The **heart** lies within
the cup-shaped posterior end of the branchial
basket in a pericardial sac that communicates
with the coelom. It consists of an auricle and
a thicker-walled ventricle, with a conus arteriosus anteriorly. Blood from the heart is pumped
forward into a **ventral aorta** that distributes in
eight pairs of afferent branches to the gill filaments, then is collected in a median **dorsal
aorta,** above the gills, that distributes both
anteriorly and posteriorly. The venous system
returns blood from the head and body and includes a hepatic system through the liver but
no renal portal system; lymphatic vessels are
also present.

29-7. Respiratory system. There are seven **gills**
in pouches on either side, between the respiratory tube and the body wall. Each contains
many gill filaments with fine capillaries in which
the blood is aerated by water in the pouches. In
an adult lamprey the water currents serving
for respiration pass both *in* and *out* of the gill
slits, a route unlike that in true fishes. This

Fig. 29-2. Class CYCLOSTOMATA. Structure of adult lamprey (*Entosphenus tridentatus*); left side of body mostly removed.

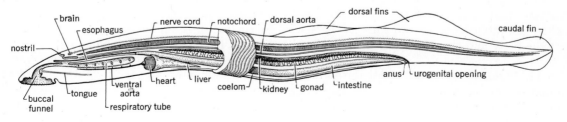

peculiar method is necessary because the lamprey often attaches by its buccal funnel to food or other objects, when the passage of water through the mouth is impossible; in a larval lamprey the respiratory current passes in through the mouth and out the gill openings, as in fishes.

29-8. Excretory system. The two *kidneys* (mesonephroi) are dorsal in the body cavity; a tubular *ureter* extends from each to the *urogenital sinus,* which empties to the exterior through the *urogenital papilla.*

29-9. Nervous system. The forebrain includes large paired *olfactory lobes,* followed by smaller *cerebral hemispheres* attached to the *diencephalon;* beneath the latter is a broad *infundibulum* and, dorsally, a *pineal structure.* On the midbrain, dorsally, is a pair of large *optic lobes.* In the hind brain, the *cerebellum* is a small transverse dorsal band, and the ventral *medulla oblongata* is much larger. Large apertures with choroid plexes containing blood vessels occur between the optic lobes and over the medulla. Within the brain are four *ventricles,* as in other vertebrates. There are 10 pairs of *cranial nerves.* The *nerve cord* is flattened and bandlike. The dorsal and ventral roots of the paired *spinal nerves* emerge alternately from the cord and are not bound together as in other vertebrates. There is a poorly defined sympathetic system.

29-10. Sense organs. The single nasal opening leads into an *olfactory sac* receiving nerve endings from both olfactory lobes of the brain. Besides the paired *eyes,* an elaborate median *pineal eye* with clear lens and pigmented retina lies behind the nasal aperture. Each internal *ear* (organ of equilibrium) has two semicircular canals. Taste buds occur in the pharynx, and there are *lateral line* sense organs on the sides of the body and the undersurface of the head.

29-11. Endocrine glands. Beneath the infundibulum is a *pituitary body;* a long sac extending posteriorly from the olfactory sac is termed the

pituitary pouch. The endostyle of the larva resembles similar structures in tunicates and amphioxus and is considered to be the forerunner of the thyroid gland of the adult lamprey.

29-12. Reproductive system. The immature gonad is hermaphroditic but later becomes either male or female in any one individual, so that in adults the sexes are separate (dioecious) as in other vertebrates. At sexual maturity a single large elongate *gonad* fills much of the abdominal cavity. There is no genital duct; eggs or sperm discharge into the abdominal cavity and pass through paired *genital pores* into the urogenital sinus, thence to the outside.

29-13. Hagfishes and slime eels. As compared with lampreys, members of the Order MYXINOIDIA differ in many ways, having (1) a soft suctorial mouth with one large dorsal epidermal tooth, but no buccal funnel; (2) four pairs of soft anterior tentacles; (3) nostril terminal and median with canal (and pituitary pouch) under brain to roof of pharynx as channel for water entering to aerate gills; (4) roof and sides of brain case membranous, branchial basket far reduced, arcualia few and posterior; (5) myomeres alternate; (6) gills 6 or 14 pairs, far posterior; (7) segmental pronephros (with nephrostomes) in adult; (8) brain primitive, of 4 lobes, no recognizable cerebrum or cerebellum, dorsal and ventral roots of spinal nerves united; (9) eyes degenerate; (10) each ear with only one semicircular canal; (11) lateral line system far reduced; and (12) adults normally monoecious, eggs large, with shells formed in ovary.

29-14. Natural history. Lampreys occur in both fresh and salt waters; the hagfishes are marine, some descending to depths of more than 300 fathoms. Some adult lampreys are nonparasitic. The parasitic species attach to fishes (Fig. 29-4) by suction of the funnel and use of the buccal teeth; a hole is rasped by the lingual teeth and an anticoagulant injected, when the host's blood flows into the mouth of the lamprey. Healthy fishes are attacked and may be killed. The hagfishes and slime eels burrow into the bodies of fishes and consume the flesh, leaving only a bag of skin and the bones. Their effects are seen on fishes caught by set nets or lines, but healthy free-swimming fishes also may be attacked.

29-15. Reproduction. When lampreys, either marine or fresh-water, become sexually mature, in the spring or early summer, the gonads swell and both sexes move into streams, sometimes "riding" on a passing fish or boat. They seek clear water on riffles in streams, and by use of the buccal funnel move stones on the bottom until a shallow rounded depression, free of silt, is prepared as a nest (Fig. 29-5C). The female then attaches to a stone on the upstream side, and the male fastens to the female, both using their buccal funnels. Partly entwined, they wriggle back and forth as eggs and sperm are discharged, fertilization being external. The eggs are small (1 mm. in the brook lamprey) and adhesive; they quickly sink and are covered by silt and sand. A female brook lamprey may contain up to 65,000 eggs and that of the large sea lamprey up to 236,000 eggs. Several pairs usually spawn close together, at times in the same nest. All adults die after spawning.

The young emerge in a month or so as minute larvae; when 12 to 15 mm. long, they quit the nest to seek quiet water. There each constructs and inhabits a U-shaped tunnel in the sand and silt but emerges to feed on ooze covering the stream bottom (Fig. 29-5D). Water is drawn into the mouth by ciliary action and passes out through the gill apertures. The food is caught in mucus secreted by the endostyle on the floor of the pharynx, as in amphioxus.

The larvae, known as "ammocoetes," are blind and toothless and have a long life, from at least 3 years (*Entosphenus tridentatus*) to perhaps 7 years (*Ichthyomyzon unicolor*), during which they grow. When metamorphosis ensues, two courses are pursued by different types of lampreys. In the more primitive group a functional digestive tract is retained and strong sharp teeth develop; such lampreys feed on fishes, continuing to live and grow in the sea or in large streams or lakes, according to the spe-

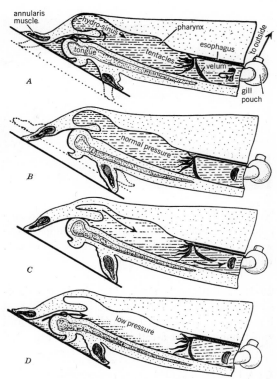

Fig. 29-4. Lamprey attaching and feeding; diagrams of the action of the buccal funnel and tongue. (*After T. E. Reynolds*, 1931.) *A.* Buccal funnel is collapsed against an object, and its interior volume is decreased by forcing water behind tongue into pharynx. *B.* Tongue closes passage between funnel and pharynx; funnel warped out to increase internal volume and degree of suction. *C.* Water in hydrosinus is forced behind velum; tongue continues to block oral passage. *D.* Velum prevents return of water from gill pouches; tongue is free to move back and forth in rasping flesh.

cies. After having existed in this state for a year (perhaps longer in the largest species), they reascend small streams in the spring to spawn and then die. Members of the second group cease feeding and growth after metamorphosis in August to October; the alimentary tract and teeth partly degenerate, and after 4 to 11 months the animals breed and die. Such degenerate lampreys have developed as offshoots of the normal type at several places, in both eastern and western states and other parts of the world.

In the hagfish the same individual produces sperm and then eggs later, being protandrous.

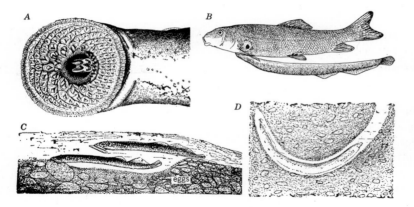

Fig. 29-5. Structure and life of lake lampreys. *A.* Buccal funnel in ventral view with many horny teeth. *B.* Lamprey attached to a fish. *C.* Nest with female attached to a stone, male carrying another stone; small eggs in rear of nest. *D.* Larval lamprey (ammocoetes) in its burrow under the water. (*After S. H. Gage*, 1893, 1929.)

The eggs are large (10 by 30 mm.) and enclosed in a horny shell that may attach to seaweeds. Growth to the adult form is direct, without a larval stage.

29-16. Relations to man. Hagfishes often damage fishes caught on lines or in nets. Larval lampreys serve as bait for both commercial and sport fishing, and adult sea lampreys are used to a small extent as food. Sea lampreys have invaded the Great Lakes in large numbers, and their attacks on lake trout have reduced the annual catch from about 15 million pounds to less than one-tenth that amount. Attempts at control include trapping and building barriers to keep lampreys from spawning in streams. Lampreys injure or destroy fishes by taking blood and causing secondary infections.

CLASSIFICATION

CLASS 1. †*OSTRACODERMI.* Ancient Jawless Vertebrates. Small; body usually depressed; covered usually with bony scales and these often fused as a shield covering the head; skull of bone or cartilage; nasal opening 1 (or 2); a pair of eyes and a pineal eye; paired gill slits numerous; median fins on tail and body; some with pectoral lobes behind head. Ordovician to Devonian; mainly in fresh waters and on the bottom. †*Cephalaspis;* †*Birkenia;* †*Pteraspis.*

CLASS 2. *CYCLOSTOMATA* (Marsipobranchii). Body cylindrical, elongate; skin smooth, without scales; mouth suctorial, with horny teeth; nasal aperture single and median; no jaws, paired appendages, or genital ducts; gills 6 to 14 pairs, in pouches; heart 2-chambered; aquatic.

Order 1. Petromyzontia. Lampreys. Mouth surrounded by a large ventral suctorial funnel with many horny teeth; nasal sac dorsal, not connected to mouth; 7 pairs of gill pouches, opening separately; "branchial basket" well developed; eggs small; a long larval stage; nearly world-wide along seacoasts and in streams and lakes. *Petromyzon marinus,* sea lamprey, Atlantic coast from Chesapeake Bay northward and in Europe, grows to 3 feet, spawns in fresh water, landlocked in Finger Lakes, N.Y., spreading in Great Lakes; *Entosphenus tridentatus,* Pacific lamprey of western shores, southern California to Alaska, spawns in fresh water; *E. amottenii* and others, brook lampreys, nonparasitic, eastern and middle-western states; *Ichthyomyzon,* brook lamprey, central United States and Canada.

Order 2. Myxinoidia. Slime Eels and Hagfishes. Mouth nearly terminal, with 4 pairs of tentacles about margin, no buccal funnel, few teeth; nasal sac near end of head, with duct to pharynx; eyes beneath skin; gill slits 10 to 14 pairs; "branchial basket" and arcualia poorly developed; eggs large, development direct; marine. *Myxine limosa,* slime eel, Cape Cod northward on the Atlantic coast; *M. glutinosa,* Europe, to 3 feet long; *Bdellostoma,* Chile; *Polistotrema (Eptatretus),* "the borer," Lower California to Alaska.

REFERENCES

(See also Chap. 31)

APPLEGATE, V. C., and J. W. MOFFETT. 1955. The sea lamprey. *Scientific American*, vol. 192, no. 4, pp. 36–41, illus.

GAGE, S. H. 1893. The lake and brook lampreys of New York. . . . Ithaca, N.Y., Wilder Quarter-Century Book. Pp. 421–493, 8 pls. Structure, function, and natural history; includes the landlocked form of the sea lamprey.

HUBBS, C. L. 1924. The life-cycle and growth of lampreys. *Michigan Academy of Science, Arts and Letters, Papers*, vol. 4, pp. 587–603, figs. 16–22.

LENNON, R. E. 1954. Feeding mechanism of the sea lamprey and its effect on host fishes. *U.S. Fish & Wildlife Service Fisheries Bull.*, vol. 56, pp. 245–293, 19 figs.

REYNOLDS, T. E. 1931. Hydrostatics of the suctorial mouth of the lamprey. *University of California Publications in Zoology*, vol. 37, pp. 15–34, 3 pls., 2 figs. Anatomy and function of the head region.

30 CLASS CHONDRICHTHYES

Cartilaginous Fishes

The sharks, rays, and chimaeras of the Class CHONDRICHTHYES (Gr. *chondros*, cartilage + *ichthys*, fish) are the lowest living vertebrates with complete and separate vertebrae, movable jaws, and paired appendages. All are predaceous, and practically all are ocean dwellers. The group is ancient and is represented by many fossil remains, especially teeth, fin spines, and scales. The shark is of major biological interest, because some of its basic anatomical features appear in early embryos of the higher vertebrates.

30-1. Characteristics. 1. Skin tough, covered with minute placoid scales and having many mucous glands; both median and paired fins present, all supported by fin rays; pelvic fins with "claspers" in males.

2. Mouth ventral, with many enamel-capped teeth; nostrils 2 (or 1), not connected to mouth cavity; both lower and upper jaws present; intestine with spiral valve.

3. Skeleton cartilaginous, no true bone; cranium joined by paired sense capsules; notochord persistent; vertebrae many, complete, and separate.

4. Heart 2-chambered (1 auricle, 1 ventricle), with sinus venosus and conus arteriosus, contains only venous blood; several pairs of aortic arches; red blood cells nucleated and oval.

5. Respiration by 5 to 7 pairs of gills, each in a separate cleft (3 pairs + two half gills in chimaeras).

6. Ten pairs of cranial nerves.

7. Body temperature variable (poikilothermous), dependent upon environment.

8. Sexes separate; gonads typically paired; reproductive ducts discharge into cloaca; fertilization internal; oviparous or ovoviviparous; eggs large, with much yolk,

segmentation meroblastic; no embryonic membranes; development direct, no metamorphosis.

The cartilaginous fishes show advances over the cyclostomes in having (1) scales covering the body; (2) two pairs of lateral fins; (3) movable jaws articulated to the cranium; (4) enamel-covered teeth on the jaws; (5) three semicircular canals in each ear; and (6) paired reproductive organs and ducts. They stand below the bony fishes in having (1) the skeleton of cartilage, with no true bone; (2) placoid scales; (3) separate gill clefts; (4) a pair of spiracles connecting to pharynx; and (5) no air bladder.

Several theories have been proposed on the origin of paired fins in fishes. That of Balfour and others would derive the paired fins from lengthwise lateroventral fin folds supported by parallel fin rays (Fig. 30-2). As evidence, (1) amphioxus has such continuous (metapleural) folds joining the ventral caudal fin; (2) a small Devonian fish, †*Climatius*, had five accessory finlets between the pectoral and pelvic fins on each side; (3) †*Cladoselache*, a late Devonian shark, had paired fins with expanded bases supported by many parallel rays; and (4) embryos of some living sharks (*Scyllium*) have lateral skin folds preceding appearance of the paired fins. Other evidence from embryology, anatomy, and paleontology favors this theory.

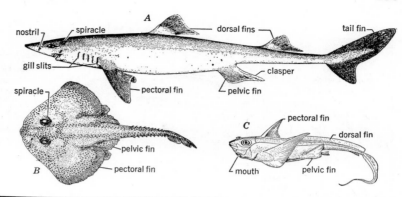

Fig. 30-1. Class CHONDRICH-THYES. *A.* Spiny dogfish or shark (*Squalus acanthias*). *B.* Ray (*Raja*). *C.* Chimaera (*Chimaera colliei*). (*A, after Goode; B, after General Biological Supply House; C, after Dean, Fishes living and fossil, The Macmillan Co.*)

Fig. 30-2. Possible origin of the fins on fishes from fin folds such as those on amphioxus. Compare Fig. 28-11. (*After Wiedersheim.*)

30-2. Size. Dogfishes (*Squalus*) grow to about 3 feet in length, and most sharks are under 8 feet long; however, both the great white shark (*Carcharodon carcharias*) and the basking shark (*Cetorhinus maximus*) may exceed 40 feet; and the whale shark (*Rhineodon typus*) reaches 50 feet in length. These are the biggest living vertebrates except whales. Most rays are 1 to 3 feet in length, but the greater devilfish (*Manta birostris*) grows to 17 feet in length and 20 feet across the pectoral fins. The chimaeras are less than 3 feet long.

STRUCTURE OF A DOGFISH OR DOG SHARK

30-3. External features. The *head* is bluntly pointed, and the *trunk* is spindle-shaped, largest near the pectoral fins, and tapering behind. There are two separate median *dorsal fins* (each preceded by a spine in the spiny dogfish, *Squalus*), a median *caudal fin,* and two pairs of *lateral fins, pectoral* and *pelvic.* Between the latter on males is a pair of slender *claspers,* used in mating. The smooth dogfish (*Mustelus*) has also a median *anal fin* ventrally. The *tail* is heterocercal, with the vertebrae extending into the larger dorsal lobe.

Ventrally on the head are two *nostrils* and the wide *mouth;* the *eyes* are lateral and with-

out lids. Five oval *gill slits* open anterior to each pectoral fin; a gill-like cleft, or *spiracle,* opens behind each eye. The *anus* is between the pelvic fins.

30-4. Body covering. The gray-colored *skin* is evenly covered with diagonal rows of minute *placoid scales* (Fig. 30-3), each with a backward pointing spine covered by enamel and a basal plate of dentine in the dermis.

30-5. Skeleton. The entire skeleton is of cartilage (gristle) more or less reinforced with limy deposits; the axial parts are the *skull* and the segmented *vertebral column.* Each *vertebra* has a spool-shaped centrum, concave on both ends (amphicoelous), and above this a neural arch to house the nerve cord; in the tail, each also bears ventrally a hemal arch shielding the caudal aorta and vein; the notochord persists

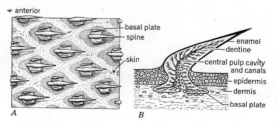

Fig. 30-3. Placoid scales (enlarged). *A.* Skin with scales in surface view. *B.* Median section through a scale. (*After Klaatsch.*)

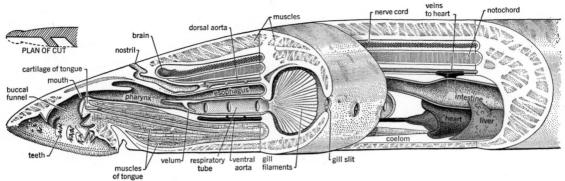

Fig. 29-3. Adult lamprey (*Entosphenus*), anterior end, with left side of body removed to median plane, leaving parts of gill region and muscular body wall.

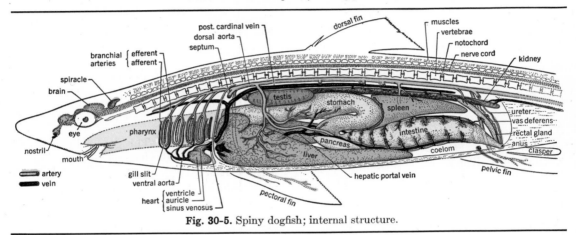

Fig. 30-5. Spiny dogfish; internal structure.

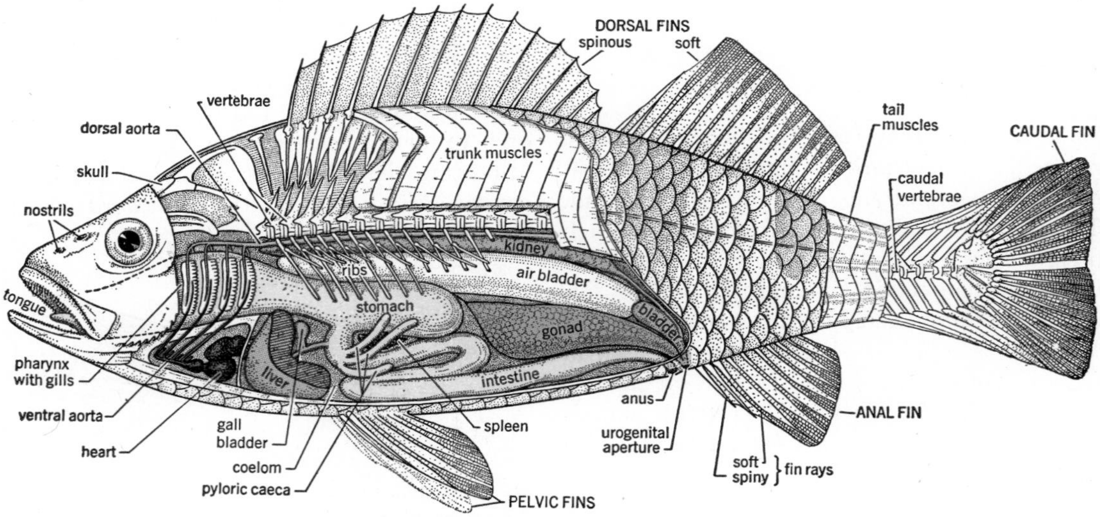

Fig. 31-3. Yellow perch; general structure. Operculum, pectoral fin, most of the skin and scales, and some trunk and tail muscles have been removed.

in the spaces between vertebrae. The skull is made up of (1) the cranium housing the brain; (2) paired capsules for the olfactory, optic, and auditory organs; and (3) the visceral skeleton, consisting of the jaws, the hyoid arch, and five pairs of branchial arches supporting the gill region. The appendicular skeleton includes (1) the U-shaped *pectoral girdle* supporting the pectoral fins; (2) the flatter *pelvic girdle* to which the pelvic fins attach; and (3) the many small jointed cartilages within and supporting each lateral fin. The median fins are supported by dermal *fin rays.*

30-6. Muscular system. The body and tail *muscles* are of segmental character and serve to produce the lateral undulations of the trunk and tail necessary for swimming. More specialized muscles serve the paired fins, gill region, and structures of the head.

30-7. Digestive system. The broad *mouth* is margined with transverse rows of sharply pointed *teeth;* these are embedded in flesh on the jaws and frequently replaced by new rows of teeth from behind. The teeth serve to grasp prey such as small fishes, which are often swallowed entire. A flat *tongue* adheres to the floor of the mouth. On the sides of the wide *pharynx* are openings leading to the separate *gill slits* and *spiracles.* The short *esophagus* leads to the J-shaped *stomach,* which ends at a circular sphincter muscle, the pyloric valve. The *intestine* follows and connects directly to the *cloaca* and *anus.* In the intestine is a spirally arranged partition, or *spiral valve,* covered with mucous membrane, that delays the passage of food and offers increased area for absorption (Fig. 30-4). The large *liver* is of two long lobes, attached at the anterior end of the body cavity. Bile from the liver collects in the greenish *gall bladder* and thence passes through the *bile duct* to the anterior part of the intestine. The *pancreas* lies between the stomach and intestine, its duct joining the latter just below the bile duct. A slim *rectal gland,* of unknown function, attaches dorsally at the junction of the intestine and cloaca.

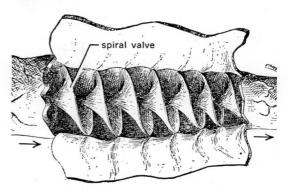

Fig. 30-4. Intestine of dogfish opened to show spiral valve. (*After Jammes.*)

30-8. Coelom. The stomach, intestine, and other internal organs lie in the large *body cavity,* or *coelom.* It is lined with a smooth glistening membrane, the *peritoneum,* which also covers the organs. The latter are supported from the middorsal wall of the coelom by thin *mesenteries,* also formed of peritoneum. A transverse *septum* separates the coelom from the cavity containing the heart.

30-9. Circulatory system. The *heart* lies beneath the gill region in a sac, the pericardium; it consists of (1) a thin-walled dorsal sinus venosus that receives blood from various veins, followed by (2) the auricle, (3) the thick-walled ventricle, and (4) the conus arteriosus. From the latter, blood passes anteriorly into the *ventral aorta,* whence five pairs of *afferent branchial arteries* distribute to capillaries in the gills for aeration; four pairs of *efferent branchial arteries* then collect the blood into the *dorsal aorta,* which extends along the middorsal wall of the coelom. The principal *arteries* are (1) paired external and internal carotids to the head; (2) paired subclavians to the pectoral fins; (3) coeliac to the stomach, liver, and intestine; (4) anterior mesenteric to the spleen and hind part of intestine; (5) posterior mesenteric to the rectal gland; (6) several renal and gonadic (ovarian or spermatic) to the kidneys and reproductive organs; and (7) paired iliacs to the pelvic fins. Beyond the latter the caudal aorta continues in the tail.

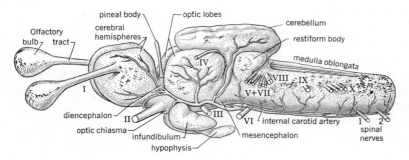

Fig. 30-6. Brain and nerves of the spiny dogfish from the left side. I–X, cranial nerves; 1, 2, spinal nerves.

In the **venous system,** blood in the caudal vein from the tail passes in (1) paired renal portal veins to the kidneys. Other blood from the posterior regions passes forward in (2) the paired postcardinal veins paralleling the kidneys and in (3) paired lateral abdominal veins on either side of the body cavity. Paired (4) jugular and (5) anterior cardinal veins return blood from the head region. All these veins enter large sinuses connected to the sinus venosus. Blood from the digestive tract flows in (6) the hepatic portal vein to be filtered through the liver, then is collected in (7) the hepatic veins connected to the sinus venosus. The blood passes through the heart but once in each circuit of the body, as in cyclostomes and most fishes, and the heart blood is all venous (unoxygenated; blue in Fig. 30-5; [1] see also Fig. 6-6).

30-10. Respiratory system. By opening and closing the mouth, the shark draws water in and forces it out the gill slits and spiracles (Fig. 31-6). The **gills** are composed of numerous parallel slender filaments that contain capillaries. The blood from the ventral aorta passes through these capillaries, discharges carbon dioxide and absorbs oxygen dissolved in the water, and then continues into the dorsal aorta.

30-11. Excretory system. The two slender **kidneys** lie immediately above the coelom on either side of the dorsal aorta. Urine from each is collected in a series of segmental tubules that join a longitudinal duct, the **ureter,** leading posteriorly, the two emptying through a single **urogenital papilla** dorsal in the cloaca.

30-12. Nervous system. The shark's **brain** (Fig. 30-6) is of a more advanced type than that of

[1] See color Fig. 30-5, p. 484.

the lamprey. From the two olfactory sacs in the snout, the large olfactory tracts extend to the **olfactory lobes,** which attach closely to the paired **cerebral hemispheres** on the **diencephalon.** Dorsally the latter bears a pineal stalk and **pineal body** and ventrally the **infundibulum** to which is attached the **hypophysis.** All these are part of the forebrain. Two rounded **optic lobes** lie dorsally on the midbrain. The hind brain comprises the large median dorsal **cerebellum** over the open-topped **medulla oblongata.** Ten pairs of **cranial nerves** serve structures, chiefly of the head, in approximately the same distribution as among other vertebrates (Table 10-1). The spinal **nerve cord** is protected by the neural arches of the vertebrae, an advance over the condition in cyclostomes. Paired **spinal nerves** to each body somite emerge between the neural arches of successive vertebrae.

30-13. Sense organs. Sharks depend importantly on olfactory stimuli received from water passing through the two shallow **olfactory sacs** on the snout. The **eyes** are capable of movement by three pairs of muscles attaching the eyeball to the eye socket. The **ears** are entirely within the head and serve the two distinct functions of (1) receiving sound impressions and (2) orientation. There are three semicircular canals at right angles to each other, as in all higher vertebrates. A slender endolymphatic duct extends from each ear to a small opening on the dorsal surface of the head.

The **lateral line** is a fine groove extending along each side of the body and tail. It contains a longitudinal canal with numerous transverse openings to the surface. Within the canal are sensory hair cells, segmentally arranged and connected to the lateralis branch of the tenth cranial nerve. On the surface of the head are many **sensory canals** opening in **pores** and containing **pit organs,** with sensory hairs surrounded by groups of supporting cells and connected to sensory nerve fibers. All these structures are derived, embryologically, from the auditory organ and are equivalent to the inner ear of higher vertebrates. They respond to slow pressure stimuli of waves and currents in the water.

30-14. Reproductive system. The sexes are separate. In the **male,** sperm develop in two long **testes** anterior in the body cavity; from each testis several **vasa efferentia** lead to a much convoluted **vas deferens** running posteriorly on the ventral surface of the kidney and emptying into the urogenital papilla. At mating, sperm are transferred from the male, by aid of the claspers, into the cloaca of the female.

The **female** system comprises a single large **ovary** attached dorsally by a stout membrane. Two **oviducts** extend the length of the body cavity, each having at the anterior end a large funnel through which the eggs enter. The anterior portion of each duct is dilated as a **shell gland,** and ovoviviparous species, like the dogfish, have the posterior part enlarged as a **"uterus"** to contain the young during development. The oviducts open separately into the cloaca.

30-15. Other cartilaginous fishes. Most other sharks resemble the dogfish in general anatomy. The rays have much depressed bodies with large pectoral fins broadly joined to the head and trunk, so that these fishes are diamond- or disc-shaped in outline. The gill openings are on the flat ventral surface, and the spiracles serve for entry of the respiratory currents of water. The tail is slender. Chimaeras are grotesque-appearing, the skin is scaleless, the gill slits on either side are covered by a membranous operculum, there is no spiracle, and the teeth are fused into bony plates.

30-16. Natural history. The sharks and rays are mostly marine, but a few inhabit rivers above

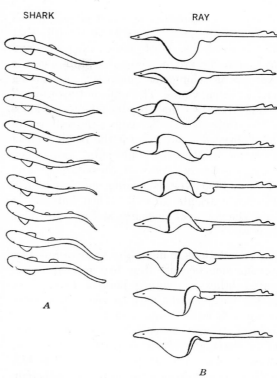

Fig. 30-7. The swimming of cartilaginous fishes. *A.* Shark (dorsal view) swims by lateral undulations of the trunk and tail. *B.* Ray (lateral view) swims by flapping movements of the pectoral fins. (*After Marey.*)

salt water. Most sharks live in open water, and rays on the bottom, but the manta and other large rays swim at or near the surface. Some tropical sharks and rays live permanently in fresh waters.

These fishes are all predaceous. Sharks are active swimmers, seeking prey appropriate to their size, and are usually common about large schools of fishes. The largest predaceous sharks may capture seals or sea lions, but the big basking and whale sharks feed upon plankton. The bottom-dwelling rays subsist upon various invertebrates.

30-17. Reproduction. The large eggs undergo meroblastic segmentation and develop slowly (16 to 25 months in the dogfish; 9 to 12 months in the chimaera). The primitive heterodont sharks, some dogfishes and rays, and the chimaeras are oviparous, depositing each egg in a brown horny capsule (mermaid purse) of distinctive shape; some cases have tendrils that affix to seaweeds. Most sharks, dogfishes, and rays, however, are ovoviviparous, retaining the eggs for development internally and giving birth to living young. The walls of the "uterus" (oviduct) in the female produce numerous loops of blood vessels that lie against the yolk sac of the embryo and provide for the respiration of the latter. In *Mustelus* a "placenta" forms when the yolk is nearly exhausted, the embryonic and maternal blood vessels coming close together to transfer nutrients as well. When hatched or born, the young of all sharks and rays resemble their parents.

30-18. Relations to man. Sharks are a nuisance to fishermen because they tear nets and steal netted fishes or remove bait or fishes from hooks. Large sharks may capsize small boats, or injure fishermen, and some tropical and subtropical species menace bathers. The great white shark (*Carcharodon carcharias*) attacks human beings in Australian waters, where half of 40 known attacks were fatal. In north temperate waters, attacks by sharks are scarce, but occasional human deaths result from injuries by the spines of sting rays.

Sharks and rays are used as human food in many countries. Shark fins are gathered and dried in Ceylon, the Philippines, and California; they are boiled and yield a gelatinous material favored for soups. Sharkskin tanned with the scales in place (then termed shagreen) was used in the Old World for casing fine books, jewel boxes, and sword handles, and as an abrasive for polishing wood and ivory. With the scales crushed, the skins make acceptable leather for shoes and bags.

Shark livers yield large quantities of oil, and fisheries for this product have existed for years in Greenland, Iceland, and Norway; a large basking shark yields about 125 gallons of oil. The oil contains large amounts of vitamin A, which is extracted for human use.

30-19. Fossil forms. Earliest of the known fossil vertebrates with jaws are the †PLACODERMI of Silurian to Permian time. The jaws were primitive, and the hyoid unspecialized and preceded by a complete gill slit. The latter, in higher classes, is a spiracle or an ear opening or is closed. Most placoderms had an operculum covering the gills that was developed from the mandibular arch. There were both median and paired fins, but the latter were more variable in number than in later fishes. The first CHONDRICHTHYES appear in mid-Devonian rocks (later than the first bony fishes) but already were well advanced in evolution of the jaws. No true bone is recognized in any shark, fossil or living, and the cartilaginous skeleton seems more likely a degenerate rather than primitive character. Some early types inhabited fresh waters, but the group has been predominantly marine; they were abundant and often well armored in the Paleozoic era but later decreased in numbers and had less armor.

CLASSIFICATION

CLASS 1. †*PLACODERMI* (Aphetohyoidea). ANCIENT FISHES. A full-sized functional gill cleft anterior to the unspecialized hyoid arch.

Order 1. †**Acanthodii.** Small; body armored with small diamond-shaped bone-like scales (ganoid-like); each fin except caudal preceded by a spine. Upper Silurian to Permian. †*Climatius*, †*Acanthodes*.

Order 2. †**Arthrodira.** JOINT-NECKED FISHES. Bony armor of two parts, head and gill region jointed to that of body. Mainly Devonian. †*Coccosteus*, †*Dinichthys*.

Order 3. †**Antiarchii.** Posterior trunk and tail fish-like, anterior trunk and head each with armor box; fresh water. Devonian. †*Pterichthyodes*.

Order 4. †**Stegoselachii.** ARMORED SHARKS. Body covered with bony plates; some of skate-like body form; marine. Devonian. †*Gemuendina*.

CLASS 2. *CHONDRICHTHYES* (Elasmobranchii). CARTILAGINOUS FISHES. Living forms with skeleton of cartilage; first gill slit a spiracle; scales minute, placoid; mouth and 2 nostrils ventral; males with claspers; ova large, much yolk, cleavage meroblastic.

Order 1. †**Cladoselachii.** Fins broad at base; no claspers. Devonian to early Permian. †*Cladoselache*.

Order 2. †Pleuracanthodii. Dorsal fin along most of body and tail; fresh water. Late Devonian to Triassic. *†Pleuracanthus.*

Order 3. Selachii. SHARKS and RAYS. Gills in separate clefts at sides of pharynx; a spiracle opening behind each eye; cloaca present; mostly marine; about 250 living species.

SUBORDER 1. SQUALI (Pleurotremata). SHARKS. Body typically spindle-shaped; tail heterocercal; gill slits lateral, 5 to 7 pairs; pectoral fins never greatly enlarged; 1st dorsal fin anterior to pelvics; swim by use of tail. Carboniferous to Recent. *Chlamydoselachus,* frilled shark, 6 pairs of gill slits; *Heterodontus,* Port Jackson shark, primitive; *Mustelus,* smooth dogfish, to 3 feet long; *Carcharias,* gray shark; *Sphyrna,* hammerhead, to 15 feet long, a large eye-bearing lobe at each side of head; *Rhineodon typus,* whale shark, to 50 feet long, harmless, feeds on plankton sieved from water by gill rakers in pharynx; *Alopias,* thresher shark, large, tail long; *Lamnia nasus,* porbeagle, to 10 feet long, sometimes in groups; *Cetorhinus maximus,* basking shark, to 40 feet long, feeds like whale shark; *Squalus (Acanthias),* spiny dogfishes, to 3 or 4 feet long, predaceous, common in shore waters; *Squatina,* angel shark, resembles rays but swims with tail, lives on bottom and eats flatfishes, mollusks, and crustaceans; *Pristiophorus* (gill slits, 5 pairs) and *Pliotrema* (6 pairs), saw sharks, resemble *Pristis* but gill slits lateral.

SUBORDER 2. BATOIDEA (Raji, Hypotremata). RAYS. Body depressed; pectoral fins enlarged and joined to sides of head and body; gill slits ventral, 5 pairs; spiracle highly functional; swim by flapping pectoral fins. Triassic to Recent; chiefly on bottom in shore waters, some down to 9,000 feet. *Pristis,* sawfish, to 20 feet long, snout long with tooth-like scales at sides, used to disable prey; *Rhinobatos,* guitar fish, somewhat shark-like; *Raja,* common rays and skates; *Torpedo,* electric rays, pectoral fins rounded, with many dorsal muscle cells modified as an electric organ producing severe shocks and used to stun prey; *Dasyatis, Urobatis, Aëtobatus,* sting rays, small, tail slender and whip-like, with 1 to 3 saw-edged spines containing poison glands that produce ugly, slow-healing wounds, sometimes complicated by gangrene or tetanus, on bathers and fishermen; *Manta,* manta, or "devilfish," size huge, swims at or near surface.

Order 4. †Bradodonti. Teeth as crushing plates. Devonian to Permian. *†Cochliodus; †Psammodus.*

Order 5. Holocephali. CHIMAERAS. Gill slits covered by operculum; no cloaca or spiracles; 1st dorsal fin far forward with strong spine; tail slender, whip-like; each jaw with large tooth plate; adults scaleless. Triassic to Recent. In cold ocean waters, down to 6,000 feet; 3 genera, 25 species. *Hydrolagus (Chimaera) colliei,* in North Pacific, from California northward, eats fish, invertebrates, and seaweed.

REFERENCES

(See also Chap. 31)

BIGELOW, H. B., and W. C. SCHROEDER. 1948. Sharks. *In* Fishes of the western North Atlantic. New Haven, Yale University, Sears Foundation for Marine Research. Pt. 1, pp. 59–576, figs. 6–106.

DANIEL, J. F. 1934. The elasmobranch fishes. 3d ed. Berkeley, University of California Press. xii + 332 pp., 270 figs.

DEAN, BASHFORD. 1906. The chimaeroid fishes and their development. *Carnegie Institution of Washington Publication No. 32,* 194 pp., 11 pls., 144 figs.

GARMAN, S. 1911. The chismopnea [chimaeroids]. *Museum of Comparative Zoology Memoirs,* vol. 40, pp. 79–101.

———. 1913. The Plagiostoma [cartilaginous fishes]. *Museum of Comparative Zoology Memoirs,* vol. 36 (2 parts), xiii + 528 pp., 77 pls. Keys and descriptions; nomenclature somewhat out of date.

GOODRICH, E. S. 1909. Chondrichthyes. *In* R. Lankester, Treatise on zoology. London, A. & C. Black, Ltd. Pt. 9, pp. 118–187, figs. 79–155.

MOY-THOMAS, J. A. 1939. Palaeozoic fishes. New York, Chemical Publishing Co. ix + 149 pp., illus.

WATSON, D. M. S. 1937. The acanthodian fishes. *Royal Society of London, Philosophical Transactions,* B, vol. 228, pp. 49–136, pls. 5–14, figs. 1–25.

31 CLASS OSTEICHTHYES
Bony Fishes

Many kinds of animals that live in water are called "fishes," from jellyfishes to starfishes, but the word applies properly to the lower aquatic vertebrates. The Greeks knew the fishes as *ichthyes*, and ichthyology is the scientific study of fishes; the common name fish derives from the Latin, *pisces*. The most typical or bony fishes have bony skeletons, are covered by dermal scales, usually have spindle-shaped bodies, swim by fins, and breathe by gills. Various species inhabit all sorts of waters, fresh, brackish, or salt, warm or cold. Fishes have been a staple protein food of mankind since antiquity, and many species provide pleasant recreation for sports fishermen.

31-1. Characteristics. 1. Skin with many mucous glands, usually with embedded dermal scales (ganoid, cycloid, or ctenoid); some naked (scaleless), a few with enamel-covered scales; both median and paired fins present (some exceptions), supported by fin rays of cartilage or bone; no limbs.

2. Mouth usually terminal and with teeth; jaws well developed, articulated to skull; olfactory sacs 2, dorsal, usually not connected to mouth cavity; eyes large, no lids.

3. Skeleton chiefly of bone (cartilage in sturgeons and some others); vertebrae many, distinct; tail usually homocercal; relics of notochord often persist.

4. Heart 2-chambered (1 auricle, 1 ventricle) with sinus venosus and conus arteriosus, containing only venous blood; 4 pairs of aortic arches; red blood cells nucleated and oval.

5. Respiration by pairs of gills on bony gill arches in a common chamber at each side of pharynx, covered by an operculum; usually with an air (swim) bladder, sometimes with duct to the pharynx, and lung-like in DIPNOI and some others.

6. Ten pairs of cranial nerves.

7. Body temperature variable, dependent upon environment (higher in tunas).

8. Gonads typically paired; usually oviparous (some ovoviviparous or viviparous); fertilization external (some exceptions), eggs minute to 12 mm., yolk various in amount; segmentation usually meroblastic; no embryonic membranes; early young (postlarvae) sometimes quite unlike adults.

The bony fishes are notable for their bony skeletons, scales, and plates, for the swim bladder, and for advances in the structure of the brain. The tail usually is altered from the heterocercal type of sharks to the homocercal and diphycercal forms (Fig. 31-11). Most modern fishes have less bony armor in the scales than did ancient types, many of which were fully armored (with cosmoid or ganoid scales). The head is encased in a true skull comprised of both cartilage or replacement bones and membrane or dermal bones. The fins in most bony fishes are supported by numerous parallel dermal rays, but in crossopterygians each paired fin has a single stout central element or lobe (sometimes jointed) that articulates with the limb girdle; this possibly became the limb skeleton in land vertebrates (Fig. 14-3). The swim bladder is lung-like in some bony fishes, and certain species have perforate nostrils and accessory structures that enable them to breathe air in shallow mucky water.

31-2. Size. The smallest fish is a Philippine goby (*Pandaka*) only 10 mm. long. Most fishes are under 3 feet in length. Some record large specimens are the halibut at 9 feet, the swordfish at 12 feet, and the Columbia River sturgeon at 12½ feet and 1,285 pounds.

STRUCTURE OF A BONY FISH: THE YELLOW PERCH

31-3. External features (Fig. 31-2 [1]). The body is spindle-shaped, higher than wide, and of oval cross section for easy passage through the water. The *head* extends from the tip of the snout to the hind edge of the operculum, the *trunk* from this point to the anus, and the remainder is the *tail*. The large *mouth* is terminal, with distinct jaws that bear fine teeth. Dorsally on the snout are two double *nostrils* (olfactory sacs), the *eyes* are lateral without lids, and behind each is a thin bony gill cover or *operculum,* with free edges below and posteriorly. Under each operculum are four comb-like *gills.* The *anus* and *urogenital aperture* precede the anal fin. Ichthyologists measure the standard length of a fish from the tip of the snout to the end of the last vertebra, to avoid error from wear of the tail fin; but fishermen include the fin.

On the back are two separate *dorsal fins,* on the end of the tail is the *caudal fin,* and ventrally on the tail is the *anal fin;* all these are median. The lateral or paired fins are the *pectoral fins* behind the opercula and the ventral or *pelvic fins* close below. The fins are membranous extensions of the integument, supported by *fin rays.* All except the first dorsal are flexible, being supported by soft rays which are calcified but with many joints and usually branched. The first dorsal has 13 to 15 solid calcified *spines,* and there are 1 or 2 similar spines in the anterior edge of the other fins. The fins aid in maintaining equilibrium, in steering, and in swimming.

[1] See also color Fig. 31-3, p. 484.

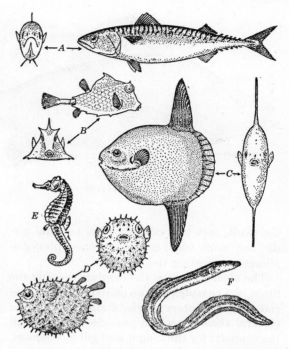

Fig. 31-1. Representative bony fishes (Class OSTEICHTHYES), of different bodily form. *A.* Mackerel (*Scomber*), streamlined and fast-swimming. *B.* Trunkfish (*Ostracion*), body rigid, only fins movable. *C.* Marine sunfish (*Mola*), huge, thin, deep-bodied. *D.* Globefish (*Chilomycterus*), body spiny, swollen, fins small. *E.* Sea horse (*Hippocampus*), swims erect by small dorsal fin, tail prehensile. *F.* Common eel (*Anguilla*), long and highly flexible. (*After Norman, History of fishes, Ernest Benn, Ltd.*)

31-4. Body covering (Fig. 31-4). The entire fish is covered by soft mucus-producing *epidermis* that facilitates easy movement in the water and is a protection against entry of disease organisms. The trunk and tail bear thin rounded dermal *scales,* in lengthwise and diagonal rows, with their free posterior edges overlapping like shingles on a roof; each lies in a dermal pocket and grows throughout life. The *lateral line,* along either side of the body, is a row of small pores connected to a lengthwise tubular canal under the scales, in which are sensory organs responsive to slow coarse vibrations in the water.

31-5. Skeleton. The scales and fins constitute an exoskeleton. The endoskeleton consists of

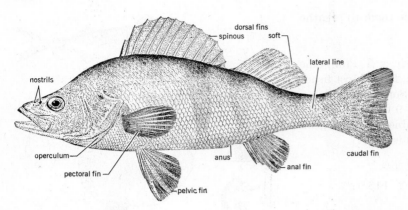

Fig. 31-2. Yellow perch (*Perca flavescens*); external features.

the skull, vertebral column, ribs, pectoral girdle, and many small accessory bones (pterygiophores) supporting the fin rays.

The **skull** comprises the **cranium** housing the brain, the **capsules** for the paired organs of special sense (olfactory, optic, auditory), and the **visceral skeleton,** which provides the jaws and the supports for the tongue and gill mechanism. The skull is so closely affixed to the vertebral column that a fish cannot "turn its head." **Teeth** are usually present on the premaxillary, dentary, vomer, and palatine bones.

In the embryo and young, the cranium is of cartilage, later largely replaced by separate **cartilage bones.** To these are added many **membrane bones** that result from ossifications in the embryonic connective tissue.

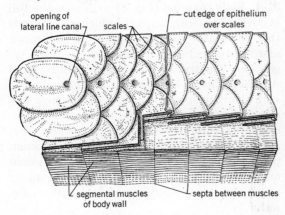

Fig. 31-4. Body wall of a bony fish (carp) near the lateral line, showing relations of the epidermis, scales, and muscles. (*Modified from Lankester, Treatise on zoology, A. & C. Black, Ltd.*)

The visceral skeleton comprises seven paired **arches,** first of cartilage and later ossified; these correspond to the arches of sharks and rays, but not to the branchial basket of lampreys. The upper part (palatoquadrate) of the **mandibular arch** (no. 1) attaches to the cranium, and each half of the upper jaw is formed of two membrane bones (premaxillary and maxillary). The primitive **lower jaw** (Meckel's cartilage) on each side is supplied with three bones, the dentary, angular, and articular, the latter hinging on the quadrate which attaches to the cranium. The **hyoid arch** (no. 2) partly supports the tongue. Four **gill arches** (nos. 3 to 6) each bear a gill on the outer curvature and a row of small spiny gill rakers on the inner or pharyngeal border; the latter form a sieve to protect the gills from injury by food. The small last arch (no. 7) has pharyngeal teeth but no gill.

The vertebral column is of many similar and separate **vertebrae;** each consists of (1) a cylindrical **centrum,** concave on both ends (amphicoelous); (2) a small dorsal **neural arch** over the spinal cord; above this (3) a slender elongate **neural spine** for muscular attachments; and (4) paired **parapophyses,** laterally on the centrum. Each caudal vertebra has also (5) a ventral or **hemal arch,** around the caudal artery and vein, and (6) a slender **hemal spine** below (Fig. 4-3). The column ends in an expanded (hypural) bone supporting the tail. The vertebrae are bound together by ligaments, and between the centra are relics of the notochord.

Slender paired rib-like bones attach to each

Fig. 31-5. Gills of a bony fish (carp). *A.* Gills in the gill chamber with operculum cut away. *B.* Part of a gill showing gill rakers and filaments, with path of blood in the latter; afferent vessels dark, efferent vessels light (in many fishes the gill rakers are slender). *C.* Portion of one filament with thin lamellae containing capillaries where blood is aerated. (*Partly after Goldschmidt, Ascaris, Prentice-Hall, Inc.*)

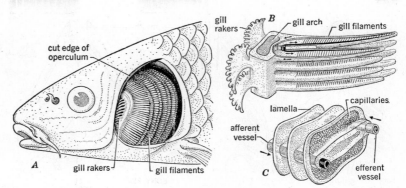

trunk vertebra, and delicate *intramuscular bones* (epipleurals) extend lengthwise between some of the ribs. In the flesh between the spines of the vertebrae are interspinal bones (pterygiophores) that support and articulate the dorsal and anal fin rays.

Each half of the *pectoral girdle* is of several bones (scapular, coracoid, clavicle, etc.), articulated dorsally to the skull and providing attachment for muscles of the pectoral fins. Four short bones with expanded tips (actinosts) and several nodules of cartilage (distal pterygiophores) articulate between the pectoral girdle and rays of each pectoral fin. There is no pelvic girdle; the ventral (pelvic) fins attach to a pubic bone (basipterygium), having a tendon or ligament to the pectoral girdle but no connection to the vertebral column.

31-6. Muscular system. The substance of the trunk and tail consists chiefly of *segmental muscles* (myomeres) that alternate with the vertebrae and produce the swimming and turning movements. Fish myomeres are broadly ≽-shaped, in four principal bands, and heaviest along the back. Between successive myomeres are delicate connective tissue septa; when a fish is cooked, these dissolve to leave the myomeres as individual "flakes." The muscles of the fins, gill region, and head are small.

31-7. Digestive system. The jaws have many small conical *teeth* to grasp food. Mucous glands are numerous, but there are no salivary glands. The small *tongue* is attached to the floor of the mouth cavity and may aid in respiratory movements. The *pharynx* has gills on

the sides and leads to a short *esophagus* followed by the recurved *stomach.* A pyloric valve separates the latter from the *intestine.* Three tubular *pyloric caeca,* secretory or absorptive in function, attach to the intestine. There is a large *liver* anteriorly in the body cavity, a *gall bladder,* and a bile duct to the intestine. The *pancreas* is usually indistinct.

31-8. Circulatory system. The two-chambered *heart* lies below the pharynx in the *pericardial cavity,* an anterior portion of the coelom. Venous blood passes into the *sinus venosus,* to the thin-walled *auricle,* thence into the muscular *ventricle,* all separated by valves that prevent reverse flow. Rhythmic contractions of the ventricle force the blood through the *conus arteriosus* and short *ventral aorta* into four pairs of *afferent branchial arteries* distributing to capillaries in the gill filaments for oxygenation. It then collects in correspondingly paired *efferent branchial arteries* leading to the *dorsal aorta,* which distributes branches to all parts of the head and body. The principal *veins* are the paired anterior cardinals and posterior cardinals and the unpaired hepatic portal circulation leading through the liver. The *blood* of fishes is pale and scanty as compared with that of terrestrial vertebrates. The fluid plasma contains nucleated oval red cells (erythrocytes) and various types of white cells (leucocytes). The *spleen,* a part of the blood system, is a large red-colored gland near the stomach. A lymphatic system is also present.

31-9. Respiratory system (Figs. 31-5, 31-6). The perch respires by means of *gills,* of which

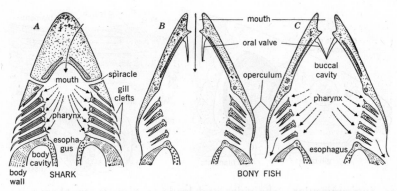

Fig. 31-6. The respiratory mechanism of fishes; diagrammatic frontal sections (lobes of oral valve actually are dorsal and ventral); arrows show paths of water currents. SHARK. *A.* Water enters ventrally placed mouth, which then closes, and floor of mouth region rises to force water over the gills and out the separate clefts. BONY FISH. *B. Inhalent,* opercula closed, oral valve open, cavity dilated, and water enters. *C. Exhalent,* oral valve closes, buccal cavity contracts, water passes over gills in common cavities at sides of pharynx and out beneath opercula. (*Modified from Boas.*)

there are four in a common gill chamber on each side of the pharynx, beneath the operculum. A gill consists of a double row of slender **gill filaments;** every filament bears many minute transverse plates covered with thin epithelium and containing capillaries between the afferent and efferent branchial arteries. Each gill is supported on a cartilaginous **gill arch,** and its inner border has expanded **gill rakers,** which protect against hard particles and keep food from passing out the gill slits. In "breathing," the opercula close against the body and the gill arches bulge laterally, whereupon water flows into the opened mouth; then the oral valve closes, the gill arches contract, the opercula lift, and the water is forced out over the filaments. Blood in the filaments gives up its carbon dioxide and absorbs oxygen from the water. The fish needs a constant supply of oxygen-bearing water and soon dies of asphyxiation if removed from water or if the water is depleted of oxygen. The phrase "to drink like a fish" is a misconception of the respiratory process, since a fish takes little or no fluid into its stomach except with food.

A large thin-walled sac, the **air bladder** or **swim bladder,** occupies the dorsal portion of the body cavity. It is connected to the pharynx by a pneumatic duct in some fishes, but not in the perch. The bladder is filled with gases (O, N, CO_2) and acts as a hydrostatic organ to adjust the specific gravity of the fish to that of the water at different depths. By secretion or absorption of the gases through blood vessels in the wall, a fish makes this adjustment slowly as it moves from one depth to another; if a fish is suddenly hauled up from a considerable depth, the greater pressure within the air bladder may, upon reaching the surface, force the stomach out of the mouth. In different fishes the bladder may aid respiration, or serve as a sense organ or in sound production. The air bladder is lung-like in the lung fishes (DIPNOI) and a few others.

31-10. Excretory system. The two slender dark **kidneys** lie dorsally between the air bladder and vertebrae. Fluid nitrogenous waste removed from the blood is carried posteriorly from each in a tubular **ureter,** both emptying into a **urinary bladder,** which in turn discharges through the **urogenital sinus** to the exterior.

31-11. Nervous system. The perch **brain** is short, the olfactory lobes, cerebral hemispheres, and diencephalon being smaller and the optic lobes and cerebellum larger than in a shark. There are 10 pairs of **cranial nerves.** The **nerve cord** is covered by the neural arches and gives

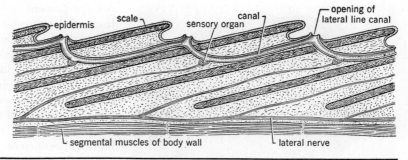

Fig. 31-7. Body wall of carp in longitudinal section, showing the lateral line sensory system; compare Fig. 31-4. (*Modified from Lankester, Treatise on zoology, A. & C. Black, Ltd.*)

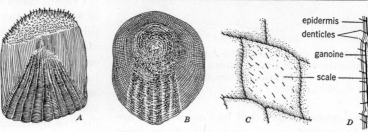

Fig. 31-8. Scales of bony fishes, enlarged. *A*. Ctenoid (with fine teeth). *B*. Cycloid. *C, D*. Ganoid (*Lepidosteus*) in surface view and vertical section.

off a pair of lateral *spinal nerves* to each body segment.

31-12. Organs of special sense. The dorsal *olfactory sacs* on the snout contain cells sensitive to substances dissolved in water. *Taste buds* are present in and around the mouth. The large *eyes* probably focus clearly only on nearby objects but serve to detect moving objects above water, such as a person walking on the bank. The internal *ear* contains three semicircular canals and an *otolith* serving the sense of equilibrium. Opinions differ as to the reactions of fishes to sound; any vibrations that are perceived must be transmitted through the head or body, since fishes have no eardrum or middle ear. The *lateral line system* (Fig. 31-7) has various extensions on the head and evidently detects slight changes in pressure or slow wave or current movements (not over 6 per second) such as might be experienced by a fish swimming close to some solid object from which water movements would be reflected; it is innervated by the lateralis branch of the tenth cranial nerve. This system is considered to survive in land vertebrates as the inner ear.

31-13. Reproductive system. In a *male* the two *testes* enlarge greatly in the breeding season,

and at mating the "milt," or sperm, passes in a *vas deferens* from each to emerge from the urogenital aperture. In a *female* the eggs pass from the two united *ovaries* through the *oviducts*.

STRUCTURE OF OTHER BONY FISHES

All bony fishes are enough alike in general form and structure to be recognized as members of the Class OSTEICHTHYES, but they differ among themselves in details. Many have the general configuration of the perch; the flounders, soles, and some tropical reef fishes are thin-bodied, the eels are slender, and the porcupine fishes are globular.

31-14. Scales. Most fishes are covered with *scales* (Fig. 31-8). While usually thin and overlapping, the scales are separate and minute on eels, small and tubercle-like on some flounders, and slender spines on porcupine fishes. The overlapping scales of tarpon are up to 2 inches in width, whereas some fishes are scaleless or naked (catfish). The scales are usually bony. On the perch and many others the exposed hind part of each has many tiny spines, making a

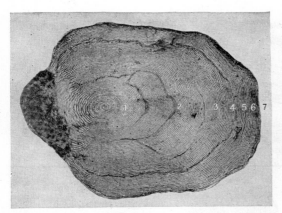

Fig. 31-9. Scale of 7-pound female rainbow trout, showing concentration of winter growth rings (numbered) which indicate age in years. (*Enlarged photograph, courtesy of C. McC. Mottley.*)

ctenoid scale. Others that lack such spines are termed *cycloid* scales, and still others have *ganoid* scales covered externally by enamel. The heads and bodies of various fishes, living and fossil, are armor-plated with large stout scales, as in the trunkfish; living species so protected are usually small or sluggish.

The scales grow throughout life, increasing in size with the fish. There is no molt of the body covering, although occasional scales may be lost and replaced. On many species growth results in a series of fine concentric ridges that end obliquely on the scale margin. After cessation of growth during winter, the first ridges of the next growth season form parallel to the scale margin, making a definite "winter line" (Fig. 31-9). These features make age determination possible in salmon, trout, bass, and others. (Otoliths also yield age data in some fishes.) This provides important data on the rate of growth, age at spawning, and other features for some food and game fishes. The scale pattern is essentially constant in a species; thus, the structure, form, number, and arrangement of scales are of much value in classification.

31-15. Coloration. Bony fishes are variously colored by pigment cells, or *chromatophores,* in the dermis, either outside or beneath the scales. Pigments of black, yellow, orange, and red are present in different species. Combinations of these result in green (black + yellow), brown (red or yellow + black), and other colors. Opaque crystals of *guanine* in other cells (iridocytes) provide the bright silvery or chalky-white appearance on various fishes. Interference phenomena, due probably to exceedingly thin layers of material over the pigments, are responsible for the prismatic hues and brilliant iridescence of some species.

Certain fishes change color by concentrating or spreading pigment in the chromatophores; this is slow in some but can be rapid in others. Some flounders can simulate the sea bottom on which they rest (Fig. 31-10). The stimulus to change is received through the eyes, as fish artificially blinded do not respond like normal ones. Some fishes, like brook trout, undergo little or no change in pattern or color but can alter in shade. Fishes living in the perennial darkness of the deep sea are often black.

31-16. Fins. The fins are diverse in form, size, and placement. The pectoral fins are usually

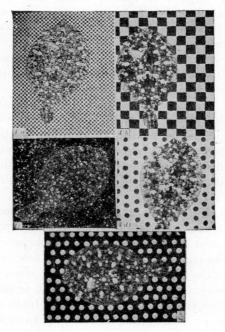

Fig. 31-10. Color changes in a flounder (*Rhomboidichthys podas*) some time after being placed on various types of backgrounds. (*After Sumner, from Guyer, Animal biology, Harper & Brothers.*)

Fig. 31-11. Types of tails in bony fishes, showing relation of the vertebrae (or notochord) and radials to the caudal fin. *A.* Heterocercal (sturgeon, *Acipenser*). *B.* Abbreviate heterocercal (bowfin, *Amia*). *C.* Diphycercal, equal lobes (lung fish). The homocercal tail, common to many fishes, is shown in Fig. 31-3.

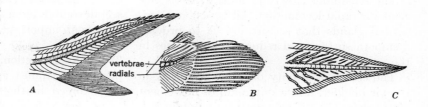

near the gill apertures; the pelvics are on the abdomen in trout, near the gill openings on perch, on the throat (jugular), in blennies, and lacking in eels. The dorsal fin may be single, multiple, or continuous along the back; salmonids and catfishes have, besides the single dorsal, a small fleshy or adipose fin posteriorly. In the top minnow and other viviparous species, the anterior part of the anal fin is modified as a copulatory organ (Fig. 31-24).

NATURAL HISTORY

31-17. Distribution. Fishes occur from the polar seas to the equator, from the surface to depths of more than 12,000 feet and up to 14,000 feet in the Andes. They live variously in open water, on sandy or rocky or muddy bottoms, in the crannies of reefs, in saline bays and estuaries, in fresh or alkaline rivers and lakes, in cave waters, and even in hot springs. Some live only in cold waters of the Arctic, the ocean depths, or deep in lakes; others are restricted to shallow and warm tropical seas; and a few minnows live in springs up to 93°F. on the American deserts. Trout thrive in waters at 55 to 70°F. Most fishes are limited by a temperature range of about 12 to 15°F. The majority live either in fresh or in salt water, but sticklebacks and sculpins are at home in either sort, and various species migrate from salt water to fresh for spawning. Some marine species range widely in the oceans, but most fishes are of restricted distribution, so that along the shores of the continents and in inland waters there are various definite "fish faunas."

Many fishes, like birds, perform seasonal *migrations.* The barracuda and swordfish move north in spring and south in autumn, in a latitudinal migration. The salmon, shad, striped bass, and some trout travel from salt water to fresh for spawning and are termed *anadromous;* the fresh-water eel, which reverses this process, is said to be *catadromous.* Cod and herring of the ocean perform an inshore migration to spawn on banks or shoals. Some deep-water (bathypelagic) fishes have a daily vertical migration.

31-18. Habits. Modern "skin divers," wearing air tanks (aqualung) for prolonged submergence and equipped with cameras and powerful lights, are learning much about the habits of fishes. Some species are active at all hours, many are quiet at night, and a few are nocturnal. Fishes of fresh-water streams habitually head against the current to maintain position, facilitate respiration, and catch food, as may be seen in a trout hatchery. Marine species are active at all seasons, but many fresh-water types become inactive during the winter, descending to deeper water in lakes and rivers. Some fishes are solitary, whereas others are gregarious and live in schools of various sizes, those of herring numbering a few thousands to many millions of individuals.

31-19. Locomotion. Most fishes swim by lateral undulations of the tail and tail fin, produced by alternate contractions of the metameric muscles on the two sides. The action is comparable to that of a man sculling a boat, with one oar at the stern moved from side to side. The other fins serve chiefly to maintain balance and change direction, but some fishes use the dorsal or anal and sometimes the pectorals for swimming.

The streamlined body of most fishes is efficient for rapid locomotion. All fishes have epidermal glands that secrete mucus to provide a smooth surface and reduce friction losses in the water.

The center of gravity of a fish is usually in the air bladder, and a minimum of movement of the paired fins is necessary to maintain balance or to keep a fixed position in water. Adjustment to depth is facilitated by altering the gases in the air bladder.

Trout and salmon and others may jump or leap from the water at times, when in pursuit of prey; they swim rapidly up to the surface when momentum alone carries them into the less dense air. The halfbeaks (HEMIRHAMPIDAE) skitter along the surface, propelled by the tail, which remains submerged. Flying fishes (EXOCOETIDAE) actually leave the water to glide or "volplane." They swim rapidly, then "taxi" with the body above the surface while the submerged tail vibrates laterally—up to 70 times per second (the pectoral fins may vibrate as a result of bodily movements); the speed may be up to 10 meters per second (22 miles per hour). Then the broad pectoral fins are instantaneously extended, and the fishes rise and glide for 3 to 8 seconds, traveling 35 to 100 yards. Flights may be repeated at short intervals.

31-20. Food. A few fresh-water fishes and some marine species feed upon aquatic vegetation, and the carp and suckers draw up bottom materials containing algae and minute invertebrates. Most fishes, however, are entirely predaceous. They feed on aquatic invertebrates or other fishes, with occasional captures of birds or mammals by some. Being "cold-blooded," most fishes require no energy to maintain the body temperature; yet their food intake is considerable. A captive trout in winter needs 10 per cent of its body weight in food per week for maintenance, but 30 per cent in summer.

31-21. Enemies. Fishes serve as staple food for other fishes, for water snakes, some turtles and alligators, many kinds of sea birds, herons and kingfishers, and mammals such as seals, mink,

otter, and bears. The eggs and young of fishes are devoured by a host of aquatic animals. Man is an important enemy of fishes.

31-22. Reproduction. Tropical species may reproduce at almost any season, but temperate fishes breed in the spring or early summer; trout, however, spawn in autumn or winter. Most fishes have one annual brood, but top minnows can produce up to six.

Fishes are mainly oviparous, but many individual species and all members of some groups are viviparous. Top minnows and the viviparous perches (EMBIOTOCIDAE) bear but few young at a time, whereas most oviparous fishes produce many eggs. Brook trout lay 80 to more than 5,600, according to size, Atlantic salmon up to 17,000, the cod to over 6,000,000, and the ocean sunfish to 300,000,000. The bodies of females are often swollen with the maturing eggs just before laying. Changes in coloration or other features, such as the hooked jaws of salmon, may occur in males for the mating season. Courting performances precede actual spawning among various kinds of fishes. Some fresh-water fishes provide "nests"; the "redds" of trout and salmon are shallow depressions, cleared of fine debris and covered with gravel or sand after egg deposition. The male stickleback (*Gasterosteus*) makes a globular nest of fine vegetable fibers bound together with a sticky secretion from the kidneys; he later guards the eggs and small young. The viviparous perches (Fig. 31-28) and top minnows retain eggs to develop in the ovaries; a male sea horse (*Hippocampus*) carries the eggs in a brood pouch; and males of some marine catfishes and African fresh-water cichlids carry the eggs in the mouth.

The eggs usually are small, and the time required for development varies with the species and the water temperature. Eggs of some marine fishes hatch as small transparent larvae within a few hours, and those of most tropical fresh-water species hatch in 20 to 48 hours. By contrast, the eggs of brook trout need about 44 days at 50 to 52°F., and 90 days or more at below 40°F (Fig. 31-12).

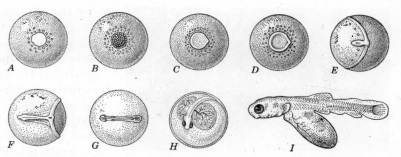

Fig. 31-12. Early development of the trout, a bony fish. *A.* Germinal disc (white) concentrates after fertilization. *B.* Meroblastic segmentation. *C, D.* Gastrula forming, blastodisc elongates in axis of future embryo. *E.* Primitive streak begins, blastodisc spreads. *F.* Neural tube forms, blastoderm surrounds yolk. *G.* Embryo with eye and ear vesicles and 18+ somites. *H.* "Eyed egg"— embryo with large eyes; blood vessels spread over yolk. *I.* "Yolk sac" stage of hatched young. (*A–G, after Henneguy,* 1888.)

The young of some viviparous fishes resemble their parents when hatched; other young are quite larval upon emergence and gradually assume the adult form. Flounders and soles (HETEROSOMATA) when hatched are bilaterally symmetrical with an eye on each side, but at an early age one eye begins to "migrate" to the opposite side, which thenceforth is the upper surface as the fish lies on the bottom. Young of the top minnow (*Gambusia*) may mature and breed before 4 months of age, whereas the king salmon of the Yukon River requires 5 or 6 years before spawning. Individuals of the Pacific salmon (*Oncorhynchus*) grow to sexual maturity, breed once, and then die.

31-23. Relations to man. Fishes have been important as human food from the time of Paleolithic man, who left fishbones in his "kitchen middens," to the present day. The world fisheries take 35 billion pounds worth over $800,-000,000 annually and employ thousands of persons. The flesh of most fishes is white (or reddish) and flaky in texture. It contains 13 to 20 per cent of protein and has a food value of 300 to 1,600 calories per pound, depending on the oil content (to 17 per cent in salmon). Fishes deteriorate rapidly after being caught and must either be consumed soon or preserved. In the fresh state they are iced or frozen. Methods of preservation include drying, smoking, and canning. Crude fish oils are used in paints and insecticidal sprays, and refined oils from livers of cod and other species comprise a concentrated source of vitamin D. The scraps from canneries as well as entire fishes of some species are ground and dried into meal, used for feeding poultry and for fertilizer. Liquid glues are rendered from heads and trimmings of fishes. Flesh of some tropical fishes is poisonous at times.

Sport fishing is an outdoor recreation for thousands of persons and also a source of food. Much money is spent each year by anglers in pursuit of trout, salmon, perch, bass, and other game fishes. In the United States the Federal and state governments rear millions of trout and other fishes in hatcheries and plant them in streams and lakes to replace some of those taken by fishermen.

Captive fishes of many kinds in ponds and aquaria are kept and bred by fish fanciers and other persons, and many public institutions maintain large glass-fronted aquaria where both native and foreign fishes are displayed. The keeping of fishes in ponds is an ancient practice of the Orient, the Romans, and the Aztecs of Middle America. Artificial rearing was on record in Europe in the fourteenth century and is now a widespread practice. Intensive pond culture of fishes, especially carp in Central Europe and the Orient, supplies considerable protein to

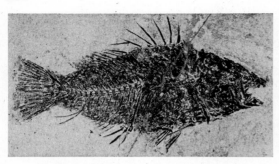

Fig. 31-13. Fossil fish (†*Priscacara*, Family CICHLIDAE) from Eocene Green River Shale, Kemmer, Wyo. (*Photo by T. I. Storer.*)

human populations in those regions. Experiments in the United States and elsewhere have shown that addition of natural or chemical fertilizers to fish ponds will increase the diatom-algae-invertebrate food chain upon which fishes depend, and 250 pounds or more of fish may be produced in an acre of water annually.

The top minnow (*Gambusia affinis*) has been propagated and distributed widely to aid in control of mosquitoes and malaria, by devouring mosquito larvae.

31-24. Fossil fishes. Bony fishes probably arose from primitive fishes in Silurian time. The Subclasses PALAEOPTERYGII (ancient fins) and CHOANICHTHYES (lobe fins) were numerous and widespread before the modern NEOPTERYGII (new fins) appeared. The PALAEOPTERYGII, of predaceous habit, were dominant in Paleozoic time and continued through the Mesozoic but are now represented only by the African bichir (*Polypterus*), spoonbill (*Polyodon*) of the Mississippi Valley, and the sturgeons (ACIPENSERIDAE) of the Northern Hemisphere.

Of the crossopterygians, the Order †RHIPIDISTIA of the Devonian and Carboniferous, with rounded lobe-like fins, simple teeth, and bodies covered by ganoid scales, are probable ancestors of the amphibians. The Order COELACANTHINI exhibits a most remarkable range, occurring almost unchanged from Lower Carboniferous to Cretaceous. More remarkable, a 5-foot living coelacanthid (*Latimeria chalumnae*) was taken off East London, South Africa, on Dec. 22, 1938. Intensive search has since produced about 10 other specimens from depths of 500 to 1,300 feet around the Comoro Islands near Madagascar, where the fish is known to the native people. It has a cartilaginous skeleton, tubular vertebrae, small spiracles, and an obscure lateral line. The Superorder DIPNOI (lungfishes) flourished during the Paleozoic and dwindled in the Triassic; but, in the latter period, species resembling the living *Neoceratodus* of Australia were of almost world-wide occurrence. The five living species of lungfishes in Australia, Africa, and South America were formerly considered possible ancestors of the amphibians but are now looked upon as somewhat degenerate forms (Fig. 31-33).

The earliest recognized modern fishes (†SEMIONOTIDAE, Triassic and Jurassic) were slow-swimming bottom dwellers with ganoid scales. The family gave rise to various offshoots, most of which in turn became extinct during Cretaceous time, save for the bowfin (*Amia*) and gar pike (*Lepidosteus*) still living in North America. Most modern families and a few existing genera probably date from the Eocene epoch (Fig. 31-13). Fossil fish remains of later periods often include impressions of soft parts.

CLASSIFICATION

CLASS OSTEICHTHYES (Pisces of many authors). BONY FISHES. Skeleton more or less bony; skin usually with embedded dermal (bony) scales of cycloid or ctenoid form, some with ganoid scales; both paired lateral and median fins usually present, and supported by fin rays; no pelvic girdle; mouth usually terminal; gills present throughout life, not in separate clefts; air bladder usually present; heart 2-chambered; no cloaca; ova small, segmentation meroblastic; Devonian to Recent, in salt, brackish, and fresh waters; about 25,000 species.

SUBCLASS 1. PALAEOPTERYGII. ANCIENT FISHES. Dermal fin rays of dorsal and anal fins usually more numerous than their internal skeletal supports; clavicles present (except in BELONORHYNCHII); nostrils not connected to mouth cavity.

Order 1. †Archistia. Body usually covered with ganoid scales; tail heterocercal; head covered with bones; snout short; teeth conical; vertebrae without centra; Lower Devonian to Jurassic. *†Cheirolepis*, *†Platysomus*.

Order 2. Cladistia. Body slender, scales thick, rhomboid, enameled; base of pectoral fins narrow and scale-covered; dorsal fin of 8 or more finlets each with a spine anteriorly; tail seemingly diphycercal; vertebrae amphicoelous, with bony centra; air bladder lung-like, possibly an accessory respiratory organ; larvae with slender external gills; Paleozoic and Recent (none known between). Africa. *Polypterus* (Fig. 31-14), tropical Africa; *Calamoichthys*, eel-like, Nigeria and Congo.

Fig. 31-14. Bichir (*Polypterus bichir*, Order CLADISTIA). Length to 36 inches. (*After Norman, Guide to fish gallery, British Museum.*)

Order 3. Chondrostei. STURGEONS, SPOONBILL. Body naked (scaleless) or with longitudinal rows of bony (ganoid) scutes; tail heterocercal; no teeth; skeleton largely cartilaginous; notochord persistent and unsegmented; vertebrae acentrous; Lower Jurassic to Recent.

POLYODONTIDAE. Two living species: *Polyodon spathula*, spoonbill or paddlefish, Mississippi drainage and south in streams, to 6 feet long, with paddle-shaped snout, practically scaleless; food of small invertebrates strained by gill rakers from bottom mud; *Psephurus*, Yangtze River.

ACIPENSERIDAE. STURGEONS. About 24 species; shark-like, mouth ventral and with barbels; 5 rows of enlarged bony scutes along body; food of worms, mollusks, small fishes, and aquatic plants; flesh palatable, eggs preserved as caviar, lining of swim bladder made into isinglass for clarifying jellies. *Acipenser sturio*, common sturgeon (Fig. 31-15), on both sides of Atlantic

Fig. 31-15. Sturgeon (*Acipenser sturio*, Order CHONDROSTEI). Length to 10 feet. (*After Norman, Guide to fish gallery, British Museum.*)

Ocean, and *A. transmontanus*, great white sturgeon, along Pacific coast, both ascend large rivers to spawn; *A. fulvescens*, rock sturgeon, and *Scaphirhynchus platorhynchus*, shovel-nosed sturgeon, both in Mississippi drainage, restricted to fresh water.

Order 4. †Belonorhynchii. Body with 4 series of bony scutes; caudal fin symmetrical; snout and lower jaw long; vertebrae acentrous; Lower Jurassic and Triassic. *†Belonorhynchus.*

SUBCLASS 2. NEOPTERYGII (Ganoids + Teleostei). MODERN FISHES. Vertebra with centra and usually amphicoelous; dermal rays of dorsal and anal fins equal in number to internal radial skeletal supports; no clavicles; caudal fin homocercal (rarely, abbreviate heterocercal); scales cycloid or ctenoid (ganoid in some fossils); nostrils not connected to mouth cavity; Upper Permian to Recent.

Order 1. Protospondyli. Tail abbreviate heterocercal; the living species with thin overlapping cycloid scales; Upper Jurassic and Lower Tertiary; one Recent species. *Amia calva*, bowfin (Fig. 31-16),

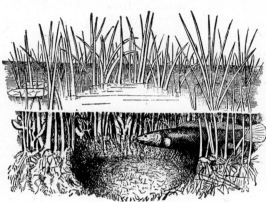

Fig. 31-16. Bowfin and nest (*Amia calva*, Order PROTOSPONDYLI). Length to 24 inches. (*After Norman, Guide to fish gallery, British Museum.*)

Great Lakes to Texas and Florida; air bladder large, cellular, aids in respiration; eats fishes and invertebrates; eggs in a crude nest, guarded by male.

Order 2. Ginglymodi. GAR PIKES and ALLIGATOR GARS. Vertebrae solid, opisthocoelous; scales ganoid, in oblique rows; snout and lower jaw long; teeth stout, conical; Eocene to Recent. *Lepidosteus osseus*, long-nosed gar (Fig. 31-17), Great Lakes and Mississippi Valley to coastal streams of

Fig. 31-17. Long-nosed gar (*Lepidosteus osseus*, Order GINGLYMODI). Length to 5 feet. (*After Norman, Guide to fish gallery, British Museum.*)

Florida, snout and body slender, grows to 5 feet; *L. spatula*, alligator gar, lower Mississippi Valley, grows to over 9 feet; all voracious, preying on smaller fishes.

(*Note: The remaining* NEOPTERYGII, *comprising the "Teleostei" or bony fishes proper, now in 29 orders, include all but a few of the living fishes; Orders 4 to 8 and 10 to 13 have only soft rays in the fins, but many of the others have some or all fins with one or more hard calcified spiny rays.*)

Order 3. †Halecostomi. Vertebral centra annular or amphicoelous. Mesozoic. *†Pholidophorus.*

Order 4. Isospondyli. HERRING, SALMON, TROUT, etc. Tail homocercal; fins without spiny rays; pelvic fins abdominal; air bladder with open duct to pharynx (no auditory ossicles); pyloric caeca usually numerous; Jurassic to Recent.

ELOPIDAE. TARPONS. Medium to large, in salt water, prized for sport. *Tarpon atlanticus*, common off Florida.

CLUPEIDAE. HERRINGS. Small, chiefly in salt water, often in schools numbering millions along both sides of North America, coming shoreward to spawn. *Clupea harengus*, common herring, over 150,000,000 pounds netted annually in New England waters and up to 3,000,000,000 pounds per year in Europe; marketed fresh, salt, smoked, or pickled, also used for bait; young canned as "sardines"; *C. pallasi*, Pacific coast; *Sardinops caerulea*, pilchard or California sardine, taken along Pacific coast for canning and for reduction to fish oil and meal; *Sardinia*, sardine of Spain and Italy; *Alosa sapidissima*, shad, native to Atlantic coast and introduced on Pacific coast, enters rivers to spawn, much esteemed for eating.

SALMONIDAE. SALMONS, TROUTS, etc. A small adipose fin on back. In cool waters of Northern Hemisphere, much prized for game and food. *Oncorhynchus*, Pacific salmon (Fig. 31-18), 5 species,

Fig. 31-18. Chinook or king salmon and young (*Oncorhynchus tschawytscha*, Family SALMONIDAE). Length 2 to 5 feet. (*After Goode, 1884.*)

central California to Alaska, others in Asia; millions of pounds taken in nets, used fresh or canned; spawn in fresh water, young migrate to sea and mature in 2 to 8 years, return to fresh water,

Fig. 31-19. Eastern brook trout (*Salvelinus fontinalis*, Family SALMONIDAE). Length to 18 inches. (*After Norman, Guide to fish gallery, British Museum.*)

spawn once, and die; *O. tschawytscha*, Chinook or tyee salmon, averages 30 pounds, some over 100 pounds; other species smaller. *Salmo salar*, Atlantic salmon, eastern North America and Europe, spawns more than once as do trouts; *S. gairdnerii*, rainbow trout, resident in fresh waters of Pacific coast, California to Alaska, has a sea-run race the "steelhead trout"; *S. clarkii*, cutthroat trout, Colorado and central California northward; *S. trutta*, brown or Loch Leven trout of Europe, widely introduced in United States; *Salvelinus fontinalis*, eastern brook or speckled trout (Fig. 31-19), Iowa and Allegheny Mountains to Saskatchewan and Labrador; *Coregonus*, whitefish, and *Thymallus*, grayling, northern states to Canada and Alaska. Various trout and salmon have been transplanted to many new localities.

Order 5. Haplomi. Pikes and Mud Minnows. Fins with soft rays only; pelvic fins abdominal; air bladder with duct to pharynx; no pyloric caeca; Miocene to Recent.

ESOCIDAE. PIKES. Slender-bodied with large mouths and conspicuous teeth, feed on other fishes. *Esox lucius*, common pike or pickerel, Arkansas and Minnesota eastward, other species there and in Eurasia; *E. masquinongy*, muskellunge, upper Mississippi basin, Great Lakes and northward, grows to 8 feet and over 100 pounds, a choice game fish.

Order 6. Iniomi. LANTERN FISHES, etc. Air bladder usually absent; deep-sea forms with phosphorescent spots on sides; Cretaceous to Recent; shore waters and deep sea to 2,500 fathoms. *Myctophum*, lantern fishes, deep seas; *Synodus*, lizard fishes, tropical seas.

Order 7. Giganturoidea. Lower lobe of caudal fin elongate; pectoral fins long with many rays, placed high above the small gill openings; pelvic fins absent; fin rays soft; no air bladder; Atlantic and Indian Oceans. *Gigantura*.

Order 8. Lyomeri. GULPERS. Body eel-shaped, naked; mouth very large; fin rays soft; tail long and slender; no ribs, caudal or pelvic fins; oceanic, at considerable depths. *Saccopharynx*.

Order 9. Ostariophysi. CHARACINS, ELECTRIC EELS, SUCKERS, MINNOWS, and CATFISHES. Anterior vertebrae fused, and lateral elements of 4 vertebrae detached to form small auditory ossicles (Weberian organ) between air bladder and ear; air bladder of 2 or 3 parts, usually with duct to pharynx; Eocene to Recent; fully 5,000 species, all in fresh waters except some catfishes.

SUBORDER 1. CYPRINOIDEA. Normally scaled. Characins, mostly small with silvery sides, many in Central and South America, some in Africa. Gymnotids, slender, long tapering tail and anal fin, no dorsal or pelvic fins, South and Central America; *Electrophorus electricus*, electric eel, Orinoco and Amazon drainages in South America, grows to 8 feet, produces powerful electric shocks.

CYPRINIFORM or CARP-LIKE FISHES. No adipose fin; mouth toothless and protractile.

CATOSTOMIDAE. SUCKERS. With fleshy lips to suck up bottom mud containing small animals and plants used as food; *Catostomus*, *Carpiodes*, and others, more than 60 species in North America and 2 in eastern Asia.

CYPRINIDAE. CARPS, CHUBS, ROACHES, MINNOWS, etc. Teeth in pharynx used to grind food; about 1,500 species. *Cyprinus carpio*, common carp, native to fresh waters in eastern Asia, where reared for food and ornament for centuries; introduced into Europe in thirteenth century and brought from Germany (hence "German" carp) to United States in 1872 where now widespread and abundant, with domestic races such as mirror carp (large scales) and leather carp (scaleless); *Carassius auratus*, goldfish (Fig. 31-20), also native to Asia and long under domestica-

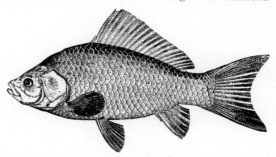

Fig. 31-20. Goldfish (*Carassius auratus*, Order OSTARIOPHYSI). Length to 12 inches. (*After Goode*, 1884.)

tion, with many artificial breeds or races of peculiar form; daces and minnows, many native to North America, of small size, often erroneously thought to be young fishes; *Notropis*, minnows, eastern North America; *Ptychocheilus lucius*, "white salmon" of Colorado River basin, grows to 5 feet and 80 pounds, the largest North American cyprinid.

SUBORDER 2. SILUROIDEA. CATFISHES. Mouth with teeth, nonprotractile, and usually with sensory barbels; body either naked (scaleless) or with bony plates; over 30 species in fresh waters of United States, others in salt waters and southward; American species naked and with adipose fin (Fig. 31-21). *Ameiurus nebulosus,* bullhead or horned pout, native to most quiet waters east of Rocky Mountains and introduced in the West; *Ictalurus lacustris (punctatus),* channel or spotted catfish, in clear flowing waters from Great Lakes region to Gulf states; *Galeichthys, Arius,* shallow coastal seas.

Fig. 31-21. Catfish or bullhead (*Ameiurus melas,* Suborder SILUROIDEA). Length 6 to 10 inches. (*After Goode, 1884.*)

Order 10. Apodes. EELS. Body long and slender; dorsal, caudal, and anal fins continuous, caudal sometimes lacking; pelvic fins usually absent; gill openings small; scales minute or absent; air bladder with duct; no oviducts; mostly marine; Cretaceous to Recent. *Anguilla,* fresh-water eels (Fig. 31-22), grow to maturity in fresh-water streams, adults migrate to sea in autumn, spawn in deep water, and die, the delicate transparent larvae (leptocephali) swim near the surface of the sea, feeding and growing, to enter the rivers perhaps a year later; *A. bostonensis,* American eel, of Atlantic coast, spawns near Bermuda islands; *Muraena,* morays, marine, highly predaceous, many of striking coloration, abound in crevices of coral reefs.

Fig. 31-22. Fresh-water eel (*Anguilla bostonensis,* Order APODES). Length to 4 feet. (*After Goode, 1884.*)

Order 11. Heteromi. Body slender; tail long, with anal fin below tapering to a point, but no caudal fin; pelvic fins abdominal; no oviducts; oceanic at considerable depths. *Notacanthus.*

Order 12. Synentognathi. GARFISHES, HALFBEAKS, FLYING FISHES. Dorsal fin above anal; pectorals high on body; lower pharyngeals united as 1 bone; marine. *Strongylura, Belone,* garfishes; *Scomberesox,* skipper; *Hemirhamphus,* halfbeak; *Exocoetus, Cypselurus,* flying fishes, chiefly in warm seas, emerge to glide in air over the water (Fig. 31-23).

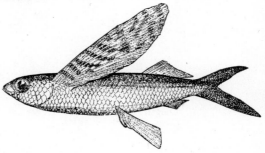

Fig. 31-23. Flying fish (*Cypselurus,* Order SYNENTOGNATHI). Length to 15 inches. (*After Norman, Guide to fish gallery, British Museum.*)

Order 13. Cyprinodontes (Microcyprini). TOP MINNOWS and CAVE FISHES. Size small; mouth protractile; lateral line weak; pelvic fins abdominal or absent; many viviparous; chiefly in North America, either fresh or salt waters; feed chiefly near the surface, on small animals or plants; some with conspicuous courtship performances. *Typhlichthys,* eyeless cave fish, in streams of limestone caves, Indiana to Alabama; *Cyprinodon macularius* and others, desert minnows, in scattered springs, streams, and artesian waters, southern Nevada and southeastern California to Sonora; *Fundulus heteroclitus*, common killifish, in brackish coastal waters, Canada to Florida; *Gambusia affinis*, top minnow (Fig. 31-24), in fresh waters, reared and planted widely to control mosquito larvae; *Anableps*, "four-eyed" fish, pupil of eye divided with upper half for vision in air and lower for seeing in water.

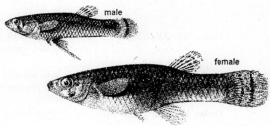

Fig. 31-24. Top minnow or "mosquito fish" (*Gambusia affinis*, Order CYPRINODONTES). About natural size. (*After Garman, 1895.*)

Order 14. Salmopercae. TROUT-PERCHES. Dorsal and anal fins preceded by 1 or 4 spines; North America (only 3 species). *Percopsis; Columbia.*

Order 15. Solenichthyes. PIPEFISHES, SEA HORSES, etc. Mouth at end of tubular snout, suctorial; male usually with brood pouch under tail to shelter eggs until hatching; marine. *Syngnathus*, pipefishes, slender, covered with ring-like exoskeleton of enlarged plates, fins minute; *Hippocampus*, sea horse (Fig. 31-25), head enlarged and at right angles with body, swims in vertical position by undulations of dorsal fin.

Fig. 31-25. Sea horse (*Hippocampus*, Order SOLENICHTHYES). Length to 6 inches. (*After Norman, Guide to fish gallery, British Museum.*)

Fig. 31-26. Sea dragon (*Phyllopteryx rex*, Order SOLENICHTHYES), with outgrowths resembling sea weeds among which the fish lives. (*After Norman, Guide to fish gallery, British Museum.*)

Order 16. Anacanthini. CODS, POLLACKS, HAKES, BURBOTS, etc. Fins soft-rayed; pelvics often many-rayed, and thoracic or jugular in position; caudal fin, when present, formed mainly of dorsal and anal rays, without expanded hypural; air bladder lacks duct; Northern Hemisphere, mostly marine bottom dwellers; of great commercial importance. *Gadus morhua*, codfish (Fig. 31-27), both sides of North Atlantic, fished from ancient times, over 50,000,000 pounds taken annually in American fisheries, and three times this amount of haddock (*Melanogrammus aeglefinus*) being sold fresh or salted; *Merluccius*, hake; *Lota*, burbot (in fresh water).

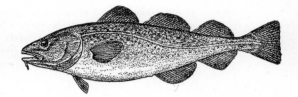

Fig. 31-27. Common cod (*Gadus morhua*, Order ANACANTHINI). Length to 4 feet. (*After Norman, Guide to fish gallery, British Museum.*)

Order 17. Allotriognathi. Eyes large; teeth feeble or none; occasional spiny fin rays; marine, mostly oceanic. *Lampris regius* (*luna*), opah; *Trachypterus*, ribbonfish; *Regalecus*, oarfish, slender, to 20 feet long.

Order 18. Berycomorphi. Pelvic fins usually with more than 5 soft rays; caudal fin generally with 19 principal rays (17-branched); some spiny rays; Cretaceous to Recent; marine, mostly in deep water. *Holocentrus*, squirrelfish.

Order 19. Zeomorphi. Anal fin preceded by 1 to 4 spines forming separate fins; marine. *Zeus faber*, "John Dory."

Order 20. Percomorphi. PERCHES, etc. Dorsal and anal fins with both spiny and soft fin rays; pectoral arch attached to skull by forked posttemporal; Upper Cretaceous to Recent; world-wide, in both fresh and salt waters; about 80 families, diverse in form and habits.

CENTRARCHIDAE. FRESH-WATER BASSES and SUNFISHES. Many species in eastern states, prized for sport fishing; some transplanted into western states. *Huro salmoides*, large-mouthed black bass; *Micropterus dolomieui*, small-mouthed black bass; *Lepomis gibbosus*, sunfish; *Pomoxis annularis*, crappie.

PERCIDAE. FRESH-WATER PERCHES. *Perca flavescens*, yellow perch; *Etheostoma*, *Hadropterus*, etc., darters, eastern United States.

CICHLIDAE. CICHLIDS. Nearly 600 species in tropical America and Africa.

EMBIOTOCIDAE. SURF FISHES or VIVIPAROUS PERCHES. California to Japan (Fig. 31-28).

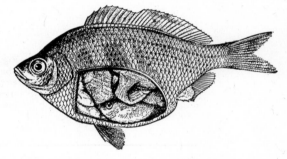

Fig. 31-28. Viviparous perch (*Cymatogaster aggregatus*, Family EMBIOTOCIDAE), cut open to show fully formed young ready for birth. Length 5 inches. (*After Jordan, 1925.*)

SCOMBRIDAE. MACKERELS, etc. More than 38,000,000 pounds of mackerel (*Scomber scombrus*, Fig. 31-1) taken annually by fishermen of United States.

THUNNIDAE. TUNAS, etc. Includes tunas, yellowfin, bluefin or horse mackerel, skipjack, bonito, and others, some of large size. More than 324,000,000 pounds obtained commercially in United States fisheries annually.

Order 21. Scleroparei. MAIL-CHEEKED FISHES. A bony stay (second suborbital) across cheek, from below eye toward operculum; many with extra spines on head or body; chiefly marine, some in fresh waters, many bottom dwellers in shallow or deep waters. *Sebastes*, rose fish or ocean perch; *Scorpaena*, scorpion fish; *Cottus*, sculpin; *Gasterosteus*, stickleback (Fig. 31-29), male builds nest of sticks and a secretion, then guards eggs.

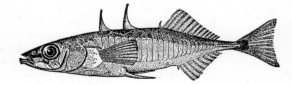

Fig. 31-29. Stickleback (*Gasterosteus aculeatus*, Order SCLEROPAREI). Length to 4 inches. (*After Norman, Guide to fish gallery, British Museum.*)

Order 22. Hypostomides. DRAGONFISHES. Small; body enclosed in a broad bony box, tail in bony rings; tropical seas of Old World. *Pegasus.*

Order 23. Heterosomata. FLATFISHES. Asymmetrical, with both eyes on one side of head and movable; body strongly compressed; dorsal and anal fins fringing the body (Fig. 31-30); bottom dwellers, lying on side, undersurface usually unpigmented; Upper Eocene to Recent; usually marine, on bottom in coastal waters; important food fishes, sought commercially; early young bilaterally

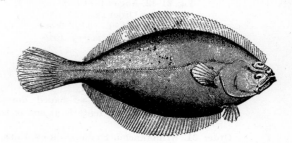

Fig. 31-30. The sand dab, a "flat fish" (*Hippoglossoides platessoides,* Order HETEROSOMATA). Length to 24 inches. (*After Goode, 1884.*)

symmetrical, but fish soon lies on one side and "lower" eye migrates around so that both eyes are on upper surface. *Hippoglossus,* halibut; *Paralichthys,* flounder; *Symphurus,* sole; *Achirus,* round sole.

Order 24. Discocephali. REMORAS. Upper surface of head with flat oval adhesive disc (modified spinous dorsal fin), transversely furrowed, by which the fish attaches to a shark or other object in the water; other fins normal and used for ordinary swimming; warm seas. *Echeneis, Remora,* remoras, or "suckfishes" (Fig. 31-31).

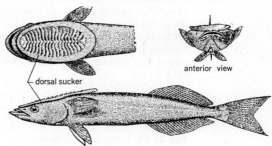

anterior view

dorsal sucker

Fig. 31-31. Remora or "suckfish" (*Remora,* Order DISCOCEPHALI). Length to 21 inches. (*After Norman, Guide to fish gallery, British Museum.*)

Order 25. Plectognathi. TRIGGERFISHES, TRUNKFISHES, PUFFERS, HEAD FISHES, etc. Body form various, some globose, some inflate by swallowing water; jaws short, powerful; teeth usually strong incisors or forming a sharp-edged beak; scales generally spiny or bony; gill openings small; warm seas. *Balistes,* triggerfish; *Diodon,* porcupine fish; *Mola mola,* ocean sunfish, body short, high, compressed (Fig. 31-1), anal and dorsal fins enlarged, literally no tail, skin leathery, specimens of 250 to 400 pounds occasional off New York, the largest nearly 11 feet long and 1 ton in weight off California.

Order 26. Malacichthyes. No spinous rays; skeleton weakly ossified, body limp; median fins long, with many rays; Pacific Ocean. *Icosteus.*

Order 27. Xenopterygii. CLINGFISHES. Naked; large subcircular adhesive disc on abdomen, by which the fish attaches to stones or shells; shore waters, tropic and temperate. *Gobiesox,* clingfish.

Order 28. Haplodoci. TOADFISHES. Head depressed, mouth wide; a spinous dorsal fin and long soft-rayed dorsal and anal fins; bottom of tropical and subtropical seas. *Opsanus,* toadfish; *Porichthys,* singing fish or "midshipman."

Order 29. Pediculati. ANGLER FISHES, DEEP-SEA FISHES. "Spinous" dorsal fin of a few flexible rays, the first located on head and with dilated bulb at tip; some luminescent organs; shore waters or ocean depths. *Lophius piscatorius,* angler fish (Fig. 31-32), broad, soft-bodied, with huge mouth, and to 4 feet in length, on both sides of North Atlantic down to 60 fathoms, captures fish, marine invertebrates and birds; *Ceratias, Melanocetus,* etc., deep-sea anglers, at 1,500 to 6,000 feet, mostly small, of blackish color, with a luminescent "bulb"; male minute and early attaches permanently to female, their bodies and blood streams growing together, such "parasitism" probably an adaptation to ensure mating in the dark depths of the sea.

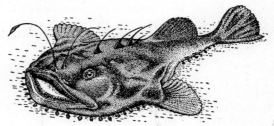

Fig. 31-32. Angler fish (*Lophius piscatorius*, Order PEDICULATI). Length to 4 feet. (*After Norman, Guide to fish gallery, British Museum.*)

Order 30. Opisthomi. Body eel-shaped; dorsal fin preceded by separate small spines; anterior nostril tubular on fleshy tentacle at end of snout; fresh waters of Africa and southeastern Asia. *Mastacembelus.*

Order 31. Symbranchii. SYMBRANCHOID EELS. Shaped like eels; dorsal and anal fins without fin rays and continuous with caudal; no pectoral fins; gill openings fused as transverse ventral slit; Africa, India, and tropical America in fresh-water streams. *Symbranchus.*

SUBCLASS 3. CHOANICHTHYES. Nostrils connecting to mouth cavity; each paired fin with large median lobe (sometimes cross-jointed), and dermal fin rays along sides.

Superorder 1. Crossopterygii. LOBE-FINNED FISHES. Premaxilla and maxilla present.

Order 1. †Rhipidistia. Head normal, skull ossified; teeth on both premaxilla and maxilla; a "pineal" eye; tail heterocercal. Devonian to Carboniferous. †*Osteolepis.*

Order 2. Coelacanthini (Actinistia). Head short, deep; skull with much cartilage; teeth only at tip of premaxilla and dentary; no pineal eye; tail 3-pronged. Devonian to Cretaceous. †*Eusthenopteron,* †*Macropoma.* Also Recent: *Latimeria chalumnae,* off South Africa.

Superorder 2. Dipnoi (Dipneusti). LUNG FISHES. Body long, slender; no premaxilla or maxilla; teeth forming pair of plates on palate and one on inner edge of each lower jaw; air bladder lung-like; paired fins narrow; Devonian to Recent, many fossil forms; food of invertebrates and plants (Fig. 31-33).

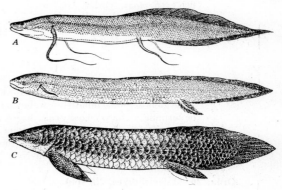

Fig. 31-33. Lung fishes (Superorder DIPNOI). *A.* African (*Protopterus*), length to 32 inches. *B.* South American (*Lepidosiren*), length to 32 inches. *C.* Australian (*Neoceratodus*), length to 40 inches or more. (*After Norman, Guide to fish gallery, British Museum.*)

CERATODONTIDAE. †*Ceratodus,* Triassic to Cretaceous, almost world-wide; *Neoceratodus forsteri,* only living species; scales large, cycloid, overlapping; fins leaf-like; in Burnett and Mary Rivers, Queensland, Australia; inhabits quiet pools that become stagnant during dry season when the fish rises to surface and takes air into lung.

LEPIDOSIRENIDAE. Body eel-like, scales small, fins filamentous; inhabit swamps and in dry season, retire to vertical burrows (nests) in mud, lined with mucus. *Lepidosiren,* South America, makes burrow at bottom of water and deposits eggs in tunnel, guarded by male; *Protopterus annectens* and 2 other species of central Africa retire to burrows in mud where mucus dries to form a "cocoon" with lid and tubular aperture leading to mouth of fish for respiration; spawns after return of water.

REFERENCES

(Some references for Chap. 30 are included)

Many publications of the U.S. Bureau of Fisheries (now part of the Fish and Wildlife Service, U.S. Department of the Interior) deal with the fishes and fisheries of the United States and dependencies. Various state game and conservation departments issue publications on the fishes of their states. The *Transactions* of the American Fisheries Society, *Annual Reports* of the North American Wild Life Conference, the quarterly periodical *Copeia*, other journals, and many books contain materials on fishes and the fisheries.

BERG, L. S. 1940. Classification of fishes, both recent and fossil. *Travaux de l'institut zoologique de l'académie des sciences de l'URSS*, vol. 5, pt. 2, pp. 87–517, 190 figs.; also available in facsimile lithoprint edition. 1947. Ann Arbor, Mich., J. W. Edwards. Best recent summary; text in both Russian and English.

DEAN, B., and OTHERS. 1916–1923. A bibliography of fishes. New York, American Museum of Natural History. 3 vols., 2,124 pp.

GOODRICH, E. S. 1909. Cyclostomes and fishes. *In* E. R. Lankester, Treatise on zoology. London, A. & C. Black, Ltd. Pt. IX: 1, pp. 58–578, figs. 39–515.

JORDAN, D. S. 1905. A guide to the study of fishes. New York, Henry Holt & Co., Inc. 2 vols., 1,271 pp., 506 figs.

——— and B. W. EVERMANN. 1896–1900. The fishes of North and Middle America . . . *U.S. National Museum Bulletin* 47 (4 vols.), ci + 3,313 pp., pls. I–CCCXCII. Keys and technical descriptions; comprehensive.

JORDAN, D. S. and B. W. EVERMANN. 1902. American food and game fishes. New York, Doubleday & Co., Inc. xlix + 573 pp., illus. Popular.

———, ———, and H. W. CLARK. 1930. Checklist of the fishes . . . of North and Middle America. . . . *U.S. Commissioner of Fisheries Report for 1928*, pt. 2, 760 pp. Scientific and common names and distribution of 4,137 species and subspecies; many errors.

NEEDHAM, P. R. 1938. Trout streams. Ithaca, N.Y., Comstock Publishing Associates, Inc. x + 233 pp., 74 figs. Trout biology and management in North America.

NORMAN, J. R. 1931. A history of fishes. London, Ernest Benn, Ltd. xv + 463 pp., 8 pls., 147 figs. Modern general account of fishes.

——— and F. C. FRASER. 1938. Giant fishes, whales and dolphins. New York, W. W. Norton & Co., Inc. xxvii + 361 pp., illus.

RADCLIFFE, W. 1936. Fishing from the earliest times. 2d ed. London, John Murray. xxi + 494 pp., illus. Historical to A.D. 500; many ancient quotations.

SCHULTZ, L. P., and E. M. STERN. 1948. The ways of fishes. New York, D. Van Nostrand Co. xii + 264 pp., 80 figs. Popular; with outline of fish classification.

TRESSLER, D. K., and J. McW. LEMON. 1951. Marine products of commerce. 2d ed. New York, Reinhold Publishing Corp. xiii + 782 pp., illus. Gathering, processing, and preserving fishes and other sea products.

WALTON, ISAAK. 1653. The compleat angler. 5th ed. (1676) and later editions with Charles Cotton. The classical discussion of the delights of fishing. Often reprinted.

32 CLASS AMPHIBIA
Amphibians

The AMPHIBIA include the living salamanders (Subclass CAUDATA), the toads and frogs (Subclass SALIENTIA), the limbless tropical caecilians (Order GYMNOPHIONA), and various fossil forms of Carboniferous and Permian times. The class name (Gr. *amphi*, dual + *bios*, life) appropriately indicates that most of the species live partly in fresh water and partly on land. In both structure and function, the amphibians stand between the fishes and reptiles, being the first group among the chordates to live out of water. Several "new" features adapt them for terrestrial life, such as legs, lungs, nostrils connecting to the mouth cavity, and sense organs that can function in both water and air. Amphibians serve as food for various vertebrates, a few species are used for biological teaching and research, and frog legs are a table delicacy.

32-1. Characteristics. 1. Skin moist and glandular; no external scales.

2. Two pairs of limbs for walking or swimming (no paired fins); toes 4–5, or fewer (no limbs on caecilians, no hind limbs on SIRENIDAE); any median fins lack fin rays.

3. Nostrils 2, connected to mouth cavity and with valves to exclude water; eyes often with movable lids; eardrums external on toads and frogs; mouth usually with fine teeth; tongue often protrusible.

4. Skeleton largely bony; skull with 2 occipital condyles; ribs, if present, not attached to sternum.

5. Heart 3-chambered, 2 auricles and 1 ventricle; 1 (or 3) pair of aortic arches; red blood cells nucleated and oval.

6. Respiration by gills, lungs, skin, or the mouth lining, separately or in combination; gills present at some stage in life history; vocal cords in toads and frogs.

7. Brain with 10 pairs of cranial nerves.

8. Body temperature variable (poikilothermous), dependent upon environment.

9. Fertilization external or internal; mostly oviparous; eggs with some yolk and enclosed in gelatinous coverings; cleavage holoblastic but unequal; no embryonic membranes; usually an aquatic larval stage with metamorphosis to adult form.

The AMPHIBIA are the lowest and earliest TETRAPODA (Gr. *tetra*, four + *podos*, foot), or land vertebrates. They undoubtedly derived from some fish-like ancestor, possibly in Devonian times. The transition from water to land involved (1) modification of the body for travel on land while retaining the ability to swim, (2) development of limbs in place of paired fins, (3) change of the skin to permit exposure to the air, (4) replacement of gills by lungs, (5) changes in the circulatory system to provide for respiration by the lungs and skin, and (6) acquisition of sense organs that function in both air and water. In the early larvae of all amphibians and in such salamanders as retain the gills throughout life, there are multiple aortic arches, as in fishes. After metamorphosis, the other salamanders and the toads and frogs have but one pair of arches, as in reptiles. The amphibian skull is simpler, with fewer bones than in fishes, but

510

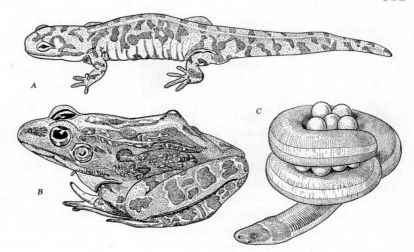

Fig. 32-1. Representative amphibians (Class AMPHIBIA). *A.* Tiger salamander (*Ambystoma tigrinum*, Subclass CAUDATA). *B.* Leopard frog (*Rana pipiens*, Subclass SALIENTIA). *C.* A tropical caecilian or limbless amphibian (*Ichthyosis glutinosus*, Subclass STEGOCEPHALIA, Order GYMNOPHIONA).

the limb muscles are more complex than those of the lateral fins in fishes. Some primitive fossil labyrinthodont amphibians probably were ancestral to the oldest reptiles and so to all higher land vertebrates.

Salamanders have the head and neck distinct, the trunk long and either cylindrical or depressed dorsoventrally, and a long tail. Toads and frogs have the head and trunk joined in a broad depressed body, with no neck or tail, small fore limbs, long hind limbs, and the eardrums exposed. Caecilians are limbless and worm-like, with annulate bodies, and their skin contains small internal scales.

32-2. Size. Most salamanders are 3 to 8 inches long. The giant salamander (*Megalobatrachus japonicus*) grows to 69 inches, whereas a Mexican salamander is only 1½ inches in length. The giant frog (*Rana goliath*) of the African Cameroons grows to 12 inches in head-and-body length, and the smallest salientian is a Cuban tree toad (*Phyllobates*) only ⅜ inch when grown. Most toads and frogs are 2 to 5 inches long.

STRUCTURE OF AMPHIBIANS

32-3. External features. The detailed description of the frog in Chap. 2 will serve as an account of general structure and physiology. The skin on salamanders and caecilians adheres closely to the muscles of the body. On most amphibians the external surface is smooth and glistening; it is rough on terrestrial newts (*Taricha*, etc.) and on toads bears many groups of **poison glands** in small or large rounded warts, over the back, sides, and legs. (Handling toads does not produce warts on human skin.) The coloration of many salamanders and toads is bright and contrasted, of green, yellow, red, brown, or black. The pattern is fixed on most species, but tree toads undergo great changes in coloration with different environmental conditions.

The palms and soles of the **feet** bear small cornified tubercles; on the hind foot in the spadefoots (*Scaphiopus*) and some other toads, the innermost tubercle becomes a horny cutting spade that these animals use to dig backward into the ground when seeking shelter. The tree toads (HYLIDAE), some frogs (PHYLLOBATIDAE), and some *Rana* in Asia have expanded discs on all toes by which they can adhere to and climb on vertical surfaces. The webbing of the hind toes is least in strictly terrestrial toads, but extensive in the more aquatic forms.

32-4. Skeleton and muscles. The skeleton in salamanders resembles that of other elongate vertebrates in having many vertebrae (up to 100 in *Amphiuma*); some caecilians have over 200. Ribs are present in salamanders, caecilians, and some toads. The pelvic girdle of salamanders is short, and caecilians lack both limbs and

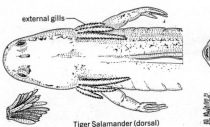
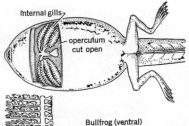

external gills

Tiger Salamander (dorsal)

Internal gills

operculum
cut open

Bullfrog (ventral)

Fig. 32-2. Gills of amphibian larvae; enlarged insets show finer structure.

girdles. Most amphibians have fine teeth on the upper jaw and roof of the mouth; some salamanders have teeth on both jaws, but toads are toothless. The teeth are somewhat conical, fastened to the surfaces of the bones, and replaced by growth of a new tooth beside the old one.

Segmental muscles are conspicuous on the trunk and tail of salamanders and caecilians. Gill-bearing species have special muscles to move the gills and to open or close the gill slits. The upper segment of each limb stands out laterally from the body, thus ⌐°⌐, as in four-legged reptiles.

32-5. Respiration. Amphibians have more means for *respiration* than any other group in the Animal Kingdom, reflecting the transition from aquatic to land habitats. In different species the gills, lungs, skin, and buccopharynx serve separately or in combination.

The heart in larvae is fish-like, with one auricle and a ventricle, and all the heart blood is venous (unoxygenated). Adults have two auricles and a double circulation of the blood through the heart. The pulmocutaneous arteries distribute blood to both lungs and skin in all adult amphibians without gills.

Three pairs of external *gills* occur in the embryos and larvae (Fig. 32-2) of all amphibians and persist in the adults of some strictly aquatic salamanders. By pumping action of the mouth cavity, water is drawn in through the nostrils and forced out the gill slits, to pass the filaments where the respiratory exchange occurs. *Necturus* waves its bushy gills in the water and does not use the mouth in respiration.

Save for the dipnoan fishes, amphibians are the lowest vertebrates with **lungs.** These are usually simple, with low internal partitions containing blood vessels (Fig. 2-16). In aquatic species the lungs also serve as hydrostatic organs, being inflated when the animals are floating. Some salamanders that inhabit swift mountain streams (*Rhyacotriton*) have the lungs reduced, and all American land salamanders (PLETHODONTIDAE) lack lungs. The skin of all amphibians contains many blood vessels that aid aeration of the blood; this permits aquatic species to remain submerged for long periods and to hibernate in ponds.

Many species have **buccopharyngeal respiration;** pulsations of the chin move air in and out of the mouth cavity, and aeration of the blood occurs in vessels under the mucous membrane there.

The vocal cords in the larynx of frogs and toads serves to make the familiar calls, distinctive for each species, that serve to bring the sexes together for mating—chiefly in the spring. Some species have resonating pouches in the chin that amplify the sounds. Salamanders lack vocal cords, but a few kinds make faint squeaks.

NATURAL HISTORY

32-6. Distribution. Amphibians live mainly in water or damp places; none is in salt water. They are commonest in moist temperate regions, but some are tropical, one frog ranges into the Arctic Circle, and a frog and tree frog occur above 12,000 feet in the Sierra Nevada of California. Some toads and tree toads live on deserts, such as in the American Southwest, where they hide in underground retreats by day to emerge only at night.

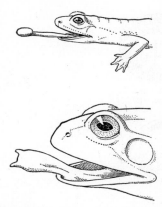

Fig. 32-3. Tongues of a plethodont salamander and a frog as extended to capture prey.

The mud puppy (*Necturus*), hellbender (*Cryptobranchus*), congo eel (*Amphiuma*), and mud eel (*Siren*) are strictly aquatic. Bullfrogs are always in or close to water, as are some other frogs, whereas the wood frog lives on the moist floor of forests. Some frogs and tree toads are partly arboreal, and others in the tropics are completely so. Land salamanders are commonly under stones or logs, and the tropical caecilians burrow in moist earth.

32-7. Seasonal activity. All amphibians must avoid temperature extremes and drought because they have no regulation of body temperature and can lose water easily from the soft skin. Frogs and aquatic salamanders hibernate during the winter by going deep into lakes or streams that do not freeze; toads and terrestrial salamanders then burrow or go below the frost line. During hibernation all bodily processes are lessened, the heartbeat is slow, and the animal subsists on materials stored within its body, including glycogen in the liver. In some southern states many amphibians are active at all seasons, but in the hot dry lowlands of California some aestivate during the summer.

32-8. Food. Adult amphibians and the larvae of salamanders eat only live moving animals, such as insects, crustaceans, worms, and small mollusks. Large aquatic species also take small fishes, the bullfrog sometimes catches small fishes, birds, or mammals, and big amphibians will devour small individuals of their own or other species. The aquatic larvae of toads and frogs feed mainly on algae and on bits of dead animals in the water, as their peculiar mouth parts do not permit swallowing large items (Fig. 2-20).

32-9. Enemies. Frogs and tree toads are staple foods of turtles, snakes, herons, certain hawks, raccoons, and large fishes. The acrid secretions of the warts on toads protect these animals from many predators, but not all. Raccoons and skunks reportedly roll toads underfoot to get rid of these secretions before eating them. Puppies soon learn by bitter experience to leave toads alone, and adult dogs rarely attack them. For the same reason, newts are seldom eaten by other animals. Amphibian larvae are preyed upon by large water bugs and beetles and by dragon-fly nymphs, as well as by the various enemies of adult amphibians.

32-10. Reproduction. Most amphibians mate in water, where their eggs are deposited and hatch and where the resulting larvae live and grow until they metamorphose into the adult stages. Each species has a characteristic type of breeding place such as a large quiet lake or pond, a stream, or a transient pool; some breed on land. With toads and frogs, the males, upon entering the water, begin croaking to attract females. As each "ripe" female enters, she is clasped by a male, who clings on her back. As she extrudes her eggs, the clasping male discharges sperm, or "milt," over them to effect fertilization (Fig.

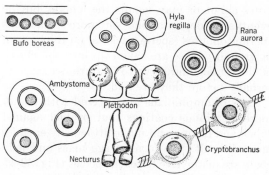

Fig. 32-4. Some amphibian eggs and their gelatinous coverings; diagrammatic.

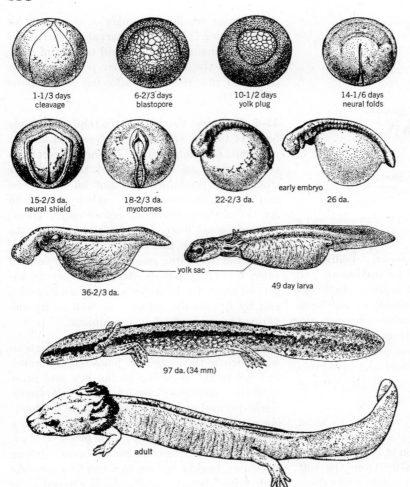

1-1/3 days
cleavage

6-2/3 days
blastopore

10-1/2 days
yolk plug

14-1/6 days
neural folds

15-2/3 da.
neural shield

18-2/3 da.
myotomes

22-2/3 da.

early embryo

26 da.

36-2/3 da.

yolk sac

49 day larva

97 da. (34 mm)

adult

Fig. 32-5. Mud puppy (*Necturus maculosus*, Order Proteida). Development and adult. (*Rearranged from Noble, Biology of the amphibia.*)

2-20). Both aquatic and terrestrial salamanders have a courting performance in which the male noses about or may mount the female, but he eventually deposits one or more gelatinous spermatophores (sperm packets) on the bottom or ground. These are taken up into the cloaca of the female and serve to fertilize her eggs internally before they are laid.

Eggs of amphibians are covered with one or more gelatinous coatings that protect against shock and drying and make attacks by enemies more difficult. The form of egg mass and jelly coats are distinctive for each species (Fig. 32-4). Toad eggs are in long strings, those of frogs in tapioca-like masses, and those of some aquatic

salamanders in small clumps; a few species deposit the eggs individually. Eggs of land salamanders (Plethodontidae) are often attached by a stalk to some object. A small frog (*Sminthillus*) of Cuba lays but one egg, some land salamanders deposit about 30, small frogs and tree toads produce up to 1,000, the bullfrog up to 25,000, and one large toad (*Bufo marinus*) may lay up to 32,000 eggs at one time. The time and rate of development vary widely— scarcely a month for spadefoot toads (*Scaphiopus*), but 2 years for the bullfrog from egg to young frog in northern regions.

Salamander larvae (Fig. 32-5) resemble their parents in general form, having limbs and feet early in life and a mouth that enables them to be predaceous feeders. Their larval characteristics of gills, gill slits, a dorsal fin on the tail and back, and peculiarities in the hyoid apparatus are usually lost at metamorphosis.

Larvae of toads and frogs are the familiar tadpoles (polliwogs) with ovoid head and body and a long tail (Fig. 2-20). The external gills are soon replaced by internal gills, under a delicate membrane (operculum). The limbs develop late in larval life. True jaws are lacking; the face has two horny plates used to scrape algae from objects in the water. The intestine is long, slender, and spirally coiled. Metamorphosis involves (1) growth of a wide mouth and loss of the horny jaws; (2) loss of the gills, closure of the gill slits, and development of lungs; (3) emergence of the forelegs; (4) reduction in length of the intestine from the long (herbivorous) type to the short (carnivorous) form of the frog; and (5) reabsorption of the tail and median fins. During metamorphosis, the young inhabit shallow water where both gill and lung respiration are possible and where insect food may be captured. Later they hide in crevices to avoid desiccation. Thousands may appear suddenly during a shower, thus accounting for the age-old belief of an occasional "rain of toads."

Fertilization is external in the hellbender (*Cryptobranchus*) and the HYNOBIIDAE, but internal in the bell toad (*Ascaphus*). Eggs of some land salamanders (PLETHODONTIDAE) are deposited in damp cavities; some hatch as larvae that have an aquatic stage, but others complete development within the egg to emerge as miniature adults, as do certain frogs. The embryos have broad thin gills that serve for air breathing. The male obstetrical toad (*Alytes*) loops the egg strings about his hind legs until the larvae are ready for release into water. The female tongueless toad (*Pipa*) carries her eggs in separate dermal pockets on her back, and the marsupial toads (Fig. 32-6) carry theirs sheltered dorsally under a flap of skin. The European salamander (*Salamandra salamandra*) retains her few embryos internally for 10 to 12 months, when they are released into water, and the alpine salamander (*S. atra*) retains one or

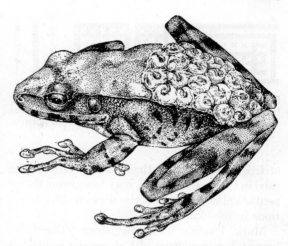

Fig. 32-6. A tropical tree toad (*Cryptobatrachus evansi,* Family HYLIDAE) with brood pouch opened to show developing eggs. (*After Noble, Biology of the amphibia.*)

two embryos that develop completely before birth.

Some ambystomid salamanders produce perennial larvae that reach adult size and even breed while retaining the gills and other larval features. This condition, known as neoteny, occurs in the tiger salamander (*Ambystoma tigrinum*) in Colorado, near Mexico City, and elsewhere and also in *Dicamptodon ensatus* of the Pacific coast.

Small amphibians may breed at two years of age, but larger forms mature more slowly. The length of life is known only for specimens in zoological gardens, a few records being giant salamander, 55 years; European toad, 36 years; tiger salamander, 25 years as a larva and 11 years as an adult.

32-11. Relations to man. Amphibians furnish art motifs (Fig. 32-7) and play a role in the religions of primitive peoples. A toad-shaped amulet from near the river Nile is dated at 3400 B.C., and a Chinese sacrificial vessel in the form of a toad belongs to an ancient dynasty (2205 to 1122 B.C.). Aesop (560 B.C.) included frogs among his fables, and Aristophanes (448–380 B.C.) dramatized their croaking choruses. The American Indian sorcerers employed parts

Fig. 32-7. Amphibian motifs in the art of American Indians. *A*. Frog pursued by snake (on basket of Guiana Indians, *from Roth*). *B*. Tadpole design (Hopi pottery, *from Fewkes*). (*After Frost*, 1932.)

of frogs and toads in their magic. Toads, long used in Chinese medicine, may have some therapeutic value because of the digitalis-like secretions in the skin.

Mark Twain's humorous story "The Celebrated Jumping Frog of Calaveras County" is now the basis for an annual "jumping-frog contest" at Angels Camp, Calif. Pet bullfrogs from all over the United States are entered in the competition.

Frogs are used for elementary courses in biology, for research in physiology and pharmacology, for fish bait, for human food, and for human pregnancy tests. Many thousands are caught annually in various states; in Louisiana, during 1938, a total of 715,540 pounds was taken, valued at $107,331. Frogs are taken by hand, with nets, with spears, or by shooting. With smaller species only the hind legs are used, but the bullfrog has enough flesh to warrant eating the entire animal. The flesh tastes somewhat like veal or chicken. Axolotls of lakes near Mexico City are also used as food. So far as known, there are no commercially practicable "frog farms," although many have been tried in the United States and elsewhere. The long developmental period of larvae and adults and low value of the final product preclude financial success.

32-12. Fossil amphibians. The earliest recognized amphibians (†*Ichthyostega*) are in Devonian rocks of Greenland and were of some size, as the skulls are 6 to 8 inches long. They possibly derived from crossopterygian fishes, had both aquatic and aerial respiration, and possessed fins with skeletal supports from which the tetrapod limb could be derived. The Devonian was evidently a time of season droughts, when the chances of survival were greater for an animal that could leave a drying pool to travel over land and seek water elsewhere. By Carboniferous time, with its coal swamps, there were three distinct orders of ancient amphibians. The skull became flattened and roofed with bone, and many had external armor of bony plates, possibly as protection against large eurypterids (arthropods) then in fresh waters. Those amphibians were from a few inches to perhaps 15 feet in length, some aquatic and some terrestrial. Some of the last types (Triassic) were permanently aquatic, and several had degenerated to become limbless, like eels or snakes. Salamanders appeared in the Cretaceous and were distinct from the earliest frogs, which appeared in the Jurassic; the latter may have been derived from fossil branchiosaurs. Both show degenerative trends in the skull by loss of bones.

Fig. 32-8. A fossil amphibian (†*Eryops*, Order LABYRINTHODONTI), restored. Length to 9 feet. (*After Noble, Biology of the amphibia.*)

CLASSIFICATION

CLASS AMPHIBIA (Batrachia). AMPHIBIANS. Living forms with moist glandular skin and no external scales; typically with 2 pairs of limbs (no paired fins); 2 nostrils connecting to mouth cavity; skull with 2 occipital condyles; heart 3-chambered; respiration by gills, lungs, or skin; eggs with gelatinous coverings, usually laid in water; larvae usually aquatic; adults aquatic or in moist places on land. Devonian to Recent; nearly 2,500 living species.

SUBCLASS 1. STEGOCEPHALIA. Cranium and cheeks completely roofed with bony plates; fossil species often with armor of small overlapping scales ventrally, some also with dorsal scales.

Order 1. †Leptospondyli. Small, of salamander or eel-like form; each vertebra usually with centrum and neural arch of one piece; ribs articulated between adjacent vertebrae. Carboniferous and Permian. *†Lysorophus; †Diplocaulus.*

Order 2. †Phyllospondylii. BRANCHIOSAURS. Small, resembling salamanders or snakes; vertebrae tubular, with nerve cord and notochord in common cavity; 3 pairs of gills on broad arches during long larval life, but none in adult. Devonian to Permian. *†Ichthyostega, †Branchiosaurus.*

Order 3. †Labyrinthodonti. Small to large, of salamander or crocodile form; both jaws with large teeth having greatly folded dentine; body usually armored with dermal plates. Lower Carboniferous to Upper Triassic. *†Eogyrinus,* to 15 feet long; *†Eryops* (Fig. 32-8), crocodile-like, to 9 feet long; *†Capitosaurus.*

Order 4. Gymnophiona (Apoda). CAECILIANS. Body slender, worm-like, no limbs or limb girdles; skull compact, roofed with bone; vertebrae many; ribs long; skin smooth, with transverse furrows, and both slime glands and "squirt glands" (discharging an irritating fluid); some with mesodermal scales embedded in skin; a small protrusible tentacle between eye and nostril; eyes lidless, often beneath skin or maxillary bones; tail short, anus near end of body; male with protrusible copulatory organ. No known fossils; about 55 Recent species.

    CAECILIIDAE. In tropics: India to Philippines, Borneo, Java, and Seychelles; east and west Africa; Mexico to Argentina. *Ichthyophis* (Fig. 32-1); *Gymnopis.* Live and burrow in moist ground; feed on invertebrates; eggs usually 24 to 30 per female, to 6 mm. in diameter, deposited in moist ground near water; some complete larval development in egg, others with aquatic larvae. *Typhlonectes,* northern South America, aquatic throughout life and viviparous, producing about 6 embryos that grow to 150 mm. long before birth.

SUBCLASS 2. CAUDATA (Urodela). SALAMANDERS, NEWTS, etc. Body with distinct head, trunk, and tail; limbs of about equal size; larvae, if aquatic, resemble adults in form and have teeth in both jaws; about 240 species.

Order 1. Proteida. Body depressed, tail with fin; gills permanent, bushy; no eyelids; lungs present; permanently aquatic.

    PROTEIDAE. *Necturus maculosus,* mud puppy or water dog (Fig. 32-5), Arkansas River to the Carolinas and Hudson River; to 12 (or 17) inches long, rusty-brown, with blackish spots; eats small fishes and invertebrates; mates in autumn when females take up spermatophores deposited by males; eggs laid in May or June, 18 to 180 in "nests," attached individually by jelly stalks to undersides of stones and guarded by female; hatch in 38 to 63 days, larvae 22 mm. long; growth slow, about 6 years to full size; *N. punctatus,* the Carolinas; *Proteus anguineus,* "olm" of southeastern Europe, in waters of deep caves, unpigmented, eyes under skin.

Order 2. Mutabilia. TRUE SALAMANDERS. Adults without gills (except *Amphiuma*); lungs present (except PLETHODONTIDAE); skull with paired vomers.

    CRYTOBRANCHIDAE. Body depressed, skin soft, flabby, with fleshy folds at sides; no eyelids; vomerine teeth in arc parallel to jaw; permanently aquatic; Oligocene to Recent. *Cryptobranchus alleganiensis,* hellbender (Fig. 32-9), Louisiana to Ohio and New York, in running water with

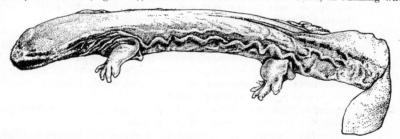

Fig. 32-9. The hellbender (*Cryptobranchus alleganiensis,* Order MUTABILIA). Length to 24 inches. (*After Noble, Biology of the amphibia.*)

rock slabs; to 24 inches long; food as with *Necturus;* fertilization external; in late summer, mates and lays about 300 eggs in rosary-like strings; larvae hatch in November, require several years to mature. *Megalobatrachus japonicus,* giant salamander, eastern China and Japan in cold brooks, to 69 inches long. *†Andrias scheuchzeri,* Miocene in Europe, first referred to several centuries ago as "*Homo diluvii testis*" (human victim of the deluge).

HYNOBIIDAE. ASIATIC LAND SALAMANDERS. Small; with eyelids; vomerine teeth in V behind nares; fertilization external; metamorphosis complete. Northern Asia, Chungking to Ural Mountains. *Hynobius; Ranodon*, lives in brooks.

(*In other salamanders the male has cloacal papillae, the female a seminal receptacle, and fertilization is internal.*)

AMBYSTOMIDAE. Teeth in transverse row across posterior margins of vomers, none on palatine bones; with eyelids; vertebrae amphicoelous; adults usually terrestrial; limited to North America. *Ambystoma*, 13 species; *A. tigrinum*, tiger salamander (Fig. 32-1), whole United States and to central Mexico, adults about 8 inches long, larva often perennial as "axolotl"; *A. opacum*, marbled salamander, eastern states, eggs laid in moist places; *Dicamptodon ensatus*, Pacific coast, to 10½ inches long, larvae often perennial; *Rhyacotriton olympicus*, Oregon and Washington, in mountain streams, lungs only ¼ inch long.

SALAMANDRIDAE. Teeth in roof of mouth behind nares and diverging posteriorly; with lungs but no gills; eyelids present; vertebrae opisthocoelous. Europe, eastern Asia, and North America. *Diemictylus viridescens*, American newt or eft (Fig. 32-10), Atlantic coast to Hudson Bay and Texas, with reddish spots along sides, to 4 inches long, eggs single, in water; *Taricha (Triturus) torosa* and others, Pacific coast newt, or "water dog," California to southern Alaska, brown

Fig. 32-10. *A*. Courtship of American newt or eft (*Diemictylus viridescens*, Family SALAMANDRIDAE), male above female. *B*. Dusky salamander (*Desmognathus fuscus*, Family PLETHODONTIDAE) with eggs. (*After Noble, Biology of the amphibia.*)

above and orange beneath, to 9 inches long, eggs in small masses in water; *T. cristatus*, European crested newt, male brilliant with dorsal crest in breeding season; *Salamandra salamandra*, European "fire" salamander, black with yellow spots, to 6 inches long, adults terrestrial; *S. atra*, European Alpine salamander.

AMPHIUMIDAE. Body cylindrical; no eyelids; adults with lungs, gills, and gill clefts; limbs small, toes 2 or 3. *Amphiuma means*, "congo eel," Louisiana to Missouri and Virginia, in swamps and rice fields, to 36 inches long, feeds on mollusks, crayfishes, and small fishes.

PLETHODONTIDAE. LUNGLESS SALAMANDERS. Mostly under 6 inches long; a minute nasolabial groove from each nostril to upper lip; teeth on vomers and also behind on parasphenoids; eyelids present; no lungs or gills; skin delicate; about 80 species in the Americas (eastern Canada to Bolivia and Lower California to Alaska, none in Great Basin or Rocky Mountains); 2 in southern Europe; most adults terrestrial in moist places where eggs are deposited, guarded by female, and young emerge with no larval stage; few in cold brooks with aquatic larvae. *Pseudotriton ruber*, red salamander; *Desmognathus fuscus*, dusky salamander (Fig. 32-10); *Plethodon glutinosus*, slimy salamander; *Aneides lugubris*, arboreal salamander of California; *Eurycea bislineata*, two-lined salamander; *Typhlomolge rathbuni*, blind, nearly colorless, permanently aquatic and neotenic, in underground waters at San Marcos, Tex.

Order 3. Meantes. Body slender; no hind limbs or eyelids; gills persistent; jaws with horny covering; fertilization probably external; strictly aquatic.

SIRENIDAE. *Siren lacertina*, "mud eel," Virginia and Indiana to Florida and Texas, in muddy ditches and ponds, grows to 30 inches, 3 pairs of gills; *Pseudobranchus striatus*, South Carolina to Florida, to 7 inches long, 1 pair of gill slits, burrows.

SUBCLASS 3. SALIENTIA (Anura). TOADS and FROGS. Head and trunk fused, no neck or tail; forelegs short, hind legs enlarged for leaping and with webs between toes; vertebrae 10, the last a slender urostyle; ribs reduced or none; egg deposition and fertilization usually external, by "clasped" pair of adults; larva (tadpole) with fused ovoid head-and-body and long tail with median fins, usually aquatic; metamorphosis conspicuous; 2,200 species.

Order 1. Amphicoela. Vertebrae amphicoelous; 2 relict "tail" muscles.

ASCAPHIDAE (LIOPELMIDAE). "Bell Toads." Only 2 genera; *Liopelma*, 2 species, the only amphibians native to New Zealand; *Ascaphus truei* (Fig. 32-11), northwestern California to Washington and Montana, in or near cool mountain streams; in mating, male grasps female around pelvis, and fertilization is internal (unique in SALIENTIA) by use of external tail-like copulatory organ on male; larva with ventral sucking disc for adhering to stones in swift stream waters.

Fig. 32-11. Male American "bell" toad (*Ascaphus truei*, Family ASCAPHIDAE) of northwestern United States. Head-and-body length to 2 inches. Enlarged inset shows cloacal appendage in ventral view. (*After Noble, Biology of the amphibia.*)

Order 2. Opisthocoela. Vertebrae opisthocoelous; free ribs in either larva or adult.

DISCOGLOSSIDAE. Tongue and eyelids present; adults with ribs. †*Latonia*, Upper Miocene; *Discoglossus*; *Bombina*, fire-bellied toad of Old World, with black and bright red or yellow on undersurface; *Alytes obstetricans*, European midwife toad.

XENOPIDAE. CLAWED TOADS. No tongue; feet fully webbed; three inner hind toes with black horny claws; strictly aquatic. Africa. *Xenopus*.

PIPIDAE. No tongue or eyelids; feet fully webbed; slender front toes end in cluster of short dermal papillae; strictly aquatic; eggs carried in separate pockets on back of female, young fully metamorphosed when hatched. Northern South America. *Pipa*, Surinam toad.

Order 3. Anomocoela. Sacral vertebrae procoelous; no free ribs.

PELOBATIDAE. SPADEFOOT TOADS. Hind foot with horny cutting spade on inner margin; pupil of eye elliptical; Northern Hemisphere to Philippine Islands. *Pelobates*, in Old World; *Scaphiopus*, United States; strictly nocturnal, hiding by day in burrows, seldom seen except when spawning; eggs laid in temporary pools after rains in spring or summer; development through metamorphosis requires about 1 month.

Order 4. Procoela. Vertebrae procoelous; urostyle with double condyle.

†PALAEOBATRACHIDAE. †*Palaeobatrachus*, Jurassic to Miocene, Europe.

BUFONIDAE. TRUE TOADS. No maxillary teeth; a large paratoid gland behind each eye; ventral parts of pectoral girdle overlap (arciferous); practically world-wide. *Eleutherodactylus*; *Leptodactylus*; *Bufo*, common toads, skin rough, many warts; terrestrial and nocturnal, hiding under logs, stones, etc., or in burrows by day; enter water briefly to spawn; eggs in gelatinous strings; over 100 species, 16 in United States. *B. terrestris*, American toad, Hudson Bay southward and eastward; *B. boreas*, Pacific states to Alaska; other species more local.

BRACHYCEPHALIDAE. Halves of pectoral girdle more or less fused ventrally. New World tropics. *Brachycephalus*; *Dendrobates*.

HYLIDAE. TREE TOADS. Mostly under 2 inches; teeth in upper or both jaws; terminal bone of each digit claw-shaped; all toes with expanded "adhesive" discs, used to climb trees, rocks, etc.;

voice often loud; eggs usually in water; commonest in American tropics. *Hyla versicolor*, tree toad, Minnesota to Texas and eastward; *H regilla*, Lower California to British Columbia; *H. crucifer*, spring peeper, Minnesota, Texas, and eastward; *Acris gryllus*, cricket frog, central Canada and Arizona eastward; *Gastrotheca,* "marsupial frog," South America, egg mass carried on back, exposed or in skin sac, whence young frogs hatch.

Fig. 32-12. Mated pair of Yosemite toads (*Bufo canorus*). The greatest sexual difference in color of any amphibians in the United States: male (above), olive green; female, black and white. (*Photo by T. I. Storer.*)

Order 5. Diplasiocoela. Pectoral girdle fused to sternum (firmisternal).

RANIDAE. TRUE FROGS. Teeth in upper jaw; tongue usually forked posteriorly; eggs usually in tapioca-like masses; Jurassic to Recent; world-wide except South America and Antipodes; only *Rana* with 27 species and subspecies in United States, the commonest being *R. catesbeiana*, bullfrog, Texas to southern Canada and eastward, introduced in western states; *R. clamitans*, green frog or spring frog, Arkansas to southern Canada and eastward; *R. palustris*, pickerel frog, Arkansas to Hudson Bay and eastward; *R. pipiens*, leopard frog or grass frog, North America east of the Sierra-Cascade mountains and into Mexico; *R. sylvatica*, wood frog, Ohio and South Carolina to Nova Scotia; *R. aurora*, red-legged frog, Lower California to Vancouver Island.

POLYPEDATIDAE. OLD WORLD "TREE FROGS." An intercalary cartilage in digits. Africa, eastern and southeastern Asia; mostly arboreal. *Polypedates* (*Rhacophorus*), eggs usually laid in gelatinous foam over water, whence tadpoles drop into water.

MICROHYLIDAE. "NARROW-MOUTH TOADS." Head small, narrow. Cosmopolitan; arboreal to burrowing. *Microhyla carolinensis*, narrow-mouth toad, Virginia and Indiana to Texas; nocturnal, hides in ground by day; larva aquatic with median spiracle, toothless expansible mouth, and no nostrils until metamorphosis; in some species the "larva" completes metamorphosis within the egg capsule.

REFERENCES

(*See also Chap. 2*)

Articles on amphibians appear in many periodicals, especially in the quarterly *Copeia* published by the American Society of Ichthyologists and Herpetologists. For many states and Canadian provinces there are state or local lists giving the distribution and natural history of amphibians occurring in those areas.

BARBOUR, T. 1934. Reptiles and amphibians, their habits and adaptations. 2d ed. Boston, Houghton Mifflin Co. xxii + 129 pp., illus.

BISHOP, S. C. 1943. Handbook of salamanders . . . of the United States, of Canada, and of Lower California. Ithaca, N.Y., Comstock Publishing Associates, Inc. xiv + 555 pp., 144 figs.

DUNN, E. R. 1926. The salamanders of the Family Plethodontidae. Northampton, Mass., Smith College. viii + 441 pp., 3 pls., 86 figs.

———. 1942. The American caecilians. *Museum of Comparative Zoology Bulletin* 91, pp. 439–540.

LIVEZEY, R. L., and A. H. WRIGHT. 1947. A synoptic key to the salientian eggs of the United States. *American Midland Naturalist*, vol. 37, pp. 179–222, 82 figs.

NOBLE, G. KINGSLEY. 1931. Biology of the Amphibia. New York, McGraw-Hill Book Co., Inc. Reprinted 1955. Dover Publications, Inc. xiii + 577 pp., 174 figs. Technical; structure, function, life histories, and classification.

OLIVER, J. A. 1955. The natural history of North American amphibians and reptiles. New York, D. Van Nostrand Co., Inc. xi + 359 pp., 74 figs.

Rosel von Rosenhof. 1758. Historia naturalis rana- rum nostrativum. Nuremberg, J. J. Fleishmann. 6 + 115 pp., 24 col. pls. Earliest comprehensive account of the toads and frogs of Germany; text in parallel columns of Latin and German.

Schmidt, K. P. 1953. A checklist of North American amphibians and reptiles [north of Mexico]. 6th ed. Chicago, American Society of Ichthyologists and Herpetologists. viii + 280 pp. Scientific and com- mon names and distribution.

Stebbins, R. C. 1954. Amphibians and reptiles of western North America. New York, McGraw-Hill Book Co., Inc. xxii + 528 pp., 90 pls., 52 figs., many maps.

Wright, A. A., and A. H. Wright. 1949. Handbook of frogs and toads . . . of the United States and Canada. 3d ed. Ithaca, N. Y., Comstock Publish- ing Associates Inc. xi + 652 pp., 163 figs. Keys and descriptions.

33 CLASS REPTILIA
Reptiles

The Class REPTILIA includes the lizards and snakes (Order SQUAMATA), the turtles and tortoises (Order CHELONIA), the crocodiles and alligators (Order CROCODILIA), and the New Zealand tuatara (*Sphenodon punctatum*, Order RHYNCHOCEPHALIA). These represent only 4 of the 14 known orders that flourished during Mesozoic time, the Age of Reptiles, when they were the dominant animals. Reptiles are the first group among vertebrates adapted for life in dry places on land. The dry cornified skin and scales resist loss of moisture from the body and facilitate living on rough surfaces. The class name refers to the mode of travel (L.

Fig. 33-1. Types of living reptiles (Class REPTILIA). Not to scale. *A*. Painted turtle (*Chrysemys picta*, Order CHELONIA). *B*. Alligator (*Alligator mississipiensis*, Order CROCODILIA). *C*. Skink, a lizard (*Eumeces*), and *D*. Boa, a snake (both Order SQUAMATA). (*After Palmer, Field book of natural history.*)

522

reptum, creep), and the study of reptiles is called herpetology (Gr. *ereptos*, reptile).

33-1. Characteristics. 1. Body covered with dry cornified skin (not slimy), usually with scales or scutes; few surface glands.

2. Two pairs of limbs, each typically with 5 toes ending in horny claws and suited to running, crawling, or climbing; limbs paddle-like in marine turtles, reduced in some lizards, and absent in a few other lizards and in all snakes (vestiges in boas).

3. Skeleton completely ossified; skull with 1 occipital condyle.

4. Heart imperfectly 4-chambered, 2 auricles and a partly divided ventricle (ventricles separate in crocodilians); one pair of aortic arches; red blood corpuscles nucleated, biconvex, and oval.

5. Respiration always by lungs; cloacal respiration in aquatic turtles.

6. Twelve pairs of cranial nerves.

7. Body temperature variable (poikilothermous), according to environment.

8. Fertilization internal, usually by copulatory organs; eggs large with much yolk, in leathery or limy shells; usually laid, but retained in female for development by some lizards and snakes.

9. Segmentation meroblastic; embryonic membranes (amnion, chorion, yolk sac, and allantois) present during development; young when hatched (or born) resemble adults; no metamorphosis.

The reptiles show advance over the amphibians in having (1) a dry scaly body covering adapted to life away from water, (2) limbs suited for rapid locomotion, (3) further separation of the oxygenated and unoxygenated blood in the heart, (4) complete ossification of the skeleton, and (5) eggs suited for development

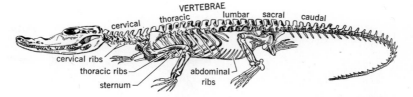

Fig. 33-2. Skeleton of the crocodile. (*Adapted from Claus.*)

on land with membranes and shells to protect the embryo. Reptiles lack the insulated body covering, regulated body temperature, and some other features of birds and mammals.

33-2. Size. Fossil reptiles were small to large, a few being the largest terrestrial animals ever known. Of living reptiles, the South American anaconda grows to 33 feet long, the Komodo lizard (*Varanus komodoensis*) to 9½ feet, and the marine leatherback turtle may exceed 7 feet. Some land tortoises of the Galápagos Islands exceed 4 feet in length, but none weighs over 250 pounds. A crocodile killed about 1825 in Luzon, Philippine Islands, was about 21 feet long. A snake (*Leptotyphlops*) of Syria is the size of a steel knitting needle, and a lizard (*Lepidoblepharis*) of Panama is about 2 inches long. Most North American snakes are 10 to 60 inches long, and the lizards usually under 12 inches.

STRUCTURE OF A REPTILE: THE ALLIGATOR

33-3. External features. The *body* comprises a distinct head, neck, trunk, and tail; each of the short *limbs* bears toes tipped with horny claws and with webs between. The long *mouth* is margined with conical teeth, set in sockets. Near the tip of the snout are two small *nostrils*. The *eyes* are large and lateral, with upper and lower eyelids, and a transparent *nictitating membrane* moves backward beneath the lids. The small *ear* opening is behind the eye and under a flap of skin. The *anus* is a longitudinal slit, behind the bases of the hind limbs.

33-4. Body covering. The tough leathery *skin* is sculptured into rectangular *horny scales* over most of the trunk and tail. The scales are generally in transverse and lengthwise rows, with furrows of softer skin between. The cornified exterior is not molted, and surface wear is replaced by additional cornified layers from the epidermis beneath. Adults have an exoskeleton of separate bony *dermal plates* under the dorsal scales from neck to tail; these are rectangular or oval, often pitted, and some have a median keel. Three pairs of epidermal *musk glands* occur on the lower side of the head, inside the mouth, and just within the cloaca.

33-5. Skeleton (Fig. 33-2). The massive *skull* includes a long snout, and the bones are usually pitted in old adults. The long lower jaw articulates at each side of the posterior margin of the skull on a fixed quadrate bone. Ventrally on the cranium is the long *hard palate* above which are the respiratory passages.

The *vertebral column* comprises five types of vertebrae: 9 cervical, 10 thoracic, 5 lumbar, 2 sacral, and about 39 caudal. On the cervical vertebrae are short free *cervical ribs;* the thoracic vertebrae and sternum are connected by *thoracic ribs,* with cartilaginous ventral extensions, and between the sternum and pubic bones there are 7 pairs of V-shaped *abdominal ribs* held in a longitudinal series by ligaments.

33-6. Muscular system (Fig. 33-3). As compared with a frog, the alligator has more diversity in its muscles, in keeping with the greater variety of its movements both on land and in water. The muscles of the head, neck, and limbs are well differentiated, though less in bulk than in a mammal. The segmental muscles of the vertebral column and ribs are conspicuous.

33-7. Digestive system. The large *mouth* (Fig. 33-4) can open widely and has stout *teeth* used for offense and defense and also to grasp and twist large items of prey. A flat *tongue* lies in the floor of the mouth cavity but cannot be

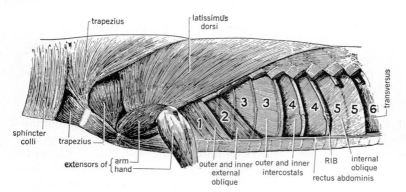

Fig. 33-3. Muscles of a lizard (*Lacerta*). Behind the "arm" successive muscle layers are removed to reveal those beneath: 1, outermost layer; 6, innermost layer. (*After Nierstrasz & Hirsch.*)

protruded. On the hind margin of the tongue, there is a transverse fold opposite a similar one on the palate; when pressed together, these shut off the mouth cavity from the pharynx, so an alligator in water may open its mouth without having water enter the lungs. Beyond the short *pharynx* is the *esophagus,* a slender tube leading to the *stomach.* The latter comprises a large spherical or fundus region and a smaller pyloric portion on the right side. This connects to the coiled *small intestine,* which joins the larger *rectum* leading to the *cloaca* and *anus.* The *liver,* of two lobes, lies anterior to the stomach, and the *pancreas* is in the first or duodenal loop of the intestine; the ducts of both enter the fore part of the intestine. The cloaca is a common end for the digestive, excretory, and reproductive systems.

33-8. Circulatory system. The *heart* lies in the anteroventral part of the thorax; it comprises a small *sinus venosus,* two *auricles,* and two *ventricles.* The ventricles are completely separated in crocodilians, but imperfectly so in other reptiles. Blood from the veins passes in turn through the (1) sinus venosus, (2) right auricle, (3) right ventricle, (4) pulmonary artery to each lung, (5) pulmonary veins from lungs, to the (6) left auricle, and (7) left ventricle. It emerges in a pair of *aortic arches* that pass dorsally around the esophagus; from the base of the right arch two *carotid arteries* lead to the neck and head, and a *subclavian artery* to each fore limb. The two aortic arches join dorsally as a *dorsal aorta* and distribute to organs in the body cavity and to the hind limbs and tail.

Venous blood is collected (1) by an *anterior vena cava* on each side from the head, neck, and fore limb; (2) by a single middorsal *posterior vena cava* from the reproductive organs and kidneys; (3) by a *hepatic portal vein* from the digestive tract that breaks to capillaries in the liver and collects as a short *hepatic vein;* and (4) by an *epigastric vein* on each side of the abdominal cavity from the posterior limbs, tail, and body. All these veins empty into the sinus venosus.

33-9. Respiratory system. Air enters the *nostrils* (external nares) and passes above the hard palate to the *internal nares* behind the velum and thence through the *glottis* in the pharynx, just behind the tongue. The glottis is composed of three cartilages and contains the paired *vocal cords;* it connects to the tubular *trachea,* which is reinforced with rings of cartilage. The trachea extends to the fore part of the thorax to divide into two short *bronchi,* one to each lung. The *lungs* are divided by higher interior partitions than in the frog and contain the pulmonary capillaries.

33-10. Excretory system. The two flat lobular *kidneys* lie in the posterior dorsal part of the body cavity; a *ureter* from each extends back to the side of the cloaca.

33-11. Nervous system and sense organs. The *brain* (Fig. 10-3) has two long olfactory lobes connected to the large cerebral hemispheres; behind the latter are two oval optic lobes. Next is the median pear-shaped cerebellum, which is larger than in amphibians. The medulla ob-

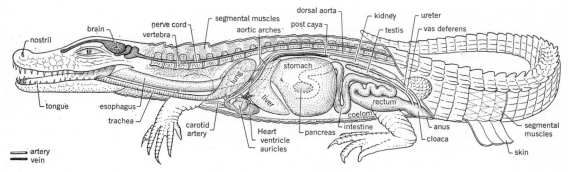

Fig. 33-4. American alligator. General structure.

longata is spread laterally below the cerebellum, then narrows to the spinal **nerve cord.** Ventrally, between the bases of the cerebral hemispheres, are the optic tracts and optic nerves, followed by the infundibulum and the hypophysis. There are 12 pairs of **cranial nerves** and paired **spinal nerves** to each body somite.

There are **taste buds** on the tongue and **olfactory organs** in each nasal cavity. The eyes have **lachrymal glands** to keep the cornea or surface of the eyeball moist when out of water. The ears are of the type characteristic of land vertebrates. Each ear has a short **external auditory canal** under a flap of skin, with a **tympanic membrane** at the inner end, a tympanic cavity or middle ear, and an inner ear containing three semicircular canals and the organ of hearing. From each tympanic cavity a **Eustachian tube** leads medially, the two having a common opening on the roof of the pharynx behind the internal nares.

33-12. Reproductive system. The paired gonads and ducts are much alike in young of the two sexes. In mature males two roundish **testes** lie near the ventromedial borders of the kidneys; a **vas deferens** from each passes back to enter the cloaca just anterior to the ureter and joins the single median **penis** on the ventral floor of the cloaca. In adult females two **ovaries** are similarly attached near the kidneys. Near the anterior end of each kidney is the open funnel of an **oviduct,** and the latter runs backward to the cloaca. Eggs form in the ovaries and pass into the funnels; in the oviducts, each is ferti-

lized and covered with albumen, shell membranes, and a shell before being laid.

33-13. Natural history. Alligators live in swamps or rivers, and some other crocodilians inhabit seacoasts. They dig burrows in stream banks for shelter and eat various kinds of animals from ants to dogs and hogs, but rarely attack man. The female American alligator builds a nest of decaying vegetation and lays 30 to 60 eggs which are incubated by decay in the nest for about 60 days. The young are $8\frac{1}{2}$ to $9\frac{1}{2}$ inches long at hatching and grow 12 inches or so per year. At 10 years a male is about 110 inches long and weighs 250 pounds, a female 87 inches and 113 pounds.

STRUCTURE OF OTHER REPTILES

33-14. Body covering. All reptiles have a dry skin consisting of a stratified epidermis and complex dermis. The epidermis produces layers of cells that pass to the surface, become cornified, and provide the body covering. The epidermal cells are bound to one another by many fine intercellular "bridges," which resist mechanical displacement. The dermis is chiefly of connective tissue and contains pigment cells, blood vessels, and nerves; in some species it includes dermal bones. The connective tissue fibers are in definite layers nearly parallel to the surface, those of each layer approximately at right angles to fibers immediately above and below, and all are "on the bias" at about 45 degrees to the body axis. Small fibers through the dermis and into the epidermis bind the whole skin together. This structural arrangement provides mechanical strength, as in a woven fabric, yet is elastic so that the skin can stretch, as when a snake is swallowing large food or a lizard puffs up in its courting performance. The pattern of dermal scales is essentially constant on each species, and the form and arrangement of the scales are useful in the classification of reptiles.

The outer cornified epidermis is molted at intervals by lizards and snakes, from two to six times a year by the latter. Prior to a molt the epidermal cells produce a new cuticle beneath the older one. The latter then loosens by cell dissolution at its base, with some production of moisture between new and old layers. In snakes, this secretion clouds the cuticle over the eye and probably impairs the animal's vision, whence the common belief that "snakes go blind in August" when many molt. The "slough" of snakes and of small-limbed or limbless lizards comes off in one piece, but some lizards molt the cuticle in pieces. The rattle of a rattlesnake results from retention of the heavier cornified covering at the end of the tail in successive molts (Fig. 33-10). Turtles and alligators do not molt, but the outer surface gradually wears away.

Some lizards and many snakes have color patterns of brilliance and beauty—stripes or bands of alternating colors, spots, and diamond or rectangular markings. Chameleons change color conspicuously. Control of pigment change in reptiles is ascribed to the adrenal glands.

33-15. Turtles. The body is incased in an oval shell, a layer of plate-like bones in definite pattern and closely sutured to one another, over which there is a covering of cornified scutes, also of regular arrangement (Fig. 33-5). The dorsal convex portion is the **carapace,** and the flatter ventral part the **plastron.** The thoracic vertebrae and ribs are usually consolidated with the bony carapace. Soft-shelled turtles have leathery integument, not divided into scutes, and the shell is poorly ossified. The head, tail, and limbs of turtles protrude between the two parts of the shell and in most species can be drawn completely within the margins for safety. Their jaws lack teeth but bear stout cornified sheaths serving to crush their food. The toes end in horny claws that are useful in crawling or digging. On terrestrial tortoises the feet are stumpy, and on marine turtles the limbs are flipper-like, for swimming. The excretory system includes a bladder, and the urine is fluid. The male has an erectile penis on the ventral wall of the cloaca. In the cloaca of aquatic turtles are thin-walled vascular sacs that serve as "cloacal gills" when the animals are submerged.

33-16. Sphenodon (Fig. 33-13). The tuatara, only living member of the Order Rhynchocephalia, is restricted to New Zealand. It is lizard-like in superficial appearance but has various primitive characters including (1) three temporal bridges in the skull, (2) a widely roofed mouth, (3) firm adfixture of the quadrate, (4) a median pineal eye, (5) persistent abdominal ribs, and (6) absence of a copulatory organ.

33-17. Lizards. The body configuration is varied; many species are slender, some compressed laterally, and some flattened dorsoventrally such as the horned toads. The limbs may be long or short, stout or delicate; they are reduced on some and entirely lacking in a number of limbless lizards ("glass snake," footless lizards, etc.). Practically all the limbless forms live in the soil, through which they progress by wriggling in the manner of a worm. In some

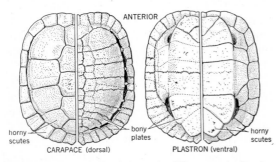

Fig. 33-5. The shell of a turtle (*Chrysemys*) showing the arrangement of external horny scutes over the bony plates beneath.

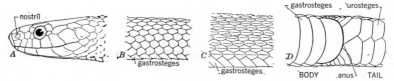

Fig. 33-6. The scales of snakes. *A.* Head of ring-necked snake. *B.* Snake body with smooth scales. *C.* Snake body with keeled scales. *D.* Lower surface of a snake in the anal region showing the enlarged ventral scales on body and tail. (*Adapted from Blanchard, 1924.*)

rapidly running lizards the long slender tail serves as a counterbalance, but in sluggish forms it is short and stumpy. The tail vertebrae in many species are incompletely ossified at their centers. If the tail of such a lizard is seized, the vertebrae separate at one or another of these "breaking points" and the animal scuttles to freedom; in time the lost part is regenerated.

The skin is usually flexible, is loosely attached to the body, and contains many scales arranged in rows, longitudinal, transverse, or diagonal. On most lizards the scales of the back and sides overlap behind, like shingles on a roof. Individual scales are variously smooth, pitted, or have a longitudinal keel. The ventral surface commonly bears small scales. An external eardrum is usually evident on each side of the head.

The tongue may be only slightly mobile or freely extensible; in chameleons it can be "shot" several inches beyond the snout to capture insects on the mucus-coated tip. The jaws are variously provided with teeth, usually short and alike, but differentiated as to form in the Old World AGAMIDAE. A bladder is present in lizards, but the excretory wastes are semisolid as in birds and most reptiles, being passed from the cloaca as whitish material (urates) with the feces. The male has two hemipenes in the sides of the cloaca; at copulation these are everted to enter the cloaca of the female.

33-18. Snakes. Loss of appendages and elongation of the body are an "experiment of nature" in several groups of vertebrates, including the eels and morays among fishes, the caecilians among amphibians, and the worm lizards (AMPHISBAENIDAE), silvery lizards (ANNIELLIDAE), "glass snake" and "slowworm" (ANGUI-

DAE), and other lizards, besides all the snakes. Vestiges of the pelvic girdle and hind limbs persist in the boas, pythons, etc. (Fig. 33-8). The snakes also lack limb girdles, a sternum, eyelids, external ear openings, and a bladder, and they show many specializations in form and function of other parts in the body.

As in lizards, the skin of snakes bears rows of scales, either smooth as on king snakes, or keeled as on rattlesnakes, garter snakes, and others (Fig. 33-6). The ventral surface on all except worm snakes has one row of large transverse scales (ventrals or gastrosteges) from chin to anus, and either one or two rows (caudals or urosteges) on the tail.

The eyes are covered with transparent cuticle; on worm snakes the vestigial eyes are beneath opaque scales. There is no external ear membrane or opening. The skull is delicate, and several of the bones can move upon one another. Teeth, having a backward slant, are present on the jaws and on bones in the roof of the mouth; they serve to hold food while being swallowed. Poisonous snakes have a pair of specialized teeth, or "fangs," on the two maxillary bones of the upper jaw that conduct the venom used to kill prey; these are fixed in the cobra and its allies but folded back, when not in use, in rattlesnakes and other vipers. The serpent tongue is narrow, flexible, and ribbonlike, with a forked tip, and can protrude through a notch in the lower jaw when the mouth is closed; it aids in the sense of smell, bringing chemical stimuli to the Jacobson's organs in the nasal cavity. The digestive tract is essentially a straight tube, from mouth to anus; practically all the other internal organs are elongated; and the right lung is reduced or absent.

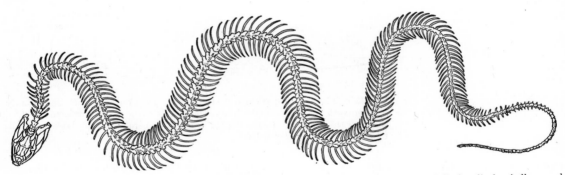

Fig. 33-7. Skeleton of a snake showing the loss of limbs, limb girdles, and sternum and the greatly increased number of vertebrae and ribs all practically alike in structure.

Hemipenes are present in the male, as in lizards.

In long snakes the vertebrae number 200 to 400 (Fig. 33-7). The segmental body muscles are slender and numerous, connecting vertebrae to vertebrae, vertebrae to ribs, ribs to ribs, ribs to skin, and skin to skin. Many extend from one body segment to the next, but others connect, by tendons, between segments far removed from one another. This arrangement makes possible the graceful sinuous movements of a snake.

Locomotion is usually due to the backward pressure of lateral loops of the body against irregularities on the surface of the ground. Snakes also travel a straight path by "hitching," part by part, the skin and body alternately, sliding the ventral scales on the ground. The sidewinder, or "horned rattlesnake" (*Crotalus cerastes*), progresses by a curious looping of the body at a sharp angle with its path of travel.

Snakes neither chew nor tear their food but swallow it entire. They can take prey greater in diameter than their own bodies (Fig. 33-9) by reason of a series of adaptive modifications, which include (1) junction of the two mandibles anteriorly by an elastic ligament; (2) loose attachment of the quadrate bone on either side to both the skull and mandible; (3) and movement of bones of the palate. In consequence of these three features the mouth can be widely distended. Other modifications are (4) the slender backward-pointing teeth on the jaws and palate, which prevent the food from slipping

forward, once swallowing has begun; (5) absence of a sternum (breastbone) and ribs free of any bony articulation ventrally, so that the thorax may be dilated; (6) presence of soft, elastic skin between scales on the back and sides of body, permitting wide distention; (7) thin and easily stretched walls of esophagus and stomach; and (8) placement of the glottis far forward, between the jaws and just behind the sheath for the slender tongue, which permits respiration during the swallowing of food.

NATURAL HISTORY

33-19. Distribution. Most reptiles, both species and individuals, live in tropical and subtropical regions; their numbers decline rapidly toward the poles and in high altitudes. Thus, Louisiana has 22 kinds of turtles, 9 lizards, 40 snakes, and the alligator, but northern Alberta has only 1, a garter snake. Turtles and snakes are more numerous in humid regions such as the southeastern states, and lizards in arid territory like that of the American Southwest.

Reptiles occupy a wide variety of habitats. Large pythons and boas dwell in the tropics, the crocodilians in swamps or rivers or along seacoasts, the biggest turtles in the ocean, and the giant land tortoises on arid oceanic islands. Most lizards and snakes are terrestrial, but some climb rocks and trees. The black snake and striped racers ascend bushes and trees in search of food, and some tropical serpents are

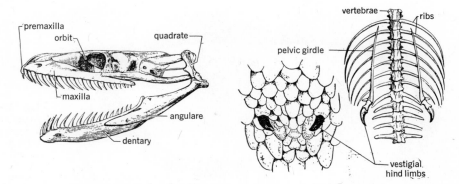

Fig. 33-8. Skeletal features of a python. *Left.* Skull with quadrate articulation of lower jaw that permits distension of the mouth when swallowing. *Center.* External appearance of pelvic region with black horny caps on vestigial hind limbs. *Right.* Vestigial pelvic girdle and limb bones. (*From Guide to reptile gallery, British Museum.*)

predominantly arboreal. Small geckos and other lizards seek shelter in crevices of rocks, trees, or buildings, snakes often use rodent burrows, and some lizards and snakes burrow into sand by aid of an upturned (rostral) plate on the snout. Most turtles live in and about water, but box turtles inhabit the open floor of forests, and the land tortoises inhabit dry ground exclusively.

33-20. Activity. Being cold-blooded or poikilothermous, reptiles are influenced markedly by the environmental temperature. In the tropics they are active throughout the year, but elsewhere they experience a period of dormancy dependent upon the length and severity of the cold season. Lizards and snakes enter crevices in the ground to hibernate, rattlesnakes and some other snakes den up in numbers in caves or large burrows, and fresh-water turtles go to the bottoms of ponds.

In temperate regions, reptiles are active during the daylight hours of the warmer months. In desert and semidesert regions during the summer, they are active in the early morning and late afternoon, but hide away during the hot midday hours. Some desert snakes are always nocturnal, and others become night prowlers during the hotter months.

Contrary to common belief, reptiles cannot withstand unlimited quantities of heat. A rise in body temperature to over 45°C. (113°F.) is quickly fatal. Lacking a mechanism for heat dissipation, they are soon killed by overheating.

33-21. Food. Most reptiles feed chiefly on animals; the land tortoises, large and small, some turtles, and a few lizards (chuckwalla and desert iguana) eat vegetation. The large crested Galápagos iguana (*Amblyrhynchus cristatus*) is unique in that it dives into the sea to obtain seaweeds (marine algae), which constitute its sole food.

Lizards and small snakes take insects and other small invertebrates; small turtles capture aquatic invertebrates; and large lizards, turtles, snakes, and crocodilians eat various vertebrates from fishes to mammals (Fig. 33-9). The total intake of food is small in amount as compared with that necessary for birds and mammals. Nonvenomous snakes that feed upon land vertebrates commonly encircle the prey quickly with one or more coils of the body, then tighten down and "constrict" the victim until death results from asphyxiation; this is the practice of boas, king snakes, and others. The poisonous snakes strike with their fangs and inject venom, whereupon the victim quickly dies.

33-22. Enemies. Racers, king snakes, coral snakes, moccasins, copperheads, and even the little ring-necked snakes feed in varying degree

Fig. 33-9. A gopher or bull snake that has just swallowed a house mouse. Extreme distension of the body skin causes the rows of scales to be widely separated during swallowing and early stages of digestion. The glottis opening just inside the lower jaw permits respiration to continue. (*Photo by T. I. Storer.*)

upon other serpents, king snakes reputedly being immune to the venom of poisonous snakes. Crows, hawks, and owls are the most important bird predators upon reptiles. Of mammals, the skunks, raccoons, badgers, foxes, and coyotes feed upon reptiles, and some ground squirrels occasionally eat lizards. Man kills many snakes, and his destruction of harmful rodents may reduce the food for large snakes.

33-23. Life span. In captivity, several tortoises have survived beyond 100 years, various turtles for 20 to 90 years, occasional crocodiles and large snakes for 25 to 40 years, and smaller species for a few years to 20 or more.

33-24. Reproduction. Reptiles are intermediate between the fishes and amphibians and the mammals in manner of reproduction. Fertilization is always internal, yet most species deposit their eggs for development outside the body. Internal development among land vertebrates may have begun as a regular phenomenon in reptiles, since some strictly oviparous turtles and snakes retain their eggs temporarily when conditions for deposition are unfavorable. When this happens in the European ring snake (*Tropidonotus*), the embryos develop, so that after laying, only 3 weeks (instead of the usual 7 or 8) ensue until hatching. Internal development

is the rule for vipers, rattlesnakes, water and garter snakes, and the sea snakes. In certain genera of lizards, some of the species lay eggs and others produce living young; horned toads are ovoviviparous except one species, but the reverse is true with the fence lizards (*Sceloporus*).

In adaptation to life on land, reptile eggs resemble somewhat those of birds, being covered by a tough flexible shell with a shell membrane inside. The shells are hardened by limy salts in crocodilians and some turtles. The shape is usually a long oval but is spherical in the eggs of land tortoises and sea turtles. An abundance of yolk is provided to nourish the embryo, so that the size of the egg is often large in proportion to that of the female. During development the embryo is surrounded by embryonic membranes, the **amnion** and **chorion** and the **allantois** (Fig. 11-15); these "new" features of vertebrates, first occurring in reptiles, are an adaptation to protect the delicate embryo against desiccation and physical shock during development. Prior to hatching a calcareous **egg tooth** develops on the tip of the upper mandible, as in birds; it serves to cut the egg membrane and shell at hatching, then drops off. The young at hatching usually resemble their parents and become independent at once.

The number of eggs produced annually by a female varies from nearly 400 in a sea turtle

(*Caretta*) to a single egg in the house gecko (*Sphaerodactylus*). Small pond turtles lay 5 to 11 eggs, the lesser snakes and lizards about 10 to 20, and the American alligator 30 to 60; and garter snakes have produced over 70 living young in a single brood. The eggs are deposited in natural cavities below or within rocks or logs, beneath vegetable debris, or in earth or sand. Female turtles seek sandbanks or hill slopes where they excavate nest cavities by digging with the hind feet. The duration of development in different reptiles is from a few weeks to several months; the New Zealand tuatara is unique in requiring about 13 months.

In ovoviviparous reptiles that retain eggs in the oviduct of the female for development, the "shell" is but a thin membrane. Blood vessels of the embryo soon grow out on either the yolk sac or the chorion and lie close to maternal vessels on the inner surface of the oviduct ("uterus"), providing respiration for the embryo in an arrangement functionally equivalent to the placenta in mammals. When development is completed, such eggs are "laid" and the young "hatch" at once.

33-25. Relations to man. Many kinds of snakes and lizards benefit man by feeding upon harmful rodents and insects, but some snakes prey on the eggs of game and song birds in season.

Skins of crocodiles and alligators have long been used for fancy leather, and in recent years those of large snakes and lizards have been made into shoes, purses, and similar articles. An estimated 2,500,000 skins were taken for such purposes in India alone during 1932, with others from Malaysia, the Philippines, Africa, and South America. Turtles are useful chiefly for food. Flesh of the green turtle, both fresh and dried, has been in such demand that the fisheries for it on tropical islands have been far depleted. The Galápagos giant land tortoises, once enormously abundant, were levied upon by Pacific Ocean mariners for three centuries as a source of fresh meat; during the whaling period, from 50 to 300 were removed by each ship, and an estimated 100,000 were taken during the nineteenth century. Some species were exterminated, and the reduced populations of others are now protected. The smaller turtles of fresh and brackish waters in the United States also serve as food, especially the snapper, diamondback terrapin, and soft-shelled turtles. Other small turtles find some use in biological laboratories. The real tortoise shell for combs and other fancy articles is obtained from the marine hawksbill turtle. Young turtles are sold extensively as pets.

Snakes have long been objects of fear and superstition to mankind. They are venerated and worshiped by many primitive peoples. Hopi Indians in northern Arizona have an annual ceremonial, part of which is a snake dance during which live snakes, including rattlesnakes, are carried in the mouths of certain priests. Many erroneous beliefs about snakes still persist among people in civilized countries, despite the amount now known about the structure and biology of snakes and their place in nature as one group of predaceous animals.

33-26. Poisonous reptiles. The two species of *Heloderma*, one of which is the Gila monster of the American Southwest, are the only poisonous reptiles other than snakes. The venom of these lizards is as poisonous as that of rattlesnakes, but the mechanism for venom transfer is poorly developed, and only rarely are human beings injured or killed. Venomous snakes occur on all the continents and on many large islands, except Madagascar and New Zealand. Venom serves for the capture of their small prey but is used defensively against large animals and man. Among the crowded populations of India, snake poisoning causes several thousand human deaths each year. In the United States several hundred persons are bitten annually, and a number of deaths result.

In North America, north of Mexico, the snakes poisonous to man include 2 coral snakes, the moccasin, the copperhead, and about 20 rattlesnakes. The coral snake has a small head and eye, an elliptical pupil, and the body marked with transverse rings of red, black, and yellow, each black ring being bordered by yellow. All other dangerous snakes in this region are "pit

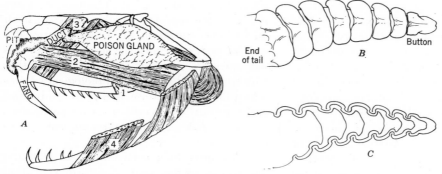

Fig. 33-10. Rattlesnake. *A.* Mechanism of the head in striking. The spheno-pterygoid muscle (1) contracts to rock the fang forward at right angles to the head; upon entering the victim's flesh the external pterygoid (2) and spheno-palatine (3) contract to draw the fang more deeply; then the anterior temporal muscle (4) draws up the lower jaw and compresses the poison gland to force venom through the duct and fang into the wound. All head and neck muscles relax for withdrawal. The whole process requires but an instant. *B, C.* The dry cornified rattle in external view and frontal section to show how the segments are held loosely together. (*After Grinnell and Storer, Animal life in the Yosemite.*)

vipers,'' with wide heads and vertically elliptical pupils. The pit, between the nostril and eye, on each side, is a thermosensory organ enabling the snake to detect the presence of warm-bodied prey. The tail on the moccasin and copperhead is slender-tipped; on all rattlesnakes it is blunt and ends with the characteristic rattle (Fig. 33-10*B, C*). The coral snake occurs from states of the Mexican border and Gulf north to Indiana and North Carolina; the copperhead from Massachusetts to Illinois and southward; and the moccasin from Virginia and Illinois southward. Rattlesnakes are present from southern Canada southward, being more numerous as to species and individuals in the arid Southwest.

The **venom** is secreted in a pair of glands, one on either side of the upper jaw, each connected by a duct to a fang. Reserve fangs develop behind the functional pair to replace the latter when lost (as with teeth in all snakes). Venom is a complex of organic materials having various physiological effects, and each kind of venom has distinctive characteristics and different toxicity. Venom of the cobra and related snakes (Elapidae) affects particularly the respiratory centers, and death results from asphyxiation; that of rattlesnakes and vipers

(Viperidae) affects the heart and nervous system more severely.

Rattlesnakes and other pit vipers strike from an S-shaped posture of the body; the fangs are buried in the victim, the snake's lower jaw clamps upward, muscles over each poison gland force the venom through the hollow fangs into the flesh, and then the head is withdrawn—all with amazing rapidity (Fig. 33-10*A*). The venom of vipers and rattlesnakes usually travels slowly in the lymphatic circulation so that the approved **treatment for rattlesnake bite** is now to (1) apply a tourniquet encircling the bitten part, toward the heart from the bite; (2) disinfect and make X-shaped cuts about ¼ inch deep near the bite; (3) apply suction by a rubber bulb, or other device, and continue this for 12 to 15 hours; and (4) administer antivenin, if available. Many other procedures long advocated are worthless or harmful to victims of snake bite.

Efforts to treat victims of snake bite date from antiquity, and many irrational means, chemical and others, have been tried. In 1887 Sewell discovered that repeated injection of minute sublethal doses of rattlesnake venom into pigeons caused development of an **antibody** (par. 6-7). For snake-bite treatment, horses are immunized to snake venom, then the blood serum is withdrawn to serve as **antivenin,** which is injected into a victim of snake bite. Each kind of venom has distinctive qualities, and no single antivenin will serve against all snakes. Antivenins for snake bite are now generally available.

Some primitive peoples use snake venom to prepare poisoned arrows for killing game and for warfare. An extract of water moccasin venom is used by physicians to check persistent bleeding in some diseases, and cobra venom has been employed to relieve the severe pain in human cases of inoperable cancer.

33-27. Fossil reptiles. The living reptiles, although numerous, are mostly small and occupy a minor role among existing animals. During the Mesozoic era, or Age of Reptiles (Triassic to Upper Cretaceous), they were the dominant vertebrates and occupied most animal habitats then available, from semideserts and dry uplands through marshes and swamps to the open ocean. They varied in size from small to large, some far exceeding elephants in length and weight, and were greatly diversified as to structure and habits.

The most primitive reptiles resembled early amphibians so closely that it is difficult to separate the two groups. During the Permian, reptiles became numerous and began to radiate in both structure and manner of life. By the end of that period they had largely replaced the amphibians, by the end of Triassic time practically all major groups of reptiles had appeared, and during the Jurassic and Cretaceous these attained a climax as to numbers of species and individuals and also in diversity of form and manner of life. Then, with the end of the Cretaceous, this great reptilian host disappeared, and only four of the 14 orders survived.

The most important evolutionary achievement of the reptiles was to become adapted for terrestrial life apart from water. The acquisition of a dry cornified integument to prevent loss of moisture from the body and the production of eggs capable of development on land were sig-

nificant in this adaptation. The small primitive reptiles had slender bodies and tails and four short five-toed limbs. From this generalized form some of the lines of radiation or specialization were (1) increase in size, as to the huge proportions of the brontosaurs; (2) acquisition of defensive armor, including plates in the skin and horns or spines on the head, as by some dinosaurs; (3) lightened build, for rapid running on four legs or two, as with other dinosaurs; (4) adaptation to flight, by increased length of fore limb and tail and development of flight membranes of skin by the pterodactyls; and (5) adaptation to strictly aquatic life, with paddle-like limbs and a fusiform body in the case of ichthyosaurs and others.

†*Brontosaurus* (Fig. 1-2) attained to a length of 75 feet, and †*Diplodocus* to $87\frac{1}{2}$ feet, the largest terrestrial animals ever known. They may have weighed 25 to 35 tons and used more than $\frac{1}{4}$ ton of food per day. †*Stegosaurus* (Fig. 33-11) had a series of enormous bony plates in a dorsal crest extending from the neck to the end of the tail. †*Triceratops* bore a skull scarcely equaled as to size and weight by any other animal save the modern whales, with a sharp cutting beak on the upper jaw, a short stout horn on the nose, and a pair of long forward-pointing horns on the top of the head. The brains of these huge dinosaurs were proportionately small; that of the 18-foot †*Stegosaurus* had an estimated weight of only 2.5 ounces.

The flying reptiles, or pterodactyls (Figs. 33-11, 14-1), were of light build. The head was long, the fifth "finger" greatly lengthened, and the hind limbs and base of the tail supported the flight membrane, somewhat as in modern bats. One form (*Pteranodon*) had a wingspread of 25 feet. The marine ichthyosaurs were whalelike but had four (instead of two) paddle-like limbs used for steering and a large tail fin. The Mesozoic reptiles included both herbivorous and carnivorous species. Nests of dinosaur eggs discovered in Mongolia prove that certain of these ancient reptiles were oviparous like their successors.

Remains of fossil reptiles have been found on all continents (except Antarctica) and are abun-

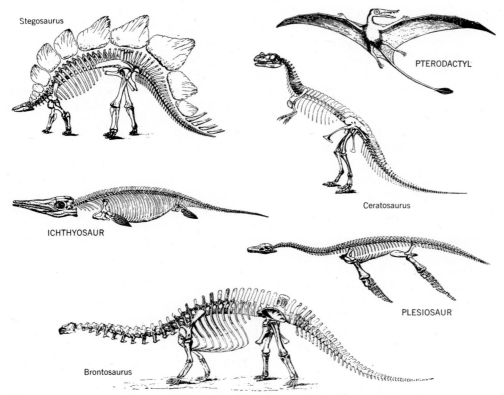

Stegosaurus

PTERODACTYL

Ceratosaurus

ICHTHYOSAUR

PLESIOSAUR

Brontosaurus

Fig. 33-11. Restored skeletons of fossil reptiles; all much reduced but not to same scale. Dinosaurs: †*Stegosaurus*, length to 18 feet, with huge dorsal armor; †*Ceratosaurus*, of bipedal form and large size; †*Brontosaurus*, length to 75 feet. Ichthyosaur: marine and fish-like, limb girdles reduced and limbs paddle-like for swimming. Plesiosaur: length to 50 feet, marine, with long neck and stout paddle-like limbs. Pterodactyl: †*Rhamphorhynchus*, fifth finger elongated to support flight membrane (compare Fig. 14-1). (*After Marsh and others.*)

dant in some rocks of the western states, especially in Wyoming, Utah, and Colorado. Footprints of Mesozoic reptiles, made on the shores of ancient waters, are found in sandstones in several places in the United States.

There has been much speculation as to why the ancient reptiles disappeared so suddenly, geologically speaking. One theory suggests that the earliest mammals preyed upon their eggs; another and more plausible explanation is that change in climate, as by reduction in temperature or altered moisture relations, affected either the reptiles themselves or their habitats, or both, adversely. Disappearance of the late Mesozoic reptiles evidently gave opportunity for primitive mammals, then small in size, to begin the spectacular development that characterized the Tertiary era.

The following outline indicates the diversity of reptiles in past geologic time.[1] Groups with living representatives are indicated by boldface type; all others are extinct.

[1] Condensed from A. S. Romer, 1937. Man and the vertebrates, University of Chicago Press.

Subclass I. ANAPSIDA.
   Order 1. Cotylosauria. Stem Reptiles. Permian, *Seymouria.*
   Order 2. **Chelonia.** Turtles. Permian, *Eunotosaurus;* Cretaceous. *Archelon;* Recent, *Chrysemys.*

Subclass II. ICHTHYOPTERYGIA.
  Order 3. Ichthyosauria. Ichthyosaurs. Marine. Triassic, *Merriamia;* Jurassic, *Ichthyosaurus;* Cretaceous, *Ophthalmosaurus.*
Subclass III. SYNAPTOSAURIA.
  Order 4. Sauropterygia. Plesiosaurs, etc. Marine. Jurassic, *Plesiosaurus;* Cretaceous, *Elasmosaurus.*
Subclass IV. LEPIDOSAURIA.
  Order 5. Eosuchia. Ancient Two-arched Reptiles. Upper Permian to Jurassic. *Proterosuchus.*
  Order 6. **Rhynchocephalia.** Triassic to Recent. *Sphenodon,* 1 living species.
  Order 7. **Squamata.**
      A. **Lacertilia.** Mosasaurs. Cretaceous, *Tylosaurus.* Lizards. Jurassic to Recent. *Sceloporus, Eumeces,* etc.
      B. **Ophidia.** Snakes. Cretaceous to Recent. *Pituophis, Crotalus.*
Subclass V. ARCHOSAURIA. Ruling Reptiles.
  Order 8. Theodontia. Phytosaurs, etc. Triassic, *Ornithosuchus, Mystriosuchus.*
  Order 9. Crocodilia. Alligators, etc. Jurassic, *Stenosaurus;* Recent, *Alligator.*
  Order 10. Pterosauria. Flying Reptiles. Jurassic, *Rhamphorhynchus;* Cretaceous, *Pteranodon.*
  Order 11. Saurischia. "Reptile-like" Dinosaurs.
      A. Theropoda (bipeds). Jurassic, *Compsognathus;* Cretaceous, *Tyrranosaurus.*
      B. Sauropoda (quadrupeds). Jurassic, *Brontosaurus, Diplodocus, Brachiosaurus.*
  Order 12. Ornithischia. "Bird-like" Dinosaurs.
      A. Ornithopoda (bipeds). "Duckbills," etc. Jurassic, *Camptosaurus;* Cretaceous, *Trachodon, Corythosaurus.*
      B. Stegosauria. Jurassic, *Stegosaurus.*
      C. Ankylosauria. Armored Dinosaurs. Cretaceous, *Ankylosaurus.*
      D. Ceratopsia. Horned Dinosaurs. Cretaceous, *Triceratops.*
Subclass VI. SYNAPSIDA (forms leading toward mammals).
  Order 13. Pelycosauria. Permian and Carboniferous, *Dimetrodon, Edaphosaurus.*
  Order 14. Therapsida. Mammal-like Reptiles. Permian and Triassic, *Cynognathus.*

CLASSIFICATION

CLASS REPTILIA. Reptiles. (Characteristics of living forms.) Skin dry, cornified, usually with scales or scutes; limbs typically 4, each with 5 clawed toes, but reduced or absent in some; skeleton bony, 1 occipital condyle; Permian to Recent; terrestrial, fresh-water, or marine, in tropics and warm temperate regions; about 6,000 species.

Order 1. Chelonia (Testudinata). Turtles, Tortoises, and Terrapins. Body broad, encased in a rigid "shell" of rounded dorsal carapace and flat ventral plastron, joined at sides, and covered by polygonal scutes or leathery skin; no teeth, jaws with horny sheaths; quadrate immovable; thoracic vertebrae and ribs usually fused to shell; anus an elongate slit; one copulatory organ; oviparous, eggs laid in holes, or "nests," dug and covered by females; Triassic to Recent; worldwide except New Zealand and western South America; in fresh or salt waters or on land; 265 species.

  Suborder 1. atheca. Large; ribs and vertebrae separate from shell; skin thick, smooth, and leathery with polygonal plates; limbs paddle-like; fore limbs slender, nearly as long as body.

    Dermochelidae. *Dermochelys coriacea,* leathery turtle, in tropical oceans, occasional on American coasts.

  Suborder 2. thecophora. Thoracic vertebrae and ribs fused to carapace.

    Superfamily A. Cryptodira. Carapace covered with horny shields; neck bends in vertical S-curve if retractile; pelvis not fused to carapace or plastron.

      Chelydridae. Snapping Turtles. Plastron small, cross-shaped; head, neck, and limbs large, cannot be withdrawn into shell; tip of upper jaw hooked; North and Central Americas. *Chelydra serpentina,* common "snapper," Gulf coast to southern Canada (Fig. 33-12*B*); *Macrochelys temminckii,* alligator snapper, Missouri, Georgia, and southward, length to 24 inches, vicious, powerful, food chiefly vertebrates.

      Dermatemyidae. Tail short; Mexico and Central America. *Dermatemys.*

      Kinosternidae. Musk and "Mud" Turtles. Both ends of plastron hinged; odor musky in life; North and Central Americas. *Sternotherus,* musk turtles, Missouri and southern Canada eastward and southward, head large, plastron reduced; *Kinosternon,* mud turtles, eastern states, Colorado River and southward, in muddy streams.

      Platysternidae. Head large; temporal region completely roofed; mandible hooked; tail long; southern Asia. *Platysternum megalocephalum.*

TESTUDINIDAE. COMMON TURTLES, TERRAPINS, and LAND TORTOISES. Pubic and ischiadic symphyses firmly joined; Eocene to Recent; world-wide, except Australian region; includes most chelonians. *Chrysemys*, painted turtle, Atlantic coast to eastern Washington, in clear waters (Fig. 33-1); *Malacoclemmys*, diamondback terrapins, Massachusetts to Texas, in salt and brackish waters, esteemed for eating; *Emys, Clemmys*, semi-box and mud turtles; *Terrapene*, box turtles,

Fig. 33-12. Turtles (Order CHELONIA). *A.* Green turtle (*Chelonia mydas*), marine, length to 42 inches. *B.* Snapping turtle (*Chelydra serpentina*), in fresh waters, to 14 inches long. *C.* Desert tortoise (*Gopherus*), to 11½ inches long, on land in arid southern states. *D.* Soft-shelled turtle (*Trionyx ferox*), in fresh waters of eastern United States, to 18 inches long. (*From Palmer, Field book of natural history.*)

plastron with transverse hinge, Arizona to Atlantic coast; *Testudo*, giant land tortoises of Galápagos Islands and islands of Indian Ocean, some over 4 feet long; *Gopherus*, smaller land tortoises, Florida to southeastern California (Fig. 33-12C); both of latter groups strictly terrestrial and vegetarian.

CHELONIDAE. SEA TURTLES. Large; limbs flipper-like; shell covered with smooth horny shields; Upper Cretaceous to Recent; tropical and subtropical seas, occasional on coasts of United States; come ashore only to lay eggs. *Caretta*, loggerhead, Atlantic coast, big-headed, 2 nails on each front flipper, to 4 feet long and 500 pounds; *Eretmochelys*, hawksbill turtle, to 24 inches long, upper jaw hooked, overlapping dorsal scutes provide true "tortoise shell" of commerce; *Chelonia*, green turtle, much prized for food, occasional adults to 3½ feet and 400 pounds (Fig. 33-12A).

SUPERFAMILY B. PLEURODIRA. Neck folds sideways under front of carapace; pelvis fused to carapace and plastron.

PELOMEDUSIDAE. Neck completely retractile; South America, Africa, and Madagascar. *Podocnemis*, "tartaruga."

CHELYIDAE. SNAKE-NECKED TURTLES. Head and neck long, not completely retractile beneath shell; South America, Australia, and New Zealand. *Chelys*, matamata; *Chelodina*.

CARETTOCHELYIDAE. Limbs flat, paddle-shaped; shell soft; New Guinea; 1 species. *Carettochelys insculpta*, highly aquatic.

SUPERFAMILY C. TRIONYCHOIDEA. Body flat, oval; skin smooth, leathery; scant bony shell; head long, snout tubular; feet broadly webbed; only 3 inner digits with claws; Cretaceous to Recent.

TRIONYCHIDAE. SOFT-SHELLED TURTLES. North America, Africa, Asia, and Malay Archipelago. *Trionyx*, Gulf states to St. Lawrence River; *T. spinifera*, most common; *T. ferox*, to 18 inches long (Fig. 33-12D).

Order 2. Rhynchocephalia. Living representative lizard-like; scales granular; a middorsal row of low spines; quadrate immovable; mandibles joined by ligament; vertebrae amphicentrous; abdominal ribs present; anal opening transverse; no copulatory organ in male; Permian to Eocene, and

Recent; New Zealand. One living species, *Sphenodon punctatum*, "tuatara" (Fig. 33-13), length to 30 inches; lives on land and in water and burrows; eats fishes, insects, and worms; eggs about 10, with hard white shells, laid in holes in ground and requiring about 13 months to hatch.

Fig. 33-13. Tuatara (*Sphenodon punctatum*). Length to 30 inches. Native to New Zealand and only living member of the Order RHYNCHOCEPHALIA. (*Photo by T. I. Storer, live specimen at California Academy of Sciences.*)

Order 3. Squamata. LIZARDS and SNAKES. Skin with horny epidermal scales or shields; quadrate bone movable; vertebrae usually procoelous; copulatory organ (hemipenes) double and eversible; anal opening transverse.

    SUBORDER 1. SAURIA (Lacertilia). LIZARDS. Body usually slender; limbs typically 4, sometimes reduced or absent; mandibles fused anteriorly; pterygoid in contact with quadrate; eyelids usually movable; pectoral girdle well developed (or vestigial); tongue usually entire; bladder ordinarily present; length usually under 12 inches (a few over 6 feet); mostly oviparous, some ovoviviparous; food chiefly insects and small invertebrates, some herbivorous; tropics and temperate regions, on continents and islands; 3,140 species.

(*Note: Of the 26 families, 6 entirely fossil, some are omitted here.*)

Fig. 33-14. Gecko (*Hemidactylus turcicus*), southern Portugal to India. Length to 4 inches. (*After Guide to reptile gallery, British Museum.*)

Division A. *Ascalabota.* Usually more than 4 rows of scales per body segment; scales, when over-lapping (imbricate), with wide free margin posteriorly.

GEKKONIDAE. GECKOS. Small; toes often with rounded adhesive plates or pads for climbing; eyes usually lack movable lids; vertebrae amphicoelous; tongue protrusible; many can produce sounds; egg shells calcified; world-wide, in warm regions; some climb rocks, trees, and buildings, other slender forms live on sandy deserts; 300 species. *Phyllodactylus* and *Coleonyx*, native to southwestern United States and Mexico; *Hemidactylus* and *Sphaerodactylus*, probably introduced at Key West, Fla. (Fig. 33-14).

IGUANIDAE. NEW WORLD LIZARDS. Limbs normal; teeth usually alike (homodont) and fixed to sides of jaws (pleurodont); tongue fleshy, not protractile; eyelids complete; chiefly in the

Fig. 33-15. Fence lizard or "swift" (*Sceloporus occidentalis*), length to 7 inches; lives on ground, rocks, and trees in western states. (*Photo by T. I. Storer.*)

Americas; includes most North American lizards, a majority of them west of the Mississippi River. *Anolis carolinensis*, American "chameleon," North Carolina to Texas, skin color changes readily, green on leaves, etc.; *Sceloporus* (Fig. 33-15), "swifts," on rocks, trees, or ground, *S. undu-*

Fig. 33-16. The horned toad (*Phrynosoma*), a common lizard on dry ground and sand in the arid western states. Length to 5½ inches. (*From Van Denburgh.*)

latus in eastern states; *Phrynosoma*, horned toads (Fig. 33-16), body broad, flat, and spiny, enlarged "horns" (scales) on head, eastern Washington and Kansas to California and Mexico, live on dry ground and sand; *Uta*, utas; *Crotaphytus*, collared lizards (Fig. 33-17); *Sauromalus*,

Fig. 33-17. Collared lizards (*Crotaphytus collaris*). Length to 13 inches. The sexes differ in colora-tion. Live on rocks and open ground in western states. (*From Van Denburgh.*)

chuckwalla; *Callisaurus*, gridiron tail; *Iguana, Cyclura*, etc., iguanas, Mexico and southward, some to 6 feet long, body compressed, tail long, a middorsal crest of lance-like spines; active in running and climbing; feed on leaves, fruits, some insects, and small vertebrates; used for human food in tropics.

AGAMIDAE. OLD WORLD LIZARDS. Limbs normal; teeth usually differentiated (heterodont) and attached to edges of jaws (acrodont); tongue short, thick; some with throat sacs or dorsal spines; southern Europe, Africa, Asia, and Australia; over 200 species. *Agama; Draco*, "flying dragon," long ribs covered by membrane and used to volplane from a height; *Moloch*, Australia, somewhat like a horned toad.

CHAMAELEONTIDAE. CHAMELEONS. Head angular; body high and narrow; tail prehensile; toes opposed (2 versus 3) for grasping; tip of tongue expanded and mucus-coated, can be "shot" several inches beyond head; eyes large, move independently; eyelids fused over eyeball, with small central circular aperture; teeth acrodont; lungs with air sacs; Africa, Madagascar, and India. *Chamaeleo (Chamaeleon)*, chameleon, changes color readily (Fig. 33-18).

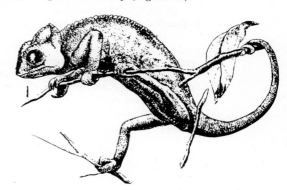

Fig. 33-18. A chameleon (*Chamaeleo chamaeleon*). Length to 6 inches. Native to warm regions of the Old World. Specialized with compressed body, prehensile tail, grasping toes, and protrusible tongue. (*After Guide to reptile gallery, British Museum.*)

Division B. *Autarchoglossa*. Less than 4 transverse rows of ventral scales to each body segment; scales when imbricate with narrow free margin posteriorly.

XANTUSIIDAE. NIGHT LIZARDS. Small; dorsal scales granular, ventral scales squarish and nonimbricate; femoral pores present; southwestern United States to Central America, and Cuba. *Xantusia*.

SCINCIDAE. SKINKS. Limbs or toes often reduced, sometimes absent; scales commonly smooth and round-margined (cycloid), with dermal ossifications beneath; tongue with scale-like papillae, tip feebly indented; viviparous; Old World tropics, Australia, and Pacific islands; few in the Americas. *Eumeces fasciatus*, and *E. skiltonianus*, blue-tailed skinks, in United States.

LACERTIDAE. OLD WORLD LIZARDS. Limbs normal; posttemporal fossa roofed; intermaxillary unpaired. Europe, Asia, and Africa. *Lacerta*.

TEIIDAE. NEW WORLD LIZARDS. Slender; limbs reduced in some; temporal fossa not roofed; ventral scales usually squarish and nonimbricate; tongue long and bifid, with scale-like papillae; the Americas and West Indies. *Cnemidophorus*, whip-tailed lizard; *Ameiva; Tupinambis*.

AMPHISBAENIDAE. "WORM" LIZARDS. Body worm-like; limbs and girdles vestigial or absent; tail short, blunt; skin soft, folded into numerous rings; eyes and ear openings concealed; subterranean; tropical America, the West Indies, and Africa. *Bipes biporus*, southern Lower California, fore limbs present, each with 5 toes; *Rhineura floridiana*, in Florida, no limbs.

VARANIDAE. MONITORS. Large, trunk and limbs stout, neck and tail long; scales small, smooth; teeth large, pointed, and pleurodont; tongue long, smooth, deeply bifid, and protrusible; Africa, southern Asia, and islands southeast to Australia. *Varanus; V. salvator*, Ceylon and Malay, to 8 feet; *V. komodoensis*, to $9\frac{1}{2}$ feet.

PYGOPODIDAE. SNAKE-LIKE LIZARDS. Body snake-like; no fore limbs; hind limbs small, under flat flaps of skin; scales rounded; tail long and fragile; no eyelids; Australia, Tasmania. *Pygopus*.

HELODERMATIDAE. BEADED (POISONOUS) LIZARDS. Trunk and tail stout, rounded, limbs short; dorsal scales bead-like, over bony tubercles (osteoderms); ventral scales flat; tongue fleshy, protrusible; teeth bluntly fang-like, grooved, with poison glands opening on outer "gum" of lower jaw; venom potent, bite fatal to small animals, rarely to man; 2 species, the only poisonous lizards. *Heloderma suspectum*, Gila monster, Arizona and Mexico to southern Utah and Nevada, pink and black, to 19 inches (Fig. 33-19); *H. horridum*, beaded lizard, Mexico and Central America, yellow and much black.

Fig. 33-19. The Gila monster (*Heloderma suspectum*) of the American Southwest. Length to 19 inches. This and a related species are the only poisonous lizards. (*From Van Denburgh.*)

ANGUIDAE. ALLIGATOR LIZARDS, etc. Body slender, a deep fold in skin along each side; limbs small or none; tail long, fragile, regenerates readily; tongue delicate, retracts into thick base; scales usually rectangular over thin bony plates; southwestern United States to northern South America, Europe, and India. *Gerrhonotus*, in United States and Mexico, limbs small; *Ophisaurus ventralis*, glass snake, New Mexico, Wisconsin, and Indiana southward and eastward, limbless, the very fragile tail about ⅔ of total length; *O. apus*, Europe; *Anguis fragilis*, slowworm or blindworm, Europe, western Asia, and northern Africa.

ANNIELLIDAE. SILVERY FOOTLESS LIZARDS. Slender, limbless; eyes and ear openings concealed; scales smooth, soft; subterranean; California. *Anniella* (2 species).

ZONURIDAE. WHORLED LIZARDS. Limbs present or absent; scales often strongly keeled and in conspicuous transverse rows; South Africa, Madagascar. *Zonurus*.

SUBORDER 2. SERPENTES (Ophidia). SNAKES. No limbs, feet, ear openings, sternum, or urinary bladder; mandibles joined anteriorly by ligament; eyes immobile and covered by transparent scales, no lids; tongue slender, bifid, and protrusible; left lung reduced; teeth slender and conical, usually on jaws and on roof of mouth (palatine and pterygoid bones); about 2,500 species.

TYPHLOPIDAE. WORM SNAKES. Eyes vestigial, under opaque scales; teeth only on transversely placed maxillary bones, none on lower jaw; scales thin, overlapping, cycloid, in multiple rows over whole body; tropics and subtropics of both hemispheres, subterranean. *Typhlops*.

LEPTOTYPHLOPIDAE. WORM SNAKES. Like TYPHLOPIDAE, but teeth only on lower jaw; vestiges of femur and all pelvic bones present; southwestern United States to Brazil, the West Indies, Africa, and southeastern Asia; subterranean. *Leptotyphlops*.

(*Note: The following families of snakes all have the eyes exposed and functional and only one row of large transverse scales along the belly.*)

BOIDAE. PYTHONS, BOAS, etc. Vestiges of pelvic girdle and hind limbs persist, latter usually as spines at each side of anus (Fig. 33-8); world-wide, except New Zealand; variously on ground, or in trees of tropical jungles, or in dry, rocky, or sandy places; includes largest living serpents, also smaller species. *Python reticulatus*, regal python of Malay region, to 29 feet long; *P. molurus*, Indian python, to 25 feet; *Eunectes murinus*, anaconda of South America, to 33 feet; *Charina bottae*, rubber snake, Montana to California, to 20 inches long (Fig. 33-20).

ANILIDAE (Ilysiidae). Vestiges of pelvic girdle and hind limbs present, latter appearing as spines at side of vent; head small; tail very short and blunt; supratemporal and quadrate bones short; scales small, smooth, and iridescent; southern Asia; South America. *Anilius* (*Ilysia*).

UROPELTIDAE. BURROWING or "EARTH" SNAKES. Head small and pointed; eyes small; tail short, ending in peculiar large shield; scales smooth and shining; no supratemporal bone; no vestiges of hind limbs or pelvic girdle; ovoviviparous; southern India and Ceylon. *Uropeltis*.

XENOPELTIDAE. Dentary bone loosely attached to articular; scales smooth, iridescent; southeastern Asia. One species, *Xenopeltis unicolor*.

COLUBRIDAE. COMMON SNAKES. Facial bones movable; squamosals loosely attached to skull; maxillaries horizontal, forming most of upper jaw; both jaws with teeth.

AGLYPHA. HARMLESS SNAKES. All teeth solid, none grooved; mostly oviparous; nearly world-wide; includes majority of harmless snakes, mostly terrestrial (Figs. 33-20 to 33-23). *Natrix,*

Fig. 33-20. The rubber snake (*Charina bottae*), a small boa of the western United States. Length to 20 inches. (*Photo by T. I. Storer.*)

water snakes, and *Thamnophis,* garter snakes, aquatic in varying degree, feed on frogs and fishes; *Coluber* and *Masticophis,* racers, speediest of snakes in United States; *C. constrictor,* black snake, climbs readily, preys on small vertebrates including birds; *Pituophis,* bull snakes and gopher

Fig. 33-21. A garter snake (*Thamnophis*). Length to 28 inches. (*Photo by T. I. Storer.*)

snakes, terrestrial; *Lampropeltis,* milk and king snakes, feed in part on reptiles, including rattle-snakes.

OPISTHOGLYPHA. BACK-FANGED SNAKES. One or more pairs of grooved teeth (fangs) on posterior parts of maxillary bones of upper jaw; usually with venom, but most species not very poisonous

Fig. 33-22. The gopher or bull snake (*Pituophis catenifer*). Length to 52 inches. (*Photo by T. I. Storer.*)

to man; world-wide, except New Zealand. *Boiga* (*Dipsadomorphus*), tree snakes; *Oxyrhopus; Tantilla,* of American Southwest, small and not particularly harmful to man.

PROTEROGLYPHA. A pair (or more) of short, rigid, erect, venom-conducting teeth (fangs), grooved or perforated, on maxilla in anterior part of upper jaw; all dangerously poisonous.

Fig. 33-23. A king snake (*Lampropeltis boylii*). Length to 38 inches. (*Photo by T. I. Storer.*)

HYDROPHIIDAE. SEA SNAKES. Tail compressed, used for swimming; venomous and dangerous to man; viviparous; in tropical seas. *Hydrophis; Hydrus platyurus*, along Pacific coast from southern Mexico to northern South America, feeds on small fishes.

ELAPIDAE. TERRESTRIAL POISONOUS SNAKES. Tail round, tapered, not compressed; venom powerful, dangerous to man; world-wide, except northern North America and northern Eurasia. *Naja*, cobra (Fig. 33-24); *Bungarus*, krait; *Denisonia; Micrurus (Elaps)*, coral snake, colored

Fig. 33-24. The Indian cobra (*Naja tripudians*), with the "hood" expanded and in the striking position; length to 6½ feet; native to the Old World and highly poisonous. (*After Guide to reptile gallery, British Museum.*)

with bands of black, red, and yellow, slow to bite and considered harmless, but strong venom causes occasional human deaths; *M. fulvius*, Ohio and North Carolina to Gulf states; *M. euryxanthus*, southern Arizona and New Mexico southward.

SOLENOGLYPHA. Paired erectile fangs in front of upper jaw, one on each maxillary bone and folded backward when not in use; maxillary short, thick, and movable in vertical plane; facial bones movable; poisonous; usually viviparous.

VIPERIDAE. OLD WORLD VIPERS. No pit between nostril and eye. Eurasia, Africa, and southern India. *Vipera*, viper; *Cerastes*, horned viper; *Bitis*, puff adder.

CROTALIDAE. PIT VIPERS, RATTLESNAKES. A pit-like depression on each side of upper jaw between nostril and eye; some with horny rattle at end of tail; the Americas (*Agkistrodon* also in Asia, west to Caspian Sea).

Tail without rattle: *A. piscivorus*, water moccasin, Virginia and Illinois southward, in swampy places; *A. mokasen*, copperhead, Massachusetts and Illinois to Gulf coast; on drier land; *Bothrops*, fer-de-lance, tropical Americas and West Indies; *Lachesis*, bushmaster, Panama to Peru and Brazil.

Tail with rattle of cornified epidermis: *Sistrurus*, pigmy rattlesnakes, and *Crotalus*, rattlesnakes; about 40 species and varieties in Western Hemisphere, 20 in United States; *C. horridus*, timber or banded rattlesnake, Maine to Florida and west to Iowa and Texas; *C. viridis (confluentus)*, prairie rattlesnake, Great Plains to Pacific coast; *C. atrox*, western diamondback rattlesnake, Texas to eastern California; *C. adamanteus*, eastern diamondback rattlesnake, North Carolina and Louisiana to Florida, over 7 feet in length; *C. cerastes*, sidewinder or "horned rattlesnake," southwestern deserts, travels by angular loops of body.

Fig. 33-25. A Pacific rattlesnake (*Crotalus viridis*), in the striking position and with the rattle elevated. Dangerously poisonous. (*Photo by T. I. Storer.*)

Order 4. Crocodilia (Loricata). ALLIGATORS, CAIMANS, GAVIALS, and CROCODILES. Body long; head large and long, jaws powerful, rimmed with numerous bluntly conical teeth; 4 short limbs ending in clawed toes with webs between; tail long, heavy, and compressed; skin thick and leathery, with horny scutes, those on back and belly rectangular and reinforced beneath by dermal bones; ear opening small, protected by small flap of skin; tongue not protrusible; heart 4-chambered, with separate ventricles; no bladder; oviparous; eggs deposited in "nests" of decaying vegetation; Triassic to Recent; tropics of New and Old Worlds and Australia, and Gulf states; about 23 species.

CROCODYLIDAE. *Crocodylus americanus*, American crocodile, southern Florida and Greater Antilles to Ecuador and Colombia, snout narrow; *C. niloticus*, Africa and river Nile, dangerous to man, many deaths; *Alligator mississippiensis*, American alligator, southern North Carolina to Florida and Rio Grande in Texas (Fig. 33-1*B*).

REFERENCES

(*See also works by Barbour, Oliver, Schmidt, and Stebbins in Chap.* 32)

Papers on reptiles will be found in the quarterly journal *Copeia*, in various scientific and popular journals, and in many books of travel dealing with tropical and other regions. Descriptive accounts of the native reptiles, their distribution and natural history, are available for many states and local areas in *Copeia*, museum publications, and other documents.

BOGERT, C. M., and R. M. DEL CAMPO. 1956. The Gila monster and its allies. *American Museum of Natural History, Bull.*, vol. 109, pt. 1, pp. 1–238, 20 pls., 35 figs.

DITMARS, RAYMOND L. 1926. Reptiles of the world. New York, The Macmillan Co. 23 + 373 pp., 89 pls. Popular.

———. 1936. The reptiles of North America. New York, Doubleday & Co., Inc. xvi + 476 pp., 135 pls. Popular.

KLAUBER, L. M. 1956. Rattlesnakes: their habits, life histories, and influence on mankind. Berkeley, University of California Press, 2 vols. I, pp. xxiv + 1–708, 1 pl., 186 figs.; II, pp. xvii + 709–1476, 1 pl., 57 figs.

McILHENNY, E. A. 1935. The alligator's life history. Boston, The Christopher Publishing House. 117 pp., 18 illus.

POPE, CLIFFORD, H. 1937. Snakes alive and how they live. New York, The Viking Press. xii + 238 pp., illus.

———. 1939. Turtles of the United States and Canada. New York, Alfred A. Knopf, Inc. xviii + 343 pp., 99 illus.

SCHMIDT, K. P., and D. D. DAVIS. 1941. Field book of snakes of the United States and Canada. New York, G. P. Putnam's Sons. xiii + 365 pp., 34 pls., 103 figs.

SMITH, H. M. 1946. Handbook of lizards [of the United States and Canada]. Ithaca, N.Y., Comstock Publishing Associates, Inc. xxi + 557 pp., 135 pls., 136 figs., 41 maps.

34 CLASS AVES
Birds

Birds are the best known and most easily recognized of all animals, because they are common, active by day, and easily seen. They are unique in having feathers that clothe and insulate their bodies to make possible a regulated body temperature and to aid in flight (Fig. 34-1); no other animals possess feathers. The ability to fly enables birds to occupy some habitats denied to other animals. The distinctive coloration and voices of birds appeal to human eyes and ears, and many bird species are of economic importance because of their food habits. Certain kinds are hunted as game,

Fig. 34-1. Class AVES. The American robin (*Turdus migratorius*), a representative bird. The contour feathers insulate the body against loss of heat and form a smooth streamlined exterior surface; the large feathers of the wings and tail provide extended surfaces for flight. The beak or bill is of bone, with a smooth cornified covering, and serves as both mouth and hands. The slender lower legs or shanks and the feet also have a cornified covering. (*After U.S. Biological Survey.*)

544

and the few domesticated species contribute to man's food supply. The ancient classical names for birds (Gr. *ornis*, L. *aves*) are perpetuated in the name of the class and the term "ornithology," the study of birds.

34-1. Characteristics. 1. Body covered with feathers.

2. Two pairs of limbs; anterior pair modified as wings for flight; posterior pair adapted for perching, walking, or swimming (with webs); each foot usually with 4 toes; shanks and toes sheathed with cornified skin.

3. Skeleton delicate, strong, fully ossified; mouth a projecting beak or bill, with horny sheath; no teeth in living birds; skull with one occipital condyle; neck very flexible; pelvis fused to numerous vertebrae but open ventrally; sternum enlarged, usually with median keel; tail vertebrae few, compressed posteriorly.

4. Heart 4-chambered (2 auricles, 2 separate ventricles); only the right aortic (systemic) arch persists; red blood corpuscles nucleated, oval, and biconvex.

5. Respiration by compact lungs attached to ribs and connected to thin-walled air sacs extending between internal organs; voice box (syrinx) at base of trachea.

6. No bladder, excretions semisolid; females usually with only left ovary and oviduct.

7. Twelve pairs of cranial nerves.

8. Body temperature regulated (homoiothermous).

9. Fertilization internal; eggs with large yolk, covered with hard limy shell, and deposited externally for incubation; segmentation meroblastic; embryonic membranes (amnion, chorion, yolk sac, and allantois) present during development within the egg; young at hatching fed and cared for by parents (except MEGAPODES).

Birds represent a significant advance over all lower animals in having (1) an insulated body covering; (2) complete separation of venous and arterial circulation in the heart, with (3) regu-

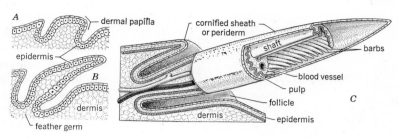

Fig. 34-2. Development of a contour feather. *A*, *B*. Early stages, as seen in section. *C*. Stereogram of later stage.

lated body temperature and (4) high rate of metabolism; (5) the ability to fly; (6) highly developed voice, hearing, and sight; and (7) specialized care for the young. In all these features they stand above the reptiles and are comparable only with the mammals, from which they differ notably in the type of body covering, in the ability to fly, and in the manner of reproduction.

34-2. Size. The largest living birds include the ostrich of Africa, which stands fully 7 feet tall and weighs 300 pounds or more, and the great condors of the Americas with wingspreads up to 10 feet; the smallest is Helena's humming-bird of Cuba, $2\frac{1}{4}$ inches long and weighing about $\frac{1}{10}$ ounce; no bird, living or fossil, approaches the largest fishes or mammals in size.

STRUCTURE OF A BIRD: THE DOMESTIC FOWL

34-3. External features. The chicken or fowl has a distinct *head,* a long flexible *neck,* and a stout spindle-shaped *body* or trunk. The two fore limbs, or *wings,* are attached high on the back and have long flight feathers (remiges); the wings are deftly folded in **Z**-shape at rest and extended in flight. On each *hind limb* the two upper segments are muscular, whereas the slender lower leg or *shank* contains tendons but little muscle and is sheathed with cornified scales, as are the four *toes* which end in horny *claws.* The short *tail* bears a fan-like group of long tail feathers (rectrices).

The mouth is extended as a pointed bill or *beak,* with horny covering. On the upper mandible are two slit-like *nostrils.* The *eyes* are large and lateral, each with an upper and lower

eyelid; beneath these is the membranous *nicti-tating membrane,* which can be drawn independently across the eyeball from the outer corner. Below and behind each eye is an *ear opening,* hidden under special feathers. The fleshy median *comb* and lateral *wattles* on the head and the cornified spurs on the legs are peculiar to the chicken, pheasant, and a few other birds. Below the base of the tail is the vent or *anus.*

34-4. Body covering. The soft, flexible *skin* is loosely attached to the muscles beneath. It lacks glands save for the *oil gland* above the base of the tail, which secretes an oily substance for "dressing" the feathers and to keep the bill from becoming brittle. The *feathers* grow from and are attached to the skin.

34-5. Feathers. These distinctive epidermal structures provide a lightweight, flexible, but resistant body covering, with innumerable dead air spaces useful as insulation; they protect the skin from wear, and the thin, flat, and overlapping wing and tail feathers form surfaces to support the bird in flight.

Growth of a feather begins, like the scale of a reptile, as a local *dermal papilla* thrusting up the overlying epidermis (Fig. 34-2). The base of this *feather bud* sinks into a circular depression, the future *follicle,* which will hold the feather in the skin. The outermost epidermal cells on the bud become a smooth cornified sheath (periderm) within which other epidermal layers are arranged in parallel ribs, a larger median one forming the future shaft and the others producing the barbs. The central soft dermal pulp (original dermal papilla) contains blood vessels and is wholly nutritive, drying

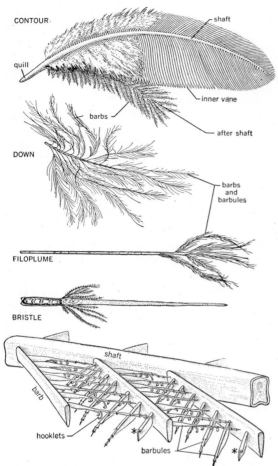

CONTOUR — shaft

quill

inner vane

barbs

after shaft

DOWN

barbs and barbules

FILOPLUME

BRISTLE

shaft

barb

hooklets

barbules

Fig. 34-3. *Above.* Four types of feathers. *Below.* Stereogram of the parts in a contour feather; *, two proximal barbules cut to show curved edge along which the hooklets slide to make the feather flexible.

upon completion of growth, so that the feather is purely an epidermal structure. Pigment for coloration is deposited in the epidermal cells during growth in the follicle, but not thereafter. When growth is completed, the sheath bursts and is removed by preening; then the feather spreads to its completed shape.

1. CONTOUR FEATHERS. These provide the external covering and establish the contour of the bird's body, including the enlarged flight feathers of the wings and tail; several thousand are present on a chicken. Each consists of a flattish **vane,** supported by the central **shaft,** which is an extension of the hollow **quill** attach-

ing to the follicle. Each half of the vane is of many narrow, parallel, and closely spaced **barbs** joining the sides of the shaft. On the proximal and distal side of each barb are numerous smaller parallel **barbules,** and these are provided with minute **barbicels** or **hooklets,** serving to hold opposing rows of barbules loosely together (Fig. 34-3). Many body feathers have a secondary shaft or aftershaft and vane, attached to the junction of the principal shaft and quill. Smooth muscles and elastic fibers in the skin enable a bird to ruffle or raise its feathers away from the body, to facilitate their rearrangement when bathing and preening, and to increase the insulation value of the feather covering during cold weather.

2. DOWN FEATHERS. Young chicks and many other birds at hatching are covered with soft downy plumage, providing excellent insulation. A down feather has a short quill, a reduced shaft, and long flexible barbs with short barbules. Down is also present beneath the contour feathers on ducks, many other water birds, and some land birds.

3. FILOPLUMES. Minute hair-like feathers, of unknown function, are sparsely distributed over the body, as seen on a plucked fowl. These grow in clusters near the follicles of some contour feathers; each has a long thread-like shaft, with a few weak barbs and barbules at the tip.

4. BRISTLES. Some birds have hair-like growths that are modified feathers, each with a short quill and slender shaft, with a few vestigial barbs at the base. These are seen about the mouths of flycatchers and whippoorwills.

The varied coloration of feathers results chiefly from pigments deposited during growth. Blue, green, and iridescent markings, as on neck feathers of some poultry and on hummingbirds, are due to microscopically thin plates in the surface structure of these feathers, with dark pigment beneath. A feather once grown changes color only by wear, fading, or other discoloration.

Feathers grow only on certain areas or feather tracts (pterylae) of the skin, between which are bare spaces (apteria), as can be seen upon parting the feathers of a bird in hand (Fig. 34-4).

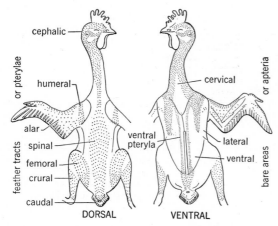

Fig. 34-4. Feather tracts of the domestic fowl. (*After Nietsch.*)

The assemblage of feathers on a bird at any one time is called a ***plumage,*** and the process of feather replacement is known as ***molt.*** The molt is an orderly and gradual process so that portions of the body are not left bare; the large feathers on the wings and tail are molted in symmetrical pairs so that flight is not hindered.

34-6. Skeleton. The bird skeleton (Fig. 34-5) is delicate as compared with that of most reptiles or mammals; many of the bones contain air cavities to lessen the weight. It is modified in relation to flight, bipedal locomotion, and the laying of large eggs with hard shells. The bones of the cranium are separate in young birds but fused in adults. The ***brain case*** is rounded, the ***orbits*** sheltering the eyes are large, and the ***jaws*** (premaxillae + maxillae, and mandibles) project forward as the bony ***beak.*** The lower jaws articulate on the movable ***quadrate*** connecting to the squamosal. The skull articulates on a single ***occipital condyle*** with the first neck vertebra.

The neck contains about 16 ***cervical vertebrae,*** each with saddle-shaped articular surfaces that permit free movements in feeding, preening, and other activities. The ***trunk vertebrae*** are closely fitted together; those of the thorax have rib articulations laterally, and the remainder are fused into a solid ***synsacrum*** to which the pelvis attaches. No lumbar region is evident.

The four free ***caudal vertebrae*** and the compressed terminal ***pygostyle*** (= 5 or 6 fused vertebrae) serve in movements of the tail feathers.

The ***bony thorax*** protects the internal organs and provides a rigid support for the flight mechanism, yet is capable of slight expansion and contraction for respiration. It consists of (1) the ***vertebrae*** dorsally, (2) the flat ***ribs*** laterally, and (3) the breastbone or ***sternum*** ventrally, with a median keel below to which the pectoral flight muscles attach. Each thoracic rib has a distinct vertebral and a sternal part, the two joining nearly at a right angle; the second cervical and first four thoracic ribs each has posteriorly an ***uncinate process*** overlapping the rib next behind to strengthen the thorax.

The ***pectoral girdle*** on each side consists of (1) the sword-like ***scapula*** (shoulder blade) lying parallel to the vertebrae and over the ribs,

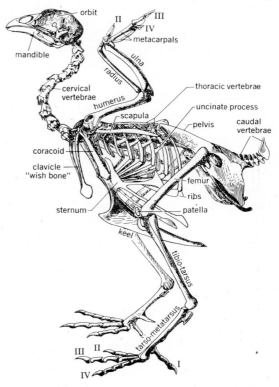

Fig. 34-5. Skeleton of the domestic fowl. (*Adapted from Ellenberger and Baum.*)

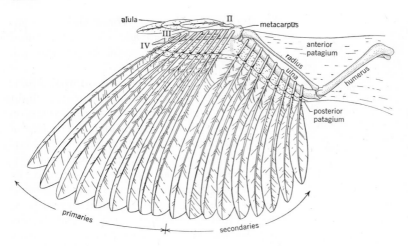

Fig. 34-6. Spread left wing of a white-crowned sparrow from the dorsal side, dissected to show how the flight feathers are supported, primaries on the "hand" and secondaries on the "forearm," by the bones and also the membranous patagium. II–IV, digits.

(2) the **coracoid** as a stout stay between the scapula and sternum, and (3) the **clavicle** hanging vertically from the scapula; the two clavicles are fused at their ventral ends to form the V-shaped **furcula** or "wishbone." The three bones meet dorsally on either side to form a circular canal as a pulley for the tendon of the pectoralis minor muscle that lifts the wing.

Each fore limb attaches high on the dorsal surface, the **humerus** articulating in the glenoid fossa on the coracoid. The "forearm" contains the **radius** and **ulna,** as in other land vertebrates. The remainder of the wing bones are greatly modified to provide stabilized supports for the flight feathers. Only two **carpals** and but three **digits** (II, III, IV) are evident, the other carpal bones being fused to the three metacarpals and forming the **carpometacarpus.** In the "hand" the anterior or second digit bears the bastard wing (alula), the next or third is longest and of two segments, and the innermost or fourth has one. The outermost and principal flight feathers, or **primaries,** are supported on digits III and IV and carpometacarpus, the **secondaries** on the radius and ulna, the **tertiaries** on the humerus. Quills of the flight feathers are kept from twisting during flight by connective tissue in extensions of the skin (patagium, Fig. 34-6).

The **pelvic girdle** is a broad thin saddle firmly united to the synsacrum, but widely open ventrally, permitting easy passage of large eggs in the female. Each half consists of the large **ilium** anteriorly, the **ischium** posteriorly, and the slender **pubis** ventrally; where the three meet, a socket, the **acetabulum,** receives the head of the thighbone.

Each leg consists of (1) the rounded **femur,** or thighbone; (2) the long and triangular-headed **tibiotarsus,** which is paralleled by the slender and often incomplete **fibula;** (3) the fused **tarsometatarsus,** or shank; (4) a knee bone or **patella,** held in ligaments before the femur-tibiotarsal joint; and (5) the four **toes,** three in front and one behind, each of two to five bones. Of the tarsals, or ankle bones, seen in other vertebrates, the proximal row in birds is fused to the tibia and the distal row to the metatarsus; the latter consists of three fused metatarsals, distinguishable only at the ends of the bone.

34-7. Muscular system. In the bodies of most lower vertebrates, segmental muscles predominate over nonsegmental ones, but the reverse is true among birds and mammals, where the limb muscles are enlarged for rapid activity. Movement of the wings in flight is due chiefly to the large pectoral muscles of the breast, the "white meat" of chickens and turkeys, a major fraction of the entire musculature (Fig. 34-7*B*). On either side, the **pectoralis major** originates on the outer part of the sternal keel and inserts on the ventrolateral head of the humerus; its contraction moves the wing downward and lifts the bird's body in flight. In other land verte-brates the fore limb is raised by muscles on the dorsal surface, but in birds such movement is also due to a ventral muscle, the *pectoralis minor.* This originates on the keel (inside or medial to p. major) and tapers to a strong tendon passing dorsally to insert on the dorso-posterior surface of the humerus. Both these muscles are symmetrically paired and in turn exert an equal and opposite pull on the thin keel of the sternum.

The muscles of the femur (drumstick) are the principal ones used for running and perch-ing. The shanks and feet contain little muscle, an adaptation to prevent loss of heat from these unfeathered parts. Movements of the toes are due to tendons connected to muscles in the upper segments of the legs. The tendons move through spaces lubricated by fluid, and their action on the toes is directed through loops of tendon (Fig. 34-7 *A*).

34-8. Digestive system. The *tongue* is small and pointed, with a horny covering. The *mouth cavity* is roofed with long *palatal folds,* a short *pharynx* follows, then the tubular and muscular *esophagus* extends to the base of the neck where it dilates into a large soft-walled *crop,* in which food is stored and moistened. The stomach comprises a soft anterior *proventricu-lus* with thick walls secreting the gastric juices, and the disc-shaped *ventriculus,* or *gizzard,* with walls of thick dense musculature, lined in-ternally by hardened epithelial secretion. Here the food is ground up by action of the muscular walls, aided by bits of gravel or other hard particles swallowed for the purpose—these are, functionally, the "hen's teeth." The *intestine* is slender, with numerous coils, and leads to the larger *rectum;* at the junction are two slender *caeca* or blind pouches. Beyond is the dilated *cloaca,* the common exit for undigested food wastes and materials from the excretory and reproductive organs, ending with the *vent* or *anus.* Dorsally, in the young, the cloacal wall bears a small outgrowth, the bursa of Fabricius, of unknown function (but useful for age deter-mination). The large reddish *liver* is bilobed,

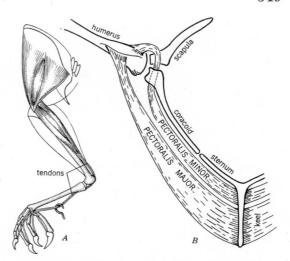

Fig. 34-7. *A.* Perching mechanism of a bird. From muscles on the thigh and lower leg tendons pass be-hind the "heel" (tarsal joint) and shank, then through an annular ligament beneath the foot to insert sepa-rately on the toes. When a bird squats down for resting or sleeping this arrangement flexes the toes and holds the bird firmly to its perch. (*Adapted from Wolcott.*) *B.* Diagram of the pectoral muscles (major and minor) that move the bird's wings in flight.

with a gall bladder and two bile ducts. The *pancreas* usually has three ducts; all the ducts discharge into the anterior loop of the intestine.

34-9. Circulatory system. The bird *heart* has two thin-walled auricles and two distinct thick-walled ventricles, separating completely the venous and arterial blood streams. This is a major factor in maintaining a regulated body temperature. The sinus venosus is incorporated in the right auricle. Blood from the two precaval veins and one postcaval enters the right auricle, passes to the right ventricle, and thence by the pulmonary artery to capillaries in the lungs for oxygenation. It all returns in the pulmonary vein to the left auricle, then the left ventricle, and into the single *right aortic arch.* The latter gives off two innominate arteries, each with three large branches, the carotid to the head and neck, brachial to the wing, and pectoral to the breast muscles of flight. The arch continues dorsally and posteriorly as the *dorsal aorta* serving the internal organs and remainder of the body. The venous system retains some

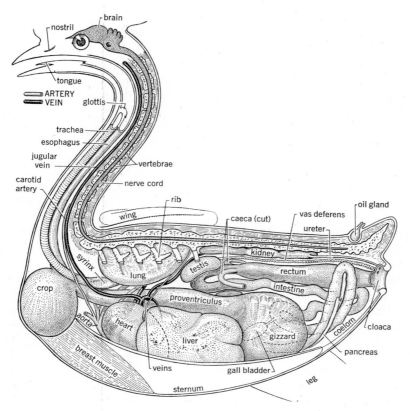

Fig. 34-8. The domestic fowl; internal structure. The two caeca are cut off.

reptilian features. Two precavals collect anteriorly, and the single postcaval vein is short, formed of two large iliac veins draining from the hind limbs and body. A *hepatic portal system* is present as in other vertebrates, but the renal portal system in the kidneys is reduced. A special adaptation is the cross connection in the jugular veins below the head that prevents stoppage of circulation if one vein is compressed by movements of the head or neck. The small rounded *spleen* lies near the stomach. Behind the pericardial sac containing the heart, a delicate *oblique septum* separates the heart and lungs from the other viscera.

34-10. Respiratory system (Fig. 34-9). The *nostrils* on the beak connect to *internal nares* above the mouth cavity. The slit-like *glottis* in the floor of the pharynx connects to the long flexible windpipe or *trachea,* which is reinforced by hoop-like cartilages, partly calcified. The

trachea continues down the neck to the *syrinx* (voice box), within which are the vocal muscles. From the syrinx a short *bronchus* leads to each *lung.* The latter are small, inelastic, and closely attached by connective tissue to the ribs and vertebrae in the dorsal part of the thorax. The lungs are penetrated by many interconnected air passages, the *bronchioles,* and by branches of pulmonary blood vessels. To the bronchioles are attached numerous thin-walled *air sacs* that extend out between organs in the body cavity, to spaces around neck vertebrae, and to cavities in the larger bones. The lungs are dilated by slight movements of muscles between the ribs, the sternum moving downward and the ribs bowing laterally, whereupon air is drawn into the lung cavities; slight contraction of the thorax reverses the flow. Such movements are possible despite the rigid nature of the thorax necessary for flight. At inspiration, air rushes through the bronchioles and on into the air sacs, then passes in reverse direction at expiration. This rapid flow of air *through* the lung and past the pulmonary capillaries explains why birds can be served by small and dense lungs, although they have the highest respiratory needs of all animals because of their high body temperature and active life. The air sacs are the principal means of dissipating the heat resulting from muscular contraction and other metabolic activities. The songs and calls of birds are produced by air forced across muscles in the syrinx, which vibrate like reeds and can be varied in tension to give notes of different pitch.

34-11. Excretory system. The paired *kidneys* are dark-brown three-lobed structures attached dorsally beneath the pelvis. From each, a slender *ureter* extends posteriorly to the dorsal wall of the cloaca; there is no bladder. Semisolid nitrogenous waste (with a high concentration of urates) passes slowly down the ureters and out the cloaca with the feces, as whitish material on the latter.

34-12. Nervous system and sense organs. The bird *brain* is proportionately larger than that of a reptile and is short and broad. The olfactory lobes are small (poor sense of smell), the cerebral hemispheres are large and smooth, and the optic lobes on the midbrain are conspicuously developed (keen sight). The cerebellum has increased surface with many superficial folds (many activities of coordination). The *nerve cord* and paired *spinal nerves* are essentially as in other vertebrates. The thoracic or brachial plexus, serving the great muscles of flight, is especially large.

Choice and rejection of food materials probably depend on the *taste buds* in the roof of the mouth and at the sides of the tongue, aided by pressure receptors on the bill and tongue. The eye is proportionately larger than in other vertebrates, and the sense of *sight* phenomenally keen. The exposed surface of the eye, beneath the eyelids, is covered by the cornea, a transparent layer kept moist by secretions of the tear glands. A protective ring of 12 to 20 bony *sclerotic plates* is embedded in the outer tissues

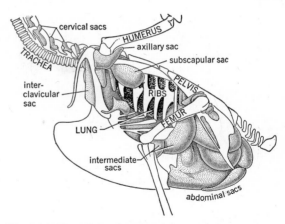

Fig. 34-9. Respiratory system of a pigeon. The air sacs are stippled, and bones are outlined; attachments of the lungs to the ribs are indicated. (*After Muller*, 1910.)

of the eyeball. Color vision is acute, and accommodation, or adjustment of focus to objects at different distances, is very rapid, as necessary in the quick changes from near to distant vision during flight and in other activities.

The sense of *hearing* is highly developed. A short *external auditory canal* at the posterior-lateral angle of the head leads to the *tympanic membrane* or eardrum. From the latter a bone, the *columella auris,* transmits sound waves across the middle-ear cavity to the "oval window" of the inner ear, as with reptiles and amphibians. From the *middle ear* on each side, a *Eustachian tube* leads to the pharynx, the two having a common opening at the back of the palate. The "cochlea" of the inner ear is a short, blind-ended tube, larger than in reptiles but less developed than in mammals.

34-13. Endocrine glands. The *pituitary* (hypophysis) is below the base of the brain. The *thyroid,* of two lateral lobes, lies beneath the jugular vein near where the subclavian and carotid arteries originate. The *pancreas* contains the islets of Langerhans. The paired *adrenals* are on the ventral surface of the kidneys, each being 8 to 10 mm. long. The endocrine secretions of the *gonads* regulate the secondary sexual characters, especially those of plumage. In many species of birds the males and females differ in feather characteristics (Fig. 9-4), and in chick-

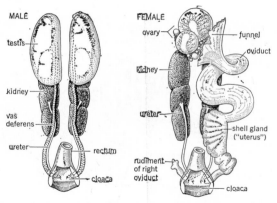

Fig. 34-10. Urogenital systems of the domestic fowl, in ventral view. Cloaca opened to show exits of the ducts.

ens and turkeys the wattles and comb are unlike in the two sexes.

Complete removal of the left ovary and rudiment of the right in a brown Leghorn hen is followed by permanent assumption of typical male plumage. If only the left ovary is removed in a young hen, the male plumage is acquired; but later, with growth of the right ovary, there is often a return toward female plumage. If the left ovary is removed after a hen has acquired her typical plumage, she assumes that of the male. Secretions of the female gonad therefore suppress the male plumage, but if eliminated, the latter type develops. Complete removal of the testis in a male chicken results in a *capon,* with feathering much like a male. Implanting an ovary in a chicken capon usually is followed by assumption of female plumage, but implantation of a testis into a normal or castrated hen (*poulard*) has no effect on its plumage.

34-14. Reproductive system (Fig. 34-10). In the male the two oval and whitish *testes* are attached near the anterior end of the kidneys. From each testis a much convoluted *vas deferens* extends posteriorly parallel to the ureter; in many birds it is dilated as a *seminal vesicle* just before entering the cloaca on a papilla close to the urinary opening. In the cloaca of ducks and ostriches there is a median *penis,* as in the alligator; this is present only as a vestige in the chick for a few days after hatching, when it provides a means of determining the sex of

downy young. The testes become enormously enlarged in the breeding season. Sperm developed in the testes are accumulated in the seminal vesicles, to be transferred from the cloaca of the male to that of the female while in contact during the act of mating.

The *female* system usually develops only on the left side. The *ovary* is near the left kidney, and close by is the open expanded funnel or *infundibulum* of the *oviduct;* the duct extends posteriorly to the cloaca. In nonlaying birds the ovary is small, containing minute eggs, and the duct is also small, but in the season of egg laying both are much enlarged. The ova then become numerous, and each receives its full quota of yolk before being released individually. A mature ovum escapes from its ovarian follicle into the abdominal cavity, is grasped by active gaping movements of the funnel and enters the oviduct; there it moves slowly down by the action of muscles in the walls and bands of cilia on the inner surface. Fertilization probably occurs in the upper oviduct; albumen (egg white) is added by glands in the middle portion; and the shell membranes and shell are secreted by glands in the posterior part ("uterus") after which the egg is ready to lay. A rudimentary right ovary is commonly present and may enlarge to function if the left one is removed.

STRUCTURE OF OTHER BIRDS

34-15. Adaptive features. As a group, the birds are more like one another than are members of other classes of vertebrates. Differences among various birds are often adaptive, enabling each kind to perform its necessary activities more efficiently. The external form is usually spindle-shaped, like two cones with their bases together; this shape offers minimum resistance to the air during flight or to water in diving, facilitates passage through vegetation, and sheds water easily.

The *coloration* is varied and striking. A few birds are all of a color, as black crows and some blackbirds and the white egrets, but the feathers of most species are marked with spots, stripes, or bars. The pattern often resembles

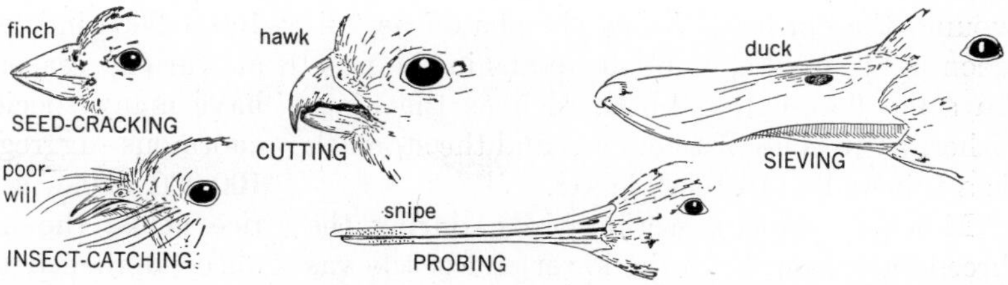

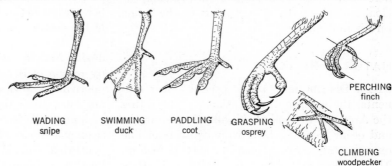

Fig. 34-11. Some types of beaks and bills in birds.

finch — SEED-CRACKING

hawk — CUTTING

duck — SIEVING

poor-will — INSECT-CATCHING

snipe — PROBING

Fig. 34-12. Some types of feet in birds.

WADING snipe

SWIMMING duck

PADDLING coot

GRASPING osprey

PERCHING finch

CLIMBING woodpecker

somewhat that of the environment, and such *protective coloration* renders the bird less visible; this is aided by *countershading,* the upper parts which receive stronger lighting being darker than the undersurface. Birds of arid regions tend to be pale-colored, and those of humid places are darker. Males are often more brilliant than and marked differently from females. In some species both sexes acquire a *nuptial plumage* by a spring or prenuptial molt and return to duller colors for the winter by a postnuptial molt in late summer.

The *bill* is at once a mouth and hands, serving to obtain and "handle" food, to preen the feathers, to gather and arrange nest materials, and for other purposes, including defense (Fig. 34-11). The cornified covering grows continually to replace that lost by wear. The form of bill usually indicates the food habits of a bird, being slender in species that probe into crevices or capture insects, stouter but still elongate in woodpeckers which dig in wood, wide but delicate in swallows and flycatchers which capture living insects in flight, stout and conical in seed-eating finches and sparrows, sharp-edged in flesh-eating hawks, owls, shrikes, and parrots, and with serrated margins in ducks that sieve small materials from water. The *tongue* in most

birds cannot be extended; but in woodpeckers it can be protruded beyond the bill for capturing insects in wood, and in hummingbirds it is an extensible siphon for obtaining nectar from flowers.

The *wings* (Fig. 34-6), by their vigorous downward strokes, serve to raise the bird's body in the air, and various tilting and banking movements aid in altering the manner of flight. The penguins, auks, and some other waterfowl use their wings to "fly" under water. The ostrich, kiwi, and a few other birds have degenerate wings and cannot fly. The *tail* serves as a rudder in flight, as a counterbalance in perching, and for display in courting by the males of many species. Creepers, woodpeckers, and some others that forage on vertical surfaces have tail feathers with stiffened shafts that help to support the body when these birds are at work. The *feet* of birds serve variously for running or climbing, for support of the body at rest, for arranging nest materials, and in some species for handling food and for offense (Fig. 34-12).

The *crop* is used by some birds to carry food for the young, which are fed either by regurgitation or by putting their heads down the parent gullet. In adult pigeons, while rearing young, the epithelial lining sloughs off as "pigeon milk" used to nourish squabs in the nest. In some flesh-eating birds, such as the kingfisher, there is no distinct crop and the stomach is a thin-walled distensible sac.

Males of some passerine birds, during the breeding season, have the lower end of the vas deferens swollen (seminal glomera), causing the cloaca to protrude, whereby sex of the living bird is indicated.

NATURAL HISTORY

34-16. Distribution. Birds occupy all continents, the seas, and most islands, penetrating the Arctic to beyond 80°N. and the Antarctic, and occur from sea level to above timber line on mountains, even to above 20,000 feet on Mount Everest. Despite the ability to fly, they conform to the "laws" of animal distribution, each species occupying a definite geographic range and particular kind of habitat. Albatrosses and petrels live on the open ocean except when nesting, gulls, auks, and murres occur along seacoasts, shore birds inhabit ocean beaches and borders of inland waters, ducks are found in marshes and on open fresh and salt water, meadow larks and savanna sparrows dwell in grasslands, fox sparrows and white-crowned sparrows inhabit thickets, and horned larks prefer open areas. Many birds utilize trees—the woodpeckers, nuthatches, and creepers foraging on trunks and large branches, the warblers, chickadees, and others in foliage, and the flycatchers using tree perches to watch for passing insects, as do hawks and owls for their larger prey. Swallows and swifts capture their insect food in the air, and some hawks soar when hunting. Owls, woodpeckers, and others use cavities for nesting and sleeping, but no bird is strictly subterranean. Insect eaters and birds of prey usually live and hunt alone; quail, ducks, robins, and juncos scatter in pairs to nest but flock at other seasons; and some seafowl, pigeons, and blackbirds are always in companies.

In polar regions the species are few but numerous as to individuals. In temperate lands, 150 to 200 kinds of birds may occur in a locality at various seasons. Tropical regions tend to have many species. Birds sometimes occur in enormous aggregations, such as "rafts" of 100,000 ducks and "clouds" of blackbirds in rice fields; the now extinct passenger pigeon once "darkened the sky" with its numbers in eastern states. There is an average of two birds per acre over the United States at the opening of the nesting season.

34-17. Activity. Birds are active at all seasons, by reason of being "warm-blooded" (only the poorwill is known to hibernate). Diurnal species are busy from dawn to dusk, and owls and whippoorwills feed at night. Diurnal land birds sleep at night, with the head turned back on or beneath a wing. Water birds may sleep by day, floating and dragging a foot to keep from drifting.

The body temperature is regulated and usually above that of the environment. The daytime temperature of adults is about 105 to 108°F., varying with the species. Poultry and passerine birds have a daily rhythm of 107 to 108° by day and down to 104°F. at night; in some swifts and hummingbirds it drops markedly at night. Young of house wrens and others are "reptilian" at birth when they assume the temperature of the environment, but their heat regulation develops within a few days.

The ability to fly gives greater opportunity to seek food and escape enemies and makes long migrations possible. Quail have a short direct flight, others can remain awing for longer periods, and the swallows, swifts, terns, and some hawks are in the air much of the time. The speed of flight varies from 20 to 50 or more miles per hour.

34-18. Voice. Most birds can utter calls and songs. Some species have only fixed calls, but most "songbirds" (Order PASSERIFORMES, Suborder OSCINES) have definite songs. Crows and jays use various notes to convey different "ideas" to others of their species, and the parrots, mynas, magpies, and mockingbirds have the power of mimicry. The average pitch in songs of 59 passerine species studied by Brand is 4,280 cycles per second, or above the highest note (C_7) on the piano. Bird notes serve (1) to assemble gregarious species; (2) to advertise nesting territory and attract mates; (3) for directional calls between parents and young; and (4) to warn in the event of danger. Some notes are used at all times of year, some songs and calls only during the nesting season, and a few only during migration. The calls and songs serve for identification of bird species by man, once he has learned them, as the voice of each is usually distinctive.

34-19. Migration. Some birds such as the bob-white are strictly resident, but many species *migrate,* or shift regularly from one region to another with the change of seasons. Most migration is north and south, or *latitudinal;* birds move into the wide land masses of the north temperate and subarctic regions, where there are facilities for feeding and nesting during the warmer months, and then retire south for the winter. A lesser and opposite movement occurs in the Southern Hemisphere, where the seasons are reversed. Some birds perform *altitudinal migrations* into mountainous regions for the summer and return to the lowlands to winter; this occurs in the Rocky Mountains and the Cascade–Sierra Nevada systems of western North America.

Most species use established routes for migration and travel more or less on schedule, arriving and disappearing regularly, "according to the calendar" (Fig. 34-13). Some birds migrate close to the earth, and others up to 3,000 or 5,000 feet but rarely higher. Although individuals may fly at 30 to 50 miles per hour, they stop to feed, are passed by others, then go on; hence the "migration front" progresses rather slowly, averaging about 25 miles per day. Many migrants "follow the sun"—like human tourists—and never experience the rigors of winter. Results from marking individual birds with numbered leg bands show that many return to places previously occupied. Both the summer and winter ranges of species are well defined.

Some migrants follow obvious landmarks,

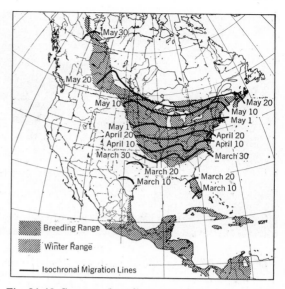

Fig. 34-13. Summer (breeding) and winter ranges of the black-and-white warbler (*Mniotilta varia*), a migratory species. The advance during the spring migration is shown by isochronal lines that connect points of arrival on certain dates. (*From U.S. Fish and Wildlife Service.*)

such as rivers, mountain ranges, or coast lines; but others pass over the sea or lands without directional features. Birds evidently are guided by instinct impressed on the nervous system in some way through countless generations. The urge to migrate is related in part to the endocrines of the gonads.

34-20. Food. The high and regulated body temperature of birds, their great activity, and their light weight make for a large requirement of food having high energy value. Since none has more than a limited fat storage, a bird cannot long survive without food—it must literally "eat to live." Quail and other gallinaceous birds take much leafy vegetation, but most species use concentrated materials such as seeds or fruits of plants and various animals, including worms, arthropods, mollusks, and vertebrates. Small flycatchers, warblers, and vireos eat little but insects; fish are the staple diet of loons, cormorants, pelicans, terns, and kingfishers; frogs are eaten by herons; both snakes and lizards are captured by some hawks; the "bird hawks" (sharp-shinned, etc., and duck hawk)

  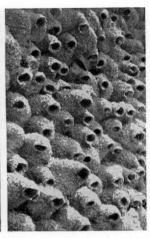

Fig. 34-14. Some types of bird nests. *Left.* Killdeer, eggs laid on ground. *Center.* Valley quail, eggs in a lined depression. *Right.* Cliff swallow, nests formed of mud pellets and closely placed in a dense colony on a rock. (*Photos by T. I. Storer.*)

feed chiefly on birds; and rodents and rabbits bulk large in the diet of many hawks and owls. Vultures feed only on carrion (dead animals), and ravens and some hawks also use such food.

Nestlings may eat more than their own weight in a day, and adults of many small species need a quarter to a half their weight daily. The crop and stomach may be filled twice a day or more often; the growing young of some species are fed several hundred times a day by their parents.

34-21. Enemies. Common predators on birds are the bird hawks, a few owls, weasels, wildcats, house cats, and foxes. Man "preys" on game birds, often kills useful hawks and owls, and at times has to destroy birds that damage crops.

Birds have various parasites—worms, protozoans, bacteria, and viruses—but their effects are poorly understood. The largest losses among birds are probably from predation, weather, and, at times, food shortage. Western duck sickness, due to *Bacillus botulinus*, Type C, in shallow warm waters of western North America containing decaying vegetation, has killed thousands of ducks.

34-22. Reproduction. Fertilization is always internal, and all birds lay eggs with much yolk and a hard limy shell, which must be warmed or *incubated* for growth of the embryo. In all birds except the "brush turkeys" (MEGAPODES) of Australia, either one or both parents sit upon the eggs to supply the necessary heat. The young of chickens, quail, ducks, shore birds, and others are *precocial,* being well formed, fully covered with down, and able to run about at once when hatched, whereas those of songbirds, woodpeckers, pigeons, and others are blind, naked, and helpless when hatched and must be fed and cared for in the nest; these are termed *altricial* (Fig. 34-15).

Each species has a characteristic season of reproduction, usually a few weeks in spring or summer—horned owls in February or March, goldfinches in July, and so on. Breeding activities follow increase in the size and functioning of the gonads and are controlled by endocrines. The latter are, in turn, evidently affected indirectly by light, since experimental exposure of birds in winter to an increased "length of day," even with a 40-watt electric light, will cause enlargement of the gonads, song, mating behavior, and even egg production long before the normal season of reproduction. Poultry farms use electric lights in laying houses during winter to increase egg production, but the hens are shorter-lived.

The breeding season for many species begins with the males uttering their characteristic songs at frequent intervals, and many go through *courting performances* in the presence of females. Each male takes up and defends a *territory* suitable to the needs of a pair for the period necessary to rear a brood, the requirements being different for each species. Other males of the same species and predaceous enemies are not tolerated. When a female joins a male so established, the pair proceeds with nest construction, mating, egg laying, incubation, and care of the young. In some species both sexes participate fully, whereas in others one sex performs most of the duties. Colonial waterfowl (murres, cormorants, gulls) on rocky sea cliffs defend nesting territories, since suitable places are scarce. Brood production usually leaves the parents with worn plumage, which is renewed at the postnuptial molt.

Some waterfowl and a few land birds lay on bare rocks or ground, but most species construct a *nest* to hold the eggs and shelter the young (Fig. 34-14). This may be a mere depression in soil or gravel (killdeer), a few bits of vegetation (gulls), a loose framework of twigs (doves), or a cup-like structure woven of grasses or other plant materials (many songbirds). Most kingfishers and some swallows dig nest tunnels in stream banks, woodpeckers usually excavate gourd-shaped nest cavities in trees, and some swallows build nests of mud. Bluebirds, titmice, and others use natural or artificial cavities, including man-made nest boxes.

The average number of *eggs* laid by a female in one clutch is smallest in birds nesting in safe locations and largest among ground nesters. The murre and the band-tailed pigeon lay but 1, the mourning dove 2, large hawks 2 or 3, most small land birds 3 to 5, and the bobwhite and California quail average 14 to a set. The *shells* are white with owls and woodpeckers, plain blue with the robin, and of a common ground color overlaid with darker spots, streaks, or blotches in many species. Shore birds and

Fig. 34-15. *Above.* Precocial young killdeer hatched with a full covering of down, eyes open, and able to get about at once. *Below.* Helpless (altricial) young of the wood pewee still in the nest some days after hatching; the down has grown out, the contour feathers are just appearing, the eyes are still closed, and the young must be fed by the parents. The killdeer shows white egg tooth on tip of bill; the leg bears a bird band for identification. (*Photos by T. I. Storer.*)

some others nesting on bare places have eggs that are *protectively colored,* closely resembling their average surroundings. The usual ovoid or

Fig. 34-16. Young goldfinch after leaving the nest but barely able to fly; some down still on the head, lax contour feathers of the juvenal plumage on the body, and wing and tail feathers not fully grown. (*Photo by T. I. Storer.*)

"egg" shape permits the eggs being closely placed and covered by the parent during incubation. *Incubation* with many small land birds requires about 14 days, the domestic fowl 21 days, pheasants 21 to 26 days, many ducks and the larger hawks 28 days, and the ostrich 42 to 60 days. Young of small altricial species require about a week after hatching before they leave the nest.

All young birds require *care after hatching.* This includes feeding, guarding, and brooding (for protection against chilling or wetting) or shielding against undue heat of the sun (Fig. 34-15). The young are attended and defended by the adults for some time after leaving the nest. Family groups form the nuclei for winter flocks in gregarious birds, such as blackbirds or quail; among solitary forms, such as hawks and insect eaters, the young scatter or are driven away by the parents, and all take up independent life.

34-23. Relations to man. Primitive people use wild birds for food and garments. Ducks, quail, herons, and other birds down to small finches have been sought as game in Europe for centuries, and today small songbirds are regularly marketed in some Mediterranean countries. Early settlers in North America used game birds for food, and later enormous numbers of wild ducks, geese, prairie chickens, pigeons, and shore birds were sold in city markets, but wild populations cannot withstand such continued slaughter. The great auk and passenger pigeon became extinct, and many others were far reduced. Ducks, geese, quail, and other game birds are now sought by several million hunters every year in the United States, under legal restrictions as to season, bag limit, and manner of capture. Means are being developed to increase the supply by "game management." Bird feathers of distinctive color or shape serve native peoples and modern women for ornamentation.

The principal domesticated forms, the wild stock whence each was derived, and the lands of origin are as follows:

OSTRICH (*Struthio camelus*), Africa.
DUCK (*Anas platyrhynchos*, mallard), Europe.
MUSCOVY DUCK (*Cairina moschata*), Central America or northern South America.
GOOSE (*Anser albifrons*, gray lag goose), Europe.
MUTE SWAN (*Cygnus olor*), Europe.
CHICKEN (*Gallus gallus*, jungle fowl), India.
PHEASANT (*Phasianus colchicus* and others), Caucasus and northern India.
PEACOCK (*Pavo cristatus*), India.
TURKEY (*Meleagris gallopavo*), Mexico.
GUINEA FOWL (*Numida meleagris*), Africa.
PIGEON (*Columba livia*, rock pigeon), western Asia or Egypt.
SHELL PARAKEET (*Melopsittacus undulatus*), Australia.
CANARY (*Serinus canarius*), western Europe.

Many small birds consume harmful insects and weed seeds, and they are one agency in reducing such pests. Most hawks and owls feed upon rodents that are injurious to crops and so are beneficial, but a few may destroy poultry, game birds, and songbirds. Certain birds sometimes damage crops by eating newly planted seeds or young plants, or the mature seeds, fruits, and berries, and control then is necessary.

Bird study with field glasses or camera is a healthful outdoor recreation for many people, and there are numerous organizations devoted to this subject; the American Ornithologists' Union and the National Audubon Society are two of the largest in North America.

For centuries man has kept wild birds as pets in cages and aviaries. Until recently this traffic depended upon capture of adults or young birds in the wild, but aviculturists now breed many species in captivity, and the drain on wild stocks has lessened.

The greatest economic contribution of birds to man's welfare is from the species he has domesticated, the "barnyard" fowls or poultry —chickens, turkeys, ducks, and geese—that serve for food, supply eggs, and provide feathers for pillows and beds. Several others have been domesticated for aesthetic reasons.

34-24. Fossil birds. Fossil remains of birds are scarcer than those of some other land vertebrates because their delicate skeletons are less likely to be preserved. Birds are probably derived from reptiles, possibly the bird-like dinosaurs, as the two groups have many similar features.

The oldest bird relics are in two slabs of limestone from the Upper Jurassic near Solnhofen in southern Germany, which contain impressions of the bird-like †*Archaeopteryx* (Fig. 34-17). This was the size of a large pigeon, with long jaws bearing bony teeth, but no horny sheaths. The wing had four (not three) digits, each with a claw, and bore long flight feathers. The long tail had more than 13 separate vertebrae, and the tail feathers formed a lateral fringe, a pair to each segment. The head, neck, and part of the body were bare. Toothed birds lived during Cretaceous time, 14 kinds having

Fig. 34-17. Fossil birds. *Left.* Restoration of the Jurassic "lizard-bird" (†*Archaeopteryx*). *Right.* Skeleton of Cretaceous toothed bird (†*Hesperornis; after Marsh*).

been found in Kansas and Montana; of these, †*Hesperornis* was a highly aquatic and flightless form about 6 feet long, and †*Ichthyornis* was a smaller flying type somewhat resembling modern birds.

From the Tertiary (Eocene) onward, the birds lack teeth and become progressively more modern in structure and appearance. The terrestrial †*Diatryma* of the Eocene in Wyoming was about 7 feet tall with a huge bill but abortive wings. The oldest known passerine bird is †*Paleospiza belli*, about the size of a bluebird, from the Miocene of Colorado. Bird remains are common in the Pleistocene of California, Florida, and elsewhere. The asphalt pits of Rancho La Brea in Los Angeles, Calif., have yielded about 60 species, including †*Teratornis merriami*, a giant condor larger than any now existing; 36 of the species found there are still living. About 437 kinds of fossil birds have been recorded in North America, and 189 of them continue in the present-day avifauna.

CLASSIFICATION

CLASS AVES. Birds. Body covered with feathers; fore limbs modified as wings, usually adapted for flight; hind limbs for walking, perching, or swimming, usually 4 toes, never more; mouth extended as a beak, no teeth (in living birds); skull with one occipital condyle; pelvis fused to numerous vertebrae, forming a synsacrum, open ventrally; heart 4-chambered; lungs compact, with air sacs; voice box at base of trachea; no bladder; body temperature regulated; oviparous; Upper Jurassic to Recent; 8,600 species.

SUBCLASS 1. †ARCHAEORNITHES. "Lizard Birds." Three fingers and metacarpals separate, each with a claw; tail long, with more than 13 vertebrae, each with a pair of rectrices; no pygostyle; both jaws with teeth in sockets (alveoli); Upper Jurassic, in Germany. †*Archaeopteryx*, 2 known specimens (Fig. 34-17).

SUBCLASS 2. NEORNITHES. True Birds. Metacarpals fused, 2d finger longest; caudal vertebrae 13 or fewer, and compressed; sternum either keeled or flat; Cretaceous to Recent.

Superorder A. †*Odontognathae.* New World Toothed Birds. Teeth present, in furrows on jaws; Upper Cretaceous (Kansas and Montana); 2 orders, 14 species. †*Hesperornis*, †*Ichthyornis* (Fig. 34-17).

Superorder B. Palaeognathae. Walking Birds. No teeth; wings reduced, usually flightless; tail vertebrae free; coracoid and scapula small.

Order 1. Struthioniformes. Ostriches. Flightless; terrestrial; sternum lacks keel; pubic symphysis present (unique in birds!); no pygostyle; only 2 toes (3d, 4th) on each foot; head, neck, and legs sparsely feathered; feathers without aftershaft; Miocene to Recent; Africa and Arabia. *Struthio camelus*, ostrich (Fig. 34-18), largest living bird, to over 7 feet tall and weight of 300 pounds or

Fig. 34-18. The ostrich (*Struthio camelus*, Order Struthioniformes) of Africa and Arabia; to over 7 feet tall; each foot with two toes; body and wing feathers lax, cannot fly. (*Photo by National Zoological Park.*)

more; inhabits arid lands in flocks of 3 to 20; omnivorous; at nesting a male defends 4 or 5 females that lay up to 30 eggs in one nest, male usually incubates; feathers of adults used by women as decorative plumes, plucked from living birds on ostrich farms in Africa and United States.

Order 2. Casuariiformes. Cassowaries and Emus. Flightless; terrestrial; sternum unkeeled; 3 front toes on each foot; wings small; neck and body densely feathered; feathers with aftershaft nearly equal to shaft; Pliocene to Recent. Australia: *Dromiceius* (*Dromaeus*), emu, to 5 feet tall, in sparsely wooded regions. New Guinea and nearby islands: *Casuarius*, cassowary, to over 5 feet tall, bare skin on head and neck, helmet-like casque on head, in forest, nocturnal.

Order 3. Aepyornithiformes. Elephant Birds. Flightless; terrestrial; sternum short, broad, and unkeeled; wings vestigial; 4 toes; Recent, but extinct for several centuries; Madagascar. *Aepyornis*, about 10 feet tall; eggs to 9½ by 13 inches, largest known animal eggs.

Order 4. Dinornithiformes. Moas. Flightless; terrestrial; sternum reduced and unkeeled; coracoid, scapula, and wing bones reduced or absent; hind limbs massive, 3 or 4 toes; feathers with large aftershaft; Recent, but extinct for several centuries; New Zealand. *Dinornis*, several species, one 8 feet tall; eggs to 5½ by 7¾ inches.

Order 5. Apterygiformes. KIWIS. Flightless; terrestrial; bill long and slender with nostrils at tip; wing degenerate (humerus vestigial, only one digit, no flight feathers); sternum unkeeled; 4 toes; body plumage fluffy, hair-like, without aftershafts; New Zealand. *Apteryx*, kiwi (Fig. 34-19), several species, mostly under 24 inches long; nocturnal; omnivorous; nest in burrows, eggs 1 or 2, about 3 by 5 inches.

Fig. 34-19. Kiwi (*Apteryx*, Order APTERYGIFORMES), wings vestigial, plumage hair-like; native to New Zealand. (*Photo by San Diego Zoological Society.*)

Order 6. Rheiformes. RHEAS. Flightless; terrestrial; sternum unkeeled; 3 front toes on each foot; head and neck partly feathered; feathers lack aftershafts; Miocene to Recent; South America. *Rhea*, to 4 feet tall, on open lands.

Order 7. Tinamiformes. TINAMOUS. Wings developed for flying; sternum keeled; pygostyle reduced; egg shells with high gloss; southern Mexico to southern South America. *Tinamus, Rhynchotus*, tinamous, size medium, flight direct, but usually run; used as game birds.

Superorder C. Neognathae. MODERN BIRDS. No teeth; sternum keeled, wings well developed; tail vertebrae 5 or 6; pygostyle present; fore limb with metacarpals joined and fingers included in wing; Eocene to Recent.

(*Note: All birds of the following orders possess the ability to fly except the penguins and an occasional species in other orders.*)

Order 8. Sphenisciformes. PENGUINS. Fightless; fore limbs ("wings") paddle-like, adapted for swimming, the bones much compressed; metatarsus incompletely fused; 4 toes (1st small), all directed forward, feet webbed; feathers small, scale-like, covering entire body (no apteria); thick layer of fat beneath skin; stand erect on metatarsi; dive readily and swim by strokes of fore limbs; nest in colonies on rocky islands or ice; southern oceans north to Galápagos Islands; about 20 kinds (Fig. 34-20). *Aptenodytes forsteri*, emperor penguin, shores of Antarctica, to 48 inches tall; other species smaller.

Order 9. Gaviiformes. LOONS. Legs short, at end of body; toes fully webbed; patella reduced; tail of 18 to 20 short stiff feathers; flight swift, direct, adept at diving; feed on fish; northern part of Northern Hemisphere; 4 species. *Gavia immer*, common loon (Fig. 34-21).

Fig. 34-20. Penguins (Order Sphenisciformes). The paddle-like wings serve for swimming but not for flight; native to the Southern Hemisphere. (*Photo by National Zoological Park.*)

Fig. 34-21. Loon (*Gavia immer*, Order Gaviiformes). Length 28 to 36 inches; strictly aquatic; native to Northern Hemisphere. (*After Hoffmann, Birds of the Pacific states, Houghton Mifflin Co.*)

Order 10. Podicipitiformes. Grebes. Tail a tuft of downy feathers; legs far back on body; patella large; tarsus compressed; feet lobed; on quiet fresh water, some on bays or ocean margins; adept at diving, "at flash of a gun"; food of small aquatic animals, some plant materials. *Podiceps* (*Colymbus*) *auritus*, horned grebe; *Podilymbus podiceps*, pied-billed grebe or "dabchick."

Order 11. Procellariiformes. Albatrosses, Fulmars, and Petrels. Nostrils tubular; horny sheath of bill compounded of several plates; skull with large nasal glands; hind toe vestigial or none (diving petrels); plumage compact, "oily" in texture; wings long, narrow; young downy when hatched; strictly oceanic, nest usually on islands.

Diomedeidae. Albatrosses. Mostly large and on southern oceans, often follow ships at sea. *Diomedea exulans*, wandering albatross, wingspread over 10 feet.

Procellariidae. *Puffinus*, shearwaters; *Oceanodroma*, petrels or "Mother Carey's chickens," small, nest in crevices or burrows.

Order 12. Pelecaniformes. Pelicans, Cormorants, Boobies, Gannets, etc. All 4 toes included in foot web; nostrils vestigial or absent; a gular pouch on throat (except in tropic birds); aquatic; young naked at hatching.

Pelecanidae. Pelicans. Body heavy, bill to 18 inches long, pouch used to scoop fish from water. *Pelecanus erythrorhynchos*, white pelican, on inland fresh waters of the West; *P. occidentalis*, brown pelican, coastwise in Gulf states and California.

Phalacrocoracidae. Cormorants. *Phalacrocorax*, many species, practically world-wide, on both coasts of North America, nests on sea cliffs, islands (Fig. 31-22), some inland waters, and trees; slender-bodied with small pouch, fish by diving; captives (with ring on neck) used by Orientals to catch fish.

Sulidae. *Sula*, booby, tropic birds; *Morus bassana*, gannet.

Fig. 34-22. Cormorants (*Phalacrocorax*, Order PELECANIFORMES). Nesting colony on islet near Carmel, Calif. Individuals can forage freely on the adjacent ocean waters, but nesting sites are few and the birds crowd closely when incubating and rearing young. (*Photo by T. I. Storer.*)

Order 13. Ciconiiformes. HERONS, STORKS, IBISES, and FLAMINGOS. Long-necked and long-legged wading birds, with either decorative plumes (herons), bare areas on head (storks), or bill abruptly decurved at middle (flamingos); little or no web between toes (except flamingos); young naked (except flamingos); chiefly tropical and subtropical, usually about water; food chiefly of fish and other aquatic animals; many nest in colonies in trees.

ARDEIDAE. HERONS and BITTERNS. *Ardea herodias*, great blue heron; *Butorides virescens*, green heron; *Nycticorax*, night heron; *Casmerodius albus*, American egret, and *Egretta thula*, snowy egret, both with pure white plumage and nuptial plumes (aigrettes) on back in nesting season.

PHOENICOPTERIDAE. *Phoenicopterus ruber*, flamingo, Brazil to Florida Keys, mandibles bent, forming box with serrated margins, bird feeds with head inverted, sieving small animals from water; nest in dense colonies, eggs on cylindrical mounds of mud.

Order 14. Anseriformes. DUCKS, GEESE, and SWANS. Bill broadened, covered with soft cornified epidermis containing numerous sense pits, with harder "nail," or cap, at tip; margins of bill with many transverse horny ridges (lamellae); tongue fleshy; legs short; feet webbed; tail usually short, of many feathers; nests lined with down; eggs plain, without spots; young downy when hatched;

Fig. 34-23. Order ANSERIFORMES. Whistling swan (*Olor columbianus*), pin-tail duck (*Dafila acuta*), lesser snow goose (*Chen hyperboreus*), and Canada goose (*Branta canadensis*). (*Photo by T. I. Storer.*)

world-wide; over 200 species; the "waterfowl" of hunters, prized for sport and eating; many kept as captives (Fig. 34-23).

ANATIDAE. Surface ducks (tip up, do not dive in feeding): *Anas platyrhynchos*, mallard, or "greenhead"; *Dafila acuta*, pintail or "sprig"; shoveler, teal, wood duck, etc. Diving ducks (more often on salt waters): *Aythya valisineria*, canvasback; *A. americana*, redhead; scaups, goldeneyes, eiders, scoters, etc. Geese (neck longer): *Branta canadensis*, Canada goose, several subspecies; *Chen*, snow goose; *Anser*, white-fronted goose. Swans (neck very long): *Cygnus columbianus*, whistling swan, winters in United States.

ANHIMIDAE. SCREAMERS. In South America, bill slender, feet not webbed. *Anhima (Palamedea)*.

Order 15. Falconiformes. VULTURES, KITES, HAWKS, FALCONS, and EAGLES. Bill stout, hooked at tip, with soft naked skin (cere) at base; mandibles sharp-edged; feet usually adapted for grasping, with sharp curved claws; predaceous, active by day; flight strong, rapid in some; food variously of vertebrates and smaller animals. CARRION FEEDERS: *Cathartes aura*, turkey vulture or "buzzard," with red head; *Coragyps atratus*, black vulture, chiefly in southeastern states, head black;

Fig. 34-24. Sparrow hawk (*Falco sparverius*, Order FALCONIFORMES), length 10 inches; feeds on insects and small mammals. (*After Hoffmann, Birds of the Pacific states, Houghton Mifflin Co.*)

Gymnogyps californianus, California condor, head yellow, wingspread to 9 feet, local in southern California. BIRD HUNTERS: *Accipiter cooperi*, Cooper's hawk; *Astur atricapillus*, goshawk. BROADWINGED soaring types, feed largely on rodents: *Buteo borealis*, red-tailed hawk; *Aquila chrysaëtos*, golden eagle. FISH-EATING: *Haliaeetus leucocephalus*, bald eagle, the United States emblem. NARROW-WINGED speedy hunters: *Falco peregrinus*, duck hawk, used in falconry; *F. sparverius*, American sparrow hawk (Fig. 34-24), feeds largely on insects.

Order 16. Galliformes. GROUSE, QUAIL, PHEASANTS, TURKEYS, etc. Bill short; feathers with aftershaft; feet usually adapted for scratching and running; young downy at hatching and precocial; the "upland game" of hunters, several species domesticated, many gregarious ground dwellers where most of them nest; food chiefly of plant materials (Fig. 34-25).

Fig. 34-25. Order GALLIFORMES. Two important upland game birds of North America. Bobwhite quail (*Colinus virginianus*), length 10 inches. Ruffed grouse (*Bonasa umbellus*), length 16 to 19 inches. (*From Pennsylvania Game News.*)

TETRAONIDAE. GROUSE. *Bonasa umbellus*, ruffed grouse, in broad-leaved woods; *Dendragapus*, blue grouse, in conifers; *Lagopus*, ptarmigan, north to Arctic, turns white in winter; *Tympanuchus*, prairie chicken; *Centrocercus urophasianus*, sage hen, in sagebrush of West.

PHASIANIDAE. PARTRIDGES, QUAILS, and PHEASANTS. *Perdix perdix*, European or Hungarian partridge, introduced successfully in northwestern prairie regions of United States and Canada; *Colinus virginianus*, bobwhite or eastern quail; *Lophortyx californica*, valley quail of Pacific coast. Native to Asia, widely introduced: *Phasianus colchicus*, ring-necked pheasant, in many states; *Pavo cristatus*, peacock or peafowl, native of India; *Gallus*, jungle fowl and domestic chickens.

MELEAGRIDIDAE. *Meleagris gallopavo*, wild turkey, eastern North America to Mexican plateau, also domesticated.

OPISTHOCOMIDAE. *Opisthocomus hoazin*, hoatzin, a peculiar species in South America, inhabits trees and feeds on leaves; young with claws on first 2 digits of wing, used for climbing until wing feathers are grown.

Order 17. Gruiformes. CRANES, RAILS, COOTS, etc. Feathers with aftershaft; either of large size and strong flight, inhabiting open marshes or prairies (cranes) or of medium to small size, of weak flight (occasionally flightless), and shy inhabitants of marshes (rails); young downy when hatched.

GRUIDAE. CRANES. Some bare skin about head; legs and neck long; all continents except South America. *Grus mexicana*, sand hill crane, tall, gray-colored, nests in temperate North America, often flocks on marshes in winter.

RALLIDAE. RAILS, COOTS, etc. Size of chickens or smaller, neck and legs moderate. *Rallus*, rails, body compressed, live in marshes, slip readily through vegetation; *Fulica americana*, coot or "mud hen," with lobate toes, common on ponds, diving or swimming, over much of North America; *Gallinula*, gallinule, toes elongate, used to walk on lily pads in ponds.

Order 18. †Diatrymiformes. Large, flightless, wing atrophied; bill huge; 4 toes on each foot. Eocene of western United States. †*Diatryma*.

Order 19. Charadriiformes. SHORE BIRDS or "WADERS," GULLS, AUKS, etc. Toes usually webbed at least at base; plumage dense and firm; more or less long-legged (shore birds), strong-winged (gulls), or with only 3 toes and legs far back on body (auks); eggs heavily spotted; young downy when hatched.

SHORE BIRDS. On seabeaches or inland watery flats—"the strand"—probing for food in sand, mud, or shallow water; many nest in Arctic regions and migrate far south for winter; formerly

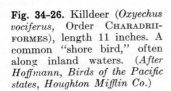

Fig. 34-26. Killdeer (*Oxyechus vociferus*, Order CHARADRII-FORMES), length 11 inches. A common "shore bird," often along inland waters. (*After Hoffmann, Birds of the Pacific states, Houghton Mifflin Co.*)

hunted for market. *Charadrius (Oxyechus) vociferus*, killdeer (Fig. 34-26), often inland; *Philohela minor*, American woodcock, in woods of eastern states; *Capella*, snipe, in marshy places; *Erolia (Pisobia)*, sandpiper.

LARIDAE. GULLS and TERNS. On seashores and inland waters; long-winged and commonly gray-backed, white beneath. *Sterna*, terns, fish activity over water, plunging to capture prey; *Larus*, gulls, feed on aquatic animals in surface waters or on shore and on garbage about harbors.

ALCIDAE. AUKS, MURRES, PUFFINS, etc. Flight in air swift, direct; swim and dive readily, "fly" under water; nest in dense colonies on sea cliffs or in burrows, each pair with 1 (or 2) eggs; on seacoasts of Northern Hemisphere. *Pinguinus (Plautus) impennis*, great auk, or garefowl, 24 inches tall, North Atlantic coasts, south to Massachusetts, extinct since 1844; *Uria aalge*, murre, eggs earlier collected for market; *Fratercula*, puffin.

Order 20. Columbiformes. Pigeons and Doves. Bill usually short and slender, with thick soft skin (cere) at base; tarsus usually shorter than toes; crop large, producing "pigeon milk" to feed small young; eggs unmarked, usually white; young naked; world-wide.

COLUMBIDAE. *Columba fasciata*, band-tailed pigeon (Fig. 34-27), forested portions of Pacific coast; *Ectopistes migratorius*, passenger pigeon, formerly in forested regions of eastern North

Fig. 34-27. Band-tailed pigeon (*Columba fasciata*, Order COLUMBIFORMES), length 15 inches; native to woods of Pacific coast states; sometimes in large flocks. (*After Hoffmann, Birds of the Pacific states, Houghton Mifflin Co.*)

America, killed extensively for market, extinct since about 1900; *Zenaidura macroura*, mourning dove, over whole of United States.

Order 21. Cuculiformes. Cuckoos, Road-runner, and Anis. Toes 2 in front and 2 behind, outer hind toe reversible; feet not adapted for grasping; tail long; bill moderate; many Old World cuckoos "parasitic," the female laying egg in nest of other small birds, for incubation and rearing; young cuckoo usually "elbows out" rightful owners; the two North American cuckoos, *Coccyzus*, not parasitic; *Geococcyx californianus*, road-runner, Kansas to Texas and California, terrestrial, legs and tail long.

Order 22. Psittaciformes. Parrots. Beak stout, narrow, sharp-edged and hooked at tip; upper mandible movable on frontal bone of skull; bill with soft cere, often feathered; toes 2 in front and 2 behind, outer hind toe not reversible; feet adapted for grasping; plumage brilliant, green, blue, yellow, or red; in forests of tropics and subtropics, many gregarious and with loud voices; food chiefly of fruits. *Rhynchopsitta pachyrhyncha*, thick-billed parrot, Mexico north to southern Arizona; *Conuropsis carolinensis*, Carolina paroquet, small, formerly to Wisconsin and Colorado, probably extinct.

Order 23. Strigiformes. Owls. Head large and rounded; eyes large and directed forward, each in a disc of radial feathers; ear opening large, often with flap-like cover, sometimes asymmetrical; beak short; feet adapted for grasping; claws sharp; plumage soft-textured and lax; eggs white; young downy at hatching; active chiefly by night; hide in retreats by day; food of land vertebrates especially mammals, some birds, and arthropods. *Tyto alba*, barn owl (Fig. 34-28); *Bubo virginianus*, horned owl; *Otus asio*, screech owl; *Nyctea scandiaca*, snowy owl, in Arctic, sometimes invades northern states in winter; *Speotyto cunicularia*, "burrowing owl," inhabits burrows in ground dug by squirrels, etc.

Order 24. Caprimulgiformes. Nighthawks, Whippoorwills, etc. Bill small and delicate, but mouth wide and margined with long bristle-like feathers (none in nighthawks); legs and feet small and weak, not adapted for grasping; plumage soft and lax; active mostly at dusk and by night, food

Fig. 34-28. Order STRIGIFORMES. Great horned owl (*Bubo virginianus*), length 18 to 23 inches. Barn owl (*Tyto alba*), length 15 to 21 inches. (*After Grinnell and Storer, Animal life in the Yosemite.*)

of night-flying insects captured in air; North American forms do not build nests. *Antrostomus vociferus*, whippoorwill, woods of eastern states, named for its call; *Phalaenoptilus nuttalli*, poorwill, brushy areas of western states, 2-syllabled call; both forage near ground; *Chordeiles minor*, nighthawk, usually forages high in air.

Order 25. Apodiformes (Micropodiformes). SWIFTS and HUMMINGBIRDS. Size usually small; legs very short and feet very small; wings pointed; bill small and weak (swifts), or slender with long tubular tongue (hummingbirds); eggs white; active by day, food captured on the wing; mostly tropical.

APODIDAE (Micropodidae). SWIFTS. Nests in rock cavities or trees and fastened with salivary secretion; latter used in Orient for "bird's-nest soup"; about 70 species, 4 in United States. *Chaetura pelagica*, chimney swift, eastern North America.

TROCHILIDAE. HUMMINGBIRDS. Only in Western Hemisphere, over 500 species, mostly in tropics, 14 in United States; length 2¼ to 8½ inches; plumage brilliant, iridescent especially on head and neck of males; food of nectar, small insects, and spiders taken from blossoms by the tubular protrusible tongue and needle-like bill; nests small, exquisitely felted of mosses, plant down, and spider web (Fig. 34-29); eggs 2, young naked, fed by regurgitation. *Archilochus*

Fig. 34-29. Anna hummingbird (*Calypte anna*, Order APODIFORMES), length 3½ inches. Nest a felted cup of plant down, leaves, feathers, and spider web. (*Photo by T. I. Storer.*)

colubris, ruby-throated hummingbird, Alberta to central Texas and eastward; others chiefly in California and far western states; *Selasphorus rufus*, rufous hummingbird, to 61°N. in Alaska for nesting.

Order 26. Coliiformes. Colies or Mouse Birds. Small, passerine-like; 1st and 4th toes reversible; tail very long; Africa. *Colius*.

Order 27. Trogoniformes. Trogons. Bill short and stout, with bristles at base; feet small and weak; plumage brilliant, often green, but soft and lax. *Trogon elegans ambiguus*, coppery-tailed trogon, Mexico and southern Arizona; *Pharomacrus moccino*, quetzal, Central America, one of the most beautiful of birds.

Order 28. Coraciiformes. Kingfishers, etc. Third and 4th toes fused at base; bill strong; includes also motmots, bee eaters, rollers, hoopoes, and hornbills, mostly in tropics. *Megaceryle alcyon*, belted kingfisher (Fig. 34-30), on fresh waters over much of North America, captures small fishes and frogs by diving from a perch; excavates horizontal tunnel in stream bank for nest.

Fig. 34-30. Belted kingfisher (*Megaceryle alcyon*, Order Coraciiformes), length 11 to 14 inches; lives about water. (*After Hoffmann, Birds of the Pacific states, Houghton Mifflin Co.*)

Order 29. Piciformes. Woodpeckers, Jacamars, Puffbirds, Barbets, Honey Guides, and Toucans. Picidae. Woodpeckers. Tail feathers stiff with pointed tips; bill stout, awl-like; tongue roughened or with barbs near tip, and protrusible; toes 2 in front and 2 (or 1) behind, not reversible; mostly in forests, cling to tree trunks, dig insects and larvae out of wood, and excavate nest cavities in trees; some on cactus in southwestern deserts. *Dendrocopos* (*Dryobates*) *villosus*,

Fig. 34-31. The flicker (*Colaptes*, Order Piciformes), length 13 inches, a woodpecker that forages both in trees and on the ground. (*After U.S. Biological Survey.*)

hairy woodpecker; *D. pubescens*, downy woodpecker; *Sphyrapicus*, sapsuckers, eat cambium of trees; *Colaptes*, flickers (Fig. 34-31), forage also on ground; *Melanerpes formicivora bairdi*, California woodpecker, stores many acorns individually in holes drilled in trees.

Order 30. Passeriformes. PERCHING BIRDS. Toes 3 in front and 1 behind, adapted for perching and neither reversible nor united; includes great majority of all known birds, 4 suborders, 69 families, about 5,100 species.

SUBORDER OSCINES. "SONGBIRDS." (52 families), so named because of structure of vocal cords; many produce beautiful songs, others are poor songsters, practically all have call notes. Size from that of raven and crow to small chickadee; in all types of habitats, some strictly terrestrial, a majority in trees and shrubs; the ouzels or dippers (*Cinclus*) swim and dive in cold fresh-water streams, and flycatchers and swallows capture insects in flight. Usually build nests, some elaborate, eggs

Fig. 34-32. Chipping sparrow (*Spizella passerina*, Order PASSERIFORMES), length 5½ inches; common in much of North America. (*After U.S. Biological Survey.*)

3 to 8, variously colored, young naked and blind at hatching, require feeding and care by parents before becoming independent. Food varied, chiefly of small size, many strictly insectivorous, some exclusively seed eaters, others have mixed diet. Common examples: *Corvus*, crow, raven; *Melospiza*, song sparrow; *Dendroica*, wood warblers; *Turdus*, American robin (Fig. 34-1).

ORDER PASSERIFORMES. FAMILIES IN NORTH AMERICA, NORTH OF MEXICO

Suborder TYRANNI
   COTINGIDAE, Cotingas
   TYRANNIDAE, New World Flycatchers
Suborder OSCINES
   ALAUDIDAE, Horned Larks
   HIRUNDINIDAE, Swallows
   CORVIDAE, Crows, Magpies, Jays
   PARIDAE, Chickadees, Titmice
   SITTIDAE, Nuthatches
   CERTHIIDAE, Creepers
   CHAMAEIDAE, Wren Tits
   CINCLIDAE, Dippers, or Water Ouzels
   TROGLODYTIDAE, Wrens
   MIMIDAE, Thrashers, Mockingbirds, Catbirds

TURDIDAE, Thrushes, Robins, Bluebirds
SYLVIIDAE, Kinglets
MOTACILLIDAE, Pipits, Wagtails
BOMBYCILLIDAE, Waxwings
PTILOGONATIDAE, Phainopeplas
LANIIDAE, Shrikes ("butcherbirds")
STURNIDAE, European Starling (introduced)
VIREONIDAE, Vireos
PARULIDAE, Wood Warblers
ICTERIDAE, Blackbirds, Orioles, Meadow Larks
THRAUPIDAE, Tanagers
FRINGILLIDAE, Grosbeaks, Finches, Sparrows, Towhees, Buntings

REFERENCES

Many special periodicals deal solely with birds, the more important for North America being as follows: *The Auk* (published by the American Ornithologists' Union) chiefly on North American birds; *The Condor* (Cooper Ornithological Society), especially for western North America; *The Wilson Bulletin* (Wilson Ornithological Club), especially for the Middle West; and *Bird Banding* (Northeastern Bird Banding Association), particularly for studies on banded birds; *Audubon Magazine*, formerly *Bird-Lore* (National Audubon Society), popular. Many separate books, museum publications, and articles in scientific journals contain extensive accounts of the birds in various regions, states, provinces, and smaller geographic areas.

American Ornithologists' Union. 1931. Checklist of North American birds. 4th ed. Lancaster, Pa., American Ornithologists' Union. xix + 526 pp.

Scientific and common name and geographic range for each living species and subspecies north of Mexico; also a list of fossil species. Supplements to checklist appear at intervals in *The Auk*.

American Ornithologists' Union. 1955. Recent studies in avian biology. Albert Wolfson, editor. Urbana, University of Illinois Press. ix + 479 pp., few figs. Thirteen summaries of research and literature on classification, biology, behavior, etc.

AUDUBON, JOHN JAMES. 1937. The birds of America. New York, The Macmillan Co. 500 colored plates (9 by 12½ inches) with footnotes and index. A popular reproduction of the famous elephant folio of the same title with plates about 28 by 38 inches, published 1827–1838 by this renowned naturalist-artist, in which all birds of North America then known were shown in color. In 1831–1839 he issued 5 text volumes, "Ornithological Biography," on the anatomy and habits of birds, and in 1840–1844 the two works were combined and reissued as 7 octavo volumes. The indefatigible Audubon collected the specimens and notes, painted the pictures, wrote the text, obtained subscriptions, and directed the printing; the most stupendous work on natural history ever produced in North America.

BENT, A. C. 1919–   . Life histories of North American birds. *U.S. National Museum Bulletins* 107 . . . 203 . . . (19 published, others planned.) Detailed account of habits, migration, and nesting for each species; many illustrations.

BRADLEY, O. C. 1950. The structure of the fowl. 3d ed. Rev. by Tom Grahame. Philadelphia, J. B. Lippincott Co. xii + 128 pp., 79 figs.

GRASSÉ, PIERRE-P. (editor). 1950. Oiseaux. *In* Traité de zoologie. Paris, Masson et Cie. Vol. 15, 1,164 pp., 743 figs. Anatomy, physiology, biology, and classification.

HELLMAYR, C. E., C. B. CORY, and B. CONOVER. 1918–1949. Catalogue of birds of the Americas and the adjacent islands. *Field Museum of Natural History Zoological Series*, vol. 13, 15 pts.

HEILMANN, GERARD. 1926. The origin of birds. London, H. F. & G. Witherby. 5 + 208 pp., 142 figs. Fossil record and relationships.

KNOWLTON, F. H. 1909. Birds of the world. New York, Henry Holt & Co., Inc. ix + 873 pp., illus. Structure, distribution, and habits of the orders and families, with mention of many species.

LINCOLN, F. C. 1952. Migration of birds. New York, Doubleday & Co., Inc. 3 + 102 pp., 23 figs.

PETERS, J. L. 1931–   . Checklist of birds of the world. Cambridge, Mass., Harvard University Press. 7 vols. to 1951.

RIDGWAY, R. 1900–   . Birds of North and Middle America. *U.S. National Museum Bulletin* 50, pts. (vols.) I–XI (unfinished). Technical keys, descriptions of plumages, measurements, and geographic distribution.

STRONG, R. M. 1939. A bibliography of birds. *Field Museum of Natural History Zoological Series*, vol. 25, 937 pp.

STURKIE, P. D. 1954. Avian physiology. Ithaca, Comstock Publishing Associates, Inc. xx + 423 pp., 77 figs. Mainly of domestic fowl.

WALLACE, G. J. 1955. An introduction to ornithology. New York, The Macmillan Co. xii + 443 pp., 178 figs.

35 CLASS MAMMALIA
Mammals

The mammals are the "highest" group in the animal kingdom. They include the moles, bats, rodents, cats, monkeys, whales, horses, deer, man, and other living forms, besides a host of extinct species and orders. All are more or less covered with hair or fur and are warm-blooded. The distinctive term "mammal" refers to the mammary glands on females that supply milk for suckling the young. Parental care is most highly developed in this class and reaches its climax in the human species (Chap. 36). Various mammals live in all sorts of habitats from polar regions to the tropics and from the sea to the densest forests and driest deserts. Many are of retiring habits or nocturnal so that they are seldom seen, but they play a leading role in the present-day world. Certain wild species are hunted as game, and others for their fur. Some rodents and flesh eaters damage man's crops and livestock, and a few species are reservoirs of disease. The domestic mammals provide man with food, clothing, and transportation.

35-1. Characteristics. 1. Body usually covered with hair (scant on some), which is molted periodically; skin with many glands (sebaceous, sweat, scent, and mammary).

2. Skull with 2 occipital condyles; neck vertebrae usually 7; tail usually long and mobile.

3. Nasal region usually slender; mouth with teeth (rarely absent) in sockets or alveoli, on both jaws and differentiated in relation to food habits; tongue usually mobile; eyes with movable lids; ears with external fleshy pinnae.

4. Four limbs (cetaceans and sirenians lack hind limbs); each foot with 5 (or fewer) toes and variously adapted for walking, running, climbing, burrowing, swimming, or flying; toes with horny claws, nails, or hoofs and often fleshy pads.

5. Heart completely 4-chambered (2 auricles, 2 distinct ventricles); only the left aortic arch persists; red blood cells nonnucleated, usually circular.

6. Respiration only by lungs; larynx with vocal cords; a complete muscular diaphragm separating lungs and heart from abdominal cavity.

7. A urinary bladder; excretions (urine) fluid.

8. Twelve pairs of cranial nerves; brain highly developed, both cerebrum and cerebellum large.

9. Body temperature regulated (homoiothermous).

10. Male with copulatory organ (penis); testes commonly in a scrotum external to abdomen; fertilization internal; eggs usually minute, without shells, and retained in uterus (modified oviduct) of female for development; embryonic membranes (amnion, chorion, and allantois) present; usually with a placenta affixing embryo to uterus for nutrition and respiration; young nourished after birth by milk secreted from mammary glands of female.

The insulated body covering (hair and subcutaneous fat) and the complete separation of venous and arterial blood in the heart make the regulated body temperature possible. With this go a high rate of metabolism and a consequent large requirement for food. The teeth are usually conspicuous and differentiated. The senses of sight, hearing, and smell are highly developed. The large cerebellum and cerebrum provide for a high degree of coordination in all activities and for learning and a retentive memory.

Fig. 35-1. Class MAMMALIA. The Norway or house rat (*Rattus norvegicus*), a representative mammal; body covered with hair, nose bearing sensory vibrissae, lips soft and movable, external ears thin, feet with fleshy sole pads, toes with claws, and slender tail serving mainly for balancing.

35-2. Size. The smallest mammals are shrews and mice less than 2 inches in head-and-body length and weighing only a fraction of an ounce. Others range variously in size up to the elephants and large whales; the blue whale (*Balaenoptera musculus*), which grows to 105 feet long and 119 tons in weight, is the biggest known animal.

STRUCTURE OF A MAMMAL: THE DOMESTIC CAT

The cat is a member of the Order CARNIVORA (L. *caro*, flesh + *voro*, devour) that feeds typically on small mammals and birds. Its forward-directed eyes, keen senses, and silent tread on padded feet make it an effective hunter. The lithe body and sharp claws enable it to pounce upon and grasp prey easily, and the sharp shearing teeth facilitate the cutting of flesh.

35-3. External features. The entire body is densely covered with *hair* or fur and consists of a rounded *head*, short *neck*, narrow *trunk*, and long flexible *tail*. Each *fore limb* has five *toes* provided with fleshy *pads* and curved retractile *claws*. The *hind limbs* are stouter, providing the principal power in locomotion; each has four toes and claws. A cat walks on its toes and hence is digitigrade (L. *digitus*, finger + *gradior*, to step; Fig. 35-6).

The tip of the nose has two narrow *nostrils*, and the *mouth* is bordered by thin fleshy *lips*. Each eye has two fleshy *eyelids*, margined with fine hairs or *eyelashes;* and beneath the lids is a transparent *nictitating membrane* that moves across the eyeball from the outer angle. About the eyes and nose are long sensory hairs, the *vibrissae* or "cat whiskers." Behind the eyes are two thin fleshy *external ears* (pinnae), each with an external auditory canal leading into the head. The trunk comprises a narrow chest or *thorax*, sheltered by the ribs, and the broader *abdomen* posteriorly; along the ventral surface on the female are four or five pairs of small elevated *teats* or *mammae*, through which the milk or mammary glands open. The *anus* is anterior to the base of the tail, and close below is the *urogenital opening*. In males the *scrotum*, containing the testes, hangs beneath the anus.

35-4. Body covering. The *skin* is soft and thin except for the thickened cornified pads of the feet. It is covered densely with closely spaced *hairs*, and all the hairs collectively are termed the coat or *pelage*.

Each hair (Fig. 4-1) grows from a *hair papilla* at the base of a deep tubular pit or *hair follicle* that is embedded in the skin and lined by epidermis. Each follicle is joined to a small *sebaceous gland* that provides an oily secretion (sebum) to lubricate the hair. The follicles lie slantingly in the skin, and to each is attached an *erector muscle* by which the hair may be made to "stand on end" when the cat is either cold or angry. Hair, when grown, is a nonliving epidermal product subject to wear and fading and therefore is periodically renewed by molt,

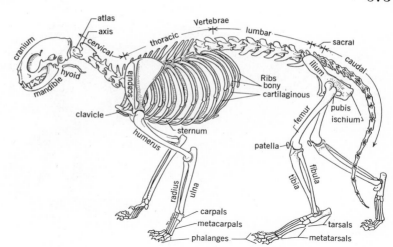

Fig. 35-2. Skeleton of the domestic cat.

usually in autumn. The hairs drop out individually, and new ones grow from the same follicles. An individual hair (Fig. 35-9) is covered by *cuticular scales* over a tubular *cortex* that surrounds an inner *medulla*. The coloration of hair and hence of the pelage is dependent upon the kind of pigment granules present in the cortex —black, brown, red, or yellow. The blue color of some cats is due to the combined effect of pigment and of light-interference phenomena in the cortex and cuticle. White cats lack pigment.

35-5. Skeleton. The skeleton is largely of bone, with cartilage over joint surfaces, on parts of the ribs, and in a few other places (Fig. 35-2). Besides the cartilage and membrane bones (Chap. 3), certain tendons contain ossifications known as *sesamoid bones;* the most conspicuous of these is the kneecap, or *patella,* but others occur on the feet. The rounded *skull* is a hard case with all the bones closely united by irregular *sutures* that may be obliterated in later life. The facial region contains, dorsally, the *nostrils* and the large *orbits* that shelter the eyes, and ventrally there is a flat *palate* margined by the teeth of the upper jaw. Outside of each orbit is a conspicuous horizontal bar, the *zygomatic arch.* On the posterior surface is a large *foramen magnum* through which the nerve cord connects to the brain, and at either side of this is a rounded *occipital condyle* by which the skull articulates to the first vertebra or atlas.

The *lower jaw,* which also bears teeth, consists of a single bone on each side that articulates to the squamosal bone of the cranium.

The *vertebral* or *spinal column* forms a flexible support for the body and shelters the nerve cord; adjacent vertebrae are separated by *intervertebral discs* of dense fibrocartilage. The column comprises five regions: (1) the short neck of 7 *cervical vertebrae;* (2) the 13 *thoracic vertebrae* on which the movable ribs articulate; (3) the 7 *lumbar vertebrae* of the lower back; (4) the 3 *sacral vertebrae* which are fused for attachment of the pelvic girdle; and (5) the 16 to 20 slender *caudal vertebrae* in the tapered tail. The 13 pairs of *ribs* and the slender midventral *sternum* form a flexible "thoracic basket" that protects vital organs within and also performs respiratory movements.

The *pectoral girdle* attaches by muscles to the thorax and supports the fore limbs. On each side it comprises a flat triangular shoulder blade or *scapula* which receives the head of the humerus, and a delicate collarbone or *clavicle* in nearby muscles. The *fore limb* comprises a humerus; distinct radius and ulna; seven carpal bones; five metacarpals (innermost short); and the phalanges of the toes. The *pelvic girdle* attaches rigidly to the sacrum; each half (the innominate bone, or hipbone) consists of an anterior dorsal *ilium,* a posterior *ischium* with a tuberosity on which the cat sits, and the ventral *pubis.* At the junction of the three bones

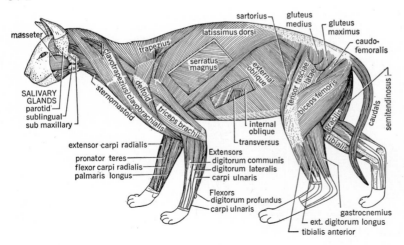

Fig. 35-3. Superficial muscles and salivary glands of the domestic cat; some of the muscles are cut to show others beneath.

is a cup-like socket or **acetabulum,** in which the head of the femur articulates. The two pubes and ischia join in symphyses ventrally below the vertebrae. The bones of each **hind limb** are the femur; separate tibia and fibula; seven tarsals of the ankle; four long metatarsals (and a vestige of the innermost, or first), and the phalanges.

35-6. Muscular system (Fig. 35-3). As compared with the lower vertebrates, mammals have a lesser bulk of segmental muscles on the vertebrae and ribs and more elaborately developed muscles on the head, neck, and limbs. The cat has facial muscles that permit some degree of "expression" in relation to emotional states. The limbs have been rotated so that the elbow is posterior and the knee is anterior and both limbs project ventrally; this is quite unlike the laterally projecting limbs of amphibians and reptiles. The cat's ability to "land on all fours" when dropped results from the freedom in its skeletal articulations and the diversity of muscular movements that it can make. A distinctive mammalian characteristic is the dome-shaped transverse muscular partition or **diaphragm,** covered by peritoneum, that separates the coelom into an anterior **thoracic cavity** containing the heart and lungs and the **abdominal cavity** behind with the other viscera.

35-7. Teeth. Mammalian teeth are fixed in sockets and of definite number. In various mammals the teeth are specialized in form and function according to the kind of food used, those of the cat being adapted for cutting and tearing flesh. On each tooth (Fig. 35-13) the exposed part or **crown** is covered by hard white **enamel** over a bone-like **dentine** that contains a pulp cavity. The base or **root** of the tooth, below the gums, is fixed by bony **cement** in a socket or **alveolus** in the jaw. Like most mammals, the cat has four kinds of teeth: short **incisors** at the ends of the jaws, to cut or scrape off food; slender stabbing **canines** used to seize or kill prey and in fighting; and angular **premolars** and **molars** for shearing and crushing the food (Fig. 35-12). Incisors, canines, and premolars comprise the "milk teeth" of a kitten; these later are all replaced, and there are added the molars having no milk predecessors. The teeth are alike on the two sides but differ in the upper and lower jaws. All the teeth collectively form the **dentition,** and their number is expressed as a dental formula that indicates those of the upper and lower jaws on one side, thus:

for a kitten

$$i\frac{3}{3},\ c\frac{1}{1},\ p\frac{3}{2}\times 2 \qquad = 26$$

and for a cat

$$I\frac{3}{3},\ C\frac{1}{1},\ P\frac{3}{2},\ M\frac{1}{1}\times 2 = 30.$$

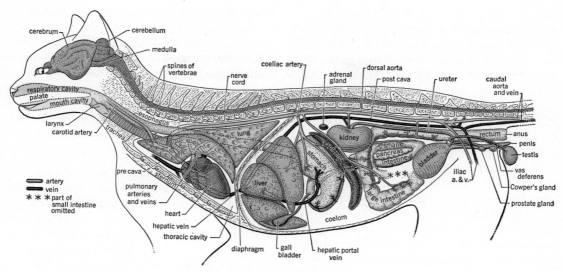

Fig. 35-4. The cat; internal structure.

35-8. Digestive system (Fig. 35-4). The mouth cavity is margined by the thin soft *lips,* within which are fleshy *gums* around the bases of the *teeth.* The lips and cavity are lined with soft mucous membrane. The *tongue* is a flexible muscular organ, attached ventrally and supported by the hyoid bones; its rough and cornified upper surface contains four kinds of *papillae* and microscopic *taste buds.* The mouth cavity is roofed by the *palate;* the anterior hard palate is formed of bone and crossed by fleshy ridges that help in holding food; the short fleshy soft palate behind closes the respiratory passage above during swallowing. At either side of the soft palate is the reddish *tonsil,* of lymphoid tissue. Four pairs of *salivary glands* pour watery and mucous secretions through ducts into the mouth to moisten the food; these are (1) the parotids, below the ears; (2) the submaxillaries, behind the lower jaws; (3) the sublinguals near the preceding; and (4) the infraorbitals below the eyes (see Fig. 5-3*A*).

The *pharynx* is the cavity behind the mouth where respiratory and food paths cross. Into its dorsal surface there open the *internal nares* from the nasal cavity above the palate, and behind these are two slit-like openings of the *Eustachian tubes.* Beyond the tongue and ventral in the pharynx is the respiratory opening, or *glottis;* when food is passing, this is covered by an anterior flap, the *epiglottis.* The *esophagus* is a narrow muscular tube through the thorax to the enlarged *stomach* behind the diaphragm. The stomach connects, through a pyloric valve, to the slender and coiled *small intestine.* To the anterior portion of the latter are joined ducts of the digestive glands, the large brownish *liver* of several lobes, and the small whitish *pancreas.* At the junction of the small and large intestine there is a short blind sac or *caecum* (but no appendix). The *large intestine* extends up the right side and across the abdomen, then descends on the left to a short muscular *rectum* opening at the *anus.* Most mammals have no cloaca; the digestive, excretory, and reproductive systems have separate external openings.

35-9. Circulatory system. The red blood corpuscles of mammals are unlike those of all lower vertebrates in being round, biconcave, and nonnucleated. The *heart,* in the thoracic cavity, is enclosed in a delicate sac of pericardium. It is completely four-chambered, as in birds, with two auricles and two thick muscular ventricles. The course of blood through the heart and lungs is the same in the cat and the bird, but in the mammal it leaves the left ventricle of the heart through a *left aortic arch.* Shortly the arch gives off an *innominate artery* (relict of the right arch), whence the two *common carotid arteries* arise, and the innominate continues as the *subclavian* artery to the right fore limb. The arch gives off a left subclavian and then turns as the *dorsal aorta,* which extends posteriorly. The latter gives branches to the internal organs, body wall, and posterior limbs, then continues as the *caudal artery* of the tail.

The *venous system* includes paired *jugular veins* from the head and neck and *subclavian veins* from the fore limbs; these all join as a *precaval vein,* which enters the right auricle. The *postcaval vein* returns blood from the tail, hind limbs, kidneys, gonads, and dorsal muscles. From the digestive organs a *hepatic portal system* carries blood to the liver, whence *hepatic veins* join the postcava as the latter enters the right auricle. There is no renal portal system. The *spleen* is a slender dark mass behind the stomach.

35-10. Respiratory system. Air enters the *nostrils* to pass above the palate through a maze of coiled turbinate bones covered by mucous epithelium, where it is cleaned and warmed. Behind the soft palate it crosses the pharynx to enter the *glottis.* This is the opening in the voice box or *larynx* (Adam's apple in man), a framework of several cartilages that contains the *vocal cords* by which the cat's calls and squalls are produced. From the larynx the air passes down the flexible wind pipe or *trachea,* which is reinforced against collapse by C-shaped cartilages. The trachea continues into the thorax to divide into two *bronchi.* These distribute air through subdividing branches that terminate in the microscopic *alveoli* of the lungs. The alveoli are surrounded by pulmonary capillaries in which the O_2-CO_2 exchange of external respiration occurs. The lungs are spongy elastic structures, each of three lobes (Fig. 7-3). The exterior of the lungs and interior of the thorax (pleural cavity) are lined by smooth peritoneum, the *pleura.* The mechanics of breathing are described in Chap. 7 (Fig. 7-5 and par. 7-8).

35-11. Excretory system. The two *kidneys* lie in the lumbar region above the peritoneum. The liquid urine passes from each kidney down a duct, the *ureter,* to be stored in the distensible *bladder* that lies midventrally below the rectum. At intervals, the muscular walls of the bladder are voluntarily contracted to force the urine out through the single *urethra.* In a female this empties at the urogenital aperture, but in a male the urethra traverses the penis.

35-12. Nervous system and sense organs. The *brain* is proportionately larger than in other land vertebrates. The *olfactory lobes* and brain stem are covered by the greatly enlarged *cerebral hemispheres.* The exterior of these is convoluted with elevations (gyri) separated by furrows (sulci); this increase of cerebral tissue is in keeping with the greater degree of intelligence displayed by the cat. The two hemispheres are joined internally by a transverse band of fibers, the *corpus callosum,* peculiar to mammals. The *cerebellum* likewise is large and conspicuously folded, being formed of a median and two lateral lobes (Figs. 10-3, 10-7). Its greater development is related to the fine coordination in the cat's activities. There are 12 pairs of *cranial nerves,* and from the *nerve cord* a pair of *spinal nerves* passes to each body somite. The trunks of the *sympathetic system* lie close below the vertebrae.

The organs of taste, smell, sight, and hearing in the cat are essentially like those of man as to location and function (see Chap. 10). Sound waves collected by the movable external ears pass into the external auditory canal that leads to the eardrum, or tympanic membrane. The middle ear of a mammal has three auditory ossicles (malleus, incus, stapes) that transfer vibrations to the inner ear—unlike the ears of birds, reptiles, and amphibians, which have only a single bone (columella)—and to the cochlea, which is spirally coiled.

35-13. Endocrine glands. In the cat these comprise the pituitary, thyroid, parathyroids, adrenals, islets of Langerhans, and gonads. Their functions are much as in other mammals (see Chap. 9).

35-14. Reproductive system (Figs. 35-5, 11-3). In a male the two *testes* lie within the *scrotum,* a skin-covered double extension of the abdominal cavity suspended below the anus. From each testis the spermatozoa are gathered in a network of minute tubules in the *epididymis* to enter the sperm duct, or *vas deferens.* This, together with blood vessels and nerves, comprises a *spermatic cord* that enters the abdomen through a small *inguinal canal.* The two vasa deferentia enter the base of the urethra, which is a common urinogenital canal through the male copulatory organ, or *penis,* that serves to transfer sperm into the vagina of a female during copulation. Two small accessory glands, the *prostate gland* around the base of the urethra and the Cowper or *bulbo-urethral glands* posteriorly, provide secretions that aid in the transfer of sperm.

The female has, behind the kidneys, two small *ovaries.* Lateral to each ovary is the funnel or *ostium,* joining a slender coiled *oviduct.* The latter is continued backward as a thick-walled *horn of the uterus.* Posteriorly the two horns unite medially as the *body of the uterus,* from which the *vagina* extends between the bladder and rectum to the *urogenital opening.* Ventral in the latter is a minute rod, the *clitoris,* corresponding to the penis of the male.

In reproduction, ova are discharged by the Graafian follicles and enter the ostia. In the oviducts they are fertilized by sperm that migrate up from the vagina after copulation. The fertilized ova settle separately against the inner wall of the uterine horns and become implanted. The fetal membranes of the developing embryo form a *placenta* (Fig. 11-16) through which the embryo receives nourishment and oxygen and disposes of wastes by way of the maternal blood circulation. The *period of gestation,* from fertilization until birth, is 60 days.

STRUCTURE OF OTHER MAMMALS

35-15. External features. The many kinds of mammals differ in size, form, proportions, nature of the pelage, and coloration. Swift-running species have narrow bodies and long limbs, large

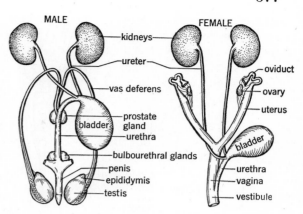

Fig. 35-5. The cat. Urogenital organs in ventral view; bladder turned aside. Compare Fig. 11-16.

sedentary species are heavy in all respects, and the whales, seals, and others that swim have spindle-shaped bodies. The mammalian *head* is proportionately large, because of the greater size of the brain, and usually has an elongate snout. The *eyes* of rodents, hoofed animals, and other plant feeders are lateral (to watch on both sides for enemies); those of primates, bats, and carnivores are directed forward to provide binocular vision. The *external ears* are large and mobile in the grazing deer, horses, and hares, reduced in the burrowing ground squirrels and pocket gophers, and small or absent in seals and other swimming mammals. The *neck* is long in grazing mammals such as deer, horses, and giraffes, but short in burrowing types and not evident in whales. The *trunk* is cylindrical in the agile weasels, cask-like in the ponderous elephants, boat-shaped in whales, compressed in deer and other speedy runners, and depressed in the burrowing gophers and moles. Mammalian *tails* are of diverse form and serve variously—being brushy "fly swatters" in hoofed mammals, stout for support and balance in kangaroos, flat as rudders in whales, beavers, and muskrats, and prehensile for grasping in opossums and some monkeys.

The *limbs* are slender and tapered in the agile deer and antelopes, huge and stump-like in the elephants and hippopotamuses, short and with broad palms in the burrowing moles, and paddle-like in the seals and whales. Kangaroos,

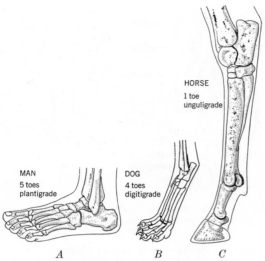

Fig. 35-6. Mammalian feet (left hind limb). *A.* Human, generalized with 5 toes and walks on entire foot. *B.* Dog, with 4 toes, "heel" raised and walks on fleshy pads under toes. *C.* Horse with only one toe (3d), "heel" raised, and walks on cornified hoof over tip of toe.

jerboas, and kangaroo rats have long hind legs, feet, and tail that serve for their jumping or bounding gait. The bats have long delicate fore limbs and fingers to support their thin flight membranes, or wings. Other "flying" mammals —squirrels, lemurs, and marsupials—have normal limbs with lateral extensions of skin along the body by which they merely volplane down from a height.

The mammalian *foot* (Fig. 35-6) ends typically in five toes; hence, man and other primates are generalized in this respect. Narrowing of the foot and reduction in the number of toes occur particularly in running mammals, the horse (Fig. 14-13) being an extreme case. Cattle, sheep, and deer are "cloven-hoofed," the third and fourth toes persist and the second and fifth show as small relict dewclaws.

35-16. Body covering. The *skin* produces hair and various horny or cornified structures, and it contains many glands. Where subjected to heavy wear, it forms a dense cornified coating such as the calluses on the human palms or soles and the foot pads of bears, mice, etc. The claws, nails, and hoofs of various mammals and the horns of cattle, sheep, and Old World ante-

lope are also cornified, resistant to wear and chemical disintegration. Growth in all of them is continuous from the base to compensate for external wear. Horns are supported by a bony core. Antlers of deer are annual growths of dense connective tissue that later become calcified (Figs. 35-7, 35-8).

The *pelage,* or covering of hair, varies in length, density, texture, and color in different species. It is heaviest on Arctic mammals but thin and short on tropical species. The elephant, rhinoceros, hippopotamus, and manatee are, like man, sparsely haired. Whales are naked save for a few bristles about the lips. The coat on many mammals is differentiated into a dense fine *underfur* for body insulation, and a lesser number of heavier long *guard hairs* that protect against wear. About the nose and eyes of carnivores and rodents are long sensory *vibrissae,* with the base of each hair surrounded by sensory nerve fibers. As the animal moves about, these receive touch stimuli. A rat deprived of its vibrissae does not run freely and behaves abnormally. Spiny anteaters, hedgehogs, and porcupines are covered by sharp pointed quills (modified hairs). Scales, with hairs between, occur on the tails of beavers, muskrats, and many rats and mice; the pangolins (*Manis*) are entirely covered by scales. The armadillo has a jointed armor of epidermal scutes over bony plates and a few hairs.

The pelage is replaced gradually by a periodic *molt,* usually in autumn so that a new coat is provided for winter. Deer and some others have

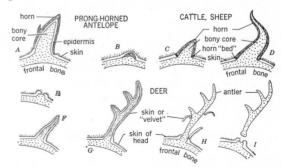

Fig. 35-7. Structure and growth stages of horns and antlers; diagrammatic sections. *A.* Prong-horned antelope. *B–D.* Horns of cow or sheep. *E–I.* Antlers of a deer or elk. Compare Fig. 32-8.

Fig. 35-8. Horns and antlers. *A.* The mountain sheep has thick permanent hollow horns (of keratin), each over a bony core. *B.* The prong-horned antelope has thin hollow horns over bony cores, and the horns are molted annually. *C.* The black-tailed deer has solid calcified antlers that are shed and grow anew each year.

also a spring molt that yields a shorter sparser pelage for the summer. In northern regions the weasels and hares have a brown summer coat that is replaced by one of white for the season of snow. Each hair usually grows to a definite length and stops, but on the scalp of mankind and the manes and tails of horses the growth is continuous. The various *color patterns* of mammals result from differences in pigmentation of the hair. Some, like black or white foxes, are practically solid color, but stripes, spots, bars, or other markings are common.

Whales and seals have a thick layer of subcutaneous fat (blubber) that insulates the body against loss of heat in water; blubber is the source of oil in the whaling industry.

35-17. Glands. The superficial *glands* include (1) sebaceous glands, as described for the cat; (2) scent glands of various types; (3) mammary glands that produce milk; (4) sweat glands on the horse and man; and (5) lachrymal (tear)

glands that moisten and cleanse the surface of the eye. *Scent glands* are variously placed: suborbital and metatarsal on deer, middorsal on

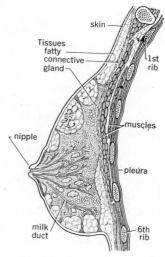

Fig. 35-10. Human mammary gland in saggital section; nonlactating. (*After Testut.*)

peccaries and some squirrels, between the toes and on the tail in the dogs, between the toes of sheep, and about the anal region in rabbits, muskrats, beavers, skunks, weasels, etc. The secretions may be abundant and odoriferous (skunks) or scant and delicate (squirrels). They serve variously (1) to convey information by an odor or scent track for animals of the same or other species; (2) to bring the sexes together for mating; and (3) as a means of defense. Such extensive use of scent is related to the keen sense of smell in mammals. *Mammary glands* (Fig. 35-10) usually occur only on females but are present on males in primates and

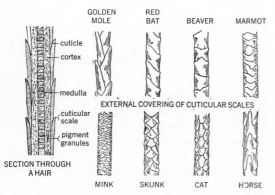

Fig. 35-9. Structure of mammalian hairs. (*After Hausman.*)

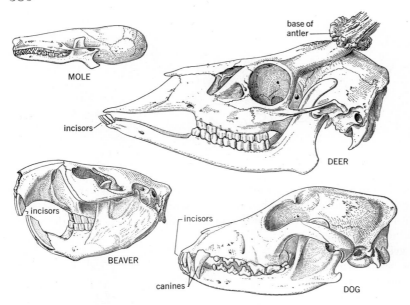

base of antler

MOLE

incisors

DEER

incisors

incisors

BEAVER

canines

DOG

Fig. 35-11. Some types of mammalian skulls and teeth; not to same scale. *Mole* (Order INSECTIVORA): teeth fine and conical for grasping insects and worms. *Mule deer* (Order ARTIODACTYLA): lower incisor teeth close against fleshy pad on the upper jaw to nip off vegetation which is ground between the enamel-ridged cheek teeth (premolars and molars); no canines. *Beaver* (Order RODENTIA): two pairs of chisel-like incisors used for gnawing; no canines; premolars and molars cross-ridged with enamel to grind food. *Dog* (Order CARNIVORA): incisors small, canines large for stabbing, and cheek teeth differentiated for shearing and crushing.

some other mammals. They become activated late in pregnancy by action of a hormone (prolactin from the anterior pituitary), to provide milk during early growth of the young, and then recede (par. 9-10). The nipples are usually more numerous than the average number of young in a litter—2 in the human female, mare, and ewe, 4 in cattle and some rodents, and 10 to 12 in swine. **Sweat glands** produce a watery secretion that, by evaporation from the surface of the skin, serves to cool the body.

35-18. Dentition. Mammalian *teeth,* unlike those in most lower vertebrates, are differentiated in form and function (Figs. 35-11 to 35-13); in each mammalian order they are specialized for the kind of food used. The teeth are narrowly pointed in moles and bats, which feed on insects, and sharp for shearing and piercing in flesh eaters such as the cat. Cheek teeth are flattened and with low cusps for crushing various foods in squirrels, pigs, and human beings, and of rasp-like structure with many enamel ridges for grinding green vegetation in hoofed animals and many rodents. The incisors of rodents have enamel only on the anterior surface, and the softer dentine behind

wears away more rapidly so that these teeth are always of chisel-like form for gnawing. Teeth may be short-crowned as in cats or long-crowned as in the cheek teeth of horses; they may have distinct roots in which growth soon ceases, or may be rootless and grow from a persistent pulp as with the incisors of rodents. Among higher mammals a full dentition never exceeds 44 teeth, and many species have fewer; some representative dental formulas are

mole and pig

$$I \frac{3}{3}, C \frac{1}{1}, P \frac{4}{4}, M \frac{3}{3} \times 2 = 44,$$

house mouse and house rat

$$I \frac{1}{1}, C \frac{0}{0}, P \frac{0}{0}, M \frac{3}{3} \times 2 = 16.$$

The tusks of pigs are enlarged canines, and those of elephants are upper incisors. Adult monotremes, some edentates, and whalebone whales lack teeth entirely.

35-19. Digestive tract. The intestine is short in species that consume such concentrated foods as insects or flesh, but long in rodents and

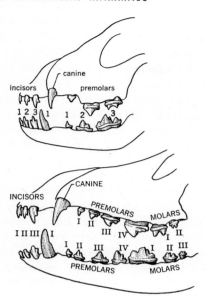

Fig. 35-12. The two dentitions of the dog. *Above.* The temporary or "milk" teeth of a puppy, all of which are later replaced. *Below.* The adult (or permanent) teeth.

hoofed mammals which eat grass or leafy vegetation. All the latter have a large **caecum** that provides additional space for such bulky food while undergoing slow digestion. In the cattle, deer, antelope, camels, etc., the ruminants which "chew the cud," the stomach is of four compartments (Fig. 35-14). Their food is gathered rapidly, mixed with saliva, chewed slightly, and passed into the rumen. Then the animal seeks a safe quiet place to ruminate. In small masses or cuds, the food is regurgitated, chewed thoroughly, and reswallowed. It then passes in turn through the other compartments, the first three of which are specialized parts of the esophagus and have cornified linings with ridges or folds that cause it to be subjected to further abrasion.

In healthy mammals the **body temperature** is closely regulated; the means and extremes for a few domestic animals are horse 100°F. (99.1–100.8); sheep 102.3 (100.9–103.8); dog and cat 101.5 (100.5–102.5); rabbit 103.1 (101.5–104.2).

NATURAL HISTORY

35-20. Distribution. Mammals inhabit practically all parts of the earth—land, water, and air. The walrus and some seals live in the Arctic seas and ice, other seals and sea lions along temperate ocean shores, and whales and porpoises in the open sea. The beaver, muskrat, mink, and otter inhabit fresh waters. Grasslands, brushlands, and forests are the homes of

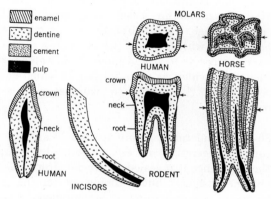

Fig. 35-13. Structure of mammalian teeth in diagrammatic sections; on the molar teeth the arrows indicate the plane of section for the figure above or below.

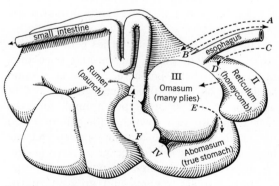

Fig. 35-14. The four-compartment stomach of the cow, a ruminant animal. Grasses and similar roughage pass down (*A*) the esophagus to the rumen, return (*B*) to the mouth for rechewing or rumination, and then pass (*C*) into the reticulum. Grain and other concentrates go at once into the reticulum. The food while being digested is moved successively (*D*) to the omasum, (*E*) abomasum, and (*F*) small intestine.

many rodents, carnivores, and hoofed animals. Still other mammals live in dense tropical jungles, on the treeless Arctic tundras, and in many desert regions. Tree squirrels, lemurs, many monkeys, and some small carnivores live chiefly in trees, moles and pocket gophers are strict inhabitants of the soil, and the insect-eating bats find their forage at night in the air. Different mammals range in altitude from sea level to high mountains where some mountain sheep and conies live above timber line. Each kind of mammal has a definite geographic and ecologic range. The habitat limitations may be narrow, as with a beaver which requires soft-barked trees as food and quiet fresh water for shelter, or wider, as with house rats which accommodate themselves to various environments.

35-21. Populations. Many mammals are nocturnal or secretive and escape notice by man; their presence is revealed by tracks, droppings, or other "signs," but trapping or hunting is necessary to determine their numbers. The mountain lion, mink, and many rodents live solitarily. Wolves and hyenas may hunt in packs, the prairie dog (*Cynomys*) and some western ground squirrels inhabit colonial burrows, and buffaloes, antelopes, fur seals, and sea lions often live in herds. Some primates live in social groups.

The population density varies with available cover and food. Small shrews and mice may number 50 to 100 per acre, and large ground squirrels from 2 to 10 per acre; American deer average 25 to 40 acres per animal, and the black bear up to a township (36 square miles) for each individual. Marine species, having large areas of the sea for foraging, often assemble in herds on the shore. The number of species is least in polar regions and greatest in the tropics.

In many species the general population is rather constant unless modified by drought, flood, food shortage, human interference, or similar factors. It reaches an annual peak when the young appear and then declines until completion of the next breeding season. Cyclical

fluctuations in population occur with meadow mice or voles (*Microtus*), lemmings (*Synaptomys*), snowshoe hares, arctic foxes, and other species in northern states, Canada, Alaska, and northern Europe. The cycle is about 4 years in meadow mice and about 10 or 11 years in arctic foxes and hares. Meadow mice and house mice (*Mus musculus*) occasionally "irrupt" with great local increase of numbers for a short time.

35-22. Nests and shelters. Many mammals provide shelters where they rest, sleep, avoid inclement weather, and rear their young. Natural crevices amid rocks serve wood rats, conies, and some carnivores. Holes in trees are used by mice, chipmunks, raccoons, opossums, and black bears. Bats resort to caves, trees, or buildings. Tree squirrels, some wood rats, and certain mice build nests amid tree foliage. Rabbits, ground squirrels, badgers, coyotes, and skunks dig burrows in the ground. Moles and pocket gophers spend their lives in elaborate systems of tunnels beneath the ground surface. Beavers construct dams to form ponds where they can float logs and build mound-like houses of sticks and mud for shelter. In regions of heavy snow deer and moose trample out winter yards where they can move about and forage. Many of the small rodents shred plant fibers lengthwise to form a fine "excelsior" that is felted into a warm soft nest.

35-23. Voice. Many mammals use their voices often to express "emotions" and transfer "ideas" between individuals. The calls and notes serve to (1) warn of danger, (2) intimidate enemies, (3) assemble gregarious species, (4) bring the sexes together for mating, and (5) locate parents or young. The "language" is usually of stereotyped calls but is more varied among the primates, leading toward the articulate speech of mankind. Small bats emit short bursts of ultrasonic notes that, echoing from nearby objects, serve to guide them in flight and may aid in capturing prey (10 to 60 bursts per second, each of 0.005 second duration, frequency 50,000 cycles per second).

35-24. Food. The hoofed mammals and most rodents (along with insects) are primary converters of vegetation, since they subsist on plant materials, and they in turn serve as food for flesh-eating animals. The *herbivorous* mammals include horses, cattle, bison, and others which *graze* on grasses and herbs, and the deer, goats, elephants, and giraffes which *browse* on leaves and twigs of shrubs and trees. Rabbits eat grasses, herbs, and bark; squirrels and chipmunks consume many seeds; tree squirrels eat nuts; beavers feed on the inner bark or cambium of willow and aspen, and porcupines take that of coniferous trees. *Omnivorous* mammals are those which take both plant and animal materials; examples are the house rats, raccoon (Fig. 35-15), bears, pigs, and man. The *carnivorous* mammals or flesh eaters include the cats, weasels, mink, seals, whales, and others. The small bats are exclusively *insectivorous,* and moles, shrews, skunks, and others subsist largely on insects. Small mammals have disproportionately large food requirements; some mice eat nearly their own weight of food daily, and a shrew has been known to consume its own weight in insects during 24 hours. Rodents and deer may forage on farm crops, coyotes and wildcats often kill sheep or turkeys, and foxes prey on poultry.

Mammals overcome a seasonal scarcity of food in several ways. The buffalos of the Great Plains performed a regular *migration* to northern grasslands for the summer and retired to others farther south for the winter. Some western deer migrate up on the Sierra-Cascade and Rocky Mountains for summer but winter in the foothills when deep snow blankets the higher ranges. Herds of antelope and zebras in Africa shift about in keeping with supplies of forage grasses. Some bats, like insectivorous birds, leave their northern summer habitats when insects become scarce and migrate southward to winter.

Squirrels, chipmunks, and kangaroo rats gather seeds in their cheek pouches and *store* them by burying in the ground. The cony (*Ochotona*) cuts and cures various plants as "hay" during the summer; this material is stored in dry, well-aired spaces ("barns")

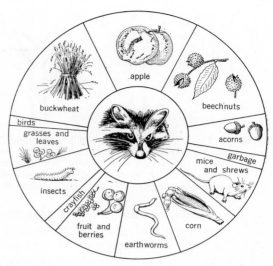

Fig. 35-15. Proportions of different foods taken by an omnivorous mammal, the raccoon (*Procyon*), in fall and winter. (*From Hamilton, American mammals.*)

among the rocks of its high mountain habitat, to be eaten when the region is blanketed with winter snow.

Winter sleep or *hibernation* is practiced by ground squirrels, chipmunks, and bats to tide over the winter scarcity of food. During hibernation all bodily metabolism drops to a low level; the respiration and heartbeat are slowed, and the body temperature is far reduced. Excess fat is accumulated prior to hibernation and serves as fuel to maintain life through the dormant period when no food is eaten. Some northern ground squirrels hibernate for about two-thirds of the year. Bears have a winter dormancy that varies with latitude.

35-25. Enemies. Herbivorous mammals fall prey to various flesh eaters according to size. Cattle are eaten by tigers, antelopes and zebras by African lions, American deer by mountain lions, wolves and coyotes, and so on, down to small mice, which are eaten by weasels. Hawks and owls prey on mice, rats, and rabbits, and some large snakes take many rodents. Man is a major enemy of many mammals. He hunts game species, traps fur bearers, and kills in various ways the predators that levy on domestic livestock and rodents that forage on

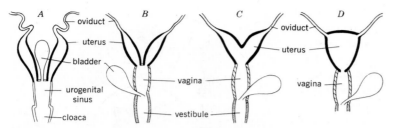

Fig. 35-16. Types of uteri. *A.* Duck-billed platypus (Monotremata): separate oviducts (uteri) enter a urogenital sinus joined to the cloaca. *B.* Rabbit (Lagomorpha): uterus duplex, of separate "horns" joined to a common vagina. *C.* Cow (Artiodactyla): uterus bicornate, "horns" partly fused. *D.* Human (Primates): uterus simplex, with a common central chamber, and no horns.

crops. Mammals are hosts to various parasites and diseases (Table 26-1) that may reduce their vitality or cause death, and some of these are probably important in the regulation of mammalian populations. Protozoans, flatworms, roundworms, lice, fleas, and ticks are among the common parasites (Chaps. 16, 19, 20, 26, 27).

35-26. Reproduction. Fertilization is always internal, and the young are nourished by milk after birth. The lowest mammals are the duck-billed platypus and spiny anteater (Monotremata) that lay reptile-like eggs of some size which are probably incubated. The opossums, kangaroos, and other Marsupialia have minute eggs that develop for some days in the uterus. Then the immature "larvae" crawl out to the ventral pouch or marsupium on the abdomen of the female, where they attach firmly to the mammary nipples for nutrition and remain until their development is complete. In all the higher mammals the minute eggs are retained for a longer period in the uterus, which becomes modified for their reception and nourishment. The circulatory system of the embryo quickly comes into close relation, but not direct connection, with maternal blood vessels in the uterus by development of the placenta, which provides a mechanism for diffusion of food and oxygen to the embryo and for removal of waste products (Fig. 11-16).

Most mammals have rather definite mating seasons, often in winter or spring. Many produce but one brood a year, some have more than one, and the alien house mouse and rats

may breed at any season. In rodents, the testes enlarge and descend into the scrotum to become functional during the mating season, then decrease and return into the abdomen. Male elk "bugle" and become more pugnacious during the mating period, and other mammals have special mating calls between the sexes, as with domestic cats and cattle.

Female mammals experience a recurrent ***estrus cycle,*** marked by cellular changes in the uterus and vagina and by differences in behavior. The successive stages are termed anestrum (quiescent period), proestrum (preparation for mating), estrum or "heat" (acceptance of male), and metestrum (regressive changes). Discharge of ova from the ovary occurs usually late in estrus or soon thereafter. The female rat is in heat for a few hours about every 4 days, the cow has recurrent periods lasting about 24 hours every 18 to 21 days, and the female dog is in estrus for 6 to 12 days about every 6 months. Female rabbits and ferrets will usually breed at any time. Estrus, pregnancy, and lactation are regulated by hormones of the pituitary gland and ovaries; environmental factors such as the length of day and temperature affect pituitary activity.

The relations between the sexes during the reproductive season are various. In some carnivores the male remains with the female and helps to gather food until the young are weaned. Many other mammals are promiscuous in mating, one or more males simply attending a female for a day or so until she is served. Polygamy, the mating of one male with several or many females, is the habit of sea lions, fur seals, cattle, wild horses, and elk.

The period of *gestation,* or pregnancy, usually varies with size. The time in days for some common mammals is as follows: house mouse, 21; Norway rat, 21.5 to 22; domestic rabbit, 30 to 32; ferret, 40; black fox, 51; house cat and domestic dog, 60; guinea pig, 68; swine, 114; sheep and goats, 149; mule deer, 203 to 208; marten, 259 to 275; cow, 280; horse, 336; elephant, about 20 months.

The number of young produced at one time is usually inversely proportional to size; elephant and horse, 1; sheep and deer, 1 or 2; carnivores, 3 to 5; rodents, 2 or 3 to 8 or 9. The black rat averages 6, and the Norway rat about 8, but females of the latter may have up to 15 embryos at one pregnancy. Large mammals usually produce but one young per year, but smaller species with short gestation time and multiple broods are more prolific. A pair of captive meadow mice has produced 13 to 17 litters, totaling 78 to 83 young, in 1 year; and a pair of white (Norway) rats, over 1,500.

The *precocial* young of hares and jack rabbits (*Lepus*), deer, and domestic livestock are fully haired at birth, have their eyes open, and are able to move about at once (Fig. 35-17). In contrast, the *altricial* young of true rabbits (*Oryctolagus*), most rodents, and carnivores are naked, blind, and helpless when born and require further development in a nest before being able to get about. The young of all mammals receive parental care before they become independent.

Some small mice may breed a few weeks after birth, whereas the larger land mammals require several years before sexual maturity; large whales, however, breed in the second or third year of life.

The average span of life is scarcely a year in some small rodents and shrews and is generally proportional to size in the larger species; yet no mammals, even among captives, attain the average life span of mankind.

35-27. Relations to man. Mammals have served or harmed man in various ways from the earliest

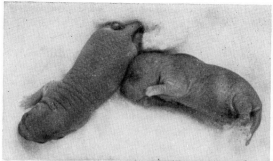

Fig. 35-17. Young mammals. *Above.* Rats, born naked, blind, and helpless; require nursing and care in a nest before becoming independent. *Below.* Jack rabbit, fully haired and with eyes open at birth, able to move about at once. (*Photos by T. I. Storer.*)

times. He depends on some for food, clothing, and other necessities, but others have been a physical menace or a source of disease, and some injure his possessions. Early cave paintings by primitive man in Europe depict the chase and the defense against large predators; the great interest in hunting by all peoples demonstrates this continuing relation between man and mammals.

Eskimos in the Arctic use whale and seal blubber as fuel oil, caribou skins for clothing, seal hides for footwear, and skins or intestines of other species for boats. The Plains Indians were supported largely by the buffalo, using its flesh for food, its hides for clothing and teepees (tents), and its sinews for sewing. Civilized races in northern countries have used animal pelts as clothing for many centuries, and much of the early exploration of North America was by trappers in search of furs. Today, the demand for fur garments supports a large industry. Dense natural furs of soft texture and pleasing colors, such as marten, ermine, fur seal, and beaver, bring the highest prices. Millions of muskrats, skunks, and opossums are still taken in the United States, and lesser numbers of other fur bearers. The rearing of black foxes and mink on fur farms has become successful. Pelts of rabbits, house cats, muskrats, and others are dyed, clipped, or otherwise altered to resemble the more expensive furs.

Civilized man hunts now for pleasure and recreation. The moose, elk, deer, mountain sheep, and bears are "big game," sought for their heads, hides, and meat; lesser forms such as the raccoons, opossums, rabbits, and tree squirrels are pursued by thousands of hunters.

Live mammals, especially the larger or rarer kinds, are exhibited in many zoological gardens; and in national parks they are protected so that visitors may see them at close range.

Harmful mammals are those which damage crops or domestic animals, those which harbor disease, and the large kinds which are dangerous to man himself. Rabbits, woodchucks, and some mice will forage in vegetable patches, gardens, and fields and may gnaw the bark of trees. In the western states ground squirrels damage grain and other crops and pocket gophers eat roots of plants in gardens and fields. The alien house rats and mice, spread by shipping and commerce to many lands, do much damage. They gnaw into buildings, consume all kinds of foodstuffs, and destroy much property. The carnivores, or "predatory mammals," in nature feed on other animals appropriate to their size, from rodents to deer. Wolves, coyotes, wildcats, and bears also prey at times on domestic cattle, sheep, hogs, and poultry. Since the beginning of agriculture, mankind has endeavored to control the damage by rodents to his crops and property and by predators to his livestock.

Important diseases in mammals that may be transmitted to man are plague, typhus, and ratbite fever in house rats; plague, relapsing fever, spotted fever, and tularemia in various wild rodents; and trichina in rats, pigs, and cats.

35-28. Domesticated mammals. Various mammals have been domesticated—tamed and reared in captivity—to serve man's needs. This began many centuries ago in Asia (par. 36-19), where many of the wild stocks are native. The horse and ox serve for transport and draft; the cattle, sheep, and goats provide meat and milk; the pig affords meat; and all yield hides to tan into leather. The wool and hair of sheep and goats is spun into yarn or thread and woven into fabrics. The dog is a guardian and friend, is used in hunting, sometimes is a beast of burden, and is eaten by some primitive races.

The domestic mammals, the wild species whence derived, and the regions of origin are as follows:

Lagomorpha

Rabbits, all breeds (*Oryctolagus cuniculus*, gray rabbit), Europe.

Rodentia

Golden hamster (*Mesocricetus auratus*), Syria.
White and colored mice (*Mus musculus*, house mouse), Asia or Europe.
White rat (*Rattus norvegicus*), western Asia.

Carnivora

Dogs, *Canis familiaris* (*Canis lupus*, wolf), Europe and Asia.
Black and silver foxes (*Vulpes fulva*, red fox), North America.
Cats, *Felis catus* (*Felis silvestris*, European wild cat), Europe.
Mink (*Mustela vison*), United States.
Ferret, *Mustela furo* (*Mustela eversmanni*, polecat), Asia.

Perissodactyla

Horses: draft types (*Equus caballus fossilis*), Europe.
    Speed types (*Equus przewalski*), western Asia.
Gray asses (*Equus onager*), western Asia.
White asses (*Equus asinus*), northern Africa.

Artiodactyla

European swine (*Sus scrofa*, European wild boar), Europe.
Asiatic swine (*Sus vittatus*), southeastern Asia.
Dromedary or Arabian camel (*Camelus dromedarius*), Mongolia.
Two-humped or Bactrian camel (*Camelus bactrianus*), Mongolia.
Llama (*Auchenia glama*), South America.
Alpaca (*Auchenia peruana*), South America.
Reindeer (*Rangifer tarandus*), northern Europe.
European cattle, *Bos taurus* (*Bos primigenius*, aurochs or ur), Europe.
Asiatic cattle, *Bos indicus* (?*Bos sondaicus*, banteng), southern Asia.

Yak (*Poephagus grunniens*), Tibet.
Water buffalo (*Bubalus bubalis*), southern Asia.
Sheep: ordinary breeds (*Ovis musimon*, moufflon), southern Europe.
  Merino and fat-tailed (*Ovis argal*), western Asia.
Goats: ordinary breeds (*Capra aegagrus*), western Asia.
  Kashmir and Angora (*Capra falconeri*), western Asia.

Many special breeds of horses, cattle, sheep, pigs, and dogs have been developed to suit particular needs, by artificial selection in breeding. Some of these differ greatly from their wild ancestors in size, conformation, color, reproductive ability, and other features, although no new animals have been created. Examples of such breeds among cattle are the Hereford (beef), Holstein-Friesian (heavy milk production), Jersey (high butterfat content of milk), and Brown Swiss of triple purpose (meat, milk, and draft). Domestic mammals and birds provide most of the protein for human food, aside from fish, and also many other necessities of modern life. The livestock industry breeds and rears domesticated mammals and birds, and the packing industry slaughters these animals, distributes meat products, and recovers by-products.

35-29. Fossil mammals. The mammals probably arose from the cynodont reptiles of Triassic time, which had differentiated teeth. The earliest forms were small, but later stocks increased in size and became varied in structure. Marsupials and insectivores appeared in the Cretaceous, and from the latter group the higher placental mammals are considered to have arisen. With the close of the Cretaceous most of the reptiles disappeared and the mammals "blossomed forth." First came a series of ungainly archaic stocks (Orders †TAENIODONTA,

†CREODONTA, †CONDYLARTHRA, †AMBLYPODA), then modern types appeared. The Cenozoic era (Paleocene to Pleistocene) is called the Age of Mammals because members of this class were dominant throughout. About half the known orders consist entirely of extinct forms, and all the others contain, besides the living representatives, some or many that have died out.

Some important structural features of mammals, as compared with reptiles, are (1) two occipital condyles instead of one; (2) each ramus of the lower jaw of one bone, not several; (3) articulation of the jaw directly on the skull, not through the quadrate; (4) teeth differentiated and of only two sets (milk, permanent), instead of alike with many replacements; and (5) centra of vertebrae and long bones ossifying from three centers instead of one.

The factors that led to development of the mammals have been inferred to be the increasing aridity from Permian time onward, which placed a premium on speed of locomotion, and the colder glacial climates, in which animals with regulated body temperature that progressed with their bodies off the ground would be more likely to survive.

Some early mammals were exceedingly abundant, to judge from the quantities of their teeth and skeletons that have been found. Fossil relics of carnivores, whales, proboscidians, horses, camels, and others are sufficiently numerous to enable paleontologists to trace their probable evolution in some detail. The phylogeny of some groups can be traced through several geological periods in one continent. In other cases a stock suddenly appears in the rocks and provides little or no clue to its immediate ancestry or probable path of migration.

CLASSIFICATION

CLASS MAMMALIA. MAMMALS. Body usually covered with hair; skin with various glands; skull with 2 occipital condyles; jaws usually with differentiated teeth, in sockets; limbs adapted for walking, climbing, burrowing, swimming, or flying; toes with claws, nails, or hoofs; heart 4-chambered, with left aortic arch only; lungs large, elastic; a diaphragm between thoracic and abdominal cavities; male with a penis; fertilization internal; eggs small or minute, usually retained in uterus for development; females with mammary glands that secrete milk to nourish the young; body temperature regulated (homoiothermous); Triassic to Recent; 4,400 living species (many subspecies) and numerous fossil forms.

SUBCLASS A. PROTOTHERIA.

Order 1. Monotremata (Ornithodelphia). Monotremes or Egg-laying Mammals. Coracoid and precoracoid present; no external pinna on ear; teeth only in young, adults with horny beak; cloaca present; ureters open in dorsal wall of urogenital passage; testes abdominal; penis conducts only sperm; oviducts distinct, entering cloaca separately; no uterus or vagina; mammary glands without nipples; females oviparous; Australian region. *Ornithorhynchus anatinus*, duck-billed platypus (Fig. 35-18), eastern Australia and Tasmania, 18 to 20 inches long; duck-like bill, internal cheek

Fig. 35-18. An egg-laying mammal, the duck-billed platypus (*Ornithorhynchus anatinus*, Order Monotremata) of Australia. (*After Vogt and Specht, The natural history of animals, Blackie & Son, Ltd.*)

pouches, feet broadly webbed, tail flat and beaver-like, male with rooster-like spur on heel, connected to poison gland; aquatic, constructs burrows; food of fresh-water invertebrates, carried in cheek pouches; during spring (August to December) female constructs nest in burrow and lays 1 to 3 eggs, each about ½ by ¾ inch, with strong flexible white shell; probably incubated; young about 1 inch long when hatched, "nurse" by lapping up milk secreted by scattered "mammary" glands on abdomen of female. *Tachyglossus*, spiny anteater, several species, Australia, Tasmania, New Guinea, and Papua. *T. aculeatus*, of Australia, 17 inches long, beak elongate, cylindrical, tongue extensile, body covered with coarse hairs and spines, limbs short, toes 3 to 5 with claws; nocturnal, feeds on ants found under stones; female lays 1 egg, probably carried in pouch (marsupium) on abdomen.

SUBCLASS B. †ALLOTHERIA. **Order 1.** †**Multituberculata.** Jurassic to Eocene.

SUBCLASS C. THERIA. Marsupials and Placental Mammals. Ear usually with external pinna; teeth usually in both young and adults, differentiated as to form and function; cloaca usually absent; ureters open into base of bladder; testes of males usually in a scrotal sac, vasa deferentia and bladder opening through a common urethra in penis; females with each oviduct differentiated into upper Fallopian and lower uterine portions, both opening into a distinct vagina; mammary glands with nipples; females produce living young (viviparous).

INFRACLASS 1. †PANTOTHERIA. **Order 1.** †**Pantotheria.** Jurassic. **Order 2.** †**Symmetrodonta.** Jurassic.

INFRACLASS 2. METATHERIA.

Order 1. Marsupialia. Marsupials or Pouched Mammals. Epipubic bones usually present; incisor teeth not equal in the 2 jaws; female usually with marsupium (ventral pouch) or marsupial folds surrounding nipples on abdomen; uterus and vagina double; usually no placenta; eggs fertilized internally and begin development in uterus, but after a few days the premature "larvae" leave and crawl to marsupium where each attaches closely by its mouth to a mammary nipple and remains (as a "mammary fetus") until fully formed; thereafter small young retreat to marsupium for shelter; Cretaceous to Recent.

Didelphidae. Opossums. In the Americas. *Didelphis marsupialis* (*virginianus*), Virginia opossum (Fig. 35-19), southern New England and Wisconsin to Gulf states and Texas, introduced into California; tail scaly and prehensile; hides by day in hollow tree near water; omnivorous. Up to 22 embryos, mammae only 13; "larvae" when 12¾ days old (11 mm. long) crawl to marsupium and remain 50 to 60 days, then become free. Adults feign death, or "play 'possum," when disturbed; favored for hunting and eating in southern states.

Caenolestidae. *Caenolestes*, two species in Andes of South America.

(Note: All other living marsupials are restricted to Australia, where they are the dominant mammals; many have the fore and hind limbs about equal, but others have long hind legs as in kangaroos; they range in size from small mice to large man-sized kangaroos.)

Fig. 35-19. American or Virginia opossum (*Didelphis marsupialis*, Order MARSUPIALIA); head-and-body to 20 inches long, tail 13 inches. (*Photo by D. R. Dickey.*)

DASYURIDAE. Limbs alike; carnivorous or insectivorous. *Thylacinus*, marsupial wolf, size of large dog; *Sarcophilus*, Tasmanian devil; *Dasyurus*, tiger cat; *Phascogale*, rat size; *Sminthopsis*, pouched mouse, 3 to 5 inches long.

NOTORYCTIDAE. Foreclaws enlarged; subterranean, insectivorous. *Notoryctes*, marsupial mole, 6½ to 8 inches long.

PERAMELIDAE. Terrestrial and burrowing, largely insectivorous. *Perameles*, bandicoot.

PHALANGERIDAE. Claws sharp, hallux opposed; arboreal, herbivorous. *Phalanger*, cuscus; *Petaurus*, flying phalanger (like flying squirrel); *Phascolarctus*, koala or "teddy bear."

PHASCOLOMYIDAE. Terrestrial and burrowing, herbivorous. *Phascolomys*, wombat.

MACROPODIDAE. Hind legs, feet, and tail long; habitat various, herbivorous. *Macropus*, kangaroo, open forest or plains (Fig. 35-20); *Petrogale*, rock wallaby, about rocks; *Lagorchestes*, hare wallaby, like hare or jack rabbit; *Dendrolagus*, tree kangaroo, arboreal.

Fig. 35-20. A marsupial mammal (Order MARSUPIALIA) of Australia; female kangaroo with young in the pouch; long tail of female not shown. (*Photo by San Diego Zoological Society.*)

INFRACLASS 3. EUTHERIA. PLACENTAL MAMMALS. No marsupial bones or pouch; vagina single; fetus developed entirely within body of female, attached by a placenta to wall of uterus, and with growth of chorion.

Order 1. Insectivora. MOLES, SHREWS, etc. Size small; snout usually long and tapered; feet usually 5-toed, with claws, inner toes not opposable; teeth sharp-pointed; Cretaceous to Recent; Northern Hemisphere, West Indies, and Africa.

TALPIDAE. MOLES. *Scalopus, Scapanus* (Fig. 35-21). Eyes covered, palms enlarged, foreclaws large; pelage short, velvety; most species strictly subterranean, in "mole runs" at ground surface and in deeper tunnels from which earth is pushed out on surface as "mole hills"; food chiefly insects and worms, some sprouted seeds.

Fig. 35-21. Mole (*Scapanus latimanus*, Order INSECTIVORA), length 6½ inches. Lives in ground, using large claws and palms for burrowing.

SORICIDAE. SHREWS. *Sorex*, etc. "Mouse-like," eyes not covered, feet and tail normal; pelage soft, short; forage on surface of ground and in animal burrows, feeding voraciously on insects, small invertebrates, and some rodents; *Echinosorex albus*, Borneo, largest, to 653 mm. long.

ERINACEIDAE. HEDGEHOGS. *Erinaceus*, in Old World, pelage with spines on back.

Order 2. Dermoptera. "FLYING LEMURS." Resemble flying squirrel in appearance; the four limbs equal and included with tail in a wide, thin, fur-covered "parachute" (patagium); incisor teeth 2/3. Southeastern Asia and adjacent islands. One living genus, *Galeopithecus*, 2 species, nocturnal, in trees, glide on extended membranes; feed on leaves and fruits.

Order 3. Chiroptera. BATS. Flying mammals; size small; fore limbs and 2d to 5th digits greatly elongated, supporting a thin integumental flight membrane, or wing, that includes hind limbs (and tail in some); only 1st digit (2d also in fruit bats) of fore limb with claw; hind feet small, with sharp curved claws; teeth sharp; mostly nocturnal, capable of true flight; Paleocene to Recent; worldwide.

SUBORDER 1. MEGACHIROPTERA. FRUIT BATS or "FLYING FOXES." Africa and s. Asia to Australia; often in great flocks; sleep by day on tree branches, hanging head downward with wings folded cloaklike around body; feed on fruits, sometimes damaging orchards. *Pteropus edulis*, of Java, largest species, head and body about 12 inches, wingspread to 5 feet.

SUBORDER 2. MICROCHIROPTERA. INSECTIVOROUS BATS or "FLITTERMICE." Hang by hind claws head downward during day, in crevices of rocks or trees or in caves or buildings; some gregarious, others solitary; forage independently at night (Fig. 35-22), in open air or beneath trees; feed on

Fig. 35-22. Pallid bat (*Antrozous pallidus*, Order CHIROPTERA), length to 5 inches. Hangs upside down by day in caves or buildings on sharp hind claws; climbs with aid of foreclaws, and flies at night to capture insects for food. (*Photo by Robert T. Orr.*)

flying insects. *Myotis, Eptesicus*, brown bats; *Tadarida mexicana*, free-tailed bat, roosts in companies of a dozen to millions, as in Carlsbad Caverns, N.M., the accumulated droppings (guano) under roosts in dry caves gathered for fertilizer; *Desmodus*, vampire bat, in American tropics, with enlarged canine teeth punctures large blood vessels on horses, cattle, and occasionally man and laps up the streaming blood as food; transmits a form of rabies and a disease of horses (trypanosomiasis).

Order 4. Primates. LEMURS, MONKEYS, APES, and MAN. Limbs long, "hands" and "feet" enlarged, each of 5 digits with flattened or cupped nails; innermost (great) toe and thumb or both, usually opposable, for climbing; orbit usually directed forward and surrounded by bony ring; molars tuberculate; usually but one young at a birth; Paleocene to Recent; chiefly tropical and subtropical, most species arboreal; structure more generalized than in many other mammals, but with highest functional development of nervous system and intelligence; food chiefly fruits and seeds, some eat animal materials.

SUBORDER 1. LEMUROIDEA. LEMURS. Second toe with claw, others with nails; tail long, never prehensile, rarely absent; coloration often conspicuous; hair thick; Madagascar, Africa, southeastern Asia to Philippines and Celebes; solitary, tree-dwelling, many crepuscular or nocturnal; food of plant materials and small animals. *Lemur.*

SUBORDER 2. TARSIOIDEA. TARSIERS. Eyes protruding; ears large, thin; tarsal region of foot long, 2d and 3d toes with claws, tips of all digits with rounded pads; tail long rat-like, not prehensile; Philippines and Indo-Australian islands. *Tarsius* (1 or more species), size of red squirrel, solitary, tree-inhabiting, nocturnal, agile, jumps like a frog; food chiefly insects and lizards.

SUBORDER 3. ANTHROPOIDEA. MONKEYS, APES, MAN. Digits with flattened or cupped nails; tree-inhabiting or terrestrial, diurnal.

SUPERFAMILY 1. CEBOIDEA (Platyrhinii). NEW WORLD MONKEYS. Wide flat interval between nostrils, no cheek pouches, Central and South America.

HAPALIDAE. MARMOSETS. Size of squirrels; head often with lateral tufts; tail not prehensile. *Hapale.*

CEBIDAE. Form and color varied; tail prehensile in some. *Ateles,* spider monkey, very slender; *Alouatta,* howlers, voice loud; *Cebus,* capuchins, mostly small.

Fig. 35-23. Mountain gorilla (*Gorilla gorilla,* Order PRIMATES). Distinctive features are dome-shaped cranium, small ears, heavy brow ridges, long arms, and both hand and foot with opposable first digit. (*Photo by T. I. Storer.*)

Fig. 35-24. Chimpanzee (*Pan troglodytes,* Order PRIMATES). Conspicuous are the flat cranium, large ear, moderate brow ridges, long arms, and opposable first digit on each foot. (*Photo by San Diego Zoological Society.*)

SUPERFAMILY 2. CERCOPITHECOIDEA (Catarrhini). OLD WORLD MONKEYS. Nostrils directed downward, a narrow space between; often with internal cheek pouches; tail never prehensile, ischial tuberosities on buttocks with calloused, exposed skin. *Nasalis*, proboscis monkey, in Borneo; *Semnopithecus*, langur, in India, includes sacred hanuman of the Hindus; *Colobus*, in Africa, hair long, black-and-white; *Cynocephalus*, baboons, mandrill, etc., head stout, dog-like, tail short, disposition savage; *Macacus*, macaques or rhesus monkeys, Asia (one species at Gibraltar), used as pets and in biological research.

SUPERFAMILY 3. HOMINOIDEA. ANTHROPOID APES and MAN. No tail or cheek pouches.

PONGIDAE. ANTHROPOID APES. *Hylobates*, gibbon, and *Siamanga*, siamang, southeastern Asia and Malay Archipelago, body slender, limbs long, height to 3 feet; chiefly arboreal, travel easily through trees, but walk slowly on ground, using only the feet; voice powerful, often used; diet omnivorous. *Pongo (Simia) satyrus*, orang-utan, Sumatra and Borneo, in swampy forests; skull high-topped, face flattish, brain man-like; to 54 inches tall; hair long, lax, and reddish, old males often with beard; lives in trees and constructs crude nests; diet of plant materials. *Gorilla gorilla* (Fig. 35-23), gorilla, West and east Central Africa, in forests; body and limbs heavy, males to 65 inches high and over 500 pounds in weight; hair and skin black; walks on soles of feet aided by knuckles of hands, with body inclined; lives chiefly on ground, in family groups; food of plant materials. *Pan (Anthropopithecus) troglodytes*, chimpanzee (Fig. 35-24), West Africa, in forests, to 54 inches tall, weight to 150 pounds; head rounded, ears large, forearms short, feeds on plant materials; resembles human beings more than other anthropoids.

HOMINIDAE. *Homo sapiens*, mankind (Chap. 36).

Order 5. †**Tillodontia.** Paleocene-Eocene.

Order 6. †**Taeniodonta.** Eocene.

Order 7. Edentata (Xenarthra). SLOTHS, etc. Teeth reduced to molars in anterior part of jaws and without enamel; Eocene to Recent.

Fig. 35-25. Captive three-toed sloths (*Bradypus*, Order EDENTATA). In nature they hang inverted by the long curved claws. The slope of hair is reversed from that of most mammals, to shed rain more effectively. (*Photo by T. I. Storer.*)

Myrmecophagidae. Anteaters. *Myrmecophagus*, in tropical America; head and snout elongate; tongue slender, protrusible, and sticky; no teeth; forefeet with stout curved claws used to open ant and termite nests; hair long.

Bradypodidae. Arboreal Sloths (Fig. 35-25). Molar teeth present, all feet with long curved claws by which sloth hangs upside down on tree branches; hair long, slopes dorsally; food of leaves, fruits, and birds. In tropical America. *Bradypus* (3-toed), *Choloepus* (2-toed).

Dasypodidae. Armadillos. Texas to South America, with dorsal horny protective shell over bony plates in the skin and commonly divided by transverse furrows of softer skin so that animal can curl up when disturbed. *Dasypus novemcincta*, nine-banded armadillo, southern Texas.

Order 8. Pholidota. Body covered by large overlapping horny plates with sparse hair between; no teeth, tongue slender and used to capture insects. *Manis*, pangolin or scaly anteater, Africa and southeastern Asia.

Order 9. Lagomorpha. Pikas, Hares, and Rabbits. Size moderate to small; toes with claws; tail stubby; incisors chisel-like, grow continually, $2/1 \times 2$ (2d upper incisor small, behind 1st); no canines; premolars 3/2; molars unrooted; total cheek teeth to 6/5, those of upper jaw wider; palate broad; jaw motion only lateral; elbow joint nonrotating; Eocene to Recent; more than 300 species and subspecies; food of leaves, stems, and bark.

Ochotonidae. Pikas or Conies (not Hyracoidea). *Ochotona*, California and Colorado to Alaska and Asia, at high altitudes; about 6 inches long, ears rounded, legs equal, tail vestigial; live about rock piles and gather plants for "winter hay."

Leporidae. Hares and Rabbits (Fig. 35-26). Ears long, hind legs long for jumping, feed on leaves and stems of plants. *Lepus americanus*, snowshoe hare (rabbit), turns white in winter;

Fig. 35-26. Order Lagomorpha. *Above.* Jack rabbit (*Lepus californicus*, a hare), living in open areas. *Below.* Cottontail (*Sylvilagus*), living about thickets. *Right.* Brush rabbit (*Sylvilagus*), native to the Pacific coast, inhabits dense brushy chaparral. (*From Storer, 1949*).

L. campestris, etc., "jack rabbit," arid western states; both surface dwellers, young fully haired when born; *Sylvilagus*, American cottontail, lives about thickets, digs burrows, young born naked and blind; *Oryctolagus cuniculus*, European gray rabbit, source of all domestic breeds, introduced and widespread in Australia and New Zealand.

Order 10. Rodentia. Rodents or Gnawing Mammals. Usually small; limbs usually with 5 toes and claws; incisors $1/1 \times 2$, exposed, chisel-like, and rootless, growing continually; no canines; a gap between incisors and cheek teeth; premolars 2/1 or fewer; molars 3/3 (rarely 2/2); upper and lower cheek teeth about equal-sized; palate narrow; jaw motion both fore-and-aft and lateral; elbow joint rotates; Eocene to Recent; world-wide, on all continents and many islands, from sea level to above 19,000 feet in Himalayas, from dry deserts to rain forests, some in swamps and fresh waters, none marine; includes majority of living mammals, more than 6,400 species and subspecies (2,156 of 3,622 mammals in North America, from Panama northward); size varies from mice only 2 inches long to capybara (*Hydrochoerus* of South America) 48 inches long, but few exceed 12 inches; food chiefly of leaves, stems, seeds, or roots, some partly or largely insectivorous; smaller species often abundant and with high reproductive potential; serve as staple food for many carnivorous mammals, birds, and reptiles.

SCIURIDAE. SQUIRRELS. Mostly diurnal, feed chiefly on seeds and nuts. *Sciurus*, tree squirrels (red, gray, fox, etc.) in forested regions, often sought by hunters; *Citellus*, ground squirrels, on open lands of western states, make burrows in ground, feed on seeds and grasses, some damage crops, and a few carry diseases transmissible to man; *Tamias, Eutamias*, chipmunks, about logs, brush, and rocks; *Marmota*, woodchuck, ground hog, or marmot, in meadowlands, feeds on grasses; *Glaucomys*, flying squirrel, with broad membranes along sides of body, in forests, nocturnal.

GEOMYIDAE. POCKET GOPHERS. With external fur-lined cheek pouches to carry food; strictly subterranean in self-constructed burrows; vegetarian; southern and western North America. *Geomys, Thomomys*.

HETEROMYIDAE. POUCHED MICE. With fur-lined cheek pouches; forage on surface of ground at night, chiefly on seeds; in arid southwestern North America. *Dipodomys*, kangaroo rat; *Perognathus*, pocket mouse.

MURIDAE. RATS and MICE. *Microtus*, meadow mice or voles, in grasslands; *Peromyscus*, white-footed or deer mice, widespread over North America; *Sigmodon*, cotton rats; *Neotoma*, wood rats or pack rats; *Ondatra zibethica*, muskrat (Fig. 35-27), in marshes, pelt valuable for fur. Also,

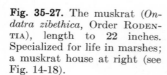
Fig. 35-27. The muskrat (*Ondatra zibethica*, Order RODENTIA), length to 22 inches. Specialized for life in marshes; a muskrat house at right (see Fig. 14-18).

Old World rats and house mouse, spread by commerce and shipping to all civilized countries, common in much of North America, damage property and food supplies and carry various diseases, including plague, typhus, and ratbite fever. *Rattus norvegicus*, Norway rat (Fig. 35-1); *R. rattus*, black and roof rats; *Mus musculus*, house mouse.

ERETHIZONTIDAE. PORCUPINES. *Erethizon*, protectively covered with slender, pointed quills (modified hairs); feeds on cambium of coniferous trees.

CASTORIDAE. BEAVERS. *Castor*, North America and Europe, formerly common; head and body to 30 inches long; tail flat, oval, scaly; body pelage soft, a desirable fur; builds dams and ponds, to float logs cut for food and to contain houses for shelter; feeds on cambium of aspen, willow, etc.

Order 11. Cetacea. WHALES, DOLPHINS, and PORPOISES. Size medium to very large; body usually spindle-shaped; head long, often pointed, joined directly to body (no neck region); some with a fleshy dorsal "fin"; fore limbs (flippers) broad and paddle-like, digits embedded, no claws; no hind limbs; tail long, ending in two broad transverse fleshy flukes, and notched in mid-line; teeth when present alike, lacking enamel; nostrils on top of head; ear openings minute; body surface smooth, no hairs save for few on muzzle; no skin glands except mammary and conjunctival glands; a thick layer of fat (blubber) under skin, affording insulation; stomach complex; Eocene to Recent; oceanic, over the world, always in water, die from crushing of internal organs if stranded on shore; whales may dive to 3,600 feet when wounded and can remain submerged many minutes without breathing; upon reaching surface, warm moist air is blown from lungs, forming a "spout" as condensed by cooler air over ocean; mate and bear young in the sea, sometimes in shallow water, young large at birth and suckled like those of other mammals (Fig. 35-28).

SUBORDER 1. †ARCHAEOCETI. ZEUGLODONTS. Eocene to Oligocene.

SUBORDER 2. ODONTOCETI. TOOTHED WHALES. Teeth 2 to 40 in various species; 1 nostril. *Physeter catodon*, sperm whale or cachalot, to 60 feet long, head squarish, about one-third total length; food of large squids and some fishes; a large "reservoir" in head yields sperm oil, a fine lubricant; ambergris, formed in the stomach, is used in perfume. *Delphinus delphis*, common dolphin, to 7 feet long, and *Phocaena phocaena*, harbor porpoise, both feed on fishes; 4 species of dolphins native to rivers in China, India, and South America; *Orcinus*, killer whale, most aggressive cetacean, attacks large fishes, seals, porpoises, and even big whales; *Monodon monoceros*, narwhal, of Arctic, with but 2 teeth, of which one in male is a slender twisted tusk 8 to 9 feet long—the "unicorn" of European fables.

Fig. 35-28. Humpback whale (*Megaptera novaeangliae*, Order CETACEA), length to 50 feet; female suckling young. (*After Scammon, Marine mammals, 1874.*)

SUBORDER 3. MYSTICETI. No teeth; 2 nostrils; mouth with many parallel horny plates of "whalebone" on sides of upper jaw, used to strain small animals from water; food chiefly of krill (*Euphasia*, a schizopod crustacean about 2 inches long, often enormously abundant). *Balaena*, "right" whale, no dorsal fin; *Balaenoptera* (*Sibbaldia*) *musculus*, blue whale, with fin on back and lengthwise grooves on throat; the largest living animal, to about 105 feet long, young 23 feet long at birth, 52 feet at weaning, and 74 to 77 feet long when sexually mature in second winter of life; *Rhachianectes glaucus*, California gray whale, of Pacific coast.

Order 12. Carnivora. CARNIVORES. Small to large; toes usually 5 (at least 4), all with claws; limbs mobile, radius and ulna, tibia and fibula, complete and separate; incisors small, usually 3/3; canines 1/1, as slender "fangs"; uterus bihorned; placenta zonary.

SUBORDER 1. †CREODONTA. Eocene to Miocene.

SUBORDER 2. FISSIPEDIA. DOGS, CATS, BEARS, etc. Toes separate; Eocene to Recent; native to all continents except Australia and New Zealand, where some now introduced; the flesh eaters or predatory animals, but some eat plant materials; pelts of many are valuable furs, hence the principal fur bearers.

CANIDAE. *Canis lupus*, wolf, once common in Europe and America, now far reduced; *C. latrans*, coyote or "prairie wolf," usually under 30 pounds in weight; open regions of arid West, but has spread to Alaska; eats rodents, deer, antelope, domestic sheep, and some plant material; *Canis*, domestic dogs, derived in Old World; *Urocyon*, gray fox, in brushlands; *Vulpes*, red fox, chiefly in woodlands, domesticated "black" and "silver" phases now reared commonly on fox farms.

PROCYONIDAE. *Procyon lotor*, raccoon (Fig. 35-15), over most of United States, especially near streams, tail black-and-white banded, food of frogs, fishes, crayfishes, fruits, a favorite for night hunting, pelts used for coats; *Ailurus*, panda, in Himalayas; *Ailuropoda*, giant panda, mountains of western China, feeds on bamboo.

URSIDAE. BEARS. *Thalarctos maritimus*, polar bear, Arctic regions to southern limit of pack ice, pelage white and dense, feet fully furred, teeth pointed, food of fishes and seals; *Euarctos americanus,* "black" bear (also with cinnamon or "brown" phase) in forests of North America from subarctic regions to Mexico, climbs readily, adults occasionally to 600 pounds, hibernates in midwinter, when young (8 to 9 inches long) are born, omnivorous; *Ursus arctos horribilis,* grizzly bear, size large, strictly terrestrial, originally in open and brushy areas, Mexico to Arctic and Great Plains to California, mostly exterminated; *U. a. gyas,* etc., brown bear of Alaska, strictly terrestrial, size huge, some possibly to 1,500 pounds, omnivorous.

MUSTELIDAE. FUR BEARERS. Many strictly predatory, eat birds, mammals, or fishes. *Martes,* marten, fisher, in woods; *Gulo,* wolverine; *Mustela,* weasels, stoats, and ferrets, live in burrows; *Taxidea,* badger, on open lands; *Mephitis,* striped skunk (Fig. 35-29), and *Spilogale,* spotted

Fig. 35-29. Striped skunk (*Mephitis,* Order CARNIVORA), length to 18 inches. (*After Pennsylvania Game News.*)

skunk, both with nauseating secretion (containing mercaptans), eat small vertebrates, insects, and fruits; *Mustela vison,* mink, and *Lutra,* river otter, both aquatic; *Enhydra lutris,* sea otter, California to Alaska, lives in ocean surf, feeds on marine invertebrates.

FELIDAE. CATS. *Felis leo,* lion, of Africa, and *F. tigris,* tiger, eastern Asia and India, both large and dangerous to man; *F. catus,* house cat, widely feral in United States; *F. cougar,* etc. mountain lion (also cougar, puma, or panther), the Americas, but exterminated in many eastern states; to about 7 feet and 160 pounds, food of deer, sometimes colts and livestock, practically never attacks man; *Lynx canadensis,* Canada lynx, and *L. rufus,* wildcat, both with short tails.

VIVERRIDAE. Mostly small, bodies slender. Africa and southern Asia. *Herpestes mungo,* common mongoose, of India, introduced into Jamaica and Hawaii; *Viverra,* civet, scent glands used to make perfume.

HYAENIDAE. HYENAS. *Hyaena,* Africa and southern Asia, dog-like in size and form, gray or brown with spots or stripes, jaws powerful, teeth large.

SUBORDER 3. PINNIPEDIA. SEALS and SEA LIONS. Size medium to large, males usually much larger than females; body spindle-shaped, limbs formed as flippers or paddles for swimming with toes included in webs; tail very short; Miocene to Recent; oceans and seacoasts, gregarious; food chiefly of fishes.

OTARIIDAE. EARED SEALS. *Eumetopias jubata (stelleri),* Steller sea lion, California to Alaska; *Zalophus californianus,* California sea lion, smaller, central California southward; *Callorhinus ursinus,* northern fur seal, adults haul out on rocky shores of Pribilof Islands in Bering Sea through summer, in assemblages (rookeries) numbering thousands. An adult male (bull) controls a group (harem) of about 60 females (cows); each female usually produces 1 young (pup), nurses it on land, later breeds; at end of summer entire population (herd) puts to sea for ensuing 9 months; summer population about 3,600,000, under supervision of United States government; more than 60,000 three-year males (bachelors) taken annually to provide sealskins of commerce.

ODOBENIDAE. WALRUSES. Skin thick, sparsely haired; 2 upper canine teeth form tusks up to 3 feet long, used to dig mollusks and crustaceans on sea bottom, and used by man as ivory. *Odobenus,* in Arctic, to 10 feet long.

Fig. 35-30. Harbor seal (*Phoca vitulina*, Order Carnivora, Suborder pinnipedia), length 5 feet; a marine, fish-eating "carnivore" of seacoasts. (*After Scammon*, 1874.)

Phocidae. Earless or Hair Seals. Hind feet cannot be turned forward, hence less agile on land. *Phoca vitulina*, harbor seal (Fig. 35-30), common on coasts and bays of North America and elsewhere; *Mirounga*, sea elephant, to 18 feet long, occasional off southern California.

Order 13. †Condylarthra. Paleocene to Eocene.

Order 14. †Litopterna. Paleocene to Pleistocene.

Order 15. †Notungulata. Paleocene to Pleistocene.

Order 16. †Astrapotheria. Paleocene to Miocene.

Order 17. Tubulidentata. Aard Varks. Body stout, somewhat pig-like, sparsely haired; ears and snout long; mouth tubular, with slender protrusible tongue; milk teeth numerous, permanent teeth fewer (no incisors or canines), unrooted, no enamel; toes 4, 5, with heavy claws; Pliocene to Recent. Africa. *Orycteropus* (2 or 4 species), nocturnal, digs open nests of ants and termites and captures the insects with its sticky tongue.

Order 18. †Pantodonta (Amblypoda). Paleocene to Eocene.

Order 19. †Dinocerata. Paleocene to Eocene.

Order 20. †Pyrotheria. Paleocene to Oligocene.

Order 21. Proboscidea. Elephants. Massive; head large, ears broad and flat, neck short, body huge, legs pillar-like, skin thick (pachyderm), loose, and sparsely haired; nose and upper lip a long flexible muscular proboscis, containing nasal passages, with nostrils at tip; 2 upper incisors elongated as tusks; each molar tooth with many transverse rows of enamel on exposed grinding surface, only 1 tooth (or 2) functional at a time in each side of jaw; feet club-like, toes 5, 3 (or 4)

Fig. 35-31. Indian elephant (*Elephas maximus*, Order Proboscidea). (*Photo by National Zoological Park.*)

each with small nail-like hoof, weight borne on elastic pad behind toes. Eocene to Recent. Africa and southeastern Asia; inhabit forests and tall grass; gregarious, in herds of 10 to 100; feed on trees, grasses, and bamboos, adults eating 600 to 700 pounds daily; gestation period about 20 months, young about 3 feet tall, weighing 200 pounds at birth; maximum recorded age about 50 years.

Elephantidae. *Elephas maximus* (*indica*), Indian elephant (Fig. 35-31), India to Ceylon and Borneo, tusks to 9 feet long; used for transport and in circuses; *Loxodonta africana*, African elephant, to over 10 feet in height, ears huge; tamed for transport in war and pageants by Carthaginians and Romans but not often since; *E. cyclotis*, pigmy elephant, West Africa, under 7 feet tall, ears small.

Order 22. †**Embrithopoda.** Oligocene.

Order 23. Hyracoidea. Coneys. Small; 4 toes on fore limb, 3 on hind; ears and tail short; incisors 1/2; no canines; Oligocene to Recent; Africa and Syria. One genus, *Procavia* (*Hyrax*), about 14 species; superficially like guinea pigs, but related to hoofed animals; inhabit rocky areas or trees.

Order 24. Sirenia. Manatees or "Sea Cows." Size large, body spindle-shaped; fore limbs paddle-like, no hind limbs, tail with lateral flukes, not notched; muzzle blunt, mouth small, lips fleshy; no external ears; teeth with enamel; hairs few, scattered; stomach complex; Paleocene to Recent; tropical and subtropical seas and rivers; herbivorous.

Three families, each of one genus: *Trichechus*, manatees, in warm rivers of Florida, West Indies, Brazil, and West Africa; *T. latirostris*, Florida manatee (Fig. 35-32), to 12 feet long;

Fig. 35-32. Manatee (*Trichechus*, Order Sirenia), length to 12 feet. (*After Goode*, 1884.)

Halicore dugong, dugong, Red Sea and coasts of India, New Guinea, and Australia; *Hydrodamalis* (*Rhytina*) *stelleri*, Steller sea cow, large, formerly on island shores in North Pacific Ocean, exterminated by hunters in 1854.

Order 25. Perissodactyla. Odd-toed Hoofed Mammals. Size large; legs long; foot with odd number of toes, each sheathed in cornified hoof, functional axis of leg passing through middle (3d) toe; stomach simple; Eocene to Recent; Eurasia, Africa, and tropical America.

Equidae. Horses, Asses, and Zebras. One functional digit and hoof on each leg (in Recent forms); inhabit open plains or deserts, diet of grass. *Equus caballus*, horse, man's principal means of transport and work for centuries, with 50 or 60 domestic races, from Shetland pony 42 inches high at shoulder and weighing scarcely 300 pounds to Shire and Percheron stallions 6 feet high, weighing to 2,600 pounds and over; *E. asinus*, ass, adapted to desert life, domesticated as donkey, or burro, for riding and transport; the mule is an F_1 hybrid of male ass ("jack") and female horse ("mare"), with stamina of ass and size of horse; *E. zebra*, zebra (Fig. 35-33), native to open lands of Africa, seldom domesticated.

Fig. 35-33. Zebra (*Equus zebra*, Order PERISSODACTYLA), about 48 inches high at shoulder; native to Africa. (*Photo by National Zoological Park.*)

TAPIRIDAE. TAPIRS. Toes 4 on front feet, 3 on hind feet; in tropical forests. *Tapirella*, 2 species, Central America and northern South America; *Tapirus*, Malay Peninsula, Borneo, and Sumatra.

RHINOCEROTIDAE. RHINOCEROSES. *Rhinoceros*, in woody or grassy areas in Africa south of Sahara Desert and in southeastern Asia; large and heavy-bodied, hide thick and armor-like; 1 or 2 median "horns" on snout; toes 3.

Order 26. Artiodactyla. EVEN-TOED HOOFED MAMMALS. Size various; legs usually long; 2 (rarely 4) functional toes on each foot, each usually sheathed in a cornified hoof; axis of leg between toes; many with antlers or horns on head; all but pigs with reduced dentition, a 4-compartment stomach, and ruminate, or "chew the cud"; Eocene to Recent; all continents except Australia. Size from antelope (dik-diks) no bigger than a hare to heavy buffalo and hippopotamus; some domesticated, others important as big game; 4 suborders and 22 families, 13 families extinct, and others all with fossil species.

SUBORDER 1. BUNODONTIA. PIGS and ALLIES. No horns or antlers, teeth 38 to 44, canines enlarged as curved tusks.

TAYASSUIDAE. PECCARIES or NEW WORLD PIGS. Patagonia to southern United States; *Pecari tajacu*, southern Texas and Arizona.

SUIDAE. OLD WORLD PIGS. Many in southern Asia; *Sus scrofa*, European wild boar, source of most domestic pigs; *Phacochoerus*, wart hog, in Africa.

HIPPOPOTAMIDAE. HIPPOPOTAMUSES ("horse of the river"). Body and legs very stout, skin heavy but scantily haired, adept at swimming, feeds on aquatic plants. *Hippopotamus amphibius*, Nile River and south in Africa (Fig. 35-34), to 12 feet long; *Choeropsis liberiensis*, pigmy hippopotamus, in West Africa, smaller.

Fig. 35-34. Hippopotamus (*Hippopotamus amphibius*, Order ARTIODACTYLA), length to 12 feet. (*Photo by National Zoological Park.*)

SUBORDER 2. PECORA. RUMINANTS. Teeth 32, canines small or none; stomach of 4 parts (Fig. 35-14).

CAMELIDAE. Feet soft and broad (no hoofs), 1 pair of upper incisors. *Camelus*, camel and dromedary (Fig. 35-35), in Africa and Asia, used for riding and transport; *Auchenia*, llama and alpaca, in western South America, provide transport, flesh, hides, and wool.

TRAGULIDAE. CHEVROTAINS or "MOUSE DEER." Intermediate between pigs, camels, and deer; some no bigger than large rodents. *Tragulus*, southeastern Asia.

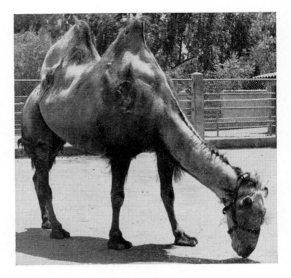

Fig. 35-35. Bactrian or two-humped camel (*Camelus bactrianus*, Order ARTIODACTYLA), of Asia. Most of the long dense winter hair has molted and the summer coat is short. (*Photo by T. I. Storer.*)

(Note: Next 4 families have 4 pairs of incisor-like teeth at front of lower jaw, none in upper.)

CERVIDAE. DEER, etc. Head of male with pair of solid calcareous antlers, shed and grown anew each year; in Northern Hemisphere. *Rangifer*, reindeer and caribou, in northern regions, antlers in both sexes; *Alces alces americanus*, moose, Canada, Maine, North Dakota, and Yellowstone Park, adult male (bull) to 6 feet at shoulder and 900 to 1,400 pounds in weight, enters water, feeds on aquatic plants; *Cervus canadensis*, American elk (wapiti), formerly over much of United States except deserts, now restricted, males to 5 feet high and 500 pounds; *C. elaphus*, European red deer; *Odocoileus*, American deer, males of larger races to 42 inches high and 300 pounds in weight: *O. virginianus*, white-tailed deer, Atlantic coast to eastern Oregon; *O. hemionus*, black- and mule-tailed deer, western North America (Fig. 35-8).

GIRAFFIDAE. GIRAFFES, etc. Africa. Neck and legs very long. *Giraffa camelopardalis*, giraffe, 18 to 20 feet tall, head with 3 to 5 skin-covered "horns"; browses on foliage of mimosa and other trees; *Ocapia*, okapi, smaller, neck shorter.

Fig. 35-36. American bison or buffalo (*Bison bison*, Order ARTIODACTYLA), in full winter coat. (*Photo by National Zoological Park.*)

ANTILOCAPRIDAE. One species, *Antilocapra americana*, prong-horned antelope (Fig. 35-8), on treeless plains and deserts from Great Plains to California, now reduced and mostly on reservations; adults 36 inches high, weight to 125 pounds; both sexes with pair of permanent bony horn cores on head, on which compressed black horns with lateral prongs grow and are shed annually.

BOVIDAE. HOLLOW-HORNED RUMINANTS. Horns hollow, paired, unbranched, composed of keratin, growing slowly and continuously from base, over bony cores on frontal bones, usually in both sexes, larger in males; over 35 genera in Northern Hemisphere, southeastern Asia and Africa. *Ovis canadensis* (and others), mountain sheep, or bighorn (Fig. 35-8), Mexico, Rocky Mountains, and California to Alaska, on rugged mountains; males (rams) to 40 inches high and 300 pounds, with horns to 40 inches long; *Oreamos americanus* (*montanus*), mountain goat, Idaho and Washington to Alaska, coat long, shaggy, and white, horns short, black; *Bison bison* (Fig. 35-36), American buffalo or bison, formerly Texas and Great Plains to southern Canada, with hump over shoulder and long crinkly hair on fore parts; adult bulls to 70 inches high and 1,800 pounds but cows smaller; millions formerly on flat lands but slaughtered for meat and hides, now few on reservations and in parks; *Bison bonasus*, European wisent, nearly extinct; domestic cattle, sheep, and goats (par. 35-28); *Bibos* (*Bos*) *gaurus*, gaur, India and Burma; *Bibos sondiacus*, banteng, southeastern Asia, Borneo, and Java; *Bubalus bubalis*, water buffalo or carabao, native of India, widely domesticated, Italy to Pacific islands. *Ovibos moschatus*, musk ox, on treeless Arctic lands from Hudson Bay to 83°N., to 52 inches high and over 500 pounds; African antelopes, many species of various sizes.

REFERENCES

The *Journal of Mammalogy* (quarterly, since 1919, published by the American Society of Mammalogists) is the principal periodical. Museums, universities, etc., publish state lists or books on mammals. The U.S. Departments of Agriculture and the Interior have many circulars and bulletins on the economic and other relations of mammals. The *North American Fauna* (60 numbers, issued by the U.S. Biological Survey; now U.S. Fish and Wildlife Service) includes accounts of mammals of various states and regions. Information on game and fur bearers may be found in books on hunting, shooting, and trapping.

AUDUBON, JOHN JAMES, and J. BACHMAN. 1851–1854. The quadrupeds of North America. 3 vols. New York, V. G. Audubon. 155 pls. and text. First issued (1845–1848) as "The Viviparous Quadrupeds of North America" in 3 folio vols. containing 150 plates and a separate text (1846–1853) of 3 quarto vols.; combined as "The Quadrupeds . . . " of 3 royal octavo vols. The first elaborate work on mammals of North America.

BOURLIÈRE, FRANÇOIS. 1954. The natural history of mammals. New York, Alfred A. Knopf, Inc. xxi + 363 + xi pp., 24 pls., 97 figs.

BURT, W. H., and R. P. GROSSENHEIDER. 1952. A field guide to the mammals [north of Mexico]. Boston, Houghton Mifflin Co. xii + 200 pp., many figs. (some colored) and maps.

EADIE, W. R. 1954. Animal [mammal] control in field, farm, and forest. New York, The Macmillan Co. viii + 257 pp. Habits, economic status, and control methods of North American species.

FLOWER, W. H., and R. LYDEKKER. 1891. An introduction to the study of mammals living and extinct. London, A. & C. Black, Ltd. xvi + 763 pp., 357 figs.

GRASSÉ, PIERRE-P. (editor). 1955. Mammifères. *In* Traité de zoologie. Paris, Masson et Cie. Vol. 17 (2 pts.), 2,300 pp., 2,106 figs.

HAMILTON, W. J., JR. 1939. American mammals: their lives, habits, and economic relations. New York, McGraw-Hill Book Co., Inc. xii + 434 pp., 92 illus.

———. 1943. The mammals of eastern United States. Ithaca, N.Y., Comstock Publishing Associates, Inc. 432 pp., 183 figs.

HENDERSON, J., and E. L. CRAIG. 1932. Economic mammalogy. Springfield, Ill., Charles C Thomas. x + 397 pp. Much detailed information and many references.

MILLER, G. S., JR., and REMINGTON KELLOGG. 1955. List of North American recent mammals. *U.S. National Museum Bulletin* 205. xii + 954 pp. Scientific name and geographic range of each species and subspecies.

PALMER, R. S. 1954. The mammal guide . . . North America north of Mexico. New York, Doubleday & Co., Inc. 384 pp., 40 col. pls., 37 figs., 145 maps. Identification, biology, and economic status.

SETON, E. T. 1925–1928. Lives of game animals. New York, Doubleday & Co., Inc. 4 vols., illus. Extensive account of hoofed mammals, carnivores, and some rodents.

SIMPSON, G. G. 1945. The principles of classification and a classification of mammals. *American Museum of Natural History Bulletin* 85. xvi + 350 pp. Technical; both fossil and Recent groups down to genera.

WEBER, MAX. 1927. Die Saügetiere. Einführung in die Anatomie und Systematik der recenten und fossilen Mammalia. 2d ed. Jena, Germany, Gustav Fischer Verlagsbuchhandlung. xxxix + 1,342 pp., 886 figs. Detailed, modern; vol. 1, anatomy; vol. 2, systematic review of genera, mentioning many species.

36 MANKIND

36-1. Man's place in nature. The place of man, *Homo sapiens*, in the realm of living things has long been a topic of great interest. Primitive races have myths that imply human origin from animals, or inanimate materials, or other sources. To other peoples, man is the creation of a supernatural power. Biologists view the origin and position of man objectively, using knowledge of the structure and physiology of the human body, its embryonic development, and the historic, prehistoric, and fossil records of mankind on earth. On this basis, the human species belongs in turn to the following groups:

1. Animal Kingdom, in requiring complex organic food, etc.
2. Phylum CHORDATA in having a notochord and gill arches and pouches during embryonic development and a dorsal brain and nerve cord throughout life.
3. Group CRANIATA (vertebrates) in having a cranium and segmented spinal column.
4. Class MAMMALIA in having hair and mammary glands.
5. Order PRIMATES in having 4 generalized limbs each with 5 digits bearing nails.
6. Superfamily HOMINOIDEA in lacking cheek pouches and a tail.
7. Family HOMINIDAE (as distinguished from the Family PONGIDAE, or anthropoid apes) in the possession of many features, including:
   a. Brain with far greater functional ability and of larger size (minimum human, 1,000 cc.; maximum gorilla, 650 cc.); brain case larger than face.
   b. Face flatter and more vertical, brow ridges reduced, lower jaw less protruding, teeth more evenly sized.
   c. Hair long and of continuous growth on head, but sparse and short on body.
   d. Hands more generalized, thumbs better developed; leg 30 per cent longer than arm, and straight; big toe not opposable to other toes.
   e. Skeleton and soft parts of different configuration and proportions.

The human species habitually walks erect on two feet, is terrestrial in habits, highly gregarious, and omnivorous in diet, and commonly uses cooked food. By contrast, the anthropoid apes (gorilla, chimpanzee, orang-utan, gibbon) are semierect in posture, literally "four-handed," chiefly tree dwellers, slightly gregarious, and fruit eaters. The human species is also notable for its extreme variability in many small structural features as compared with other animal species.

Mankind surpasses all other living organisms in many functional abilities such as (1) the construction and use of tools, (2) modification of the environment to his own advantage, (3) possession of articulate speech and language, (4) organization of a complex social life, and (5) formation of mental and abstract concepts. These are possible by reason of having generalized hands, but more importantly by the superior development of the human brain as to size, structure, and functional capacity. By use of articulate speech, language, writing, and records, mankind is able to assemble and transmit accumulated knowledge to succeeding generations. Material, social, cultural, and ethical advances have thus resulted. In all other animals, transmission of abilities between generations is limited to such instincts and reflexes as are fixed by heredity.

STRUCTURE AND PHYSIOLOGY

36-2. Size. Normal human adults are 56 to 78 inches tall, although occasional midgets are only 18 to 36 inches high and exceptional giants (due to excessive pituitary function) grow to 9 feet. Native races vary in average height from 51 inches (African pygmies) to 72 inches (Patagonian and Australian natives). Peoples lacking suitable food or living in extreme climates tend to be small, but active races in temperate lands and with better food are taller. Recent generations in the United States show a definite increase in average height, due to improved nutrition and more healthful living. Daughters of alumnae in several colleges average 1.1 to 1.5 inches taller than their mothers; and native-born children of immigrants average taller than their parents. In most races the males are taller than the females; American men average 68 inches and the women 64 inches.

The weight varies with race, sex, height, and age; white males average about 150 pounds and females 140 pounds. Exceptional fat (obese) persons have weighed 700 pounds or more, and occasional individuals of average height weigh scarcely 50 pounds. Increase in weight after maturity is usually due to accumulation of fat.

36-3. Body covering.[1] Human skin is thin and delicate, except for calluses (functional adaptations) on the palms of "horny-handed sons of toil" and on the soles, especially among barefoot natives. The skin coloration results from the presence of blood capillaries containing red cells (with hemoglobin) in the dermis and also of pigment, including melanin (black) and carotene (yellow). The white, yellow, brown, and black races differ as to the amounts of melanin pigment in the skin. Blonds of the white race

---

[1] Many features of human structure and physiology are described in Chaps. 4 to 10, and some aspects of human heredity in Chap. 12.

have less melanin than brunets, and women usually less than men. The yellow tinge of the palms, soles, and eyelids is ascribed to carotene. Pigmentation is commonly more pronounced in races exposed to severe sunlight. The tanning or darkening of the skin in white persons is a defensive mechanism against undue amounts of ultraviolet radiation.

The human skin (Fig. 4-1) differs from that of most mammals in having sweat glands that produce watery perspiration, containing some salts and excretory products. Evaporation of perspiration aids in cooling and regulating the body temperature.

36-4. Hair. Human hair is mammalian as to structure and manner of growth but differs (1) in being long or dense chiefly on the head; (2) in amount, distribution, and form at various ages of an individual; (3) between the sexes as to amount and length; and (4) in amount and structure between races of men.

Long hair of continuous growth on the scalp is a distinctive human characteristic. The eyebrows and eyelids (lashes), external ear canals, and nostrils all bear specialized hairs. The body elsewhere has a scant covering, and the lips, soles, palms, outer (extensor) surface on the terminal segment of each finger, and parts of the genitalia are hairless.

The human fetus at about the twentieth week is covered with fine soft hair (lanugo) which is lost at or before birth. The newborn usually has dark scalp hair that later may change color. Body hair is scant during childhood but begins to grow at puberty (14± years), especially in the armpits (axillae) and in the pubic region. As boys become men, the beard and chest hairs grow out. Dense facial hair is characteristic of males after puberty; but women have varying small amounts, and there are occasional "bearded ladies."

Further changes occur later in life, when the hair gradually becomes gray and then white through failure of the hair papillae to produce pigment—but no one's hair ever "turns white overnight," despite popular belief. The head hair usually becomes sparse with advancing

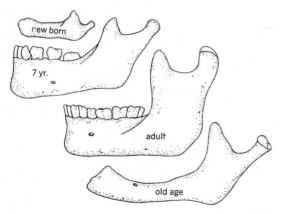

Fig. 36-1. Change in outline and relative shape of the human mandible with age. (*Altered from Heitzmann.*)

years, and definite patterns then develop, leading to graying of the scalp and beard and, on men, to baldness. These are probably hereditary changes, although pathological ones also occur; baldness is probably transmitted by females, but not evidenced by them. Some of the patterns are gray hair on the temples, a dark patch on top of the scalp, a bald spot on the crown or above each eye, a completely bald crown, a dark beard with white patch on each cheek, or a gray beard with black moustache. Curiously enough, for each type of human hair pattern, one or another occurs in some species of lower primate!

Racial differences in human hair are exemplified by the straight black hair of Orientals and American Indians, the kinky hair of Negroes, and the yellowish hair of Scandinavians. In cross section, the hair varies from nearly round in Mongolians to elliptical in kinky-haired Hottentots.

All human hairs are replaced at intervals, those of the eyebrows and eyelashes every few months and scalp hairs at from a few months to 4 or 5 years. There is evidence of slight "spring" and "autumn" molts in human beings. The scalp includes about 100,000 hairs.

36-5. Skeleton and teeth. The human cranium is a rounded bony box, lacking the sagittal crest of many other mammals. The occipital condyles are ventral rather than posterior, in keeping with the upright posture, the brain case is larger, the nasal region is short, and the lower jaw is U-shaped rather than V-shaped. The skull increases in size until about seven years and again at puberty, and final closure of the sutures may be delayed until old age. Other notable features of the human skeleton are the absence of caudal (tail) vertebrae and the complete and generalized skeleton of the limbs, hands, and feet.

The human teeth are less conspicuously differentiated than in other mammals and of nearly equal height. The first or deciduous (milk) teeth number 20, and the permanent or adult dentition includes 28 to 32, depending on how many of the third molars (wisdom teeth)

TABLE 36-1. Approximate Age for Eruption and Loss of Teeth in Human Beings

	Incisors		Canines	Premolars		Molars		
	Central	Lateral		1st	2d	1st	2d	3d
Deciduous teeth								
Erupted (months).....	6–8	7–9	17–18	14–15	18–24	None present		
Shed (years).........	7	8	10	10	11–12			
Permanent teeth								
Erupted (years):								
Upper.............	7–8	7–8	12–13	8–11	11–12	6–7	12–14	17–20
Lower	7–8	8–9	12–13	10–11	11–12	6–7	14–16	16–20

appear, these being irregular as to time and manner of eruption (Table 36-1).

36-6. Muscular system. The 500 or more muscles of the human body are much like those of other mammals. The names for muscles that were first applied by early anatomists to the human subject serve in the main for mammals as well, with minor differences as to origin, insertion, and size. Most of the peculiarities of human muscles relate to the upright posture, the support of the body and walking on the "hind" limbs, and to the greater flexibility of the arms, hands, and fingers. Of especial interest are the facial muscles (Fig. 36-2) that make possible the expression of pleasure, anger, and other emotional states. Man and the primates have the greatest development of these muscles; a few carnivores, such as the cat, may indicate pleasure and anger, but in all vertebrates below the mammals the face is a rigid mask.

36-7. Internal organs. In the abdominal cavity the organs are supported by mesenteries attached to the posterior wall, and a large sheet called the greater omentum hangs apron-like between the intestines and the inner front wall of the abdomen. It is composed of four layers of peritoneum and contains deposits of fat, serving to cushion the internal organs and protect them against loss of heat.

36-8. Nervous system. The human brain (Fig. 10-7) is notable for proportionately large size and great development of the cerebral hemispheres (gray matter) which have a much convoluted surface and are spread so as to cover completely the other parts of the brain.

The average human brain weighs about 1,250 (women) to 1,350 grams (men), and the volume is around 1,500 cc. Brain size and mental ability are not closely correlated, although the brains of people of distinction tend to be somewhat larger; two extremes were Baron Georges Cuvier (1,830 grams) and Anatole France (1,190 grams). The human brain far surpasses that of other animals in proportionate size as well as functional development. Thus a dog, gorilla,

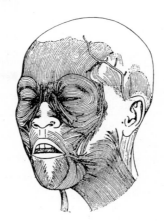

Fig. 36-2. The facial muscles of man. (*After Hube* 1930.)

and man of about equal weights have brains of 135, 430, and 1,350 grams, respectively.

NATURAL HISTORY

36-9. Distribution. Man inhabits a wider geographic range than any other animal, from the Arctic ice to islands beyond the southern continents, from sea level to over 20,000 feet in some mountain regions, and from moist tropical jungles to the driest of deserts. The local races in these various habitats differ as to stature, configuration, and coloration, in mode of life, foods and shelters utilized, and in social organization and customs. The white race thrives best in north temperate regions and does not persist in many tropic localities without renewed immigration.

36-10. Numbers. The total human population of the earth is unknown. Estimates for some earlier times (by Pearl and Gould) were, in millions of persons: A.D. 1650—453; 1750—550; 1820—814; 1880—1,341; 1900—1,520. Recent estimates (by United Nations) are: 1920—1,810; 1940—2,250; 1954—2,652 million. World population is currently estimated to be increasing at the rate of 37 million annually. The six fold increase in the past three centuries can be attributed to improved agricultural practices, better nutrition, and latterly to public-health measures. Decreased infant and juvenile mor-

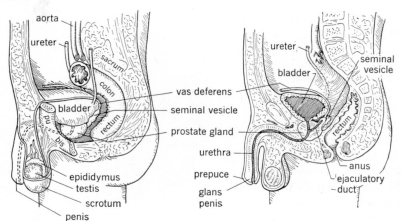

Fig. 36-3. The male urogenital system. *Left.* In perspective. *Right.* Median section.

tality combined with medical care have made for increase in many lands.

The ultimate human population of any region depends upon the fertility of the soil and also, in arid regions, upon the availability of water for irrigation. Human populations in Asia Minor, North Africa, and parts of the United States have decreased because of depletion of soil fertility, loss of top soil by erosion, and increasing aridity.

36-11. Factors regulating human populations. Man surpasses animals in being able to control his environment in some degree, by (1) *food production* (agriculture) and *food storage* (warehouses, canning, refrigeration) against seasonal shortage and deterioration; (2) improved *shelter* for adults and offspring against unfavorable weather and against enemies (housing, flood protection, police protection, national defense); (3) *destruction of animal enemies* (wolves, rats and mice, household insects); (4) *reducing competition* from other animals (fencing crops and livestock; shooting, trapping, or poisoning species that attack his food, crops, and domesticated livestock); and (5) *control of diseases* that attack human beings (sanitation, immunization). By these means, modern man in civilized countries has increased in numbers over the population possible for primitive natives.

Human beings are reduced in numbers by several agencies, some being comparable to those affecting wild animals; these include: (1) *food shortage* or famine due to crop failure,

as from unfavorable weather, especially in densely populated lands such as China and India where food reserves are scant or unequally distributed; malnutrition (improper diet) may lead to physical impairment with greater susceptibility to disease and death; (2) *inadequate shelter,* especially during the cold of winter outside the tropics; (3) *calamities in nature,* including floods, hurricanes, volcanic eruptions, etc.; (4) *enemies,* such as large predatory mammals (lion, tiger) and poisonous snakes, which cause many deaths in less civilized regions; (5) *warfare,* a form of competition between races or nations for land, natural resources, trade routes, or other desired features of human environment; war and slavery have long been major factors in depopulation; and (6) *disease,* uncontrolled as among primitive peoples, the result of neglect as is common among "civilized" peoples, or uncontrollable as with epidemic influenza; probably the largest single factor in reducing populations.

Where many diseases are under control by public-health measures in civilized countries, fewer individuals die in childhood or early life from disease. Proportionately more die from diseases of later life or from old age (senility). Explosions, fire, earthquake, shipwreck, and transportation accidents cause many deaths in modern civilizations.

36-12. Reproduction. During childhood the features relating to sex are usually undeveloped. When an individual reaches about 14 (10 to 17)

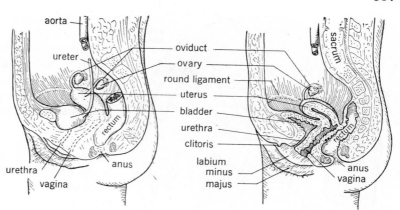

Fig. 36-4. The female urogenital system. *Left.* In perspective. *Right.* Median section.

years of age, conspicuous changes take place that lead toward sexual maturity and the ability to reproduce. This time is known as **puberty.** There then appear gradually the characteristics that differentiate the sexes. With males the beard and body hair begin growth, the shoulders broaden, the voice becomes deeper-pitched, and more attention is paid to the opposite sex. In females the mammary glands and hips enlarge, subcutaneous fat is deposited, the reproductive tract begins a series of cyclic changes, and the attentions of young men become of interest.

Healthy females from puberty onward experience a recurrent discharge of blood, mucus, and epithelial cells from the lining of the uterus, termed **menstruation** (L. *menses,* months); on the average, this occurs every 28 days (1 lunar month) and lasts 4 or 5 days. Menstruation is regulated by endocrine secretions (especially from the corpus luteum of the ovary) and prepares the uterus for implantation of an ovum. It usually ceases during pregnancy and lactation and stops if the ovaries are removed. Menstruation gradually stops at about age forty-five to fifty, and its cessation (the menopause) marks the end of reproductive ability. This "change of life" is a time of physiological and emotional distress for many women. There is no comparable cycle in the male.

Each ovary in a female child contains perhaps 50,000 immature ova, all of which disappear before puberty. New ova are then developed from the germinal epithelium covering the ovary, and one (occasionally more) is released

to pass down the oviduct some days after each menstruation, possibly 400 ova in all during the life of an average woman.

Exceptional human females only eight or nine years old have borne children, but there is usually a time after menstruation begins (the menarche), termed "adolescent sterility," before pregnancy occurs in any considerable percentage of young women. In the white race of north temperate latitudes, first children are common only at about age twenty. The time at which a young male becomes capable of procreation varies with individuals, and the same is true as to cessation of potency, as some men of advanced age have become fathers.

If, as a result of sexual union, an ovum in a female is fertilized, it becomes implanted in the mucosa of the uterus, begins embryonic development, and is surrounded by embryonic membranes. Shortly a placenta develops whereby the maternal and embryonic circulations are brought close together for transfer of nutrients, respiration, and removal of wastes (Fig. 36-5). The human embryo normally requires about 280 (243 to 298) days from conception to birth. In the vast majority of cases a single infant is produced. Twins occur about once in 88 births, triplets once in 7,600, and quadruplets once in 670,000; some families produce a greater percentage of twins. About 50 instances of quintuplets are known, but only exceptionally do all survive. The average infant weighs about 7 pounds (3,250 grams) at birth but may be from less than 5 to 13 pounds or more.

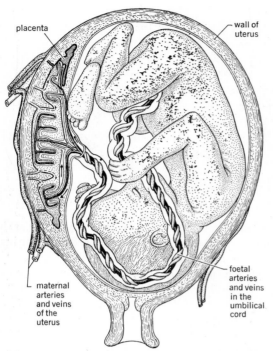

placenta

wall of uterus

maternal arteries and veins of the uterus

foetal arteries and veins in the umbilical cord

Fig. 36-5. Section of the human uterus with a fetus connected by the umbilical cord to the placenta; maternal blood circulation indicated by broken arrows, embryonic circulation by solid arrows. (*Adapted from Ahlfeld and Spanner.*)

The sex ratio at birth is about 105 to 106 males per 100 females, and even more disproportionate before birth. A higher mortality rate occurs in males, before birth and during the early years of life, so that from about age forty to eighty the females decidedly outnumber the males.

36-13. Growth. The human individual has the longest period of development after birth of any living creature, and its growth curve (age to weight) differs both quantitatively and qualitatively from that of other animals, except the chimpanzee (Figs. 36-6, 36-7). Five stages are recognized in mankind: (1) *prenatal,* 9 months; (2) *infantile,* birth to 10 months; (3) *early childhood,* 10 months to 4 or 5 years; (4) *juvenile,* 4 or 5 to about 14 years, the time of puberty; and (5) *adolescent* plus postadolescent, 14 to 20 or 22 years. There is accelerated growth in the prenatal and puberty periods, but retarda-

tion in the juvenile and postadolescent stages. Little or no living tissue is added after the latter; any subsequent increase in weight is due chiefly to the addition of fat, dehydration of tissues, and further mineralization of bone. The long juvenile period, about 10 years, is a most distinctive human characteristic not approached by any other animal.

36-14. Length of life. The extreme limit of life is the *life span,* which is about 100 years for mankind, the longest-lived animal. Accounts of persons living 900 years are purely legendary, and reports of those living well over a century must be carefully authenticated. Reports of extreme age among Indians and Negroes are often unsupported by documentary records. The human life span has not changed materially within historic times, since the average age at death of 52 eminent Greeks and Romans of antiquity was 67 years, a figure close to that of similar persons today. The Biblical "threescore years and ten" thus remains a fairly good approximation.

The *mean length of life* is the average number of years lived by all persons born at a given period. This is least among primitive and tropical native populations. In white populations of the North Temperate region, it has increased during the twentieth century, with improved sanitation, control of communicable diseases, corrective surgery, and bettered nutrition. For white persons in the United States the average in 1900 was 47.6 years; in 1920, 54.9 years; in 1936, 60.18 for males and 64.36 for females; in 1940, 64.2 years; and in 1954, 67.4 for males and 73.6 for females. The effect of increased mean length of life has been a general aging of the population. Thus the persons aged 65 and over represented about 4 per cent of the population of the United States in 1900, 6 per cent in 1935, and 8 per cent in 1950.

In ancient Egypt and Rome the *average expectation of life* during the first 5 years was never over 30 years, whereas in the United States in 1954 for age 20 it was 50.3 for boys and 55.9 for girls. This results from great reductions in infant mortality and the other factors just mentioned.

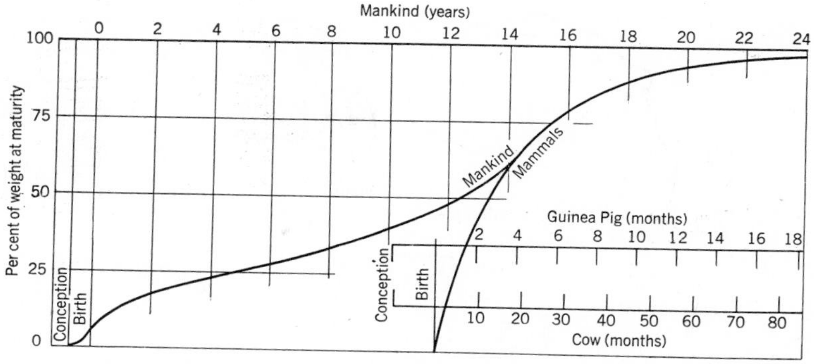

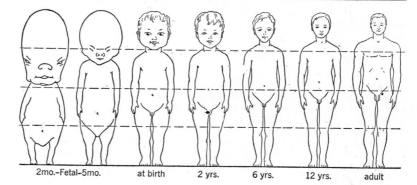

Fig. 36-6. Comparison of growth curve for weight in mankind and mammals (guinea pig and cow). (*After Brody,* 1927.)

Fig. 36-7. Changes in proportions of the human body with age. (*After Stratz.*)

2mo.–Fetal–5mo.   at birth   2 yrs.   6 yrs.   12 yrs.   adult

HISTORY OF MANKIND

36-15. The fossil record. An understanding of the gradual evolution of mankind from prehuman ancestry has been obtained in the last century since the significance of fossils has been recognized. The available evidence points to derivation of existing races from stocks dating back to early Pleistocene time and those in turn from earlier primates. The story is a continuous one, but for convenience it may be divided into (1) the fossil record, from bones, especially skulls and teeth, always rare and usually fragmentary; (2) the prehistoric record (Recent, to about 5000 B.C. but before the invention of writing) based on tools, weapons, and other evidence from places of habitation; and (3) the historic record (about 5000 B.C. in Egypt and later elsewhere), from the earliest accounts usually carved upon stone (Fig. 13-17).

The earliest known fossil primates (*Notharctus*) are small and found in the basal Eocene

of North America and Europe. The first apes (*Propliopithecus*) with a reduced muzzle and somewhat enlarged brain case are in the Oligocene. Anthropoid stocks branched widely during the long Miocene and Pliocene epochs, some leading toward the modern gorilla and chimpanzee, others showing prehuman features in the jaws and molar teeth. *Dryopithecus* of Europe and India is close to the point of divergence of the two lines. The subsequent record of human ancestry rests upon the following forms (Fig. 36-8).[1]

JAVA APE MAN, *Pithecanthropus erectus.* Mid-Pleistocene from near Trinil, Java. Skullcap, portion of mandible, femur, and 3 teeth, 1891; 4 more femurs, 1931; cranium and mandible with 4 teeth, 1937; 4 skulls in all up to 1945. Skull low-vaulted with heavy brow ridges, estimated cranial capacity (brain volume) about 750 to 900 cc.; imprint of brain on interior of skullcap suggests extremely primitive human status, possibly with power of speech; femur somewhat curved, suggesting only semierect posture. No associated stone implements.

[1] The "Piltdown man," first reported in 1908 from Sussex, England, subsequently proved to be a fake!

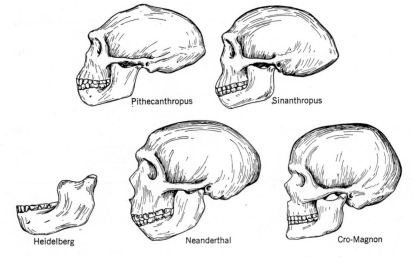

Pithecanthropus   Sinanthropus

Heidelberg   Neanderthal   Cro-Magnon

Fig. 36-8. Skulls of prehistoric species and races of mankind; all but the Cro-Magnon are restored in varying amount. (*After various authors.*)

PEKING MAN, *Sinanthropus pekinensis*. Mid-Pleistocene near Peking (Peiping), China. One tooth, 1903; many others, broken mandibles, and 15 skulls or fragments up to 1943. Crania small, low-vaulted, brow ridges well developed, capacity 915 to 1,220 cc.; imprint of brain suggests better development for motor control of speech, but "thinking area" deficient. With numerous crude chipped flake tools, seemingly some of deer antler and bone, and definite evidence of use of fire.

HEIDELBERG MAN, *Homo heidelbergensis*. Second (or first) warm interglacial period of mid-Pleistocene. Mauer (near Heidelberg), Germany. One complete mandible with teeth, 1907. Stronger and more massive than that of any living people. Teeth robust, jaw muscles evidently powerful, chin not prominent; form intermediate between simian and human, possibly ancestral to Neanderthal man. No associated implements.

NEANDERTHAL MAN, *Homo neanderthalensis*. Pleistocene, 3d and 4th warm interglacial periods. Crimea to Germany, France, and Spain; also central Asia (southeast of Aral Sea). First found ?1700; again at Gibraltar, 1848; described from Neanderthal Valley near Düsseldorf, Germany, 1861; others subsequently totaling over 100 individuals, in caves and rock shelters. Cranium flattened and elongate, also widened laterally and bulging at back; forehead sloping, brow ridges heavy but arched, cranial capacity 1,300 to 1,600 cc. Impressions of brain convolutions on interior simpler than in modern man. Face large and prominent, jaws protruding (prognathous); lower molars large and deep-bodied. Posture slightly stooping, head and neck inclined forward, as suggested by slight curvature of femur and vertebral column, attachments for heavy neck muscles, and more posterior position of foramen magnum in skull; males 63 to 65 inches high. Remains found in debris and in definite burials in floors of caves and rock shelters, often associated with chipped stone tools and weapons (Mousterian culture) and evidence of fire. Estimated age 100,000 years.

RHODESIAN MAN, *Homo rhodesiensis*. Probably Pleistocene. In cave at Broken Hill, Rhodesia, South Africa.

One skull, 1921. Cranium compressed, orbits huge, with most massive brow ridges, capacity about 1,280 cc. Upper jaw and palate "gigantic," but teeth distinctly of human character. Nondescript stone implements and quantities of broken animal bones (?food relics) in the debris-filled cave with the skull, may relate either to this or another race.

CRO-MAGNON MAN, *Homo sapiens fossilis*. Close of Glacial period onward. Many specimens since 1864; caves of northwest Italy and France to Czechoslovakia and Poland. Related races in Africa. Cranium high, face broad and upright, cranial capacity 1,590 cc.; males to 70 inches high, robust. Remains often in caves, with stone implements, sculpture, and paintings. Estimated age 40,000 B.C. and later.

MISCELLANEOUS REMAINS. (1) Java, 1938, skull fragments of *Pithecanthropus robustus*, heavier than *P. erectus*. (2) Java, 1941, part of a giant jaw (*Meganthropus paleojavanicus*) heavier than any known hominid relic. (3) From chemist shops in Hongkong, 1935-1939, possibly originally from caves in South China, three huge molars (*Gigantopithecus blacki*) of human type, each 5 or 6 times the bulk of those in modern man. (4) Java, 1933, 11 crania of *H. soloensis*, Ngandong man, in ancient lime-cemented gravels of the Solo River, near Ngandong, resemble but differ from *H. neanderthalensis*. Associated animal fossils indicate late Pleistocene, probably the 3d interglacial period. Rude bone implements and many split bones with the remains. (5) In caves of Palestine, near Mount Carmel (1925-1932), 13 individuals, including several complete skeletons. Characteristics of both Neanderthal and Cro-Magnon, but showing greater variability than in most modern communities; associated with Mousterian-like stone implements.

36-16. Modern man (*Homo sapiens*). After the Old Stone Age of the Neanderthal and Cro-Magnon, there were several transitional stocks in Europe (Mesolithic; Tardenoisian culture, with very small flints). New broad-headed people appeared, and narrow-headed races came from the south. Cro-Magnon art was replaced by conventional silhouettes of men and animals, tools were improved, some being fitted to the side of a shaft. Remains of huts and of flint implements include axes and adzes for felling trees and building boats. There are also millstones, implying agriculture with cereal production, and crude pottery.

The New Stone Age came with waning of the glacial cold. The people polished their chipped stone implements, made pottery, wove textiles, and were food producers rather than food gatherers. In Europe, they included narrow-headed light-statured Mediterraneans in the south, broad-headed stocky swarthy Alpines in the center and east, and narrow-headed tall blond Nordics to the north. These, by complex mixing and with some additional invasions from the east, have formed the present racial stocks of Europe. In turn, came the Ages of Copper, Bronze, and Iron; these led to the early civilizations recorded in history of the eastern Mediterranean and thence onward to the modern Age of Steel, steel alloys, and plastics.

The "cradle of the human race" was presumably in Central Asia, whence stocks radiated in various directions, especially westward; similar migrations occurred also in the historical period, which, geologically speaking, began but yesterday (Fig. 13-17).

36-17. Man in the Western Hemisphere.
The time and route of man's arrival in the Americas is not known. The native races of the Western Hemisphere differ less among themselves in physical features and language than do races in the Old World. American Indians are much like some stocks of eastern Asia. The route of entry was probably near Bering Strait between Asia and Alaska (see front end paper), where but 30 miles of shallow water separate the two continents and solid ice sometimes connects the two in winter.

Prehistoric American "camp sites" are gradually being found and studied. Some have charcoal (evidence of man's use of fire), some have

chipped flint tools, and some yield both. A few in the West contain bones indicating that early man was contemporaneous with and hunted certain large mammals now extinct here—elephant, camel, llama, horse, and dire wolf, besides bison. First he used the spear and followed game herds; later, in the Great Basin (about 6,000 years ago), increasing aridity caused a decrease in big mammals and he shifted to the bow and arrow for smaller game. The approximate age of some sites has been learned by carbon-14 dating. Some of the older are:

Gypsum Cave, Nevada, 10,500 years (with dung of ground sloth); Lubbock, Tex., nearly 9,000 years (burned bison bones and "Folsom" flints); Medicine Creek, Nebr., nearly 11,000 years; rock shelter near Prairie du Rocher, Ill., 11,000 years; cave at Sandia, N.M. (below the Folsom level), more than 20,000 years; and Tule Springs, Nev., more than 23,800 years (charcoal).

Man may have been in North America more than 25,000 years. Sites east of the Mississippi River are all dated at less than 5,000 years. In southern Chile, however, burned animal bones, associated with human bones, are dated at about 8,600 years.

Prior to the discovery of America by Columbus in 1492, two great human cultures had developed, one by the Incas in the Andes of South America, from Colombia to Chile, at elevations up to 13,000 feet, and another by the Mayas and Aztecs of Central America. The Maya chronology points to a beginning date in 3400 (or 3140) B.C. The Inca civilization dates from about A.D. 1000 but rests on other earlier cultures extending backward to before the Christian era. Of the old empire of the Mayas, chiefly in Guatemala and Honduras, the earliest dated relic is a stone from near Tres Zapotes, Veracruz, dated Nov. 4, 291 (or 31) B.C. That empire ended about A.D. 600, and a new one culminated in the tenth to twelfth centuries but declined before the Spanish explorers arrived. Those civilizations had none of the Old World domestic animals except the dog; their agricultural plants were exclusively of the New World and included maize or corn, beans, squashes, manoic or cassava, sweet potatoes, cotton, tobacco, peppers, tomatoes, and peanuts. Some tribes of

North American Indians practiced agriculture but were far less advanced culturally than either the Incas or Mayas.

36-18. Shelter. The anthropoid apes live in tropical forests and have little need of shelter; at most, they construct crude nests of leaves and branches in trees. Man, long a dweller on the earth both in and beyond the tropics, requires protection against weather and enemies. During the Glacial period, early man in Europe lived in natural caves. The hunting Plains Indians of North America, who followed buffalo and other game, made conical shelters (teepees) of animal skins supported on poles; nomad tribesmen with herds of sheep and goats in Central Asia today use crude tents of skins or woven fabrics of animal fibers. The oldest fixed human shelters in Egypt were of wattle (woven sticks); sun-dried (adobe) bricks later served as building material in the eastern Mediterranean countries. Rough (unhewn) stones were first employed to form burial tombs in the Mediterranean region, in England (at Stonehenge), and in Scandinavia. Dressed stone for building was possible only after the discovery of copper and development of copper tools for shaping the stone. Structures wholly of wood were built in forested regions as by the "Danube people," who moved up the river of that name about 2600 B.C.; such structures are made by Indians of the Pacific Northwest today. Man has continued to use all these materials, improving his work with wood and stone by invention and development of iron and steel tools. To these have been added, in the past century, concrete (with reinforcement) and iron or steel for construction.

36-19. Food. Mankind was first a *food gatherer,* either hunting wild animals for their flesh and marrow (using the hides for clothing), or gathering wild roots, seeds, and fruits, as did American Indians in recent centuries. Later he became a *food producer,* when flesh-producing animals were domesticated and reared in captivity and seeds were planted and tended to produce more abundant harvests. In Arizona these two stages existed side by side up to the last century with the hunting Apaches and the agricultural Papagos. Conscious food production is solely an attribute of the later human races. Man and the cultivated cereals now exist symbiotically, as neither can survive without the other. The only instinctive food producers among animals are a few specialized fungus-growing ants and termites and some ants that colonize aphids ("ant cows") on plants to afford honeydew for the ants.

Domestication of animals (pars. 34-23, 35-28) to furnish meat for food, hides for clothing, and fibers for weaving and for use in draft and transport began long ago. Stone Age people in Europe after the Glacial period may have had the first domestic dogs. Horses for transport and cattle for milk production are on record in Asia Minor about 3000 B.C. but probably were used earlier in western Asia. Sheep and asses were under domestication in early Egypt. The gathering and planting of seeds of native wheat and barley began long ago, as did the use of scythes of wood with blades of flint. Storage of harvested grain in pits lined with mud and straw began in Egypt between 5000 and 4000 B.C. Of all living creatures, only mankind uses cooked food.

36-20. Implements. Use of fire is associated with Peking man of the early Pleistocene; later its use spread to all peoples. The spear is known from Mesolithic time. A progressive series in the development of tools (artifacts) can be traced from association with the older human relics down to the present day (Fig. 36-9). At first, stones of convenient size and shape (eoliths) probably were selected as tools. Then crude implements of flint were formed through flaking off chips by striking with another stone (percussion method of Paleolithic time, the Early Stone Age). The wedge-shaped fist ax was one of the earliest tools thus produced. Next the flints were shaped more accurately through flaking off bits by pressure with a piece of deer antler (pressure method of the later Paleolithic). Still later, such implements were smoothed by grinding on some abrasive stone (polished implements of the Neolithic or New Stone Age).

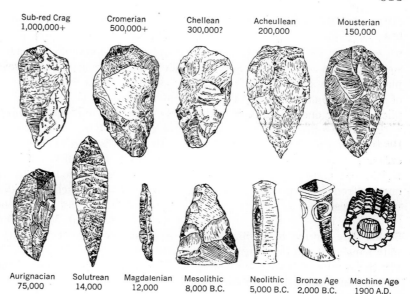

Sub-red Crag 1,000,000+   Cromerian 500,000+   Chellean 300,000?   Acheullean 200,000   Mousterian 150,000

Aurignacian 75,000   Solutrean 14,000   Magdalenian 12,000   Mesolithic 8,000 B.C.   Neolithic 5,000 B.C.   Bronze Age 2,000 B.C.   Machine Age 1900 A.D.

Fig. 36-9. Evolution of cutting tools used by mankind. Names are of the successive human "cultures" recognized by anthropologists, and figures are estimated age in years, B.C. (*After Fairchild and Hart, 1929.*)

Meanwhile, some prehistoric races made awls, needles, and fishhooks of bone, antler, or mollusk shell. Finally, copper was discovered and smelted into metallic form by the use of fire (about 3000 B.C. in eastern Europe and 2000 B.C. in the west). By heating and hammering, it became possible to fashion tools suited to special tasks. Then small amounts of tin (from Bohemia, before 2000 B.C.) were added to the copper to make bronze, an alloy of lower melting point yet of superior hardness and better suited to making edge tools (about 1800 B.C. in Europe). In turn, there followed the recovery of iron by smelting (Roman times), and much later the production of steel by adding a trace of carbon to the iron. The special alloys of steel and other metals in the twentieth century are but a further development of this ancient practice.

Other early inventions of fundamental significance in the social development of mankind were (1) drawing as first practiced on cave walls by Paleolithic man in France and Spain; (2) pictorial records (hieroglyphics) leading to phonetic signs and writing (Egypt, about 3500 B.C.); (3) baking of clay to make pottery; and (4) clay tablets and then papyrus sheets on which written records were preserved. In the realm of mechanics, the wheel for carts and much later for machines and the arch in stone construction were great advances, as were the boat and sail for water transport. Development of counting and computation systems led to means for calculating the movements of heavenly bodies, determination of the length of the year, the size of the earth, etc., and slowly paved the way for the scientific research and technical knowledge of the present day.

36-21. Energy supplies. During the past 500,000,000 years, a fraction of the organisms living on the earth have been entombed in sediments under conditions that preserved some of their energy content derived from solar radiation. Coal, oil shale, petroleum, and natural gas are rich in such "fossil energy."

Through his long early history, man existed almost entirely on energy from food, perhaps 2,000 gram-calories per day, with a little added heat later from wood fires. In the ecologic complex of nature he was merely one animal species competing for the immediate products of solar energy. Civilization is essentially a means for using more energy, both current and fossil supplies. It has upset the ecologic balance to favor increase in numbers of the human species at the expense of the environment, and this process goes on at an ever accelerated rate. Wind and water power are derived from replaceable resources, and wood for fuel may be strictly replaceable for a small human population. Beasts of burden are sustained by the recurrent supplies of solar energy in their plant foods, but with some eventual decline in fertility of crop lands. Modern civilization, however, with its enlarged human populations and complex activities, depends largely on "mining" the fossil energy from past geological periods, a nonrenewable resource.

36-22. The future of civilized man. Against man's ingenuity in devising machines to multiply the results of his labor must be set the effects of increasing the human population and of the consequent greater struggle for lands (territory) and the natural resources required in modern life. He has already modified his environment profoundly by agriculture, drainage, irrigation, deforestation, planting, and the construction of huge cities with manifold biological requirements. Unwise use of land has destroyed

the productive capacity of many areas by loss of topsoil through erosion by water and wind. Commerce and agriculture have spread pests, parasites, and diseases to countries and continents where these were not native and where they levy on the human population, its domestic animals, and its agriculture. Efforts to alleviate sickness and suffering by applying the discoveries of modern medicine have offset some of the effects of natural selection that formerly eliminated less fit individuals from the population. Such individuals now produce offspring that may in the end be less suited to natural survival. Modern knowledge of the mechanism of heredity and its application in the field of eugenics has as yet made only small beginnings to offset some of these adverse features. There have been great losses of good human germ plasm from the human race through wars, immigration, and other later developments of human "society." Man's future, as a species, will depend upon his ability to recognize and take account of these many changes when planning the manner of life for later generations.

CLASSIFICATION

All living human beings belong to the one highly variable species *Homo sapiens*. They are divided into numerous races, all able to produce fertile offspring when intercrossed. A *race* is a stock of common ancestry and physical characteristics, whereas a *people* is the assemblage of individuals occupying a given area; the two terms are not synonymous. The culture and languages of a people are of sociological interest but do not necessarily indicate its origin, as some habits and inventions are borrowed from other peoples and some are independently developed. The races have been blended by intermarriage following migrations, war, conquest, and slavery so that few are sharply distinct. Their number is uncertain, classification is difficult, and anthropologists disagree as to how they should be divided. Many races of Africa, Europe, and Asia are variously mixed, and no true races have yet resulted from settlement of the Americas by Europeans.

The characters most useful for classification are (1) hair form—straight, smooth, wavy, or curly, and its color and amount; (2) skin color—white, yellow, brown, red, or black; (3) form of head—the length to breadth ratio, long, medium, or short, and other measurements; (4) facial features—general shape, form of forehead, shape and proportions of nose, lips, and jaw, and color and form of eyes; and (5) stature or average height of mature adults— pigmy up to 58 inches; short to 62 inches; medium to 66 inches; tall to 68 inches; very tall, over 68 inches.

GROUP I. NEGROIDS. Hair woolly.

1. **Negrillo.** CONGO PIGMY. Skin yellow; hair very short, dark rusty-brown; stature 53½ to 56 inches. Equatorial Africa, in forests.

2. **Bushman.** Skin yellow, hair short, often knotted; buttocks enlarged (steatopygia) in females; stature to 60 inches. Africa, Kalahari Desert. Hottentot of southwest Africa is Bushman × Bantu.

3. **Negro.** Skin dark brown to black; head long; forehead often bulging; legs short; stature tall, to 68 inches. Guinea coast, formerly also tropical Africa.

4. **Nigritian.** NILE NEGRO. Skin very dark; head long; forehead retreating; legs long; stature to 70 inches or more. Upper Nile Valley and eastern Sudan.

5. **Bantu.** Skin black, chocolate, or yellow; head various; stature 66 to 68 inches. Central and South Africa.

6. **Negrito.** Skin dark to medium; head medium; hair short; stature short, 57 to 60 inches. Philippines, Malay Peninsula, Andaman Islands, Dutch New Guinea.

7. **Melanesian** (and **Papuan**). Skin chocolate; head long, high; face squarish or ovoid; stature to 63 inches. New Guinea to Fiji and Micronesian islands.

GROUP II. MONGOLOIDS. Hair usually straight, stiff, and black, sparse on face.

1. **Eskimo.** Skin yellow-brown; head long, face round and flat; stature to 66 inches. Arctic coasts of Greenland, North America, and northeastern Asia.

2. **Northwestern Amerind.** NORTH COAST INDIAN. Skin and hair lighter than Northern Amerind. Washington to southeastern Alaska.

3. **Northern Amerind.** RED INDIAN. Skin red to yellow; head long to short; face large, oval; nose straight or convex; tall, 66 to 69 inches. Plains and eastern woodlands of North America.

4. **Neoamerind.** Skin reddish to warm yellow; nose straight to concave; head short. Western North America, Central and South America.

5. **Patagonian** (Tehuelche). Skin deep brown; head short; face square; very tall, 68 to 72 inches. Southern South America.

6. **Ugrian** (Lapp, Tungus, Chukchi). Skin yellow-white to brown; hair black to reddish; head flat; cheekbones prominent. Arctic Eurasia, Scandinavia to Siberia.

7. **Northern Mongol.** Skin pale yellow to brown; face oval to round; stature medium to tall. North central Asia.

8. **Southern Mongol.** Skin pale yellow; face squarish; cheekbones prominent; stature medium. China and Indo-China.

9. **Indonesian** (Malaysian). Skin yellow to light brown; hair black; head long; face elliptic; cheekbones prominent; nose flat or concave; stature short. South China to East Indies.

10. **Polynesian.** Skin yellow to light brown; hair straight or wavy; head various; face elliptic, nose prominent; stature tall. Hawaii to New Zealand, and Samoa to Easter Island.

11. **Turko-Tatar.** Skin yellowish-white; head short, high; face long, oval; nose straight; lips thick. European Turkey across central Asia.

GROUP III. CAUCASOIDS. Hair smooth to wavy.

1. **Australian.** Skin dark brown; hair straight to wavy; head long, forehead retreating, jaw prominent; nose flat; stature medium. Australia.

2. **Ainu.** Skin light brown; hair black; face and body very hairy; head long; nose broad, concave; stature short. Islands of northeastern Asia.

3. **Dravidian.** Skin brownish-black; hair brownish-black, curly, abundant; head long; stature short. Southern India.

4. **Indo-Afghan.** Skin light brown; hair black, wavy; head and face long; eyes dark; stature tall. Northwestern India.

5. **Ethiopian** (Hamite). Skin reddish-brown to brown-black; hair brown to black; head long; face oval; stature medium. Northeastern Africa.

6. **Berber.** Skin usually pinkish-white; hair black to brown, curly; head long; face various; eyes brown; stature medium. Northwestern Africa.

7. **Armenoid** (Assyroid). Skin swarthy; hair abundant, dark brown, wavy; head short; nose narrow, hooked; eyes brown; stature medium. Northeast of Mediterranean Sea.

8. **Arab** (Semite). Skin tawny-white; hair black; face elliptical; nose convex; stature medium. Arabia.

9. **Ibero-insular** (Pyrenean). Skin tawny-white; hair black to dark brown; head long; nose straight; stature short. Northern Spain and Western Isles.

10. **Littoral** (Atlanto-) **Mediterranean.** Skin tawny-white; hair black; head medium; face long, oval; nose straight; stature medium. Western Ireland to Spain, the Mediterranean, and eastward.

11. **Alpine.** Skin pale-tawny; hair light brown to black; head short; stature medium to tall. Central France to Russia, Persia, and eastward.

12. **Nordic.** Skin reddish-white; hair yellow, reddish, or pale brown; head and face long; eyes blue or gray; nose and chin prominent; stature tall. Northern Europe.

REFERENCES

(See also titles in Chap. 14)

BAITSELL, G. A. 1950. Human biology. 2d ed. New York, McGraw-Hill Book Co., Inc. xvii + 730 pp., 361 figs.

BEALS, R. L., and HARRY HOIJER. 1953. An introduction to anthropology. New York, The Macmillan Co xxi + 658 pp., illus.

BOULE, MARCELLIN, et H. V. VALLOIS. 1952. Les hommes fossiles. 4th ed. Paris, Masson et Cie. x + 583 pp., 299 figs.

CHILDE, V. G. 1953. New light on the most ancient East. 4th ed. London, Praeger. 255 pp., illus.

CLARK, W. E. LeG. 1955. Fossil evidence for human evolution. Chicago, University of Chicago Press. 180 pp., illus.

COON, C. S. 1954. Story of man from the first human to primitive culture. New York, A. A. Knopf, Inc. xxii + 437 pp., illus.

HADDON, A. C. 1925. The races of men and their distribution. New York, The Macmillan Co. vii + 201 pp., 10 pls.

HOOTON, E. A. 1947. Up from the ape. Rev. ed. New York, The Macmillan Co. xxii + 788 pp., 41 pls., 68 figs.

HOWELLS, WILLIAM. 1954. Back of history; the story of our own origins. New York, Doubleday & Co. 384 pp., illus.

KROEBER, A. L. 1948. Anthropology. New York, Harcourt, Brace & Co., Inc. xii + 856 + xxxix pp., 42 figs.

LEAKEY, L. S. B. 1953. Adam's ancestors . . . Old Stone Age . . . and . . . man's . . . evolution. 4th ed. London, Methuen & Co., Ltd. 235 pp., illus.

SELLARDS, E. H. 1952. Early man in America: a study in prehistory. Austin, Tex., University of Texas Press. xvi + 211 pp., 55 figs.

GLOSSARY

L. = Latin; Gr. = Greek; dim. = diminutive.

Definitions of many other terms not included in the glossary can be found by referring to the index for the pages on which they occur in the text.

Pronunciation is indicated by the division of words into syllables (by hyphens) and by accent marks; on long words with two accented syllables both the primary (″) and the secondary (′) accents are shown.

Latin and Greek plurals are usually formed as follows: sing. *us*, to plural, *i* (nucleus, nuclei); *a* to *ae* (larva, larvae); *um* to *a* (cilium, cilia); *on* to *a* (pleuron, pleura); *is* to *es* (testis, testes); others are formed by adding *s* (digit, digits). A few exceptions are genus, genera; species, species; vas, vasa.

Ab-do′men. The major body division posterior to the thorax; behind the diaphragm in mammals. (L.)

Ab-duc′tor. A muscle that draws a part away from the axis of the body or a limb, or separates two parts. (L. *ab*, away + *duco*, lead)

Ab-o′ral. Opposite the mouth. (L. *ab*, from + *os*, mouth)

Ab-sorp′tion. The selective taking up of fluids or substances in solution by cells or absorbent vessels. (L. *ab*, from + *sorbeo*, suck in)

Ac-cli′ma-tize. To become habituated to an environment where not native. (L. *ad*, to + *clima*, climate)

Ac′i-nus. A small terminal sac in a lung or multicellular gland. (L., grape)

Acquired character. One that originates during the life of an individual owing to the environment or a functional cause.

Ad′ap-ta″tion. The fitness of a structure, function, or entire organism for a particular environment; the process of becoming so fitted. (L. *ad*, to + *apto*, fit)

Ad-duc′tor. A muscle that draws a part toward the median axis or that draws parts together. (L. *ad*, to + *duco*, lead)

Ad′i-pose. Pertaining to fat. (L. *adeps*, fat)

Ad-sorp′tion. Adhesion of an extremely thin layer of gas molecules, dissolved substance, or liquid to a solid surface. Compare Absorption. (L. *ad*, to + *sorbeo*, suck in)

A-e′ri-al. Living or occurring in air. (Gr. *aer*, air)

Aes′ti-vate. Passing the summer in a quiet, torpid condition. (L. *aestas*, summer)

Af′fer-ent. A vessel or structure leading to or toward a given position. (L. *ad*, to + *fero*, bear)

Al′bin-ism. Lack of pigment when normally present. (L. *albus*, white)

Al′i-men″ta-ry. Pertaining to food, digestion, or the digestive tract. (L. *alimentum*, food)

Al-lan′to-is. An embryonic membrane outpocketed from the hind-gut and serving for respiration and excretion in embryos of reptiles and birds; becomes part of umbilical cord and unites with the chorion to form the placenta in mammals. (Gr. *allas*, stem + *eidos*, form)

Al-le′le. The alternative forms of a gene, having the same locus in homologous chromosomes; also, the alternative forms of a Mendelian character. (Gr. *allelon*, of one another)

Al-le′lo-morph. See Allele.

Alternation of generations. See Metagenesis.

Al-ve′o-lus. A small cavity or pit; a tooth socket; a minute terminal air sac in a lung; a terminal unit in an alveolar gland; one droplet in an emulsion. (L., a small cavity)

Am′i-no acid. Any organic acid containing an amino radical (NH_2); amino acids are the "building stones" of proteins.

Am′ni-on. The innermost thin double membrane, filled with watery amniotic fluid, that encloses the developing embryo of a reptile, bird, or mammal. A similar single membrane around the insect embryo. (Gr., fetal membrane)

A-moe′boid. Putting forth pseudopodia like an amoeba or a white blood cell. (Gr. *amoibe*, change)

Am-phib′i-ous. Capable of living either on land or in water, as a frog. (Gr. *amphi*, on both sides + *bios*, life)

Am′phi-coe″lous. Concave at both ends, as the centrum of some vertebrae. (Gr. *amphi*, on both sides + *koilos*, hollow)

Am′phi-mix″is. Union of egg and sperm nuclei to form a zygote; mingling of the germ plasm of 2 individuals. (Gr. *amphi*, on both sides + *mix*)

Am-pul′la. A small bladder-like enlargement. (L., flask)

A-nab′o-lism. Constructive stages in metabolism, including digestion to assimilation. (Gr. *ana*, up + *ballo*, throw)

A-nal'o-gy. Similarity of external features or function, but not of structural plan or origin. (Gr. *analogia*, ratio)

An-am'nia. Vertebrates in which the embryo is not enclosed by an amnion during development—the cyclostomes, fishes, and amphibians. (Gr. *an*, without + *amnion*)

A-nas'to-mo"sis. A union or joining as of 2 or more arteries, veins, or other vessels. (Gr. *ana*, again + *stoma*, mouth)

An-ten'na. A sensory appendage, especially on arthropods, not concerned with light perception or sight. (Gr. *ana*, up + *teino*, stretch)

An-te'ri-or. The forward-moving or head end of an animal, or toward that end. Opposite of posterior. (L. *ante*, before)

An'ti-mere. One of the several similar or equivalent parts into which a radially symmetrical animal may be divided. (Gr. *anti*, against + *meros*, part)

A'nus. The posterior opening of the digestive tract. (L.)

A-or'ta. A large artery, especially one connected to the heart. (Gr. *aorte*, artery)

A-or'tic arch. A large artery arising from the heart in vertebrates; one of paired arteries connecting the ventral aorta and dorsal aorta in the region of the pharynx or gills.

Ap'i-cal. At the apex or top, as of a conical structure. (L.)

Ap-pend'age. A movable projecting part on a metazoan body having an active function. (L. *ad*, to + *pendeo*, hang)

A-quat'ic. Pertaining to or living in water. (L. *aqua*, water)

Ar-bor'e-al. Pertaining to or living in trees, as tree-inhabiting animals. (L. *arbor*, tree)

Ar-chen'ter-on. The primitive digestive cavity of a metazoan embryo, formed by gastrulation. (Gr. *archo*, rule + *enteron*, intestine)

Ar'ter-y. A tubular vessel conveying blood away from the heart. (Gr. *arteria*, artery)

A-sex'u-al. Not related to sex; not involving gametes or fusion of their nuclei.

As-sim'i-la"tion. Incorporation of digested nutriment, after absorption, into living protoplasm. (L. *ad*, to + *similis*, like)

A'sym-met"ri-cal. Without symmetry.

A'tri-um. An outer cavity or chamber, as an auricle of the heart. (L., court)

Au"di-to'ry. Pertaining to the organ or sense of hearing. (L. *audio*, hear)

Au'ri-cle. The receiving chamber (atrium) of the heart; also, the external pinna of the ear in mammals. (L.)

Au'to-some. Any ordinary chromosome as contrasted with a sex chromosome. (Gr. *autos*, self + *soma*, body)

Au-tot'o-my. The automatic "voluntary" breaking off of a part by an animal. (Gr. *autos*, self + *temno*, to cut)

Au'to-tro"phic nu-tri'tion. That process by which an organism manufactures its own food from inorganic compounds, as in a plant. (Gr. *autos*, self + *trepho*, to feed)

Ax'i-al skel'e-ton. That part of the vertebrate skeleton in the axis of the body—skull, vertebrae, ribs, and sternum.

Ax'is. A line of reference or one about which parts are arranged symmetrically. (L.)

Ax'on. Ax'one. The process of a nerve cell that conducts impulses away from the cell body of which it is a part. (Gr., *axon*, axle)

Bi-lat'er-al sym'me-try. Symmetry of a kind so that a body or part can be divided by one median plane into equivalent right and left halves, each a mirror image of the other.

Bi-ra'mous. Consisting of or possessing 2 branches, as a crustacean appendage. (L. *bis*, twice + *ramus*, branch)

Blad'der. A thin-walled sac, or bag, that contains fluid or gas.

Blas'to-disc. The germinal area on a large yolked egg that gives rise to the embryo. (Gr. *blastos*, germ + *diskos*, platter)

Blas'to-mere. One of the early cells formed by the division of an ovum. (Gr. *blastos*, germ + *meros*, part)

Blas'to-pore. The mouth-like opening of a gastrula. (Gr. *blastos*, germ + *poros*, passage)

Blas'tu-la. Early stage of an embryo, usually a hollow sphere of cells. (Gr. dim. of *blastos*, germ)

Blood. The fluid that circulates in the vascular system of many animals.

Bod'y cav'i-ty. The cavity between the body wall and internal organs of an animal. See Coelom.

Bra'chi-al. Referring to the fore limb or pectoral appendage. (L. *brachium*, forearm)

Bran'chi-al. Referring to gills. (Gr. *branchia*, gills)

Bron'chus. One of the larger divisions of the trachea conveying air into the lungs. (Gr. *bronchos*, windpipe)

Buc'cal. Pertaining to the mouth or cheek. (L. *bucca*, cheek)

Bud. Part of an animal that grows out to produce a new individual or new part.

Bur'sa. A pouch, or sac, as the bursa of a joint. (Gr., hide or skin)

Cae'cum; pl. cae'ca. A pouch or sac-like extension on the digestive tract, closed at the outer end. (L. *caecus*, blind)

Cal-car'e-ous. Composed of or containing calcium carbonate ($CaCO_3$); limy. [L. *calx* (*calc*), lime]

Cap'il-la-ry. A minute tubular vessel with walls composed of a single layer of thin cells, through which diffusion may occur; commonly in a connecting network between arteries and veins. (L. *capillus*, hair)

Car'di-ac. Pertaining to or near the heart. (Gr. *kardia*, heart)

Car-niv'o-rous. Eating or living on flesh or other animals. (L. *caro*, flesh + *voro*, eat)

Cas-tra'tion. Removal of the gonads, or sex glands, especially of the male. (L. *castro*, to castrate)

Ca-tab'o-lism. Destructive metabolism; the breaking down of more complex substances in protoplasm. (Gr. *kata*, down + *ballo*, throw)

Cau'dal. Pertaining to the tail, or posterior part of the body. (L. *cauda*, tail)

Cell. A small mass of living matter usually containing a nucleus or nuclear material; the fundamental unit of structure and function in plants and animals. (L. *cella*, small room)

Cel'lu-lar. Pertaining to or consisting of cells. (L. dim. of *cella*, small room)

Cel′lu-lose. The carbohydrate forming the wall of plant cells; also in the mantle of tunicates.

Cen′trum. The spool-like body of a vertebra, which bears various processes. (L., center)

Ce-phal′ic. Pertaining to or toward the head. (Gr. *kephale*, head)

Ceph′a-lo-tho″rax. A body division with the head and thorax combined. (Gr. *kephale*, head + *thorax*, chest)

Cer′e-bel″lum. The anterior development from the hind brain. (L. dim. of *cerebrum*, brain)

Cer′e-bral. Of or pertaining to the brain as a whole or the anterior dorsal (cerebral) hemisphere; also to the anterior brain-like nerve ganglia of various invertebrates. (L. *cerebrum*, brain)

Cer′e-brum. The dorsal anterior part of the vertebrate forebrain, consisting of 2 "hemispherical" masses. (L., brain)

Cer′vi-cal. Pertaining to a neck. (L. *cervix*, neck)

Chae′ta. See Seta.

Char′ac-ter, Characteristic. A distinguishing feature, trait, or property of an organism. (Gr.)

Che-lic′e-ra. One of the most anterior pair of appendages on arachnoids such as spiders, scorpions, and the king crab. (Gr. *chele*, claw + *keras*, horn)

Che′li-ped. The first thoracic appendage (pincer) of a crayfish and related crustaceans. (Gr. *chele*, claw + L. *pes*, foot)

Chi′tin. The nonprotein secreted in the exoskeleton on arthropods and some other animals. (Gr. *chiton*, tunic)

Chlo′ro-phyll. The green pigment of plants and certain animals, involved in photosynthesis. (Gr. *chloros*, green + *phyllon*, leaf)

Cho′a-na. A funnel, especially the opening between the nasal passages and pharynx (or mouth). (Gr.)

Chon′dro-cra″ni-um. The cartilaginous skull of cyclostomes and elasmobranchs; also that part of the embryonic skull in higher vertebrates first formed as cartilage. (Gr. *chondros*, cartilage + *kranion*, skull)

Chor-da′ta. The phylum of animals with a notochord, persistent or transient; includes the vertebrates, amphioxus, tunicates, and tongue worm; the chordates. (L. *chorda*, cord or string)

Cho′ri-on. The outer double membrane surrounding the embryo of a reptile, bird, or mammal; in mammals it unites with the allantois to form the placenta; the outer membrane of an insect egg. (Gr., membrane)

Chro′ma-tin. The easily and deeply staining substance in a cell nucleus, conspicuous in the nuclear network and in the chromosomes at mitosis. (Gr. *chroma*, color)

Chro″ma-to-phore′. A pigment cell containing granules or coloring material and responsible for color markings on many animals. (Gr. *chroma*, color + *phero*, bear)

Chro′mo-mere. An individual chromatin granule in a chromosome. (Gr. *chroma*, color + *meros*, part)

Chro′mo-somes. Characteristic deeply staining bodies, formed of chromatin in the nucleus of a cell during mitosis, that bear the genes or determiners of heredity. (Gr. *chroma*, color + *soma*, body)

Cil′i-um; pl. cil′i-a. A microscopic hair-like process attached to a free cell surface; usually numerous, often arranged in rows, and capable of vibration. (L., eyelid)

Cir′rus; pl. cir′ri. A small, slender, and usually flexible structure or appendage. (L., tuft of hair)

Cleav′age. The early stages in the division of an egg cell into many cells.

Clo-a′ca. The terminal portion of the digestive tract in many insects; the common passage from the digestive, excretory, and reproductive organs in various vertebrates. (L., sewer)

Co-coon′. A protective case or covering about a mass of eggs, a larva or pupa, or even an adult animal.

Coe-lom′. The body cavity or space between the body wall and internal organs in many metazoan animals, lined with peritoneum (mesoderm). (Gr., *koilos*, hollow)

Col′o-ny. A group of organisms of the same species living together; colonial. Opposite of solitary. (L. *colonus*, farmer)

Com-men′sal-ism. The association of 2 or more individuals of different species in which one kind or more is benefited and the others are not harmed. (L. *cum*, together + *mensa*, table)

Com-mu′ni-ty. A group of organisms of one or more species living together and related by environmental requirements. (L. *communis*, common)

Com-pressed′. Reduced in breadth; flattened laterally. (L. *cum*, together + *premo*, press)

Con-ver′gent. Approaching each other or tending toward a common point. (L. *cum*, together + *vergo*, incline)

Cop′u-la″tion. Sexual union. (L. *copulo*, join together)

Co′ri-um. The dermal portion of the skin beneath the epidermis. The dermis. (L., skin, hide)

Cor′ne-a. The outer transparent coat of an eye. (L. *corneus*, horny)

Cor′pus-cle. A small or minute structure, or a cell free or attached, as a blood corpuscle or bone corpuscle. (L. dim. of *corpus*, body)

Cor′tex. The outer or covering layer of a structure. (L., rind, bark)

Cra′ni-al. Of or pertaining to the skull or brain, as a cranial nerve. (Gr., *kranion*, skull)

Cra′ni-um. The skull, specifically the brain case. (Gr. *kranion*, skull)

Crop. A thin-walled and expanded portion of the digestive tract, primarily for food storage.

Cross fer′til-i-za″tion. Union of an egg cell from one individual with a sperm cell from another. Opposite of self-fertilization.

Cu-ta′ne-ous. Pertaining to the skin. (L. *cutis*, skin)

Cu′ti-cle. A thin noncellular external covering on an organism. (L. dim. of *cutis*, skin)

Cyst. A resistant protective covering formed about a protozoan or other small organism during unfavorable conditions or reproduction; a small sac or capsule. (Gr. *kystis*, bladder)

Cy′to-plasm. That part of a cell outside the nucleus and within the cell membrane. (Gr. *kytos*, hollow + *plasma*, form)

Cy′to-some. See Cytoplasm.

Def′e-cate. To discharge food residues (feces) through the anus. (L. *de*, from + *faex*, dung)

Den′drite. The process on a nerve cell that conducts impulses to the cell body; often branched. (Gr. *dendron*, tree)

De-pressed′. Flattened vertically, from above. (L. *de*, down + *premo*, press)

619

Der'mal. Pertaining to the skin, especially the inner connective-tissue layers of vertebrate skin. (Gr. *derma*, skin)

Der'mis. The deeper or "true" portion of the skin beneath the epidermis in a vertebrate, derived from mesoderm. (Gr. *derma*, skin)

Deu'to-plasm. Substance other than the nucleus and cytoplasm in a cell, especially yolk in an egg cell. (Gr. *deuteros*, second + *plasma*, form)

Di'a-phragm. A dividing membrane, as the diaphragm of the ear; the muscular partition between the thoracic and abdominal cavities in mammals. (Gr. *dia*, through + *phragma*, fence)

Di-ges'tion. The process of preparing food for absorption and assimilation. (L.)

Dig'it. A finger or toe; one of the terminal divisions of a limb in tetrapods. (L. *digitus*, finger)

Dig'i-ti-grade. Walking on the toes. (L. *digitus*, finger + *gradior*, to step)

Di-mor'phism. Existing under 2 distinct forms. (Gr. *di*, two + *morphe*, form)

Di-oe'cious. With the male and female organs in separate individuals. (Gr. *di*, two + *oikos*, house)

Dip'lo-blas"tic. Derived from 2 embryonic germ layers, ectoderm and endoderm. (Gr. *diplous*, double + *blastos*, germ)

Dip'loid. The dual or somatic number of chromosomes ($2n$), the normal number in all but the matured germ cells of any particular organism. (Gr. *diplous*, double + *eidos*, form)

Dis-sim'i-la"tion. The chemical disintegration of protoplasm, usually by oxidation, with release of energy; catabolism. (L. *dissimilis*, different)

Dis'tal. Away from the point of attachment or place of reference. (L. *disto*, stand apart)

Di-ur'nal. Pertaining to the daytime. (L. *dies*, day)

Di-ver'gent. Going farther apart; separating from a common source. (L. *di*, doubly + *vergo*, incline)

Dom'i-nant char'ac-ter. A character from one parent that manifests itself in offspring to the exclusion of a contrasted (recessive) character from the other parent. (L. *dominor*, rule)

Dor'sal. Toward or pertaining to the back, or upper surface. (L. *dorsum*, back)

Duct. A tube by which a liquid or other product of metabolism is conveyed, as of a secretion from a gland; usually opening on a surface or in a larger compartment. (L. *duco*, lead)

Duct'less gland. A gland that elaborates and secretes a hormone, or "internal secretion," directly into the blood stream; an endocrine gland.

E-col'o-gy. The relations of an organism to its environment. (Gr. *oikos*, home + *logos*, knowledge)

Ec'to-derm. The outer germ layer or cell layer of an early embryo. (Gr. *ektos*, outside + *derma*, skin)

Ec'to-par"a-site. One that lives on the exterior of its host. (Gr. *ektos*, outside + parasite)

Ef-fec'tor. A structure that transforms motor impulses into motor action. (L. *efficio*, effect, bring to pass)

Ef'fer-ent. A structure leading away from a given point of reference, as an efferent artery. (L. *ex*, out + *fero*, carry)

E-gest'. To discharge unabsorbed food or residues from the digestive tract. (L. *e*, out + *gero*, bear)

Egg. A germ cell produced by a functionally female organism; an ovum.

Em'bry-o. A newly forming young animal in the stages of development before hatching or birth. (Gr.)

Em'bry-og"e-ny. The process of development of the embryo. (Gr. *embryon* + *genesis*, generation)

Em'bry-on"ic mem'branes. Cellular membranes formed as part of an embryo during its development and necessary for its metabolism; the amnion, chorion and allantois of reptiles, birds, and mammals; some also in insects.

En-am'el. The dense whitish covering on teeth of vertebrates, the hardest substance produced by animal bodies.

En'do-crine. A ductless gland; also, its internal secretion or hormone, which is diffused into and carried by the blood stream. (Gr. *endon*, within + *krino*, separate)

En'do-derm (or **entoderm**). The layer or group of cells lining the primitive gut, or gastrocoel, in an early embryo, beginning in the gastrula stage. (Gr. *endon*, within + *derma*, skin)

En'do-par"a-site. One that lives within its host. (Gr. *endon*, within + parasite)

En'do-skel"e-ton. An internal supporting framework or structure. (Gr. *endon*, within + skeleton)

En'do-style. The ventral ciliated groove in the pharynx of tunicates, amphioxus, and larval lampreys, used in food getting; homologous with the thyroid gland of vertebrates. (Gr. *endon*, within + *stylos*, column)

En'do-the"li-um. Layer of simple squamous cells lining the inner surface of circulatory organs and other closed cavities. (Gr. *endon*, within + *thele*, nipple)

En'ter-on. The digestive cavity, especially that part lined by endoderm. (Gr., intestine)

Entoderm. See Endoderm.

En-vir'on-ment. The total of conditions surrounding an entire organism.

En'zyme. A substance produced by living cells that in minute amount causes specific chemical transformation such as hydrolysis, oxidation, or reduction but that is not used up in the process; a ferment or catalyst. (Gr. *en*, in + *zyme*, leaven)

Ep'i-der"mis. A layer of cells (sometimes stratified) covering an external surface; the ectodermal portion of the skin of most animals; secretes cuticle on some animals. (Gr. *epi*, upon + *derma*, skin)

Ep'i-did"y-mis. Structure containing the efferent tubules of the mammalian testis. (Gr. *epi*, upon + *didymos*, testicle)

E-piph'y-sis. The end or other external part of a bone that ossifies separately; also, the pineal body, a dorsal outgrowth on the diencephalon of the vertebrate brain. (Gr. *epi*, upon + *phyto*, to grow)

Ep'i-the"li-um. A layer (or layers) of cells covering a surface or lining a cavity. (Gr. *epi*, upon + *thele*, nipple)

E-ryth'ro-cyte. A red blood cell or corpuscle; characteristic of vertebrates. (Gr. *erythros*, red + *kytos*, hollow vessel)

E-soph'a-gus. That part of the digestive tract between the pharynx and stomach. (Gr.)

Eu-sta'chi-an tube. The passage between the pharynx and middle ear in land vertebrates. (Eustachio, an Italian anatomist)

620

E-vag'i-na"tion. An outpocketing from a hollow structure. (L. *e*, out, from + *vagina*, a sheath)

E'vo-lu"tion. The process by which living organisms have come to be what they are, structurally and functionally, complex forms being derived from simpler forms; hence, descent with modification. (L. *evolvo*, unroll, unfold)

Ex-cre'tion. Waste material resulting from metabolism and discharged from the body as useless; also the process of its elimination. Compare Secretion, and Feces. (L. *excerno*, separate, secrete)

Ex'o-skel"e-ton. An external supporting structure or covering. (Gr. *exo*, outside + skeleton)

F₁, F₂, etc. Abbreviations for 1st filial, 2d filial, etc., indicating the successive generations following crossbreeding.

Fac'tor. An agent or cause; in genetics, a specific germinal cause of a hereditary character; same as gene.

Fas'ci-a. A sheet of connective tissue covering an organ or attaching a muscle. (L., a band)

Fau'na. All the animal life in a given region or period of time.

Fe'ces. Excrement; unabsorbed or indigestible food residues discharged from the digestive tract as waste. (L., dregs)

Fer'til-i-za"tion. Union of two gametes (egg and sperm) to form a zygote and initiate the development of an embryo. (L. *fertil*, fruitful, from *fero*, to bear)

Fe'tus. The later stages of an embryo while within the egg or uterus. (L., offspring)

Fi'ber. A delicate thread-like part in a tissue. (L.)

Fi'bril. A small fiber. (L.)

Fin. An extension of the body on an aquatic animal used in locomotion or steering.

Fis'sion. Asexual reproduction by division into 2 or more parts, usually equivalent. (L. *findo*, split)

Fla-gel'lum. A long lash or thread-like extension capable of vibration; on flagellate protozoans and on collar cells of sponges. (L., little whip)

Flame cell. A type of hollow terminal excretory cell in certain invertebrates that contains a beating (flamelike) group of cilia.

Foetus. See Fetus.

Fol'li-cle. A minute cellular sac or covering. (L. dim. of *follis*, bag)

Food vac'u-ole. An intracellular digestive organelle.

Fo-ra'men. An opening or perforation through a bone, membrane, or partition. (L. *foro*, bore)

Fos'sil. Any relic of an organism buried in the earth or rocks by natural causes in past geologic time. (L. *fodio*, dig)

Free-liv'ing. Not attached or parasitic; capable of independent movement and existence. Compare Sessile.

Fron'tal. Of or pertaining to the front, or forehead; also, a plane or section parallel to the main body axis and at right angles to the sagittal plane. (L. *frons*, the brow)

Func'tion. The activity or action of any part of an organism. (L. *functio*, to perform)

Gam'ete. A mature reproductive or germ cell, either male (sperm) or female (ovum). (Gr. *gamos*, marriage)

Gam'e-to-gen"e-sis. The process of formation of mature germ cells, or gametes; maturation.

Gan'gli-on; pl. gan'gli-a. A group or concentration of nerve cell bodies, set apart, and acting as a center of nervous influence.

Gas'tro-coel. The primitive digestive cavity of a metazoan embryo, formed by gastrulation. (Gr. *gaster*, stomach + *koilos*, hollow)

Gas'tro-der"mis. Lining of the digestive cavity in coelenterates. (Gr. *gaster*, stomach + *derma*, skin)

Gas'tro-vas"cu-lar. Serving for both digestion and circulation.

Gas'tru-la. Early stage in embryonic development; an invaginated blastula. (Gr. *gaster*, stomach)

Gene. The unit of inheritance, which is transmitted from one generation to another in the gametes and controls the development of a character in the new individual; the factor, or hereditary determiner.

Gen'i-tal. Referring to reproductive organs or the process of generation. (L. *gigno*, beget)

Gen'o-type. The internal genetic or hereditary constitution of an organism without regard to its external appearance. Compare Phenotype. (Gr. *genos*, race + *typos*, impression, form)

Germ cell. A reproductive cell in a multicellular organism.

Germ lay'er. One of the (2 or 3) fundamental cell layers (ecto-, endo-, mesoderm) in an early embryo of a multicellular animal from which tissues and organs of the adult are formed.

Germ plasm. The material basis of inheritance; the gametes and the cells and tissues from which they form, considered as a unit.

Ger'min-al va'ri-a"tions. Those due to some modification in the germ cells.

Gill. An organ for aquatic respiration.

Giz'zard. A heavily muscled portion of the digestive tract.

Gland. An organ of secretion or excretion. (L. *glans*, acorn)

Glo-mer'u-lus. A small rounded clump of vessels; the knot of capillaries in a renal corpuscle. (L. dim. of *glomus*, ball)

Glot'tis. The opening from the pharynx into the trachea. (Gr. *glotta*, tongue)

Gly'co-gen. A carbohydrate (polysaccharid) stored in the muscles and liver; "animal starch." (Gr. *glykys*, sweet + *gen*, come into being)

Gon'ad. A reproductive organ (ovary, testis) in which gametes (ova or sperm) are produced. (Gr. *gonos*, generation, seed)

Gre-ga'ri-ous. Habitually living in groups, flocks, etc., of numerous individuals. (L. *grex*, herd)

Gy-nan'dro-morph. An individual in a dioecious species having one part of the body female and another part male in constitution. (Gr. *gyne*, woman + *aner*, man)

Hab'i-tat. The natural or usual dwelling place of an individual or group of organisms. (L. *habitus*, condition)

Hair. A slender filamentous growth on the skin of mammals and on the exposed surfaces of some arthropods.

Hap'loid. The single or halved number of chromosomes (n) as found in matured germ cells. (Gr. *haplous*, single + *eidos*, form)

Hem'al. Pertaining to the blood or the blood-vascular system. (Gr. *aima*, blood)

Hem'o-coel. Portion of a body cavity reduced in size

and functioning as part of a blood-vascular system. (Gr. *aima*, blood + *koilos*, cavity)

Hem'o-glo"bin. The coloring matter of red corpuscles in vertebrate blood and of blood plasma in some invertebrates; a protein containing iron that combines with and transports oxygen to the tissues. (Gr. *aima*, blood + globe)

He-pat'ic. Pertaining to the liver. (Gr. *hepar*, liver)

He-pat'ic por'tal sys'tem. A system of veins leading from the digestive tract to capillaries (sinusoids) in the liver of a vertebrate.

Her-biv'o-rous. Feeding only or chiefly on herbs, grasses, or other vegetable matter. (L. *herba*, grass + *voro*, devour)

He-red"i-tar'y. Passing by inheritance from one generation to another.

He-red'i-ty. The transmission of characters, physical and others, from parent to offspring; the tendency of offspring to resemble their parents. (L. *heres*, heir)

Her-maph'ro-dite. An animal with both male and female reproductive organs. (Gr. *Hermes* + *Aphrodite*)

Het'er-o-zy"gote. An individual produced by union of 2 germ cells that contain unlike genes for a given character, either both genes of an allelomorphic pair or 2 different genes of an allelomorphic series. Compare Homozygote. (Gr. *heteros*, another + *zygon*, yoke)

Hi'ber-nate. Passing the winter in an inactive or torpid condition. (L. *hiberno*, pass the winter)

Hol'o-blas"tic. Cleavage in which an entire egg cell divides. (Gr. *holos*, whole + *blastos*, germ)

Hol'o-phyt"ic nu-tri'tion. Nutrition involving photosynthesis of simple inorganic chemical substances, as in green plants and some flagellate protozoans. (Gr. *holos*, whole + *phyton*, plant)

Hol'o-zo"ic nu-tri'tion. Nutrition requiring complex organic foodstuffs, and characteristic of most animals. (Gr. *holos*, whole + *zoön*, animal)

Ho-mol'o-gous. Of like source in structure and embryonic development from primitive origin. (Gr. *homos*, same + *lego*, speak)

Ho-mol'o-gous chro'mo-somes. A pair of chromosomes having relatively similar structure and value, one from each parent. (Gr. *homologos*, agreeing)

Ho-mol'o-gy. Fundamental similarity; structural likeness of an organ or part in one kind of animal with the comparable unit in another resulting from descent from a common ancestry. Compare Analogy. (Gr.)

Ho'mo-zy"gote. An individual produced by union of 2 germ cells that contain like genes for a given character. Compare Heterozygote. (Gr. *homos*, like + *zygon*, yoke)

Hor'mone. A chemical regulator or coordinator secreted by cells or ductless glands and carried in the blood stream. See Endocrine. (Gr. *hormao*, urge on, spur)

Host. An organism that harbors another as a parasite. (L. *hospes*, entertainer)

Hy'a-line. Glassy or semitransparent. (Gr. *hyalos*, glass)

Hy'brid. The offspring of 2 parents that differ in 1 or more heritable characters; a heterozygote. (L. *hybrida*, mongrel)

Hy-per'tro-phy. Abnormal increase or overgrowth in the size of a part or organ. (Gr. *hyper*, over + *tropho*, nourish)

In-breed'. To mate related animals or plants.

In-gest'. To take food into a place of digestion. (L. *in* + *gero*, bear)

In-her'i-tance. The sum of all characters that are transmitted by the germ cells from generation to generation. (L. *in*, in + *heres*, heir)

In'stinct. An inherited type of action, invoked by a certain stimulus and often of complex nature, combining associated reflex acts and leading to a particular end.

In-teg'u-ment. An outer covering, especially the skin of a vertebrate and its derivatives. (L. *intego*, to cover)

In'ter-cel"lu-lar. Between or among cells.

In-tes'tine. That part of the digestive or alimentary canal between the stomach and anus (or cloaca). (L. *intus*, inside)

In'tra-cel"lu-lar. Within a cell or cells.

In-vag'i-na"tion. An inpocketing or folding in, as of the vegetal pole of a blastula to form the gastrula. (L. *in* + *vagina*, a sheath)

In-ver'te-brate. Any animal without a dorsal column of vertebrae; protozoans to amphioxus, inclusive.

Ir'ri-ta-bil"i-ty. The capacity of responding to stimuli. (L. *irrito*, excite)

Joint. A place of union between two separate bones or other hardened structures. (L. *junctus*, from *jungo*, to join)

La'bi-al. Pertaining to the lips.

La-mel'la. A thin sheet-like layer. (L. *lamina*, plate)

Lar'va. The early and usually active feeding stage of an animal, after the embryo, and unlike the adult. (L., mask)

Leu'co-cyte. A white blood cell or corpuscle. (Gr. *leukos*, white + *kytos*, hollow vessel)

Lim'y. Calcareous; containing calcium salts, especially $CaCO_3$.

Lin'gual. Pertaining to the tongue. (L., tongue)

Link'age. Inheritance of characters in groups, probably because their genes lie in the same chromosome.

Lip'oid. Of fatty nature. (Gr. *lipos*, fat)

Lo'pho-phore. A ridge about the mouth region bearing tentacles in some invertebrates. (Gr. *lophos*, crest + *phero*, bear)

Lu'men. The cavity in a gland, duct, vessel, or organ.

Lu'mi-nes"cence. Emission of light as a result of chemical reactions within cells. (L. *lumen*, light)

Lung. An organ for aerial respiration.

Lymph. Colorless blood fluid (without red blood cells) found among tissues and in lymph capillaries or vessels. (L. *lympha*, water)

Lym-phat'ic sys'tem. A system of delicate vessels in vertebrates that lead from spaces between tissues to large veins entering the heart; part of the circulatory system.

Lymph'o-cyte. A white blood cell with one large undivided and nongranular nucleus; present in blood and lymph vessels. (L. *lympha*, water + Gr. *kytos*, hollow vessel)

Man'di-ble. The lower jaw of a vertebrate; either jaw of an arthropod. (L. *mandibula*, jaw)

Ma-rine'. Pertaining to or inhabiting the sea, ocean, or other salt waters. (L. *mare*, sea)

Mat'u-ra"tion. Final stages in preparation of sex cells

for mating, with segregation of homologous chromosomes so that each cell or gamete contains half the usual (diploid) number.

Mei-o'sis. Nuclear changes in maturation.

Mem'brane. A thin soft sheet of cells or of material secreted by cells.

Mer'o-blas"tic. Cleavage of an egg in which only part of the protoplasm divides, leaving the yolk undivided; characteristic of eggs with much yolk. (Gr. *meros*, part + *blastos*, germ)

Mes'en-chyme. Part of the mesoderm in a vertebrate embryo that produces connective and circulatory tissues. (Gr. *mesos*, middle + *chyma*, fluid)

Mes'en-ter-y. The sheet of tissue that suspends organs in the body cavity and is continuous with the peritoneum lining that cavity. (Gr. *mesos*, middle + *enteron*, intestine)

Mes'o-derm. The embryonic cells or cell layers between ectoderm and endoderm. (Gr. *mesos*, middle + *derma*, skin)

Mes'o-gle"a. The gelatinous filling between the outer and inner cell layers of a two-layered animal such as a jellyfish. (Gr. *mesos*, middle + *gloios*, glutinous)

Me-tab'o-lism. The sum of the constructive and destructive processes (anabolism and catabolism), mainly chemical, that occur in living organisms. (Gr. *metabolos*, changeable)

Met'a-gen"e-sis. Alternation of sexual and asexual reproduction in the life cycle of certain animals; alternation of generations. (Gr. *meta*, after + *genesis*, origin)

Met'a-mere. Any one of a series of homologous parts in the body, as with annelids, arthropods, or chordates; a somite. (Gr. *meta*, after + *meros*, part)

Me-tam'er-ism. Segmental repetition of homologous parts (metameres).

Met'a-mor"pho-sis. Marked change in form from one stage of development to another, as of a larva to an adult. (Gr.)

Met'a-ne-phrid"i-um. A tubular excretory organ, the open inner end draining from the coelom and the outer discharging to the exterior, as in the earthworm. (Gr. *meta*, after + *nephros*, kidney)

Met'a-zo"a. Multicellular animals with cells usually arranged into tissues; includes all animals above the sponges. (Gr. *meta*, after + *zoön*, animal)

Mi'cron; pl. mi'cra. The unit of microscopic measurement, 1/1,000 of a millimeter; represented by μ (Greek letter mu). (Gr. *mikros*, small)

Mi-to'sis. Indirect cell division, characterized by the appearance of a fibrous spindle and a definite number of chromosomes, which split longitudinally to form 2 equal sets of daughter chromosomes; the latter diverge to opposite poles of the spindle to become parts of the 2 new nuclei. (Gr. *mitos*, thread)

Mo'lar. The posterior permanent teeth of a mammal. (L. *molo*, grind)

Molt. To cast off an outer covering such as cuticle, scales, feathers, or hair.

Mo-noe'cious. Having both male and female gonads in the same individual; hermaphroditic. (Gr. *monos*, single + *oikos*, house)

Mon'o-hy"brid. The offspring of parents differing in 1 character. (Gr. *monos*, single + L. *hybrida*, mongrel)

Mon'o-phy-let"ic. From a single known evolutionary derivation. (Gr. *monos*, single + *phyle*, tribe)

Mu'cous. Secreting mucus or similar sticky slimy substance, as by a mucous cell, gland, or membrane. (L.)

Mu-ta'tion. Abrupt and heritable modification of a character; also, the change in a gene responsible for it. (L. *mutatus*, changed)

Mu'tu-al-ism. Jointly beneficial association between individuals of 2 different species. (L. *mutuus*, exchanged)

My'o-mere. A muscle segment or somite. (Gr. *mys*, muscle + *meros*, part)

Na'ris; pl. na'res. The opening of the air passages, both internal and external, in the head of a vertebrate. (L., nostril)

Na'sal. Pertaining to the nose.

Nat'u-ral se-lec'tion. The elimination of less fit individuals in the struggle to live.

Ne-phrid'i-um. A tubular excretory organ found in mollusks, annelids, arthropods, and other invertebrates. (Gr. *nephros*, kidney)

Neph'ro-stome. The ciliated entrance from the coelomic cavity into a nephridium, or kidney tubule. (Gr. *nephros*, kidney + *stoma*, mouth)

Nerve. A bundle of nerve fibers lying outside the central nervous system.

Nerve cord. A compact cord, composed of neurons and usually with ganglia, forming part of a central nervous system.

Neu'ral. Pertaining to the nervous system. (Gr. *neuron*, nerve)

Neu'ron. A nerve cell with cytoplasmic extensions (dendrites, axon) over which nervous impulses pass.

Noc-tur'nal. Active at night. (L. *nocturnus*, nightly)

No'to-chord. The elastic cellular axial support formed ventral to the nerve cord in the early embryo of all chordates; later surrounded or supplanted by the vertebrae in most vertebrates. (Gr. *notos*, the back + *chorde*, string)

Nu-cle'o-lus. An oval mass within the nucleus of most cells; of uncertain function but disappears during mitosis. (L. dim. of *nucleus*)

Nu'cle-us. A differentiated structure of specialized protoplasm within a cell, refractile and with deeply staining chromatin, that controls metabolic activities; in cells of all organisms except bacteria. (L. dim. of *nux*, nut)

O-cel'lus. A small simple eye as on many invertebrates. (L. dim. of *oculus*, eye)

Oc'u-lar. Pertaining to the eye.

Ol-fac'to-ry. Pertaining to the sense of smell. (L. *olfacto*, smell)

Om-niv'o-rous. Eating all kinds of food; feeding upon both plants and animals. (L. *omnis*, all + *voro*, eat)

On-tog'e-ny. Development of the individual. (Gr. *on*, being + *gen*, become)

O'ö-sperm. A fertilized egg, a zygote. (Gr. *oön*, egg + *sperma*, seed)

O-per'cu-lum. The plate covering the gills of a bony fish; also, the plate serving to cover the opening of some snail shells. (L.)

Oph-thal'mic. Pertaining to the eye. (Gr. *ophthalmos*, eye)

O-pis'tho-coe"lous. Concave behind, as the centrum of

some vertebrae. (Gr. *opisthen*, behind + *koilos*, hollow)

Op'tic. Pertaining to the eye or sense of sight. (Gr. *optos*, seen)

O'ral. Pertaining to or near the mouth. (L. *os*, mouth)

Or'bit. The eye socket. (L. *orbis*, circle)

Or'gan. Any part of an animal performing some definite function; a group of cells or tissues acting as a unit for some special purpose. (Gr. *organon*, instrument)

Or-gan-elle'. A specialized part in a protozoan that performs some special function (like an organ in a metazoan). (Gr. dim. of *organon*, instrument)

Or'gan-ism. A single plant or animal; one that functions as a unit.

Os-mo'sis. Diffusion through a differentially permeable membrane. (Gr. *osmos*, pushing)

Os'ti-um; pl. **os'ti-a.** An opening to a passage, usually guarded by a valve or circular muscle. (L. *os*, mouth)

O'tic. Pertaining to the ear. (Gr. *otikos*, pertaining to the ear)

O'to-lith. A concretion of calcium salts in the inner ear of vertebrates or in the auditory organ of some invertebrates. (Gr. *otikos*, pertaining to the ear + *lithos*, stone)

O'va-ry. The organ in which the egg cells multiply and are nourished. (L. *ovum*, egg)

O'vi-duct. The tube by which eggs are conveyed from the ovary to the uterus or to the exterior. (L. *ovum*, egg + *duco*, lead)

O-vip'a-rous. Egg-laying; producing eggs that hatch outside the mother's body. (L. *ovum*, egg + *pario*, produce)

O'vo-vi-vip"a-rous. Producing eggs that are incubated and hatched within the parent's body, as with some fishes, reptiles, and invertebrates. (L. *ovum*, egg + *vivus*, alive + *pario*, produce)

O'vum. An egg, the sex cell of a female. (L.)

P. The first parental generation—parents of a given individual of the F_1 generation.

Palp (or **palpus**). A projecting part or appendage, often sensory, on the head or near the mouth in some invertebrates. (L. *palpo*, stroke)

Pa-pil'la. Any nipple-like structure, large or small. (L., nipple)

Par'a-site. An organism that lives on or in another more or less at the expense of the latter (the host). (Gr. *para*, beside + *sitos*, food)

Pa-ren'chy-ma. Soft cellular substance filling space between organs. (Gr. *para*, beside + *en*, in + *chyma*, fluid)

Par'the-no-gen"e-sis. Development of a new individual from an unfertilized egg, as in rotifers, plant lice, etc. (Gr. *parthenos*, virgin + *genesis*, origin)

Path'o-gen"ic. Causing or productive of disease. (Gr. *pathos*, suffering + *genesis*, origin)

Pec'to-ral. Pertaining to the upper thoracic region, or breast. (L. *pectoralis*, pertaining to the breast)

Pe-lag'ic. Pertaining to the open sea, away from the shore. (Gr. *pelagos*, open sea)

Pel'vic. Pertaining to the posterior girdle and paired appendages of vertebrates; the posterior abdominal region of a mammal. (L., a basin)

Pe'nis. The copulatory organ of a male for conveying sperm to the genital tract of a female. (L.)

Pen'ta-dac"tyl. Having 5 fingers, toes, or digits. (Gr. *pente*, five + *daktylos*, finger)

Per'i-car"di-um. The cavity enclosing the heart; also, the membranes lining the cavity and covering the heart. (Gr. *peri*, around + *kardia*, heart)

Pe-riph'er-al. To or toward the surface, away from the center. (Gr. *peri*, around + *phero*, to bear)

Per'i-stal"sis. Rhythmic involuntary muscular contractions passing along a hollow organ, especially of the digestive tract. (Gr. *peri*, around + *stalsis*, constriction)

Per'i-to-ne"um. The thin serous membrane (mesodermal) that lines the body cavity and covers the organs therein in many animals. (Gr. *peri*, around + *teino*, stretch)

Phag'o-cyte. A white blood cell that engulfs and digests bacteria and other foreign materials. (Gr. *phagein*, to eat + *kytos*, hollow vessel)

Phar'ynx. The region of the digestive tract between the mouth cavity and the esophagus; often muscular and sometimes with teeth in invertebrates; the gill region of many aquatic vertebrates. (Gr., throat)

Phe'no-type. The external appearance of an individual without regard to its genetic or hereditary constitution. Compare Genotype. (Gr. *phaino*, show + *typos*, impression, type)

Pho'to-syn"the-sis. The formation of carbohydrates from carbon dioxide and water by the chlorophyll in green plants or flagellate protozoans in the presence of light. (Gr. *phos*, light + *synthesis*, place together)

Phy-log'e-ny. The history (evolution) of a species or higher group. (Gr. *phylon*, race + *gen*, become)

Pig'ment. Coloring matter.

Pin'na. A wing or fin; also, the projecting part of the external ear in mammals. (L., feather)

Pla-cen'ta. The organ by which the fetus (embryo) of higher mammals is attached in the uterus of the mother and through which diffusible substances pass for the metabolism of the fetus. See Chorion. (L., flat cake)

Plan'ti-grade. Walking on the whole sole of the foot, as a man or bear. (L. *planta*, sole + *gradior*, walk)

Plas'ma. The fluid portion of blood or lymph. (Gr., a thing molded)

Pleu'ra. The membrane covering the lung and lining the inner wall of the thorax. (Gr., rib, side)

Pleu'ron. The lateral plate on either side of a somite in arthropods. (Gr., rib, side)

Plex'us. A network of interlaced nerves or blood vessels. (L., a plaiting)

Pol'y-mor"phism. Existence of individuals of more than one form in a species. (Gr. *poly*, many + *morphe*, form)

Pol'y-phy-let"ic. From more than one known evolutionary derivation. (Gr. *poly*, many + *phyle*, tribe)

Por'tal vein. One that divides into capillaries before reaching the heart. (L. *porta*, gate)

Pos-te'ri-or. The hinder part or toward the hinder (tail) end, away from the head. Opposite of anterior. (L., following)

Pred'a-tor. An animal that captures or preys upon other animals for its food. (L. *praeda*, booty)

Pre-hen'sile. Adapted for grasping or holding. (L. *prehendo*, seize)

Prim′i-tive. Not specialized; the early or beginning type or stage. (L. *primus*, first)

Pro-coe′lous. Concave in front, as the centrum in some vertebrae. (Gr. *pro*, before + *koilos*, hollow)

Proc′to-de″um. The ectoderm-lined terminal part of the digestive tract near the anus. (Gr. *proktos*, anus + *hodos*, a road)

Pro-tan′dry. Production of sperm and later of eggs by the same gonad. (Gr. *protos*, first + *aner*, man)

Pro′to-ne-phrid″i-um. An invertebrate excretory organ (of 1 or more cells), the inner end closed and either branched or with one terminal cell (solenocyte). (Gr. *protos*, first + *nephros*, kidney)

Pro′to-plasm. Living substance; the complex colloidal physicochemical system that constitutes living matter and is the viscid, semifluid material of animal and plant cells. (Gr. *protos*, first + *plasma*, form)

Prox′i-mal. Toward or nearer the place of attachment or reference of the center of the body. Opposite of distal. (L. *proximus*, nearest)

Pseu′do-coel. A body cavity not lined with peritoneum and not part of a blood-vascular system, as in hematodes and some other invertebrates. Compare Coelom, Hemocoel. (Gr. *pseudes*, false + *koilos*, hollow)

Pseu′do-po″di-um. A flowing extension of protoplasm used in locomotion or feeding by a cell or protozoan. (Gr. *pseudes*, false + *podion*, foot)

Pul′mo-na-ry. Pertaining to the lungs. (L. *pulmo*, lungs)

Ra′di-al sym′me-try. Having similar parts arranged around a common central axis, as in a starfish.

Ra′mus. A branch or outgrowth of a structure. (L., branch)

Re′cent. The present or Holocene epoch in geology. Compare Fossil. (L. *recens*, fresh)

Re-cep′tor. A free nerve ending or sense organ capable of receiving and transforming certain environmental stimuli into sensory nerve impulses. (L., receiver)

Re-ces′sive char′ac-ter. A character from one parent that remains undeveloped in offspring when associated with the corresponding dominant character from the other parent. (L. *recessus*, a going back)

Rec′tum. The terminal enlarged portion of the digestive tract. (L. *rectus*, straight)

Re-duc′tion di-vi′sion. That division of the maturing germ cells by which the somatic or diploid number of chromosomes is reduced to the haploid number.

Re′flex ac′tion. Action resulting from an afferent sensory impulse on a nerve center and its reflection as an efferent motor impulse independent of higher nerve centers or the brain. An automatic response to a stimulus. (L. *re*, back + *flecto*, bend)

Re-gen′er-a″tion. Replacement of parts lost through mutilation or otherwise

Re′nal. Pertaining to a kidney. (L. *renes*, kidneys)

Re′pro-duc″tion. The maintenance of a species from generation to generation.

Res′pi-ra″tion. Obtaining oxygen from the surrounding medium and giving off carbon dioxide. (L. *re*, back + *spiro*, breathe)

Ret′i-na. The cell layer of an eye containing the receptors of light impulses. (L. *rete*, net)

Re-ver′sion. The reappearance of ancestral traits that have been in abeyance for one or more generations. (L. *re*, back + *verto*, turn)

Ros′trum. A projecting snout or similar process on the head. (L., beak)

Ru′di-men″ta-ry. Incompletely developed or having no function. Compare Vestigial. (L. *rudis*, unwrought)

Ru′mi-nant. A herbivorous land mammal that chews a cud, as a cow or deer. (L. *rumen*, throat)

Sa′crum. The posterior part of the vertebral column that is attached to the pelvic girdle. (L. from *sacer*, sacred, offered in sacrifice)

Sag′it-tal. Of or pertaining to the median anteroposterior plane in a bilaterally symmetrical animal, or a section parallel to that plane. (L. *sagitta*, arrow)

Sal′i-va-ry. Pertaining to the glands of the mouth that secrete saliva. (L. *saliva*, spittle)

Sap′ro-phyte. An organism that lives upon dead organic matter. (Gr. *sapros*, rotten + *phyton*, plant)

Scan-so′ri-al. Pertaining to or adapted for climbing. (L. *scando*, climb)

Sec′on-da-ry sex′u-al char′ac-ters. Those characters which distinguish one sex from the other, not functioning directly in reproduction.

Se-cre′tion. A useful substance produced in the body by a cell or multicellular gland; also, the process of its production and passage. Compare Excretion. (L. *secretus*, separated)

Sed′en-ta-ry. Remaining in one place. (L. *sedeo*, sit)

Sed′i-men″ta-ry. In geology, rocks formed of calcium carbonates, clay, mud, sand, or gravel, deposited in water or depressions on land and cemented or pressed into solid form. Fossils occur in such rocks. (L. *sedimentum*, settling)

Seg′ment. A part that is marked off or separate from others; any of the several serial divisions of a body or an appendage. Compare Somite.

Sem′i-nal. Pertaining to structures or fluid containing spermatozoa (semen). (L. *semen*, seed)

Sense or′gan. An organ containing a part sensitive to a particular kind of stimulus.

Sep′tum. A dividing wall or partition between two cavities or structures. (L. *sepes*, fence)

Se′rous. Secreting watery colorless serum, as by a gland or serous membrane. (L.)

Se′rum. The plasma of blood that separates from a clot and contains no cells or fibrin. (L.)

Ses′sile. Permanently fixed, sedentary, not free-moving. (L. *sedeo*, sit)

Se′ta. A bristle or slender, stiff bristle-like structure. (L., bristle)

Sex chro′mo-somes. Special chromosomes different in males and females and concerned in the determination of sex; the X and Y chromosomes.

Sex-lim′i-ted char′ac-ter. A character belonging to one sex only; commonly a secondary sexual character.

Sex-linked char′ac-ter. A character the gene of which is located in the sex chromosome.

Sex′u-al u′nion. Temporary connection of a male and female for transfer of sperm into the female's reproductive tract.

Si-li′ceous. Containing silica or silicon dioxide (SiO_2). (L. *silex*, flint)

Si′nus. A cavity in a bone or an enlargement in a blood vessel. (L., fold, hollow)

Skel′e-ton. The hardened framework of an animal body serving for support and to protect the soft parts; it may be external or internal and either solid or jointed. (Gr.)

Sol'i-ta-ry. Living alone; not in colonies or groups. (L. *solus*, alone)

Sol'ute. A substance that will dissolve or go into solution, as salt in water. (L. *se*, apart + *lus*, set free)

Sol'vent. A fluid capable of dissolving substances.

So'ma, So-mat'ic. Pertaining to the body or body cells, as contrasted with germ cells. (Gr. *soma*, body)

So'mite. A serial segment or homologous part of the body; a metamere. (Gr. *soma*, body)

Spe'cial-ized. Not primitive; adapted by structure or function for a particular purpose or mode of life.

Spe'cies (pl. also **species**). The unit in classification of animals or plants. (See par. 15-3)

Sperm. See Spermatozoa.

Sper'ma-to-zo"a. The matured and functional male sex cells or male gametes. (Gr. *sperma*, seed + *zoön*, animal)

Spir'a-cle. In insects, an external opening to the tracheal or respiratory system; in cartilaginous fishes, the modified first gill slit. (L. *spiraculum*, air hole)

Spore. A cell in a resistant covering, capable of developing independently into a new individual. (Gr. *spora*, seed)

Stat'o-cyst. An organ of equilibrium in some invertebrates. (Gr. *statos*, standing + *kystis*, bladder)

Stat'o-lith. A calcareous granule in a statocyst.

Stim'u-lus. A change in the external or internal environment capable of influencing some activity in an organism or its parts.

Sto'mo-de"um. The ectoderm-lined portion of the mouth cavity. (Gr. *stoma*, mouth + *hodos*, a road)

Strat'i-fied. A series of layers, one above another. (L.)

Stra'tum. A layer or sheet of tissue (anatomy); a layer or sheet of sedimentary rock (geology). (L., covering)

Su'ture. Line of junction between 2 bones or between 2 parts of an exoskeleton. (L. *suo*, sew)

Sym'bi-o"sis. Interrelation between 2 organisms of different species; see commensalism, mutualism, parasitism. (Gr. *syn*, together + *bios*, life)

Sym'phy-sis. A union between 2 parts. (Gr. *syn*, together + *phyein*, grow)

Syn-apse'. The contact of one nerve cell with another, across which impulses are transmitted. (Gr. *syn*, together + *hapto*, unite)

Syn-ap'sis. Temporary union of the chromosomes in pairs preliminary to the first maturation division. (Gr. *syn*, together + *hapto*, unite)

Syn-cyt'i-um. A mass or layer of protoplasm containing several or many nuclei not separated by cell membranes. (Gr. *syn*, together + *kytos*, cell)

Sys-tem'ic. Portion of the circulatory system not directly involved in respiration.

Tac'tile. Pertaining to the organs or the sense of touch. (L. *tactus*, touch)

Tec'tin. The organic material in skeletons of some protozoans; pseudochitin.

Ten'don. A connective tissue band attaching a muscle. (L. *tendo*, to stretch)

Ten'ta-cle. An elongate flexible appendage usually near the mouth. (L. *tento* from *teneo*, hold)

Ter-res'tri-al. Belonging to or living on the ground or earth. (L. *terra*, earth)

Tes'tis; pl. tes'tes. The male germ gland or gonad, in which spermatozoa are formed. (L.)

Tet'ra-pod. A vertebrate typically with 4 limbs—the amphibians, reptiles, birds, and mammals. (Gr. *tetra*, four + *pous*, foot)

Tho'rax. The major division of an animal next behind the head; in land vertebrates, the part enclosed by the ribs. (Gr.)

Tis'sue. A layer or group of cells in an organ or body part having essentially the same structure and function. (L. *texo*, weave)

Tra'che-a. An air tube; the windpipe of land vertebrates from the glottis to the lungs; part of the respiratory system in insects and other arthropods. (Gr. *trachys*, rough)

Trip'lo-blas"tic. Derived from 3 embryonic germ layers —ectoderm, endoderm, and mesoderm. (Gr. *triplous*, threefold + *blastos*, germ)

Tro'cho-phore. An invertebrate larva, commonly pear-shaped and with an equatorial band of cilia. (Gr. *trochos*, wheel + *phoros*, bearing)

Tym'pa-num. A vibrating membrane involved in hearing; the eardrum, or tympanic membrane. (Gr. *tympanon*, drum)

Um-bil'i-cal cord. The cord containing blood vessels supported by connective tissue that unites the embryo or fetus of a mammal with the mother during development in the uterus. (L. *umbilicus*, navel)

Un-guic'u-late. Having claws, as a cat. (L. *unguis*, claw)

Un'gu-late. Having hoofs, as a deer or horse. (L. *ungula*, hoof)

Un"gu-li-grade'. Walking or adapted for walking on hoofs. (L. *ungula*, hoof + *gradior*, to step)

Unit character. A trait that behaves more or less as a unit in heredity, and may be inherited independently of other traits.

U-re'ter. The duct carrying urine from the kidney to the urinary bladder or to the cloaca. (Gr. from *ouron*, urine)

U-re'thra. The duct by which urine is discharged from the bladder to the outside in mammals; joined by the vasa deferentia in the male. (Gr. from *ouron*, urine)

U'ri-no-gen"i-tal. See Urogenital.

U'ro-gen"i-tal. Pertaining to the excretory and reproductive organs and functions. (L. *urina*, urine + *genitalis*, genital)

U'ter-us. The enlarged posterior portion of an oviduct in which eggs may be retained for development. (L., womb)

Vac'u-ole. A minute cavity within a cell, usually filled with some liquid product of protoplasmic activity. (L. dim. of *vacuus*, empty)

Va-gi'na. The terminal portion of the female reproductive tract, which receives the copulatory organ of a male in mating. (L., sheath)

Valve. In animals, any structure that limits or closes an opening; the thin folds in veins, lymph vessels, or hearts or the circular muscles about a tubular exit; also, either external shell of a bivalve mollusk, brachiopod, or some crustaceans.

Vas; pl. va'sa. A small tubular vessel, or duct, especially one leading from the testis. (L., vessel)

Vas de′fer-ens. The sperm duct from the vasa efferentia to the cloaca or ejaculatory duct. (L. *deferens*, carrying out)

Va′sa ef′fe-ren″ti-a. Short ducts carrying sperm from the testis to the vas deferens. (L. *ex*, out + *fero*, carry)

Vas′cu-lar. Pertaining to vessels or ducts for conveying or circulating blood or lymph. (L. dim. of *vas*, vessel)

Vein. A vessel carrying blood from capillaries toward the heart. (L. *vena*, vein)

Ven′tral. Toward the lower side or belly; away from the back. Opposite to dorsal. (L. *venter*, belly)

Ven′tri-cle. The muscular chamber in a heart; also, a cavity in the brain of a vertebrate. (L. dim. of *venter*, belly)

Ver′te-bra. One of the segmental structural units of the axial skeleton or spinal column in a vertebrate. (L., joint)

Ver′te-brate. An animal having a segmental "backbone" or vertebral column; the cyclostomes to mammals. (L. *vertebratus*, jointed)

Ves′sel. A tubular structure that conveys fluid, especially blood or lymph. (L. *vascellum*, dim. of *vas*, vessel)

Ves-tig′i-al. Small or degenerate but representing a structure that formerly was more fully developed or functional. Compare Rudimentary. (L. *vestigium*, footstep, a trace)

Vil′lus; pl. **vil′li.** A minute finger-like projection; especially those numerous on the intestinal lining of vertebrates. (L. *villus*, shaggy hair)

Vis′cer-a. The organs within the cranium, thorax, and abdomen, especially the latter. (L., internal organs)

Vis′cer-al skel′e-ton. The supporting framework of the jaws and gill arches and their derivatives, in vertebrates.

Vis′u-al. Pertaining to sight.

Vi′ta-min. An organic substance that is an essential food factor needed in minute amounts for normal growth and function. (L. *vita*, life + *amin*, a chemical radical)

Vi-vip′a-rous. Producing living young that develop from eggs retained within the mother's body and nourished by her blood stream, as with most mammals. (L. *vivo*, live + *pario*, to bear)

X, Y chromosomes. Chromosomes associated with sex in many animals.

Yolk. Nutritive materials (fats and others) stored within or with an egg for nourishment of the future embryo.

Zy′gote. A fertilized egg resulting from the union of 2 gametes of opposite kind, ovum and sperm. (Gr. *zygon*, yoke)

INDEX

All numbers refer to pages. Numbers in boldface refer to pages on which illustrations occur. Scientific names of genera and species are in italics and those of higher groups in small capitals. Names of fossil species or groups are preceded by a dagger (†). The index omits incidental references to common structures such as stomach, heart, etc., but contains entries for pages where these are described in detail. Such items may be sought under entries to Digestive system, Circulatory system, etc., or to an animal type such as Cat, Crayfish, etc.

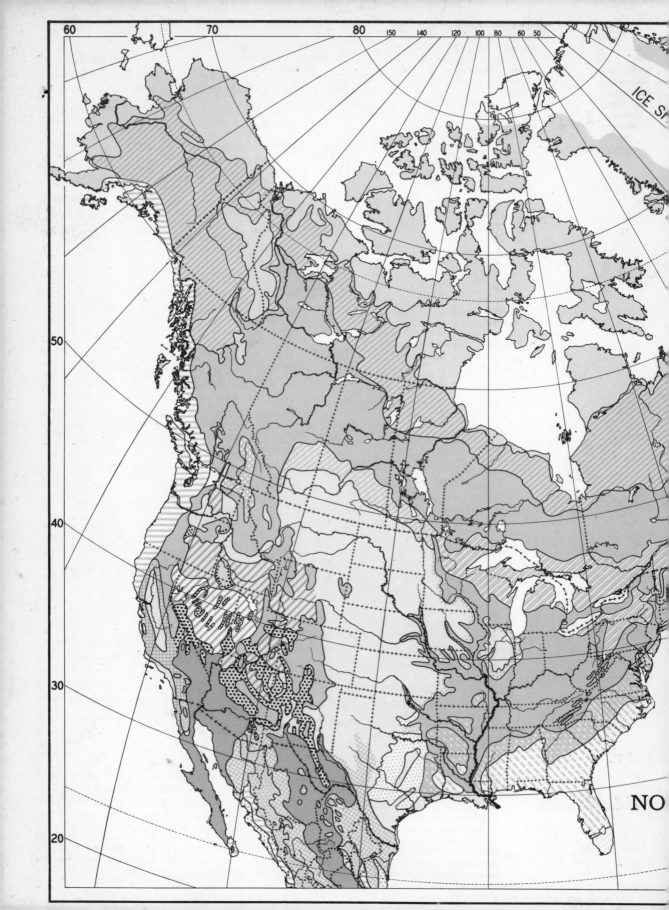

60 70 80 150 140 120 100 80 60 50

ICE SI

50

40

30

20

NO